MAT 090

FUNDAMENTALS
of MATHEMATICS

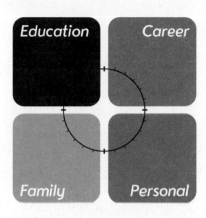

SECOND CUSTOM EDITION

Edited by Brian K. Saltzer

Taken from:

Prealgebra, Fourth Edition
by Marvin L. Bittinger and David Ellenbogen

Mathematics for New Technologies
by Don Hutchinson and Mark Yannotta

*Instructor's Solutions Manual
for Mathematics for New Technologies*
by Don Hutchinson and Mark Yannotta

STRAYER
UNIVERSITY

 PEARSON
Custom
Publishing

 PEARSON
Addison
Wesley

Cover art courtesy of Photodisc by Getty Images.

Taken from:

Prealgebra, Fourth Edition
by Marvin L. Bittinger and David J. Ellenbogen
Copyright © 2004 by Pearson Education, Inc.
Published by Addison Wesley
Boston, Massachusetts 02116

Mathematics for New Technologies
by Don Hutchison and Mark Yannotta
Copyright © 2004 by Pearson Education, Inc.
Published by Addison Wesley

Instructor's Solutions Manual for Mathematics for New Technologies
by Don Hutchison and Mark Yannotta
Copyright © 2004 by Pearson Education, Inc.
Published by Addison Wesley

This special edition published in cooperation with Pearson Custom Publishing.

Printed in the United States of America

10 9 8 7 6 5 4

ISBN 0-536-50934-4

2007361331

SB

Please visit our web site at *www.pearsoncustom.com*

PEARSON CUSTOM PUBLISHING
501 Boylston Street, Suite 900, Boston, MA 02116
A Pearson Education Company

Contents

3 FRACTION NOTATION: MULTIPLICATION AND DIVISION

4 FRACTION NOTATION: ADDITION AND SUBTRACTION

Feature Walkthrough

Chapter Openers

To engage students and prepare them for the upcoming chapter material, two-page gateway chapter openers are designed with exceptional artwork that is tied to a motivating real-world application.

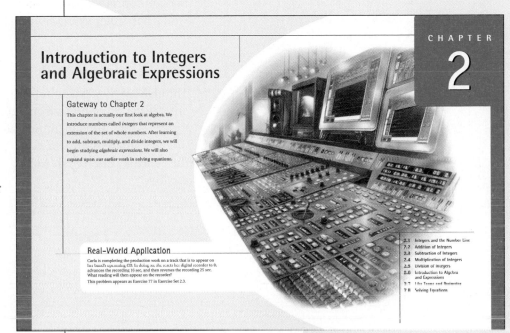

Chapter Pretests

Allowing students to test themselves before beginning each chapter, Chapter Pretests help them to identify material that may be familiar as well as target material that is new or especially challenging. Instructors can use these results to assess student needs.

Objectives Boxes

At the beginning of each section, a boxed list of objectives is keyed by letter to the section subheadings, the exercises in the Pretest, that section's exercise set, the exercises in the Summary and Review, and the answers to the Chapter Test and Cumulative Review questions. This correlation enables students to easily find appropriate review material if they need help with a particular exercise or skill.

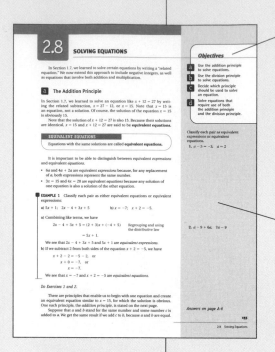

Margin Exercises

Throughout the text, students are directed to numerous margin exercises that provide immediate practice and reinforcement of the concepts covered in each section.

Annotated Examples

Detailed annotations and color highlights lead the student through the structured steps of the examples.

Study Tips

New! A different Study Tip now appears in each and every section of the text. These tips provide students with pointers on how to get the most out of their course. At times short snippets and at other times more lengthy discussions, these Study Tips encourage students to reflect upon and adjust to how they can best learn mathematics.

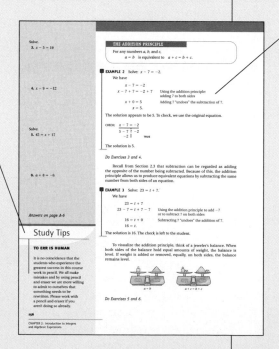

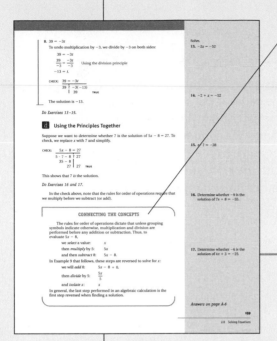

Connecting the Concepts

New! This feature highlights the importance of connecting concepts and invites students to pause and check that they understand the "big picture." This helps ensure that students understand how concepts work together in several sections at once. For example, students are alerted to shifts made from solving equations to writing equivalent expressions. The pacing of this feature helps students increase their comprehension and maximize their retention of key concepts.

Calculator Corners

Where appropriate throughout the text, students see optional Calculator Corners. This feature is designed specifically with students of prealgebra in mind, enabling them to use a calculator (either scientific or graphing, as appropriate) to better visualize a concept that they have just learned. Popular in the Third Edition, the new edition has several more Calculator Corners and the revised content is now more accessible to students.

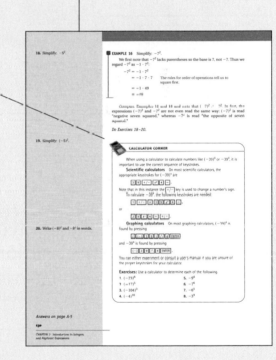

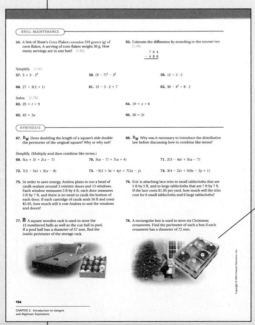

Art Program

Today's students are often visually oriented and their approach to a printed page is no exception. To appeal to students, the situational art in this edition is more dynamic and there are more photographs and art pieces overall. Where possible, mathematics is included in the art pieces to help students visualize the problem at hand.

Real-Data Applications

This text encourages students to see and interpret the mathematics that appears every day in the world around them. Throughout the writing process, an energetic search for real-data applications was conducted, and the result is a variety of examples and exercises that connect the mathematical content with the real world. Most of these applications feature source lines and many include charts and graphs.

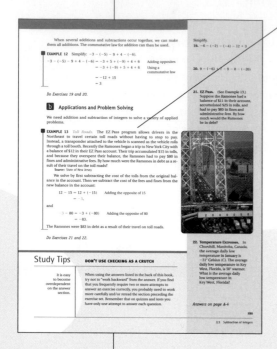

Highlighted Information

Important definitions, rules, and procedures are highlighted in titled boxes.

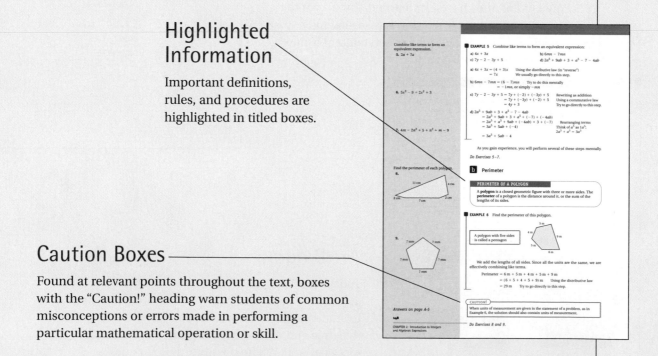

Caution Boxes

Found at relevant points throughout the text, boxes with the "Caution!" heading warn students of common misconceptions or errors made in performing a particular mathematical operation or skill.

EXERCISE SETS

To give students the opportunity to reinforce the concepts they have just learned, each section is followed by an extensive exercise set. In addition, students have the opportunity to synthesize the concepts of the current section with those from preceding sections.

For Extra Help

Many valuable study aids accompany this text. Located just before each exercise set, "For Extra Help" lists appropriate video, tutorial, and Web resources so students can easily find related support materials.

Exercises

Exercises are keyed by letter to the section objectives for easy review.

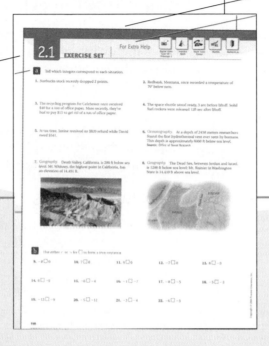

Discussion and Writing Exercises

Designed to help students develop deeper comprehension of critical concepts, Discussion and Writing exercises (indicated by the D_W symbol) are suitable for individual or group work. These exercises encourage students to both think and write about key mathematical ideas in each section.

Skill Maintenance Exercises

Found in each exercise set, these exercises review concepts from earlier sections in the text to keep skills sharp. Section and objective codes appear next to each Skill Maintenance exercise for easy reference, and in response to user feedback, the overall number of Skill Maintenance exercises has been increased and many are designed as preparation for the next section of the text.

Synthesis Exercises

In every exercise set, Synthesis exercises help build critical-thinking skills by requiring students to merge concepts from the current section with those from preceding text sections.

END-OF-CHAPTER MATERIAL

At the end of each chapter, students can practice all they have learned and also tie the current chapter material to material covered in earlier chapters.

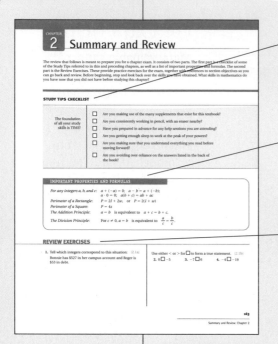

Study Tips Checklist

Each chapter review begins with a Study Tips Checklist that reviews Study Tips introduced in the current chapter, making the use of these Study Tips more interactive.

Important Properties and Formulas

Following the Study Tips Checklist, most chapters include a summary of Important Properties and Formulas. This provides students with a place to find a quick review before beginning the exercises.

Review Exercises

At the end of each chapter, students are provided with an extensive set of Review exercises. Reference codes beside each exercise or direction line allow students to easily review the related objective.

Chapter Test

Following the Review exercises, a sample Chapter Test allows students to review and test comprehension of chapter skills prior to taking an instructor's exam.

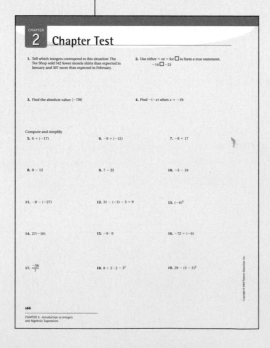

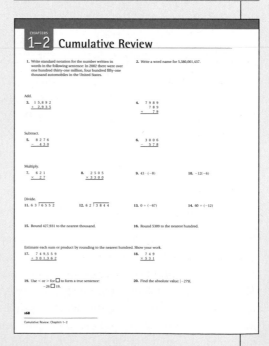

Cumulative Review

Following each chapter (beginning with Chapter 2), students encounter a Cumulative Review. This exercise set reviews skills and concepts from all preceding chapters to help students recall previously learned material and prepare for a final exam.

To the Student

Whatever your experience in math has been, it is important for you to regard this mathematics course as a fresh start. Approaching your course with a positive attitude will have a great impact on how much success you experience. A successful experience in this course can, in turn, provide a solid base for your college studies, your personal career, your household finances, and ultimately life in general.

As authors we have done our best to create a book that you can count on to be consistently understandable and comprehensive. We make very few assumptions regarding previous experience in math and, whenever possible, include real-life applications to make the material as relevant as possible. However, no matter how much effort we put into writing this book, it is *your* effort that will have the greatest impact on how well you do in this course. In past courses, you may have allowed yourself to sit back and let the instructor "pour in" the learning, with little or no active involvement on your part. This approach is unlikely to work in your current course. Math is not a spectator sport, and to succeed it is not enough to simply listen and read—you will have to actually do the mathematics, check your work, correct yourself as needed, ask questions, and accept primary responsibility for your learning. As soon as possible after class, you should thoroughly read the textbook, use the various supplements as needed, and work on the assigned exercises. In short, do all you can to learn on your own. When a student approaches an instructor for help, the instructor can quickly sense how much effort the student has devoted to becoming an independent learner. You will likely find that there are many people who will gladly help you if you can convince them that you consistently put forth your best effort when working on your own.

Perhaps the most important suggestion that we can make is that you provide yourself with enough time to learn. You can have the best book, the best instructor, and the best supplements, but if you do not give yourself time to learn, these will not be enough. If you can succeed in giving yourself the "gift of time" at the beginning of the course, you will be developing a healthy study habit for all future work in mathematics. Better yet, by giving yourself ample time, you may discover that you really enjoy the subject.

Good luck!

M.L.B.
D.J.E.

Review

This review is designed for those students who may wish to refresh themselves on the basic arithmetic operations of addition, subtraction, multiplication, and division before beginning to use the book.

R

Add; think of joining sets of objects.

1. $4 + 5$ **2.** $5 + 2$

3.   9
     + 5

4.   8
     + 8

5.   9
     + 7

6.   7
     + 9

The first printed use of the + symbol was in a book by a German, Johann Widmann, in 1498.

Answers on page A-1

R.1 ADDITION

a Basic Addition

Basic addition can be explained by counting. The sum

$$3 + 4$$

can be found by counting out a set of 3 objects and a separate set of 4 objects, putting them together, and counting all the objects.

| A set of 3 | + | A set of 4 | = | A set of 7 |

The numbers to be added are called **addends.** The result is the **sum.**

$$3 \quad + \quad 4 \quad = \quad 7$$

 ↑   ↑   ↑

Addend   Addend   Sum

EXAMPLES Add. Think of putting sets of objects together.

1. $5 + 6 = 11$

    5
  + 6
   11

2. $8 + 5 = 13$

    8
  + 5
   13

We can also do these problems by counting up from one of the numbers. For example, in Example 2, we start at 8 and count up 5 times: 9, 10, 11, 12, 13.

Do Exercises 1–6.

What happens when we add 0? Think of a set of 5 objects. If we add 0 objects to it, we still have 5 objects. Similarly, if we have a set with 0 objects in it and add 5 objects to it, we have a set with 5 objects. Thus,

$$5 + 0 = 5 \quad \text{and} \quad 0 + 5 = 5.$$

ADDITION OF 0

Adding 0 to a number does not change the number:
$$a + 0 = 0 + a = a.$$
We say that 0 is the **additive identity.**

EXAMPLES Add.

3. $0 + 9 = 9$

$$\begin{array}{r} 0 \\ + 9 \\ \hline 9 \end{array}$$

4. $0 + 0 = 0$

$$\begin{array}{r} 0 \\ + 0 \\ \hline 0 \end{array}$$

5. $97 + 0 = 97$

$$\begin{array}{r} 97 \\ + 0 \\ \hline 97 \end{array}$$

Do Exercises 7–12.

Your objective for this part of the section is to be able to add any of the numbers 0, 1, 2, 3, 4, 5, 6, 7, 8, 9. Adding 0 is easy. The rest of the sums are listed in this table. Memorize the table by saying it to yourself over and over or by using flash cards.

+	1	2	3	4	5	6	7	8	9
1	2	3	4	5	6	7	8	9	10
2	3	4	5	6	7	8	9	10	11
3	4	5	6	7	8	9	10	11	12
4	5	6	7	8	9	10	11	12	13
5	6	7	8	9	10	11	12	13	14
6	7	8	9	10	11	12	13	14	15
7	8	9	10	11	12	13	14	15	16
8	9	10	11	12	13	14	15	16	17
9	10	11	12	13	14	15	16	17	18

$6 + 7 = 13$
Find 6 at the left, and 7 at the top.

$7 + 6 = 13$
Find 7 at the left, and 6 at the top.

It is very important that you *memorize* the basic addition facts! If you do not, you will always have trouble with addition.

Note the following.

$$3 + 4 = 7 \qquad 7 + 6 = 13 \qquad 7 + 2 = 9$$
$$4 + 3 = 7 \qquad 6 + 7 = 13 \qquad 2 + 7 = 9$$

We can add whole numbers in any order. This is the *commutative law of addition.* Because of this law, you need to learn only about half the table above, as shown by the shading.

Do Exercises 13 and 14.

b Certain Sums of Three Numbers

To add $3 + 5 + 4$, we can add 3 and 5, then 4:

$$3 + 5 + 4$$
$$\searrow \swarrow$$
$$8 + 4$$
$$\searrow \swarrow$$
$$12.$$

We can also add 5 and 4, then 3:

$$3 + 5 + 4$$
$$\searrow \swarrow$$
$$3 + 9$$
$$\searrow \swarrow$$
$$12.$$

Either way we get 12.

Add.

7. $8 + 0$

8. $0 + 8$

9. $\begin{array}{r} 7 \\ + 0 \end{array}$

10. $\begin{array}{r} 46 \\ + 0 \end{array}$

11. $0 + 13$

12. $58 + 0$

Complete the table.

13.

+	1	2	3	4	5
1			4		
2					
3				7	
4					
5					

14.

+	6	5	7	4	9
7			14		
9					
5			9		
8					
4					

Answers on page A-1

Add from the top mentally.

15.　　1
　　　　 6
　　　+ 9

16.　　2
　　　　 3
　　　+ 4

17.　　6
　　　　 1
　　　+ 4

18.　　5
　　　　 2
　　　+ 8

Add.

19.　　2 4
　　　+ 3 5

20.　　3 4 6
　　　+ 2 0 3

21.　　8 3 2 7
　　　+ 1 6 5 2

22.　　3 4 6 1
　　　+ 2 0 3 5

EXAMPLE 6　Add from the top mentally.

　　1
　　7　　　We first add 1 and 7,
　+ 9　　　getting 8. Then we add
　　　　　8 and 9, getting 17.

　　1
　　7 → 8
　+ 9　　9 → 17
　　17 ←

EXAMPLE 7　Add from the top mentally.

　　2
　　4 → 6
　+ 8　　8 → 14
　　14 ←

Do Exercises 15–18.

C　Addition (No Carrying)

We now move to a more gradual, conceptual development of the addition procedure. It is intended to provide you with a greater understanding so that your skill level will increase.

To add larger numbers, we can add the ones first, then the tens, then the hundreds, and so on.

EXAMPLE 8　Add: 5722 + 3234.

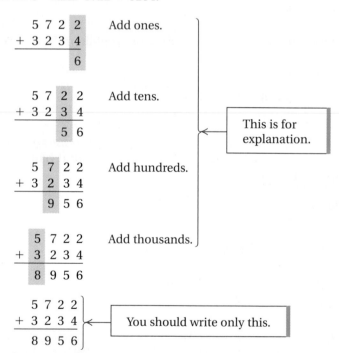

　　5 7 2 **2**　　Add ones.
　+ 3 2 3 **4**
　　　　 6

　　5 7 **2** 2　　Add tens.
　+ 3 2 **3** 4
　　　 5 6

　　5 **7** 2 2　　Add hundreds.
　+ 3 **2** 3 4
　　 9 5 6

　　5 7 2 2　　Add thousands.
　+ **3** 2 3 4
　　8 9 5 6

This is for explanation.

　　5 7 2 2
　+ 3 2 3 4
　　8 9 5 6

You should write only this.

Do Exercises 19–22.

d Addition (with Carrying)

CARRYING TENS

EXAMPLE 9 Add: 18 + 27.

$$\begin{array}{r} 1\ 8 \\ +\ 2\ 7 \\ \hline ? \end{array}$$ Add ones.   *Think:*

$$\begin{array}{r} 8 \\ +\ 7 \\ \hline 1\ 5 \end{array}$$ 15 ones = 10 ones + 5 ones
= 1 ten + 5 ones

$$\begin{array}{r} \overset{1}{1}\ 8 \\ +\ 2\ 7 \\ \hline 5 \end{array}$$ Write 5 in the ones column.
Write 1 as a reminder above the tens.
This is called *carrying*.

$$\begin{array}{r} \overset{1}{1}\ 8 \\ +\ 2\ 7 \\ \hline 4\ 5 \end{array}$$ Add tens.

We can use money to help explain Example 9.

$$\begin{array}{r} 1\ 8¢ \\ +\ 2\ 7¢ \\ \hline 1\ 5¢ \end{array}$$ ⟶ 1 dime and 8 pennies
⟶ 2 dimes and 7 pennies
We first add the pennies

$$\begin{array}{r} 1\ \text{dime} \\ 1\ 8 \\ +\ 2\ 7 \\ \hline 5\ \text{pennies} \end{array}$$ We regard ten pennies as one dime.

$$\begin{array}{r} \overset{1}{1}\ 8 \\ +\ 2\ 7 \\ \hline 4\ 5 \end{array}$$ We now add the dimes. The result is
4 dimes and 5 pennies.

Do Exercises 23 and 24.

CARRYING HUNDREDS

EXAMPLE 10 Add: 256 + 391.

$$\begin{array}{r} 2\ 5\ 6 \\ +\ 3\ 9\ 1 \\ \hline 7 \end{array}$$ Add ones.

$$\begin{array}{r} \overset{1}{2}\ 5\ 6 \\ +\ 3\ 9\ 1 \\ \hline 4\ 7 \end{array}$$ Add tens. We get 14 tens.
Now 14 tens = 10 tens + 4 tens = 1 hundred + 4 tens.
Write 4 in the tens column and a 1 above the hundreds.

> The carrying here is like exchanging 14 dimes for a 1 dollar bill and 4 dimes.

$$\begin{array}{r} \overset{1}{2}\ 5\ 6 \\ +\ 3\ 9\ 1 \\ \hline 6\ 4\ 7 \end{array}$$ Add hundreds.

Do Exercises 25 and 26.

Add.

23.
$$\begin{array}{r} 1\ 9 \\ +\ 3\ 7 \end{array}$$

24.
$$\begin{array}{r} 4\ 6 \\ +\ 3\ 9 \end{array}$$

Add.

25.
$$\begin{array}{r} 3\ 4\ 1 \\ +\ 4\ 8\ 8 \end{array}$$

26.
$$\begin{array}{r} 7\ 3\ 0 \\ +\ 2\ 9\ 6 \end{array}$$

Answers on page A-1

27. Add.

$$
\begin{array}{r}
7\ 8\ 5\ 0 \\
+\ 4\ 8\ 4\ 8 \\
\hline
\end{array}
$$

Add.

28.

$$
\begin{array}{r}
7\ 9\ 8\ 9 \\
+\ 5\ 6\ 7\ 2 \\
\hline
\end{array}
$$

29.

$$
\begin{array}{r}
5\ 6{,}7\ 8\ 9 \\
+\ 1\ 4{,}5\ 3\ 9 \\
\hline
\end{array}
$$

CARRYING THOUSANDS

■ **EXAMPLE 11** Add: 4803 + 3792.

$$
\begin{array}{r}
4\ 8\ 0\ \boxed{3} \\
+\ 3\ 7\ 9\ \boxed{2} \\
\hline
\boxed{5}
\end{array}
$$
Add ones.

$$
\begin{array}{r}
4\ 8\ \boxed{0}\ 3 \\
+\ 3\ 7\ \boxed{9}\ 2 \\
\hline
\boxed{9}\ 5
\end{array}
$$
Add tens.

$$
\begin{array}{r}
^{1} \\
4\ \boxed{8}\ 0\ 3 \\
+\ 3\ \boxed{7}\ 9\ 2 \\
\hline
\boxed{5}\ 9\ 5
\end{array}
$$
Add hundreds. We get 15 hundreds. Now 15 hundreds = 10 hundreds + 5 hundreds = 1 thousand + 5 hundreds. Write 5 in the hundreds column and 1 above the thousands.

$$
\begin{array}{r}
^{1} \\
\boxed{4}\ 8\ 0\ 3 \\
+\ \boxed{3}\ 7\ 9\ 2 \\
\hline
\boxed{8}\ 5\ 9\ 5
\end{array}
$$
Add thousands.

Do Exercise 27.

CARRYING MORE THAN ONCE

Sometimes we must carry more than once.

■ **EXAMPLE 12** Add: 5767 + 4993.

$$
\begin{array}{r}
^{\quad 1} \\
5\ 7\ 6\ \boxed{7} \\
+\ 4\ 9\ 9\ \boxed{3} \\
\hline
\boxed{0}
\end{array}
$$
Add ones. We get 10 ones. Now 10 ones = 1 ten + 0 ones. Write 0 in the ones column and 1 above the tens.

$$
\begin{array}{r}
^{\ 1\ 1} \\
5\ 7\ \boxed{6}\ 7 \\
+\ 4\ 9\ \boxed{9}\ 3 \\
\hline
\boxed{6}\ 0
\end{array}
$$
Add tens. We get 16 tens. Now 16 tens = 1 hundred + 6 tens. Write 6 in the tens column and 1 above the hundreds.

$$
\begin{array}{r}
^{1\ 1\ 1} \\
5\ \boxed{7}\ 6\ 7 \\
+\ 4\ \boxed{9}\ 9\ 3 \\
\hline
\boxed{7}\ 6\ 0
\end{array}
$$
Add hundreds. We get 17 hundreds. Now 17 hundreds = 1 thousand + 7 hundreds. Write 7 in the hundreds column and 1 above the thousands.

$$
\begin{array}{r}
^{1\ 1\ 1} \\
\boxed{5}\ 7\ 6\ 7 \\
+\ \boxed{4}\ 9\ 9\ 3 \\
\hline
\boxed{1\ 0}\ 7\ 6\ 0
\end{array}
$$
Add thousands. We get 10 thousands.

Do Exercises 28 and 29.

R.1

a   Add. Try to do these mentally. If you have trouble, think of putting sets of objects together.

1.	8 + 9	2.	8 + 7	3.	6 + 7	4.	9 + 5	5.	5 + 7	6.	5 + 6
7.	9 + 8	8.	9 + 7	9.	8 + 4	10.	9 + 1	11.	8 + 2	12.	3 + 8
13.	0 + 7	14.	4 + 3	15.	2 + 9	16.	0 + 0	17.	3 + 0	18.	9 + 9
19.	8 + 6	20.	3 + 7	21.	2 + 2	22.	7 + 7	23.	6 + 5	24.	7 + 8
25.	8 + 8	26.	8 + 1	27.	5 + 8	28.	5 + 9	29.	4 + 7	30.	6 + 1

31. 6 + 7   **32.** 7 + 7   **33.** 3 + 9   **34.** 6 + 0   **35.** 6 + 4

36. 9 + 3   **37.** 5 + 5   **38.** 5 + 3   **39.** 1 + 1   **40.** 4 + 5

41. 9 + 4   **42.** 0 + 8   **43.** 4 + 6   **44.** 2 + 7   **45.** 3 + 7

46. 3 + 3   **47.** 5 + 8   **48.** 3 + 6   **49.** 4 + 4   **50.** 4 + 7

b   Add from the top mentally.

51.	1 8 + 3	52.	1 7 + 5	53.	3 2 + 5	54.	4 3 + 5	55.	1 7 + 9
56.	5 2 + 6	57.	4 5 + 1	58.	1 9 + 6	59.	1 8 + 7	60.	1 6 + 8

61. $\begin{array}{r} 23 \\ +16 \\ \hline \end{array}$

62. $\begin{array}{r} 54 \\ +35 \\ \hline \end{array}$

63. $\begin{array}{r} 67 \\ +20 \\ \hline \end{array}$

64. $\begin{array}{r} 496 \\ +503 \\ \hline \end{array}$

65. $\begin{array}{r} 700 \\ +200 \\ \hline \end{array}$

66. $\begin{array}{r} 801 \\ +67 \\ \hline \end{array}$

67. $\begin{array}{r} 666 \\ +333 \\ \hline \end{array}$

68. $\begin{array}{r} 523 \\ +325 \\ \hline \end{array}$

69. $\begin{array}{r} 747 \\ +130 \\ \hline \end{array}$

70. $\begin{array}{r} 8250 \\ +9430 \\ \hline \end{array}$

71. $\begin{array}{r} 6552 \\ +4321 \\ \hline \end{array}$

72. $\begin{array}{r} 3406 \\ +1293 \\ \hline \end{array}$

73. $\begin{array}{r} 7340 \\ +3527 \\ \hline \end{array}$

74. $\begin{array}{r} 4825 \\ +5070 \\ \hline \end{array}$

75. $\begin{array}{r} 2073 \\ +1925 \\ \hline \end{array}$

76. $\begin{array}{r} 9111 \\ +9111 \\ \hline \end{array}$

77. $\begin{array}{r} 7889 \\ +9000 \\ \hline \end{array}$

78. $\begin{array}{r} 52{,}433 \\ +12{,}056 \\ \hline \end{array}$

79. $\begin{array}{r} 43{,}723 \\ +56{,}276 \\ \hline \end{array}$

80. $\begin{array}{r} 51{,}670 \\ +26{,}107 \\ \hline \end{array}$

81. $\begin{array}{r} 38 \\ +8 \\ \hline \end{array}$

82. $\begin{array}{r} 17 \\ +9 \\ \hline \end{array}$

83. $\begin{array}{r} 17 \\ +38 \\ \hline \end{array}$

84. $\begin{array}{r} 95 \\ +6 \\ \hline \end{array}$

85. $\begin{array}{r} 862 \\ +781 \\ \hline \end{array}$

86. $\begin{array}{r} 613 \\ +799 \\ \hline \end{array}$

87. $\begin{array}{r} 355 \\ +491 \\ \hline \end{array}$

88. $\begin{array}{r} 280 \\ +348 \\ \hline \end{array}$

89. $\begin{array}{r} 814 \\ +390 \\ \hline \end{array}$

90. $\begin{array}{r} 274 \\ +333 \\ \hline \end{array}$

91. $\begin{array}{r} 9990 \\ +10 \\ \hline \end{array}$

92. $\begin{array}{r} 999 \\ +11 \\ \hline \end{array}$

93. $\begin{array}{r} 999 \\ +111 \\ \hline \end{array}$

94. $\begin{array}{r} 839 \\ +388 \\ \hline \end{array}$

95. $\begin{array}{r} 909 \\ +202 \\ \hline \end{array}$

96. $\begin{array}{r} 808 \\ +909 \\ \hline \end{array}$

97. $\begin{array}{r} 8718 \\ +1420 \\ \hline \end{array}$

98. $\begin{array}{r} 3854 \\ +2700 \\ \hline \end{array}$

99. $\begin{array}{r} 4828 \\ +1283 \\ \hline \end{array}$

100. $\begin{array}{r} 6995 \\ +1432 \\ \hline \end{array}$

101. $\begin{array}{r} 9889 \\ +1 \\ \hline \end{array}$

102. $\begin{array}{r} 6889 \\ +4723 \\ \hline \end{array}$

103. $\begin{array}{r} 9128 \\ +1997 \\ \hline \end{array}$

104. $\begin{array}{r} 8898 \\ +6645 \\ \hline \end{array}$

105. $\begin{array}{r} 9989 \\ +6785 \\ \hline \end{array}$

106. $\begin{array}{r} 46{,}889 \\ +21{,}786 \\ \hline \end{array}$

107. $\begin{array}{r} 23{,}448 \\ +10{,}989 \\ \hline \end{array}$

108. $\begin{array}{r} 67{,}658 \\ +98{,}786 \\ \hline \end{array}$

109. $\begin{array}{r} 77{,}548 \\ +23{,}767 \\ \hline \end{array}$

110. $\begin{array}{r} 44{,}684 \\ +4{,}765 \\ \hline \end{array}$

R.2

SUBTRACTION

a   Basic Subtraction

Subtraction can be explained by taking away part of a set.

■ **EXAMPLE 1** Subtract: $7 - 3$.

We can do this by counting out 7 objects and then taking away 3 of them. Then we count the number that remain: $7 - 3 = 4$.

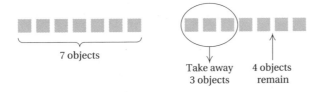

7 objects

Take away   4 objects
3 objects   remain

We could also do this mentally by starting at 7 and counting down 3 times: 6, 5, 4.

■ **EXAMPLES** Subtract. Think of "take away."

2. $11 - 6 = 5$ *Take away*: "11 take away 6 is 5."

$$\begin{array}{r} 11 \\ -\ 6 \\ \hline 5 \end{array}$$

3. $17 - 9 = 8$

$$\begin{array}{r} 17 \\ -\ 9 \\ \hline 8 \end{array}$$

Do Exercises 1–4.

In R.1, you memorized an addition table. That table will enable you to subtract also. First, let's recall how addition and subtraction are related.

An addition:

4   +   3   =   7

Two related subtractions:

A.

$7 - 3$ ←   =   4

B.

$7 - 4$ ←   =   3

Objectives

a Find basic differences such as $5 - 3$, $13 - 8$, and so on.

b Subtract one whole number from another when borrowing is not necessary.

c Subtract one whole number from another when borrowing is necessary.

Subtract.

1. $10 - 6$

2. $11 - 4$

3. $\begin{array}{r} 16 \\ -\ 8 \\ \hline \end{array}$

4. $\begin{array}{r} 10 \\ -\ 7 \\ \hline \end{array}$

Answers on page A-1

For each addition fact, write two subtraction facts.

5. $8 + 4 = 12$

6. $6 + 7 = 13$

Subtract. Try to do these mentally.

7. $14 - 6$

8. $12 - 5$

9. $\begin{array}{r} 1\ 3 \\ -\ \ \ 4 \\ \hline \end{array}$

10. $\begin{array}{r} 1\ 1 \\ -\ \ \ 7 \\ \hline \end{array}$

Answers on page A-1

CHAPTER R: Review

Since we know that

$$4 + 3 = 7, \qquad \text{A basic addition fact}$$

we also know the two subtraction facts

$$7 - 3 = 4 \quad \text{and} \quad 7 - 4 = 3.$$

EXAMPLE 4 From $8 + 9 = 17$, write two subtraction facts.

a) The addend 8 is subtracted from the sum 17.

$8 + 9 = 17$ The related sentence is $17 - 8 = 9.$

b) The addend 9 is subtracted from the sum 17.

$8 + 9 = 17$ The related sentence is $17 - 9 = 8.$

Do Exercises 5 and 6.

We can use the idea that subtraction is defined in terms of addition to think of subtraction as "how much more."

EXAMPLE 5 Find: $13 - 6$.

To find $13 - 6$, we ask, "6 plus what number is 13?"

$$6 + \square = 13$$

+	1	2	3	4	5	6	7	8	9
1	2	3	4	5	6	7	8	9	10
2	3	4	5	6	7	8	9	10	11
3	4	5	6	7	8	9	10	11	12
4	5	6	7	8	9	10	11	12	13
5	6	7	8	9	10	11	12	13	14
6	7	8	9	10	11	12	13	14	15
7	8	9	10	11	12	13	14	15	16
8	9	10	11	12	13	14	15	16	17
9	10	11	12	13	14	15	16	17	18

$13 - 6 = 7$

Using the addition table above, we find 13 inside the table and 6 at the left. Then we read the answer 7 from the top. Thus we have $13 - 6 = 7$. Strive to do this kind of thinking mentally as fast as you can, without having to use the table.

Do Exercises 7–10.

b Subtraction (No Borrowing)

We now move to a more gradual, conceptual development of the subtraction procedure. It is intended to provide you with a greater understanding so that your skill level will increase.

To subtract larger numbers, we can subtract the ones first, then the tens, then the hundreds, and so on.

EXAMPLE 6 Subtract: $5787 - 3214$.

$$
\begin{array}{r}
5\ 7\ 8\ \boxed{7} \\
-\ 3\ 2\ 1\ \boxed{4} \\
\hline
\boxed{3}
\end{array}
$$ Subtract ones.

$$
\begin{array}{r}
5\ 7\ \boxed{8}\ 7 \\
-\ 3\ 2\ \boxed{1}\ 4 \\
\hline
\boxed{7}\ 3
\end{array}
$$ Subtract tens.

This is the explanation.

$$
\begin{array}{r}
5\ \boxed{7}\ 8\ 7 \\
-\ 3\ \boxed{2}\ 1\ 4 \\
\hline
\boxed{5}\ 7\ 3
\end{array}
$$ Subtract hundreds.

$$
\begin{array}{r}
\boxed{5}\ 7\ 8\ 7 \\
-\ \boxed{3}\ 2\ 1\ 4 \\
\hline
\boxed{2}\ 5\ 7\ 3
\end{array}
$$ Subtract thousands.

$$
\begin{array}{r}
5\ 7\ 8\ 7 \\
-\ 3\ 2\ 1\ 4 \\
\hline
2\ 5\ 7\ 3
\end{array}
$$ You should write only this.

Do Exercises 11–14.

c Subtraction (with Borrowing)

We now consider subtraction when borrowing, or regrouping, is necessary.

BORROWING FROM THE TENS PLACE

EXAMPLE 7 Subtract: $37 - 18$.

$$
\begin{array}{r}
3\ \boxed{7} \\
-\ 1\ \boxed{8} \\
\hline
\boxed{?}
\end{array}
$$ Try to subtract ones: $7 - 8$ is not a whole number.

$$
\begin{array}{r}
\overset{2\ 17}{\cancel{3}\ \cancel{7}} \\
-\ 1\ 8 \\
\hline
\end{array}
$$ Borrow a ten. That is, 1 ten = 10 ones, and 10 ones + 7 ones = 17 ones. Write 2 above the tens column and 17 above the ones. We regard 37 as $20 + 17$.

$$
\begin{array}{r}
\overset{2\ 17}{\cancel{3}\ \cancel{7}} \\
-\ 1\ 8 \\
\hline
\boxed{9}
\end{array}
$$ Subtract ones.

The borrowing here is like exchanging 3 dimes and 7 pennies for 2 dimes and 17 pennies.

11. $\quad\begin{array}{r} 7\ 8 \\ -\ 6\ 4 \\ \hline \end{array}$

12. $\quad\begin{array}{r} 2\ 9 \\ -\ \ \ 9 \\ \hline \end{array}$

13. $\quad\begin{array}{r} 5\ 4\ 2 \\ -\ 3\ 0\ 1 \\ \hline \end{array}$

14. $\quad\begin{array}{r} 6\ 8\ 9\ 6 \\ -\ 4\ 8\ 7\ 1 \\ \hline \end{array}$

Answers on page A-1

Subtract.

15.   4 6
       − 2 9

$$\begin{array}{cc} & \overset{2}{\cancel{3}}\ \overset{17}{\cancel{7}} \\ - & 1\ 8 \\ \hline & 1\ 9 \end{array}$$ Subtract tens.

$$\begin{array}{cc} & \overset{2}{\cancel{3}}\ \overset{17}{\cancel{7}} \\ - & 1\ 8 \\ \hline & 1\ 9 \end{array}$$ You should write only this.

Do Exercises 15 and 16.

BORROWING HUNDREDS

16.   7 4
       − 3 8

■ **EXAMPLE 8**   Subtract: 538 − 275.

$$\begin{array}{c} 5\ 3\ \boxed{8} \\ -\ 2\ 7\ \boxed{5} \\ \hline \boxed{3} \end{array}$$ Subtract ones.

$$\begin{array}{c} 5\ \boxed{3}\ 8 \\ -\ 2\ \boxed{7}\ 5 \\ \hline \boxed{?}\ 3 \end{array}$$ Try to subtract tens: 3 tens − 7 tens is not a whole number.

$$\begin{array}{c} \overset{4}{\cancel{5}}\ \overset{13}{\cancel{3}}\ 8 \\ -\ 2\ 7\ 5 \\ \hline 3 \end{array}$$ Borrow a hundred. That is, 1 hundred = 10 tens, and 10 tens + 3 tens = 13 tens. Write 4 above the hundreds column and 13 above the tens.

Subtract.

17.   6 4 6
       − 1 9 2

> The borrowing is like exchanging 5 dollars and 3 dimes for 4 dollars and 13 dimes.

$$\begin{array}{c} \overset{4}{\cancel{5}}\ \overset{13}{\boxed{\cancel{3}}}\ 8 \\ -\ 2\ \boxed{7}\ 5 \\ \hline \boxed{6}\ 3 \end{array}$$ Subtract tens.

$$\begin{array}{c} \boxed{\overset{4}{\cancel{5}}}\ \overset{13}{\cancel{3}}\ 8 \\ -\ \boxed{2}\ 7\ 5 \\ \hline \boxed{2}\ 6\ 3 \end{array}$$ Subtract hundreds.

18.   7 3 3
       − 4 8 3

$$\begin{array}{c} \overset{4}{\cancel{5}}\ \overset{13}{\cancel{3}}\ 8 \\ -\ 2\ 7\ 5 \\ \hline 2\ 6\ 3 \end{array}$$ You should write only this.

Do Exercises 17 and 18.

Answers on page A-1

CHAPTER R: Review

BORROWING MORE THAN ONCE

Sometimes we must borrow more than once.

EXAMPLE 9 Subtract: $672 - 394$.

$$
\begin{array}{r}
6\ \overset{6}{\cancel{7}}\ \overset{12}{\cancel{2}} \\
-\ 3\ 9\ 4 \\
\hline
8
\end{array}
$$
Borrowing a ten to subtract ones

$$
\begin{array}{r}
\overset{16}{\cancel{6}}\ \overset{6}{\cancel{7}}\ \overset{12}{\cancel{2}} \\
-\ 3\ 9\ 4 \\
\hline
2\ 7\ 8
\end{array}
$$
Borrowing a hundred to subtract tens

Do Exercises 19 and 20.

EXAMPLE 10 Subtract: $6357 - 1769$.

$$
\begin{array}{r}
6\ 3\ \overset{4}{\cancel{5}}\ \overset{17}{\cancel{7}} \\
-\ 1\ 7\ 6\ 9 \\
\hline
8
\end{array}
$$
$7 - 9$ is not a whole number.
We borrow a ten.

$$
\begin{array}{r}
6\ \overset{2}{\cancel{3}}\ \overset{14}{\overset{4}{\cancel{5}}}\ \overset{17}{\cancel{7}} \\
1\ 7\ 6\ 9 \\
\hline
8\ 8
\end{array}
$$
4 tens minus 6 tens is not a whole number.
We borrow a hundred.

$$
\begin{array}{r}
\overset{5}{\cancel{6}}\ \overset{12}{\overset{2}{\cancel{3}}}\ \overset{14}{\overset{4}{\cancel{5}}}\ \overset{17}{\cancel{7}} \\
-\ 1\ 7\ 6\ 9 \\
\hline
4\ 5\ 8\ 8
\end{array}
$$
2 hundreds minus 7 hundreds is not a whole number.
We borrow a thousand.

We can always check by adding the answer to the number being subtracted.

EXAMPLE 11 Subtract: $8341 - 2673$. Check by adding.

We check by adding 5668 and 2673.

$$
\begin{array}{r}
7\ \overset{12}{\cancel{2}}\ \overset{13}{\cancel{3}}\ 11 \\
\cancel{8}\ \cancel{3}\ \cancel{4}\ \cancel{1} \\
-\ 2\ 6\ 7\ 3 \\
\hline
5\ 6\ 6\ 8
\end{array}
\qquad
Check:\quad
\begin{array}{r}
\overset{1}{5}\ \overset{1}{6}\ \overset{1}{6}\ 8 \\
+\ 2\ 6\ 7\ 3 \\
\hline
8\ 3\ 4\ 1
\end{array}
$$

Do Exercises 21 and 22.

ZEROS IN SUBTRACTION

Before subtracting, note the following:

50 is 5 tens;

70 is 7 tens.

Then

100 is 10 tens;

200 is 20 tens.

Do Exercises 23–26.

Subtract.

19.
$$
\begin{array}{r}
5\ 6\ 3 \\
-\ 1\ 8\ 7 \\
\hline
\end{array}
$$

20.
$$
\begin{array}{r}
7\ 3\ 3 \\
-\ 4\ 8\ 8 \\
\hline
\end{array}
$$

Subtract. Check by adding.

21.
$$
\begin{array}{r}
4\ 2\ 3\ 6 \\
-\ 1\ 6\ 7\ 9 \\
\hline
\end{array}
$$

22.
$$
\begin{array}{r}
7\ 5\ 4\ 1 \\
-\ 3\ 0\ 6\ 7 \\
\hline
\end{array}
$$

Complete.

23. $80 = \underline{\qquad}$ tens

24. $60 = \underline{\qquad}$ tens

25. $300 = \underline{\qquad}$ tens

26. $900 = \underline{\qquad}$ tens

Answers on page A-1

Complete.

27. 5000 = _____ tens

28. 9000 = _____ tens

29. 5380 = _____ tens

30. 6770 = _____ tens

Subtract.

31.　　6 0　　　　**32.**　　4 8 0
　　　− 1 8　　　　　　　− 2 5 6

Subtract.

33.　　6 0 2　　　**34.**　　4 0 8
　　　− 4 6 4　　　　　　− 3 6 4

Subtract.

35.　4 0 0 6　　　**36.**　9 0 0 1
　　　− 1 2 3 8　　　　　− 7 8 0 4

Subtract.

37.　3 0 0 0　　　**38.**　8 0 1 7
　　　− 1 7 5 4　　　　　− 3 2 8 9

Also,

　　230 is 2 hundreds + 3 tens
　　or 20 tens + 3 tens
　　or 23 tens.

Similarly,

　　1000 is 100 tens;
　　2000 is 200 tens;
　　4670 is 467 tens.

Do Exercises 27–30.

EXAMPLE 12　Subtract: 50 − 37.

$$\overset{4\ \ 10}{\cancel{5}\ \cancel{0}}$$
$$-\ 3\ 7$$
$$1\ 3$$

We have 5 tens. We keep 4 of them in the tens column and put 1 ten, or 10 ones, with the ones.

Do Exercises 31 and 32.

EXAMPLE 13　Subtract: 803 − 547.

$$\overset{7\ \ 9\ \ 13}{8\ \cancel{0}\ \cancel{3}}$$
$$-\ 5\ 4\ 7$$
$$2\ 5\ 6$$

We have 8 hundreds, or 80 tens. We keep 79 tens and put 1 ten, or 10 ones, with the ones.

Do Exercises 33 and 34.

EXAMPLE 14　Subtract: 9003 − 2789.

$$\overset{8\ \ 9\ \ 9\ \ 13}{9\ \cancel{0}\ \cancel{0}\ \cancel{3}}$$
$$-\ 2\ 7\ 8\ 9$$
$$6\ 2\ 1\ 4$$

We have 9 thousands, or 900 tens. We keep 899 tens and put 1 ten, or 10 ones, with the ones.

Do Exercises 35 and 36.

EXAMPLES　Subtract.

15.　$\overset{4\ \ 9\ \ 9\ \ 10}{5\ \cancel{0}\ \cancel{0}\ \cancel{0}}$
　　　$-\ 2\ 8\ 6\ 1$
　　　$\ \ 2\ 1\ 3\ 9$

16.　$\overset{4\ \ 9\ \ \overset{10}{\cancel{0}}\ \ 13}{5\ \cancel{0}\ \cancel{1}\ \cancel{3}}$
　　　$-\ 1\ 8\ 5\ 7$
　　　$\ \ 3\ 1\ 5\ 6$

We have 5 thousands, or 49 hundreds and 10 tens.

Do Exercises 37 and 38.

EXERCISE SET

a Subtract. Try to do these mentally.

1.	7	2.	8	3.	7	4.	8	5.	5
	− 0		− 8		− 7		− 3		− 2

6.	1 6	7.	1 7	8.	1 2	9.	1 1	10.	1 2
	− 8		− 9		− 6		− 4		− 9

11.	1 4	12.	1 8	13.	1 3	14.	1 5	15.	9
	− 7		− 9		− 7		− 9		− 7

16. $7 - 3$ **17.** $4 - 1$ **18.** $2 - 0$ **19.** $3 - 3$ **20.** $6 - 3$

21. $7 - 6$ **22.** $9 - 8$ **23.** $10 - 3$ **24.** $6 - 6$ **25.** $11 - 7$

26. $12 - 8$ **27.** $5 - 0$ **28.** $4 - 0$ **29.** $13 - 9$ **30.** $14 - 9$

31. $11 - 2$ **32.** $12 - 3$ **33.** $16 - 9$ **34.** $18 - 9$ **35.** $11 - 5$

36. $10 - 4$ **37.** $10 - 8$ **38.** $14 - 8$ **39.** $15 - 8$ **40.** $10 - 2$

b Subtract.

41.	6 4	42.	5 5	43.	5 4 8	44.	5 9 6	45.	7 0 0
	− 3 1		− 3 4		− 3 0 1		− 4 0 3		− 2 0 0

46.
$$765 - 111$$

47.
$$525 - 323$$

48.
$$747 - 130$$

49.
$$988 - 700$$

50.
$$9450 - 8230$$

51.
$$6552 - 4321$$

52.
$$7547 - 3421$$

53.
$$5875 - 2111$$

54.
$$38{,}695 - 37{,}004$$

55.
$$67{,}899 - 66{,}673$$

56.
$$99{,}999 - 1$$

57.
$$56{,}780 - 56{,}770$$

58.
$$42{,}111 - 32{,}010$$

59.
$$77{,}654 - 66{,}611$$

60.
$$23{,}456 - 12{,}345$$

C Subtract.

61.
$$93 - 28$$

62.
$$42 - 13$$

63.
$$86 - 78$$

64.
$$98 - 89$$

65.
$$625 - 317$$

66.
$$735 - 609$$

67.
$$853 - 236$$

68.
$$961 - 747$$

69.
$$787 - 698$$

70.
$$6769 - 2367$$

71.
$$6431 - 2876$$

72.
$$7654 - 1765$$

73.
$$5246 - 2859$$

74.
$$6328 - 2679$$

75.
$$7641 - 3809$$

76.
$$8743 - 599$$

77.
$$12{,}647 - 4{,}897$$

78.
$$16{,}222 - 5{,}777$$

79.
$$46{,}781 - 12{,}988$$

80.
$$470 - 189$$

81.
$$690 - 235$$

82.
$$703 - 132$$

83.
$$6406 - 258$$

84.
$$2309 - 109$$

85.
$$3406 - 1293$$

86.
$$6807 - 3059$$

87.
$$8000 - 2794$$

88.
$$8002 - 6543$$

89.
$$38{,}000 - 37{,}695$$

90.
$$16{,}043 - 11{,}588$$

R.3 MULTIPLICATION

Objectives

a Multiply any two of the numbers 0, 1, 2, 3, 4, 5, 6, 7, 8, 9.

b Multiply by multiples of 10, 100, and 1000.

c Multiply larger numbers by 0, 1, 2, 3, 4, 5, 6, 7, 8, 9.

d Multiply by multiples of 10, 100, and 1000.

a   Basic Multiplication

To multiply, we begin with two numbers, called **factors,** and get a third number, called a **product.** Multiplication can be explained by counting. The product 3×5 can be found by counting out 3 sets of 5 objects each, joining them (in a rectangular array if desired), and counting all the objects.

Factor   Factor   Product

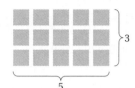

We can also think of multiplication as repeated addition.

$$3 \times 5 = \underbrace{5 + 5 + 5}_{\text{3 addends of 5}} = 15$$

■ **EXAMPLES**   Multiply. If you have trouble, think either of putting sets of objects together in a rectangular array or of repeated addition.

1. $5 \times 6 = 30$

$$\begin{array}{r} 6 \\ \times\ 5 \\ \hline 30 \end{array}$$

2. $8 \times 4 = 32$

$$\begin{array}{r} 4 \\ \times\ 8 \\ \hline 32 \end{array}$$

Do Exercises 1–4.

MULTIPLYING BY 0

How do we multiply by 0? Consider $4 \cdot 0$. Using repeated addition, we see that

$$4 \cdot 0 = \underbrace{0 + 0 + 0 + 0}_{\text{4 addends of 0}} = 0.$$

We can also think of this using sets. That is, $4 \cdot 0$ is 4 sets with 0 objects in each set, so the total is 0.

Consider $0 \cdot 4$. Using repeated addition, we say that this is 0 addends of 4, which is 0. Using sets, we say that this is 0 sets with 4 objects in each set, which is 0. Thus we have the following.

MULTIPLICATION BY 0

Multiplying by 0 gives 0.

■ **EXAMPLES**   Multiply.

3. $13 \times 0 = 0$

$$\begin{array}{r} 0 \\ \times\ 13 \\ \hline 0 \end{array}$$

4. $0 \cdot 11 = 0$

$$\begin{array}{r} 11 \\ \times\ 0 \\ \hline 0 \end{array}$$

5. $0 \cdot 0 = 0$

$$\begin{array}{r} 0 \\ \times\ 0 \\ \hline 0 \end{array}$$

Do Exercises 5 and 6.

Multiply. Think of joining sets in a rectangular array or of repeated addition.

1. $7 \cdot 8$ (The dot "$\cdot$" means the same as "$\times$".)

2. $\begin{array}{r} 9 \\ \times\ 4 \\ \hline \end{array}$

3. $4 \cdot 7$

4. $\begin{array}{r} 7 \\ \times\ 6 \\ \hline \end{array}$

Multiply.

5. $8 \cdot 0$

6. $\begin{array}{r} 17 \\ \times\ 0 \\ \hline \end{array}$

Answers on page A-2

Multiply.

7. $8 \cdot 1$

8. $\begin{array}{r} 2\,3 \\ \times\ \ \ 1 \\ \hline \end{array}$

9. Complete the table.

×	2	3	4	5
2				
3			12	
4				
5		15		
6				

10.

×	6	7	8	9
5				
6			48	
7				
8		56		
9				

Answers on page A-2

MULTIPLYING BY 1

How do we multiply by 1? Consider $5 \cdot 1$. Using repeated addition, we see that

$$5 \cdot 1 = \underbrace{1 + 1 + 1 + 1 + 1}_{5 \text{ addends of } 1} = 5.$$

We can also think of this using sets. That is, $5 \cdot 1$ is 5 sets with 1 object in each set, for a total of 5 objects.

Consider $1 \cdot 5$. Using repeated addition, we say that this is 1 addend of 5, which is 5. Using sets, we say that this is 1 set of 5 objects, which is again 5 objects. Thus we have the following.

MULTIPLICATION BY 1

Multiplying a number by 1 does not change the number:
$$a \cdot 1 = 1 \cdot a = a.$$
We say that 1 is the **multiplicative identity.**

This is a very important property.

EXAMPLES Multiply.

6. $13 \cdot 1 = 13$

$\begin{array}{r} 1 \\ \times\ 13 \\ \hline 13 \end{array}$

7. $1 \cdot 7 = 7$

$\begin{array}{r} 7 \\ \times\ 1 \\ \hline 7 \end{array}$

8. $1 \cdot 1 = 1$

$\begin{array}{r} 1 \\ \times\ 1 \\ \hline 1 \end{array}$

Do Exercises 7 and 8.

You should be able to multiply any two of the numbers 0, 1, 2, 3, 4, 5, 6, 7, 8, 9. Multiplying by 0 and 1 is easy. The rest of the products are listed in the following table.

×	2	3	4	5	6	7	8	9
2	4	6	8	10	12	14	16	18
3	6	9	12	15	18	21	24	27
4	8	12	16	20	24	28	32	36
5	10	15	20	25	30	35	40	45
6	12	18	24	30	36	42	48	54
7	14	21	28	35	42	49	56	63
8	16	24	32	40	48	56	64	72
9	18	27	36	45	54	63	72	81

$5 \times 7 = 35$
Find 5 at the left, and 7 at the top.

$8 \cdot 4 = 32$
Find 8 at the left, and 4 at the top.

It is *very* important that you have the basic multiplication facts *memorized.* If you do not, you will always have trouble with multiplication.

The *commutative law of multiplication* says that we can multiply numbers in any order. Thus you need to learn only about half the table, as shown by the shading.

Do Exercises 9 and 10.

b Multiplying by 10, 100, and 1000

We now move to a more gradual, conceptual development of the multiplication procedure. It is intended to provide you with a greater understanding so that your skill level will increase.

We begin by considering multiplication by 10, 100, and 1000.

MULTIPLYING BY 10

We know that

$$50 = 5 \text{ tens} \qquad 340 = 34 \text{ tens} \quad \text{and} \quad 2340 = 234 \text{ tens}$$
$$= 5 \cdot 10, \qquad = 34 \cdot 10, \qquad = 234 \cdot 10.$$

Turning this around, we see that to multiply any number by 10, all we need do is write a 0 on the end of the number.

> **MULTIPLICATION BY 10**
>
> To multiply a number by 10, write 0 on the end of the number.

EXAMPLES Multiply.

9. $10 \cdot 6 = 60$

10. $10 \cdot 47 = 470$

11. $10 \cdot 583 = 5830$

Do Exercises 11–15.

Let's find $4 \cdot 90$. This is $4 \cdot (9 \text{ tens})$, or 36 tens. The procedure is the same as multiplying 4 and 9 and writing a 0 on the end. Thus, $4 \cdot 90 = 360$.

EXAMPLES Multiply.

12. $5 \cdot 70 = 350$
    ———— $5 \cdot 7$, then write a 0

13. $8 \cdot 80 = 640$

14. $5 \cdot 60 = 300$

Do Exercises 16 and 17.

MULTIPLYING BY 100

Note the following:

$$300 = 3 \text{ hundreds} \qquad 4700 = 47 \text{ hundreds} \quad \text{and} \quad 56,800 = 568 \text{ hundreds}$$
$$= 3 \cdot 100, \qquad = 47 \cdot 100, \qquad = 568 \cdot 100.$$

Turning this around, we see that to multiply any number by 100, all we need do is write two 0's on the end of the number.

> **MULTIPLICATION BY 100**
>
> To multiply a number by 100, write two 0's on the end of the number.

Multiply.

11. $10 \cdot 7$

12. $10 \cdot 45$

13. $10 \cdot 273$

14. $10 \cdot 10$

15. $10 \cdot 100$

Multiply.

16. $\begin{array}{r} 7\,0 \\ \times \quad 8 \\ \hline \end{array}$

17. $\begin{array}{r} 6\,0 \\ \times \quad 6 \\ \hline \end{array}$

Answers on page A-2

Multiply.

18. $100 \cdot 7$ **19.** $100 \cdot 23$

20. $100 \cdot 723$ **21.** $100 \cdot 100$

22. $100 \cdot 1000$

Multiply.

23.
$$\begin{array}{r} 7\,0\,0 \\ \times \quad\ 8 \\ \hline \end{array}$$

24.
$$\begin{array}{r} 4\,0\,0 \\ \times \quad\ 4 \\ \hline \end{array}$$

Multiply.

25. $1000 \cdot 9$ **26.** $1000 \cdot 852$

27. $1000 \cdot 10$ **28.** $3 \cdot 4000$

29. $9 \cdot 8000$

■ **EXAMPLES** Multiply.

15. $100 \cdot 6 = 600$

16. $100 \cdot 39 = 3900$

17. $100 \cdot 448 = 44{,}800$

Do Exercises 18–22.

Let's find $4 \cdot 900$. This is $4 \cdot (9 \text{ hundreds})$, or 36 hundreds. The procedure is the same as multiplying 4 and 9 and writing two 0's on the end. Thus, $4 \cdot 900 = 3600$.

■ **EXAMPLES** Multiply.

18. $6 \cdot 800 = 4800$ $6 \cdot 8$, then write 00

19. $9 \cdot 700 = 6300$

20. $5 \cdot 500 = 2500$

Do Exercises 23 and 24.

MULTIPLYING BY 1000

Note the following:

$$6000 = 6 \text{ thousands} \quad \text{and} \quad 19{,}000 = 19 \text{ thousands}$$
$$= 6 \cdot 1000 \qquad\qquad\qquad = 19 \cdot 1000.$$

Turning this around, we see that to multiply any number by 1000, all we need do is write three 0's on the end of the number.

> **MULTIPLYING BY 1000**
>
> To multiply a number by 1000, write three 0's on the end of the number.

■ **EXAMPLES** Multiply.

21. $1000 \cdot 8 = 8000$

22. $2000 \cdot 13 = 26{,}000$ $2 \cdot 13$, then write 000.

23. $1000 \cdot 567 = 567{,}000$

Do Exercises 25–29.

MULTIPLYING MULTIPLES BY MULTIPLES

Let's multiply 50 and 30. This is $50 \cdot (3 \text{ tens})$, or 150 tens, or 1500. The procedure is the same as multiplying 5 and 3 and writing two 0's on the end.

To multiply multiples of tens, hundreds, thousands, and so on:

a) Multiply the one-digit numbers.

b) Count the number of zeros.

c) Write that many 0's on the end.

EXAMPLES Multiply.

24.
```
      80     1 zero at end
×     60     1 zero at end
    4800
      ↑────── 6 · 8, then write 00
```

25.
```
     800     2 zeros at end
×     60     1 zero at end
   48,000
      ↑────── 6 · 8, then write 000
```

26.
```
     800     2 zeros at end
×    600     2 zeros at end
  480,000
      ↑────── 6 · 8, then write 0,000
```

27.
```
     800     2 zeros at end
×     50     1 zero at end
   40,000
      ↑────── 5 · 8, then write 000
```

Do Exercises 30–33.

C Multiplying Larger Numbers

The product 3 × 24 can be represented as

$$3 \times (2 \text{ tens} + 4) = (2 \text{ tens} + 4) + (2 \text{ tens} + 4) + (2 \text{ tens} + 4)$$
$$= 6 \text{ tens} + 12$$
$$= 6 \text{ tens} + 1 \text{ ten} + 2$$
$$= 7 \text{ tens} + 2$$
$$= 72.$$

We multiply the 4 ones by 3, getting   12
We multiply the 2 tens by 3, getting   + 60
               Then we add: 72

EXAMPLE 28 Multiply: 3 × 24.

```
    2 4     We use the approach described above.
×     3
    1 2 ← Multiply the 4 ones by 3.
    6 0 ← Multiply the 2 tens by 3.
    7 2 ← Add.
```

Do Exercises 34–36.

EXAMPLE 29 Multiply: 5 × 734.

```
      7 3 4
×         5
      2 0 ← Multiply the 4 ones by 5.
    1 5 0 ← Multiply the 3 tens by 5.
  3 5 0 0 ← Multiply the 7 hundreds by 5.
  3 6 7 0 ← Add.
```

Do Exercises 37 and 38.

Multiply.

30.
```
  9 0 0 0
×       6
```

31.
```
    8 0
× 7 0
```

32.
```
  8 0 0
× 7 0
```

33.
```
  6 0 0
× 3 0
```

Multiply.

34.
```
  1 4
× 2
```

35.
```
  5 8
× 2
```

36.
```
  3 7
× 4
```

Multiply.

37.
```
  8 2 3
×     6
```

38.
```
  1 3 4 8
×       5
```

Answers on page A-2

Multiply using the short form.

39.
$$\begin{array}{r} 5\ 8 \\ \times\ \ \ 2 \\ \hline \end{array}$$

40.
$$\begin{array}{r} 3\ 7 \\ \times\ \ \ 4 \\ \hline \end{array}$$

41.
$$\begin{array}{r} 8\ 2\ 3 \\ \times\ \ \ \ \ 6 \\ \hline \end{array}$$

42.
$$\begin{array}{r} 1\ 3\ 4\ 8 \\ \times\ \ \ \ \ \ \ 5 \\ \hline \end{array}$$

Multiply.

43.
$$\begin{array}{r} 7\ 4\ 6 \\ \times\ \ \ \ \ 8 \\ \hline \end{array}$$

44.
$$\begin{array}{r} 7\ 4\ 6 \\ \times\ \ 8\ 0 \\ \hline \end{array}$$

45.
$$\begin{array}{r} 7\ 4\ 6 \\ \times\ 8\ 0\ 0 \\ \hline \end{array}$$

Let's look at Example 29 again. Instead of writing each product on a separate line, we can use a shorter form.

EXAMPLE 30 Multiply: 5×734.

$$\begin{array}{r} 7\ \overset{2}{3}\ 4 \\ \times\ \ \ \ \ 5 \\ \hline 0 \end{array}$$

Multiply the ones by 5: $5 \cdot (4\text{ ones}) = 20$ ones $= 2$ tens $+ 0$ ones. Write 0 in the ones column and 2 above the tens.

$$\begin{array}{r} 7\ \overset{1}{3}\ \overset{2}{4} \\ \times\ \ \ \ \ 5 \\ \hline 7\ 0 \end{array}$$

Multiply 3 tens by 5 and add 2 tens: $5 \cdot (3\text{ tens}) = 15$ tens; 15 tens $+ 2$ tens $= 17$ tens $= 1$ hundred $+ 7$ tens. Write 7 in the tens column and 1 above the hundreds.

$$\begin{array}{r} \overset{1}{7}\ \overset{2}{3}\ 4 \\ \times\ \ \ \ \ 5 \\ \hline 3\ 6\ 7\ 0 \end{array}$$

Multiply the 7 hundreds by 5 and add 1 hundred: $5 \cdot (7\text{ hundreds}) = 35$ hundreds, 35 hundreds $+ 1$ hundred $= 36$ hundreds.

$$\left.\begin{array}{r} \overset{1}{7}\ \overset{2}{3}\ 4 \\ \times\ \ \ \ \ 5 \\ \hline 3\ 6\ 7\ 0 \end{array}\right\}$$ You should write only this.

Try to avoid writing the reminders unless necessary.

Do Exercises 39–42.

d Multiplying by Multiples of 10, 100, and 1000

To multiply 327 by 50, we multiply by 10 (write a 0), and then multiply 327 by 5.

$$\begin{array}{r} 3\ 2\ 7 \\ \times\ \ \ \ 5\ \boxed{0} \\ \hline 1\ 6,3\ 5\ 0 \end{array}$$

← Write a 0.

Multiply $5 \cdot 327$.

EXAMPLE 31 Multiply: 400×289.

$$\begin{array}{r} 2\ 8\ 9 \\ \times\ 4\ \boxed{0\ 0} \\ \hline 0\ 0 \end{array}$$

← Write two 0's.

$$\begin{array}{r} 2\ 8\ 9 \\ \times\ \ \ 4\ 0\ 0 \\ \hline 1\ 1\ 5,6\ 0\ 0 \end{array}$$

Multiply 4 and 289:

$$\begin{array}{r} \overset{3}{2}\ \overset{3}{8}\ 9 \\ \times\ \ \ \ \ 4 \\ \hline 1\ 1\ 5\ 6 \end{array}$$

$$\left.\begin{array}{r} \overset{3}{2}\ \overset{3}{8}\ 9 \\ \times\ \ \ 4\ 0\ 0 \\ \hline 1\ 1\ 5,6\ 0\ 0 \end{array}\right\}$$ Try to write only this.

Do Exercises 43–45.

R.3 EXERCISE SET

For Extra Help

Math Tutor Center   MyMathLab

a Multiply. Try to do these mentally.

1. $\begin{array}{r} 3 \\ \times\ 4 \\ \hline \end{array}$	**2.** $\begin{array}{r} 6 \\ \times\ 0 \\ \hline \end{array}$	**3.** $\begin{array}{r} 7 \\ \times\ 1 \\ \hline \end{array}$	**4.** $\begin{array}{r} 0 \\ \times\ 2 \\ \hline \end{array}$	**5.** $\begin{array}{r} 10 \\ \times\ 1 \\ \hline \end{array}$	**6.** $\begin{array}{r} 6 \\ \times\ 5 \\ \hline \end{array}$
7. $\begin{array}{r} 5 \\ \times\ 2 \\ \hline \end{array}$	**8.** $\begin{array}{r} 9 \\ \times\ 7 \\ \hline \end{array}$	**9.** $\begin{array}{r} 9 \\ \times\ 6 \\ \hline \end{array}$	**10.** $\begin{array}{r} 2 \\ \times\ 6 \\ \hline \end{array}$	**11.** $\begin{array}{r} 7 \\ \times\ 0 \\ \hline \end{array}$	**12.** $\begin{array}{r} 8 \\ \times\ 9 \\ \hline \end{array}$
13. $\begin{array}{r} 1 \\ \times\ 8 \\ \hline \end{array}$	**14.** $\begin{array}{r} 8 \\ \times\ 0 \\ \hline \end{array}$	**15.** $\begin{array}{r} 4 \\ \times\ 7 \\ \hline \end{array}$	**16.** $\begin{array}{r} 3 \\ \times\ 8 \\ \hline \end{array}$	**17.** $\begin{array}{r} 5 \\ \times\ 9 \\ \hline \end{array}$	**18.** $\begin{array}{r} 2 \\ \times\ 9 \\ \hline \end{array}$
19. $\begin{array}{r} 0 \\ \times\ 7 \\ \hline \end{array}$	**20.** $\begin{array}{r} 5 \\ \times\ 7 \\ \hline \end{array}$	**21.** $\begin{array}{r} 9 \\ \times\ 5 \\ \hline \end{array}$	**22.** $\begin{array}{r} 5 \\ \times\ 8 \\ \hline \end{array}$	**23.** $\begin{array}{r} 0 \\ \times\ 0 \\ \hline \end{array}$	**24.** $\begin{array}{r} 2 \\ \times\ 8 \\ \hline \end{array}$

25. $5 \cdot 5$

26. $9 \cdot 9$

27. $1 \cdot 1$

28. $0 \cdot 0$

29. $2 \cdot 2$

30. $6 \cdot 6$

31. $1 \cdot 8$

32. $0 \cdot 1$

33. $3 \cdot 9$

34. $2 \cdot 9$

35. $6 \cdot 0$

36. $10 \cdot 1$

37. $6 \cdot 8$

38. $9 \cdot 6$

39. $8 \cdot 0$

40. $9 \cdot 8$

41. $3 \cdot 5$

42. $1 \cdot 8$

43. $1 \cdot 9$

44. $2 \cdot 1$

45. $8 \cdot 4$

46. $3 \cdot 2$

47. $5 \cdot 3$

48. $1 \cdot 6$

49. $4 \cdot 2$

50. $4 \cdot 5$

51. $5 \cdot 4$

52. $4 \cdot 4$

53. $5 \cdot 2$

54. $8 \cdot 0$

b Multiply.

55.
$$\begin{array}{r} 1\,0 \\ \times\quad 8 \\ \hline \end{array}$$

56.
$$\begin{array}{r} 7 \\ \times\,1\,0 \\ \hline \end{array}$$

57.
$$\begin{array}{r} 2\,0 \\ \times\quad 8 \\ \hline \end{array}$$

58.
$$\begin{array}{r} 3\,0 \\ \times\quad 7 \\ \hline \end{array}$$

59.
$$\begin{array}{r} 4\,5 \\ \times\,1\,0 \\ \hline \end{array}$$

60.
$$\begin{array}{r} 7\,8 \\ \times\,1\,0 \\ \hline \end{array}$$

61.
$$\begin{array}{r} 8\,0 \\ \times\quad 7 \\ \hline \end{array}$$

62.
$$\begin{array}{r} 9\,0 \\ \times\quad 4 \\ \hline \end{array}$$

63.
$$\begin{array}{r} 1\,0\,0 \\ \times\quad 8 \\ \hline \end{array}$$

64.
$$\begin{array}{r} 1\,0\,0 \\ \times\quad 3 \\ \hline \end{array}$$

65.
$$\begin{array}{r} 1\,0\,0 \\ \times\quad 9 \\ \hline \end{array}$$

66.
$$\begin{array}{r} 1\,0\,0 \\ \times\,1\,0 \\ \hline \end{array}$$

67.
$$\begin{array}{r} 3\,4\,5\,7 \\ \times\,1\,0\,0 \\ \hline \end{array}$$

68.
$$\begin{array}{r} 4\,0\,0 \\ \times\quad 3 \\ \hline \end{array}$$

69.
$$\begin{array}{r} 7\,0\,0 \\ \times\quad 7 \\ \hline \end{array}$$

70.
$$\begin{array}{r} 5\,0\,0 \\ \times\quad 8 \\ \hline \end{array}$$

71.
$$\begin{array}{r} 1\,0\,0 \\ \times\,1\,0\,0 \\ \hline \end{array}$$

72.
$$\begin{array}{r} 1\,0\,0\,0 \\ \times\quad 7 \\ \hline \end{array}$$

73.
$$\begin{array}{r} 1\,0\,0\,0 \\ \times\quad 9 \\ \hline \end{array}$$

74.
$$\begin{array}{r} 1\,0\,0\,0 \\ \times\quad 2 \\ \hline \end{array}$$

75.
$$\begin{array}{r} 4\,5\,7 \\ \times\,1\,0\,0\,0 \\ \hline \end{array}$$

76.
$$\begin{array}{r} 6\,7\,6\,9 \\ \times\,1\,0\,0\,0 \\ \hline \end{array}$$

77.
$$\begin{array}{r} 2\,0\,0\,0 \\ \times\quad 9 \\ \hline \end{array}$$

78.
$$\begin{array}{r} 5\,0\,0\,0 \\ \times\quad 4 \\ \hline \end{array}$$

79.
$$\begin{array}{r} 6\,0\,0\,0 \\ \times\quad 8 \\ \hline \end{array}$$

80.
$$\begin{array}{r} 8\,0\,0\,0 \\ \times\quad 2 \\ \hline \end{array}$$

81.
$$\begin{array}{r} 3\,0\,0\,0 \\ \times\quad 2 \\ \hline \end{array}$$

82.
$$\begin{array}{r} 1\,0\,0\,0 \\ \times\,1\,0\,0\,0 \\ \hline \end{array}$$

83.
$$\begin{array}{r} 4\,0 \\ \times\,3\,0 \\ \hline \end{array}$$

84.
$$\begin{array}{r} 2\,0 \\ \times\,1\,0 \\ \hline \end{array}$$

85.
$$\begin{array}{r} 8\,0 \\ \times\,5\,0 \\ \hline \end{array}$$

86.
$$\begin{array}{r} 5\,0 \\ \times\,5\,0 \\ \hline \end{array}$$

87.
$$\begin{array}{r} 4\,0\,0 \\ \times\quad 3\,0 \\ \hline \end{array}$$

88.
$$\begin{array}{r} 2\,0\,0 \\ \times\quad 3\,0 \\ \hline \end{array}$$

89.
$$\begin{array}{r} 7\,0\,0 \\ \times\quad 9\,0 \\ \hline \end{array}$$

90.
$$\begin{array}{r} 4\,0\,0 \\ \times\,3\,0\,0 \\ \hline \end{array}$$

91.
$$\begin{array}{r} 4\,0\,0\,0 \\ \times\quad 2\,0\,0 \\ \hline \end{array}$$

92.
$$\begin{array}{r} 6\,0\,0\,0 \\ \times\quad 2\,0 \\ \hline \end{array}$$

93.
$$\begin{array}{r} 4\,0\,0\,0 \\ \times\,4\,0\,0\,0 \\ \hline \end{array}$$

94.
$$\begin{array}{r} 8\,0\,0\,0 \\ \times\quad 1\,0 \\ \hline \end{array}$$

c Multiply.

95.
$$\begin{array}{r} 4\,9 \\ \times\quad 3 \\ \hline \end{array}$$

96.
$$\begin{array}{r} 7\,4 \\ \times\quad 6 \\ \hline \end{array}$$

97.
$$\begin{array}{r} 5\,9\,3 \\ \times\quad 5 \\ \hline \end{array}$$

98.
$$\begin{array}{r} 6\,0\,9 \\ \times\quad 8 \\ \hline \end{array}$$

99.
$$\begin{array}{r} 8\,9\,9 \\ \times\quad 7 \\ \hline \end{array}$$

100.
$$\begin{array}{r} 8\,6\,5 \\ \times\quad 4 \\ \hline \end{array}$$

101.
$$\begin{array}{r} 8\,1\,1\,8 \\ \times\quad 2 \\ \hline \end{array}$$

102.
$$\begin{array}{r} 6\,7\,5\,4 \\ \times\quad 2 \\ \hline \end{array}$$

103.
$$\begin{array}{r} 4\,3\,,7\,7\,7 \\ \times\quad 2 \\ \hline \end{array}$$

104.
$$\begin{array}{r} 3\,2\,,5\,6\,4 \\ \times\quad 6 \\ \hline \end{array}$$

d Multiply.

105.
$$\begin{array}{r} 5\,8 \\ \times\,6\,0 \\ \hline \end{array}$$

106.
$$\begin{array}{r} 9\,3 \\ \times\,3\,0 \\ \hline \end{array}$$

107.
$$\begin{array}{r} 4\,2 \\ \times\,8\,0 \\ \hline \end{array}$$

108.
$$\begin{array}{r} 7\,8 \\ \times\,9\,0 \\ \hline \end{array}$$

109.
$$\begin{array}{r} 3\,4\,6 \\ \times\quad 6\,0 \\ \hline \end{array}$$

110.
$$\begin{array}{r} 2\,6\,7 \\ \times\quad 4\,0 \\ \hline \end{array}$$

111.
$$\begin{array}{r} 8\,9\,7 \\ \times\,4\,0\,0 \\ \hline \end{array}$$

112.
$$\begin{array}{r} 3\,6\,6 \\ \times\,3\,0\,0 \\ \hline \end{array}$$

113.
$$\begin{array}{r} 8\,3\,4 \\ \times\,7\,0\,0 \\ \hline \end{array}$$

114.
$$\begin{array}{r} 3\,3\,3 \\ \times\,9\,0\,0 \\ \hline \end{array}$$

115.
$$\begin{array}{r} 5\,6\,7\,3 \\ \times\,2\,0\,0\,0 \\ \hline \end{array}$$

116.
$$\begin{array}{r} 4\,6\,7\,8 \\ \times\,5\,0\,0\,0 \\ \hline \end{array}$$

117.
$$\begin{array}{r} 6\,7\,8\,8 \\ \times\,9\,0\,0\,0 \\ \hline \end{array}$$

118.
$$\begin{array}{r} 9\,1\,2\,9 \\ \times\,8\,0\,0\,0 \\ \hline \end{array}$$

R.4 DIVISION

Objectives

a   Find basic quotients such as $20 \div 5$, $56 \div 7$, and so on.

b   Divide using the "guess, multiply, and subtract" method.

c   Divide by estimating multiples of thousands, hundreds, tens, and ones.

a   Basic Division

Division can be explained by arranging a set of objects in a rectangular array. This can be done in two ways.

EXAMPLE 1   Divide: $18 \div 6$.

METHOD 1   We can do this division by taking 18 objects and determining how many rows, each with 6 objects, we can form.

3 rows of 6 objects

Since there are 3 rows of 6 objects, we have

$$18 \div 6 = 3.$$

METHOD 2   We can also arrange the objects into 6 rows and determine how many objects are in each row.

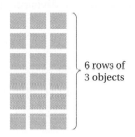

6 rows of 3 objects

Since there are 3 objects in each of the 6 rows, we have

$$18 \div 6 = 3.$$

We can also use fraction notation for division. That is,

$$18 \div 6 = 18/6 = \frac{18}{6}.$$

EXAMPLES   Divide.

2. $9 \overline{)\ 3\ 6}^{\ \ 4}$ *Think*: 36 objects: How many rows, each with 9 objects? or 36 objects: How many objects in each of 9 rows?

3. $42 \div 7 = 6$

4. $\dfrac{24}{3} = 8$

Do Exercises 1–4.

Divide.

1. $24 \div 6$

2. $64 \div 8$

3. $\dfrac{63}{7}$

4. $\dfrac{27}{9}$

Answers on page A-2

For each multiplication fact, write two division facts.

5. $6 \cdot 2 = 12$

In R.3, you memorized a multiplication table. That table will enable you to divide as well. First, let's recall how multiplication and division are related.

A multiplication: $5 \cdot 4 = 20$.

Two related divisions:

A.  $20 \div 5 = 4.$

B. 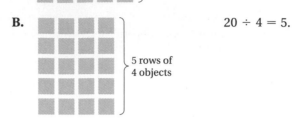 $20 \div 4 = 5.$

Since we know that

$$5 \cdot 4 = 20, \qquad \text{A basic multiplication fact}$$

we also know the two division facts

$$20 \div 5 = 4 \quad \text{and} \quad 20 \div 4 = 5.$$

EXAMPLE 5 From $7 \cdot 8 = 56$, write two division facts.

a) We have

$$7 \cdot 8 = 56 \qquad \text{Multiplication sentence}$$

$$7 = 56 \div 8. \qquad \text{Related division sentence}$$

b) We also have

$$7 \cdot 8 = 56 \qquad \text{Multiplication sentence}$$

$$8 = 56 \div 7. \qquad \text{Related division sentence}$$

Do Exercises 5 and 6.

6. $7 \times 6 = 42$

Answers on page A-2

We can use the idea that division is defined in terms of multiplication to do basic divisions.

EXAMPLE 6 Find: $35 \div 5$.

To find $35 \div 5$, we ask, "5 times what number is 35?"

$$5 \cdot \square = 35$$

×	2	3	4	5	6	7	8	9
2	4	6	8	10	12	14	16	18
3	6	9	12	15	18	21	24	27
4	8	12	16	20	24	28	32	36
5	10	15	20	25	30	35	40	45
6	12	18	24	30	36	42	48	54
7	14	21	28	35	42	49	56	63
8	16	24	32	40	48	56	64	72
9	18	27	36	45	54	63	72	81

$35 \div 5 = 7$

Using the multiplication table above, we find 35 inside the table and 5 at the left. Then we read the answer 7 from the top. Thus we have $35 \div 5 = 7$. Strive to do this kind of thinking mentally as fast as you can, without having to use the table.

Do Exercises 7–10.

DIVISION BY 1

Note that

$$3 \div 1 = 3 \quad \text{because} \quad 3 \cdot 1 = 3; \qquad \frac{14}{1} = 14 \quad \text{because} \quad 14 \cdot 1 = 14.$$

> **DIVISION BY 1**
>
> Any number divided by 1 is that same number:
>
> $$a \div 1 = \frac{a}{1} = a.$$

EXAMPLES Divide.

7. $\dfrac{8}{1} = 8$ **8.** $6 \div 1 = 6$ **9.** $34 \div 1 = 34$

Do Exercises 11–13.

DIVISION BY 0

Why can't we divide by 0? Suppose the number 4 *could* be divided by 0. Then if $\square$ were the answer,

$$4 \div 0 = \square,$$

and since 0 times any number is 0, we would have

$$4 = \square \cdot 0 = 0. \quad \text{False!}$$

Divide.

7. $28 \div 4$

8. $81 \div 9$

9. $\dfrac{16}{2}$

10. $\dfrac{54}{6}$

Divide.

11. $6 \div 1$

12. $\dfrac{13}{1}$

13. $1 \div 1$

Answers on page A-2

Divide, if possible. If not possible, write "undefined."

14. $\dfrac{8}{4}$

15. $\dfrac{5}{0}$

16. $\dfrac{0}{5}$

17. $\dfrac{0}{0}$

18. $12 \div 0$

19. $100 \div 10$

20. $\dfrac{5}{3-3}$

21. $\dfrac{8-8}{4}$

Similarly, suppose 12 could be divided by 0. If $\square$ were the answer,

$$12 \div 0 = \square$$

and since 0 times any number is 0, we would have

$$12 = \square \cdot 0 = 0. \qquad \text{False!}$$

Thus, $a \div 0$ would have to be some number $\square$ such that $a = \square \cdot 0 = 0$. So the only number that could possibly be divided by 0 would be 0 itself.

But such a division would give us any number we wish, for

$$\left.\begin{array}{l} 0 \div 0 = 8 \quad \text{because} \quad 8 \cdot 0 = 0; \\ 0 \div 0 = 3 \quad \text{because} \quad 3 \cdot 0 = 0; \\ 0 \div 0 = 7 \quad \text{because} \quad 7 \cdot 0 = 0. \end{array}\right\} \quad \text{All true!}$$

We avoid these difficulties by agreeing to not divide *any* number by 0.

DIVISION BY 0

Division by 0 is not defined. (We agree not to divide by 0.)

DIVIDING 0 BY OTHER NUMBERS

Note that

$$0 \div 3 = 0 \quad \text{because} \quad 0 \cdot 3 = 0; \qquad \dfrac{0}{12} = 0 \quad \text{because } 0 \cdot 12 = 0.$$

DIVISION INTO 0

Zero divided by any number other than 0 is 0:

$$\dfrac{0}{a} = 0, \quad a \neq 0.$$

EXAMPLES Divide.

10. $0 \div 8 = 0$

11. $0 \div 22 = 0$

12. $\dfrac{0}{9} = 0$

Do Exercises 14–21.

DIVIDING A NUMBER BY ITSELF

Note that

$$3 \div 3 = 1 \quad \text{because} \quad 1 \cdot 3 = 3; \qquad \dfrac{34}{34} = 1 \quad \text{because} \quad 1 \cdot 34 = 34.$$

Answers on page A-2

DIVISION OF A NUMBER BY ITSELF

Any number other than 0 divided by itself is 1:

$$\frac{a}{a} = 1, \quad a \neq 0.$$

EXAMPLES Divide.

13. $8 \div 8 = 1$ *Check:* $1 \cdot 8 = 8$

14. $27 \div 27 = 1$ *Check:* $1 \cdot 27 = 27$

15. $\dfrac{32}{32} = 1$ *Check:* $1 \cdot 32 = 32$

Do Exercises 22–27.

b   Dividing by "Guess, Multiply, and Subtract"

To understand the process of division, we use a method known as "guess, multiply, and subtract." We do this to develop a shorter way that is both understandable and easier to use.

EXAMPLE 16 Divide $275 \div 4$. Use "guess, multiply, and subtract."

We *guess* a partial quotient of 35. We could guess *any* number — say, 4, 16, or 30. We *multiply* and *subtract* as follows:

```
      3 5 ← Partial quotient
  4 ) 2 7 5
      1 4 0 ← 35 · 4
      1 3 5 ← Remainder
```

Next, we look at 135 and *guess* another partial quotient—say, 20. Then we *multiply* and *subtract*:

```
      2 0 ← Second partial quotient
      3 5
  4 ) 2 7 5
      1 4 0
      1 3 5
        8 0 ← 20 · 4
        5 5 ← Remainder
```

Next, we look at 55 and *guess* another partial quotient—say, 13. Then we *multiply* and *subtract*:

```
      1 3 ← Third partial quotient
      2 0
      3 5
  4 ) 2 7 5
      1 4 0
      1 3 5
        8 0
        5 5
        5 2 ← 13 · 4
          3 ← Remainder is less than 4
```

Divide.

22. $23 \div 23$

23. $\dfrac{67}{67}$

24. $\dfrac{41}{41}$

25. $17 \div 17$

26. $17 \div 1$

27. $\dfrac{54}{54}$

Divide using the "guess, multiply, and subtract" method.

28. $6 \overline{)\ 4\ 5\ 4}$

29. $3\ 2 \overline{)\ 7\ 4\ 7}$

Answers on page A-2

Divide using the "guess, multiply, and subtract" method.

30. $7 \overline{)6789}$

31. $64 \overline{)3012}$

Since we cannot subtract any more multiples of 4, the division is finished. We add our partial quotients.

$$
\begin{array}{r}
6\ 8 \leftarrow \text{Quotient (sum of guesses)} \\
\hline
1\ 3 \\
2\ 0 \\
3\ 5 \\
4\ )\ 2\ 7\ 5 \\
1\ 4\ 0 \\
\hline
1\ 3\ 5 \\
8\ 0 \\
\hline
5\ 5 \\
5\ 2 \\
\hline
3
\end{array}
$$

CHECK:
$$
275 = (4 \times 68) + 3
$$
$$
275 \overset{?}{=} 272 + 3
$$
$$
275
$$

The answer is 68 R 3. This tells us that with 275 objects, we could make 68 rows of 4 and have 3 left over.

The partial quotients (guesses) can be made in any manner so long as subtraction is possible.

Do Exercises 28 and 29 on the preceding page.

EXAMPLE 17 Divide: $1506 \div 32$.

$$
\begin{array}{r}
4\ 7 \leftarrow \text{Quotient (sum of guesses)} \\
\hline
2\ 0 \\
2 \\
2\ 0 \\
5 \\
3\ 2\ )\ 1\ 5\ 0\ 6 \\
1\ 6\ 0 \leftarrow 5 \cdot 32 \\
\hline
1\ 3\ 4\ 6 \\
6\ 4\ 0 \leftarrow 20 \cdot 32 \\
\hline
7\ 0\ 6 \\
6\ 4 \leftarrow 2 \cdot 32 \\
\hline
6\ 4\ 2 \\
6\ 4\ 0 \leftarrow 20 \cdot 32 \\
\hline
2 \leftarrow \text{Remainder: smaller than the divisor, 32}
\end{array}
$$

with "Guesses" bracketing 20, 2, 20, 5.

The answer is 47 R 2.

Remember, you can *guess any partial quotient* so long as subtraction is possible.

Do Exercises 30 and 31.

C **Dividing by Estimating Multiples**

Let's refine the guessing process. We guess multiples of 10, 100, and 1000, and so on.

EXAMPLE 18 Divide: $7643 \div 3$.

a) Are there any thousands in the quotient? Yes, $3 \cdot 1000 = 3000$, which is less than 7643. To find how many thousands, we find products of 3 and multiples of 1000.

$3 \cdot 1000 = 3000$

$3 \cdot 2000 = 6000$ ← 7643 is here, so there

$3 \cdot 3000 = 9000$ are over 2000 threes in the quotient.

$$
\begin{array}{r}
2\ 0\ 0\ 0 \\
3\ )\overline{7\ 6\ 4\ 3} \\
6\ 0\ 0\ 0 \\
\hline
1\ 6\ 4\ 3
\end{array}
$$

b) Now go to the hundreds place. Are there any hundreds in the quotient?

$3 \cdot 100 = 300$

$3 \cdot 200 = 600$

$3 \cdot 300 = 900$

$3 \cdot 400 = 1200$

$3 \cdot 500 = 1500$ ← 1643

$3 \cdot 600 = 1800$

$$
\begin{array}{r}
5\ 0\ 0 \\
2\ 0\ 0\ 0 \\
3\ )\overline{7\ 6\ 4\ 3} \\
6\ 0\ 0\ 0 \\
\hline
1\ 6\ 4\ 3 \\
1\ 5\ 0\ 0 \\
\hline
1\ 4\ 3
\end{array}
$$

c) Now go to the tens place. Are there any tens in the quotient?

$3 \cdot 10 = 30$

$3 \cdot 20 = 60$

$3 \cdot 30 = 90$

$3 \cdot 40 = 120$ ← 143

$3 \cdot 50 = 150$

$$
\begin{array}{r}
4\ 0 \\
5\ 0\ 0 \\
2\ 0\ 0\ 0 \\
3\ )\overline{7\ 6\ 4\ 3} \\
6\ 0\ 0\ 0 \\
\hline
1\ 6\ 4\ 3 \\
1\ 5\ 0\ 0 \\
\hline
1\ 4\ 3 \\
1\ 2\ 0 \\
\hline
2\ 3
\end{array}
$$

d) Now go to the ones place. Are there any ones in the quotient?

$3 \cdot 1 = 3$

$3 \cdot 2 = 6$

$3 \cdot 3 = 9$

$3 \cdot 4 = 12$

$3 \cdot 5 = 15$

$3 \cdot 6 = 18$

$3 \cdot 7 = 21$ ← 23

$3 \cdot 8 = 24$

$$
\begin{array}{r}
2\ 5\ 4\ 7 \\
7 \\
4\ 0 \\
5\ 0\ 0 \\
2\ 0\ 0\ 0 \\
3\ )\overline{7\ 6\ 4\ 3} \\
6\ 0\ 0\ 0 \\
\hline
1\ 6\ 4\ 3 \\
1\ 5\ 0\ 0 \\
\hline
1\ 4\ 3 \\
1\ 2\ 0 \\
\hline
2\ 3 \\
2\ 1 \\
\hline
2
\end{array}
$$

The answer is 2547 R 2.

Do Exercises 32 and 33.

Divide.

32. $4\,)\overline{3\ 8\ 5}$

33. $7\,)\overline{8\ 8\ 4\ 6}$

Answers on page A-2

Divide using the short form.

34. 2) 6 4 8

35. 9) 3 7 5 8

Divide.

36. 1 1) 4 1 5

37. 4 6) 1 0 7 5

A SHORT FORM

Here is a shorter way to write Example 18.

Instead of this,

$$
\begin{array}{r}
2\ 5\ 4\ 7 \\
\hline
7 \\
4\ 0 \\
5\ 0\ 0 \\
2\ 0\ 0\ 0 \\
3\ \overline{)\ 7\ 6\ 4\ 3} \\
6\ 0\ 0\ 0 \\
\hline
1\ 6\ 4\ 3 \\
1\ 5\ 0\ 0 \\
\hline
1\ 4\ 3 \\
1\ 2\ 0 \\
\hline
2\ 3 \\
2\ 1 \\
\hline
2
\end{array}
$$

Short form

we write this.

$$
\begin{array}{r}
2\ 5\ 4\ 7 \\
\hline
3\ )\ 7\ 6\ 4\ 3 \\
6\ 0\ 0\ 0 \\
\hline
1\ 6\ 4\ 3 \\
1\ 5\ 0\ 0 \\
\hline
1\ 4\ 3 \\
1\ 2\ 0 \\
\hline
2\ 3 \\
2\ 1 \\
\hline
2
\end{array}
$$

We write a 2 above the thousands digit in the dividend to record 2000. We write a 5 to record 500. We write a 4 to record 40. We write a 7 to record 7.

Do Exercises 34 and 35.

EXAMPLE 19 Divide 2637 ÷ 41. Use the short form.

$$
\begin{array}{r}
6 \\
\hline
4\ 1\ )\ 2\ 6\ 3\ 7 \\
2\ 4\ 6\ 0 \\
\hline
1\ 7\ 7
\end{array}
$$

60 times 41 is 2460. Since the remainder, 177, is greater than 41, we continue.

$$
\begin{array}{r}
6\ 4 \\
\hline
4\ 1\ )\ 2\ 6\ 3\ 7 \\
2\ 4\ 6\ 0 \\
\hline
1\ 7\ 7 \\
1\ 6\ 4 \\
\hline
1\ 3
\end{array}
$$

Try to just write this.

The answer is 64 R 13.

Do Exercises 36 and 37.

Answers on page A-2

R.4

EXERCISE SET

a   Divide, if possible.

1. $24 \div 8$ **2.** $72 \div 9$ **3.** $28 \div 7$ **4.** $22 \div 22$ **5.** $32 \div 1$

6. $45 \div 5$ **7.** $14 \div 2$ **8.** $40 \div 8$ **9.** $37 \div 1$ **10.** $10 \div 2$

11. $36 \div 4$ **12.** $12 \div 3$ **13.** $54 \div 9$ **14.** $18 \div 2$ **15.** $20 \div 4$

16. $16 \div 2$ **17.** $72 \div 8$ **18.** $42 \div 7$ **19.** $12 \div 4$ **20.** $8 \div 4$

21. $54 \div 6$ **22.** $18 \div 9$ **23.** $9 \div 3$ **24.** $28 \div 4$ **25.** $56 \div 7$

26. $24 \div 6$ **27.** $14 \div 2$ **28.** $14 \div 7$ **29.** $21 \div 7$ **30.** $36 \div 6$

31. $8 \div 8$ **32.** $32 \div 8$ **33.** $30 \div 5$ **34.** $18 \div 6$ **35.** $49 \div 7$

36. $81 \div 9$ **37.** $0 \div 7$ **38.** $9 \div 0$ **39.** $16 \div 0$ **40.** $42 \div 6$

41. $\dfrac{48}{6}$ **42.** $\dfrac{35}{5}$ **43.** $\dfrac{9}{9}$ **44.** $\dfrac{45}{9}$ **45.** $\dfrac{0}{5}$ **46.** $\dfrac{0}{8}$

47. $\dfrac{6}{2}$ **48.** $\dfrac{3}{3}$ **49.** $\dfrac{8}{2}$ **50.** $\dfrac{7}{1}$ **51.** $\dfrac{5}{5}$ **52.** $\dfrac{6}{1}$

53. $\dfrac{2}{2}$ **54.** $\dfrac{25}{5}$ **55.** $\dfrac{4}{2}$ **56.** $\dfrac{24}{3}$ **57.** $\dfrac{0}{9}$ **58.** $\dfrac{0}{4}$

59. $\dfrac{40}{5}$ **60.** $\dfrac{3}{1}$ **61.** $\dfrac{16}{4}$ **62.** $\dfrac{9}{0}$ **63.** $\dfrac{32}{8}$ **64.** $\dfrac{9}{9}$

b Divide using the "guess, multiply, and subtract" method.

65. $4 \overline{)277}$ **66.** $2 \overline{)399}$ **67.** $8 \overline{)737}$ **68.** $6 \overline{)831}$

69. $5 \overline{)8619}$ **70.** $3 \overline{)8775}$ **71.** $9 \overline{)7777}$ **72.** $8 \overline{)4179}$

73. $7 \overline{)3691}$ **74.** $2 \overline{)5794}$ **75.** $20 \overline{)875}$ **76.** $30 \overline{)987}$

77. $21 \overline{)999}$ **78.** $23 \overline{)975}$ **79.** $85 \overline{)7757}$ **80.** $54 \overline{)2821}$

81. $111 \overline{)3219}$ **82.** $102 \overline{)5612}$ **83.** $346 \overline{)78,910}$ **84.** $781 \overline{)15,999}$

c Divide.

85. $5 \overline{)105}$ **86.** $6 \overline{)708}$ **87.** $9 \overline{)820}$ **88.** $3 \overline{)965}$

89. $5 \overline{)4823}$ **90.** $8 \overline{)5437}$ **91.** $7 \overline{)9298}$ **92.** $41 \overline{)1115}$

93. $46 \overline{)1058}$ **94.** $24 \overline{)7722}$ **95.** $38 \overline{)8522}$ **96.** $81 \overline{)2247}$

97. $94 \overline{)2153}$ **98.** $82 \overline{)4064}$ **99.** $117 \overline{)44{,}902}$ **100.** $740 \overline{)55{,}200}$

Whole Numbers

Gateway to Chapter 1

You are beginning a study of Prealgebra. In this chapter, we consider addition, subtraction, multiplication, and division of whole numbers, as well as exponential notation and order of operations. We also introduce the idea of using variables to form equations. Then we solve simple equations and use the skills of this chapter to solve applied problems.

Before starting, be sure to read the preface and the introduction from the authors to the student.

Real–World Application

Boeing Corporation builds commercial aircraft. A Boeing 767 has a seating configuration with 4 rows of 6 seats across in first class and 35 rows of 7 seats across in economy class. Find the total seating capacity of the plane.

Sources: The Boeing Corporation; Delta Airlines

This problem appears as Example 8 in Section 1.8.

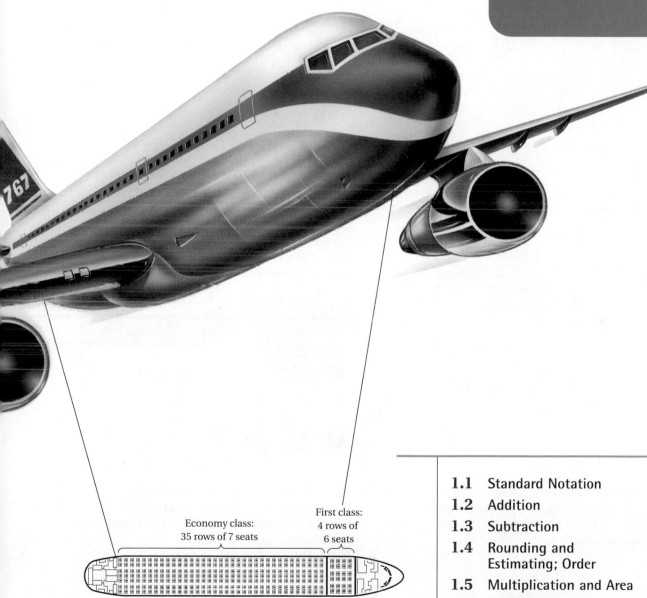

Economy class:
35 rows of 7 seats

First class:
4 rows of
6 seats

1. Write a word name: 3,078,059.   [1.1c]

2. Write expanded notation: 6987.   [1.1b]

3. Write standard notation: Two billion, forty-seven million, three hundred ninety-eight thousand, five hundred eighty-nine.   [1.1c]

4. What does the digit 6 mean in 2,967,342?   [1.1a]

5. Round 956,449 to the nearest thousand.   [1.4a]

6. Estimate the product 594 · 126 by first rounding the numbers to the nearest hundred.   [1.5b]

7. Add.   [1.2b]
$$\begin{array}{r} 7\ 3\ 1\ 2 \\ +\ 2\ 9\ 0\ 4 \end{array}$$

8. Subtract.   [1.3d]
$$\begin{array}{r} 7\ 0\ 1\ 2 \\ -\ 2\ 9\ 0\ 4 \end{array}$$

9. Multiply: 359 · 64.   [1.5a]

10. Divide: 23,149 ÷ 46.   [1.6c]

Use either < or > for ☐ to write a true sentence.   [1.4c]

11. 346 ☐ 364

12. 54 ☐ 45

Solve.   [1.7b]

13. $326 \cdot 17 = m$

14. $y = 924 \div 42$

15. $19 + x = 53$

16. $34 \cdot n = 850$

Solve.   [1.8a]

17. **Paper Quantity.**   There are 500 sheets in a ream of paper. How many sheets are in 9 reams?

9 reams

500 sheets in each

18. **Digital Cameras.**   A group of 63 language students from VaMard University is planning a year abroad to study German. They decide that each of them will buy a digital camera like the one shown in the ad below. The total cost of the purchase is $12,537. What is the cost per camera?

OPUS
Digital Camera

19. **Checking Account.**   You have $756 in your checking account. Using your debit card, you pay $387 for a VCR for your dorm room. How much is left in your account?

20. **College Costs.**   In 2001, tuition and fees at public 2-yr colleges averaged $1359, board was $1900, and dormitory charges were $1603. Find the total cost to the student.
Source: Based on figures from U.S. National Center for Education Statistics

Evaluate.   [1.9b]

21. 5^2

22. 4^3

Simplify.

23. $8^2 \div 8 \cdot 2 - (2 + 2 \cdot 7)$ [1.9c]

24. $108 \div 9 - \{3 \cdot [18 - (5 \cdot 3)]\}$ [1.9d]

1.1 STANDARD NOTATION

Objectives

a Give the meaning of digits in standard notation.

b Convert between standard notation and expanded notation.

c Convert between standard notation and word names.

We study mathematics in order to be able to solve problems. In this section, we study how numbers are named. We begin with the concept of place value.

a Place Value

Consider the number named in the following sentence:

By the year 2008, there will be approximately 160,795,000 workers in the United States.

Source: U.S. Bureau of Labor Statistics

A **digit** is a number 0, 1, 2, 3, 4, 5, 6, 7, 8, or 9 that names a place-value location. For large numbers, digits are separated by commas into groups of three, called **periods.** Each period has a name: *ones, thousands, millions, billions, trillions,* and so on. To understand the number in the sentence, we can use a **place-value chart,** as shown below.

PLACE-VALUE CHART														
Periods →	Trillions			Billions			Millions			Thousands			Ones		
							1	6	0	7	9	5	0	0	0
	Hundreds	Tens	Ones	Hundreds	Tens	Ones	Hundreds	Tens	Ones	Hundreds	Tens	Ones	Hundreds	Tens	Ones

160 millions, 795 thousands, 0 ones

EXAMPLES What does the digit 8 mean in each number?

1. 278,342   8 thousands
2. 872,342   8 hundred thousands
3. 28,343,399,223   8 billions

Do Exercises 1–4.

What does the digit 2 mean in each number?

1. 526,555

2. 265,789

3. 42,789,654

4. 24,789,654

Answers on page A-2

5. Golf Balls. It is estimated that in one day Americans buy 486,575 golf balls. What does each digit name?
Source: U.S. Golf Association

Write expanded notation.

6. 1895

7. $14,280, the average salary for a day-care worker in 2002
Source: Based on information from U.S. Dept. of Labor

8. 3031 mi, the diameter of Mercury

9. 4100 mi, the length of the Nile River, the longest in the world

10. 3860 mi, the length of the Missouri–Mississippi River, the longest in the United States

Answers on page A-3

EXAMPLE 4 *Pacific Ocean.* The area of the Pacific Ocean is 64,186,000 square miles. What does each digit name?

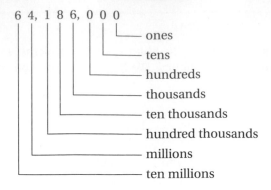

6 4, 1 8 6, 0 0 0

- ones
- tens
- hundreds
- thousands
- ten thousands
- hundred thousands
- millions
- ten millions

Do Exercise 5.

b Converting Between Standard Notation and Expanded Notation

To answer questions such as "How many?", "How much?", and "How tall?", we use whole numbers. The set, or collection, of **whole numbers** is

$$0, 1, 2, 3, 4, 5, 6, 7, 8, 9, 10, 11, 12, \ldots.$$

The set goes on indefinitely. There is no largest whole number, and the smallest whole number is 0. Each whole number can be named using various notations. The set $1, 2, 3, 4, 5, \ldots$, without 0, is called the set of **natural numbers.**

Let's look at the data from the line graph shown here.

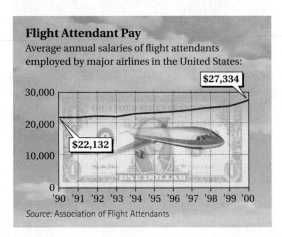

Flight Attendant Pay
Average annual salaries of flight attendants employed by major airlines in the United States:

$27,334

$22,132

30,000
20,000
10,000
0
'90 '91 '92 '93 '94 '95 '96 '97 '98 '99 '00

Source: Association of Flight Attendants

The average salary for a flight attendant in 2000 was $27,334. **Standard notation** for the salary is 27,334. We write **expanded notation** for 27,334 as follows:

27,334 = 2 ten thousands + 7 thousands
        + 3 hundreds + 3 tens + 4 ones.

EXAMPLE 5 Write expanded notation for 4218 mi (miles), the diameter of Mars.

4218 = 4 thousands + 2 hundreds + 1 ten + 8 ones

EXAMPLE 6   Write expanded notation for 3400.

$$3400 = 3 \text{ thousands} + 4 \text{ hundreds} + 0 \text{ tens} + 0 \text{ ones, or}$$
$$3 \text{ thousands} + 4 \text{ hundreds}$$

Do Exercises 6–10 on the preceding page.

EXAMPLE 7   Write standard notation for 9 ten thousands + 6 thousands + 7 hundreds + 1 ten + 8 ones.

Standard notation is 96,718.

EXAMPLE 8   Write standard notation for 2 thousands + 3 tens.

Standard notation is 2030.

Do Exercises 11–13.

C   Converting Between Standard Notation and Word Names

We often use **word names** for numbers. When we pronounce a number, we are speaking its word name. The People's Republic of China won 59 medals in the 2000 Summer Olympics in Sydney, Australia. A word name for 59 is "fifty-nine."

TOP COUNTRIES IN SUMMER OLYMPICS 2000	GOLD	SILVER	BRONZE	TOTAL
United States of America	39	25	33	97
Russia	32	28	28	88
People's Republic of China	28	16	15	59
Australia	16	25	17	58
Germany	14	17	26	57

Source: 2000 Olympics, Sydney, Australia

Word names for some two-digit numbers like 59, 88, and 97 use hyphens. Others like 17 use only one word, "seventeen." Let's write some word names.

Write standard notation.

11. 5 thousands + 6 hundreds + 8 tens + 9 ones

12. 8 ten thousands + 7 thousands + 1 hundred + 2 tens + 8 ones

13. 9 thousands + 3 ones

Write a word name. (Refer to the figure at left.)

14. 88, the total number of medals won by Russia

15. 16, the number of silver medals won by the People's Republic of China

16. 32, the number of gold medals won by Russia

Answers on page A-3

Write a word name.

17. 204

18. $45,678, the average salary in 1999 for those who have a bachelor's degree
Source: U.S. Bureau of the Census

19. 1,879,204

20. 6,254,540,000, the world population in 2002
Source: U.S. Bureau of the Census

21. Write standard notation.

Two hundred thirteen million, one hundred five thousand, three hundred twenty-nine

EXAMPLES   Write a word name.

9. 97, the total number of medals won by the United States

   Ninety-seven

10. 15, the number of bronze medals won by the People's Republic of China

   Fifteen

Do Exercises 14–16 on the preceding page.

For word names for larger numbers, we begin at the left with the largest period. The number named in the period is followed by the name of the period; then a comma is written and the next period is named.

EXAMPLE 11   Write a word name for 46,605,314,732.

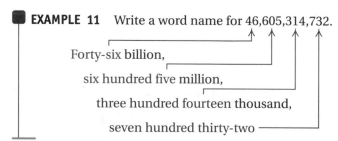

Forty-six billion,

   six hundred five million,

      three hundred fourteen thousand,

         seven hundred thirty-two

The word "and" *should not* appear in word names for whole numbers. Although we commonly hear such expressions as "two hundred *and* one," the use of "and" is not, strictly speaking, correct in word names for whole numbers. For decimal notation, it is appropriate to use "and" for the decimal point. For example, 317.4 is read as "three hundred seventeen *and* four tenths."

Do Exercises 17–20.

EXAMPLE 12   Write standard notation.

Five hundred six million,

   three hundred forty-five thousand,

      two hundred twelve

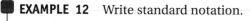

Standard notation is 506,345,212.

Do Exercise 21.

Study Tips

Throughout this textbook, you will find a feature called *Study Tips*. These tips are intended to help improve your math study skills. On the first day of class, you should complete this chart.

GET THE FACTS

Instructor: Name _____

Office hours and location

_____

Phone number _____

Fax number _____

E-mail address _____

Find the names of two students whom you could contact for information or study questions:

1. Name _____

   Phone number _____

   E-mail address _____

2. Name _____

   Phone number _____

   E-mail address _____

Math lab on campus:

Location _____

Hours _____

Phone _____

Tutoring:

Campus location _____

Hours _____

AW Math Tutor Center _____

To order, call _____ .

(See the preface for important information concerning this tutoring.)

Important supplements:
(See the preface for a complete list of available supplements.)

Supplements recommended by the instructor

_____

_____

1.1 EXERCISE SET

Digital Video Tutor CD 1 Videotape 1   InterAct Math   Math Tutor Center   MathXL   MyMathLab

a What does the digit 5 mean in each case?

1. 235,888   **2.** 253,777   **3.** 1,488,526   **4.** 500,736

Lift Tickets. In 2000–2001, a total of 2,974,574 ski or snowboard lift tickets were sold in Utah. In the number 2,974,574, what digit names the number of:

5. Ones?   **6.** Ten thousands?

7. Millions?   **8.** Hundred thousands?

Source: *The Salt Lake Tribune,* 6/12/02

b Write expanded notation.

9. 5702   **10.** 3097

11. 93,986   **12.** 38,453

Step-Climbing Races. Races in which runners climb the steps inside a building are called "run-up" races. The graph below shows the number of steps in four buildings. In Exercises 13–16, write expanded notation for the number of steps in each race.

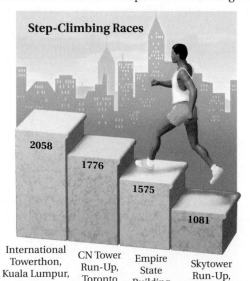

Step-Climbing Races

2058 — International Towerthon, Kuala Lumpur, Malaysia
1776 — CN Tower Run-Up, Toronto
1575 — Empire State Building Run-Up
1081 — Skytower Run-Up, Auckland, New Zealand

Source: New York Road Runners Club

13. 2058 steps in the International Towerthon, Kuala Lumpur, Malaysia

14. 1776 steps in the CN Tower Run-Up, Toronto, Ontario, Canada

15. 1575 steps in the Empire State Building Run-Up, New York City, United States

16. 1081 steps in the Skytower Run-Up, Auckland, New Zealand

Write standard notation.

17. 2 thousands + 4 hundreds + 7 tens + 5 ones

18. 7 thousands + 9 hundreds + 8 tens + 3 ones

19. 6 ten thousands + 8 thousands + 9 hundreds + 3 tens + 9 ones

20. 1 ten thousand + 8 thousands + 4 hundreds + 6 tens + 1 one

21. 7 thousands + 3 hundreds + 0 tens + 4 ones

22. 8 thousands + 0 hundreds + 2 tens + 0 ones

23. 1 thousand + 9 ones

24. 2 thousands + 4 hundreds + 5 tens

C Write a word name.

25. 85

26. 48

27. 88,000

28. 45,987

29. 123,765

30. 111,013

31. 7,754,211,577

32. 43,550,651,808

Write standard notation.

33. Two million, two hundred thirty-three thousand, eight hundred twelve

34. Three hundred fifty-four thousand, seven hundred two

35. Eight billion

36. Seven hundred million

Write a word name for the number in each sentence.

37. *Great Pyramid.* The area of the base of the Great Pyramid in Egypt is 566,280 square feet.
Source: NOVA, "This Old Pyramid," Airdate 2/4/97, PBS, WGBH.

38. *Population of the United States.* The population of the United States in 2002 was estimated to be 288,445,700.
Source: U.S. Bureau of the Census

39. *Monopoly.* In a recent Monopoly® game sponsored by McDonald's® restaurants, the odds of winning the grand prize were estimated to be 467,322,388 to 1.
Source: McDonald's Corporation

40. *Native American Population.* In a recent year, the population of Native Americans in Arizona was 165,385.
Source: U.S. Bureau of the Census

Write standard notation for the number in each sentence.

41. Light travels nine trillion, four hundred sixty billion kilometers in one year.

42. The distance from the sun to Pluto is three billion, six hundred sixty-four million miles.

43. *Pacific Ocean.* The area of the Pacific Ocean is sixty-four million, one hundred eighty-six thousand square miles.

44. *Gigabyte.* On a computer hard disk, one gigabyte is one billion, seventy-three million, seven hundred forty-one thousand, eight hundred twenty-four bytes of memory.

To the student and the instructor: The Discussion and Writing exercises are meant to be answered with one or more sentences. They can be discussed and answered collaboratively by the entire class or by small groups. Because of their open-ended nature, the answers to these exercises do not appear at the back of the book. Discussion and Writing exercises are denoted by the symbol **D**_W.

45. **D**_W Explain why we use commas when writing large numbers.

46. **D**_W Write an English sentence in which the number 370,000,000 is used.

SYNTHESIS

To the student and the instructor: The Synthesis exercises at the end of every exercise set challenge you to combine concepts or skills studied in that section or in preceding parts of the text. Exercises marked with a ▦ symbol are meant to be solved using a calculator.

47. How many whole numbers between 100 and 400 contain the digit 2 in their standard notation?

48. ▦ What is the largest number that you can name on your calculator? How many digits does that number have? How many periods?

1.2 ADDITION

a — Addition and Related Sentences

Addition of whole numbers corresponds to combining or putting things together.

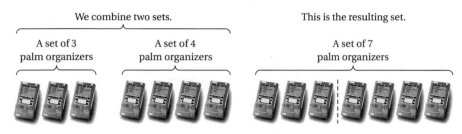

We combine two sets.

A set of 3 palm organizers — A set of 4 palm organizers

This is the resulting set.

A set of 7 palm organizers

The addition that corresponds to the figure above is

$$3 + 4 = 7.$$

The number of objects in a set can be found by counting. We count and find that the two sets have 3 palm organizers and 4 palm organizers, respectively. After combining, we count and find that there are 7 palm organizers. We say that the **sum** of 3 and 4 is **7**. The numbers added are called **addends.**

$$\underset{\text{Addend}}{3} \; + \; \underset{\text{Addend}}{4} \; = \; \underset{\text{Sum}}{7}$$ This is read "3 plus 4 equals 7."

EXAMPLE 1   Write an addition sentence that corresponds to this situation.

Kelly has $3 and earns $10 more. How much money does she have?

An addition that corresponds is $3 + $10 = $13.

Do Exercises 1 and 2.

Addition also corresponds to combining distances or lengths.

EXAMPLE 2   Write an addition sentence that corresponds to this situation.

A car is driven 44 mi from San Francisco to San Jose. It is then driven 42 mi from San Jose to Oakland. How far is it from San Francisco to Oakland along the same route?

$$44 \text{ mi} + 42 \text{ mi} = 86 \text{ mi}$$

Do Exercises 3 and 4.

Objectives

a Write an addition sentence that corresponds to a situation.

b Add whole numbers.

c Use addition in finding perimeter.

Write an addition sentence that corresponds to each situation.

1. John has 8 music CD-ROMs in his backpack. Then he buys 2 educational CD-ROMs at the bookstore. How many CD-ROMs does John have in all?

2. Sue earns $20 in overtime pay on Thursday and $13 on Friday. How much overtime pay does she earn altogether on the two days?

Write an addition sentence that corresponds to each situation.

3. A car is driven 100 mi from Austin to Waco. It is then driven 93 mi from Waco to Dallas. How far is it from Austin to Dallas along the same route?

4. A coaxial cable 5 feet (ft) long is connected to a cable 7 ft long. How long is the resulting cable?

Answers on page A-3

5. Add.

$$
\begin{array}{r}
6\ 2\ 0\ 3 \\
+\ 3\ 5\ 4\ 2 \\
\hline
\end{array}
$$

b Addition of Whole Numbers

To add numbers, we add the ones digits first, then the tens, then the hundreds, and so on.

EXAMPLE 3 Add: 7312 + 2504.

Place values are lined up in columns.

$$
\begin{array}{r}
7\ 3\ 1\ \boxed{2} \\
+\ 2\ 5\ 0\ \boxed{4} \\
\hline
6
\end{array}
$$ Add ones.

$$
\begin{array}{r}
7\ 3\ \boxed{1}\ 2 \\
+\ 2\ 5\ \boxed{0}\ 4 \\
\hline
1\ 6
\end{array}
$$ Add tens.

We show you this for explanation.

$$
\begin{array}{r}
7\ \boxed{3}\ 1\ 2 \\
+\ 2\ \boxed{5}\ 0\ 4 \\
\hline
8\ 1\ 6
\end{array}
$$ Add hundreds.

You need write only this.

$$
\begin{array}{r}
\boxed{7}\ 3\ 1\ 2 \\
+\ \boxed{2}\ 5\ 0\ 4 \\
\hline
9\ 8\ 1\ 6
\end{array}
$$ Add thousands.

$$
\begin{array}{r}
7\ 3\ 1\ 2 \\
+\ 2\ 5\ 0\ 4 \\
\hline
9\ 8\ 1\ 6
\end{array}
$$
←—Addends
←—Sum

Do Exercise 5.

Answer on page A-3

Study Tips

We began our "Study Tips" in Section 1.1. You will find many of these tips throughout the book. One of the most important ways to improve your math study skills is to learn the proper use of the textbook. Here we highlight a few points that we consider most helpful.

MAKE THE MOST OF THIS TEXTBOOK

■ **Be sure to note the special symbols** a , b , c , **and so on, that correspond to the objectives you are to be able to perform.** The first time you see them is in the margin at the beginning of each section; the second time is in the subheadings of each section; and the third time is in the exercise set for the section. You will also find them next to the skill maintenance exercises in each exercise set and the review exercises at the end of the chapter, as well as in the answers to the chapter tests and the cumulative reviews. These objective symbols allow you to refer to the appropriate place in the text whenever you need to review a topic.

■ **Read and study each step of each example.** The examples include important side comments that explain each step. These carefully chosen examples and notes prepare you for success in the exercise set.

■ **Stop and do the margin exercises as you study a section.** Doing the margin exercises is one of the most effective ways to enhance your ability to learn mathematics from this text. Don't deprive yourself of this benefit!

■ **Note the icons labeled "For Extra Help" that appear at the top of each exercise set.** They refer to the many distinctive multimedia study aids that accompany the book.

EXAMPLE 4 Add: 6878 + 4995.

$$
\begin{array}{cccc}
 & & \overset{1}{} & \\
6 & 8 & 7 & 8 \\
+\ 4 & 9 & 9 & 5 \\
\hline
 & & & 3
\end{array}
$$

Add ones. We get 13 ones, or 1 ten + 3 ones. Write 3 in the ones column and 1 above the tens. This is called *carrying*, or *regrouping*.

$$
\begin{array}{cccc}
 & \overset{1}{} & \overset{1}{} & \\
6 & 8 & 7 & 8 \\
+\ 4 & 9 & 9 & 5 \\
\hline
 & & 7 & 3
\end{array}
$$

Add tens. We get 17 tens, or 1 hundred + 7 tens. Write 7 in the tens column and 1 above the hundreds.

$$
\begin{array}{cccc}
\overset{1}{} & \overset{1}{} & \overset{1}{} & \\
6 & 8 & 7 & 8 \\
+\ 4 & 9 & 9 & 5 \\
\hline
 & 8 & 7 & 3
\end{array}
$$

Add hundreds. We get 18 hundreds, or 1 thousand + 8 hundreds. Write 8 in the hundreds column and 1 above the thousands.

$$
\begin{array}{cccc}
\overset{1}{} & \overset{1}{} & \overset{1}{} & \\
6 & 8 & 7 & 8 \\
+\ 4 & 9 & 9 & 5 \\
\hline
1\ \ 1 & 8 & 7 & 3
\end{array}
$$

Add thousands. We get 11 thousands.

Do Exercises 6 and 7.

How do we do an addition of three numbers, like 2 + 3 + 6? We do so by adding 3 and 6, and then 2. We can show this with parentheses:

$2 + (3 + 6) = 2 + 9 = 11.$ Parentheses tell what to do first.

We could also add 2 and 3, and then 6:

$(2 + 3) + 6 = 5 + 6 = 11.$

Either way we get 11. It does not matter how we group the numbers. This illustrates the **associative law of addition**, $a + (b + c) = (a + b) + c$.

EXAMPLE 5 Insert parentheses to illustrate the associative law of addition:

$5 + (1 + 7) = \ 5 \ + \ 1 \ + \ 7$

We group as follows:

$5 + (1 + 7) = (5 + 1) + 7.$

Do Exercises 8 and 9.

We can also add whole numbers in any order. That is, 2 + 3 = 3 + 2. This illustrates the **commutative law of addition**, $a + b = b + a$.

EXAMPLE 6 Complete the following to illustrate the commutative law of addition:

$5 + 4 = \square + \square$

We reverse the appearance of the two addends:

$5 + 4 = 4 + 5.$

Do Exercises 10 and 11.

Add.

6.
$$
\begin{array}{r}
7\ 9\ 6\ 8 \\
+\ 5\ 4\ 9\ 7 \\
\hline
\end{array}
$$

7.
$$
\begin{array}{r}
9\ 8\ 0\ 4 \\
+\ 6\ 3\ 7\ 8 \\
\hline
\end{array}
$$

Insert parentheses to illustrate the associative law of addition.

8. $2 + (6 + 3) = \ 2 \ + \ 6 \ + \ 3$

9. $(5 + 1) + 4 = \ 5 \ + \ 1 \ + \ 4$

Complete the following to illustrate the commutative law of addition.

10. $2 + 6 = \square + \square$

11. $7 + 1 = \square + \square$

Answers on page A-3

Add from the top.

12.
```
   9
   9
   4
+  5
```

13.
```
   8
   6
   9
   7
+  4
```

14. Add from the bottom.
```
      9
      9
      4
   +  5
```

Add. Look for pairs of numbers whose sums are 10, 20, 30, and so on.

15.
```
   1 5
     7
     5
     3
+    8
```

16. $6 + 12 + 14 + 8 + 7$

17. $27 + 8 + 13 + 2 + 11$

THE ASSOCIATIVE LAW OF ADDITION

For any numbers a, b, and c,
$$(a + b) + c = a + (b + c).$$

THE COMMUTATIVE LAW OF ADDITION

For any numbers a and b,
$$a + b = b + a.$$

Together the commutative and associative laws tell us that to add more than two numbers, we can use any order and grouping we wish.

EXAMPLE 7 Add from the top.
```
   8
   9
   7
+  6
```

We first add 8 and 9, getting 17; then 17 and 7, getting 24; then 24 and 6, getting 30.

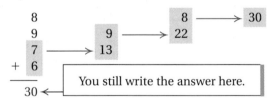

Try to write only this.

Do Exercises 12 and 13.

EXAMPLE 8 Add from the bottom.

You still write the answer here.

Do Exercise 14.

Sometimes it is easier to look for pairs of numbers whose sums are 10 or 20 or 30, and so on.

 **EXAMPLES** Add.

9.
```
14 ──────→  20
 8  ╲    ╱
 6   ╲  ╱
 2 ──────→  10
+ 9 ──────→   9
───          ──
39           39
```

Try to write only the answer in the position shown.

10. 23 + 19 + 7 + 21 + 4

= 30 + 40 + 4

= 74

Do Exercises 15–17 on the previous page.

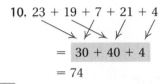 **EXAMPLE 11** Add: 2391 + 3276 + 8789 + 1498

```
        2
  2  3  9  1
  3  2  7  6
  8  7  8  9
+ 1  4  9  8
           4
```
Add ones. We get 24, so we have 2 tens + 4 ones. Write 4 in the ones column and 2 above the tens.

```
     3  2
  2  3  9  1
  3  2  7  6
  8  7  8  9
+ 1  4  9  8
        5  4
```
Add tens. We get 35 tens, so we have 30 tens + 5 tens. This is also 3 hundreds + 5 tens. Write 5 in the tens column and 3 above the hundreds.

```
  1  3  2
  2  3  9  1
  3  2  7  6
  8  7  8  9
+ 1  4  9  8
     9  5  4
```
Add hundreds. We get 19 hundreds, or 1 thousand + 9 hundreds. Write 9 in the hundreds column and 1 above the thousands.

```
  1  3  2
  2  3  9  1
  3  2  7  6
  8  7  8  9
+ 1  4  9  8
  1  5  9  5  4
```
Add thousands. We get 15 thousands.

Do Exercise 18.

18. Add.
```
  1  9  3  2
  6  7  2  3
  9  8  7  8
+ 8  9  4  1
```

Answer on page A-3

 CALCULATOR CORNER

To the student and the instructor: This is the first of a series of *optional* discussions on using a calculator. A calculator is *not* a requirement for this textbook. There are many kinds of calculators and different instructions for their usage. We include instructions here for most low-cost calculators. Be sure to consult a user's manual as well. Also, check with your instructor about whether you are allowed to use a calculator in the course.

To add on a calculator, we use the ⊞ and ⊟ keys. For example, to add 57 and 34, we press ⑤ ⑦ ⊞ ③ ④ ⊟ . The display is ⌷⌷⌷⌷⌷ 91, so 57 + 34 = 91. For 314 + 259 + 478, we press ③ ① ④ ⊞ ② ⑤ ⑨ ⊞ ④ ⑦ ⑧ ⊟ . The display reads ⌷⌷⌷⌷ 1051, so 314 + 259 + 478 = 1051.

Exercises: Use a calculator to find each sum.

1. 19 + 36

2. 73 + 48

3. 925 + 677

4. 276 + 458

5.
```
   8  2  6
   4  1  5
+  6  9  1
```

6.
```
   2  5  3
   4  9  0
+  1  2  1
```

Solve.

19. Index Cards. Two standard sizes for index cards are 3 in. (inches) by 5 in. and 5 in. by 8 in. Find the perimeter of each card.

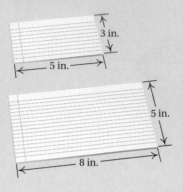

Find the perimeter of each figure.

20.

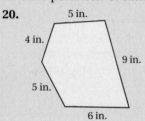

21.

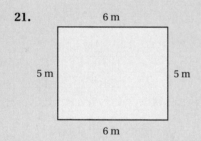

C   Finding Perimeter

Addition can be used when finding perimeter.

PERIMETER

The distance around an object is its **perimeter.**

EXAMPLE 12   Find the perimeter of the soccer field shown.

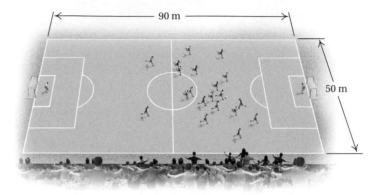

The letter m denotes *meters* (a meter is slightly more than 3 ft). Note that for any rectangle, the opposite sides are the same length. Thus

$$50 \text{ m} + 90 \text{ m} + 50 \text{ m} + 90 \text{ m} = \text{Perimeter}$$

$$100 \text{ m} + 180 \text{ m} = 280 \text{ m}$$

The perimeter is 280 m.

Do Exercises 19–21.

Answers on page A-3

a Write an addition sentence that corresponds to each situation.

1. Two trucks haul sand to a construction site to use in a driveway. One carries 6 cu yd (cubic yards) and the other 8 cu yd. Altogether, how many cubic yards of sand are they hauling to the site?

2. At a construction site, there are two gasoline containers to be used by earth-moving vehicles. One contains 400 gal and the other 200 gal. How many gallons do both contain together?

3. A builder buys two parcels of land to build a housing development. One contains 500 acres and the other 300 acres. What is the total number of acres purchased?

4. During March and April, Deron earns extra money doing income taxes part time. In March he earned $220, and in April he earned $340. How much extra did he earn altogether in March and April?

b Add.

5.
$$\begin{array}{r} 3\ 6\ 4 \\ +\ \ \ 2\ 3 \\ \hline \end{array}$$

6.
$$\begin{array}{r} 1\ 5\ 2\ 1 \\ +\ \ \ 3\ 4\ 8 \\ \hline \end{array}$$

7.
$$\begin{array}{r} 1\ 7\ 1\ 6 \\ +\ 3\ 4\ 8\ 2 \\ \hline \end{array}$$

8.
$$\begin{array}{r} 7\ 5\ 0\ 3 \\ +\ 2\ 6\ 8\ 3 \\ \hline \end{array}$$

9.
$$\begin{array}{r} 8\ 6 \\ +\ 7\ 8 \\ \hline \end{array}$$

10.
$$\begin{array}{r} 7\ 3 \\ |\ 6\ 9 \\ \hline \end{array}$$

11.
$$\begin{array}{r} 9\ 9 \\ +\ \ \ 1 \\ \hline \end{array}$$

12.
$$\begin{array}{r} 9\ 9\ 9 \\ +\ \ \ 1\ 1 \\ \hline \end{array}$$

13. 8113 + 390

14. 271 + 3338

15. 356 + 4910

16. 280 + 34,702

17. 3870 + 92 + 7 + 497

18. 10,120 + 12,989 + 5738

19.
$$\begin{array}{r} 5\ 0\ 9\ 3 \\ +\ 3\ 2\ 1\ 7 \\ \hline \end{array}$$

20.
$$\begin{array}{r} 3\ 6\ 5\ 4 \\ +\ 2\ 7\ 0\ 0 \\ \hline \end{array}$$

21.
$$\begin{array}{r} 4\ 8\ 2\ 5 \\ +\ 1\ 7\ 8\ 3 \\ \hline \end{array}$$

22.
$$\begin{array}{r} 6\ 7\ 7\ 5 \\ +\ 1\ 4\ 3\ 2 \\ \hline \end{array}$$

23.
$$\begin{array}{r} 9999 \\ +\ 6785 \\ \hline \end{array}$$

24.
$$\begin{array}{r} 45{,}879 \\ +\ 21{,}786 \\ \hline \end{array}$$

25.
$$\begin{array}{r} 23{,}443 \\ +\ 10{,}989 \\ \hline \end{array}$$

26.
$$\begin{array}{r} 67{,}654 \\ +\ 98{,}786 \\ \hline \end{array}$$

27.
$$\begin{array}{r} 77{,}543 \\ +\ 23{,}767 \\ \hline \end{array}$$

28.
$$\begin{array}{r} 44{,}654 \\ +\ 4{,}765 \\ \hline \end{array}$$

29.
$$\begin{array}{r} 99{,}999 \\ +\ 112 \\ \hline \end{array}$$

30.
$$\begin{array}{r} 127{,}556 \\ +\ 68{,}766 \\ \hline \end{array}$$

Insert parentheses to illustrate the associative law of addition.

31. $(2 + 5) + 4 = 2\ +\ 5\ +\ 4$

32. $(7 + 1) + 5 = 7\ +\ 1\ +\ 5$

33. $6 + (3 + 2) = 6\ +\ 3\ +\ 2$

34. $5 + (1 + 4) = 5\ +\ 1\ +\ 4$

35. $(2 + 4) + 6 = 2\ +\ 4\ +\ 6$

36. $3 + (5 + 7) = 3\ +\ 5\ +\ 7$

Complete each equation to illustrate the commutative law of addition.

37. $2 + 7 = \square + \square$

38. $5 + 2 = \square + \square$

39. $6 + 1 = \square + \square$

40. $1 + 9 = \square + \square$

41. $2 + 9 = \square + \square$

42. $7 + 5 = \square + \square$

Add from the top. Then check by adding from the bottom.

43.
$$\begin{array}{r} 7 \\ 9 \\ 4 \\ +\ 8 \\ \hline \end{array}$$

44.
$$\begin{array}{r} 4 \\ 3 \\ 9 \\ 1 \\ +\ 8 \\ \hline \end{array}$$

45.
$$\begin{array}{r} 8 \\ 6 \\ 2 \\ 3 \\ +\ 7 \\ \hline \end{array}$$

46.
$$\begin{array}{r} 9 \\ 4 \\ 7 \\ 8 \\ +\ 7 \\ \hline \end{array}$$

Add. Look for pairs of numbers whose sums are 10, 20, 30, and so on.

47.
```
      7
    1 8
      3
    3 7
 +    2
```

48.
```
    2 3
    1 6
    1 1
    1 8
 + 1 9
```

49.
```
    4 5
    2 5
    3 6
    4 4
 + 8 0
```

50.
```
    3 8
    2 7
    3 2
    1 4
 + 7 6
```

51.
```
    4 5 1
      3 6
  + 8 6 2
```

52.
```
      3 1
      7 5 3
    + 9 2 4
```

53.
```
  1 2,0 7 0
     2,9 5 4
  +  3,4 0 0
```

54.
```
    4 2,4 8 7
    8 3,1 4 1
  + 3 6,7 1 2
```

55.
```
    3 2 7
    4 2 8
    5 6 9
    7 8 7
  + 2 0 9
```

56.
```
    9 8 9
    5 6 6
    8 3 4
    9 2 0
  + 7 0 3
```

57.
```
    4 8 3 5
      7 2 9
    9 2 0 4
    8 9 8 6
  + 7 9 3 1
```

58.
```
        5,9 4 6
          8 3 4
      1 2,9 5 6
    9 2 8,3 4 2
      3 4,9 0 1
  +   5 6,0 0 0
```

C Find the perimeter of (the distance around) each figure.

59.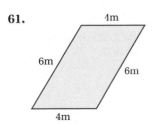

60.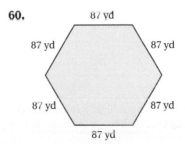

61.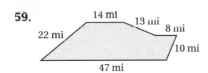

62.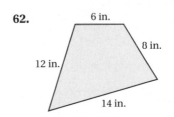

63.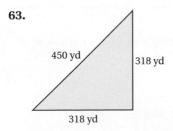

64.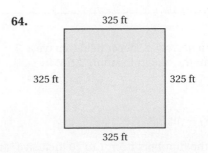

65. Find the perimeter of a standard hockey rink.

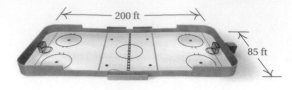

66. In major league baseball, how far does a batter travel in circling the bases when a home run has been hit?

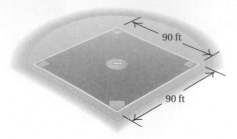

67. **D_W** Describe a situation that corresponds to the addition 12 mi + 7 mi. (See Examples 1 and 2.)

68. **D_W** Explain in your own words the associative law of addition.

The exercises that follow begin an important feature called Skill Maintenance Exercises. These exercises provide an ongoing review of any preceding objective in the book and you will see them in virtually every exercise set. It has been found that this kind of extensive review can significantly improve your retention of concepts. When possible, skill maintenance exercises are chosen to provide practice with skills needed in the following section.

69. Write standard notation for 7 thousands + 9 hundreds + 9 tens + 2 ones.   [1.1b]

70. Write a word name for the number in the following sentence: [1.1c]

Recently, the National Basketball Association's gross revenue was $924,600,000.
Source: *Wall Street Journal*

71. What does the digit 8 mean in 486,205?   [1.1a]

72. Write in standard notation: [1.1c]

Twenty-three million

73. **D_W** Is it possible for a narrower soccer field to have a greater perimeter than the one in Example 12? Why or why not?

74. **D_W** Is it possible for a rectangle to have a perimeter of 12 cu yd? Why or why not?

Add.

75. 🖩 5,987,943 + 328,959 + 49,738,765

76. 🖩 39,487,981 + 8,709,486 + 989,765

77. A fast way to add all the numbers from 1 to 20 inclusive is to pair 1 with 19, 2 with 18, and so on. Use a similar approach to add all the numbers from 1 to 100 inclusive.

1.3 SUBTRACTION

Objectives

a Write a subtraction sentence that corresponds to a situation involving "take away."

b Given a subtraction sentence, write a related addition sentence; and given an addition sentence, write two related subtraction sentences.

c Write a subtraction sentence that corresponds to a situation of "How much do I need?"

d Subtract whole numbers.

a Subtraction and Related Sentences

TAKE AWAY

Subtraction of whole numbers applies to two kinds of situations. The first is called "take away." Consider the following example.

A bowler starts with 10 pins and knocks down 8 of them.

From 10 pins, the bowler "takes away" 8 pins. There are 2 pins left. The subtraction is $10 - 8 = 2$.

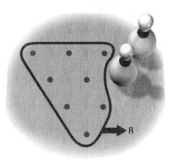

10                                 $10 - 8 = 2$

We use the following terminology with subtraction:

$$\underset{\text{Minuend}}{10} \quad - \quad \underset{\text{Subtrahend}}{8} \quad = \quad \underset{\text{Difference}}{2} \; .$$

The **minuend** is the number from which another number is being subtracted. The **subtrahend** is the number being subtracted. The **difference** is the result of subtracting the subtrahend from the minuend.

EXAMPLES Write a subtraction sentence that corresponds to each situation.

1. Juan goes to a music store and chooses 10 CDs to take to the listening station. He rejects 7 of them, but buys the rest. How many CDs does Juan buy?

There are 10 CDs   He rejects 7 of them.   He buys the remaining 3.
to begin with.

10   —   7   =   3

Write a subtraction sentence that corresponds to each situation.

1. A contractor removes 5 cu yd of sand from a pile containing 67 cu yd. How many cubic yards of sand are left in the pile?

2. Sparks Electronics owns a field next door that has an area of 20,000 sq ft. Deciding they need more room for parking, the owners have 12,000 sq ft paved. How many square feet of field are left unpaved?

Write a related addition sentence.

3. $7 - 5 = 2$

4. $17 - 8 = 9$

2. Kaitlin has $300 and spends $85 for office supplies. How much money is left?

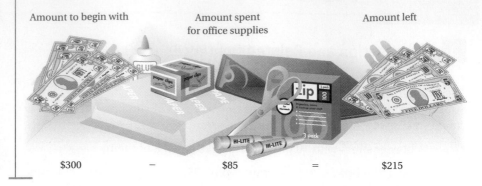

Amount to begin with		Amount spent for office supplies		Amount left
$300	$-$	$85	$=$	$215

Do Exercises 1 and 2.

b   Related Sentences

Subtraction is defined in terms of addition. For example, $5 - 2$ is that number which when added to 2 gives 5. Thus for the subtraction sentence

$$5 - 2 = 3, \qquad \text{Taking away 2 from 5 gives 3.}$$

there is a *related addition* sentence

$$5 = 3 + 2. \qquad \text{Putting back the 2 gives 5 again.}$$

In fact, we know that answers we find to subtractions are correct only because of the related addition, which provides a handy way to *check* a subtraction.

> **SUBTRACTION**
>
> The difference $a - b$ is that unique number c for which $a = c + b$.

EXAMPLE 3   Write a related addition sentence: $8 - 5 = 3$.

$$8 - 5 = 3$$
This number gets added (to 3).
$$8 = 3 + 5$$

By the commutative law of addition, there is also another addition sentence:

$$8 = 5 + 3.$$

The related addition sentence is $8 = 3 + 5$.

Do Exercises 3 and 4.

Answers on page A-3

■ **EXAMPLE 4** Write two related subtraction sentences: $4 + 3 = 7$.

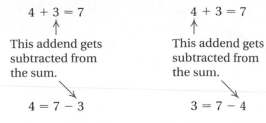

$4 = 7 - 3$ $3 = 7 - 4$

(7 take away 3 is 4.)   (7 take away 4 is 3.)

The related subtraction sentences are $4 = 7 - 3$ and $3 = 7 - 4$.

Do Exercises 5 and 6.

C   How Much Do I Need?

The second kind of situation to which subtraction can apply is called a "missing addend." You have 2 notebooks, but you need 7. You can think of this as "How much do I need to add to 2 to get 7?" Finding the answer can be thought of as finding a missing addend, and can be found by subtracting 2 from 7.

What must be added to 2 to get 7? From the related sentence, we see that the answer is 5.

$$\underbrace{\text{Missing addend}}_{2 + \square = 7} \qquad \underbrace{\text{Difference}}_{7 - 2 = 5.}$$

■ **EXAMPLES** Write a subtraction sentence that corresponds to each situation.

5. Jason wants to buy the CD player shown in this ad. He has \$30. He needs \$79. How much more does he need in order to buy the CD player?

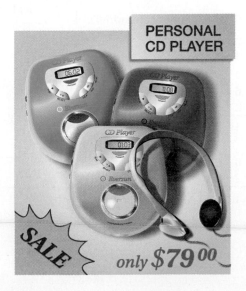

Write two related su[btraction]
sentences.

5. $5 + 8 = 13$

6. $8 + 4 = 12$

Answers on page A-3

Study Tips

Write an addition sentence and a related subtraction sentence corresponding to each situation.

7. It is 348 mi from Miami to Jacksonville. Alice has completed 200 miles of the drive. How much farther does she need to travel?

8. Cedric estimates that it will take 1200 bricks to complete the side of a building, but he has only 800 bricks. How many more bricks will be needed?

9. Subtract.

$$
\begin{array}{r}
7\,8\,9\,3 \\
-\,4\,0\,9\,2 \\
\hline
\end{array}
$$

Answers on page A-3

Answers on page A-3

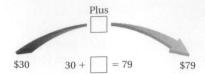

CALCULATOR CORNER

To subtract whole numbers on a calculator, we use the $-$ and $=$ keys. For example, to find $63 - 47$, we press $6\ 3\ -\ 4\ 7\ =$. The calculator displays $\boxed{16}$, so $63 - 47 = 16$. We can check this result by adding the subtrahend, 47, and the difference, 16. To do this, we press $1\ 6\ +\ 4\ 7\ =$. The sum is the minuend, 63, so the subtraction is correct.

Exercises: Use a calculator to perform each subtraction. Check by adding.

1. $57 - 29$

2. $81 - 34$

3. $145 - 78$

4. $612 - 493$

5.
$$
\begin{array}{r}
4\,9\,7\,6 \\
-\,2\,8\,4\,8 \\
\hline
\end{array}
$$

6.
$$
\begin{array}{r}
1\,2{,}4\,0\,6 \\
-\ \ \ 9{,}8\,1\,3 \\
\hline
\end{array}
$$

Thinking of this situation in terms of a missing addend, we have:

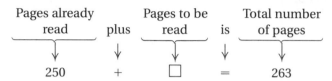

$$30 \qquad 30 + \boxed{} = 79 \qquad \$79$$

To find the answer, we think of the related subtraction sentence:

$$79 - \$30 = \$49. \qquad \text{The addend 30 gets subtracted.}$$

6. Cathy is reading *Ishmael* by Daniel Quinn as part of her philosophy class. It contains 263 pages, of which she has read 250. How many more pages does she have left?

Pages already read	plus	Pages to be read	is	Total number of pages
↓	↓	↓	↓	↓
250	+	☐	=	263

Now we write a related subtraction sentence:

$$263 - 250 = 13 \qquad \text{250 gets subtracted.}$$

Do Exercises 7 and 8.

d Subtraction of Whole Numbers

To subtract numbers, we subtract the ones digits first, then the tens, then the hundreds, and so on.

EXAMPLE 7 Subtract: $9768 - 4320$.

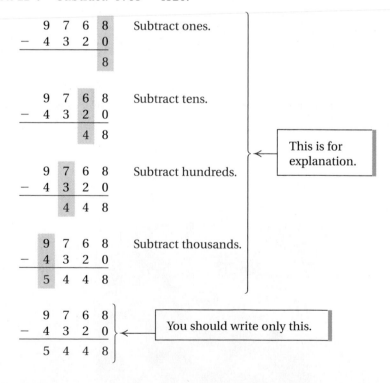

$$
\begin{array}{r}
9\,7\,6\,\boxed{8} \\
-\,4\,3\,2\,\boxed{0} \\
\hline
\boxed{8}
\end{array}
\qquad \text{Subtract ones.}
$$

$$
\begin{array}{r}
9\,7\,\boxed{6}\,8 \\
-\,4\,3\,\boxed{2}\,0 \\
\hline
\boxed{4}\,8
\end{array}
\qquad \text{Subtract tens.}
$$

$$
\begin{array}{r}
9\,\boxed{7}\,6\,8 \\
-\,4\,\boxed{3}\,2\,0 \\
\hline
\boxed{4}\,4\,8
\end{array}
\qquad \text{Subtract hundreds.}
$$

This is for explanation.

$$
\begin{array}{r}
\boxed{9}\,7\,6\,8 \\
-\,\boxed{4}\,3\,2\,0 \\
\hline
\boxed{5}\,4\,4\,8
\end{array}
\qquad \text{Subtract thousands.}
$$

$$
\begin{array}{r}
9\,7\,6\,8 \\
-\,4\,3\,2\,0 \\
\hline
5\,4\,4\,8
\end{array}
$$

You should write only this.

Do Exercise 9.

Sometimes we need to borrow.

EXAMPLE 8 Subtract: 6246 − 1879.

$$\begin{array}{r} {\scriptstyle 3\ 16} \\ 6\ 2\ \cancel{4}\ \cancel{6} \\ -\ 1\ 8\ 7\ 9 \\ \hline 7 \end{array}$$

We cannot subtract 9 ones from 6 ones, but we can subtract 9 ones from 16 ones. We borrow 1 ten to get 16 ones.

$$\begin{array}{r} {\scriptstyle 13} \\ {\scriptstyle 1\ \ 3\ 16} \\ 6\ \cancel{2}\ \cancel{4}\ \cancel{6} \\ -\ 1\ 8\ 7\ 9 \\ \hline 6\ 7 \end{array}$$

We cannot subtract 7 tens from 3 tens, but we can subtract 7 tens from 13 tens. We borrow 1 hundred to get 13 tens.

$$\begin{array}{r} {\scriptstyle 11\ 13} \\ {\scriptstyle 5\ \ \cancel{Y}\ \ 3\ 16} \\ \cancel{6}\ \cancel{2}\ \cancel{4}\ \cancel{6} \\ -\ 1\ 8\ 7\ 9 \\ \hline 4\ 3\ 6\ 7 \end{array}$$

We cannot subtract 8 hundreds from 1 hundred, but we can subtract 8 hundreds from 11 hundreds. We borrow 1 thousand to get 11 hundreds.

We can always check the answer by adding it to the number being subtracted.

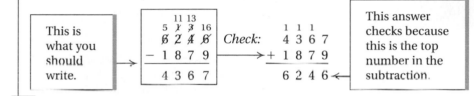

| This is what you should write. | $\begin{array}{r} {\scriptstyle 11\ 13} \\ {\scriptstyle 5\ \cancel{Y}\ 3\ 16} \\ \cancel{6}\ \cancel{2}\ \cancel{4}\ \cancel{6} \\ -\ 1\ 8\ 7\ 9 \\ \hline 4\ 3\ 6\ 7 \end{array}$ | *Check:* | $\begin{array}{r} {\scriptstyle 1\ 1\ 1} \\ 4\ 3\ 6\ 7 \\ +\ 1\ 8\ 7\ 9 \\ \hline 6\ 2\ 4\ 6 \end{array}$ | This answer checks because this is the top number in the subtraction. |

Do Exercises 10 and 11.

EXAMPLE 9 Subtract: 902 − 477.

$$\begin{array}{r} {\scriptstyle 8\ \ 9\ 12} \\ \cancel{9}\ \cancel{0}\ \cancel{2} \\ -\ 4\ 7\ 7 \\ \hline 4\ 2\ 5 \end{array}$$

We cannot subtract 7 ones from 2 ones. We have 9 hundreds, or 90 tens. We borrow 1 ten to get 12 ones. We then have 89 tens.

Do Exercises 12 and 13.

EXAMPLE 10 Subtract: 8003 − 3667.

$$\begin{array}{r} {\scriptstyle 7\ \ 9\ 9\ 13} \\ \cancel{8}\ \cancel{0}\ \cancel{0}\ \cancel{3} \\ -\ 3\ 6\ 6\ 7 \\ \hline 4\ 3\ 3\ 6 \end{array}$$

We have 8 thousands, or 800 tens. We borrow 1 ten to get 13 ones. We then have 799 tens.

EXAMPLES

11. Subtract: 6000 − 3762.

$$\begin{array}{r} {\scriptstyle 5\ 9\ 9\ 10} \\ \cancel{6}\ \cancel{0}\ \cancel{0}\ \cancel{0} \\ -\ 3\ 7\ 6\ 2 \\ \hline 2\ 2\ 3\ 8 \end{array}$$

12. Subtract: 6024 − 2968.

$$\begin{array}{r} {\scriptstyle 11} \\ {\scriptstyle 5\ 9\ \cancel{Y}\ 14} \\ \cancel{6}\ \cancel{0}\ \cancel{2}\ \cancel{4} \\ -\ 2\ 9\ 6\ 8 \\ \hline 3\ 0\ 5\ 6 \end{array}$$

Do Exercises 14–16.

Subtract. Check by adding.

10.
$$\begin{array}{r} 8\ 6\ 8\ 6 \\ -\ 2\ 3\ 5\ 8 \\ \hline \end{array}$$

11.
$$\begin{array}{r} 7\ 1\ 4\ 5 \\ -\ 2\ 3\ 9\ 8 \\ \hline \end{array}$$

Subtract.

12.
$$\begin{array}{r} 7\ 0 \\ -\ 1\ 4 \\ \hline \end{array}$$

13.
$$\begin{array}{r} 5\ 0\ 3 \\ -\ 2\ 9\ 8 \\ \hline \end{array}$$

Subtract.

14.
$$\begin{array}{r} 7\ 0\ 0\ 7 \\ -\ 6\ 3\ 4\ 9 \\ \hline \end{array}$$

15.
$$\begin{array}{r} 6\ 0\ 0\ 0 \\ -\ 3\ 1\ 4\ 9 \\ \hline \end{array}$$

16.
$$\begin{array}{r} 9\ 0\ 3\ 5 \\ -\ 7\ 4\ 8\ 9 \\ \hline \end{array}$$

Answers on page A-3

1.3 EXERCISE SET

a   Write a subtraction sentence that corresponds to each situation.

1. Lauren arrives at the Evergreen State Fair with 20 ride tickets and uses 4 to ride the Upside Down Ride. How many tickets remain?

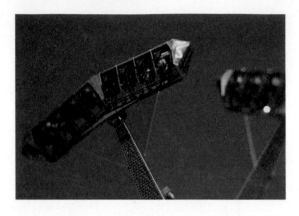

2. *Frozen Yogurt.*   A dispenser at a frozen yogurt store contains 126 ounces (oz) of strawberry yogurt. A 13-oz cup is sold to a customer. How much is left in the dispenser?

3. A host pours 5 oz of salsa from a jar containing 16 oz. How many ounces are left?

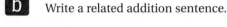

4. *Chocolate Cake.*   One slice of chocolate cake with fudge frosting contains 564 calories (cal). One cup of hot cocoa made with skim milk contains 188 calories. How many more calories are in the cake than in the cocoa?

b   Write a related addition sentence.

5. $7 - 4 = 3$

6. $12 - 5 = 7$

7. $13 - 8 = 5$

8. $9 - 9 = 0$

9. $23 - 9 = 14$

10. $20 - 8 = 12$

11. $43 - 16 = 27$

12. $51 - 18 = 33$

Write two related subtraction sentences.

13. $6 + 9 = 15$

14. $7 + 9 = 16$

15. $8 + 7 = 15$

16. $8 + 0 = 8$

17. $17 + 6 = 23$

18. $11 + 8 = 19$

19. $23 + 9 = 32$

20. $42 + 10 = 52$

c   Write an addition sentence and a related subtraction sentence corresponding to each situation.

21. *Kangaroos.*   There are 32 million kangaroos in Australia and 17 million people. How many more kangaroos are there than people?

22. *Interstate Speeds.*   Recently, speed limits on interstate highways in many western states were raised from 65 mph to 75 mph. By how many miles per hour were they raised?

23. A set of drapes requires 23 yards (yd) of material. The decorator has 10 yd of material in stock. How much more must be ordered?

24. Marv needs to bowl a score of 223 in order to win his tournament. His score with one frame to go is 195. How many pins does Marv need in the last frame to win the tournament?

 Subtract.

25.
```
   1 7
 -   5
```

26.
```
   8 6
 - 1 3
```

27.
```
   6 5
 - 2 1
```

28.
```
   8 7
 - 3 4
```

29.
```
   5 6 7
 - 2 3 4
```

30.
```
   5 2 6
 - 3 2 3
```

31.
```
   4 5 4 7
 - 3 4 2 1
```

32.
```
   6 8 7 5
 - 2 1 1 1
```

33. 86 − 47

34. 73 − 28

35. 625 − 327

36. 726 − 509

37. 835 − 609

38. 953 − 246

39. 981 − 747

40. 887 − 698

41.
```
   9 7 6 8
 - 4 3 8 6
```

42.
```
   6 4 3 2
 - 2 8 9 7
```

43.
```
   3 9 8 2
 - 2 4 8 9
```

44.
```
   7 6 5 0
 - 1 7 6 5
```

45.
```
   5 0 4 6
 - 2 8 5 9
```

46.
```
   6 3 0 8
 - 2 6 7 9
```

47.
```
   7 6 4 0
 - 3 8 0 9
```

48.
```
   8 0 0 3
 -   5 9 9
```

49.
$$12{,}647 - 4{,}899$$

50.
$$16{,}222 - 5{,}888$$

51.
$$46{,}771 - 12{,}977$$

52.
$$95{,}654 - 48{,}985$$

53. $10{,}002 - 7834$

54. $23{,}048 - 17{,}592$

55. $90{,}237 - 47{,}209$

56. $84{,}703 - 298$

57.
$$90 - 37$$

58.
$$40 - 37$$

59.
$$90 - 54$$

60.
$$90 - 78$$

61.
$$160 - 74$$

62.
$$470 - 188$$

63.
$$690 - 236$$

64.
$$803 - 418$$

65.
$$903 - 132$$

66.
$$6408 - 258$$

67.
$$2300 - 109$$

68.
$$3506 - 1293$$

69.
$$6808 - 3059$$

70.
$$7840 - 3027$$

71.
$$8092 - 1073$$

72.
$$6007 - 1589$$

73. 5843 − 98

74. 10,002 − 398

75. 101,734 − 5760

76. 15,017 − 7809

77. 10,004 − 29

78. 21,043 − 8909

79. 83,907 − 89

80. 311,568 − 19,394

81.
```
   7 0 0 0
 − 2 7 9 4
```

82.
```
   8 0 0 1
 − 6 5 4 3
```

83.
```
   4 8,0 0 0
 − 3 7,6 9 5
```

84.
```
   1 7,0 4 3
 − 1 1,5 9 8
```

85. **D**W Describe two situations that correspond to the subtraction $20 − $17, one "take away" and one "missing addend."

86. **D**W Is subtraction commutative (is there a commutative law of subtraction)? Why or why not?

SKILL MAINTENANCE

Add. [1.2b]

87.
```
   9 4 6
 +   7 8
```

88.
```
   9 0 7 8
 + 3 6 5 4
```

89.
```
   5 7,8 7 7
 + 3 2,4 0 6
```

90.
```
   8 0 0 4
   6 7 8 9
   7 7 2 0
 + 6 8 5 1
```

91. 567 + 778

92. 901 + 23

93. 12,885 + 9807

94. 9909 + 1011

95. Write a word name for 6,375,602.   [1.1c]

96. What does the digit 7 mean in 6,375,602?   [1.1a]

SYNTHESIS

97. **D**W Describe the one situation in which subtraction *is* commutative (see Exercise 86).

98. **D**W Explain what it means to "borrow" in subtraction.

Subtract.

99. ▦ 3,928,124 − 1,098,947

100. ▦ 21,431,206 − 9,724,837

101. Fill in the missing digits to make the subtraction true:
9,☐48,621 − 2,097,☐81 = 7,251,140.

Objectives

a Round to the nearest ten, hundred, or thousand.

b Estimate sums and differences by rounding.

c Use < or > for ☐ to write a true sentence in a situation like 6 ☐ 10.

Round to the nearest ten.

1. 37

2. 52

3. 73

4. 98

Round to the nearest ten.

5. 35

6. 75

7. 85

Answers on page A-4

1.4 ROUNDING AND ESTIMATING; ORDER

a Rounding

We round numbers in situations for which we do not need an exact answer. For example, we might round to check if an answer to a problem is reasonable or to check a calculation done by hand or on a calculator. We might also round to see if we are being charged the correct amount in a store.

To understand how to round, we first look at some examples using number lines, even though this is not the way we generally do rounding.

EXAMPLE 1 Round 47 to the nearest ten.

Here is a part of a number line; 47 is between 40 and 50.

Since 47 is closer to 50, we round up to 50.

EXAMPLE 2 Round 42 to the nearest ten.

42 is between 40 and 50.

Since 42 is closer to 40, we round down to 40.

Do Exercises 1–4.

EXAMPLE 3 Round 45 to the nearest ten.

45 is halfway between 40 and 50.

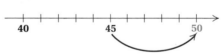

We could round 45 down to 40 or up to 50. We agree to round up to 50.

When a number is halfway between rounding numbers, round up.

Do Exercises 5–7.

Here is a rule for rounding.

Round to the nearest ten.

8. 137

> ### ROUNDING WHOLE NUMBERS
>
> To round to a certain place:
> **a)** Locate the digit in that place.
> **b)** Consider the next digit to the right.
> **c)** If the digit to the right is 5 or higher, round up. If the digit to the right is 4 or lower, round down.
> **d)** Change all digits to the right of the rounding location to zeros.

9. 473

10. 235

EXAMPLE 4 Round 6485 to the nearest ten.

a) Locate the digit in the tens place, 8.

   6 4 8 5
       ↑

11. 285

b) Consider the next digit to the right, 5.

   6 4 8 5
       ↑

c) Since that digit is 5 or higher, round 8 tens up to 9 tens.

d) Change all digits to the right of the tens digit to zeros.

    6 4 9 0 ← This is the answer.

Round to the nearest hundred.
12. 641

EXAMPLE 5 Round 6485 to the nearest hundred.

a) Locate the digit in the hundreds place, 4.

   6 4 8 5
     ↑

b) Consider the next digit to the right, 8.

   6 4 8 5
     ↑

13. 759

c) Since that digit is 5 or higher, round 4 hundreds up to 5 hundreds.

d) Change all digits to the right of the hundreds digit to zeros.

    6 5 0 0 ← This is the answer.

14. 750

15. 9325

EXAMPLE 6 Round 6485 to the nearest thousand.

a) Locate the digit in the thousands place, 6.

   6 4 8 5
  ↑

b) Consider the next digit to the right, 4.

   6 4 8 5
  ↑

Round to the nearest thousand.
16. 7896

c) Since that digit is 4 or lower, round down, meaning that 6 thousands stays as 6 thousands.

d) Change all digits to the right of the thousands digit to zeros.

    6 0 0 0 ← This is the answer.

17. 8459

18. 19,343

Do Exercises 8–19.

19. 68,500

Answers on page A-4

20. Round 48,968 to the nearest ten; to the nearest hundred; to the nearest thousand.

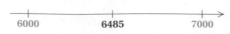
Sometimes rounding involves changing more than one digit in a number.

EXAMPLE 7　Round 78,595 to the nearest ten.

a) Locate the digit in the tens place, 9.

　　7 8,5 9 5
　　　　　↑

b) Consider the next digit to the right, 5.

　　7 8,5 9 5
　　　　　↑

c) Since that digit is 5 or higher, round 9 tens to 10 tens. To carry this out, we think of 10 tens as 1 hundred + 0 tens, and increase the hundreds digit by 1, to get 6 hundreds + 0 tens. We then write 6 in the hundreds place and 0 in the tens place.

d) Change the digit to the right of the tens digit to zero.

　　7 8,6 0 0 ← This is the answer.

Note that if we round this number to the nearest hundred, we get the same answer.

21. Round 269,582 to the nearest ten; to the nearest hundred; to the nearest thousand.

Do Exercises 20 and 21.

There are many methods of rounding. For example, in computer applications, rounding 8563 to the nearest hundred might be done using a rule called **truncating,** meaning that we simply change all digits to the right of the rounding location to zeros. Thus, 8563 would round to 8500, a different result from what we would get using the rule discussed in this section.

b　Estimating

In the following example, we see how estimation can be used in making a purchase.

EXAMPLE 8　*Estimating the Price of an Automobile.*　Recently Maria and Luis Vasquez considered buying an Oldsmobile Alero. There are three basic models of this car, and each has options beyond the basic price, as shown in the chart on the following page. Maria and Luis had a budget of $20,000. Make a quick estimate to determine if the GL3 with all the options was within their budget.

Answers on page A-4

To estimate, we round to the nearest hundred the cost of the GL3 with all the options and decide whether it fit into their budget.

MODEL GL1 SEDAN (4 DOOR) 2.4-liter engine, 5 SPEED MANUAL TRANSMISSION	MODEL GL2 SEDAN (4 DOOR) 2.4-liter engine, 4 SPEED AUTOMATIC TRANSMISSION	MODEL GL3 SEDAN (4 DOOR) 3.4-liter engine, 4 SPEED AUTOMATIC TRANSMISSION	
Base price: $17,650	*Base price:* $18,270	*Base price:* $18,875	
Destination charges: $535	*Destination charges:* $535	*Destination charges:* $535	
Each of these vehicles comes with several options.			
Driver's seat: with 6-way power adjustment		$305	
Sunroof:		$650	
Feature package: 15" aluminum wheels, remote keyless entry, foglamps, leather-wrapped steering wheel and shift knob		$585	
Sport package: 16" aluminum wheels, performance radial tires, and performance suspension		$450	
Rear decklid spoiler:		$225	
Radio: AM/FM cassette/CD with 6 speaker dimensional sound system		$200	

Source: General Motors

First, we list the base price of the GL3 and then the cost of each of the options. We then round each number to the nearest hundred and add.

```
  1 8,8 7 5        1 8,9 0 0
      5 3 5            5 0 0
      3 0 5            3 0 0
      6 5 0            7 0 0
      5 8 5            6 0 0
      4 5 0            5 0 0
      2 2 5            2 0 0
+     2 0 0      +     2 0 0
                 2 1,9 0 0  ← Estimated answer
```

The estimated total cost is $21,900. Since Maria and Luis allowed themselves a budget of $20,000 for their car, they needed to forego some options or buy a different car.

Do Exercises 22 and 23.

Refer to the chart below to answer Margin Exercises 22 and 23.

22. Suppose Maria and Luis wanted to buy a GL1 with all options except the sunroof and the sport package.

a) Estimate this cost by rounding to the nearest hundred.

b) Could they have bought this car with a budget of $20,000?

23. By eliminating options, find a way that Luis and Maria could have bought the GL3 and stayed within their $20,000 budget. Answers may vary.

Answers on page A-4

1.4 Rounding and Estimating; Order

24. Estimate the sum by first rounding to the nearest ten. Show your work.

$$
\begin{array}{r}
7\ 4 \\
2\ 3 \\
3\ 5 \\
+\ 6\ 6 \\
\end{array}
$$

25. Estimate the sum by first rounding to the nearest hundred. Show your work.

$$
\begin{array}{r}
6\ 5\ 0 \\
6\ 8\ 5 \\
2\ 3\ 8 \\
+\ 1\ 6\ 8 \\
\end{array}
$$

26. Estimate the difference by first rounding to the nearest hundred. Show your work.

$$
\begin{array}{r}
9\ 2\ 8\ 5 \\
-\ 6\ 7\ 3\ 9 \\
\end{array}
$$

27. Estimate the difference by first rounding to the nearest thousand. Show your work.

$$
\begin{array}{r}
2\ 3,2\ 7\ 8 \\
-\ 1\ 1,6\ 9\ 8 \\
\end{array}
$$

Answers on page A-4

Estimating can be done in many ways and can have many results, even though in the problems that follow we ask you to round in a specific way.

■ **EXAMPLE 9**   Estimate this sum by first rounding to the nearest ten:

$$78 + 49 + 31 + 85.$$

We round each number to the nearest ten. Then we add.

$$
\begin{array}{rr}
7\ 8 & \quad 8\ 0 \\
4\ 9 & 5\ 0 \\
3\ 1 & 3\ 0 \\
+\ 8\ 5 & +\ 9\ 0 \\
\hline
& 2\ 5\ 0 \leftarrow \text{Estimated answer}
\end{array}
$$

■ **EXAMPLE 10**   Estimate this sum by first rounding to the nearest hundred:

$$850 + 674 + 986 + 839.$$

We have

$$
\begin{array}{rr}
8\ 5\ 0 & \quad 9\ 0\ 0 \\
6\ 7\ 4 & 7\ 0\ 0 \\
9\ 8\ 6 & 1\ 0\ 0\ 0 \\
+\ 8\ 3\ 9 & +\ \ 8\ 0\ 0 \\
\hline
& 3\ 4\ 0\ 0
\end{array}
$$

Do Exercises 24 and 25.

■ **EXAMPLE 11**   Estimate the difference by first rounding to the nearest thousand: $9324 - 2849.$

We have

$$
\begin{array}{rr}
9\ 3\ 2\ 4 & \quad 9\ 0\ 0\ 0 \\
-\ 2\ 8\ 4\ 9 & -\ 3\ 0\ 0\ 0 \\
\hline
& 6\ 0\ 0\ 0
\end{array}
$$

Do Exercises 26 and 27.

The sentence $7 - 5 = 2$ says that $7 - 5$ is the same as 2. When we round, the result is rarely the same as the number we started with. Thus we use the symbol $\approx$ when rounding. This symbol means "**is approximately equal to.**" For example, when 687 is rounded to the nearest ten, we can write

$$687 \approx 690.$$

C   **Order**

We know that 2 is not the same as 5. We express this by the sentence $2 \neq 5$. We also know that 2 is less than 5. We symbolize this by the expression $2 < 5$. We can see this order on a number line: 2 is to the left of 5.

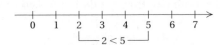

Note that 0 is the smallest whole number. We have $0 < a$ for any whole number a.

ORDER OF WHOLE NUMBERS

For any whole numbers *a* and *b*:

1. $a < b$ (read "*a* is less than *b*") is true when *a* is to the left of *b* on a number line.

2. $a > b$ (read "*a* is greater than *b*") is true when *a* is to the right of *b* on a number line.

We call < and > **inequality symbols.**

EXAMPLE 12 Use < or > for ☐ to write a true sentence: 7 ☐ 11.

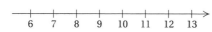

Since 7 is to the left of 11 on a number line, 7 < 11.

EXAMPLE 13 Use < or > for ☐ to write a true sentence: 92 ☐ 87.

Since 92 is to the right of 87 on a number line, 92 > 87.

A sentence like $8 + 5 = 13$ is called an **equation.** It is a *true* equation. The equation $4 + 8 = 11$ is a *false* equation. A sentence like 7 < 11 is called an **inequality.** The sentence 7 < 11 is a *true* inequality. The sentence 23 > 69 is a *false* inequality.

Do Exercises 28–33.

Use < or > for ☐ to write a true sentence. Draw a number line if necessary.

28. 8 ☐ 12

29. 12 ☐ 8

30. 76 ☐ 64

31. 64 ☐ 76

32. 217 ☐ 345

33. 345 ☐ 217

Answers on page A-4

EXERCISE SET

a   Round to the nearest ten.

1. 48   **2.** 532   **3.** 467   **4.** 8945

5. 731   **6.** 17   **7.** 895   **8.** 798

Round to the nearest hundred.

9. 146   **10.** 874   **11.** 957   **12.** 650

13. 9079   **14.** 4645   **15.** 32,850   **16.** 198,402

Round to the nearest thousand.

17. 5876   **18.** 4500   **19.** 7500   **20.** 2001

21. 45,340   **22.** 735,562   **23.** 373,405   **24.** 6,713,855

b   Estimate the sum or difference by first rounding to the nearest ten. Show your work.

25.
```
   7 8
 + 9 7
```

26.
```
   6 2
   9 7
   4 6
 + 8 8
```

27.
```
  8 0 7 4
 - 2 3 4 7
```

28.
```
   6 7 3
 -    2 8
```

Estimate each sum by first rounding to the nearest ten. If the given sum seems to be incorrect when compared to the estimate, state so.

29.
```
   4 1
   2 1
   5 5
 + 6 0
 ─────
 1 7 7
```

30.
```
   4 5
   7 7
   2 5
 + 5 6
 ─────
 3 4 3
```

31.
```
   6 2 2
     7 8
     8 1
 + 1 1 1
 ───────
   9 3 2
```

32.
```
   8 3 6
   3 7 4
   7 9 4
 + 9 3 8
 ───────
 3 9 4 7
```

Estimate each sum or difference by first rounding to the nearest hundred. Show your work.

33.
```
   7 3 4 8
 + 9 2 4 7
```

34.
```
   5 6 8
   4 7 2
   9 3 8
 + 4 0 2
```

35.
```
  6 8 5 2
 - 1 7 4 8
```

36.
```
  9 4 3 8
 - 2 7 8 7
```

Gateway Computers. Gateway, Inc., recently sold a model of computer called the Performance 1600. The base price for this model, with the features shown in the following ad, was $1399. Options that could be included when ordering are shown in the table below.

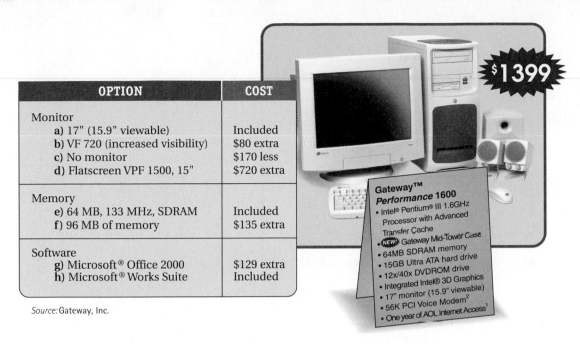

OPTION	COST
Monitor	
a) 17" (15.9" viewable)	Included
b) VF 720 (increased visibility)	$80 extra
c) No monitor	$170 less
d) Flatscreen VPF 1500, 15"	$720 extra
Memory	
e) 64 MB, 133 MHz, SDRAM	Included
f) 96 MB of memory	$135 extra
Software	
g) Microsoft® Office 2000	$129 extra
h) Microsoft® Works Suite	Included

Source: Gateway, Inc.

37. Estimate the cost, by rounding to the nearest hundred, of the computer with options (a), (f), and (h).

38. Estimate the cost, by rounding to the nearest hundred, of the computer with options (b), (f), and (h).

39. Jamaal and Natasha are shopping for a computer and have a budget of $1700. Estimate the cost, by rounding to the nearest hundred, of the computer with options (c), (e), and (g). Can they afford the computer?

40. Max is shopping for a computer and has a budget of $2100. Estimate the cost, by rounding to the nearest hundred, of the computer with options (d), (f), and (g). Can he afford the computer?

41. Suppose you need to buy a computer with a monitor, and you select this model. Decide on the options you would like and estimate the cost to the nearest ten dollars. Answers will vary.

42. Suppose you had decided on this computer and already had a monitor. Select any of the remaining options and estimate the cost to the nearest ten dollars. Answers will vary.

Estimate each sum by first rounding to the nearest hundred. If the given sum seems to be incorrect when compared to the estimate, state so.

43.
```
    2 1 6
      8 4
    7 4 5
  + 5 9 5
  ---------
  1 6 4 0
```

44.
```
      4 8 1
      7 0 2
      6 2 3
  + 1 0 4 3
  ---------
    1 8 4 9
```

45.
```
    7 5 0
    4 2 8
      6 3
  + 2 0 5
  ---------
  1 4 4 6
```

46.
```
    3 2 6
    2 7 5
    7 5 8
  + 9 4 3
  ---------
  2 3 0 2
```

Estimate each sum or difference by first rounding to the nearest thousand. Show your work.

47.
```
    9 6 4 3
    4 8 2 1
    8 9 4 3
  + 7 0 0 4
```

48.
```
    7 6 4 8
    9 3 4 8
    7 8 4 2
  + 2 2 2 2
```

49.
```
    9 2,1 4 9
  - 2 2,5 5 5
```

50.
```
    8 4,8 9 0
  - 1 1,1 1 0
```

C   Use < or > for ☐ to write a true sentence. Draw a number line if necessary.

51. 0 ☐ 17

52. 32 ☐ 0

53. 34 ☐ 12

54. 28 ☐ 18

55. 1000 ☐ 1001

56. 77 ☐ 117

57. 133 ☐ 132

58. 999 ☐ 997

59. 460 ☐ 17

60. 345 ☐ 456

61. 37 ☐ 11

62. 12 ☐ 32

Land-Speed Cars.   Two competing jet-powered cars can now travel faster than the speed of sound. The Thrust SCC is 54 ft long and weighs 7 tons. The Spirit of America is 47 ft long and weighs 4 tons. Use this information to answer Exercises 63 and 64.

Sources: *Car & Driver*, September 1996; *Advanced Materials and Processes*, January 1998; *Guinness Book of Records*, 2002

63. Which is longer, the Thrust SCC or the Spirit of America? Express the numbers in the situation as an inequality.

64. Which is heavier, the Thrust SCC or the Spirit of America? Express the numbers in the situation as an inequality.

65. *Life Expectancy.* The life expectancy in 2050 is predicted to be about 87 yr for a female and about 81 yr for a male. Use an inequality to compare these life expectancies.

Life Expectancy

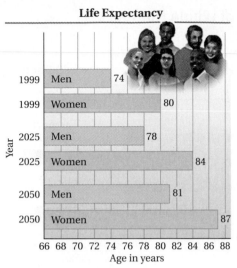

Source: U.S. Census Bureau

66. *Utilities.* The average yearly cost of utilities for households in the Northeast is $1644 and for households in the West is $1014. Use an inequality to compare the costs.

Utility Costs

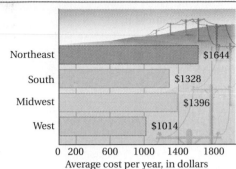

Source: Energy Information Administration

67. **D**w Explain how estimating and rounding can be useful when shopping for groceries.

68. **D**w When rounding 748 to the nearest hundred, Gerry rounds to 750 and then to 800. What mistake is he making?

SKILL MAINTENANCE

Write standard notation.

69. 7 thousands + 9 hundreds + 9 tens + 2 ones   [1.1b]

70. Twenty-three million   [1.1c]

71. Write a word name for 246,605,004,032.   [1.1c]

72. Write expanded notation for 8017.   [1.1b]

Add.   [1.2b]

73. $\begin{array}{r} 6\,7,7\,8\,9 \\ +\ 1\,8,9\,6\,5 \\ \hline \end{array}$

74. $\begin{array}{r} 9\,0\,0\,2 \\ +\ 4\,5\,8\,7 \\ \hline \end{array}$

Subtract.   [1.3d]

75. $\begin{array}{r} 6\,7,7\,8\,9 \\ -\ 1\,8,9\,6\,5 \\ \hline \end{array}$

76. $\begin{array}{r} 9\,0\,0\,2 \\ -\ 4\,5\,8\,7 \\ \hline \end{array}$

SYNTHESIS

77. **D**w Consider two numbers a and b, with $a < b$. Is it possible that when a and b are each rounded down, the result of rounding a is greater than the result of rounding b? Why or why not?

78. **D**w Why do you think we round *up* when a 5 is the next digit to the right of the place in which we are rounding?

79.–82. Use a calculator to find the sums and differences in each of Exercises 47–50. Then check your answers using estimation. Even when using a calculator, it is possible to make an error if you press the wrong buttons, so it is a good idea to check by estimating.

MULTIPLICATION AND AREA

a Multiplication of Whole Numbers

REPEATED ADDITION

The multiplication 3×5 corresponds to this repeated addition:

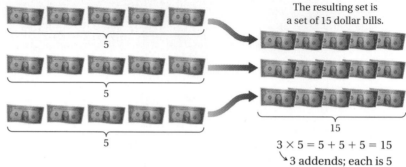

We combine 3 sets with 5 bills in each set.

The resulting set is a set of 15 dollar bills.

$$3 \times 5 = 5 + 5 + 5 = 15$$
3 addends; each is 5

The numbers that we multiply are called **factors.** The result of the multiplication is called a **product.**

$$\begin{array}{ccc} 3 & \times & 5 & = & 15 \\ \downarrow & & \downarrow & & \downarrow \\ \text{Factor} & & \text{Factor} & & \text{Product} \end{array}$$

RECTANGULAR ARRAYS

Multiplications can also be thought of as rectangular arrays. Each of the following corresponds to the multiplication 3×5.

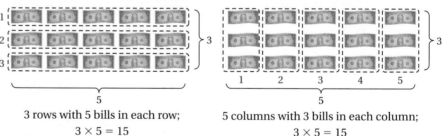

3 rows with 5 bills in each row;
$3 \times 5 = 15$

5 columns with 3 bills in each column;
$3 \times 5 = 15$

When you write a multiplication sentence corresponding to a real-world situation, you should think of either a rectangular array or an addition with identical addends. In some cases, it may help to think both ways.

We have used an "$\times$" to denote multiplication. A dot "$\cdot$" is also commonly used. (Use of the dot is attributed to the German mathematician Gottfried Wilhelm von Leibniz in 1698.) Parentheses are also used to denote multiplication. For example,

$$3 \times 5 = 3 \cdot 5 = (3)(5) = 3(5) = 15.$$

■ **EXAMPLES**   Write a multiplication sentence that corresponds to each situation.

1. It is known that Americans drink 24 million gal of soft drinks per day (*per day* means *each day*). What quantity of soft drinks is consumed every 5 days?

We draw a picture in which 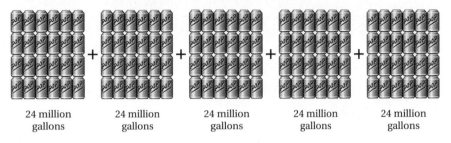 = 1 million gallons or we can simply visualize the situation. Repeated addition fits best in this case.

24 million gallons + 24 million gallons + 24 million gallons + 24 million gallons + 24 million gallons

5 · 24 million gallons = 120 million gallons

2. One side of a building has 6 floors with 7 windows on each floor. How many windows are on that side of the building?

We have a rectangular array and can easily draw a sketch.

6 · 7 = 42

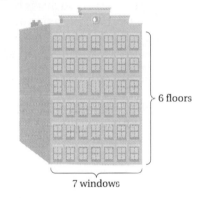

6 floors

7 windows

Do Exercises 1–3.

Repeated addition of 0 results in 0, so $0 \cdot a = a \cdot 0 = 0$. When 1 is added to itself *a* times, the result is *a*, so $1 \cdot a = a \cdot 1 = a$. We say that the number 1 is the **multiplicative identity.**

■ **EXAMPLE 3**   Multiply: 37×2.

We have

$$\begin{array}{r} 3\ 7 \\ \times\quad 2 \\ \hline 1\ 4 \\ 6\ 0 \\ \hline 7\ 4 \end{array}$$

1 4 ← Multiply the 7 ones by 2: $2 \times 7 = 14$.
6 0 ← Multiply the 3 tens by 2: $2 \times 30 = 60$.
7 4 ← Add.

Write a multiplication sentence that corresponds to each situation.

1. Marv practices for the U.S. Open bowling tournament. He bowls 8 games each day for 7 days. How many games does he bowl altogether for practice?

2. A lab technician pours 75 milliliters (mL) of acid into each of 10 beakers. How much acid is poured in all?

3. **Checkerboard.**   A checkerboard consists of 8 rows with 8 squares in each row. How many squares in all are there on a checkerboard?

Answers on page A-4

Multiply.

4. 5 8
   ×   2

5. 3 7
   ×   4

6. 8 2 3
   ×   6

7. 1 3 4 8
   ×   5

Multiply.

8. 4 5
   × 2 3

9. 48 × 63

We can simplify what we write by writing just one line for the products.

$$\begin{array}{r} \overset{1}{} \\ 3\;7 \\ \times\;\;\; 2 \\ \hline 4 \end{array}$$

Multiply the ones by 2: $2 \cdot (7 \text{ ones}) = 14 \text{ ones} = 1 \text{ ten} + 4 \text{ ones}$. Write 4 in the ones column and 1 above the tens.

$$\begin{array}{r} \overset{1}{} \\ 3\;7 \\ \times\;\;\; 2 \\ \hline 7\;4 \end{array}$$

Multiply the 3 tens by 2 and add 1 ten: $2 \cdot (3 \text{ tens}) = 6 \text{ tens}$, $6 \text{ tens} + 1 \text{ ten} = 7 \text{ tens}$. Write 7 in the tens column.

$$\left.\begin{array}{r} \overset{1}{} \\ 3\;7 \\ \times\;\;\; 2 \\ \hline 7\;4 \end{array}\right\}$$ Try to write only this.

Do Exercises 4–7.

The fact that we can do this is based on a property called the **distributive law.** It says that to multiply a number by a sum, $a \cdot (b + c)$, we can multiply each part by a and then add like this: $(a \cdot b) + (a \cdot c)$. Thus, $a \cdot (b + c) = (a \cdot b) + (a \cdot c)$. Applied to the example above, the distributive law gives us

$$2 \cdot 37 = 2 \cdot (30 + 7) = (2 \cdot 30) + (2 \cdot 7).$$

■ **EXAMPLE 4** Multiply: 43×57.

$$\begin{array}{r} \overset{2}{} \\ 5\;7 \\ \times\;\;4\;3 \\ \hline 1\;7\;1 \end{array}$$ Multiplying by 3

$$\begin{array}{r} \overset{2}{\overset{2}{}} \\ 5\;7 \\ \times\;\;4\;3 \\ \hline 1\;7\;1 \\ 2\;2\;8\;0 \end{array}$$ Multiplying by 40. (We write a 0 and then multiply 57 by 4).

> You may have learned that such a 0 does not have to be written. You may omit it if you wish. If you do omit it, remember, when multiplying by tens, to put the answer in the tens place.

$$\begin{array}{r} \overset{2}{\overset{2}{}} \\ 5\;7 \\ \times\;\;4\;3 \\ \hline 1\;7\;1 \\ 2\;2\;8\;0 \\ \hline 2\;4\;5\;1 \end{array}$$ Adding to obtain the product

Do Exercises 8 and 9.

EXAMPLE 5 Multiply: 457×683.

```
        5 2
      6 8 3
  ×   4 5 7
  ───────────
  4 7 8 1        Multiplying 683 by 7
```

```
      4 1
      5 2
      6 8 3
  ×   4 5 7
  ───────────
  4 7 8 1
3 4 1 5 0        Multiplying 683 by 50
```

```
      3 1
      4 1
      5 2
      6 8 3
  ×   4 5 7
  ───────────
    4 7 8 1
  3 4 1 5 0
2 7 3 2 0 0      Multiplying 683 by 400
───────────
3 1 2 , 1 3 1    Adding
```

Do Exercises 10 and 11.

EXAMPLE 6 Multiply: 306×274.

Note that $306 = 3$ hundreds $+ 6$ ones.

```
      2 7 4
  ×   3 0 6
  ───────────
    1 6 4 4 ←── Multiplying by 6 ones
  8 2 2 0 0 ←── Multiplying by 3 hundreds. (We write 00
  ───────────     and then multiply 274 by 3.)
  8 3 , 8 4 4 ←─ Adding
```

Do Exercises 12–14.

EXAMPLE 7 Multiply: 360×274.

Note that $360 = 3$ hundreds $+ 6$ tens.

```
      2 7 4   ┌─ Multiplying by 6 tens. (We write 0 and
  ×   3 6 0   │    then multiply 274 by 6.)
  ───────────
  1 6 4 4 0 ←─┘  Multiplying by 3 hundreds. (We write 00
  8 2 2 0 0 ←─   and then multiply 274 by 3.)
  ───────────
  9 8 , 6 4 0    Adding
```

Do Exercises 15–18.

Multiply.

10.
```
    7 4 6
  ×   6 2
```

11. 245×837

Multiply.

12.
```
    4 7 2
  × 3 0 6
```

13. 408×704

14.
```
    2 3 4 4
  × 6 0 0 5
```

Multiply.

15.
```
    4 7 2
  × 8 3 0
```

16.
```
    2 3 4 4
  × 7 4 0 0
```

17. 100×562

18. 1000×562

Answers on page A-4

Complete the following to illustrate the commutative law of multiplication.

19. $8 \cdot 7 = \square \cdot \square$

20. $2 \cdot 6 = \square \cdot \square$

Insert parentheses to illustrate the associative law of multiplication.

21. $3 \cdot (7 \cdot 9) = 3 \cdot 7 \cdot 9$

22. $(5 \cdot 4) \cdot 8 = 5 \cdot 4 \cdot 8$

Multiply.

23. $5 \cdot 2 \cdot 4$

24. $5 \cdot 1 \cdot 3$

Answers on page A-4

Check on your own that $17 \cdot 37 = 629$ and that $37 \cdot 17 = 629$. This illustrates the **commutative law of multiplication.** It says that we can multiply two numbers in any order, $a \cdot b = b \cdot a$, and get the same answer.

EXAMPLE 8 Complete the following to illustrate the commutative law of multiplication:

$$6 \cdot 9 = \square \cdot \square.$$

We reverse the order of the multiplication:

$$6 \cdot 9 = 9 \cdot 6.$$

Do Exercises 19 and 20.

To multiply three or more numbers, we group them so that we multiply two at a time. Consider $2 \cdot (3 \cdot 4)$ and $(2 \cdot 3) \cdot 4$. The parentheses tell what to do first:

$$2 \cdot (3 \cdot 4) = 2 \cdot (12) = 24. \qquad \text{We multiply 3 and 4, then 2.}$$

We can also multiply 2 and 3, then 4:

$$(2 \cdot 3) \cdot 4 = (6) \cdot 4 = 24.$$

Either way we get 24. It does not matter how we group the numbers. This illustrates that **multiplication is associative:** $a \cdot (b \cdot c) = (a \cdot b) \cdot c$.

EXAMPLE 9 Insert parentheses to illustrate the associative law of multiplication:

$$6 \cdot (2 \cdot 5) = 6 \cdot 2 \cdot 5.$$

We regroup as follows:

$$6 \cdot (2 \cdot 5) = (6 \cdot 2) \cdot 5.$$

Do Exercises 21–24.

> ### THE COMMUTATIVE LAW OF MULTIPLICATION
>
> For any numbers a and b,
> $$a \cdot b = b \cdot a.$$

> ### THE ASSOCIATIVE LAW OF MULTIPLICATION
>
> For any numbers a, b, and c,
> $$a \cdot (b \cdot c) = (a \cdot b) \cdot c.$$

CAUTION!

Do not confuse the associative law with the distributive law. When you multiply $2 \cdot (3 \cdot 4)$, do *not* use the 2 twice. When you multiply $2 \cdot (3 + 4)$ using the distributive law, use the 2 twice: $2 \cdot 3 + 2 \cdot 4$.

b Estimating Products by Rounding

EXAMPLE 10 *Computer Memory.* Gladys is buying a Gateway Performance 300 computer. She wants to add memory and finds that each additional block of 128 MB memory costs $80. By rounding to the nearest ten, estimate the cost if she purchases 11 additional blocks of memory.
Source: 2000 Gateway, Inc.

We want to estimate the product of 80 and 11. To do so, we round each factor to the nearest ten and multiply the rounded numbers:

Exact	*Nearest ten*
8 0	8 0
× 1 1	× 1 0
8 8 0	8 0 0

The additional memory will cost about $800.

Do Exercise 25.

EXAMPLE 11 Estimate the following product by first rounding to the nearest ten and to the nearest hundred: 683 × 457.

Nearest ten	*Nearest hundred*	*Exact*
6 8 0	7 0 0	6 8 3
× 4 6 0	× 5 0 0	× 4 5 7
4 0 8 0 0	3 5 0,0 0 0	4 7 8 1
2 7 2 0 0 0		3 4 1 5 0
3 1 2,8 0 0		2 7 3 2 0 0
		3 1 2,1 3 1

Do Exercise 26.

CALCULATOR CORNER

To multiply whole numbers on a calculator, we use the ☒ and ☐ keys. For example, to find 13 × 47, we press ⬚1⬚ ⬚3⬚ ☒ ⬚4⬚ ⬚7⬚ ☐ . The calculator displays 611, so 13 × 47 = 611.

Exercises: Use a calculator to find each product.

1. 56 × 8

2. 845 × 26

3. 5 · 1276

4. 126(314)

5.   3 7 6 0
  ×   4 8

6.   5 2 1 8
  ×   4 5 3

---

25. Computer Memory. See Example 10. By rounding to the nearest ten, estimate the cost to Gladys of 17 extra blocks of memory.

26. Estimate the product by first rounding to the nearest ten and to the nearest hundred. Show your work.

     8 3 7
  × 2 4 5

Answers on page A-4

27. Table Tennis. Find the area of a standard table tennis table that has dimensions of 9 ft by 5 ft.

Professional pool player Jeanette Lee (also known as the "Black Widow")

To the instructor and the student: This section presented a review of multiplication of whole numbers. Students who are successful should go on to Section 1.6. Those who have trouble should study developmental unit M near the back of this text and then repeat Section 1.5.

Answer on page A-4

C Finding Area

The area of a rectangular region is often expressed as the number of square units needed to fill it. Here is a rectangle that is exactly 4 cm (centimeters) long and 3 cm wide. It takes 12 square centimeters (sq cm) to fill it.

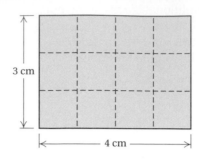

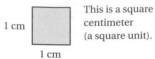

This is a square centimeter (a square unit).

In this case, we have a rectangular array of 3 rows, each of which contains 4 squares. The number of square units is given by $3 \cdot 4$, or 12.

> **AREA**
>
> The area of a shape is a measure of its surface using square units.

■ **EXAMPLE 12** *Professional Pool Table.* The playing area of a standard pool table has dimensions of 50 in. by 100 in. (There are rails 6 in. wide on the outside not included in the playing area.) Find the playing area.

If we think of filling the rectangle with square inches, we have a rectangular array. The length is $l = 100$ in. and the width is $w = 50$ in. Thus, the area A is given by the formula

$$A = l \cdot w = 100 \cdot 50 = 5000 \text{ sq in.}$$

Do Exercise 27.

a   Write a multiplication sentence that corresponds to each situation.

1. The *Los Angeles Sunday Times* crossword puzzle is arranged rectangularly with squares in 21 rows and 21 columns. How many squares does the puzzle have altogether?

2. *Pixels.* A computer screen consists of small rectangular dots called *pixels*. How many pixels are there on a screen that has 600 rows with 800 pixels in each row?

3. A new soft drink beverage carton contains 8 cans, each of which holds 12 oz. How many ounces are there in the carton?

4. There are 7 days in a week. How many days are there in 18 weeks?

5. *Computer Printers.* The HP Inkjet 2600 can print 1200 × 600 dots per square inch (dpi). How many dots can it print in one square inch?

6. *Computer Printers.* The Epson Stylus C60 prints 2880 × 720 dots per square inch (dpi). How many dots does it print in one square inch?

Multiply.

7.
$$\begin{array}{r} 2\ 3 \\ \times\ \ \ 2 \\ \hline \end{array}$$

8.
$$\begin{array}{r} 3\ 1 \\ \times\ \ \ 2 \\ \hline \end{array}$$

9.
$$\begin{array}{r} 4\ 6 \\ \times\ \ \ 3 \\ \hline \end{array}$$

10.
$$\begin{array}{r} 3\ 9 \\ \times\ \ \ 6 \\ \hline \end{array}$$

11.
$$\begin{array}{r} 8\ 7 \\ \times\ \ \ 4 \\ \hline \end{array}$$

12.
$$\begin{array}{r} 6\ 5 \\ \times\ \ \ 8 \\ \hline \end{array}$$

13.
$$\begin{array}{r} 7\ 6 \\ \times\ \ \ 9 \\ \hline \end{array}$$

14.
$$\begin{array}{r} 9\ 4 \\ \times\ \ \ 6 \\ \hline \end{array}$$

15.
$$\begin{array}{r} 1\ 0\ 0 \\ \times\ \ \ 9\ 6 \\ \hline \end{array}$$

16.
$$\begin{array}{r} 8\ 7 \\ \times\ 1\ 0 \\ \hline \end{array}$$

17.
$$\begin{array}{r} 8\ 0\ 0 \\ \times\ \ \ 7\ 0 \\ \hline \end{array}$$

18.
$$\begin{array}{r} 2\ 3\ 4\ 0 \\ \times\ 1\ 0\ 0\ 0 \\ \hline \end{array}$$

19.
$$\begin{array}{r} 652 \\ \times\ 100 \\ \hline \end{array}$$

20.
$$\begin{array}{r} 652 \\ \times\ \ 10 \\ \hline \end{array}$$

21.
$$\begin{array}{r} 4371 \\ \times\ 1000 \\ \hline \end{array}$$

22.
$$\begin{array}{r} 4371 \\ \times\ \ 100 \\ \hline \end{array}$$

23. $3 \cdot 509$

24. $7 \cdot 806$

25. $7(9229)$

26. $4(7867)$

27. $90(53)$

28. $60(78)$

29. $(47)(85)$

30. $(34)(87)$

31.
$$\begin{array}{r} 640 \\ \times\ \ 72 \\ \hline \end{array}$$

32.
$$\begin{array}{r} 666 \\ \times\ \ 66 \\ \hline \end{array}$$

33.
$$\begin{array}{r} 444 \\ \times\ \ 33 \\ \hline \end{array}$$

34.
$$\begin{array}{r} 509 \\ \times\ \ 88 \\ \hline \end{array}$$

35.
$$\begin{array}{r} 509 \\ \times\ 408 \\ \hline \end{array}$$

36.
$$\begin{array}{r} 432 \\ \times\ 375 \\ \hline \end{array}$$

37.
$$\begin{array}{r} 853 \\ \times\ 936 \\ \hline \end{array}$$

38.
$$\begin{array}{r} 346 \\ \times\ 650 \\ \hline \end{array}$$

39.
$$\begin{array}{r} 489 \\ \times\ 340 \\ \hline \end{array}$$

40.
$$\begin{array}{r} 7080 \\ \times\ \ 160 \\ \hline \end{array}$$

41.
$$\begin{array}{r} 4378 \\ \times\ 2694 \\ \hline \end{array}$$

42.
$$\begin{array}{r} 8007 \\ \times\ \ 480 \\ \hline \end{array}$$

43.
$$\begin{array}{r} 6428 \\ \times\ 3224 \\ \hline \end{array}$$

44.
$$\begin{array}{r} 8928 \\ \times\ 3172 \\ \hline \end{array}$$

45.
$$\begin{array}{r} 3482 \\ \times\ \ 104 \\ \hline \end{array}$$

46.
$$\begin{array}{r} 6408 \\ \times\ 6064 \\ \hline \end{array}$$

47.
```
    5 0 0 6
  × 4 0 0 8
```

48.
```
    6 7 8 9
  × 2 3 3 0
```

49.
```
    5 6 0 8
  × 4 5 0 0
```

50.
```
    4 5 6 0
  × 7 8 9 0
```

51.
```
    8 7 6
  × 3 4 5
```

52.
```
    3 5 5
  × 2 9 9
```

53.
```
    7 8 8 9
  × 6 2 2 4
```

54.
```
    6 5 0 1
  × 3 4 4 9
```

55.
```
    5 5 5
  ×   5 5
```

56.
```
    8 8 8
  ×   8 8
```

57.
```
    7 3 4
  × 4 0 7
```

58.
```
    5 0 8 0
  ×   3 0 2
```

b Estimate each product by first rounding to the nearest ten. Show your work.

59.
```
    4 5
  × 6 7
```

60.
```
    5 1
  × 7 8
```

61.
```
    3 4
  × 2 9
```

62.
```
    6 3
  × 5 4
```

Estimate each product by first rounding to the nearest hundred. Show your work.

63.
```
    8 7 6
  × 3 4 5
```

64.
```
    3 5 5
  × 2 9 9
```

65.
```
    4 3 2
  × 1 9 9
```

66.
```
    7 8 9
  × 4 3 4
```

Estimate each product by first rounding to the nearest thousand. Show your work.

67.
```
    5 6 0 8
  × 4 5 7 6
```

68.
```
    2 3 4 4
  × 6 1 2 3
```

69.
```
    7 8 8 8
  × 6 2 2 4
```

70.
```
    6 5 0 1
  × 3 4 4 9
```

71. *Oldsmobile Intrigue.* Pure-Health Medical Supplies, Inc., buys an Oldsmobile Intrigue, Model GLS, for each of its 185 sales representatives. Each car costs $25,720 plus $560 in destination charges.

a) Estimate the total cost of the purchase by rounding the final cost of each car and the number of sales representatives to the nearest hundred.

b) Estimate the total cost of the purchase by rounding both the cost of each car and the destination charges to the nearest thousand and the number of reps to the nearest hundred.

Source: General Motors

72. A travel club of 248 people decides to fly from New York to Paris. The cost of a round-trip ticket is $376.

a) Estimate the total cost of the trip by rounding the cost of the airfare and the number of travelers to the nearest ten.

b) Estimate the total cost of the trip by rounding the cost of the airfare to the nearest hundred and the number of travelers to the nearest ten.

C Find the area of each region.

73.

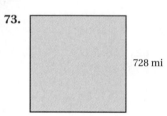

728 mi (right side)
728 mi (bottom)

74. 129 yd

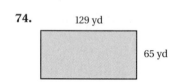

65 yd

75.

3 ft
6 ft

76.

7 mi
7 mi

77.

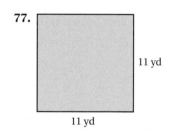

11 yd

11 yd

78.

16 cm
9 cm

79.

48 mm
3 mm

80.

247 mi
19 mi

81. Find the area of the region formed by the base lines on a Major League baseball diamond.

90 ft
90 ft

82. Find the area of a standard-sized hockey rink.

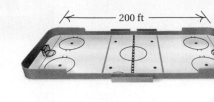

200 ft
85 ft

83. D_W Describe a situation that corresponds to each multiplication: $4 \cdot \$150$; $\$4 \cdot 150$.

84. D_W Explain in your own words what the associative law of multiplication means.

SKILL MAINTENANCE

Add. [1.2b]

85.
```
   4 9 0 8
   5 6 6 7
 + 2 1 1 0
```

86.
```
   9 8 7 6
     8 7 6
       7 6
 +      6
```

87.
```
   3 4 0,7 9 8
 +   8 6,6 7 9
```

88.
```
   8 8,7 7 7
 + 2 2,3 3 3
```

Subtract. [1.3d]

89.
```
   4 9 0 8
 - 3 6 6 7
```

90.
```
   9 8 7 6
 -   9 8 7
```

91.
```
   3 4 0,7 9 8
 -   8 6,6 7 9
```

92.
```
   8 8,7 7 7
 - 2 2,3 3 3
```

93. Round 6,375,602 to the nearest thousand. [1.4a]

94. Round 6,375,602 to the nearest ten. [1.4a]

SYNTHESIS

95. D_W What do the commutative laws of addition and multiplication have in common?

96. D_W Explain how the distributive law differs from the associative law.

97. An 18-story office building is box-shaped. Each floor measures 172 ft by 84 ft with a 20-ft by 35-ft rectangular area lost to an elevator, lobby, and stairwell. How much area is available as office space?

98. *Computer Printers.* Eva prints a 5 in. by 7 in. photo on her Epson C60 printer (see Exercise 6). How many dots will be printed when the printer produces the photo?

99. *Computer Printers.* Adam's HP2600 is printing an 8 in. by 10 in. photo (see Exercise 5). How many dots will be printed when the printer finishes the photo?

Objectives

a Write a division sentence that corresponds to a situation.

b Given a division sentence, write a related multiplication sentence; and given a multiplication sentence, write two related division sentences.

c Divide whole numbers.

Study Tips

DO THE EXERCISES

■ Usually an instructor assigns some odd-numbered exercises. When you complete these, you can check your answers at the back of the book. If you miss any, closely examine your work, and if necessary, consult the *Student's Solutions Manual* or your instructor for guidance.

■ Whether or not your instructor assigns the even-numbered exercises, try to do some on your own. There are no answers given for the even exercises, so you will gain practice doing exercises that are similar to quiz or test problems. Check your answers later with a friend or your instructor.

1.6 DIVISION

a Division and the Real World

Division of whole numbers applies to two kinds of situations. The first is repeated subtraction. Suppose we have 20 notebooks in a pile, and we want to find out how many sets of 5 there are. One way to do this is to repeatedly subtract sets of 5 as follows.

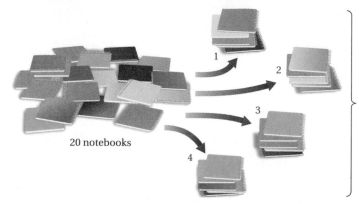

20 notebooks

How many sets of 5 notebooks each?

Since there are 4 sets of 5 notebooks each, we have

$$20 \div 5 = 4.$$

The division $20 \div 5$, read "20 divided by 5," corresponds to the figure above. We say that the **dividend** is 20, the **divisor** is 5, and the **quotient** is 4.

$$
\begin{array}{ccccc}
20 & \div & 5 & = & 4 \\
\downarrow & & \downarrow & & \downarrow \\
\text{Dividend} & & \text{Divisor} & & \text{Quotient}
\end{array}
$$

We divide the *dividend* by the *divisor* to get the *quotient*.

We can also express the division $20 \div 5 = 4$ as

$$\frac{20}{5} = 4 \quad \text{or} \quad 5\overline{)20} \; ^{4}$$

EXAMPLE 1 Write a division sentence that corresponds to this situation.

A parent directs 3 children to share $24, with each child getting the same amount. How much does each child get?

We think of an array with 3 rows. Each row will go to a child. How many dollars will be in each row?

3 rows with 8 in each row

$$24 \div 3 = 8$$

We can also think of division in terms of rectangular arrays. Consider again the pile of 20 notebooks and division by 5. We can arrange the notebooks in a rectangular array with 5 rows and ask, "How many are in each row?"

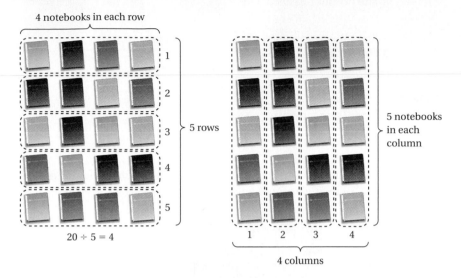

We can also consider a rectangular array with 5 notebooks in each column and ask, "How many columns are there?" The answer is still 4.

In each case, we are asking, "What do we multiply 5 by in order to get 20?"

$$\underbrace{5 \cdot \square = 20}_{\text{Missing factor}} \qquad \underbrace{20 \div 5 = \square}_{\text{Quotient}}$$

This leads us to the following definition of division.

DIVISION

The quotient $a \div b$, where $b \neq 0$, is that unique whole number c for which $a = b \cdot c$.

EXAMPLE 2 Write a division sentence that corresponds to this situation. You need not carry out the division.

How many uniforms that cost $45 each can be purchased for $495?

We think of an array with 45 dollar bills in each row. The money in each row will buy one uniform. How many rows will there be?

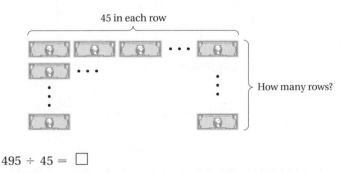

$$495 \div 45 = \square$$

1. There are 112 students in a college band, and they are marching with 14 in each row. How many rows are there?

2. A college band is in a rectangular array. There are 112 students in the band, and they are marching in 8 rows. How many students are there in each row?

Write a related multiplication sentence.

3. $15 \div 3 = 5$

4. $72 \div 8 = 9$

Whenever we have a rectangular array, we know the following:

> (The total number) ÷ (The number of rows) =
> (The number in each row).

Also:

> (The total number) ÷ (The number in each row) =
> (The number of rows).

Do Exercises 1 and 2.

b   Related Sentences

By looking at rectangular arrays, we can see how multiplication and division are related. The following array of palm pilots shows that $4 \cdot 5 = 20$.

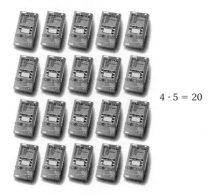

$$4 \cdot 5 = 20$$

The array also shows the following:

$$20 \div 5 = 4 \quad \text{and} \quad 20 \div 4 = 5.$$

Division is actually defined in terms of multiplication. For example, $20 \div 5$ is defined to be the number that when multiplied by 5 gives 20. Thus, for every division sentence, there is a related multiplication sentence that can serve as a check.

$$20 \div 5 = 4 \qquad \text{Division sentence}$$

$$20 = 4 \cdot 5 \qquad \text{The related multiplication sentence is true, so the division above is correct.}$$

> To get the related multiplication sentence, we use
> Dividend = Quotient · Divisor.

EXAMPLE 3   Write a related multiplication sentence: $12 \div 6 = 2$.

We have

$$12 \div 6 = 2 \qquad \text{Division sentence}$$

$$12 = 2 \cdot 6. \qquad \text{Related multiplication sentence}$$

The related multiplication sentence is $12 = 2 \cdot 6$. Because of the commutative law of multiplication, there is also another multiplication sentence: $12 = 6 \cdot 2$.

Do Exercises 3 and 4.

Answers on page A-4

For every multiplication sentence, we can write related divisions, as we can see from the preceding array.

EXAMPLE 4 Write two related division sentences: $7 \cdot 8 = 56$.

We have

$$7 \cdot 8 = 56 \qquad\qquad 7 \cdot 8 = 56$$

This factor becomes a divisor.   This factor becomes a divisor.

$$7 = 56 \div 8. \qquad\qquad 8 = 56 \div 7.$$

The related division sentences are $7 = 56 \div 8$ and $8 = 56 \div 7$.

Do Exercises 5 and 6.

C Division of Whole Numbers

Before we consider division with remainders, let's recall four basic facts about division.

DIVIDING BY 1

Any number divided by 1 is that same number:

$$a \div 1 = \frac{a}{1} = a.$$

DIVIDING A NUMBER BY ITSELF

Any nonzero number divided by itself is 1:

$$\frac{a}{a} = 1, \quad a \neq 0.$$

DIVIDING INTO 0

Zero divided by any nonzero number is 0:

$$\frac{0}{a} = 0, \quad a \neq 0.$$

EXCLUDING DIVISION BY 0

Division by 0 is not defined. (We agree not to divide by 0.)

$$\frac{a}{0} \text{ is } \textbf{undefined} \quad \text{or} \quad \textbf{not defined.}$$

Write two related division sentences.

5. $6 \cdot 2 = 12$

6. $7 \cdot 6 = 42$

Answers on page A-4

Why can't we divide by 0? Suppose the number 4 could be divided by 0. Then if r were the answer, we would have

$$4 \div 0 = r$$

and

$$r \cdot 0 = 4 \longleftarrow \text{False!}$$

Since any number times 0 is 0, it follows that there is no number r for which $4 \div 0$ is r. We say that division by 0 is undefined.

REMAINDERS

Suppose we have 18 cans of soda and want to pack them in six-packs. How many six-packs will we fill? We can determine this by repeated subtraction. We keep track of the number of times we subtract. We stop when the number of objects remaining, the **remainder,** is smaller than the divisor.

EXAMPLE 5 Divide by repeated subtraction: $18 \div 6$.

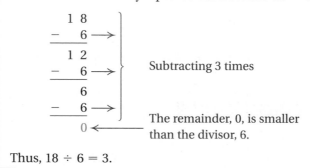

Subtracting 3 times

The remainder, 0, is smaller than the divisor, 6.

Thus, $18 \div 6 = 3$.

Suppose we have 22 cans of soda and want to pack them in cartons of 6 cans each. We end up with 3 cartons and 4 cans left over.

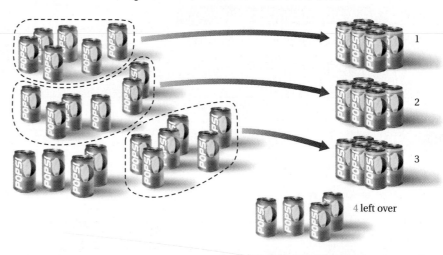

1

2

3

4 left over

■ **EXAMPLE 6** Divide by repeated subtraction: $23 \div 5$.

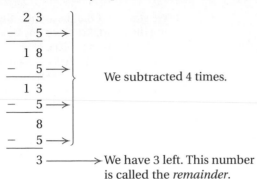

We subtracted 4 times.

3 ⟶ We have 3 left. This number is called the *remainder*.

We write

$$23 \div 5 = 4 \text{ R } 3$$

Dividend   Divisor   Quotient   Remainder

CHECKING DIVISIONS

To check a division, we multiply. Suppose we divide 98 by 2 and get 49:

$$98 \div 2 = 49.$$

To check, we think of the related multiplication sentence $49 \cdot 2 = \square$. We multiply 49 by 2 and see if we get 98.

If there is a remainder, we add it after multiplying.

■ **EXAMPLE 7** Check the division in Example 6.

We found that $23 \div 5 = 4 \text{ R } 3$. To check, we multiply 5 by 4. This gives us 20. Then we add 3 to get 23. The dividend is 23, so the answer checks.

Do Exercises 7–10.

When we use the process of long division, we are doing repeated subtraction, even though we are going about it in a different way.

To divide, we start from the digit of highest place value in the dividend and work down to the lowest place value through the remainders. At each step, we ask if there are multiples of the divisor in the remainder.

Divide by repeated subtraction. Then check.

7. $54 \div 9$

8. $61 \div 9$

9. $53 \div 12$

10. $157 \div 24$

Answers on page A-4

Divide and check.

11. 4) 2 3 9

12. 6) 8 8 5 5

13. 5) 5 0 7 5

EXAMPLE 8 Divide and check: 3642 ÷ 5.

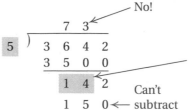

1. We start with the thousands digit in the dividend. Are there any thousands in the thousands place of the quotient? No; 5 · 1000 = 5000, and 5000 is larger than 3000.

2. Next we ask if there are any hundreds in the quotient. Think of the dividend as 36 hundreds. Estimate that 5 goes into 36 hundred 7 hundred times. Write 7 in the hundreds place, multiply 700 by 5, write the answer below 3642, and subtract.

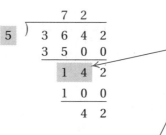

3. a) We go to the tens place of the first remainder. Are there any tens in the tens place of the quotient? To answer, think of the first remainder as 14 tens. Estimate that 5 goes into 140 about 30 times, which is 3 tens. When we multiply, we get 150, which is too large.

   b) We lower our estimate to 2 tens. Write 2 in the tens place, multiply 20 by 5, and subtract.

4. We go to the ones place of the second remainder. Are there any ones in the ones place of the quotient? To answer, think of the second remainder as 42 ones. Estimate 8 ones. Write 8 in the ones place, multiply 8 by 5, and subtract.

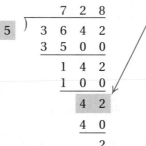

You may have learned to divide like this, without writing the extra zeros. You may omit them if desired.

```
        7 2 8
  5 ) 3 6 4 2
      3 5 ↓
        1 4
        1 0 ↓
          4 2
          4 0
            2
```

The answer is 728 R 2. To check, we multiply the quotient 728 by the divisor 5. This gives us 3640. Then we add 2 to get 3642. The dividend is 3642, so the answer checks.

CAUTION!

Be careful to keep the digits lined up correctly.

Do Exercises 11–13.

We can summarize our division procedure as follows.

To do division of whole numbers:

a) Estimate.   **b)** Multiply.   **c)** Subtract.

Answers on page A-4

Sometimes rounding the divisor helps us find estimates.

EXAMPLE 9 Divide: $8904 \div 42$.

We mentally round 42 to 40.

$$
\begin{array}{r}
2\\
42\,\overline{\smash{)}\,8\ 9\ 0\ 4}\\
8\ 4\ 0\ 0\\
\hline
5\ 0\ 4
\end{array}
$$
← *Think*: 89 hundreds ÷ 40.
Estimate 2 hundreds, but write
$2 \times 42 = 84$.

$$
\begin{array}{r}
2\ 1\\
42\,\overline{\smash{)}\,8\ 9\ 0\ 4}\\
8\ 4\ 0\ 0\\
\hline
5\ 0\ 4\\
4\ 2\ 0\\
\hline
8\ 4
\end{array}
$$
← *Think*: 50 tens ÷ 40.
Estimate 1 ten, but write
$1 \times 42 = 42$.

$$
\begin{array}{r}
2\ 1\ 2\\
42\,\overline{\smash{)}\,8\ 9\ 0\ 4}\\
8\ 4\ 0\ 0\\
\hline
5\ 0\ 4\\
4\ 2\ 0\\
\hline
8\ 4\\
8\ 4\\
\hline
0
\end{array}
$$
← *Think*: 84 ones ÷ 40.
Estimate 2 ones, but write
$2 \times 42 = 84$.

The answer is 212. *Remember*: If after estimating and multiplying you get a number larger than the dividend, you must then lower your estimate.

Do Exercises 14 and 15.

Divide.

14. $45\,\overline{\smash{)}\,6\ 0\ 3\ 0}$

15. $52\,\overline{\smash{)}\,3\ 2\ 8\ 8}$

Answers on page A-4

CALCULATOR CORNER

To divide on a calculator, we use the ⊞ and ⊟ keys. For example, to divide 711 by 9, we press ⑦①①⊞ ⑨⊟. The display reads 79, so $711 \div 9 = 79$.

When we enter $453 \div 15$, the display reads 30.2. Note that the result is not a whole number. This tells us that there is a remainder. The number 30.2 is expressed in decimal notation. The symbol "." is called a decimal point. (Decimal notation will be studied in Chapter 5.) The number to the left of the decimal point, 30, is the quotient. We can use the number to the right of the decimal point to find the remainder. To do this, first subtract 30 from 30.2. Then multiply the difference by the divisor, 15. We get 3. This is the remainder. Thus, $453 \div 15 = 30$ R 3. The steps that we performed to find this result can be summarized as follows:

$$453 \div 15 = 30.2,$$
$$30.2 - 30 = .2,$$
$$0.2 \times 15 = 3.$$

To follow these steps, we press ④⑤③⊞①⑤⊟ and write the number that appears to the left of the decimal point. This is the quotient. Then we press ⊟③⓪ ⊟⊠①⑤⊟. The last number that appears is the remainder. We may need to round to the nearest one.

To check, we multiply and add:

$$30 \times 15 = 450,$$
$$450 + 3 = 453.$$

Exercises: Use a calculator to perform each division. Check the results with a calculator also.

1. $92 \div 27$

2. $19\,\overline{\smash{)}\,5\ 3\ 2}$

3. $6\,\overline{\smash{)}\,7\ 4\ 6}$

4. $3817 \div 29$

5. $126\,\overline{\smash{)}\,3\ 5,7\ 1\ 5}$

6. $308\,\overline{\smash{)}\,2\ 5\ 9,8\ 3\ 1}$

Divide.

16. $6\overline{)4846}$

17. $7\overline{)7616}$

Divide.

18. $27\overline{)9724}$

19. $56\overline{)44{,}847}$

ZEROS IN QUOTIENTS

■ **EXAMPLE 10** Divide: $6341 \div 7$.

$$
\begin{array}{r}
9 \\
7\,\overline{)\,6\;3\;4\;1\;} \\
6\;3\;0\;0 \\
\hline
4\;1
\end{array}
$$
← *Think*: 63 hundreds ÷ 7.
Estimate 9 hundreds.

$$
\begin{array}{r}
9\;0 \\
7\,\overline{)\,6\;3\;4\;1\;} \\
6\;3\;0\;0 \\
\hline
4\;1
\end{array}
$$
← *Think*: 4 tens ÷ 7. There are no tens in the quotient (other than the tens in 900). We write a 0 to show this.

$$
\begin{array}{r}
9\;0\;5 \\
7\,\overline{)\,6\;3\;4\;1\;} \\
6\;3\;0\;0 \\
\hline
4\;1 \\
3\;5 \\
\hline
6
\end{array}
$$
← *Think*: 41 ones ÷ 7.
Estimate 5 ones.

The answer is 905 R 6.

Do Exercises 16 and 17.

■ **EXAMPLE 11** Divide: $8889 \div 37$.

We mentally round 37 to 40.

$$
\begin{array}{r}
2 \\
37\,\overline{)\,8\;8\;8\;9\;} \\
7\;4\;0\;0 \\
\hline
1\;4\;8\;9
\end{array}
$$
← *Think*: 37 ≈ 40; 88 hundreds ÷ 40. Estimate 2 hundreds, but write $2 \times 37 = 74$.

$$
\begin{array}{r}
2\;4 \\
37\,\overline{)\,8\;8\;8\;9\;} \\
7\;4\;0\;0 \\
\hline
1\;4\;8\;9 \\
1\;4\;8\;0 \\
\hline
9
\end{array}
$$
← *Think*: 148 tens ÷ 40. Estimate 4 tens, but write $4 \times 37 = 148$.

$$
\begin{array}{r}
2\;4\;0 \\
37\,\overline{)\,8\;8\;8\;9\;} \\
7\;4\;0\;0 \\
\hline
1\;4\;8\;9 \\
1\;4\;8\;0 \\
\hline
9
\end{array}
$$
← *Think*: 9 ones ÷ 40. There are no ones in the quotient.

The answer is 240 R 9.

Do Exercises 18 and 19.

1.6

EXERCISE SET

For Extra Help

Digital Video Tutor CD 1 Videotape 1 | InterAct Math | Math Tutor Center | MathXL | MyMathLab

a   Write a division sentence that corresponds to each situation.

1. *Canyonlands.* The trail boss for a trip into Canyonlands National Park divides 760 pounds (lb) of equipment among 4 mules. How many pounds does each mule carry?

2. *Surf Expo.* In a swimwear showing at Surf Expo, a trade show for retailers of beach supplies, each swimsuit test takes 8 minutes (min). If the show runs for 240 min, how many tests can be scheduled?

3. A lab technician pours 455 mL of sulfuric acid into 5 beakers, putting the same amount in each. How much acid is in each beaker?

4. A computer screen is made up of a rectangular array of pixels. There are 480,000 pixels in all, with 800 pixels in each row. How many rows are there on the screen?

b   Write a related multiplication sentence.

5. $18 \div 3 = 6$

6. $72 \div 9 = 8$

7. $22 \div 22 = 1$

8. $32 \div 1 = 32$

9. $54 \div 6 = 9$

10. $40 \div 8 = 5$

11. $37 \div 1 = 37$

12. $28 \div 28 = 1$

Write two related division sentences.

13. $9 \times 5 = 45$

14. $2 \cdot 7 = 14$

15. $37 \cdot 1 = 37$

16. $4 \cdot 12 = 48$

17. $8 \times 8 = 64$

18. $9 \cdot 7 = 63$

19. $11 \cdot 6 = 66$

20. $1 \cdot 43 = 43$

C Divide, if possible. If not possible, write "undefined."

21. $72 \div 6$

22. $54 \div 9$

23. $\dfrac{23}{23}$

24. $\dfrac{37}{37}$

25. $22 \div 1$

26. $\dfrac{56}{1}$

27. $\dfrac{16}{0}$

28. $74 \div 0$

Divide.

29. $277 \div 5$

30. $699 \div 3$

31. $864 \div 8$

32. $869 \div 8$

33. $4 \overline{)\,1\ 2\ 2\ 8}$

34. $3 \overline{)\,2\ 1\ 2\ 4}$

35. $6 \overline{)\,4\ 5\ 2\ 1}$

36. $9 \overline{)\,9\ 1\ 1\ 0}$

37. $297 \div 4$

38. $389 \div 2$

39. $738 \div 8$

40. $881 \div 6$

41. $5 \overline{)8\ 5\ 1\ 5}$

42. $3 \overline{)6\ 0\ 2\ 7}$

43. $9 \overline{)8\ 8\ 8\ 8}$

44. $8 \overline{)4\ 1\ 3\ 9}$

45. $127{,}000 \div 10$

46. $127{,}000 \div 100$

47. $127{,}000 \div 1000$

48. $4260 \div 10$

49. $7\ 0 \overline{)3\ 6\ 9\ 2}$

50. $2\ 0 \overline{)5\ 7\ 9\ 8}$

51. $3\ 0 \overline{)8\ 7\ 5}$

52. $4\ 0 \overline{)9\ 8\ 7}$

53. $852 \div 21$

54. $942 \div 23$

55. $8\ 5 \overline{)7\ 6\ 7\ 2}$

56. $5\ 4 \overline{)2\ 7\ 2\ 9}$

57. $1\ 1\ 1 \overline{)3\ 2\ 1\ 9}$

58. $1\ 0\ 2 \overline{)5\ 6\ 1\ 2}$

59. $8 \overline{)8\ 4\ 3}$

60. $7 \overline{)7\ 4\ 9}$

61. $5 \overline{)8\ 0\ 4\ 7}$ **62.** $9 \overline{)7\ 2\ 7\ 3}$ **63.** $5 \overline{)5\ 0\ 3\ 6}$ **64.** $7 \overline{)7\ 0\ 7\ 4}$

65. $1058 \div 46$ **66.** $7242 \div 24$ **67.** $3425 \div 32$ **68.** $4\ 8 \overline{)4\ 8\ 9\ 9}$

69. $2\ 4 \overline{)8\ 8\ 8\ 0}$ **70.** $3\ 6 \overline{)7\ 5\ 6\ 3}$ **71.** $2\ 8 \overline{)1\ 7,0\ 6\ 7}$ **72.** $3\ 6 \overline{)2\ 8,9\ 2\ 9}$

73. $8\ 0 \overline{)2\ 4,3\ 2\ 0}$ **74.** $9\ 0 \overline{)8\ 8,5\ 6\ 0}$ **75.** $2\ 8\ 5 \overline{)9\ 9\ 9,9\ 9\ 9}$

76. $3\ 0\ 6 \overline{)8\ 8\ 8,8\ 8\ 8}$ **77.** $4\ 5\ 6 \overline{)3,6\ 7\ 9,9\ 2\ 0}$ **78.** $8\ 0\ 3 \overline{)5,6\ 2\ 2,6\ 0\ 6}$

79. D_W Is division associative? Why or why not? Give an example.

80. D_W Suppose a student asserts that "$0 \div 0 = 0$ because nothing divided by nothing is nothing." Devise an explanation to persuade the student that the assertion is false.

SKILL MAINTENANCE

81. Write expanded notation for 7882.   [1.1b]

82. Use $<$ or $>$ for $\square$ to write a true sentence: [1.4c]
$888 \;\square\; 788$.

Write a related addition sentence.   [1.3b]

83. $21 - 16 = 5$

84. $56 - 14 = 42$

Write two related subtraction sentences.   [1.3b]

85. $47 + 9 = 56$

86. $350 + 64 = 414$

87. Add: $284 + 75$.   [1.2b]

88. Multiply: 284×75.   [1.5a]

SYNTHESIS

89. D_W Describe a situation that corresponds to the division $1180 \div 295$. (See Examples 1 and 2.)

90. D_W What is it about division that makes it more difficult than addition, subtraction, or multiplication?

91. Complete the following table.

a	b	$a \cdot b$	$a + b$
	68	3672	
84			117
		32	12
		304	35

92. Find a pair of factors whose product is 36 and:

a) whose sum is 13.
b) whose difference is 0.
c) whose sum is 20.
d) whose difference is 9.

93. A group of 1231 college students is going to take buses to a demonstration. Each bus can hold only 42 students. How many buses are needed?

94. ▦ Fill in the missing digits to make the equation true:
$34,584,132 \div 76\square = 4\square,386$.

Objectives

a Solve simple equations by trial.

b Solve equations like $x + 28 = 54$, $28 \cdot x = 168$, and $98 \div 2 = y$.

1. Determine whether 7 is a solution of $\square + 5 = 9$.

2. Determine whether 4 is a solution of $\square + 5 = 9$.

Find a number that makes the sentence true.

3. $8 = 2 + \square$

4. $\square + 2 = 7$

Solve by trial.

5. $n + 3 = 8$

6. $x - 2 = 8$

7. $45 \div 9 = y$

8. $10 + t = 32$

a Solutions by Trial

A sentence with $=$ is called an **equation.** We have already seen many equations. When an equation contains a blank, as in $9 = 3 + \square$, any replacement for the blank that makes the equation true is a **solution** of the equation. Thus, 6 is a solution of

$$9 = 3 + \square \quad \text{because} \quad 9 = 3 + \boxed{6} \text{ is true.}$$

However, 7 is not a solution of

$$9 = 3 + \square \quad \text{because} \quad 9 = 3 + \boxed{7} \text{ is false.}$$

Do Exercises 1–4.

We can use a letter instead of a blank. For example,

$$9 = 3 + x.$$

We call x a **variable** because it can represent any number. If a replacement for a variable makes an equation true, it is a **solution** of the equation.

SOLUTIONS OF AN EQUATION

A **solution** is a replacement for the variable that makes the equation true. When we find all the solutions, we say that we have **solved** the equation.

EXAMPLE 1 Solve $x + 12 = 27$ by trial.

We replace x with several numbers.

If we replace x with 13, we get a false equation: $13 + 12 = 27$.
If we replace x with 14, we get a false equation: $14 + 12 = 27$.
If we replace x with 15, we get a true equation: $15 + 12 = 27$.

No other replacement makes the equation true, so the solution is 15.

EXAMPLES Solve.

2. $7 + n = 22$
(7 plus what number is 22?)
The solution is 15.

3. $8 \cdot 23 = y$
(8 times 23 is what?)
The solution is 184.

Do Exercises 5–8.

Answers on page A-4

b Solving Equations

We now begin to develop more efficient ways to solve certain equations. When an equation has a variable alone on one side, it is easy to see the solution or to compute it. For example, the solution of

$$x = 12$$

is 12. When a calculation is on one side and the variable is alone on the other, we can find the solution by carrying out the calculation.

EXAMPLE 4 Solve: $x = 245 \times 34$.

To solve the equation, we carry out the calculation.

$$
\begin{array}{r}
2\ 4\ 5 \\
\times\ \ 3\ 4 \\
\hline
9\ 8\ 0 \\
7\ 3\ 5\ 0 \\
\hline
8\ 3\ 3\ 0
\end{array}
\qquad
\begin{aligned}
x &= 245 \times 34 \\
x &= 8330
\end{aligned}
$$

The solution is 8330.

Do Exercises 9–12.

Consider the equation

$$x + 12 = 27.$$

We can get x alone on one side of the equation by writing a related subtraction sentence:

$$x = 27 - 12 \qquad \text{12 gets subtracted to find the related subtraction sentence.}$$

$$x = 15. \qquad \text{Doing the subtraction}$$

It will be useful in our later study to think of this as forming an "equivalent" equation by "*subtracting* 12 *from both sides.*" Thus

$$x + 12 - 12 = 27 - 12 \qquad \text{Subtracting 12 from both sides}$$

$$x + 0 = 15 \qquad \text{Carrying out the subtraction}$$

$$x = 15.$$

SOLVING $x + a = b$

To solve $x + a = b$ for x, subtract a from both sides.

If we can get an equation in a form with the variable alone on one side, we can "see" the solution.

EXAMPLE 5 Solve: $t + 28 = 54$.

We have

$$t + 28 = 54$$

$$t + 28 - 28 = 54 - 28 \qquad \text{Subtracting 28 from both sides}$$

$$t + 0 = 26$$

$$t = 26.$$

Solve.

9. $346 \times 65 = y$

10. $x = 2347 + 6675$

11. $4560 \div 8 = t$

12. $x = 6007 - 2346$

Answers on page A-4

Study Tips

ORGANIZE YOUR WORK

When doing homework, consider using a spiral or three-ring binder. You want to be able to go over your homework when studying for a test. Therefore, you need to be able to easily access any problem. Write legibly, label each section and each exercise clearly, and show all steps. Writing clearly will also be appreciated by your instructor if homework is collected. Most tutors and instructors can be more helpful if they can see and understand all the steps in your work.

When you are finished with your homework, check the answers to the odd-numbered exercises at the back of the book or in the *Student's Solutions Manual* and make corrections. If you do not understand why an answer is wrong, draw a star by it so you can ask questions in class or during your instructor's office hours.

13. $x + 9 = 17$

14. $77 = m + 32$

15. Solve: $155 = t + 78$. Be sure to check.

Solve. Be sure to check.
16. $4566 + x = 7877$

17. $8172 = h + 2058$

Answers on page A-5

To check the answer, we substitute 26 for t in the original equation.

CHECK:
$$t + 28 = 54$$
$$\underline{}$$
$$26 + 28 \ ? \ 54$$
$$54 \ | \qquad \text{TRUE}$$

The solution is 26.

Do Exercises 13 and 14.

EXAMPLE 6 Solve: $182 = 65 + n$.

We have

$$182 = 65 + n$$
$$182 - 65 = 65 + n - 65 \qquad \text{Subtracting 65 from both sides}$$
$$117 = 0 + n \qquad \qquad \text{65 plus } n \text{ minus 65 is } 0 + n.$$
$$117 = n.$$

CHECK:
$$182 = 65 + n$$
$$\underline{}$$
$$182 \ ? \ 65 + 117$$
$$| \ 182 \qquad \text{TRUE}$$

The solution is 117.

Do Exercise 15.

EXAMPLE 7 Solve: $7381 + x = 8067$.

We have

$$7381 + x = 8067$$
$$7381 + x - 7381 = 8067 - 7381 \qquad \text{Subtracting 7381 from both sides}$$
$$x = 686.$$

The check is left to the student. The solution is 686.

Do Exercises 16 and 17.

To solve equations like $8 \cdot n = 96$, we can get n alone by writing a related division sentence:

$$n = 96 \div 8 \qquad \text{96 is divided by 8.}$$
$$n = 12. \qquad \text{Doing the division}$$

Note that $n = 12$ is easier to solve than $8 \cdot n = 96$. This is because we see easily that if we replace n on the left side with 12, we get a true sentence: $12 = 12$. The solution of $n = 12$ is 12, which is also the solution of $8 \cdot n = 96$.

It will be useful in our later study to think of the preceding as forming an equivalent equation by "*dividing both sides* by 8." Thus,

$$\frac{8 \cdot n}{8} = \frac{96}{8} \qquad \text{Dividing both sides by 8}$$
$$n = 12. \qquad \text{8 times } n \text{ divided by 8 is } n.$$

SOLVING $a \cdot x = b$

To solve $a \cdot x = b$ for x, divide both sides by a.

EXAMPLE 8 Solve: $10 \cdot x = 240$.

We have

$$10 \cdot x = 240$$

$$\frac{10 \cdot x}{10} = \frac{240}{10} \qquad \text{Dividing both sides by 10}$$

$$x = 24.$$

CHECK:
$$\frac{10 \cdot x = 240}{10 \cdot 24 \; ? \; 240}$$
$$240 \; | \qquad \textbf{TRUE}$$

The solution is 24.

Do Exercises 18 and 19.

EXAMPLE 9 Solve: $5202 = 9 \cdot t$.

We have

$$5202 = 9 \cdot t$$

$$\frac{5202}{9} = \frac{9 \cdot t}{9} \qquad \text{Dividing both sides by 9}$$

$$578 = t.$$

The check is left to the student. The solution is 578.

Do Exercise 20.

EXAMPLE 10 Solve: $14 \cdot y = 1092$.

We have

$$14 \cdot y = 1092$$

$$\frac{14 \cdot y}{14} = \frac{1092}{14} \qquad \text{Dividing both sides by 14}$$

$$y = 78.$$

The check is left to the student. The solution is 78.

Do Exercise 21.

EXAMPLE 11 Solve: $n \cdot 56 = 4648$.

We have

$$n \cdot 56 = 4648$$

$$\frac{n \cdot 56}{56} = \frac{4648}{56} \qquad \text{Dividing both sides by 56}$$

$$n = 83.$$

The check is left to the student. The solution is 83.

Do Exercise 22.

Solve. Be sure to check.

18. $8 \cdot x = 64$

19. $144 = 9 \cdot n$

20. Solve: $5152 = 8 \cdot t$.

21. Solve: $18 \cdot y = 1728$.

22. Solve: $n \cdot 48 = 4512$.

Answers on page A-5

a   Solve by trial.

1. $x + 0 = 14$

2. $x - 7 = 18$

3. $y \cdot 17 = 0$

4. $56 \div m = 7$

b   Solve. Be sure to check.

5. $12 + x = 41$

6. $15 + t = 22$

7. $12 = 12 + m$

8. $16 = t + 16$

9. $3 \cdot x = 24$

10. $6 \cdot x = 42$

11. $112 = n \cdot 8$

12. $162 = 9 \cdot m$

13. $45 \times 23 = x$

14. $23 \times 78 = y$

15. $t = 125 \div 5$

16. $w = 256 \div 16$

17. $p = 908 - 458$

18. $9007 - 5667 = m$

19. $x = 12{,}345 + 78{,}555$

20. $5678 + 9034 = t$

21. $3 \cdot m = 96$

22. $4 \cdot y = 96$

23. $715 = 5 \cdot z$

24. $741 = 3 \cdot t$

25. $10 + x = 89$

26. $20 + x = 57$

27. $61 = 16 + y$

28. $53 = 17 + w$

29. $6 \cdot p = 1944$

30. $4 \cdot w = 3404$

31. $5 \cdot x = 3715$

32. $9 \cdot x = 1269$

33. $47 + n = 84$

34. $56 + p = 92$

35. $x + 78 = 144$

36. $z + 67 = 133$

37. $165 = 11 \cdot n$

38. $660 = 12 \cdot n$

39. $624 = t \cdot 13$

40. $784 = y \cdot 16$

41. $x + 214 = 389$

42. $x + 221 = 333$

43. $567 + x = 902$

44. $438 + x = 807$

45. $18 \cdot x = 1872$

46. $19 \cdot x = 6080$

47. $40 \cdot x = 1800$

48. $20 \cdot x = 1500$

49. $2344 + y = 6400$

50. $9281 = 8322 + t$

51. $14{,}531 + 2150 = x$

52. $8172 - 5309 = y$

53. $234 \times 78 = y$

54. $10{,}534 \div 458 = q$

55. $58 \cdot m = 11{,}890$

56. $233 \cdot x = 22{,}135$

57. $\mathbf{D_W}$ Describe a procedure that can be used to convert any equation of the form $a \cdot b = c$ to a related division equation.

58. $\mathbf{D_W}$ Describe a procedure that can be used to convert any equation of the form $a + b = c$ to a related subtraction equation.

SKILL MAINTENANCE

59. Write two related subtraction sentences: $7 + 9 = 16$. [1.3b]

60. Write two related division sentences: $6 \cdot 8 = 48$. [1.6b]

Use $>$ or $<$ for $\square$ to write a true sentence. [1.4c]

61. $123 \;\square\; 789$

62. $342 \;\square\; 339$

63. $688 \;\square\; 0$

64. $0 \;\square\; 11$

Divide. [1.6c]

65. $1283 \div 9$

66. $1278 \div 9$

67. $1\,7 \overline{)\,5\,6\,7\,8}$

68. $1\,7 \overline{)\,5\,6\,8\,9}$

SYNTHESIS

69. $\mathbf{D_W}$ Give an example of an equation in which a variable appears but for which there is no solution. Then explain why no solution exists.

70. $\mathbf{D_W}$ Is it possible for an equation to have many solutions? If not, explain why, and if so, explain how to write such equations.

Solve.

71. ▦ $23{,}465 \cdot x = 8{,}142{,}355$

72. ▦ $48{,}916 \cdot x = 14{,}332{,}388$

1.8 APPLICATIONS AND PROBLEM SOLVING

Objective

a Solve applied problems involving addition, subtraction, multiplication, or division of whole numbers.

a A Problem-Solving Strategy

Applications and problem solving are the most important uses of mathematics. To solve a problem using addition, subtraction, multiplication, and division of whole numbers, we first look at the situation. We then try to translate the problem to an equation. Next we solve the equation and check to see if the solution of the equation is a solution of the original problem. Finally, we state the answer. We are using the following five-step strategy.

FIVE STEPS FOR PROBLEM SOLVING

1. *Familiarize* yourself with the situation.
   a) Carefully read and reread until you understand *what* you are being asked to find.
   b) Draw a diagram or see if there is a formula that applies to the situation.
   c) Assign a letter, or *variable*, to the unknown.
2. *Translate* the problem to an equation using the letter or variable.
3. *Solve* the equation.
4. *Check* the answer in the original wording of the problem.
5. *State* the answer to the problem clearly with appropriate units.

EXAMPLE 1 *Baseball's Power Hitters.* Three of the top home-run hitters in the major leagues over the years 1998 to 2002 were Sammy Sosa, Barry Bonds, and Alex Rodriguez. The numbers of home runs hit per year for each player are listed in the table below. Find the total number of home runs hit by Sammy Sosa over the 5-yr period.

YEAR	SAMMY SOSA	BARRY BONDS	ALEX RODRIGUEZ
1998	66	37	42
1999	63	34	42
2000	50	49	41
2001	64	73	52
2002	49	46	57
Total	?	?	?

Source: Major League Baseball

Sammy Sosa

1. **Familiarize.** We can make a drawing or at least visualize the situation.

$$66 + 63 + 50 + 64 + 49$$

in	in	in	in	in
1998	1999	2000	2001	2002

Since we are combining numbers of home runs, addition can be used. First, we define the unknown. We let $n = $ the total number of home runs hit by Sosa in the 5-yr period.

2. **Translate.** We translate to an equation:

$$66 + 63 + 50 + 64 + 49 = n.$$

3. **Solve.** We solve the equation by carrying out the addition.

$$\begin{array}{r} \overset{2}{6}\,6 \\ 6\,3 \\ 5\,0 \\ 6\,4 \\ +\,4\,9 \\ \hline 2\,9\,2 \end{array}$$

$$66 + 63 + 50 + 64 + 49 = n$$
$$292 = n$$

4. **Check.** We check 292 in the original problem. There are many ways in which this can be done. For example, we can repeat the calculation. (We leave this to the student.) Another way is to check whether the answer is reasonable. In this case, we would expect the total to be greater than the number of home runs in any of the individual years, which it is. We can also estimate by rounding to the nearest ten:

$$66 + 63 + 50 + 64 + 49 \approx 70 + 60 + 50 + 60 + 50$$
$$= 290$$

Since $292 \approx 290$, we have a partial check. If we had an estimate like 340 or 400, we might be suspicious that our calculated answer is incorrect. Since our estimated answer is close to our calculation, we are further convinced that our answer checks.

5. **State.** The total number of home runs hit by Sammy Sosa from 1998 to 2002 was 292.

Do Exercises 1–3.

---

1. **Teacher Needs in 2005.** The data in the table shows the estimated number of new jobs for teachers in the year 2005. The reason is an expected boom in the number of youngsters under the age of 18. Find the total number of new jobs available for teachers in 2005.

TYPE OF TEACHER	NUMBER OF NEW JOBS
Secondary	386,000
Aide	364,000
Childcare worker	248,000
Elementary	220,000
Special education	206,000

Source: Bureau of Labor Statistics

Refer to the table on the preceding page to answer Margin Exercises 2 and 3.

2. Find the total number of home runs hit by Alex Rodriguez from 1998 to 2002.

3. Find the total number of home runs hit by Barry Bonds from 1998 to 2002.

Answers on page A-5

Study Tips

DOUBLE-CHECK THE NUMBERS

Solving problems is challenging enough, without miscopying information. Always double-check that you have accurately transferred numbers from the correct exercise in the exercise set.

4. Checking Account Balance.
The balance in Heidi's checking account is $2003. She uses her debit card to buy the same Roto Zip Spiral Saw Combo, featured in Example 2, that Tyler did. Find the new balance in her checking account.

EXAMPLE 2 *Checking Account Balance.* The balance in Tyler's checking account is $528. He uses his debit card to buy the Roto Zip Spiral Saw Combo shown in this ad. Find the new balance in his checking account.

NOW
$**129**⁰⁰

Source: Roto Zip Tool Corporation

1. **Familiarize.** We first make a drawing or at least visualize the situation. We let M = the new balance in his account. This gives us the following:

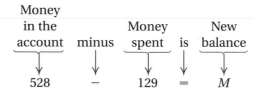

Take away
$129

$528   New balance

2. **Translate.** We can think of this as a "take-away" situation. We translate to an equation.

Money in the account	minus	Money spent	is	New balance
528	−	129	=	M

3. **Solve.** This sentence tells us what to do. We subtract.

$$\begin{array}{r} \overset{\scriptstyle 11}{\overset{\scriptstyle 4\ \cancel{2}\ 18}{\cancel{5}\ \cancel{2}\ \cancel{8}}} \\ -\ 1\ 2\ 9 \\ \hline 3\ 9\ 9 \end{array}$$
        $528 - 129 = M$
        $399 = M$

4. **Check.** To check our answer of $399, we can repeat the calculation. We note that the answer should be less than the original amount, $528, which it is. We can add the difference, 399, to the purchase price, 129: $129 + 399 = 528$. We can also estimate:

$$528 - 129 \approx 530 - 130 = 400 \approx 399.$$

5. **State.** Tyler has a new balance of $399 in his checking account.

Do Exercise 4.

Answer on page A-5

In the real world, problems may not be stated in written words. You must still become familiar with the situation before you can solve the problem.

EXAMPLE 3 *Travel Distance.* Vicki drove from Indianapolis to Salt Lake City to work during the 2002 Winter Olympics. The distance from Indianapolis to Salt Lake City is 1634 mi. She drove 1154 mi to reach Denver. How much farther did she still need to travel?

1. **Familiarize.** We first make a drawing or at least visualize the situation. We let x = the remaining distance to Salt Lake City.

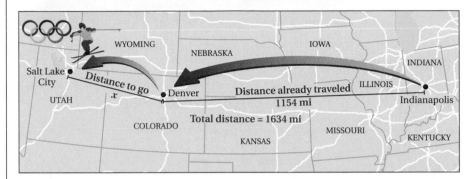

2. **Translate.** We see that this is a "missing-addend" situation. We translate to an equation.

Distance already traveled	plus	Distance to go	is	Total distance of trip
↓	↓	↓	↓	↓
1154	+	x	=	1634

3. **Solve.** To solve the equation, we subtract 1154 from both sides:

$$1154 + x = 1634$$
$$1154 + x - 1154 = 1634 - 1154$$
$$x = 480.$$

$$
\begin{array}{r}
\overset{\scriptstyle 5\ 13}{1\,\cancel{6}\,\cancel{3}\,4} \\
-\ 1\,1\,5\,4 \\
\hline
4\,8\,0
\end{array}
$$

4. **Check.** We check our answer of 480 mi in the original problem. This number should be less than the total distance, 1634 mi, which it is. We can add the difference, 480, to the subtrahend, 1154: $1154 + 480 = 1634$. We can also estimate:

$$1634 - 1154 \approx 1600 - 1200$$
$$= 400 \approx 480.$$

The answer, 480 mi, checks.

5. **State.** Vicki needed to travel 480 mi farther to Salt Lake City.

Do Exercise 5.

---

5. **Home Theatre Audio System.** Bernardo has $376. He wants to purchase the Home Theatre Audio System shown in the ad below. How much more does he need?

Answer on page A-5

6. Total Cost of Laptop Computers. What is the total cost of 12 IBM laptop computers if each one costs $1298?

EXAMPLE 4 *Total Cost of DVD/VCR Players.* What is the total cost of 5 combination DVD/VCR players if each one costs $249?

1. **Familiarize.** We first make a drawing or at least visualize the situation. We let $T =$ the cost of 5 DVD/VCR players. Multiplication or repeated addition works well in this case.

2. **Translate.** We translate to an equation.

Number of DVD/VCR players	times	Cost of each player	is	Total cost
5	×	$249	=	T

3. **Solve.** This sentence tells us what to do. We multiply.

$$\begin{array}{r} \overset{2\;4}{2\,4\,9} \\ \times\qquad 5 \\ \hline 1\,2\,4\,5 \end{array}$$

$$5 \times 249 = T$$
$$1245 = T$$

4. **Check.** We have an answer, 1245, that is much greater than the cost of one player, which is reasonable. We can repeat our calculation or we can check by estimating:

$$5 \times 249 \approx 5 \times 250 = 1250 \approx 1245.$$

The answer checks.

5. **State.** The total cost of 5 DVD/VCR players is $1245.

Do Exercise 6.

EXAMPLE 5 *Bed Sheets.* The dimensions of a flat sheet for a king-size bed are 108 in. by 102 in. What is the area of the sheet? (The dimension labels on sheets list width × length.)

1. **Familiarize.** We first make a drawing. We let $A =$ the area.

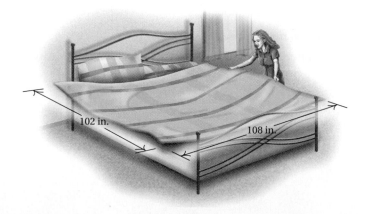

102 in.

108 in.

Answer on page A-5

2. Translate. Using a formula for area, we have

$$A = \text{length} \cdot \text{width} = l \cdot w = 102 \cdot 108.$$

3. Solve. We carry out the multiplication.

$$
\begin{array}{r}
1\ 0\ 8 \\
\times\ \ 1\ 0\ 2 \\
\hline
2\ 1\ 6 \\
1\ 0\ 8\ 0\ 0 \\
\hline
1\ 1\ 0\ 1\ 6
\end{array}
\qquad
\begin{array}{l}
A = 102 \cdot 108 \\
A = 11{,}016
\end{array}
$$

4. Check. We repeat our calculation. We also note that the answer is greater than either the length or the width, which it should be. (This might not be the case if we were using fractions or decimals.) The answer checks.

5. State. The area of a king-size bed sheet is 11,016 sq in.

Do Exercise 7.

■ **EXAMPLE 6** *Cartons of Soda.* A bottling company produces 3304 cans of soda. How many 12-can cartons can be filled? How many cans will be left over?

1. Familiarize. We first make a drawing. We let n = the number of 12-can cartons that can be filled. The problem can be considered as division or repeated subtraction, taking successive sets of 12 cans and putting them into n cartons.

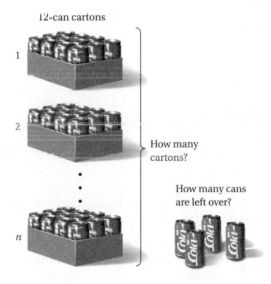

12-can cartons

1

2

How many cartons?

How many cans are left over?

n

2. Translate. We translate to an equation.

Number of cans	divided by	Number in each carton	is	Number of cartons
↓	↓	↓	↓	↓
3304	÷	12	=	n

Answer on page A-5

8. Cartons of Soda. The bottling company in Example 6 also uses 6-can cartons. How many 6-can cartons can be filled with 2269 cans of cola? How many cans will be left over?

3. Solve. We solve the equation by carrying out the division.

$$
\begin{array}{r}
2\ 7\ 5 \\
1\ 2\ )\overline{3\ 3\ 0\ 4} \\
2\ 4\ 0\ 0 \\
\hline
9\ 0\ 4 \\
8\ 4\ 0 \\
\hline
6\ 4 \\
6\ 0 \\
\hline
4
\end{array}
$$

$3304 \div 12 = n$
$275 \text{ R } 4 = n$

4. Check. We can check by multiplying the number of cartons by 12 and adding the remainder, 4:

$12 \cdot 275 = 3300,$
$3300 + 4 = 3304.$

5. State. Thus, 275 twelve-can cartons can be filled. There will be 4 cans left over.

Do Exercise 8.

EXAMPLE 7 *Automobile Mileage.* The Chrysler PT Cruiser gets 22 miles to the gallon (mpg) in city driving. How many gallons will it use in 6028 mi of city driving?
Source: DaimlerChrysler Corporation

1. Familiarize. We first make a drawing. It is often helpful to be descriptive about how we define a variable. In this case, we let g = the number of gallons ("g" comes from "gallons").

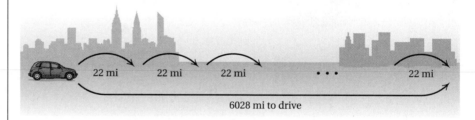

22 mi   22 mi   22 mi   • • •   22 mi

6028 mi to drive

2. Translate. Repeated addition applies here. Thus, the following multiplication applies to the situation.

Number of miles per gallon	times	Number of gallons needed	is	Number of miles to drive
22	$\cdot$	g	=	6028

3. Solve. To solve the equation, we divide by 22 on both sides.

$22 \cdot g = 6028$

$\dfrac{22 \cdot g}{22} = \dfrac{6028}{22}$

$g = 274$

$$
\begin{array}{r}
2\ 7\ 4 \\
2\ 2\ )\overline{6\ 0\ 2\ 8} \\
4\ 4\ 0\ 0 \\
\hline
1\ 6\ 2\ 8 \\
1\ 5\ 4\ 0 \\
\hline
8\ 8 \\
8\ 8 \\
\hline
0
\end{array}
$$

Answer on page A-5

4. Check. To check, we multiply 274 by 22: $22 \cdot 274 = 6028$.

5. State. The PT Cruiser will use 274 gal.

Do Exercise 9.

MULTISTEP PROBLEMS

Sometimes we must use more than one operation to solve a problem, as in the following example.

■ **EXAMPLE 8** *Aircraft Seating.* Boeing Corporation builds commercial aircraft. A Boeing 767 has a seating configuration with 4 rows of 6 seats across in first class and 35 rows of 7 seats across in economy class. Find the total seating capacity of the plane.
Sources: The Boeing Corporation; Delta Airlines

1. Familiarize. We first make a drawing.

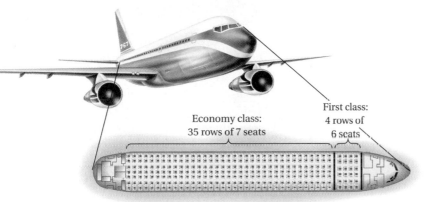

First class:
4 rows of
6 seats

Economy class:
35 rows of 7 seats

2. Translate. There are three parts to the problem. We first find the number of seats in each class. Then we add.

First class: Repeated addition applies here. Thus, the following multiplication corresponds to the situation. We let $F =$ the number of seats in first class.

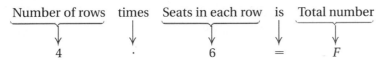

Economy class: Repeated addition applies here. Thus, the following multiplication corresponds to the situation. We let $E =$ the number of seats in economy class.

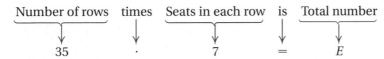

We let $T =$ the total number of seats in both classes.

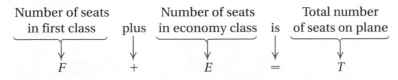

Answer on page A-5

9. Automobile Mileage. The Chrysler PT Cruiser gets 26 miles to the gallon (mpg) in highway driving. How many gallons will it take to drive 884 mi of highway driving?
Source: DaimlerChrysler Corporation

10. Aircraft Seating. A Boeing 767 used for foreign travel has three classes of seats. First class has 3 rows of 5 seats across. Business class has 6 rows with 6 seats across and 1 row with 2 seats on each of the outside aisles. Economy class has 18 rows with 7 seats across. Find the total seating capacity of the plane.

Sources: The Boeing Corporation; Delta Airlines

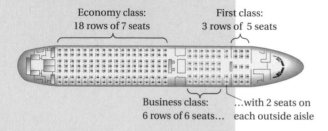

Economy class: 18 rows of 7 seats

First class: 3 rows of 5 seats

Business class: 6 rows of 6 seats...

...with 2 seats on each outside aisle

3. Solve. We solve each equation and add the solutions.

$$4 \cdot 6 = F \qquad 35 \cdot 7 = E \qquad F + E = T$$
$$24 = F \qquad 245 = E \qquad 24 + 245 = T$$
$$269 = T$$

4. Check. To check, we repeat our calculations. (We leave this to the student.) We could also check by rounding, multiplying, and adding.

5. State. There are 269 seats in a Boeing 767.

Do Exercise 10.

As you consider the following exercises, here are some words and phrases that may be helpful to look for when you are translating problems to equations.

KEY WORDS, PHRASES, AND CONCEPTS	
Addition (+)	**Subtraction (−)**
add	subtract
added to	subtracted from
sum	difference
total	minus
plus	less than
more than	decreased by
increased by	take away
	how much more
	missing addend
Multiplication (·)	**Division (÷)**
multiply	divide
multiplied by	divided by
product	quotient
times	repeated subtraction
of	missing factor
repeated addition	finding equal quantities
rectangular arrays	

Answer on page A-5

1.8

EXERCISE SET

For Extra Help

Digital Video
Tutor CD 1
Videotape 1

InterAct
Math

Math Tutor
Center

MathXL

MyMathLab

a   Solve.

Top Web Properties.   The bar graph below shows the four most frequently visited Web sites, in terms of the number of visits for a recent month. Use this graph for Exercises 1–4.

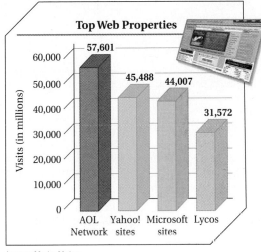

Source: Media Matrix

1. What was the total number of visits to all the sites?

2. What was the total number of visits to the three most-visited sites?

3. How many more visits were there to the AOL Network site than to the Yahoo! sites?

4. How many more visits were there to the Microsoft sites than to the Lycos site?

5. *Concorde Crash.*   The Anglo-French Concorde entered service in 1976. It had its first crash 24 yrs later. In what year did it have its first crash?

6. Dwight D. Eisenhower was the 34th president of the United States. He left office in 1961 and lived another 8 yrs. In what year did he die?

New England. The following table lists various data about the New England states.

NEW ENGLAND STATES	TOTAL AREA (in square miles)	TOTAL INLAND WATER AREA (in square miles)	SALARY OF THE GOVERNOR	POPULATION IN 2001
Maine	33,265	2,270	$70,000	1,286,670
New Hampshire	9,279	286	86,235	1,259,181
Vermont	9,614	341	80,725	613,090
Massachusetts	8,284	460	75,000	6,379,304
Connecticut	5,018	146	78,000	3,425,074
Rhode Island	1,212	157	69,900	1,058,920

Source: Based on information from the U.S. Census Bureau

7. Find the total area of New England.

8. Find the total area of inland water in New England.

9. Find the total amount paid in salaries to the governors of the New England states.

10. Find the total population of New England in 2001.

11. *Military Downsizing.* In 2002, there were approximately 383,500 people in the Navy. This was down from the 583,000 who were in the Navy in 1990. How many more people were in the Navy in 1990 than in 2002?
Source: The United States Navy

12. *Baseball Salaries.* The New York Yankees led the major leagues in 2002 with a total payroll of $125,928,583. The Minnesota Twins had the lowest payroll at $40,225,000. How much more would the Twins have to spend on payroll to equal the Yankees?
Source: Major League Baseball

13. *Longest Rivers.* The longest river in the world is the Nile in Africa at 4100 mi. The longest river in the United States is the Missouri–Mississippi at 3860 mi. How much longer is the Nile?

14. *Speeds on Interstates.* During the 1990s speed limits on most interstate highways were raised from 55 mph to 65 mph. By how many miles per hour were they raised?

15. *Automobile Mileage.* The 2002 Volkswagen New Beetle (Diesel) gets 42 miles to the gallon (mpg) in city driving. How many gallons will it use in 10,752 mi of city driving?
Source: Volkswagen of America, Inc.

16. *Automobile Mileage.* The 2002 Volkswagen New Beetle (Diesel) gets 49 miles to the gallon (mpg) in highway driving. How many gallons will it use in 9261 mi of highway driving?
Source: Volkswagen of America, Inc.

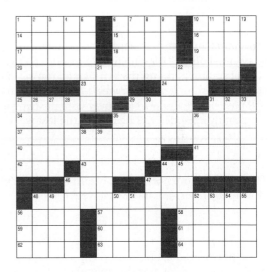

17. *Pixels.* A computer screen consists of small rectangular dots called *pixels*. How many pixels are there on a screen that has 600 rows with 800 pixels in each row?

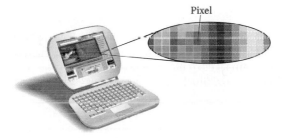

Pixel

18. *Crossword.* The *USA Today* crossword puzzle is a rectangle containing 15 rows with 15 squares in each row. How many squares does the puzzle have altogether?

19. *Refrigerator Purchase.* Cometbucks Deli has a chain of 24 restaurants. It buys a refrigerator for each store at a cost of $499 each. Find the total cost of the purchase.

20. *Microwave Purchase.* Bridgeway College is constructing new dorms, in which each room has a small kitchen. It buys 96 microwave ovens at $88 each. Find the total cost of the purchase.

Music CD Sales. The bar graph below shows the sales of music CDs, in millions, for the years from 1997 to 2001. Use this graph for Exercises 21–24.

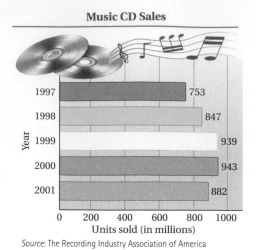

Music CD Sales

Year	Units sold (in millions)
1997	753
1998	847
1999	939
2000	943
2001	882

Source: The Recording Industry Association of America

21. How many more CDs were sold in 2001 than in 1997?

22. How many more CDs were sold in 1999 than in 1998?

23. What was the total number of CDs sold from 1997 through 1999?

24. What was the total number of CDs sold from 1999 through 2001?

25. *"Seinfeld" Episodes.* "Seinfeld" was a long-running television comedy for which 177 episodes were created. A local station picks up the syndicated reruns. If the station runs 5 episodes per week, how many full weeks will pass before it must start over with past episodes? How many episodes will be left for the last week?

26. A lab technician separates a vial containing 70 cubic centimeters (cc) of blood into test tubes, each of which contains 3 cc of blood. How many test tubes can be filled? How much blood is left over?

27. There are 24 hours (hr) in a day and 7 days in a week. How many hours are there in a week?

28. There are 60 min in an hour and 24 hr in a day. How many minutes are there in a day?

29. Dana borrows $5928 for a used car. The loan is to be paid off in 24 equal monthly payments. How much is each payment (excluding interest)?

30. A family borrows $4824 to build a sunroom on the back of their home. The loan is to be paid off in equal monthly payments of $134 (excluding interest). How many months will it take to pay off the loan?

31. *Atlanta Population.* The population of Atlanta was 4,112,198 in 2000. This was an increase of 1,152,698 from its population in 1990. What was the population of Atlanta in 1990?
Source: U.S. Bureau of the Census

32. *Orlando Population.* The population of Orlando was 1,644,561 in 2000. This was an increase of 419,717 from its population in 1990. What was the population of Orlando in 1990?
Source: U.S. Bureau of the Census

33. *Crossword.* The *Los Angeles Times* crossword puzzle is a rectangle containing 441 squares arranged in 21 rows. How many columns does the puzzle have?

34. *Sheet of Stamps.* A sheet of 100 stamps typically has 10 rows of stamps. How many stamps are in each row?

35. *Hershey Bars®.* Hershey Chocolate USA makes small, fun-size chocolate bars. How many 20-bar packages can be filled with 11,267 bars? How many bars will be left over?

36. *Reese's Peanut Butter Cups®.* H. B. Reese Candy Co. makes small, fun-size peanut butter cups. The company manufactures 23,579 cups and fills 1025 packages. How many cups are in a package? How many cups will be left over?

37. *High School Court.* The standard basketball court used by high school players has dimensions of 50 ft by 84 ft.
   a) What is its area?
   b) What is its perimeter?

38. *NBA Court.* The standard basketball court used by college and NBA players has dimensions of 50 ft by 94 ft.
   a) What is its area?
   b) What is its perimeter?
   c) How much greater is the area of an NBA court than a high school court? (See Exercise 37.)

39. Copies of this book are generally shipped from the Addison-Wesley warehouse in cartons containing 24 books each. How many cartons are needed to ship 840 books?

40. According to the H. J. Heinz Company, 16-oz bottles of catsup are generally shipped in cartons containing 12 bottles each. How many cartons are needed to ship 528 bottles of catsup?

41. Copies of this book are generally shipped from the warehouse in cartons containing 24 books each. How many cartons are needed to ship 1355 books?

42. Sixteen-ounce bottles of catsup are generally shipped in cartons containing 12 bottles each. How many cartons are needed to ship 1033 bottles of catsup?

43. *Map Drawing.* A map has a scale of 64 mi to the inch. How far apart *in reality* are two cities that are 6 in. apart on the map? How far apart *on the map* are two cities that, in reality, are 1728 mi apart?

44. *Map Drawing.* A map has a scale of 150 mi to the inch. How far apart *on the map* are two cities that, in reality, are 2400 mi apart? How far apart *in reality* are two cities that are 13 in. apart on the map?

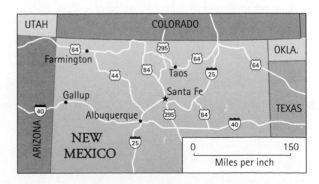

45. A carpenter drills 216 holes in a rectangular array in a pegboard. There are 12 holes in each row. How many rows are there?

46. Lou works as a CPA. He arranges 504 entries on a spreadsheet in a rectangular array that has 36 rows. How many entries are in each row?

47. Elena buys 5 video games at $64 each and pays for them with $10 bills. How many $10 bills did it take?

48. Pedro buys 5 video games at $64 each and pays for them with $20 bills. How many $20 bills did it take?

49. You have $568 in your checking account. You write checks for $46, $87, and $129. Then you deposit $94 back in the account after the return of some books. How much is left in your account?

50. The balance in your checking account is $749. You write checks for $34 and $65. Then you make a deposit of $123 from your paycheck. What is your new balance?

Weight Loss. Many Americans exercise for weight control. It is known that one must burn off about 3500 calories in order to lose one pound. The chart shown here details how much of certain types of exercise is required to burn 100 calories. Use this chart for Exercises 51–54.

Source: Based on information from the American College of Sports Medicine

51. How long must you run at a brisk pace in order to lose one pound?

52. How long must you swim in order to lose one pound?

53. How long must you do aerobic exercises in order to lose one pound?

54. How long must you bicycle at 11 mph in order to lose one pound?

55. *Bones in the Hands and Feet.* There are 27 bones in each human hand and 26 bones in each human foot. How many bones are there in all in the hands and feet?

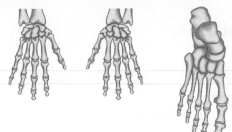

56. *Index Cards.* Index cards of dimension 3 in. by 5 in. are normally shipped in packages containing 100 cards each. How much writing area is available if one uses the front and back sides of a package of these cards?

57. Before going back to college, David buys 4 shirts at $59 each and 6 pairs of pants at $78 each. What is the total cost of this clothing?

58. An office for adjunct instructors at a community college has 6 bookshelves, each of which is 3 ft long. The office is moved to a new location that has dimensions of 16 ft by 21 ft. Is it possible for the bookshelves to be put side by side on the 16-ft wall?

59. **D_W** In the newspaper article, "When Girls Play, Knees Fail," the author discusses the fact that female athletes have six times the number of knee injuries that male athletes have. What information would be needed if you were to write a math problem based on the article? What might the problem be?
Source: *The Arizona Republic,* 2/9/00, p. C1

60. **D_W** Write a problem for a classmate to solve. Design the problem so that the solution is "The driver still has 329 mi to travel."

SKILL MAINTENANCE

Round 234,562 to the nearest: [1.4a]

61. Hundred.   **62.** Ten.   **63.** Thousand.

Estimate the computation by rounding to the nearest thousand.   [1.4b]

64. 2783 + 4602 + 5797 + 8111   **65.** 28,430 − 11,977

66. 2100 + 5800   **67.** 5800 − 2100

Estimate the product by rounding to the nearest hundred.   [1.5b]

68. 787 · 363   **69.** 887 · 799   **70.** 10,362 · 4531

SYNTHESIS

71. **D_W** Karen translates a problem into a multiplication equation, whereas Don translates the same problem into a division equation. Can they both be correct? Explain.

72. **D_W** Of the five problem-solving steps listed at the beginning of this section, which is the most difficult for you? Why?

73. ▦ *Speed of Light.* Light travels about 186,000 miles per second (mi/sec) in a vacuum as in outer space. In ice it travels about 142,000 mi/sec, and in glass it travels about 109,000 mi/sec. In 18 sec, how many more miles will light travel in a vacuum than in ice? in glass?

74. Carney Community College has 1200 students. Each professor teaches 4 classes and each student takes 5 classes. There are 30 students and 1 teacher in each classroom. How many professors are there at Carney Community College?

EXPONENTIAL NOTATION AND ORDER OF OPERATIONS

Objectives

a Write exponential notation for products such as 4 · 4 · 4.

b Evaluate exponential notation.

c Simplify expressions using the rules for order of operations.

d Remove parentheses within parentheses.

a Writing Exponential Notation

Consider the product $3 \cdot 3 \cdot 3 \cdot 3$. Such products occur often enough that mathematicians have found it convenient to create a shorter notation, called **exponential notation,** explained as follows.

$$\underbrace{3 \cdot 3 \cdot 3 \cdot 3}_{4 \text{ factors}} \text{ is shortened to } 3^4 \leftarrow \text{exponent}$$
$$\uparrow_{\text{base}}$$

We read exponential notation as follows.

NOTATION	WORD DESCRIPTION
3^4	"three to the fourth power," or "the fourth power of three"
5^3	"five to the third power," or "the third power of five," or "five-cubed," or "the cube of five"
7^2	"seven to the second power," or "the second power of seven," or "seven squared," or "the square of seven"

The wording "seven squared" for 7^2 comes from the fact that a square with side s has area A given by $A = s^2$.

$$A = s^2$$

An expression like $3 \cdot 5^2$ is read "three times five squared" or "three times the square of five."

EXAMPLE 1 Write exponential notation for $10 \cdot 10 \cdot 10 \cdot 10 \cdot 10$.

Exponential notation is 10^5. 5 is the *exponent*.
10 is the *base*.

EXAMPLE 2 Write exponential notation for $2 \cdot 2 \cdot 2$.

Exponential notation is 2^3.

Do Exercises 1–4.

Write in exponential notation.

1. $5 \cdot 5 \cdot 5 \cdot 5$

2. $5 \cdot 5 \cdot 5 \cdot 5 \cdot 5$

3. $13 \cdot 13$

4. $10 \cdot 10 \cdot 10 \cdot 10$

Answers on page A-5

b Evaluating Exponential Notation

We evaluate exponential notation by rewriting it as a product and computing the product.

EXAMPLE 3 Evaluate: 10^3.

$$10^3 = 10 \cdot 10 \cdot 10 = 1000$$

EXAMPLE 4 Evaluate: 5^4.

$$5^4 = 5 \cdot 5 \cdot 5 \cdot 5 = 625$$

> **CAUTION!**
>
> 5^4 does not mean $5 \cdot 4$.

Do Exercises 5–8.

c Simplifying Expressions

Suppose we have a calculation like the following:

$$3 + 4 \cdot 8.$$

How do we find the answer? Do we add 3 to 4 and then multiply by 8, or do we multiply 4 by 8 and then add 3? In the first case, the answer is 56. In the second, the answer is 35. We agree to compute as in the second case.

Consider the calculation

$$7 \cdot 14 - (12 + 18).$$

What do the parentheses mean? To deal with these questions, we must make some agreement regarding the order in which we perform operations. The rules are as follows.

RULES FOR ORDER OF OPERATIONS

1. Do all calculations within parentheses ( ), brackets [ ], or braces { } before operations outside.
2. Evaluate all exponential expressions.
3. Do all multiplications and divisions in order from left to right.
4. Do all additions and subtractions in order from left to right.

It is worth noting that these are the rules that computers and most scientific calculators use to do computations.

EXAMPLE 5 Simplify: $16 \div 8 \times 2$.

There are no parentheses or exponents, so we start with the third step.

$$16 \div 8 \times 2 = 2 \times 2 \qquad \text{Doing all multiplications and divisions in order from left to right}$$

$$= 4$$

CALCULATOR CORNER

Many calculators have a y^x or x^y key for raising a base to a power. To find 16^3, for example, we press

[1][6][y^x][3][=] or

[1][6][x^y][3][=] . The result is 4096.

Exercises: Use a calculator to find each of the following.

1. 3^5
2. 5^6
3. 12^4
4. 2^{11}

Evaluate.

5. 10^5 6. 15^2

7. 8^3 8. 2^5

Answers on page A-5

Simplify.

9. $93 - 14 \cdot 3$

10. $104 \div 4 + 4$

11. $25 \cdot 26 - (56 + 10)$

12. $75 \div 5 + (83 - 14)$

Simplify and compare.

13. $64 \div (32 \div 2)$ and $(64 \div 32) \div 2$

14. $(28 + 13) + 11$ and $28 + (13 + 11)$

15. Simplify:

$9 \times 4 - (20 + 4) \div 8 - (6 - 2)$.

EXAMPLE 6 Simplify: $7 \cdot 14 - (12 + 18)$.

$$7 \cdot 14 - (12 + 18) = 7 \cdot 14 - 30 \qquad \text{Carrying out operations inside parentheses}$$
$$= 98 - 30 \qquad \text{Doing all multiplications and divisions}$$
$$= 68 \qquad \text{Doing all additions and subtractions}$$

Do Exercises 9–12.

EXAMPLE 7 Simplify and compare: $23 - (10 - 9)$ and $(23 - 10) - 9$.

We have

$$23 - (10 - 9) = 23 - 1 = 22;$$
$$(23 - 10) - 9 = 13 - 9 = 4.$$

We can see that $23 - (10 - 9)$ and $(23 - 10) - 9$ represent different numbers. Thus, subtraction is not associative.

Do Exercises 13 and 14.

EXAMPLE 8 Simplify: $7 \cdot 2 - (12 + 0) \div 3 - (5 - 2)$.

$$7 \cdot 2 - (12 + 0) \div 3 - (5 - 2) = 7 \cdot 2 - 12 \div 3 - 3 \qquad \text{Carrying out operations inside parentheses}$$
$$= 14 - 4 - 3 \qquad \text{Doing all multiplications and divisions in order from left to right}$$
$$= 7 \qquad \text{Doing all additions and subtractions in order from left to right}$$

Do Exercise 15.

EXAMPLE 9 Simplify: $15 \div 3 \cdot 2 \div (10 - 8)$.

$$15 \div 3 \cdot 2 \div (10 - 8) = 15 \div 3 \cdot 2 \div 2 \qquad \text{Carrying out operations inside parentheses}$$
$$= 5 \cdot 2 \div 2 \qquad$$
$$= 10 \div 2 \qquad \text{Doing all multiplications and divisions in order from left to right}$$
$$= 5 \qquad$$

Do Exercises 16–18 on the next page.

EXAMPLE 10 Simplify: $4^2 \div (10 - 9 + 1)^3 \cdot 3 - 5$.

$$4^2 \div (10 - 9 + 1)^3 \cdot 3 - 5$$
$$= 4^2 \div (1 + 1)^3 \cdot 3 - 5 \qquad \text{Subtracting inside parentheses}$$
$$= 4^2 \div 2^3 \cdot 3 - 5 \qquad \text{Adding inside parentheses}$$
$$= 16 \div 8 \cdot 3 - 5 \qquad \text{Evaluating exponential expressions}$$
$$\left. \begin{array}{l} = 2 \cdot 3 - 5 \\ = 6 - 5 \end{array} \right\} \qquad \text{Doing all multiplications and divisions in order from left to right}$$
$$= 1 \qquad \text{Subtracting}$$

Do Exercises 19–21.

EXAMPLE 11 Simplify: $2^9 \div 2^6 \cdot 2^3$.

$$2^9 \div 2^6 \cdot 2^3 = 512 \div 64 \cdot 8 \qquad \text{There are no parentheses. Evaluating exponential expressions}$$
$$\left. \begin{array}{l} = 8 \cdot 8 \\ = 64 \end{array} \right\} \qquad \text{Doing all multiplications and divisions in order from left to right}$$

Do Exercise 22.

CALCULATOR CORNER

To determine whether a calculator is programmed to follow the rules for order of operations, we can enter a simple calculation that requires using those rules. For example, we can enter $\boxed{3} \ \boxed{+} \ \boxed{4} \ \boxed{\times} \ \boxed{2} \ \boxed{-}$. If the result is 11, we know that the rules for order of operations have been followed. That is, the multiplication $4 \times 2 = 8$ was performed first and then 3 was added to produce a result of 11. If the result is 14, we know that the calculator performs operations as they are entered rather than following the rules for order of operations. That means, in this case, that 3 and 4 were added first to get 7 and then that sum was multiplied by 2 to produce the result of 14. For such calculators, we would have to enter the operations in the order in which we want them performed. In this case, we would press $\boxed{4} \ \boxed{\times} \ \boxed{2} \ \boxed{+} \ \boxed{3} \ \boxed{=}$.

Many calculators have parenthesis keys that can be used to enter an expression containing parentheses. To enter $5(4 + 3)$, for example, we press $\boxed{5} \ \boxed{(} \ \boxed{4} \ \boxed{+} \ \boxed{3} \ \boxed{)} \ \boxed{=}$. The result is 35.

Exercises: Simplify.

1. $84 - 5 \cdot 7$ 2. $80 + 50 \div 10$

3. $3^2 + 9^2 \div 3$ 4. $4^4 \div 64 - 4$

5. $15 \cdot 7 - (23 + 9)$ 6. $(4 + 3)^2$

Simplify.

16. $5 \cdot 5 \cdot 5 + 26 \cdot 71 - (16 + 25 \cdot 3)$

17. $30 \div 5 \cdot 2 + 10 \cdot 20 + 8 \cdot 8 - 23$

18. $95 - 2 \cdot 2 \cdot 2 \cdot 5 \div (24 - 4)$

Simplify.

19. $4^3 + 9 \cdot 12 - (4 + 3 \cdot 17)$

20. $(1 + 3)^3 + 10 \cdot 20 + 8^2 - 23$

21. $81 - 3^2 \cdot 2 \div (12 - 9)$

22. Simplify: $2^3 \cdot 2^8 \div 2^9$.

Answers on page A-5

23. NBA Tall Men. The heights, in inches, of several of the tallest players in the NBA are given in the bar graph below. Find the average height of these players.

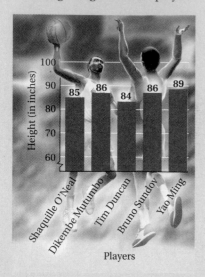

Height (in inches)

85 86 84 86 89

Shaquille O'Neal
Dikembe Mutumbo
Tim Duncan
Bruno Sundov
Yao Ming

Players

Source: NBA

AVERAGES

In order to find the average of a set of numbers, we use addition and then division. For example, the average of 2, 6, and 7 is found as follows.

The number of addends is 3.

$$\text{Average} = \frac{2 + 6 + 7}{3} = \frac{15}{3} = 5$$

Divide by 3.

AVERAGE

The **average** of a set of numbers is the sum of the numbers divided by the number of addends.

EXAMPLE 12 *Average Height of Waterfalls.* The heights of the four highest waterfalls in the world are given in the bar graph at right. Find the average height of all four.

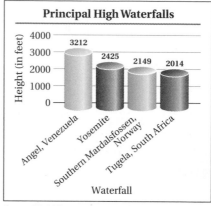

Principal High Waterfalls

Height (in feet)

4000 3000 2000 1000 0

3212   2425   2149   2014

Angel, Venezuela
Yosemite
Southern Mardalsfossen, Norway
Tugela, South Africa

Waterfall

Source: World Almanac

The average is given by $\dfrac{3212 + 2425 + 2149 + 2014}{4} = \dfrac{9800}{4} = 2450$.

Thus, the average height of the four highest waterfalls is 2450 ft.

Do Exercise 23.

d ## Removing Parentheses within Parentheses

When parentheses occur within parentheses, we can make them different shapes, such as [ ] (also called "brackets") and { } (also called "braces"). All of these have the same meaning. When parentheses occur within parentheses, computations in the innermost ones are to be done first.

EXAMPLE 13 Simplify: $[25 - (4 + 3) \times 3] \div (11 - 7)$.

$$[25 - (4 + 3) \times 3] \div (11 - 7)$$

$= [25 - 7 \times 3] \div (11 - 7)$	Doing the calculations in the innermost parentheses first
$= [25 - 21] \div (11 - 7)$	Doing the multiplication in the brackets
$= 4 \div 4$	Subtracting
$= 1$	Dividing

Answer on page A-5

EXAMPLE 14 Simplify: $16 \div 2 + \{40 - [13 - (4 + 2)]\}$.

$16 \div 2 + \{40 - [13 - (4 + 2)]\}$

$= 16 \div 2 + \{40 - [13 - 6]\}$ Doing the calculations in the innermost parentheses first

$= 16 \div 2 + \{40 - 7\}$ Again, doing the calculations in the innermost parentheses

$= 16 \div 2 + 33$ Subtracting inside the braces

$= 8 + 33$ Doing all multiplications and divisions in order from left to right

$= 41$ Doing all additions and subtractions in order from left to right

Do Exercises 24 and 25.

Simplify.

24. $9 \times 5 + \{6 \div [14 - (5 + 3)]\}$

25. $[18 - (2 + 7) \div 3]$
$- (31 - 10 \times 2)$

Answers on page A-5

Study Tips

PREPARE WELL FOR TESTS

You are probably ready to begin preparing for your first test. Here are some test-taking study tips.

■ **Make up your own test questions as you study.** After you have done your homework over a particular objective, write one or two questions on your own that you think might be on a test. You will be amazed at the insight this will provide.

■ **Do an overall review of the chapter, focusing on the objectives and the examples.** This should be accompanied by a study of any class notes you may have taken.

■ **Do the review exercises at the end of the chapter.** Check your answers at the back of the book. If you have trouble with an exercise, use the objective symbol as a guide to go back and do further study of that objective.

■ **Call the AW Math Tutor Center if you need extra help at 1-888-777-0463.**

■ **Do the chapter test at the end of the chapter.** Check the answers and use the objective symbols at the back of the book as a reference for where to review.

■ **Ask former students for old exams.** Working such exams can be very helpful and allows you to see what various professors think is important.

■ **When taking a test, read each question carefully and try to do all the questions the first time through, but pace yourself.** Answer all the questions, and mark those to recheck if you have time at the end. Very often, your first hunch will be correct.

■ **Try to write your test in a neat and orderly manner.** Very often, your instructor tries to give you partial credit when grading an exam. If your test paper is sloppy and disorderly, it is difficult to award partial credit. Working neatly, you can ease such a task for the instructor.

a Write exponential notation.

1. $3 \cdot 3 \cdot 3 \cdot 3 \cdot 3$

2. $2 \cdot 2 \cdot 2 \cdot 2 \cdot 2$

3. $5 \cdot 5$

4. $13 \cdot 13 \cdot 13$

5. $7 \cdot 7 \cdot 7 \cdot 7 \cdot 7$

6. $10 \cdot 10$

7. $10 \cdot 10 \cdot 10$

8. $1 \cdot 1 \cdot 1 \cdot 1$

b Evaluate.

9. 7^2

10. 5^3

11. 9^3

12. 10^2

13. 12^4

14. 10^5

15. 11^2

16. 6^3

c Simplify.

17. $12 + (6 + 4)$

18. $(12 + 6) + 18$

19. $52 - (40 - 8)$

20. $(52 - 40) - 8$

21. $1000 \div (100 \div 10)$

22. $(1000 \div 100) \div 10$

23. $(256 \div 64) \div 4$

24. $256 \div (64 \div 4)$

25. $(2 + 5)^2$

26. $2^2 + 5^2$

27. $(11 - 8)^2 - (18 - 16)^2$

28. $(32 - 27)^3 + (19 + 1)^3$

29. $16 \cdot 24 + 50$

30. $23 + 18 \cdot 20$

31. $83 - 7 \cdot 6$

32. $10 \cdot 7 - 4$

33. $10 \cdot 10 - 3 \cdot 4$

34. $90 - 5 \cdot 5 \cdot 2$

35. $4^3 \div 8 - 4$

36. $8^2 - 8 \cdot 2$

37. $17 \cdot 20 - (17 + 20)$

38. $1000 \div 25 - (15 + 5)$

39. $6 \cdot 10 - 4 \cdot 10$

40. $3 \cdot 8 + 5 \cdot 8$

41. $300 \div 5 + 10$

42. $144 \div 4 - 2$

43. $3 \cdot (2 + 8)^2 - 5 \cdot (4 - 3)^2$

44. $7 \cdot (10 - 3)^2 - 2 \cdot (3 + 1)^2$

45. $4^2 + 8^2 \div 2^2$

46. $6^2 - 3^4 \div 3^3$

47. $10^3 - 10 \cdot 6 - (4 + 5 \cdot 6)$

48. $7^2 + 20 \cdot 4 - (28 + 9 \cdot 2)$

49. $6 \cdot 11 - (7 + 3) \div 5 - (6 - 4)$

50. $8 \times 9 - (12 - 8) \div 4 - (10 - 7)$

51. $120 - 3^3 \cdot 4 \div (5 \cdot 6 - 6 \cdot 4)$

52. $80 - 2^4 \cdot 15 \div (7 \cdot 5 - 45 \div 3)$

53. Find the average of 10 sec, 9 sec, 8 sec, 12 sec, and 11 sec.

54. Find the average of 28 days, 29 days, and 36 days.

55. Find the average of $64, $97, and $121.

56. Find the average of four test grades of 86, 92, 80, and 78.

d Simplify.

57. $8 \times 13 + \{42 \div [18 - (6 + 5)]\}$

58. $72 \div 6 - \{2 \times [9 - (4 \times 2)]\}$

59. $[14 - (3 + 5) \div 2] - [18 \div (8 - 2)]$

60. $[92 \times (6 - 4) \div 8] + [7 \times (8 - 3)]$

61. $(82 - 14) \times [(10 + 45 \div 5) - (6 \cdot 6 - 5 \cdot 5)]$

62. $(18 \div 2) \cdot \{[(9 \cdot 9 - 1) \div 2] - [5 \cdot 20 - (7 \cdot 9 - 2)]\}$

63. $4 \times \{(200 - 50 \div 5) - [(35 \div 7) \cdot (35 \div 7) - 4 \times 3]\}$

64. $15(23 - 4 \cdot 2)^3 \div (3 \cdot 25)$

65. $\{[18 - 2 \cdot 6] - [40 \div (17 - 9)]\} + \{48 - 13 \times 3 + [(50 - 7 \cdot 5) + 2]\}$

66. $(19 - 2^4)^5 - (141 \div 47)^2$

67. $\mathbf{D_W}$ Consider the problem in Example 8 of Section 1.8. How can you translate the problem to a single equation involving what you have learned about order of operations? How does the single equation relate to how we solved the problem?

68. $\mathbf{D_W}$ Consider the expressions $9 - (4 \cdot 2)$ and $(3 \cdot 4)^2$. Are the parentheses necessary in each case? Explain.

SKILL MAINTENANCE

Solve. [1.7b]

69. $x + 341 = 793$

70. $4197 + x = 5032$

71. $7 \cdot x = 91$

72. $1554 = 42 \cdot y$

73. $3240 = y + 898$

74. $6000 = 1102 + t$

75. $25 \cdot t = 625$

76. $10{,}000 = 100 \cdot t$

Solve. [1.8a]

77. *Colorado.* The state of Colorado is roughly the shape of a rectangle that is 270 mi by 380 mi. What is its area?

78. On a long four-day trip, a family bought the following amounts of gasoline for their motor home:

23 gallons, 24 gallons,
26 gallons, 25 gallons.

How much gasoline did they buy in all?

SYNTHESIS

79. $\mathbf{D_W}$ Is it possible to compute an average of several numbers on a calculator without using parentheses or the $\boxed{=}$ key?

80. $\mathbf{D_W}$ Is the average of two sets of numbers the same as the average of the two averages? Why or why not?

Each of the answers in Exercises 81–83 is incorrect. First find the correct answer. Then place as many parentheses as needed in the expression in order to make the incorrect answer correct.

81. $1 + 5 \cdot 4 + 3 = 36$

82. $12 \div 4 + 2 \cdot 3 - 2 = 2$

83. $12 \div 4 + 2 \cdot 3 - 2 = 4$

84. Use one occurrence each of 1, 2, 3, 4, 5, 6, 7, 8, and 9 and any of the symbols $+$, $-$, $\times$, $\div$, and $(\,)$ to represent 100.

The review that follows is meant to prepare you for a chapter exam. It consists of two parts. The first part is a checklist of the Study Tips referred to in this chapter. The second part is the Review Exercises. These provide practice exercises for the exam, together with references to section objectives so you can go back and review. Before beginning, stop and look back over the skills you have obtained. What skills in mathematics do you have now that you did not have before studying this chapter?

STUDY TIPS CHECKLIST

The foundation of all your study skills is TIME!	☐ Have you found adequate time to study?
	☐ Have you determined the location of the learning resource centers on your campus, such as a mathlab, tutor center, and your instructor's office?
	☐ Are you stopping to work the margin exercises when directed to do so?
	☐ Are you doing your homework as soon as possible after class?
	☐ Are you using the textbook supplements, such as the Math Tutor Center, the *Student's Solutions Manual*, and the videotapes?

REVIEW EXERCISES

The review exercises that follow are for practice. Answers are given at the back of the book. If you miss an exercise, restudy the objective indicated in blue square brackets next to the exercise or direction line.

Write expanded notation.   [1.1b]

1. 2793

2. 56,078

Write standard notation.   [1.1b]

3. 8 thousands + 6 hundreds + 6 tens + 9 ones

4. 9 ten thousands + 8 hundreds + 4 tens + 4 ones

Write a word name.   [1.1c]

5. 67,819

6. 2,781,427

Write standard notation.   [1.1c]

7. Four hundred seventy-six thousand, five hundred eighty-eight

8. *e-books.* The publishing industry predicts that sales of digital books will reach two billion, four hundred thousand by 2005.
Source: Andersen Consulting

9. What does the digit 8 mean in 4,678,952? [1.1a]

10. In 13,768,940, what digit tells the number of millions? [1.1a]

Add. [1.2b]

11. 7304 + 6968

12. 27,609 + 38,415

13. 2743 + 4125 + 6274 + 8956

14. $\begin{array}{r} 9\ 1,4\ 2\ 6 \\ +\ \ \ \ 7,4\ 9\ 5 \\ \hline \end{array}$

15. Write a related addition sentence: [1.3b]
$10 - 6 = 4.$

16. Write two related subtraction sentences: [1.3b]
$8 + 3 = 11.$

Subtract. [1.3d]

17. 8045 − 2897   **18.** 8465 − 7312

19. 6003 − 3729   **20.** $\begin{array}{r} 3\ 7,4\ 0\ 5 \\ -\ 1\ 9,6\ 4\ 8 \\ \hline \end{array}$

Round 345,759 to the nearest: [1.4a]

21. Hundred.   **22.** Ten.

23. Thousand.

Estimate the sum, difference, or product by first rounding to the nearest hundred. Show your work. [1.4b], [1.5b]

24. 41,348 + 19,749   **25.** 38,652 − 24,549

26. 396 · 748

Use < or > for ☐ to write a true sentence. [1.4c]

27. 67 ☐ 56   **28.** 1 ☐ 23

Multiply. [1.5a]

29. 700 · 600   **30.** 7846 · 800

31. 726 · 698   **32.** 587 · 47

33. $\begin{array}{r} 8\ 3\ 0\ 5 \\ \times\ \ \ \ 6\ 4\ 2 \\ \hline \end{array}$

34. Write a related multiplication sentence: [1.6b]
$56 \div 8 = 7.$

35. Write two related division sentences: [1.6b]
$13 \cdot 4 = 52.$

Divide. [1.6c]

36. 63 ÷ 5   **37.** 80 ÷ 16

38. $7\overline{)6\ 3\ 9\ 4}$ **39.** 3073 ÷ 8

40. $6\ 0\overline{)2\ 8\ 6}$ **41.** 4266 ÷ 79

42. $3\ 8\overline{)1\ 7,1\ 7\ 6}$ **43.** $1\ 4\overline{)7\ 0,1\ 1\ 2}$

44. 52,668 ÷ 12

Solve. [1.7b]

45. $46 \cdot n = 368$ **46.** $47 + x = 92$

47. $x = 782 - 236$

48. Write exponential notation: $4 \cdot 4 \cdot 4.$ [1.9a]

Evaluate. [1.9b]

49. 10^4 **50.** 6^2

Simplify. [1.9c, d]

51. $8 \cdot 6 + 17$

52. $10 \cdot 24 - (18 + 2) \div 4 - (9 - 7)$

53. $7 + (4 + 3)^2$

54. $7 + 4^2 + 3^2$

55. $(80 \div 16) \times [(20 - 56 \div 8) + (8 \cdot 8 - 5 \cdot 5)]$

56. Find the average of 157, 170, and 168.

Solve. [1.8a]

57. *Oak Desk.* Natasha has $196 and wants to buy an oak computer roll-top desk for $698. How much more does she need?
Source: Oak Express®

Desk Just... $698

Oak Express Excalibur 48"
Computer Roll-Top Desk
Accommodates most tower or desk-top computers. Slide-out mouse pad and keyboard tray. Available in light and dark finishes.Constructed of solid oak and oak veneers.

58. Toni has $406 in her checking account. She is paid $78 for a part-time job and deposits that in her checking account. How much is then in her account?

59. *Lincoln-Head Pennies.* In 1909, the first Lincoln-head pennies were minted. Seventy-three years later, these pennies were first minted with a decreased copper content. In what year was the copper content reduced?

60. A beverage company packed 222 cans of soda into 6-can cartons. How many cartons did they fill?

61. An apple farmer keeps bees in her orchard to help pollinate the apple blossoms so more apples will be produced. The bees from an average beehive can pollinate 30 surrounding trees during one growing season. The farmer has 420 trees. How many beehives does she need to pollinate them all?
Source: Jordan Orchards, Westminster, PA

62. An apartment builder bought 3 electric ranges at $299 each and 4 dishwashers at $379 each. What was the total cost?

63. A family budgets $4950 for food and clothing and $3585 for entertainment. The yearly income of the family was $28,283. How much of this income remained after these two allotments?

64. A chemist has 2753 mL of alcohol. How many 20-mL beakers can be filled? How much will be left over?

65. *Olympic Trampoline.* Shown below is an Olympic trampoline. Find the area and the perimeter of the trampoline. [1.2c], [1.5c]
Source: International Trampoline Industry Association, Inc.

14 ft

7 ft

66. $^{\mathbf{D}}\mathbf{W}$ Write a problem for a classmate to solve. Design the problem so that the solution is "Each of the 144 bottles will contain 8 oz of hot sauce." [1.8a]

67. $^{\mathbf{D}}\mathbf{W}$ Is subtraction associative? Why or why not? [1.3b]

SYNTHESIS

68. 🖩 Determine the missing digit d. [1.5a]

$$\begin{array}{r} 9\,d \\ \times\ d\,2 \\ \hline 8\,0\,3\,6 \end{array}$$

69. 🖩 Determine the missing digits a and b. [1.6c]

$$\begin{array}{r} 9\,a\,1 \\ 2\,b\,1\,\overline{)\,2\,3\,6{,}4\,2\,1} \end{array}$$

70. A mining company calculates that a crew must tunnel 2000 ft into a mountain to reach a deposit of copper ore. Each day the crew tunnels about 500 ft. Each night, if they haven't reached the copper, about 200 ft of loose rocks roll back into the tunnel. How many days will it take the mining company to reach the copper deposit? [1.8a]

Chapter Test

1. Write expanded notation: 8843.

2. Write a word name: 38,403,277.

3. In the number 546,789, which digit tells the number of hundred thousands?

Add.

4.
```
  6 8 1 1
+ 3 1 7 8
```

5.
```
  4 5,8 8 9
+ 1 7,9 0 2
```

6.
```
  1 2
    8
    3
    7
+   4
```

7.
```
  6 2 0 3
+ 4 3 1 2
```

Subtract.

8.
```
  7 9 8 3
- 4 3 5 3
```

9.
```
  2 9 7 4
- 1 9 3 5
```

10.
```
  8 9 0 7
- 2 0 5 9
```

11.
```
  2 3,0 6 7
- 1 7,8 9 2
```

Multiply.

12.
```
  4 5 6 8
×       9
```

13.
```
  8 8 7 6
×     6 0 0
```

14.
```
  6 5
× 3 7
```

15.
```
  6 7 8
× 7 8 8
```

Divide.

16. 15 ÷ 4

17. 420 ÷ 6

18. 8 9) 8 6 3 3

19. 4 4) 3 5,4 2 8

Solve.

20. *Hostess DingDongs®.* Hostess packages its DingDong® snack products in 12-packs. It manufactures 22,231 cakes. How many 12-packs can it fill? How many will be left over?

21. *Largest States.* The following table lists the five largest states in terms of their area. Find the total area of these states.

STATE	AREA (square miles)
Alaska	591,004
Texas	266,807
California	158,706
Montana	147,046
New Mexico	121,593

Source: The New York Times Almanac

22. *Pool Tables.* The Hartford™ pool table made by Brunswick Billiards comes in three sizes of playing area: 50 in. by 100 in., 44 in. by 88 in., and 38 in. by 76 in.

    a) Find the perimeter and the area of the playing area of each table.

    b) By how much area does the large table exceed the small table?

Source: Brunswick Billiards

23. *Patents Issued.* There were 169,094 patents issued in 1999. This was 70,018 more than in 1990. How many patents were issued in 1990?

Source: U.S. Patent and Trademark Office

24. A sack of oranges weighs 27 lb. A sack of apples weighs 32 lb. Find the total weight of 16 bags of oranges and 43 bags of apples.

25. A box contains 5000 staples. How many staplers can be filled from the box if each stapler holds 250 staples?

Solve.

26. $28 + x = 74$

27. $169 \div 13 = n$

28. $38 \cdot y = 532$

Round 34,578 to the nearest:

29. Thousand.

30. Ten.

31. Hundred.

Estimate the sum, difference, or product by first rounding to the nearest hundred. Show your work.

32.
$$\begin{array}{r} 2\,3{,}6\,4\,9 \\ +\ 5\,4{,}7\,4\,6 \\ \hline \end{array}$$

33.
$$\begin{array}{r} 5\,4{,}7\,5\,1 \\ -\ 2\,3{,}6\,4\,9 \\ \hline \end{array}$$

34.
$$\begin{array}{r} 8\,2\,4 \\ \times\ 4\,8\,9 \\ \hline \end{array}$$

Use $<$ or $>$ for $\square$ to write a true sentence.

35. $34 \,\square\, 17$

36. $117 \,\square\, 157$

37. Write exponential notation: $12 \cdot 12 \cdot 12 \cdot 12$.

Evaluate.

38. 7^3

39. 2^3

Simplify.

40. $(10 - 2)^2$

41. $10^2 - 2^2$

42. $(25 - 15) \div 5$

43. $8 \times \{(20 - 11) \cdot [(12 + 48) \div 6 - (9 - 2)]\}$

44. $2^4 + 24 \div 12$

45. Find the average of 97, 98, 87, and 86.

$\boxed{\text{SYNTHESIS}}$

46. An open cardboard shoe box is 8 in. wide, 12 in. long, and 6 in. high. How many square inches of cardboard are used?

47. Cara spends $229 a month to repay her student loan. If she has already paid $9160 on the 10-yr loan, how many payments remain?

48. Jennie scores three 90's, four 80's, and a 74 on her eight quizzes. Find her average.

49. Use trials to find the single-digit number a for which
$$359 - 46 + a \div 3 \times 25 - 7^2 = 339.$$

Introduction to Integers and Algebraic Expressions

Gateway to Chapter 2

This chapter is actually our first look at algebra. We introduce numbers called *integers* that represent an extension of the set of whole numbers. After learning to add, subtract, multiply, and divide integers, we will begin studying *algebraic expressions*. We will also expand upon our earlier work in solving equations.

Real-World Application

Carla is completing the production work on a track that is to appear on her band's upcoming CD. In doing so, she resets her digital recorder to 0, advances the recording 16 sec, and then reverses the recording 25 sec. What reading will then appear on the recorder?

This problem appears as Exercise 77 in Exercise Set 2.3.

1. Tell which integers correspond to the following situation: Bill lost $75 in Reno and Janet won $67 in Las Vegas. [2.1a]

Use either < or > for ☐ to form a true sentence. [2.1b]

2. -9 ☐ 0

3. -2 ☐ -17

4. -12 ☐ 7

Find the absolute value. [2.1c]

5. $|73|$

6. $|-57|$

7. Find $-x$ when x is -32. [2.1d]

8. Find the opposite, or additive inverse, of -17. [2.1d]

Compute and simplify.

9. $-6 + (-12)$ [2.2a]

10. $15 + (-9)$ [2.2a]

11. $-19 + 10$ [2.2a]

12. $-13 + 13$ [2.2a]

13. $-9 - 7$ [2.3a]

14. $-8 - (-10)$ [2.3a]

15. $7 - (-11)$ [2.3a]

16. $3 - 9$ [2.3a]

17. $-37 \cdot 0$ [2.4a]

18. $-8 \cdot (-6)$ [2.4a]

19. -3^4 [2.4b]

20. $45 \div (-9)$ [2.5a]

21. $(-33) \div (-3)$ [2.5a]

22. $\dfrac{-400}{5}$ [2.5a]

23. $\dfrac{0}{-7}$ [2.5a]

24. $10 \div 2 \cdot 5 - (-4)^2$ [2.5b]

25. Evaluate $7a - b$ for $a = -2$ and $b = -1$. [2.6a]

Use the distributive law to write an equivalent expression. [2.6b]

26. $4(x + 9)$

27. $7(2x - 3y - 1)$

Combine like terms. [2.7a]

28. $3a + 12a$

29. $-9x + 7 - x + 8$

30. Find the perimeter of a 12-ft by 20-ft deck. [2.7b]

Solve.

31. $-3x = 54$ [2.8b]

32. $-5 + t = 17$ [2.8a]

33. $4x - 7 = 29$ [2.8d]

34. Add: $(5x^2 - 6x + 3) + (7x^2 + 4x - 13)$. [2.9a]

35. Write two equivalent expressions for the opposite of $6a^3b^2 - 7a^2b - 5$. [2.9b]

36. Subtract: $(3x^2 - 6x + 8) - (7x^2 + 11x - 13)$. [2.9c]

Evaluate.

37. 57^1 [2.10a]

38. $(-18)^0$ [2.10a]

39. $2x^3 - 5x^2$, for $x = 4$ [2.10d]

2.1 INTEGERS AND THE NUMBER LINE

Objectives

a   Tell which integers correspond to a real-world situation.

b   Form a true sentence using $<$ or $>$.

c   Find the absolute value of any integer.

d   Find the opposite of any integer.

In this section, we extend the set of whole numbers to form the set of *integers*. You have probably already used negative numbers. For example, the outside temperature could drop to *negative five* degrees and a credit card statement could indicate activity of *negative forty-eight* dollars.

To create the set of integers, we begin with the set of whole numbers, 0, 1, 2, 3, and so on. For each number 1, 2, 3, and so on, we obtain a new number the same number of units to the left of zero.

For the number 1, there is the *opposite* number -1 (negative 1).

For the number 2, there is the *opposite* number -2 (negative 2).

For the number 3, there is the *opposite* number -3 (negative 3), and so on.

The **integers** consist of the whole numbers and these new numbers. We illustrate them on a number line as follows.

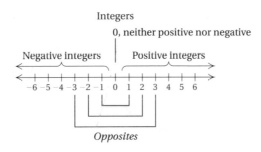

The integers to the left of zero on the number line are called **negative integers** and those to the right of zero are called **positive integers.** Zero is neither positive nor negative and serves as its own opposite.

INTEGERS

The **integers:** $\ldots, -5, -4, -3, -2, -1, 0, 1, 2, 3, 4, 5, \ldots$

---

a   Integers and the Real World

Integers correspond to many real-world problems and situations. The following examples will help you get ready to translate problem situations to mathematical language.

EXAMPLE 1   Tell which integer corresponds to this situation: Researcher Robert Ballard discovered the wreck of the *Titanic* 12,500 ft below sea level.
Source: Office of Naval Research

12,500 below sea level corresponds to the integer $-12,500$.

EXAMPLE 2   Tell which integers correspond to this situation: Elaine reversed the disc in her DVD player 17 min and then advanced it 25 min.

The integers -17 and 25 correspond to the situation. The integer -17 corresponds to the reversing and 25 corresponds to the advancing.

Tell which integers correspond to each situation.

1. Golf Score. Tiger Woods' score in winning the 2000 PGA Championship was 18 under par.
Source: U.S. Golf Association

2. The highest temperature ever recorded in the United States was 134° in Death Valley, California, on July 10, 1913. The coldest temperature ever recorded in the United States was 80° below zero in Prospect Creek, Alaska, in January 1971.

3. At 10 sec before liftoff, ignition occurs. At 148 sec after liftoff, the first stage is detached from the rocket.

4. Jacob owes $137 to the bookstore. Fortunately, he has $289 in a savings account.

Answers on page A-6

Some common uses for negative integers are as follows:

Time:	Before an event
Temperature:	Degrees below zero
Money:	Amount lost, spent, owed, or withdrawn
Elevation:	Depth below sea level
Travel:	Motion in the backward (reverse) direction

Do Exercises 1–4.

b   Order on the Number Line

Numbers are written in order on the number line, increasing as we move to the right. For any two numbers on the line, the one to the left is *less than* the one to the right.

Since the symbol < means "is less than," the sentence $-5 < 9$ is read "-5 is less than 9." The symbol > means "is greater than," so the sentence $-4 > -8$ is read "-4 is greater than -8."

EXAMPLES Use either < or > for □ to form a true sentence.

3. $-9 \,□\, 2$ \quad Since -9 is to the left of 2, we have $-9 < 2$.

4. $7 \,□\, -13$ \quad Since 7 is to the right of -13, we have $7 > -13$.

5. $-19 \,□\, -6$ \quad Since -19 is to the left of -6, we have $-19 < -6$.

Do Exercises 5–8 on the next page.

c   Absolute Value

From the number line, we see that some integers, like 5 and -5, are the same distance from zero.

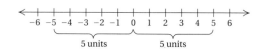

How far is 5 from 0? How far is -5 from 0? Since distance is never negative (it is "nonnegative," that is, either positive or zero), it follows that both 5 and -5 are 5 units from 0.

ABSOLUTE VALUE

The **absolute value** of a number is its distance from zero on a number line. We use the symbol $|x|$ to represent the absolute value of a number x.

Like distance, the absolute value of a number is never negative; it is always either positive or zero.

EXAMPLES Find the absolute value of each number.

6. $|-3|$ The distance of -3 from 0 is 3, so $|-3| = 3$.
7. $|25|$ The distance of 25 from 0 is 25, so $|25| = 25$.
8. $|0|$ The distance of 0 from 0 is 0, so $|0| = 0$.
9. $|-17|$ The distance of -17 from 0 is 17, so $|-17| = 17$.
10. $|9|$ The distance of 9 from 0 is 9, so $|9| = 9$.

> **To find a number's absolute value:**
> 1. If a number is positive or zero, use the number itself.
> 2. If a number is negative, make the number positive.

Do Exercises 9–12.

d   Opposites, or Additive Inverses

The set of integers is represented below on a number line.

Given a number on one side of 0, we can get a number on the other side by *reflecting* the number across zero. For example, the *reflection* of 2 is -2.

We can read -2 as "negative 2," "the opposite of 2," or "the additive inverse of 2." We read $-x$ as "the opposite of x."

NOTATION FOR OPPOSITES

The **opposite** of a number x is written $-x$.

EXAMPLE 11 If x is -3, find $-x$.

To find the opposite of x when x is -3, we reflect -3 to the other side of 0.

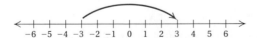

We have $-(-3) = 3$. The opposite of -3 is 3.

EXAMPLE 12 Find $-x$ when x is 0.

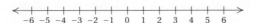

When we try to reflect 0 "to the other side of 0," we go nowhere:

$-x = 0$ when x is 0.

Use either $<$ or $>$ for $\square$ to form a true sentence.

5. $13 \; \square \; 7$ **6.** $12 \; \square \; -3$

7. $-13 \; \square \; -3$ **8.** $-4 \; \square \; -20$

Find the absolute value.

9. $|18|$ **10.** $|-9|$

11. $|-29|$ **12.** $|52|$

Answers on page A-6

CALCULATOR CORNER

To enter a negative number on most calculators, we use the $\boxed{+/-}$ key. This key gives the opposite of whatever number is currently displayed. Thus, to enter -27, we press $\boxed{2}\boxed{7}\boxed{+/-}$. Some graphing calculators have a $\boxed{(-)}$ key. To enter -27 on such a graphing calculator, we simply press $\boxed{(-)}\boxed{2}\boxed{7}$. Be careful not to confuse the $\boxed{+/-}$ or $\boxed{(-)}$ key with the $\boxed{-}$ key which is used for subtraction.

Exercises: Press the appropriate keys so that your calculator displays each of the following numbers.

1. -63
2. -419
3. -2004
4. List the keystrokes needed to compute $-(7 - 4)$.

In each case draw a number line, if necessary.

13. Find $-x$ when x is 1.

14. Find $-x$ when x is -2.

15. Evaluate $-x$ when x is 0.

Change the sign. (Find the opposite, or additive inverse.)

16. -4 **17.** -13

18. 39   **19.** 0

20. If x is 7, find $-(-x)$.

21. If x is 1, find $-(-x)$.

22. Evaluate $-(-x)$ for $x = -6$.

23. Evaluate $-(-x)$ for $x = -2$.

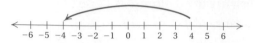

In Examples 11 and 12, the variable was replaced with a number. When this occurs, we say that we are **evaluating** the expression.

EXAMPLE 13 Evaluate $-x$ when x is 4.

To find the opposite of x when x is 4, we reflect 4 to the other side of 0.

We have $-(4) = -4$. The opposite of 4 is -4.

Do Exercises 13–15.

A negative number is sometimes said to have a negative *sign*. A positive number is said to have a positive sign, even though it rarely is written in.

EXAMPLES Determine the sign of each number.

14. -7 Negative   **15.** 23   Positive

Replacing a number with its opposite, or additive inverse, is sometimes called *changing the sign*.

EXAMPLES Change the sign (find the opposite, or additive inverse) of each number.

16. -6 $-(-6) = 6$ **17.** -10 $-(-10) = 10$
18. 0 $-(0) = 0$ **19.** 14 $-(14) = -14$

Do Exercises 16–19.

Note that when we change a number's sign twice, we return to the original number.

EXAMPLE 20 If x is 2, find $-(-x)$.

We replace x with 2 and find $-(-2)$.

We see from the figure that $-(-2) = 2$.

EXAMPLE 21 Evaluate $-(-x)$ for $x = -4$.

We replace x with -4 and find $-(-(-4))$.

Reflecting -4 to the other side of 0 and then back again gives us -4. Thus, $-(-(-4)) = -(4) = -4$.

Do Exercises 20–23.

It is important not to confuse parentheses with absolute value symbols.

EXAMPLE 22 Evaluate $-|-x|$ for $x = 2$.

We have $-|-x| = -|-2|$. Since $|-2| = 2$, it follows that $-|-2| = -2$.

Contrast the results of Examples 20 and 22. Note that $-(-2) = 2$, whereas $-|-2| = -2$.

Do Exercises 24 and 25.

24. Find $-|-7|$.

25. Find $-|-39|$.

Study Tips

SEEKING HELP?

Using some or all of these resources can make studying easier and more enjoyable.

A variety of resources are available to help you learn math.

- **Textbook supplements.** Are you aware of all the supplements that exist for this textbook? See the preface for a description of each supplement: the *Student Solutions Manual*, a complete set of lessons in video or CD form, tutorial software, and the new Web site at www.MyMathLab.com.

- **The Internet.** Our on-line World Wide Web supplement provides additional practice resources. If you have Internet access, you can reach this site through the address:

    http://www.MyMathLab.com

    It contains many helpful ideas as well as many links to other resources for learning mathematics.

- **Your college or university.** Your own college or university probably has resources to enhance your math learning.

    1. There may be a learning lab or tutoring center for drop-in tutoring.

    2. There may be study skills workshops or group tutoring sessions tailored for the specific course you are taking.

    3. Often, there is a bulletin board or network where you can locate the names of experienced private tutors.

    4. You might be able to find classmates interested in forming a study group.

- **Your instructor.** Although it may seem obvious, you should consider an often overlooked resource: your instructor. Find out your instructor's office hours and make it a point to visit when you need additional help. Many instructors welcome student e-mail. If you are hesitant to visit your instructor, e-mail may prove quite useful.

Answers on page A-6

For Extra Help

Digital Video Tutor CD 1 Videotape 2   InterAct Math   Math Tutor Center   MathXL   MyMathLab

a   Tell which integers correspond to each situation.

1. Starbucks stock recently dropped 2 points.

2. Redbank, Montana, once recorded a temperature of 70° below zero.

3. The recycling program for Colchester once received $40 for a ton of office paper. More recently, they've had to pay $15 to get rid of a ton of office paper.

4. The space shuttle stood ready, 3 sec before liftoff. Solid fuel rockets were released 128 sec after liftoff.

5. At tax time, Janine received an $820 refund while David owed $541.

6. *Oceanography.* At a depth of 2438 meters researchers found the first hydrothermal vent ever seen by humans. This depth is approximately 8000 ft below sea level.
Source: Office of Naval Research

7. *Geography.* Death Valley, California, is 280 ft below sea level. Mt. Whitney, the highest point in California, has an elevation of 14,491 ft.

8. *Geography.* The Dead Sea, between Jordan and Israel, is 1286 ft below sea level; Mt. Rainier in Washington State is 14,410 ft above sea level.

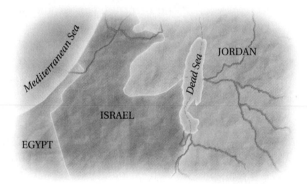

b   Use either < or > for ☐ to form a true sentence.

9. −8 ☐ 0   **10.** 7 ☐ 0   **11.** 9 ☐ 0   **12.** −7 ☐ 0   **13.** 8 ☐ −8

14. 6 ☐ −6   **15.** −6 ☐ −4   **16.** −1 ☐ −7   **17.** −8 ☐ −5   **18.** −5 ☐ −3

19. −13 ☐ −9   **20.** −5 ☐ −11   **21.** −3 ☐ −4   **22.** −6 ☐ −5

c Find the absolute value.

23. $|57|$ **24.** $|11|$ **25.** $|0|$ **26.** $|-4|$ **27.** $|-24|$

28. $|-36|$ **29.** $|53|$ **30.** $|54|$ **31.** $|-8|$ **32.** $|-79|$

d Find $-x$ when x is each of the following.

33. -7 **34.** -6 **35.** 7 **36.** 6 **37.** 0

38. -15 **39.** -19 **40.** 50 **41.** 42 **42.** -73

Change the sign. (Find the opposite, or additive inverse.)

43. -8 **44.** -7 **45.** 7 **46.** 10 **47.** -29

48. -14 **49.** -22 **50.** 0 **51.** 1 **52.** -53

Evaluate $-(-x)$ when x is each of the following.

53. 7 **54.** -8 **55.** -9 **56.** 3 **57.** -17 **58.** -19

59. 23 **60.** 0 **61.** -49 **62.** 73 **63.** 85 **64.** -37

Evaluate $-|-x|$ when x is each of the following.

65. 47 **66.** 92 **67.** 345 **68.** 729

69. 0 **70.** 1 **71.** -8 **72.** -3

73. $\mathbf{D_W}$ Does $-x$ always represent a negative number? Why or why not?

74. $\mathbf{D_W}$ Explain in your own words why $-(-x) = x$.

SKILL MAINTENANCE

75. Add: $327 + 498$. [1.2b]

76. Evaluate: 5^3. [1.9b]

77. Multiply: $209 \cdot 34$. [1.5a]

78. Solve: $300 \cdot x = 1200$. [1.7b]

79. Evaluate: 9^2. [1.9b]

80. Multiply: $31 \cdot 50$. [1.5a]

81. Simplify: $5(8 - 6)$. [1.9c]

82. Simplify: $7(9 - 3)$. [1.9c]

SYNTHESIS

83. $\mathbf{D_W}$ If $a > b$ is true, does it follow that $-b > -a$ is also true? Why or why not?

84. $\mathbf{D_W}$ Does $|x|$ always represent a positive number? Why or why not?

85. ▦ On your calculator list the sequence of keystrokes needed to find the opposite of the sum of 549 and 387.

86. ▦ On your calculator list the sequence of keystrokes needed to find the opposite of the product of 438 and 97.

87. ▦ List the sequence of keystrokes needed to find the opposite of the absolute value of the difference of 37 and 29.

Simplify.

88. $-|3|$

89. $-|-8|$

90. $-|-2|$

91. $-|7|$

Solve. Consider only integer replacements.

92. $|x| = 7$

93. $|x| < 2$

94. Simplify $-(-x)$, $-(-(-x))$, and $-(-(-(-x)))$.

95. List these integers in order from least to greatest.
$$2^{10}, \ -5, \ |-6|, \ 4, \ |3|, \ -100, \ 0, \ 2^7, \ 7^2, \ 10^2$$

CHAPTER 2: Introduction to Integers
and Algebraic Expressions

2.2

ADDITION OF INTEGERS

Objective

a Add integers without using a number line.

a Addition

To explain addition of integers, we can use the number line. Once our understanding is developed, we will streamline our approach.

> **ADDING INTEGERS**
>
> To perform the addition $a + b$, we start at a, and then move according to b.
>
> **a)** If b is positive, we move to the right.
> **b)** If b is negative, we move to the left.
> **c)** If b is 0, we stay at a.

EXAMPLE 1 Add: $2 + (-5)$.

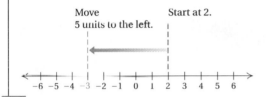

$2 + (-5) = -3$

EXAMPLE 2 Add: $-1 + (-3)$.

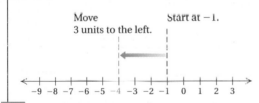

$-1 + (-3) = -4$

EXAMPLE 3 Add: $-4 + 9$.

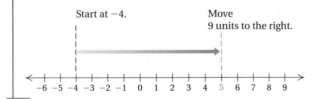

$-4 + 9 = 5$

Do Exercises 1–7.

You may have noticed a pattern in Example 2 and Margin Exercises 2 and 6. When two negative integers are added, the result is negative.

> **ADDING NEGATIVE INTEGERS**
>
> To add two negative integers, add their absolute values and change the sign (making the answer negative).

Add, using a number line.
1. $3 + (-4)$

2. $-3 + (-5)$

3. $-3 + 7$

4. $-5 + 5$

For each illustration, write a corresponding addition sentence.
5.

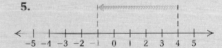

6.

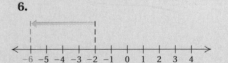

7.

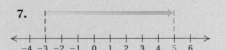

Answers on page A-6

Add. Do not use a number line except as a check.

8. $-5 + (-6)$

9. $-9 + (-3)$

10. $-20 + (-14)$

11. $-11 + (-11)$

Add.

12. $0 + (-17)$

13. $49 + 0$

14. $-56 + 0$

Add, using a number line only as a check.

15. $-4 + 6$

16. $-7 + 3$

17. $5 + (-7)$

18. $10 + (-7)$

EXAMPLES Add.

4. $-5 + (-7) = -12$ *Think*: Add the absolute values: $5 + 7 = 12$. Make the answer negative, -12.

5. $-8 + (-2) = -10$ We can visualize the number line without actually drawing it.

Do Exercises 8–11.

When the number 0 is added to any number, that number remains unchanged. For this reason, the number 0 is referred to as the *additive identity*.

EXAMPLES Add.

6. $-4 + 0 = -4$ **7.** $0 + (-9) = -9$ **8.** $17 + 0 = 17$

Do Exercises 12–14.

When we add a positive integer and a negative integer, as in Examples 1 and 3, the sign of the number with the greater absolute value is the sign of the answer.

ADDING POSITIVE AND NEGATIVE INTEGERS

To add a positive integer and a negative integer, find the difference of their absolute values.

a) If the negative integer has the greater absolute value, the answer is negative.

b) If the positive integer has the greater absolute value, the answer is positive.

EXAMPLES Add.

9. $3 + (-5) = -2$ *Think*: The absolute values are 3 and 5. The difference is 2. Since the negative number has the larger absolute value, the answer is *negative*, -2.

10. $11 + (-8) = 3$ *Think*: The absolute values are 11 and 8. The difference is 3. The positive number has the larger absolute value, so the answer is *positive*, 3.

11. $1 + (-6) = -5$ **12.** $-7 + 4 = -3$

13. $7 + (-3) = 4$ **14.** $-6 + 10 = 4$

Do Exercises 15–18.

Sometimes $-a$ is referred to as the *additive inverse* of a. This terminology is used because adding any number to its additive inverse always results in the additive identity, 0.

$$-8 + 8 = 0, \quad 14 + (-14) = 0, \quad \text{and} \quad 0 + 0 = 0.$$

Answers on page A-6

ADDING OPPOSITES

For any integer a,
$$a + (-a) = -a + a = 0.$$
(The sum of any number and its additive inverse, or opposite, is 0.)

Do Exercises 19–22.

Suppose we wish to add several numbers, positive and negative:

$$15 + (-2) + 7 + 14 + (-5) + (-12).$$

Because of the commutative and associative laws for addition, we can group the positive numbers together and the negative numbers together and add them separately. Then we add the two results.

EXAMPLE 15   Add: $15 + (-2) + 7 + 14 + (-5) + (-12)$.

First add the positive numbers: $15 + 7 + 14 = 36.$
Then add the negative numbers: $-2 + (-5) + (-12) = -19.$
Finally, add the results: $36 + (-19) = 17.$

We can also add in any other order we wish, say, from left to right:

$$
\begin{aligned}
15 + (-2) + 7 + 14 + (-5) + (-12) &= 13 + 7 + 14 + (-5) + (-12) \\
&= 20 + 14 + (-5) + (-12) \\
&= 34 + (-5) + (-12) \\
&= 29 + (-12) \\
&= 17.
\end{aligned}
$$

Do Exercises 23–25.

Add, using a number line only as a check.

19. $5 + (-5)$

20. $-6 + 6$

21. $-10 + 10$

22. $89 + (-89)$

Add.

23. $(-15) + (-37) + 25 + 42 + (-59) + (-14)$

24. $42 + (-81) + (-28) + 24 + 18 + (-31)$

25. $-35 + 17 + 14 + (-27) + 31 + (-12)$

Answers on page A-6

Study Tips

MAKING THE MOST OF HELP SESSIONS

Make the most of tutoring sessions by doing what you can ahead of time and knowing the topics with which you need help.

Often students find that a tutoring session would be helpful. The following comments may help you to make the most of such sessions.

- **Work on the topics *before* you go to the help or tutoring session.** Do not regard yourself as an empty cup that the tutor will fill with knowledge. The primary source of your ability to learn is within you. We have seen many students over the years go to help or tutoring sessions unprepared. When students do this they waste time and, in many cases, money. Go to class, study the textbook, and mark trouble spots. *Then* use the help and tutoring sessions to work on the trouble spots.

- **Do not be afraid to ask questions in these sessions!** The more you talk to your tutor, the more the tutor can help you.

- **Try being a "tutor" yourself.** Explaining a topic to someone else—a classmate, your instructor—is often the best way to master it.

2.2

EXERCISE SET

Digital Video Tutor CD 1 Videotape 2   InterAct Math   Math Tutor Center   MathXL   MyMathLab

a   Add, using a number line.

1. $-7 + 2$ **2.** $1 + (-5)$ **3.** $-9 + 5$ **4.** $8 + (-3)$ **5.** $-3 + 9$

6. $9 + (-9)$ **7.** $-7 + 7$ **8.** $-8 + (-5)$ **9.** $-3 + (-1)$ **10.** $-2 + (-9)$

11. $4 + (-9)$ **12.** $-4 + 13$ **13.** $-7 + (12)$ **14.** $-3 + 2$

Add. Use a number line only as a check.

15. $-3 + (-9)$ **16.** $-3 + (-7)$ **17.** $-6 + (-5)$ **18.** $-10 + (-14)$

19. $5 + (-5)$ **20.** $10 + (-10)$ **21.** $-2 + 2$ **22.** $-3 + 3$

23. $0 + 6$ **24.** $7 + 0$ **25.** $0 + (-8)$ **26.** $-7 + 0$

27. $-25 + 0$ **28.** $-43 + 0$ **29.** $0 + (-27)$ **30.** $0 + (-19)$

31. $17 + (-17)$ **32.** $-12 + 12$ **33.** $-23 + 23$ **34.** $11 + (-11)$

35. $9 + (-4)$ **36.** $-7 + 8$ **37.** $-4 + (-5)$ **38.** $0 + (-3)$

39. $0 + (-5)$ **40.** $10 + (-12)$ **41.** $14 + (-5)$ **42.** $-3 + 14$

43. $-11 + 8$ **44.** $0 + (-34)$ **45.** $-19 + 19$ **46.** $-10 + 3$

47. $-16 + 6$ **48.** $-15 + 5$ **49.** $-17 + (-7)$ **50.** $-15 + (-5)$

51. $11 + (-16)$ **52.** $-8 + 14$ **53.** $-15 + (-6)$ **54.** $-8 + 8$

55. $11 + (-9)$ **56.** $-14 + (-19)$ **57.** $-20 + (-6)$ **58.** $19 + (-19)$

59. $-15 + (-7) + 1$ **60.** $23 + (-5) + 4$ **61.** $30 + (-10) + 5$ **62.** $40 + (-8) + 5$

63. $-23 + (-9) + 15$ **64.** $-25 + 25 + (-9)$

65. $40 + (-40) + 6$ **66.** $63 + (-18) + 12$

67. $12 + (-65) + (-12)$ **68.** $-35 + (-63) + 35$

69. $-24 + (-37) + (-19) + (-45) + (-35)$ **70.** $75 + (-14) + (-17) + (-5)$

71. $28 + (-44) + 17 + 31 + (-94)$ **72.** $27 + (-54) + (-32) + 65 + 46$

73. $-19 + 73 + (-23) + 19 + (-73)$ **74.** $35 + (-51) + 29 + 51 + (-35)$

75. **Dw** Explain in your own words why the sum of two negative numbers is always negative.

76. **Dw** A student states "−45 is bigger than −21." What mistake do you think the student is making?

Subtract. [1.3d]

77. 543
       − 219

78. 6314
       − 2689

79. 2891
       − 1407

80. 43,213
       − 19,876

81. Write in expanded notation: 39,417. [1.1b]

82. Round to the nearest hundred: 746. [1.4a]

83. Round to the nearest thousand: 32,831. [1.4a]

84. Multiply: 42 · 56. [1.5a]

85. Divide: 288 ÷ 9. [1.6c]

86. Round to the nearest ten: 3496. [1.4a]

87. **Dw** Without using the words "absolute value," explain how to find the sum of a positive number and a negative number.

88. **Dw** Why is it important to understand the associative and commutative laws when adding more than two integers at a time?

Add.

89. $-|27| + (-|-13|)$

90. $|-32| + (-|15|)$

91. ⊞ $-3496 + (-2987)$

92. ⊞ $497 + (-3028)$

93. ⊞ $-7846 + 5978$

94. ⊞ $-7623 + 4839$

95. For what numbers x is $x + (-7)$ positive?

96. For what numbers x is $-7 + x$ negative?

Tell whether each sum is positive, negative, or zero.

97. If n is positive and m is negative, then $-n + m$ is _____.

98. If $n = m$ and n is negative, then $-n + (-m)$ is _____.

99. If n is negative and m is less than n, then $n + m$ is _____.

100. If n is positive and m is greater than n, then $n + m$ is _____.

CHAPTER 2: Introduction to Integers
and Algebraic Expressions

2.3 SUBTRACTION OF INTEGERS

Objectives

a Subtract integers and simplify combinations of additions and subtractions.

b Solve applied problems involving addition and subtraction of integers.

a Subtraction

We now consider subtraction of integers. To find the difference $a - b$, we look for a number to add to b that gives us a.

> **THE DIFFERENCE $a - b$**
>
> The difference $a - b$ is the number that when added to b gives a.

For example, $45 - 17 = 28$ because $28 + 17 = 45$. Let's consider an example in which the answer is a negative number.

EXAMPLE 1 Subtract: $5 - 8$.

Think: $5 - 8$ is the number that when added to 8 gives 5. What number can we add to 8 to get 5? The number must be negative. The number is -3:

$$5 - 8 = -3.$$

That is, $5 - 8 = -3$ because $8 + (-3) = 5$.

Do Exercises 1–3.

The definition of $a - b$ above does not always provide the most efficient way to subtract. From that definition, however, a faster way can be developed. Look for a pattern in the following table.

SUBTRACTIONS	ADDING AN OPPOSITE
$5 - 8 = -3$	$5 + (-8) = -3$
$6 - 4 = 10$	$6 + (-4) = -10$
$-7 - (-10) = 3$	$-7 + 10 = 3$
$-7 - (-2) = -5$	$-7 + 2 = -5$

Do Exercises 4–7.

Perhaps you have noticed that we can subtract by adding the opposite of the number being subtracted. This can always be done.

> **SUBTRACTING BY ADDING THE OPPOSITE**
>
> To subtract, add the opposite, or additive inverse, of the number being subtracted:
> $$a - b = a + (-b).$$

This is the method generally used for quick subtraction of integers.

Subtract.

1. $-6 - 4$

Think: What number can be added to 4 to get -6?

2. $-7 - (-10)$

Think: What number can be added to 10 to get -7?

3. $-7 - (-2)$

Think: What number can be added to -2 to get -7?

Complete the addition and compare with the subtraction.

4. $4 - 6 = -2$;

$4 + (-6) =$ _____

5. $-3 - 8 = -11$;

$-3 + (-8) =$ _____

6. $-5 - (-9) = 4$;

$-5 + 9 =$ _____

7. $-5 - (-3) = -2$;

$-5 + 3 =$ _____

Answers on page A-6

Equate each subtraction with a corresponding addition. Then write the equation in words.

8. $3 - 10$

9. $13 - 5$

10. $-12 - (-9)$

11. $-12 - 10$

12. $-14 - (-14)$

Subtract.

13. $7 - 11$

14. $-6 - 10$

15. $13 - 8$

16. $-7 - (-9)$

17. $-8 - (-2)$

18. $5 - (-8)$

Answers on page A-6

■ **EXAMPLES** Equate each subtraction with a corresponding addition. Then write the equation in words.

2. $3 - 7$;
  $3 - 7 = 3 + (-7)$ Adding the opposite of 7

Three minus seven is three plus negative seven.

3. $-14 - (-23)$;
  $-14 - (-23) = -14 + 23$ Adding the opposite of -23

Negative fourteen minus negative twenty-three is negative fourteen plus twenty-three.

4. $-12 - 30$;
  $-12 - 30 = -12 + (-30)$ Adding the opposite of 30

Negative twelve minus thirty is negative twelve plus negative thirty.

5. $-20 - (-17)$;
  $-20 - (-17) = -20 + 17$ Adding the opposite of -17

Negative twenty minus negative seventeen is negative twenty plus seventeen.

Do Exercises 8–12.

Once the subtraction has been rewritten as addition, we add as in Section 2.2.

■ **EXAMPLES**   Subtract.

6. $2 - 6 = 2 + (-6)$ The opposite of 6 is -6. We change the subtraction to addition and add the opposite. Instead of subtracting 6, we add -6.

  $= -4$

7. $4 - (-9) = 4 + 9$ The opposite of -9 is 9. We change the subtraction to addition and add the opposite. Instead of subtracting -9, we add 9.

  $= 13$

8. $-4 - 8 = -4 + (-8)$ We change the subtraction to addition and add the opposite. Instead of subtracting 8, we add -8.

  $= -12$

9. $10 - 7 = 10 + (-7)$ We change the subtraction to addition and add the opposite. Instead of subtracting 7, we add -7.

  $= 3$

10. $-4 - (-9) = -4 + 9$ Instead of subtracting -9, we add 9.
  $= 5$ To check, note that $5 + (-9) = -4$.

11. $-7 - (-3) = -7 + 3$ Instead of subtracting -3, we add 3.
  $= -4$ *Check:* $-4 + (-3) = -7$.

Do Exercises 13–18.

When several additions and subtractions occur together, we can make them all additions. The commutative law for addition can then be used.

EXAMPLE 12 Simplify: $-3 - (-5) - 9 + 4 - (-6)$.

$$
\begin{aligned}
-3 - (-5) - 9 + 4 - (-6) &= -3 + 5 + (-9) + 4 + 6 & \text{Adding opposites} \\
&= -3 + (-9) + 5 + 4 + 6 & \text{Using a} \\
& & \text{commutative law} \\
&= -12 + 15 \\
&= 3
\end{aligned}
$$

Do Exercises 19 and 20.

b   Applications and Problem Solving

We need addition and subtraction of integers to solve a variety of applied problems.

EXAMPLE 13 *Toll Roads.* The EZ Pass program allows drivers in the Northeast to travel certain toll roads without having to stop to pay. Instead, a transponder attached to the vehicle is scanned as the vehicle rolls through a toll booth. Recently the Ramones began a trip to New York City with a balance of $12 in their EZ Pass account. Their trip accumulated $15 in tolls, and because they overspent their balance, the Ramones had to pay $80 in fines and administrative fees. By how much were the Ramones in debt as a result of their travel on the toll roads?
  Source: State of New Jersey

  We solve by first subtracting the cost of the tolls from the original balance in the account. Then we subtract the cost of the fees and fines from the new balance in the account:

$$
\begin{aligned}
12 - 15 &= 12 + (-15) & \text{Adding the opposite of 15} \\
&= -3,
\end{aligned}
$$

and

$$
\begin{aligned}
-3 - 80 &= -3 + (-80) & \text{Adding the opposite of 80} \\
&= -83.
\end{aligned}
$$

The Ramones were $83 in debt as a result of their travel on toll roads.

Do Exercises 21 and 22.

Simplify.

19. $-6 - (-2) - (-4) - 12 + 3$

20. $9 - (-6) + 7 - 9 - 8 - (-20)$

21. EZ Pass.   (See Example 13.) Suppose the Ramones had a balance of $11 in their account, accumulated $25 in tolls, and had to pay $85 in fines and administrative fees. By how much would the Ramones be in debt?

22. Temperature Extremes.   In Churchill, Manitoba, Canada, the average daily low temperature in January is $-31°$ Celsius (C). The average daily low temperature in Key West, Florida, is 50° warmer. What is the average daily low temperature in Key West, Florida?

Answers on page A-6

Study Tips

DON'T USE CHECKING AS A CRUTCH

It is easy to become overdependent on the answer section.

When using the answers listed in the back of this book, try not to "work backward" from the answer. If you find that you frequently require two or more attempts to answer an exercise correctly, you probably need to work more carefully and/or reread the section preceding the exercise set. Remember that on quizzes and tests you have only one attempt to answer each question.

2.3

EXERCISE SET

Digital Video Tutor CD 1 Videotape 2 | InterAct Math | Math Tutor Center | MathXL | MyMathLab

a Subtract.

1. $2 - 7$

2. $3 - 8$

3. $0 - 8$

4. $0 - 9$

5. $-7 - (-4)$

6. $-6 - (-8)$

7. $-11 - (-11)$

8. $-6 - (-6)$

9. $13 - 17$

10. $14 - 19$

11. $20 - 27$

12. $30 - 4$

13. $-9 - (-4)$

14. $-7 - (-9)$

15. $-40 - (-40)$

16. $-9 - (-9)$

17. $7 - 7$

18. $9 - 9$

19. $7 - (-7)$

20. $4 - (-4)$

21. $8 - (-3)$

22. $-7 - 4$

23. $-6 - 8$

24. $6 - (-10)$

25. $-3 - (-9)$

26. $-14 - 2$

27. $1 - 9$

28. $2 - 8$

29. $-6 - (-5)$

30. $-4 - (-3)$

31. $8 - (-10)$

32. $5 - (-6)$

33. $0 - 10$

34. $0 - 23$

35. $-5 - (-2)$

36. $-3 - (-1)$

37. $-7 - 14$

38. $-9 - 16$

39. $0 - (-5)$

40. $0 - (-1)$

41. $-8 - 0$

42. $-9 - 0$

43. $7 - (-5)$

44. $7 - (-4)$

CHAPTER 2: Introduction to Integers
and Algebraic Expressions

45. $6 - 25$

46. $18 - 63$

47. $-42 - 26$

48. $-18 - 63$

49. $-72 - 9$

50. $-49 - 3$

51. $24 - (-92)$

52. $48 - (-73)$

53. $-50 - (-50)$

54. $-70 - (-70)$

55. $-30 - (-85)$

56. $-25 - (-15)$

Simplify.

57. $7 - (-5) + 4 - (-3)$

58. $-5 - (-8) + 3 - (-7)$

59. $-31 + (-28) - (-14) - 17$

60. $-43 - (-19) - (-21) + 25$

61. $-34 - 28 + (-33) - 44$

62. $39 + (-88) - 29 - (-83)$

63. $-93 - (-84) - 41 - (-56)$

64. $84 + (-99) + 44 - (-18) - 43$

65. $-5 - (-30) + 30 + 40 - (-12)$

66. $14 - (-50) + 20 - (-32)$

67. $132 - (-21) + 45 - (-21)$

68. $81 - (-20) - 14 - (-50) + 53$

b   Solve.

69. *Reading.*   Before falling asleep, Alicia read from the top of page 37 to the top of page 62 of her book. How many pages did she read?

70. *Writing.*   During a weekend retreat James wrote from the bottom of page 29 to the bottom of page 37 of his memoirs. How many pages did he write?

71. *Driving.*   At the start of his vacation the mileage reading on Cyrille's Echo was 23,409. If the reading at the end of the trip was 24,382, how far did Cyrille drive on his trip?

72. *Driving.*   Erin drove from mileage marker 72 to mileage marker 91. How far did she drive?

73. Through exercise, Rod went from 8 lb above his "ideal" body weight to 9 lb below it. How many pounds did Rod lose?

74. Laura has a charge of $476.89 on her credit card, but she then returns a sweater that cost $128.95. How much does she now owe on her credit card?

75. While recording a 60-minute television show, the reading on Kate's VCR changed from −21 minutes to 29 minutes. How many minutes have been recorded? Has she recorded the entire show?

76. As a result of coaching, Cedric's average golf score improved from 3 over par to 2 under. By how many strokes did his score change?

77. Carla is completing the production work on a track that is to appear on her band's upcoming CD. In doing so, she resets the digital recorder to 0, advances the recording 16 sec, and then reverses the recording 25 sec. What reading will the recorder then display?

78. Midway through a movie, Lisa resets the counter on her DVD player to 0. She then reverses the disc 8 min, and then advances the movie 11 min. What does the counter now read?

79. *Offshore Oil.* In 1998, the elevation of the world's deepwater drilling record was −7718 ft. In 2001, the deepwater drilling record was 1969 ft deeper. What was the elevation of the deepwater drilling record in 2001?
Source: U.S. Department of the Interior

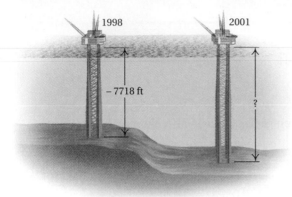

1998   2001

−7718 ft

?

80. *Oceanography.* The deepest point in the Pacific Ocean is the Marianas Trench, with a depth of 11,033 m. The deepest point in the Atlantic Ocean is the Puerto Rico Trench, with a depth of 8648 m. What is the difference in the elevation of the two trenches?

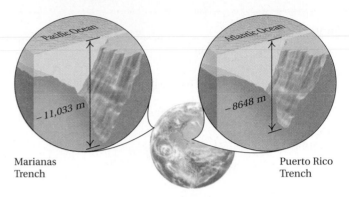

Pacific Ocean

Atlantic Ocean

−11,033 m

−8648 m

Marianas
Trench

Puerto Rico
Trench

81. *Toll Roads.* The Murrays began a trip with $13 in their EZ Pass account (see Example 13). They accumulated $20 in tolls and had to pay $80 in fines and administrative fees. By how much were the Murrays in debt as a result of their travel on toll roads?

82. *Toll Roads.* Suppose the Murrays (see Exercise 81) incurred $25 in tolls and $85 in fines and administrative fees. By how much would the Murrays be in debt?

83. ^{D}w Write a subtraction problem for a classmate to solve. Design the problem so that the solution is "Clara ends up $15 in debt."

84. ^{D}w If a negative number is subtracted from a positive number, will the result always be positive? Why or why not?

(**SKILL MAINTENANCE**)

Evaluate.

85. 4^3 [1.9b]

86. $68 \cdot 72$ [1.5a]

87. 1^7 [1.9b]

88. $143 \cdot 29$ [1.5a]

89. How many 12-oz cans of soda can be filled with 96 oz of soda? [1.8a]

90. A case of soda contains 24 bottles. If each bottle contains 12 oz, how many ounces of soda are in the case? [1.8a]

Simplify.

91. $5 + 4^2 + 2 \cdot 7$ [1.9c]

92. $45 \div (2^2 + 11)$ [1.9c]

93. $(9 + 7)(9 − 7)$ [1.9c]

94. $(13 − 2)(13 + 2)$ [1.9c]

95. D_W Explain why the commutative law was used in Example 12.

96. D_W Is subtraction of integers associative? Why or why not?

Subtract.

97. ▦ $123,907 - 433,789$

98. ▦ $23,011 - (-60,432)$

For Exercises 99–104, tell whether each statement is true or false for all integers a and b. If false, show why.

99. $a - 0 = 0 - a$

100. $0 - a = a$

101. If $a \neq b$, then $a - b \neq 0$.

102. If $a = -b$, then $a + b = 0$.

103. If $a + b = 0$, then a and b are opposites.

104. If $a - b = 0$, then $a = -b$.

105. If $a - 54$ is -37, find the value of a.

106. If $x - 48$ is -15, find the value of x.

107. Doreen is a stockbroker. She kept track of the weekly changes in the stock market over a period of 5 weeks. By how many points (pts) had the market risen or fallen over this time?

WEEK 1	WEEK 2	WEEK 3	WEEK 4	WEEK 5
Down 13 pts	Down 16 pts	Up 36 pts	Down 11 pts	Up 19 pts

108. *Blackjack Counting System.* The casino game of blackjack makes use of many card-counting systems to give players an advantage if the count becomes negative. One such system is called *High–Low*, first developed by Harvey Dubner in 1963. Each card counts as -1, 0, or 1 as follows:

2, 3, 4, 5, 6   count as $+1$;
7, 8, 9   count as 0;
10, J, Q, K, A   count as -1.

Source: Patterson, Jerry L. *Casino Gambling.* New York: Perigee, 1982.

a) Find the total count on the sequence of cards

K, A, 2, 4, 5, 10, J, 8, Q, K, 5.

b) Does the player have a winning edge?

2.4

MULTIPLICATION OF INTEGERS

Objectives

a Multiply integers.

b Find products of three or more integers and simplify powers of integers.

a Multiplication

Multiplication of integers is like multiplication of whole numbers. The difference is that we must determine whether the answer is positive or negative.

MULTIPLICATION OF A POSITIVE INTEGER AND A NEGATIVE INTEGER

To see how to multiply a positive integer and a negative integer, consider the pattern of the following.

This number decreases by 1 each time.

This number decreases by 5 each time.

$$4 \cdot 5 = 20$$
$$3 \cdot 5 = 15$$
$$2 \cdot 5 = 10$$
$$1 \cdot 5 = 5$$
$$0 \cdot 5 = 0$$
$$-1 \cdot 5 = -5$$
$$-2 \cdot 5 = -10$$
$$-3 \cdot 5 = -15$$

Do Exercise 1.

According to this pattern, it looks as though the product of a negative integer and a positive integer is negative. To confirm this, use repeated addition:

$$-1 \cdot 5 = 5 \cdot (-1) = -1 + (-1) + (-1) + (-1) + (-1) = -5$$
$$-2 \cdot 5 = 5 \cdot (-2) = -2 + (-2) + (-2) + (-2) + (-2) = -10$$
$$-3 \cdot 5 = 5 \cdot (-3) = -3 + (-3) + (-3) + (-3) + (-3) = -15$$

MULTIPLYING A POSITIVE AND A NEGATIVE NUMBER

To multiply a positive integer and a negative integer, multiply their absolute values and make the answer negative.

EXAMPLES Multiply.

1. $8(-5) = -40$ **2.** $50(-1) = -50$ **3.** $-7 \cdot 6 = -42$

Do Exercises 2–4.

MULTIPLICATION OF TWO NEGATIVE INTEGERS

How do we multiply two negative integers? Again we look for a pattern.

This number decreases by 1 each time.

This number increases by 5 each time.

$$4 \cdot (-5) = -20$$
$$3 \cdot (-5) = -15$$
$$2 \cdot (-5) = -10$$
$$1 \cdot (-5) = -5$$
$$0 \cdot (-5) = 0$$
$$-1 \cdot (-5) = 5$$
$$-2 \cdot (-5) = 10$$
$$-3 \cdot (-5) = 15$$

Do Exercise 5.

1. Complete, as in the example.

$$4 \cdot 10 = 40$$
$$3 \cdot 10 = 30$$
$$2 \cdot 10 =$$
$$1 \cdot 10 =$$
$$0 \cdot 10 =$$
$$-1 \cdot 10 =$$
$$-2 \cdot 10 =$$
$$-3 \cdot 10 =$$

Multiply.

2. $-3 \cdot 6$

3. $20 \cdot (-5)$

4. $9(-1)$

5. Complete, as in the example.

$$3 \cdot (-10) = -30$$
$$2 \cdot (-10) = -20$$
$$1 \cdot (-10) =$$
$$0 \cdot (-10) =$$
$$-1 \cdot (-10) =$$
$$-2 \cdot (-10) =$$
$$-3 \cdot (-10) =$$

Answers on page A-6

Multiply.

6. $(-3)(-4)$

7. $-9(-5)$

8. $(-1)(-6)$

Multiply.

9. $0 \cdot (-5)$

10. $-23 \cdot 0$

Answers on page A-6

Study Tips

SLEEP WELL

Being well rested, alert, and focused is very important when studying math. Often, problems that may seem confusing to a sleepy person are easily understood after a good night's sleep. Using your time efficiently is always important, so you should be aware that an alert, wide-awake student can often accomplish more in 10 minutes than a sleepy student can accomplish in 30 minutes.

According to the pattern, the product of two negative integers is positive. This leads to the second part of the rule for multiplying integers.

MULTIPLYING TWO NEGATIVE INTEGERS

To multiply two negative integers, multiply their absolute values. The answer is positive.

EXAMPLES Multiply.

4. $(-2)(-4) = 8$

5. $(-10)(-7) = 70$

6. $(-9)(-1) = 9$

Do Exercises 6–8.

The following is another way to state the rules for multiplication.

To multiply two integers:

a) Multiply the absolute values.

b) If the signs are the same, the answer is positive.

c) If the signs are different, the answer is negative.

MULTIPLICATION BY ZERO

No matter how many times 0 is added to itself, the answer is 0. This leads to the following result.

For any integer a,
$$a \cdot 0 = 0.$$
(The product of 0 and any integer is 0.)

EXAMPLES Multiply.

7. $-19 \cdot 0 = 0$

8. $0(-7) = 0$

Do Exercises 9 and 10.

b   Multiplication of More Than Two Integers

Because of the commutative and the associative laws, to multiply three or more integers, we can group as we please.

EXAMPLES Multiply.

9. a) $-8 \cdot 2(-3) = -16(-3)$ Multiplying the first two numbers
$\qquad\qquad\quad = 48$ Multiplying the results

b) $-8 \cdot 2(-3) = 24 \cdot 2$ Multiplying the negatives
$\qquad\qquad\quad = 48$ The result is the same as above.

10. $7(-1)(-4)(-2) = (-7)8$ Multiplying the first two numbers and the last two numbers

$$= -56$$

11. a) $-5 \cdot (-2) \cdot (-3) \cdot (-6) = 10 \cdot 18$ Each pair of negatives gives a positive product.

$$= 180$$

b) $-5 \cdot (-2) \cdot (-3) \cdot (-6) \cdot (-1) = 10 \cdot 18 \cdot (-1)$ Making use of Example 11(a)

$$= -180$$

We can see the following pattern in the results of Examples 9–11.

> The product of an even number of negative integers is positive.
> The product of an odd number of negative integers is negative.

Do Exercises 11–13.

POWERS OF INTEGERS

The result of raising a negative number to a power is positive or negative, depending on whether the exponent is even or odd.

EXAMPLES Simplify.

12. $(-7)^2 = (-7)(-7) = 49$ The result is positive.

13. $(-4)^3 = (-4)(-4)(-4)$
$$= 16(-4)$$
$$= -64$$ The result is negative.

14. $(-3)^4 = (-3)(-3)(-3)(-3)$
$$= 9 \cdot 9$$
$$= 81$$ The result is positive.

15. $(-2)^5 = (-2)(-2)(-2)(-2)(-2)$
$$= 4 \cdot 4 \cdot (-2)$$
$$= 16(-2)$$
$$= -32$$ The result is negative.

Perhaps you noted the following.

> When a negative number is raised to an even exponent, the result is positive.
> When a negative number is raised to an odd exponent, the result is negative.

As always, a positive number raised to any power is positive.

Do Exercises 14–17.

We have seen that when an integer is multiplied by -1, the result is the opposite of that integer.

> For any integer a,
> $$-1 \cdot a = -a$$

Multiply.

11. $-2 \cdot (-5) \cdot (-4) \cdot (-3)$

12. $(-4)(-5)(-2)(-3)(-1)$

13. $(-1)(-1)(-2)(-3)(-1)(-1)$

Simplify.

14. $(-2)^3$

15. $(-9)^2$

16. $(-1)^9$

17. 2^5

Answers on page A-6

18. Simplify: -5^2.

EXAMPLE 16 Simplify: -7^2.

We first note that -7^2 lacks parentheses so the base is 7, not -7. Thus we regard -7^2 as $-1 \cdot 7^2$:

$$-7^2 = -1 \cdot 7^2$$
$$= -1 \cdot 7 \cdot 7 \qquad \text{The rules for order of operations tell us to square first.}$$
$$= -1 \cdot 49$$
$$= -49.$$

Compare Examples 12 and 16 and note that $(-7)^2 \neq -7^2$. In fact, the expressions $(-7)^2$ and -7^2 are not even read the same way: $(-7)^2$ is read "negative seven squared," whereas -7^2 is read "the opposite of seven squared."

Do Exercises 18–20.

19. Simplify: $(-5)^2$.

CALCULATOR CORNER

When using a calculator to calculate numbers like $(-39)^4$ or -39^4, it is important to use the correct sequence of keystrokes.

Scientific calculators On most scientific calculators, the appropriate keystrokes for $(-39)^4$ are

$$\boxed{3}\,\boxed{9}\,\boxed{+/-}\,\boxed{x^y}\,\boxed{4}\,\boxed{=}.$$

Note that in this instance the $\boxed{+/-}$ key is used to change a number's sign.

To calculate -39^4, the following keystrokes are needed:

$$\boxed{1}\,\boxed{+/-}\,\boxed{\times}\,\boxed{3}\,\boxed{9}\,\boxed{x^y}\,\boxed{4}\,\boxed{=},$$

or

$$\boxed{3}\,\boxed{9}\,\boxed{x^y}\,\boxed{4}\,\boxed{=}\,\boxed{+/-}.$$

Graphing calculators On most graphing calculators, $(-39)^4$ is found by pressing

$$\boxed{(}\,\boxed{(-)}\,\boxed{3}\,\boxed{9}\,\boxed{)}\,\boxed{\wedge}\,\boxed{4}\,\boxed{\text{ENTER}}$$

20. Write $(-8)^2$ and -8^2 in words.

and -39^4 is found by pressing

$$\boxed{(-)}\,\boxed{3}\,\boxed{9}\,\boxed{\wedge}\,\boxed{4}\,\boxed{\text{ENTER}}.$$

You can either experiment or consult a user's manual if you are unsure of the proper keystrokes for your calculator.

Exercises: Use a calculator to determine each of the following.

1. $(-23)^6$ **5.** -9^6

2. $(-17)^5$ **6.** -7^6

3. $(-104)^3$ **7.** -6^5

4. $(-4)^{10}$ **8.** -3^9

Answers on page A-6

2.4 EXERCISE SET

a Multiply.

1. $-2 \cdot 8$ **2.** $-7 \cdot 3$ **3.** $-9 \cdot 2$ **4.** $-7 \cdot 7$

5. $8 \cdot (-6)$ **6.** $8 \cdot (-3)$ **7.** $-10 \cdot 3$ **8.** $-9 \cdot 8$

9. $-3(-5)$ **10.** $-8 \cdot (-2)$ **11.** $-9 \cdot (-2)$ **12.** $(-8)(-9)$

13. $-7 \cdot (-6)$ **14.** $-8 \cdot (-3)$ **15.** $-10(-2)$ **16.** $-9(-8)$

17. $12(-10)$ **18.** $15(-8)$ **19.** $-6(-50)$ **20.** $-25(-8)$

21. $(-72)(-1)$ **22.** $41(-3)$ **23.** $(-20)17$ **24.** $(-1)43$

25. $-47 \cdot 0$ **26.** $-17 \cdot 0$ **27.** $0(-14)$ **28.** $0(-38)$

b Multiply.

29. $3 \cdot (-8) \cdot (-1)$ **30.** $(-7) \cdot (-4) \cdot (-1)$ **31.** $7(-4)(-3)5$

32. $9(-2)(-6)7$ **33.** $-2(-5)(-7)$ **34.** $(-2)(-5)(-3)(-5)$

35. $(-5)(-2)(-3)(-1)$ **36.** $-6(-5)(-9)$ **37.** $(-15)(-29)0 \cdot 8$

38. $19(-7)(-8)0 \cdot 6$ **39.** $(-7)(-1)(7)(-6)$ **40.** $(-5)6(-4)5$

Simplify.

41. $(-6)^2$

42. $(-8)^2$

43. $(-5)^3$

44. $(-2)^4$

45. $(-10)^4$

46. $(-1)^5$

47. -2^4

48. $(-2)^6$

49. $(-3)^5$

50. -10^4

51. $(-1)^{12}$

52. $(-1)^{13}$

53. -3^6

54. -2^6

55. -4^3

56. -2^5

Write each of the following expressions in words.

57. -8^4

58. $(-6)^8$

59. $(-9)^{10}$

60. -5^4

61. $\mathbf{D_W}$ Explain in your own words why $(-9)^{10}$ is positive.

62. $\mathbf{D_W}$ Explain in your own words why -9^{10} is negative.

SKILL MAINTENANCE

63. Round 532,451 to the nearest hundred.   [1.4a]

64. Write standard notation for sixty million.   [1.1c]

65. Divide: $2880 \div 36$.   [1.6c]

66. Multiply: 75×34.   [1.5a]

67. Simplify: $10 - 2^3 + 6 \div 2$.   [1.9c]

68. Simplify: $2 \cdot 5^2 - 3 \cdot 2^3 \div (3 + 3^2)$.   [1.9c]

69. A rectangular rug measures 5 ft by 8 ft. What is the area of the rug?   [1.8a]

70. How many 12-egg cartons can be filled with 2880 eggs?   [1.8a]

71. A ferry can accommodate 12 cars and 53 cars are waiting. How many trips will be required to ferry them all?   [1.8a]

72. An elevator can hold 16 people and 50 people are waiting to go up. How many trips will be required to transport all of them?   [1.8a]

SYNTHESIS

73. $\mathbf{D_W}$ Which number is larger, $(-3)^{79}$ or $(-5)^{79}$? Why?

74. $\mathbf{D_W}$ Describe all conditions for which a^x is negative.

Simplify.

75. $(-3)^5(-1)^{379}$

76. $(-2)^3 \cdot [(-1)^{29}]^{46}$

77. $-9^4 + (-9)^4$

78. $-5^2(-1)^{29}$

79. $|(-2)^5 + 3^2| - (3 - 7)^2$

80. $|-12(-3)^2 - 5^3 - 6^2 - (-5)^2|$

81. 🖩 -47^2

82. 🖩 -53^2

83. 🖩 $(-19)^4$

84. 🖩 $(-23)^4$

85. 🖩 $(73 - 86)^3$

86. 🖩 $(-49 + 34)^3$

87. 🖩 $-935(238 - 243)^3$

88. 🖩 $(-17)^4(129 - 133)^5$

89. Jo wrote seven checks for $13 each. If she had a balance of $68 in her account, what was her balance after writing the checks?

90. After diving 95 m below the surface, a diver rises at a rate of 7 meters per minute for 9 min. What is the diver's new elevation?

91. What must be true of m and n if $[(-5)^m]^n$ is to be **(a)** negative? **(b)** positive?

92. What must be true of m and n if $-mn$ is to be **(a)** positive? **(b)** zero? **(c)** negative?

CHAPTER 2: Introduction to Integers
and Algebraic Expressions

2.5 DIVISION OF INTEGERS

Objectives

a Divide integers.

b Use the rules for order of operations with integers.

We now consider division of integers. Because of the way in which division is defined, its rules are similar to those for multiplication.

a Division of Integers

> **THE QUOTIENT a/b**
>
> The quotient $\dfrac{a}{b}$ (or $a \div b$, or a/b) is the number, if there is one, that when multiplied by b gives a.

Let's use the definition to divide integers.

■ **EXAMPLES** Divide, if possible. Check each answer.

1. $14 \div (-7) = -2$ *Think*: What number multiplied by -7 gives 14? The number is -2. *Check*: $(-2)(-7) = 14$.

2. $\dfrac{-32}{-4} = 8$ *Think*: What number multiplied by -4 gives -32? The number is 8. *Check*: $8(-4) = -32$.

3. $\dfrac{-21}{7} = -3$ *Think*: What number multiplied by 7 gives -21? The number is -3. *Check*: $(-3) \cdot 7 = -21$.

4. $0 \div (-5) = 0$ *Think*: What number multiplied by -5 gives 0? The number is 0. *Check*: $0(-5) = 0$.

The rules for determining the sign of a quotient are the same as for determining the sign of a product. We state them together.

> To multiply or divide two integers:
>
> **a)** Multiply or divide the absolute values.
> **b)** If the signs are the same, the answer is positive.
> **c)** If the signs are different, the answer is negative.

Do Exercises 1–6.

Recall that, in general, $a \div b$ and $b \div a$ are different numbers. In Example 4, we divided *into* 0. Consider now division of a number *by* 0, as in $9 \div 0$. The expression $9 \div 0$ represents the number that when multiplied by 0 gives 9. But any number times 0 gives 0, not 9. For this reason, we say that $9 \div 0$ is **not defined** or is **undefined.** This result is generalized as follows.

> Division by zero is not defined: $a \div 0$, or $\dfrac{a}{0}$, is undefined for all integers a.

Divide.

1. $6 \div (-2)$

Think: What number multiplied by -2 gives 6?

2. $\dfrac{-15}{-3}$

Think: What number multiplied by -3 gives -15?

3. $-24 \div 8$

Think: What number multiplied by 8 gives -24?

4. $\dfrac{0}{-4}$

5. $\dfrac{30}{-5}$

6. $\dfrac{-45}{9}$

Answers on page A-7

Divide, if possible.

7. $34 \div 0$

8. $0 \div (-4)$

9. $-52 \div 0$

Answers on page A-7

Study Tips

TAKE A POWER NAP

If you must study when you are tired, consider closing your eyes and resting your head on your arms for a 10 minute "power nap." Often a brief rest like this can greatly improve your concentration.

CHAPTER 2: Introduction to Integers
and Algebraic Expressions

EXAMPLE 5 Divide, if possible: $-17 \div 0$.

$\dfrac{-17}{0}$ is undefined.

Think: What number multiplied by 0 gives -17? There is no such number because anything times 0 is 0.

Do Exercises 7–9.

> ### CONNECTING THE CONCEPTS
>
> As mentioned in Chapter 1, thorough understanding of the rules for order of operations—that is, the sequence in which numbers are added, subtracted, multiplied, divided, raised to powers, and grouped—is essential for success in mathematics. Now that we know how to work with a "new" type of number (in this case, negative integers), it is time to extend our work with order of operations. Look for this pattern to repeat in future chapters, when fractions and decimals are studied.

b Rules for Order of Operations

When more than one operation appears in a calculation or problem, we apply the same rules that were used in Section 1.9. We repeat them here for review, now including absolute-value symbols.

> **RULES FOR ORDER OF OPERATIONS**
>
> 1. Do all calculations within parentheses, brackets, braces, absolute-value symbols, numerators, or denominators.
> 2. Evaluate all exponential expressions.
> 3. Do all multiplications and divisions in order from left to right.
> 4. Do all additions and subtractions in order from left to right.

EXAMPLES Simplify.

6. $17 - 10 \div 2 \cdot 4$

With no grouping symbols or exponents, we begin with the third rule.

$$
\begin{aligned}
17 - 10 \div 2 \cdot 4 &= 17 - 5 \cdot 4 \\
&= 17 - 20 \\
&= -3
\end{aligned}
$$

Carrying out all multiplications and divisions in order from left to right

7. $|(-2)^3 \div 4| - 5(-2)$

We first simplify within the absolute-value symbols.

$$
\begin{aligned}
|(-2)^3 \div 4| - 5(-2) &= |-8 \div 4| - 5(-2) \qquad (-2)(-2)(-2) = -8 \\
&= |-2| - 5(-2) \qquad \text{Dividing} \\
&= 2 - 5(-2) \qquad \text{Finding the absolute value of } -2 \\
&= 2 - (-10) \qquad \text{Multiplying} \\
&= 12 \qquad \text{Subtracting by adding the opposite of } -10
\end{aligned}
$$

Always regard a fraction bar as a grouping symbol. It separates any calculations in the numerator from those in the denominator.

 EXAMPLE 8 Simplify: $\dfrac{5 - (-3)^2}{-2}$.

$$\dfrac{5 - (-3)^2}{-2} = \dfrac{5 - 9}{-2}$$

$$= \dfrac{-4}{-2}$$

Calculating within the numerator:
$(-3)^2 = (-3)(-3) = 9$ and $5 - 9 = -4$

$$= 2$$ Dividing

Do Exercises 10–12.

CALCULATOR CORNER

Most calculators now provide grouping symbols. Such keys may appear as ⟨ and ⟩ or [(... and ...)] . Grouping symbols can be useful when we are simplifying expressions written in fraction form. For example, to simplify an expression like

$$\dfrac{38 + 142}{2 - 47},$$

we press (3 8 + 1 4 2) ÷ (2 − 4 7) = . Failure to include grouping symbols in the above keystrokes would mean that we are simplifying a different expression:

$$38 + \dfrac{142}{2} - 47.$$

Exercises: Use a calculator with grouping symbols to simplify each of the following.

1. $\dfrac{38 - 178}{5 + 30}$

2. $\dfrac{311 - 17^2}{2 - 13}$

3. $785 - \dfrac{285 - 5^4}{17 + 3 \cdot 51}$

Simplify.

10. $5 - (-7)(-3)^2$

11. $(-2) \cdot |3 - 2^2| + 5$

12. $\dfrac{(-5)(-9)}{1 - 2 \cdot 2}$

2.5 EXERCISE SET

For Extra Help

Digital Video Tutor CD 2 Videotape 2   InterAct Math   Math Tutor Center   MathXL   MyMathLab

a Divide, if possible, and check each answer by multiplying. If an answer is undefined, state so.

1. $28 \div (-4)$

2. $\dfrac{35}{-7}$

3. $\dfrac{28}{-2}$

4. $26 \div (-13)$

5. $\dfrac{18}{-2}$

6. $-22 \div (-2)$

7. $\dfrac{-48}{-12}$

8. $-63 \div (-9)$

9. $\dfrac{-72}{8}$

10. $\dfrac{-50}{25}$

11. $-100 \div (-50)$

12. $\dfrac{-400}{8}$

13. $-344 \div 8$

14. $\dfrac{-128}{8}$

15. $\dfrac{200}{-25}$

16. $-651 \div (-31)$

17. $\dfrac{-56}{0}$

18. $\dfrac{0}{-5}$

19. $\dfrac{88}{-11}$

20. $\dfrac{-145}{-5}$

21. $-\dfrac{276}{12}$

22. $-\dfrac{217}{7}$

23. $\dfrac{0}{-2}$

24. $\dfrac{-13}{0}$

25. $\dfrac{19}{-1}$

26. $\dfrac{-17}{1}$

27. $-41 \div 1$

28. $23 \div (-1)$

b Simplify, if possible. If an answer is undefined, state so.

29. $5 - 2 \cdot 3 - 6$

30. $5 - (2 \cdot 3 - 7)$

31. $9 - 2(3 - 8)$

32. $(8 - 2)(3 - 9)$

33. $16 \cdot (-24) + 50$

34. $10 \cdot 20 - 15 \cdot 24$

35. $40 - 3^2 - 2^3$

36. $2^4 + 2^2 - 10$

172

CHAPTER 2: Introduction to Integers and Algebraic Expressions

Copyright © 2004 Pearson Education, Inc.

37. $4 \cdot (6 + 8)/(4 + 3)$

38. $4^3 + 10 \cdot 20 + 8^2 - 23$

39. $4 \cdot 5 - 2 \cdot 6 + 4$

40. $5^3 + 4 \cdot 9 - (8 + 9 \cdot 3)$

41. $\dfrac{9^2 - 1}{1 - 3^2}$

42. $\dfrac{100 - 6^2}{(-5)^2 - 3^2}$

43. $8(-7) + 6(-5)$

44. $10(-5) \div 1(-1)$

45. $20 \div 5(-3) + 3$

46. $14 \div 2(-6) + 7$

47. $18 - 0(3^2 - 5^2 \cdot 7 - 4)$

48. $9 \cdot 0 \div 5 \cdot 4$

49. $4 \cdot 5^2 \div 10$

50. $(2 - 5)^2 \div (-9)$

51. $(3 - 8)^2 \div (-1)$

52. $3 - 3^2$

53. $17 - 10^3$

54. $30 + (-5)^3$

55. $2 + 10^2 \div 5 \cdot 2^2$

56. $5 + 6^2 \div 3 \cdot 2^2$

57. $12 - 20^3$

58. $20 + 4^3 \div (-8)$

59. $2 \times 10^3 - 5000$

60. $-7(3^4) + 18$

61. $6[9 - (3 - 4)]$

62. $8[(6 - 13) - 11]$

63. $-1000 \div (-100) \div 10$

64. $256 + (-32) \div (-4)$

65. $8 - |7 - 9| \cdot 3$

66. $|8 - 7 - 9| \cdot 2 + 1$

67. $9 - |7 - 3^2|$

68. $9 - |5 - 7|^3$

69. $\dfrac{6^3 - 7 \cdot 3^4 - 2^5 \cdot 9}{(1 - 2^3)^3 + 7^3}$

70. $\dfrac{4 \div 2 \cdot 4^2 - 3 \cdot 2}{(7 - 4)^3 - 2 \cdot 5 - 4}$

71. $\dfrac{2 \cdot 3^2 \div (3^2 - (2 + 1))}{5^2 - 6^2 - 2^2(-3)}$

72. $\dfrac{5 \cdot 6^2 \div (2^2 \cdot 5) - 7^2}{3^2 - 4^2 - (-2)^3 - 2}$

73. $\dfrac{(-5)^3 + 17}{10(2 - 6) - 2(5 + 2)}$

74. $\dfrac{(3 - 5)^2 - (7 - 13)}{(2 - 5)3 + 2 \cdot 4}$

75. $\dfrac{2 \cdot 4^3 - 4 \cdot 32}{19^3 - 17^4}$

76. $\dfrac{-16 \cdot 28 \div 2^2}{5 \cdot 25 - 5^3}$

77. $\mathbf{D_W}$ Explain in your own words why $17 \div 0$ is undefined.

78. $\mathbf{D_W}$ Without performing any calculations, Stefan reports that $(19^2 - 17^2)/(16^2 - 18^2)$ is negative. How do you think he reached this conclusion?

79. Fabrikant Fine Diamonds ran a 4-in. by 7-in. advertisement in *The New York Times*. Find the area of the ad.   [1.8a]

80. A classroom contains 7 rows of chairs with 6 chairs in each row. How many chairs are there in the classroom?   [1.8a]

81. Etta's Ford Focus gets 32 miles per gallon (mpg). How many gallons will it take to travel 384 mi?   [1.8a]

82. Tim's Chevy Blazer gets 14 mpg. How many gallons will it take to travel 378 mi?   [1.8a]

83. A 7-oz bag of tortilla chips contains 1050 calories. How many calories are in a 1-oz serving?   [1.8a]

84. A 7-oz bag of tortilla chips contains 8 grams (g) of fat. How many grams of fat are in a carton containing 12 bags of chips?   [1.8a]

85. There are 18 sticks in a large pack of Trident gum. If 4 people share the pack equally, how many whole pieces will each person receive? How many extra pieces will remain?   [1.8a]

86. A bag of Ricola throat lozenges contains 24 cough drops. If 5 people share the bag equally, how many lozenges will each person receive? How many extra lozenges will remain?   [1.8a]

87. $^{D}\!\mathbf{w}$ Cito claims that $8 - 3^2 + 1$ is -2. What mistake do you think he is making?

88. $^{D}\!\mathbf{w}$ Amelie contends that $13 - 10/2 - 5$ is -1. What mistake do you think she is making?

Simplify, if possible.

89. $\dfrac{9 - 3^2}{2 \cdot 4^2 - 5^2 \cdot 9 + 8^2 \cdot 7}$

90. $\dfrac{7^3 \cdot 9 - 6^2 \cdot 8 + 4^3 \cdot 6}{5^2 - 25}$

91. $\dfrac{(25 - 4^2)^3}{17^2 - 16^2} \cdot ((-6)^2 - 6^2)$

92. $\dfrac{(7 - 8)^{37}}{7^2 - 8^2} \cdot (98 - 7^2 \cdot 2)$

93. 🔲 $\dfrac{19 - 17^2}{13^2 - 34}$

94. 🔲 $\dfrac{195 + (-15)^3}{195 - 7 \cdot 5^2}$

95. 🔲 $28^2 - 36^2/4^2 + 17^2$

96. 🔲 $9^3 - 36^3/12^2 + 9^2$

97. 🔲 Write down the keystrokes needed to calculate $\dfrac{15^2 - 5^3}{3^2 + 4^2}$.

98. 🔲 Write down the keystrokes needed to calculate $\dfrac{16^2 - 24 \cdot 23}{3 \cdot 4 + 5^2}$.

99. Evaluate the expression for which the keystrokes are as follows: 4 − 1 0 ÷ 2 + 6 .

100. Evaluate the expression for which the keystrokes are 4 − 1 6 ÷ (2 + 6) .

Determine the sign of each expression if m is negative and n is positive.

101. $\dfrac{-n}{m}$

102. $\dfrac{-n}{-m}$

103. $-\left(\dfrac{-n}{m}\right)$

104. $-\left(\dfrac{n}{-m}\right)$

105. $-\left(\dfrac{-n}{-m}\right)$

2.6 INTRODUCTION TO ALGEBRA AND EXPRESSIONS

One of the most important skills to master in algebra is the ability to write *equivalent expressions*. In this section we will learn to do this by making use of the *distributive law*, which itself is a very important concept.

a Algebraic Expressions

In arithmetic, we work with expressions such as

$$37 + 86, \quad 7 \cdot 8, \quad 19 - 7, \quad \text{and} \quad \frac{3}{8}.$$

In algebra, we use both numbers and variables and work with *algebraic expressions* such as

$$x + 86, \quad 7 \cdot t, \quad 19 - y, \quad \text{and} \quad \frac{a}{b}.$$

Expressions like these should be familiar from the equation and problem solving that we have already done.

When a letter can stand for various numbers, we call the letter a **variable.** A number or a letter that stands for just one number is called a **constant.** Let c = the speed of light. Then c is a constant. Let a = the speed of an AMTRAK metroliner. Then a is a variable since the value of a can vary.

An **algebraic expression** consists of variables, numerals, and operation signs. When we replace a variable with a number, we say that we are **substituting** for the variable. This process is called **evaluating the expression.**

EXAMPLE 1 Evaluate $x + y$ for $x = 37$ and $y = 29$.

We substitute 37 for x and 29 for y and carry out the addition:

$$x + y = 37 + 29 = 66.$$

The number 66 is called the **value** of the expression.

Algebraic expressions involving multiplication, like "8 times a," can be written as $8 \times a$, $8 \cdot a$, $8(a)$, or simply $8a$. Two letters written together without an operation symbol, such as ab, also indicate multiplication.

EXAMPLE 2 Evaluate $3y$ for $y = -14$.

$$3y = 3(-14) = -42 \qquad \text{Parentheses are required here.}$$

Do Exercises 1–3.

Algebraic expressions involving division can also be written several ways. For example, "8 divided by t" can be written as $8 \div t$, $8/t$, or $\frac{8}{t}$.

EXAMPLE 3 Evaluate $\frac{a}{b}$ and $\frac{-a}{-b}$ for $a = 35$ and $b = 7$.

We substitute 35 for a and 7 for b:

$$\frac{a}{b} = \frac{35}{7} = 5; \qquad \frac{-a}{-b} = \frac{-35}{-7} = 5.$$

Note that $\frac{-a}{-b} = \frac{a}{b}$, as the rules for division would lead us to expect.

1. Evaluate $a + b$ for $a = 38$ and $b = 26$.

2. Evaluate $x - y$ for $x = 57$ and $y = 29$.

3. Evaluate $5t$ for $t = -14$.

Answers on page A-7

Study Tips

A TEXT IS NOT LIGHT READING

Do not expect a math text to read like a magazine or novel. On one hand, most assigned readings in a math text consist of only a few pages. On the other hand, every sentence and word is important and should make sense. If they don't, seek help as soon as possible.

For each number, find two equivalent expressions with negative signs in different places.

4. $\dfrac{-6}{x}$

5. $-\dfrac{m}{n}$

6. $\dfrac{r}{-4}$

7. Evaluate $\dfrac{a}{-b}, \dfrac{-a}{b}$, and $-\dfrac{a}{b}$ for $a = 28$ and $b = 4$.

8. Find the Fahrenheit temperature that corresponds to 10 degrees Celsius (see Example 5).

9. Evaluate $3x^2$ for $x = 4$ and $x = -4$.

10. Evaluate a^4 for $a = 3$ and $a = -3$.

11. Evaluate $(-x)^2$ and $-x^2$ for $x = 3$.

12. Evaluate $(-x)^2$ and $-x^2$ for $x = 2$.

13. Evaluate x^5 for $x = 2$ and $x = -2$.

Answers on page A-7

■ **EXAMPLE 4**   Evaluate $-\dfrac{a}{b}, \dfrac{-a}{b}$, and $\dfrac{a}{-b}$ for $a = 15$ and $b = 3$.

We substitute 15 for a and 3 for b:

$$-\frac{a}{b} = -\frac{15}{3} = -5; \qquad \frac{-a}{b} = \frac{-15}{3} = -5; \qquad \frac{a}{-b} = \frac{15}{-3} = -5.$$

Note that $-\dfrac{a}{b}, \dfrac{-a}{b}$, and $\dfrac{a}{-b}$ all represent the same number.

Do Exercises 4–7.

■ **EXAMPLE 5**   Evaluate $\dfrac{9C}{5} + 32$ for $C = 20$.

This expression can be used to find the Fahrenheit temperature that corresponds to 20 degrees Celsius:

$$\frac{9C}{5} + 32 = \frac{9 \cdot 20}{5} + 32 = \frac{180}{5} + 32 = 36 + 32 = 68.$$

Do Exercise 8.

■ **EXAMPLE 6**   Evaluate $5x^2$ for $x = 3$ and $x = -3$.

The rules for order of operations specify that the replacement for x be squared. That result is then multiplied by 5:

$$5x^2 = 5(3)^2 = 5(9) = 45;$$
$$5x^2 = 5(-3)^2 = 5(9) = 45.$$

Example 6 shows that when opposites are raised to an even power, the results are the same.

Do Exercises 9 and 10.

■ **EXAMPLE 7**   Evaluate $(-x)^2$ and $-x^2$ for $x = 7$.

We have

$$(-x)^2 = (-7)^2 = (-7)(-7) = 49.$$ Substitute 7 for x. Then evaluate the power.

Be very careful when evaluating $-x^2$. Recall from Section 2.4 that taking the opposite of a number is the same as multiplying that number by -1. Thus,

$$-x^2 = -1 \cdot x^2.$$

Next, recall that the rules for the order of operations indicate that powers are calculated before ordinary multiplication. Thus,

$$-7^2 = -1 \cdot 7^2$$
$$= -1 \cdot 49 = -49.$$

> **CAUTION!**
> Example 7 shows that $(-x)^2 \neq -x^2$.

Do Exercises 11–13.

b   **Equivalent Expressions and the Distributive Law**

It is useful to know when two algebraic expressions will represent the same number. In many situations, this will help with problem solving.

EXAMPLE 8 Evaluate $x + x$ and $2x$ for $x = 3$ and $x = -5$ and compare the results.

We substitute 3 for x in $x + x$ and again in $2x$:

$$x + x = 3 + 3 = 6; \qquad 2x = 2 \cdot 3 = 6.$$

Next we repeat the procedure, substituting -5 for x:

$$x + x = -5 + (-5) = -10; \qquad 2x = 2(-5) = -10.$$

The results can be shown in a table. It appears that $x + x$ and $2x$ represent the same number.

	$x + x$	$2x$
$x = 3$	6	6
$x = -5$	-10	-10

Do Exercises 14 and 15.

Example 8 suggests that $x + x$ and $2x$ represent the same number for any replacement of x. When this is known to be the case, we can say that $x + x$ and $2x$ are **equivalent expressions.**

EQUIVALENT EXPRESSIONS

Two expressions that have the same value for all allowable replacements are called **equivalent.**

In Examples 3 and 7 we saw that the expressions $\dfrac{-a}{-b}$ and $\dfrac{a}{b}$ are equivalent but that the expressions $(-x)^2$ and $-x^2$ are *not* equivalent.

An important concept, known as the **distributive law,** is useful for finding equivalent algebraic expressions. The distributive law involves two operations: multiplication and either addition or subtraction.

To review how the distributive law works, consider the following:

$$
\begin{array}{r}
4\ 5 \\
\times\ \ \ 7 \\
\hline
3\ 5 \\
2\ 8\ 0 \\
3\ 1\ 5 \\
\end{array}
$$

3 5 ←— This is $7 \cdot 5$.
2 8 0 ←— This is $7 \cdot 40$.
3 1 5 ←— This is the sum $7 \cdot 40 + 7 \cdot 5$.

To carry out the multiplication, we actually added two products. That is,

$$7 \cdot 45 = 7(40 + 5) = 7 \cdot 40 + 7 \cdot 5.$$

The distributive law says that if we want to multiply a sum of several numbers by a number, we can either add within the grouping symbols and then multiply, or multiply each of the terms separately and then add.

THE DISTRIBUTIVE LAW

For any numbers a, b, and c,
$$a(b + c) = ab + ac.$$

Complete each table by evaluating each expression for the given values.

14.

	$3x + 2x$	$5x$
$x = 4$		
$x = -2$		
$x = 0$		

15.

	$4x - x$	$3x$
$x = 2$		
$x = -2$		
$x = 0$		

Answers on page A-7

 CALCULATOR CORNER

To evaluate an expression like $-x^3$ for $x = -14$ with a calculator, it is imperative that we keep in mind the rules for order of operations. On most calculators, this is accomplished by pressing $\boxed{1}\ \boxed{4}\ \boxed{+/-}\ \boxed{a^x}\ \boxed{3}\ \boxed{=}$ $\boxed{+/-}$. Consult your owner's manual, an instructor, or simply experiment if your calculator behaves differently.

Exercises: Evaluate.

1. $-a^5$ for $a = -3$
2. $-x^5$ for $x = -4$
3. $-x^5$ for $x = 2$
4. $-x^5$ for $x = 5$

Use the distributive law to write an equivalent expression.

16. $5(a + b)$

17. $6(x + y + z)$

Use the distributive law to write an equivalent expression.

18. $4(x - y)$

19. $3(a - b + c)$

20. $(m - 4)6$

21. $-8(2a - b + 3c)$

Answers on page A-7

CHAPTER 2: Introduction to Integers and Algebraic Expressions

■ **EXAMPLE 9** Evaluate $a(b + c)$ and $ab + ac$ for $a = 3$, $b = 4$, and $c = 2$.

We have

$$a(b + c) = 3(4 + 2) = 3 \cdot 6 = 18 \quad \text{and}$$
$$ab + ac = 3 \cdot 4 + 3 \cdot 2 = 12 + 6 = 18.$$

It is impossible to overemphasize the importance of the parentheses in the statement of the distributive law. Were we to omit the parentheses, we would have $ab + c$. To see that $a(b + c) \neq ab + c$, note that

$$3(4 + 2) \neq 3 \cdot 4 + 2$$
$$3 \cdot 6 \quad \neq \quad 12 \quad + 2$$
$$18 \neq 14.$$

■ **EXAMPLE 10** Use the distributive law to write an expression equivalent to $2(l + w)$.

$$2(l + w) = 2 \cdot l + 2 \cdot w$$
$$= 2l + 2w. \qquad \text{Try to go directly to this step.}$$

Exercises 11 and 13 on the next page can serve as a check.

Do Exercises 16 and 17.

Since subtraction can be regarded as addition of the opposite, it follows that the distributive law holds in cases involving subtraction.

■ **EXAMPLE 11** Use the distributive law to write an expression equivalent to each of the following:

a) $7(a - b);$ **b)** $9(x - 5);$ **c)** $(a - 7)b;$ **d)** $-4(x - 2y + 3z)$

a) $7(a - b) = 7 \cdot a - 7 \cdot b$
$$= 7a - 7b \qquad \text{Try to go directly to this step.}$$

Exercises 15 and 17 on the next page can serve as a check.

b) $9(x - 5) = 9x - 9(5)$
$$= 9x - 45 \qquad \text{Again, try to go directly to this step.}$$

c) $(a - 7)b = b(a - 7)$ Using a commutative law
$$= b \cdot a - b \cdot 7 \qquad \text{Using the distributive law}$$
$$= ab - 7b \qquad \text{Using a commutative law to write } ba$$
                             alphabetically and $b \cdot 7$ with the constant first.

d) $-4(x - 2y + 3z) = -4 \cdot x - (-4)(2y) + (-4)(3z)$ Using the distributive law
$$= -4x - (-4 \cdot 2)y + (-4 \cdot 3)z \qquad \text{Using an associative law (twice)}$$
$$= -4x - (-8y) + (-12z)$$
$$= -4x + 8y - 12z \qquad \text{Try to go directly to this step.}$$

Do Exercises 18–21.

EXERCISE SET

For Extra Help

Digital Video
Tutor CD 2
Videotape 2

InterAct
Math

Math Tutor
Center

MathXL

MyMathLab

a Evaluate.

1. $7t$, for $t = 2$

(The cost, in cents, of using a handheld hair dryer for 2 hr)

2. $40t$, for $t = 2$

(The cost, in cents, of using an electric range for 2 hr)

3. $\dfrac{x}{y}$, for $x = 6$ and $y = -3$

4. $\dfrac{m}{n}$, for $m = 18$ and n $= 2$

5. $\dfrac{2q}{p}$, for $p = 6$ and $q = 3$

6. $\dfrac{5y}{z}$, for $y = 15$ and $z = -25$

7. $\dfrac{72}{r}$, for $r = 6$

(The doubling time, in years, for an investment earning 6% interest per year)

8. $\dfrac{72}{i}$, for $i = 8$

(The doubling time, in years, for an investment earning 8% interest per year)

9. $3 + 5 \cdot x$, for $x = 2$

10. $9 - 2 \cdot x$, for $x = 3$

11. $2l + 2w$, for $l = 3$ and $w = 4$

(The perimeter, in feet, of a 3-ft by 4-ft rectangle)

12. $3(a + b)$, for $a = 2$ and $b = 4$

13. $2(l + w)$, for $l = 3$ and $w = 4$

(The perimeter, in feet, of a 3-ft by 4-ft rectangle)

14. $3a + 3b$, for $a = 2$ and b $= 4$

15. $7a - 7b$, for $a = 5$ and $b = 2$

16. $4x - 4y$, for $x = 6$ and $y = 1$

17. $7(a - b)$, for $a = 5$ and $b = 2$

18. $4(x - y)$, for $x = 6$ and $y = 1$

19. $16t^2$, for $t = 5$

(The distance, in feet, that an object falls in 5 sec)

20. $\dfrac{49t^2}{10}$, for $t = 10$

(The distance, in meters, that an object falls in 10 sec)

21. $a + (b - a)^2$, for $a = 6$ and $b = 4$

22. $(x + y)^2$, for $x = 2$ and $y = 3$

23. $9a + 9b$, for $a = 13$ and $b = -13$

24. $8x + 8y$, for $x = 17$ and $y = -17$

25. $\dfrac{n^2 - n}{2}$, for $n = 9$

(For determining the number of handshakes possible among 9 people)

26. $\dfrac{5(F - 32)}{9}$, for $F = 50$

(For converting 50 degrees Fahrenheit to degrees Celsius)

27. $m^3 - m^2$, for $m = 5$

28. $a^6 - a$, for $a = -2$

For each expression, write two equivalent expressions with negative signs in different places.

29. $-\dfrac{5}{t}$

30. $\dfrac{7}{-x}$

31. $\dfrac{-n}{b}$

32. $-\dfrac{3}{r}$

33. $\dfrac{9}{-p}$

34. $\dfrac{-u}{5}$

35. $\dfrac{-14}{w}$

36. $\dfrac{-23}{m}$

Evaluate $\dfrac{-a}{b}$, $\dfrac{a}{-b}$, and $-\dfrac{a}{b}$ for the given values.

37. $a = 45, b = 9$

38. $a = 40, b = 5$

39. $a = 81, b = 3$

40. $a = 56, b = 7$

CHAPTER 2: Introduction to Integers
and Algebraic Expressions

Evaluate.

41. $(-3x)^2$ and $-3x^2$, for $x = 2$

42. $(-2x)^2$ and $-2x^2$, for $x = 3$

43. $5x^2$, for $x = 3$ and $x = -3$

44. $2x^2$, for $x = 5$ and $x = -5$

45. x^3, for $x = 6$ and $x = -6$

46. x^6, for $x = 2$ and $x = -2$

47. x^8, for $x = 1$ and $x = -1$

48. x^5, for $x = 3$ and $x = -3$

49. a^7, for $a = 2$ and $a = -2$

50. a^7, for $a = 1$ and $a = -1$

b   Use the distributive law to write an equivalent expression.

51. $5(a + b)$

52. $7(x + y)$

53. $4(x + 1)$

54. $6(a + 1)$

55. $2(b + 5)$

56. $4(x + 3)$

57. $7(1 - t)$

58. $4(1 - y)$

59. $6(5x + 2)$

60. $9(6m + 7)$

61. $8(x + 7 + 6y)$

62. $4(5x + 8 + 3p)$

63. $-7(y - 2)$

64. $-9(y - 7)$

65. $(x + 2)3$

66. $(x + 4)2$

67. $-4(x - 3y - 2z)$

68. $8(2x - 5y - 8z)$

69. $8(a - 3b + c)$

70. $-6(a + 2b - c)$

71. $4(x - 3y - 7z)$

72. $5(9x - y + 8z)$

73. $(4a - 5b + c - 2d)5$

74. $(9a - 4b + 3c - d)7$

75. **D_W**   Does $-\dfrac{x}{y}$ always represent a negative number?
Why or why not?

76. **D_W**   Is $-x^2$ always negative? Why or why not?

77. Write a word name for 23,043,921. [1.1c]

78. Multiply: $17 \cdot 53$. [1.5a]

79. Estimate by rounding to the nearest ten. Show your work. [1.4b]

$$\begin{array}{r} 5\ 2\ 8\ 3 \\ -\ 2\ 4\ 7\ 5 \\ \hline \end{array}$$

80. Divide: $2982 \div 3$. [1.6c]

81. On January 6, it snowed 9 in., and on January 7, it snowed 8 in. How much did it snow altogether? [1.8a]

82. On March 9, it snowed 12 in., but on March 10, the sun melted 7 in. How much snow remained? [1.8a]

83. For Chucko's party his wife ordered two plain pizzas at $11 apiece and two pepperoni pizzas for $13 apiece. How much did she pay for the pizza? [1.8a]

84. For Tania's graduation party her husband ordered three buckets of chicken wings at $12 apiece and 3 trays of nachos at $9 a tray. How much did he pay for the wings and nachos? [1.8a]

85. ^{D}W Under what condition(s) will the expression ax^2 be nonnegative? Explain.

86. ^{D}W Ted evaluates $a + a^2$ for $a = 5$ and gets 100 as the result. What mistake did he probably make?

87. A car's catalytic converter works most efficiently after it is heated to about 370° Celsius. To what Fahrenheit temperature does this correspond? (*Hint*: see Example 5.)

Evaluate.

88. $\boxplus$ $x^2 - xy^2 \div 2 \cdot y$, for $x = 24$ and $y = 6$

89. $\boxplus$ $a - b^3 + 17a$, for $a = 19$ and $b = -16$

90. $\boxplus$ $x^2 - 23y + y^3$, for $x = 18$ and $y = -21$

91. $\boxplus$ $r^3 + r^2t - rt^2$, for $r = -9$ and $t = 7$

92. $\boxplus$ $a^3b - a^2b^2 + ab^3$, for $a = -8$ and $b = -6$

93. $a^{1996} - a^{1997}$, for $a = -1$

94. $x^{1492} - x^{1493}$, for $x = -1$

95. $(m^3 - mn)^m$, for $m = 4$ and $n = 6$

96. $5a^{3a-4}$, for $a = 2$

Replace the blanks with $\boxed{+}$, $\boxed{-}$, $\boxed{\times}$, or $\boxed{\div}$ to make each statement true.

97. $\boxplus$ $-32 \,\square\, (88 \,\square\, 29) = -1888$

98. $\boxplus$ $59 \,\square\, 17 \,\square\, 59 \,\square\, 8 = 1475$

Classify each statement as true or false. If false, write an example showing why.

99. For any choice of x, $x^2 = (-x)^2$.

100. For any choice of x, $x^3 = -x^3$.

101. For any choice of x, $x^6 + x^4 = (-x)^6 + (-x)^4$.

102. For any choice of x, $(-3x)^2 = 9x^2$.

103. ^{D}W If the Fahrenheit temperature is doubled, does it follow that the corresponding Celsius temperature is also doubled?

2.7 LIKE TERMS AND PERIMETER

a Combine like terms.

b Determine the perimeter of a polygon.

One common way in which equivalent expressions are formed is by *combining like terms*. In this section we learn how this is accomplished and apply the concept to geometry.

a Combining Like Terms

A **term** is a number, a variable, a product of numbers and/or variables, or a quotient of numbers and/or variables. Terms are separated by addition signs. If there are subtraction signs, we can find an equivalent expression that uses addition signs.

EXAMPLE 1 What are the terms of $3x - 4y + \dfrac{2}{z}$?

$$3x - 4y + \frac{2}{z} = 3x + (-4y) + \frac{2}{z} \quad \text{Separating parts with + signs}$$

The terms are $3x$, $-4y$, and $\dfrac{2}{z}$.

EXAMPLE 2 What are the terms of $5xy + 3x^2 - 8$?

$$5xy + 3x^2 - 8 = 5xy + 3x^2 + (-8) \quad \text{Separating parts with + signs}$$

The terms are $5xy$, $3x^2$, and 8.

Do Exercises 1 and 2.

Terms in which the variable factors are exactly the same, such as $9x$ and $-4x$, are called **like**, or **similar, terms.** For example, $3y^2$ and $7y^2$ are like terms, whereas $5x$ and $6x^2$ are not. Constants, like 7 and 3, are also like terms.

EXAMPLES Identify the like terms.

3. $7x + 5x^2 + 2x + 8 + 5x^3 + 1$

   $7x$ and $2x$ are like terms; 8 and 1 are like terms.

4. $5ab + a^3 - a^2b - 2ab + 7a^3$

   $5ab$ and $-2ab$ are like terms; a^3 and $7a^3$ are like terms.

Do Exercises 3 and 4.

When an algebraic expression contains like terms, an equivalent expression can be formed by **combining, or collecting, like terms.** To combine like terms, we rely on the distributive law even though that step is often not written out.

What are the terms of each expression?

1. $5x - 4y + 3$

2. $-4y - 2x + \dfrac{x}{y}$

Identify the like terms.

3. $9a^3 + 4ab + a^3 + 3ab + 7$

4. $3xy - 5x^2 + y^2 - 4xy + y$

Answers on page A-7

183

2.7 Like Terms and Perimeter

Combine like terms to form an equivalent expression.

5. $2a + 7a$

6. $5x^2 - 9 + 2x^2 + 3$

7. $4m - 2n^2 + 5 + n^2 + m - 9$

Find the perimeter of each polygon.

8.

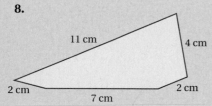

9.

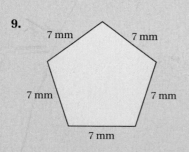

Answers on page A-7

EXAMPLE 5 Combine like terms to form an equivalent expression:

a) $4x + 3x$ b) $6mn - 7mn$

c) $7y - 2 - 3y + 5$ d) $2a^5 + 9ab + 3 + a^5 - 7 - 4ab$

a) $4x + 3x = (4 + 3)x$ Using the distributive law (in "reverse")
        $= 7x$ We usually go directly to this step.

b) $6mn - 7mn = (6 - 7)mn$ Try to do this mentally
              $= -1mn$, or simply $-mn$

c) $7y - 2 - 3y + 5 = 7y + (-2) + (-3y) + 5$ Rewriting as addition
                 $= 7y + (-3y) + (-2) + 5$ Using a commutative law
                 $= 4y + 3$ Try to go directly to this step.

d) $2a^5 + 9ab + 3 + a^5 - 7 - 4ab$
    $= 2a^5 + 9ab + 3 + a^5 + (-7) + (-4ab)$
    $= 2a^5 + a^5 + 9ab + (-4ab) + 3 + (-7)$ Rearranging terms
    $= 3a^5 + 5ab + (-4)$ Think of a^5 as $1a^5$;
                            $2a^5 + a^5 = 3a^5$

    $= 3a^5 + 5ab - 4$

As you gain experience, you will perform several of these steps mentally.

Do Exercises 5–7.

b   Perimeter

PERIMETER OF A POLYGON

A **polygon** is a closed geometric figure with three or more sides. The **perimeter** of a polygon is the distance around it, or the sum of the lengths of its sides.

EXAMPLE 6 Find the perimeter of this polygon.

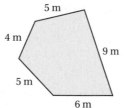

A polygon with five sides is called a pentagon

We add the lengths of all sides. Since all the units are the same, we are effectively combining like terms.

     Perimeter $= 6\,m + 5\,m + 4\,m + 5\,m + 9\,m$

              $= (6 + 5 + 4 + 5 + 9)\,m$ Using the distributive law

              $= 29\,m$ Try to go directly to this step.

CAUTION!

When units of measurement are given in the statement of a problem, as in Example 6, the solution should also contain units of measurement.

Do Exercises 8 and 9.

A **rectangle** is a polygon with four sides and four 90° angles. Opposite sides of a rectangle have the same measure. The symbol ⌐ or ⌐ indicates a 90° angle. A 90° angle is often referred to as a **right angle.**

EXAMPLE 7 Find the perimeter of a rectangle that is 3 cm by 4 cm.

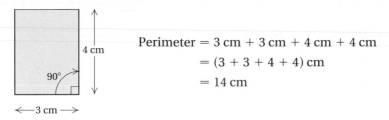

Perimeter = 3 cm + 3 cm + 4 cm + 4 cm

= (3 + 3 + 4 + 4) cm

= 14 cm

Do Exercise 10.

The perimeter of the rectangle in Example 7 is 2 · 3 cm + 2 · 4 cm, or equivalently 2(3 cm + 4 cm). This can be generalized, as follows.

PERIMETER OF A RECTANGLE

The **perimeter P of a rectangle** of length l and width w is given by

$$P = 2l + 2w, \quad \text{or} \quad P = 2 \cdot (l + w).$$

EXAMPLE 8 A common door size is 3 ft by 7 ft. Find the perimeter of such a door.

$P = 2l + 2w$ We could also use $P = 2(l + w)$.

$= 2 \cdot 7 \text{ ft} + 2 \cdot 3 \text{ ft}$

$= (2 \cdot 7) \text{ ft} + (2 \cdot 3) \text{ ft}$ Try to do this mentally.

$= 14 \text{ ft} + 6 \text{ ft}$

$= 20 \text{ ft}$ Combining like terms

The perimeter of the door is 20 ft.

Do Exercise 11.

A **square** is a rectangle in which all sides have the same length.

EXAMPLE 9 Find the perimeter of a square with sides of length 9 mm.

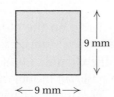

$P = 9 \text{ mm} + 9 \text{ mm} + 9 \text{ mm} + 9 \text{ mm}$

$= (9 + 9 + 9 + 9) \text{ mm}$ Note that $9 + 9 + 9 + 9 = 4 \cdot 9$

$= 36 \text{ mm}$

Do Exercise 12.

10. Find the perimeter of a rectangle that is 2 cm by 4 cm.

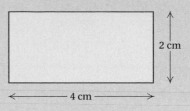

11. Find the perimeter of a 4-ft by 8-ft sheet of plywood.

12. Find the perimeter of a square with sides of length 10 km.

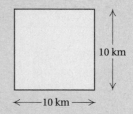

Answers on page A-7

13. Find the perimeter of a square sandbox with sides of length 6 ft.

Answers on page A-7

PERIMETER OF A SQUARE

The **perimeter P of a square** is four times s, the length of a side:

$$P = s + s + s + s$$
$$= 4s.$$

■ **EXAMPLE 10** Find the perimeter of a square garden with sides of length 12 ft.

$$P = 4s$$
$$= 4 \cdot 12 \text{ ft}$$
$$= 48 \text{ ft}$$

The perimeter of the garden is 48 ft.

Do Exercise 13.

Study Tips

PROPER PREPARATION PREVENTS POOR PERFORMANCE

The best way to prepare for taking tests is by working consistently throughout the course. That said, here are some extra suggestions.

- ■ **Make up your own test questions as you study.** You have probably become accustomed by now to the section and objective codes that appear throughout the book. After you have done your homework for a particular objective, write one or two questions on your own like those that might be on a test. This allows you to carry out a task similar to what a teacher does in preparing an exam. You will be amazed at the insight this will provide.
- ■ **Do an overall review of the chapter focusing on the objectives and the examples.** This should be accomplished by a thorough review of any class notes you have taken.
- ■ **Do the review exercises at the end of the chapter.** Check your answers at the back of the book. If you have trouble with an exercise, use the objective symbol as a guide to go back for further study of that objective. These review exercises are very much like a sample test.
- ■ **Do the chapter test at the end of the chapter.** This is like taking a second sample test. Check the answers and objective symbols at the back of the book.
- ■ **Ask your instructor or former students for old exams.** Working such exams can be very helpful and allows you to see what your instructor thinks is important.

EXERCISE SET

For Extra Help

a   List the terms of each expression.

1. $2a + 5b - 7c$

2. $4x - 6y + 7z$

3. $9mn - 6n + 8$

4. $7rs + 4s - 5$

5. $3x^2y - 4y^2 - 2z^3$

6. $4a^3b + ab^2 - 9b^3$

Combine like terms to form an equivalent expression.

7. $5x + 9x$

8. $9a + 7a$

9. $10a - 13a$

10. $-16x + x$

11. $2x + 6z + 9x$

12. $3a - 5b + 7a$

13. $27a + 70 - 40a - 8$

14. $42x - 6 - 4x + 2$

15. $9 + 5t + 7y - t - y - 13$

16. $8 - 4a + 9b + 7a - 3b - 15$

17. $a + 3b + 5a - 2 + b$

18. $x + 7y + 5 - 2y + 3x$

19. $-8 + 11a - 5b + 6a - 7b + 7$

20. $8x - 5x + 6 + 3y - 2y - 4$

21. $8x^2 + 3y - 2x^2$

22. $8y^3 - 3z + 4y^3$

23. $11x^4 + 2y^3 - 4x^4 - y^3$

24. $13a^5 + 9b^4 - 2a^5 - 4b^4$

25. $9a^2 - 4a + a - 3a^2$

26. $3a^2 + 7a^3 - a^2 + 5 + a^3$

27. $x^3 - 5x^2 + 2x^3 - 3x^2 + 4$

28. $9xy + 4y^2 - 2xy + 2y^2 - 1$

29. $7a^3 + 4ab - 5 - 7ab + 8$

30. $8a^2b - 3ab^2 - 4a^2b + 2ab$

31. $9x^3y + 4xy^3 - 6xy^3 + 3xy$

32. $3x^4 - 2y^4 + 8x^4y^4 - 7x^4 + 8y^4$

33. $3a^6 - 9b^4 + 2a^6b^4 - 7a^6 - 2b^4$

34. $9x^6 - 5y^5 + 3x^6y - 8x^6 + 4y^5$

b   Find the perimeter of each polygon.

35.
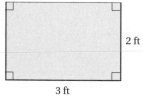
2 ft
3 ft

36.
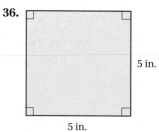
5 in.
5 in.

37.
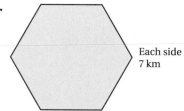
Each side
7 km

38.
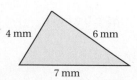
4 mm   6 mm
7 mm

39.
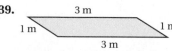
3 m
1 m   1 m
3 m

40.
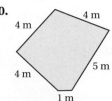
4 m
4 m
4 m
5 m
1 m

Soccer Field. A soccer field contains many rectangles. Use the diagram of a regulation soccer field (at right) to find the perimeter of each of the following rectangles.

41. The perimeter of the largest possible regulation field

42. The perimeter of the smallest possible regulation field

43. The perimeter of each goal area

44. The perimeter of each penalty area

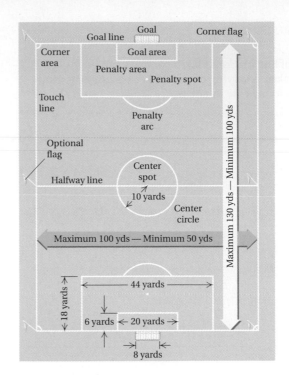

45. Find the perimeter of an 8-ft by 10-ft bedroom.

46. Find the perimeter of a 3-ft by 4-ft doghouse.

47. Find the perimeter of a checkerboard that is 14 in. on each side.

48. Find the perimeter of a square skylight that is 2 m on each side.

49. Find the perimeter of a square frame that is 65 cm on each side.

50. Find the perimeter of a square garden that is 12 yd on each side.

51. Find the perimeter of a 12-ft by 20-ft deck.

52. Find the perimeter of a 40-ft by 35-ft backyard.

53. **D**_W Explain in your own words what it means for two algebraic expressions to be equivalent.

54. **D**_W Can the formula for the perimeter of a rectangle be used to find the perimeter of a square? Why or why not?

55. A box of Shaw's Corn Flakes contains 510 grams (g) of corn flakes. A serving of corn flakes weighs 30 g. How many servings are in one box?   [1.8a]

56. Estimate the difference by rounding to the nearest ten. [1.4b]

$$\begin{array}{r} 7\ 0\ 4 \\ -\ 4\ 8\ 6 \end{array}$$

Simplify.   [1.9c]

57. $5 + 3 \cdot 2^3$

58. $(9 - 7)^4 - 3^2$

59. $12 \div 3 \cdot 2$

60. $27 \div 3(2 + 1)$

61. $15 - 3 \cdot 2 + 7$

62. $30 - 4^2 \div 8 \cdot 2$

Solve.   [1.7b]

63. $25 = t + 9$

64. $19 = x + 6$

65. $45 = 3x$

66. $50 = 2t$

67. **D**_W Does doubling the length of a square's side double the perimeter of the original square? Why or why not?

68. **D**_W Why was it necessary to introduce the distributive law before discussing how to combine like terms?

Simplify. (Multiply and then combine like terms.)

69. $5(x + 3) + 2(x - 7)$

70. $3(a - 7) + 7(a + 4)$

71. $2(3 - 4a) + 5(a - 7)$

72. $7(2 - 5x) + 3(x - 8)$

73. $-5(2 + 3x + 4y) + 7(2x - y)$

74. $3(4 - 2x) + 5(9x - 3y + 1)$

75. In order to save energy, Andrea plans to run a bead of caulk sealant around 3 exterior doors and 13 windows. Each window measures 3 ft by 4 ft, each door measures 3 ft by 7 ft, and there is no need to caulk the bottom of each door. If each cartridge of caulk seals 56 ft and costs $5.95, how much will it cost Andrea to seal the windows and doors?

76. Eric is attaching lace trim to small tablecloths that are 5 ft by 5 ft, and to large tablecloths that are 7 ft by 7 ft. If the lace costs $1.95 per yard, how much will the trim cost for 6 small tablecloths and 6 large tablecloths?

77. 🖩 A square wooden rack is used to store the 15 numbered balls as well as the cue ball in pool. If a pool ball has a diameter of 57 mm, find the inside perimeter of the storage rack.

78. A rectangular box is used to store six Christmas ornaments. Find the perimeter of such a box if each ornament has a diameter of 72 mm.

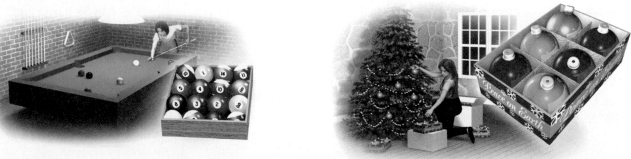

2.8 SOLVING EQUATIONS

Objectives

a Use the addition principle to solve equations.

b Use the division principle to solve equations.

c Decide which principle should be used to solve an equation.

d Solve equations that require use of both the addition principle and the division principle.

In Section 1.7, we learned to solve certain equations by writing a "related equation." We now extend this approach to include negative integers, as well as equations that involve both addition and multiplication.

a The Addition Principle

In Section 1.7, we learned to solve an equation like $x + 12 = 27$ by writing the related subtraction, $x = 27 - 12$, or $x = 15$. Note that $x = 15$ is an equation, not a solution. Of course, the solution of the equation $x = 15$ is obviously 15.

Note that the solution of $x + 12 = 27$ is also 15. Because their solutions are identical, $x = 15$ and $x + 12 = 27$ are said to be **equivalent equations.**

> **EQUIVALENT EQUATIONS**
>
> Equations with the same solutions are called **equivalent equations.**

It is important to be able to distinguish between equivalent *expressions* and equivalent *equations.*

- $6a$ and $4a + 2a$ are equivalent *expressions* because, for any replacement of a, both expressions represent the same number.
- $3x = 15$ and $4x - 20$ are equivalent *equations* because any solution of one equation is also a solution of the other equation.

EXAMPLE 1 Classify each pair as either equivalent equations or equivalent expressions:

a) $5x + 1$; $2x$ $4 + 3x + 5$

b) $x = -7$; $x + 2 = -5.$

a) Combining like terms, we have

$$2x - 4 + 3x + 5 = (2 + 3)x + (-4 + 5) \qquad \text{Regrouping and using the distributive law}$$

$$= 5x + 1.$$

We see that $2x - 4 + 3x + 5$ and $5x + 1$ are *equivalent expressions*.

b) If we subtract 2 from both sides of the equation $x + 2 = -5$, we have

$$x + 2 - 2 = -5 - 2, \quad \text{or}$$
$$x + 0 = -7, \quad \text{or}$$
$$x = -7.$$

We see that $x = -7$ and $x + 2 = -5$ are *equivalent equations*.

Do Exercises 1 and 2.

There are principles that enable us to begin with one equation and create an equivalent equation similar to $x = 15$, for which the solution is obvious. One such principle, the *addition principle*, is stated on the next page.

Suppose that a and b stand for the same number and some number c is added to a. We get the same result if we add c to b, because a and b are equal.

Classify each pair as equivalent expressions or equivalent equations.

1. $a - 5 = -3$; $a = 2$

2. $a - 9 + 6a$; $7a - 9$

Answers on page A-8

Solve.

3. $x - 5 = 19$

4. $x - 9 = -12$

Solve.

5. $42 = x + 17$

6. $a + 8 = -6$

Answers on page A-8

Study Tips

TO ERR IS HUMAN

It is no coincidence that the students who experience the greatest success in this course work in pencil. We all make mistakes and by using pencil and eraser we are more willing to admit to ourselves that something needs to be rewritten. Please work with a pencil and eraser if you aren't doing so already.

THE ADDITION PRINCIPLE

For any numbers a, b, and c,
$$a = b \quad \text{is equivalent to} \quad a + c = b + c.$$

EXAMPLE 2 Solve: $x - 7 = -2$.

We have

$$x - 7 = -2$$
$$x - 7 + 7 = -2 + 7 \qquad \text{Using the addition principle:} \\ \text{adding 7 to both sides}$$
$$x + 0 = 5 \qquad \text{Adding 7 "undoes" the subtraction of 7.}$$
$$x = 5.$$

The solution appears to be 5. To check, we use the original equation.

CHECK: $\quad x - 7 = -2$
$$\overline{5 - 7 \; ? \; -2}$$
$$-2 \;| \qquad \text{TRUE}$$

The solution is 5.

Do Exercises 3 and 4.

Recall from Section 2.3 that subtraction can be regarded as adding the opposite of the number being subtracted. Because of this, the addition principle allows us to produce equivalent equations by subtracting the same number from both sides of an equation.

EXAMPLE 3 Solve: $23 = t + 7$.

We have

$$23 = t + 7$$
$$23 - 7 = t + 7 - 7 \qquad \text{Using the addition principle to add } -7 \\ \text{or to subtract 7 on both sides}$$
$$16 = t + 0 \qquad \text{Subtracting 7 "undoes" the addition of 7.}$$
$$16 = t.$$

The solution is 16. The check is left to the student.

To visualize the addition principle, think of a jeweler's balance. When both sides of the balance hold equal amounts of weight, the balance is level. If weight is added or removed, equally, on both sides, the balance remains level.

$a = b$ $\qquad\qquad$ $a + c = b + c$

Do Exercises 5 and 6.

b The Division Principle

In Section 1.7, we solved $8n = 96$ by dividing both sides by 8:

$$8 \cdot n = 96$$

$$\frac{8 \cdot n}{8} = \frac{96}{8} \qquad \text{Dividing both sides by 8}$$

$$n = 12. \qquad \text{8 times } n \text{, divided by 8, is } n. \ 96 \div 8 \text{ is 12.}$$

You can check that $8 \cdot n = 96$ and $n = 12$ are equivalent. We can divide both sides of an equation by any nonzero number in order to find an equivalent equation.

> ### THE DIVISION PRINCIPLE
>
> For any numbers a, b, and c ($c \neq 0$),
>
> $$a = b \quad \text{is equivalent to} \quad \frac{a}{c} = \frac{b}{c}.$$

In Chapter 3, after we have discussed multiplication of fractions, we will use an equivalent form of this principle: the multiplication principle.

EXAMPLE 4 Solve: $9x = 63$.

We have

$$9x = 63$$

$$\frac{9x}{9} = \frac{63}{9} \qquad \begin{array}{l}\text{Using the division principle to} \\ \text{divide both sides by 9}\end{array}$$

$$x = 7.$$

CHECK: $$\frac{9x = 63}{9 \cdot 7 \ ? \ 63}$$
$$63 \ | \qquad \textbf{TRUE}$$

The solution is 7.

Do Exercises 7 and 8.

EXAMPLE 5 Solve: $48 = -8n$.

It is important to distinguish between a negative sign, as we have in $-8n$, and a minus sign, as we had in $x - 5 = 19$ (margin exercise 3). To undo multiplication by -8, we use the division principle:

$$48 = -8n$$

$$\frac{48}{-8} = \frac{-8n}{-8} \qquad \text{Dividing both sides by } -8$$

$$-6 = n.$$

CHECK: $$\frac{48 = -8n}{48 \ ? \ -8(-6)}$$
$$| \ 48 \qquad \textbf{TRUE}$$

The solution is -6.

Solve.

7. $7x = 42$

8. $-24 = 3t$

Solve.

9. $63 = -7n$

10. $-6x = 72$

Answers on page A-8

Solve.

11. $-x = 23$

12. $-t = -3$

Be sure that you understand why the addition principle is used in Example 2 and the division principle is used in Example 5.

Do Exercises 9 and 10 on the previous page.

Equations like $-x = 7$ or $-t = -3$ often give students difficulty. One way to handle problems of this sort is to multiply both sides of the equation by -1.

EXAMPLE 6 Solve: $-x = 7$.

To solve an equation like $-x = 7$, remember that when an expression is multiplied or divided by -1, its sign is changed. Here we multiply on both sides by -1 to change the sign of $-x$:

$$-x = 7$$
$$(-1)(-x) = (-1) \cdot 7 \qquad \text{Multiplying both sides by } -1$$
$$x = -7 \qquad \text{Note that } (-1)(-x) \text{ is the same as } (-1)(-1)x.$$

CHECK: $\dfrac{-x = 7}{-(-7) \ ? \ 7}$
$$7 \ | \ 7 \quad \textbf{TRUE}$$

The solution is -7.

Do Exercises 11 and 12.

C Selecting the Correct Approach

It is important for you to be able to determine which principle should be used to solve a particular equation.

EXAMPLES Solve.

7. $39 = -3 + t$

To undo addition of -3, we subtract -3 or simply add 3 on both sides:

$$3 + 39 = 3 + (-3) + t \qquad \text{Using the addition principle}$$
$$42 = 0 + t$$
$$42 = t.$$

CHECK: $\dfrac{39 = -3 + t}{39 \ ? \ -3 + 42}$
$$| \ 39 \qquad \textbf{TRUE}$$

The solution is 42.

8. $39 = -3t$

To undo multiplication by -3, we divide by -3 on both sides:

$$39 = -3t$$

$$\frac{39}{-3} = \frac{-3t}{-3} \qquad \text{Using the division principle}$$

$$-13 = t.$$

CHECK: $\dfrac{39 = -3t}{39 \;?\; -3(-13)}$

$\qquad\qquad \begin{array}{c|c} & 39 \end{array}$ **TRUE**

The solution is -13.

Do Exercises 13–15.

d Using the Principles Together

Suppose we want to determine whether 7 is the solution of $5x - 8 = 27$. To check, we replace x with 7 and simplify.

CHECK: $\dfrac{5x - 8 = 27}{5 \cdot 7 - 8 \;?\; 27}$

$\qquad\quad \begin{array}{c|c} 35 - 8 & \\ 27 & 27 \end{array}$ **TRUE**

This shows that 7 *is* the solution.

Do Exercises 16 and 17.

In the check above, note that the rules for order of operations require that we multiply before we subtract (or add).

CONNECTING THE CONCEPTS

The rules for order of operations dictate that unless grouping symbols indicate otherwise, multiplication and division are performed before any addition or subtraction. Thus, to evaluate $5x - 8$,

we *select* a value: $\qquad x$

then *multiply* by 5: $\qquad 5x$

and then *subtract* 8: $\qquad 5x - 8.$

In Example 9 that follows, these steps are reversed to solve for x:

we will *add* 8: $\qquad 5x - 8 + 8,$

then *divide* by 5: $\qquad \dfrac{5x}{5}$

and *isolate* x: $\qquad x$

In general, the last step performed in an algebraic calculation is the first step reversed when finding a solution.

Solve.

13. $-2x = -52$

14. $-2 + x = -52$

15. $x \cdot 7 = -28$

16. Determine whether -9 is the solution of $7x + 8 = -55.$

17. Determine whether -6 is the solution of $4x + 3 = -25.$

Answers on page A-8

18. Solve: $2x - 9 = 43$

19. Solve: $-3x + 2 = 47$

EXAMPLE 9 Solve: $5x - 8 = 27$.

We first isolate $5x$ by adding 8 on both sides:

$$5x - 8 = 27$$
$$5x - 8 + 8 = 27 + 8 \qquad \text{Using the addition principle}$$
$$5x + 0 = 35 \qquad \text{Try to do this step mentally.}$$
$$5x = 35.$$

Next, we isolate x by dividing by 5 on both sides:

$$5x = 35$$
$$\frac{5x}{5} = \frac{35}{5} \qquad \text{Using the division principle}$$
$$1x = 7 \qquad \text{Try to do this step mentally.}$$
$$x = 7.$$

The check was performed on the previous page. The solution is 7.

Do Exercise 18.

EXAMPLE 10 Solve: $38 = 9x + 2$.

We first isolate $9x$ by subtracting 2 on both sides:

$$38 = 9x + 2$$
$$38 - 2 = 9x + 2 - 2 \qquad \text{Subtracting 2 (or adding } -2\text{) from both sides}$$
$$36 = 9x + 0 \qquad \text{Try to do this step mentally.}$$
$$36 = 9x.$$

Now that we have isolated $9x$ on one side of the equation, we can divide by 9 to isolate x:

$$36 = 9x$$
$$\frac{36}{9} = \frac{9x}{9} \qquad \text{Dividing both sides by 9}$$
$$4 = x. \qquad \text{Simplifying}$$

CHECK: $\dfrac{38 = 9x + 2}{38 \ ? \ 9 \cdot 4 + 2}$
$$\begin{array}{c|c} & 36 + 2 \\ 38 & 38 \qquad \textbf{TRUE} \end{array}$$

The solution is 4.

Do Exercise 19.

Answer on page A-8

196

CHAPTER 2: Introduction to Integers
and Algebraic Expressions

2.8
EXERCISE SET

For Extra Help

Digital Video
Tutor CD 2
Videotape 2

InterAct
Math

Math Tutor
Center

MathXL

MyMathLab

a Classify each pair as either equivalent expressions or equivalent equations.

1. $2x = 10; 5x = 25$

2. $4x + 1; 3x + 1 + x$

3. $7a - 3; 4a - 3 + 3a$

4. $7t = 14; 4t = 8$

5. $4r + 3; 8 + 4r - 5$

6. $2r - 7; r - 7 + r$

7. $x - 9 = 8; x + 3 = 20$

8. $t - 4 = 9; t + 8 = 21$

9. $3(t + 2); 5 + 3t + 1$

10. $2x = -14; x - 2 = -9$

11. $x + 4 = -8; 2x = -24$

12. $4(x - 7); 3x - 28 + x$

Solve.

13. $x - 6 = -9$

14. $x - 5 = -7$

15. $x - 4 = -12$

16. $x - 7 = 5$

17. $a + 7 = 25$

18. $x + 9 = -3$

19. $x + 8 = -6$

20. $t + 5 = 13$

21. $24 = t - 8$

22. $-9 - x + 3$

23. $-12 = x + 5$

24. $17 = n - 6$

25. $-5 + a = 12$

26. $3 = 17 + x$

27. $-8 = -8 + t$

28. $-7 + t = 7$

b Solve.

29. $6x = -24$

30. $-8t = 40$

31. $-3t = 42$

32. $3x = 24$

33. $-7n = -35$

34. $64 = -2t$

35. $0 = 6x$

36. $-5n = -65$

37. $55 = -5t$

38. $-x = 83$

39. $-x = 56$

40. $-2x = 0$

41. $n(-4) = -48$

42. $-x = -475$

43. $-x = -390$

44. $n(-6) = -42$

c Solve.

45. $t - 6 = -2$

46. $3t = -45$

47. $6x = -54$

48. $x + 9 = -15$

49. $8 + x = 43$

50. $37 = -x$

51. $18 = x - 27$

52. $-42 = -x$

53. $35 = -7t$

54. $7 + t = -18$

55. $17x = -68$

56. $-34 = x + 10$

57. $18 + t = -160$

58. $-48 = t(-12)$

59. $-27 = x + 23$

60. $-135 = -9t$

d Solve.

61. $5x - 1 = 34$

62. $7x - 3 = 25$

63. $4t + 2 = 14$

64. $3t + 5 = 26$

65. $6a + 1 = -17$

66. $8a + 3 = -37$

67. $2x - 9 = -23$

68. $3x - 5 = -35$

69. $-2x + 1 = 17$

70. $-4t + 3 = -17$

71. $-8t - 3 = -67$

72. $-7x - 4 = -46$

73. $-x + 9 = -15$

74. $-x - 6 = 8$

75. $7 = 2x - 5$

76. $9 = 4x - 7$

77. $13 = 3 + 2x$

78. $33 = 5 - 4x$

79. $13 = 5 - x$

80. $12 = 7 - x$

81. **Dw** To solve $-5x = 13$, Eva decides to add 5 to both sides of the equation. Is there anything wrong with her doing this? Why or why not?

82. **Dw** Gary decides to solve $x - 9 = -5$ by adding 5 to both sides of the equation. Is there anything wrong with his doing this? Why or why not?

SKILL MAINTENANCE

Perform the indicated operation.   [1.5a, 1.6c]

83. $3 \cdot 59$

84. $5 \cdot 43$

85. $249 \div 3$

86. $462 \div 3$

87. $5 \cdot 91$

88. $3 \cdot 83$

89. $5481 \div 9$

90. $7353 \div 9$

91. $437 \cdot 9$

92. $724 \cdot 9$

93. $7320 \div 6$

94. $6894 \div 6$

SYNTHESIS

95. **Dw** Explain how equivalent expressions can be used to write equivalent equations.

96. **Dw** To solve $2x + 8 = 24$, Wilma divides both sides by 2. Can this first step lead to a solution? Why or why not?

Solve.

97. $2x - 7x = -40$

98. $9 + x - 5 = 23$

99. $17 - 3^2 = 4 + t - 5^2$

100. $(-9)^2 = 2^3 t + (3 \cdot 6 + 1)t$

101. $(-7)^2 - 5 = t + 4^3$

102. ▦ $(-42)^3 = 14^2 t$

103. ▦ $x - (19)^3 = -18^3$

104. ▦ $23^2 = x + 22^2$

105. ▦ $35^3 = -125t$

106. ▦ $248 = 24 - 32x$

107. ▦ $529 - 143x = -1902$

CHAPTER 2: Introduction to Integers
and Algebraic Expressions

2.9

ADDITION AND SUBTRACTION OF POLYNOMIALS

Objectives

a Add polynomials.

b Find the opposite of a polynomial.

c Subtract polynomials.

d Evaluate a polynomial.

In Section 2.7, we defined a *term* as a number, a variable, a product of numbers and/or variables, or a quotient of numbers and/or variables. Thus, expressions like

$$5x^2, \quad -34, \quad \frac{3}{4}ab^2, \quad xy^3z^5, \quad \text{and} \quad \frac{7n}{m}$$

are terms. A term is called a **monomial** if there is no division by a variable expression. Thus all of the terms above, except for $7n/m$, are monomials. Monomials are used to form **polynomials** like the following:

$$a^2b + c^3, \quad 5y + 3, \quad 3x^2 + 2x - 5, \quad -7a^3 + \tfrac{1}{2}a, \quad 37p^4, \quad x, \quad 0.$$

POLYNOMIAL

A **polynomial** is a monomial or a combination of sums and/or differences of monomials.

The following algebraic expressions are *not* polynomials, because each involves division by a variable expression:

$$\frac{x + 3}{x - 4}, \quad 5x^3 - 2x^2 + \frac{1}{x}, \quad \frac{1}{x^3 - 2}.$$

a   Adding Polynomials

Recall that the commutative and associative laws are often used to make addition easier to perform. For example,

$$(9 + 17) + (1 + 13)$$

can be rewritten as the equivalent expression

$$(9 + 1) + (17 + 13), \quad \text{or} \quad 10 + 30.$$

A similar approach can be used for adding polynomials. Recall that when two terms have the same variable(s) raised to the same power(s), they are "like" terms and can be combined.

EXAMPLE 1   Add: $(5x^3 + 4x^2 + 3x) + (2x^3 + 5x^2 - x)$.

$$(5x^3 + 4x^2 + 3x) + (2x^3 + 5x^2 - x)$$
$$= (5x^3 + 2x^3) + (4x^2 + 5x^2) + (3x - x) \qquad \text{Using the commutative and associative laws to pair up like terms}$$

$$= 7x^3 + 9x^2 + 2x \qquad \text{Combining like terms. Remember that } x \text{ means } 1x.$$

Often, the terms do not all form pairs of like terms.

Add.

1. $(7a^2 + 2a + 8) + (2a^2 + a - 9)$

2. $(5x^2y + 3x^2 + 4) + (2x^2y + 4x)$

3. $(2a^3 + 17) + (2a^2 - 9a)$

EXAMPLE 2 Add: $(3a^2 + 7a^2b) + (5a^2 - 6ab^2)$.

$(3a^2 + 7a^2b) + (5a^2 - 6ab^2) = (3a^2 + 5a^2) + 7a^2b - 6ab^2$ $7a^2b$ and $-6ab^2$ are *not* like terms.

$= 8a^2 + 7a^2b - 6ab^2$ Combining like terms

EXAMPLE 3 Add: $(7x^2 + 5) + (5x^3 + 4x)$.

$(7x^2 + 5) + (5x^3 + 4x) = 7x^2 + 5 + 5x^3 + 4x$ There are no like terms here.

$= 5x^3 + 7x^2 + 4x + 5$ Rearranging the order

Note that in Example 3 we wrote the answer so that the powers of x decrease as we read from left to right. This **descending order** is the traditional way of expressing an answer, especially when the polynomials in the statement of the problem are given in descending order.

Do Exercises 1–3.

b   Opposites of Polynomials

To subtract a number, we can add its opposite. We can similarly subtract a polynomial by adding its opposite. To check if two polynomials are opposites, recall that 5 and -5 are opposites, because $5 + (-5) = 0$.

> ### THE OPPOSITE OF A POLYNOMIAL
>
> Two polynomials are **opposites,** or **additive inverses,** of each other if their sum is zero.

To understand how to take the opposite of a polynomial, note that

$(5t^3 - 2) + (-5t^3 + 2) = 0$ and $(-9x^2 + x - 7) + (9x^2 - x + 7) = 0$.

We see that the opposite of $(5t^3 - 2)$ is $(-5t^3 + 2)$ and the opposite of $(-9x^2 + x - 7)$ is $(9x^2 - x + 7)$. This can be said using algebraic symbolism:

The opposite of $(5t^3 - 2)$ is $-5t^3 + 2$.

$-$ $(5t^3 - 2)$ $=$ $-5t^3 + 2$.

Similarly,

The opposite of $(-9x^2 + x - 7)$ is $9x^2 - x + 7$.

$-$ $(-9x^2 + x - 7)$ $=$ $9x^2 - x + 7$.

> ### TO FIND THE OPPOSITE OF A POLYNOMIAL
>
> We can find an equivalent polynomial for the opposite, or additive inverse, of a polynomial by replacing each term with its opposite— that is, *changing the sign of every term.*

EXAMPLE 4 Find two equivalent expressions for the opposite of
$$4x^5 - 7x^3 - 8x + \tfrac{5}{6}.$$

a) $-\left(4x^5 - 7x^3 - 8x + \tfrac{5}{6}\right)$ This is one expression for the opposite of $4x^5 - 7x^3 - 8x + \tfrac{5}{6}$.

b) $-4x^5 + 7x^3 + 8x - \tfrac{5}{6}$ Changing the sign of every term

Thus, $-\left(4x^5 - 7x^3 - 8x + \tfrac{5}{6}\right)$ is equivalent to $-4x^5 + 7x^3 + 8x - \tfrac{5}{6}$, and each is the opposite of the original polynomial $4x^5 - 7x^3 - 8x + \tfrac{5}{6}$.

Do Exercises 4–7.

EXAMPLE 5 Simplify: $-\left(-7x^4 - \tfrac{5}{9}x^3 + 8x^2 - x + 67\right)$.
$$-\left(-7x^4 - \tfrac{5}{9}x^3 + 8x^2 - x + 67\right) = 7x^4 + \tfrac{5}{9}x^3 - 8x^2 + x - 67$$

Do Exercises 8–10.

C   Subtracting Polynomials

We can now subtract a polynomial by adding the opposite of that polynomial. That is, for any polynomials p and q, $p - q = p + (-q)$.

EXAMPLE 6 Subtract:
$$(9x^5 + x^3 - 2x^2 + 4) - (2x^5 + x^4 - 4x^3 - 3x^2).$$

We have

$(9x^5 + x^3 - 2x^2 + 4) - (2x^5 + x^4 - 4x^3 - 3x^2)$

$= (9x^5 + x^3 - 2x^2 + 4) + [-(2x^5 + x^4 - 4x^3 - 3x^2)]$ Adding the opposite

$= (9x^5 + x^3 - 2x^2 + 4) + [-2x^5 - x^4 + 4x^3 + 3x^2]$ Finding the opposite by changing the sign of every term

$= 9x^5 + x^3 - 2x^2 + 4 - 2x^5 - x^4 + 4x^3 + 3x^2$

$= 7x^5 - x^4 + 5x^3 + x^2 + 4.$ Combining like terms

Do Exercises 11 and 12.

To shorten our work, we often begin by changing the sign of each term in the polynomial being subtracted.

EXAMPLE 7 Subtract:
$$(5a^4 - 7a^3 + 5a^2b) - (-3a^4 + 4a^2b + 6).$$

We have
$(5a^4 - 7a^3 + 5a^2b) - (-3a^4 + 4a^2b + 6)$

$= 5a^4 - 7a^3 + 5a^2b + 3a^4 - 4a^2b - 6$

$= 8a^4 - 7a^3 + a^2b - 6.$ Combining like terms

Do Exercise 13.

Find two equivalent expressions for the opposite of each polynomial.

4. $12x^4 - 3x^2 + 4x$

5. $-4x^4 + 3x^2 - 4x$

6. $-13x^6 + 2x^4 - 3x^2 + x - \tfrac{5}{13}$

7. $-8a^3b + 5ab^2 - 2ab$

Simplify.

8. $-(4x^3 - 6x + 3)$

9. $-(5x^3y + 3x^2y^2 - 7xy^3)$

10. $-\left(14x^{10} - \tfrac{1}{2}x^5 + 5x^3 - x^2 + 3x\right)$

Subtract.

11. $(7x^3 + 2x + 4) - (5x^3 - 4)$

12. $(-3x^2 + 5x - 4) - (-4x^2 + 11x - 2)$

13. Subtract
$(7x^3 + 3x^2 - xy) - (5x^3 + 3xy + 2).$

Answers on page A-8

14. Evaluate each expression for
$a = 2$. (See Margin Exercise 1.)

14. Evaluate each expression for
$a = 2$. (See Margin Exercise 1.)

a) $(7a^2 + 2a + 8) + (2a^2 + a - 9)$

b) $9a^2 + 3a - 1$

15. In the situation of Example 9,
how many games are played in
a league with 12 teams?

Wendy is pedaling down a hill. Her
distance from the top of the hill, in
meters, can be approximated by

$$\frac{1}{2}t^2 + 3t,$$

where t is the number of seconds
she has been pedaling and $t < 30$.

16. How far has Wendy traveled in
4 seconds?

17. How far has Wendy traveled in
10 seconds?

Answers on page A-8

d   Evaluating Polynomials and Applications

It is important to keep in mind that when we add or subtract polynomials,
we are *not* solving an equation. Rather, we are finding an equivalent expression that is usually more concise. One reason we do this is to make it easier
to evaluate.

EXAMPLE 8   Evaluate both $(5x^3 + 4x^2 + 3x) + (2x^3 + 5x^2 - x)$ and
$7x^3 + 9x^2 + 2x$ for $x = 2$ (see Example 1).

a) When x is replaced by 2 in $(5x^3 + 4x^2 + 3x) + (2x^3 + 5x^2 - x)$, we have

$$5 \cdot 2^3 + 4 \cdot 2^2 + 3 \cdot 2 + 2 \cdot 2^3 + 5 \cdot 2^2 - 2,$$

or $5 \cdot 8 + 4 \cdot 4 + 6 + 2 \cdot 8 + 5 \cdot 4 - 2,$

or $40 + 16 + 6 + 16 + 20 - 2,$ which is 96.

b) Similarly, when x is replaced by 2 in $7x^3 + 9x^2 + 2x$, we have

$$7 \cdot 2^3 + 9 \cdot 2^2 + 2 \cdot 2,$$

or $7 \cdot 8 + 9 \cdot 4 + 4,$

or $56 + 36 + 4.$ As expected, this is also 96.

Note how much easier it is to evaluate the simplified sum in part (b)
rather than the original expression.

Do Exercise 14.

Polynomials are frequently evaluated in real-world situations.

EXAMPLE 9   *Athletics.*   In a sports league of n teams in which all teams
play each other twice, the total number of games played is given by the
polynomial

$$n^2 - n.$$

A women's softball league has 10 teams. If each team plays every other team
twice, what is the total number of games played?

We evaluate the polynomial for $n = 10$:

$$n^2 - n = 10^2 - 10 = 100 - 10 = 90.$$

The league plays 90 games.

Do Exercises 15–17.

Study Tips

It is never too early to start studying for your final exam.

Best Scenario: Two Weeks of Study Time

1. **Begin by browsing through each chapter, reviewing the highlighted or boxed information regarding important formulas in both the text and the Summary and Review.** There may be some formulas that you will need to memorize.
2. **Retake all tests that your instructor has returned.** Restudy the objectives in the text that correspond to each question you miss.
3. **Then work the Chapter Tests and Cumulative Reviews in the portion of the text that you covered.** Be careful to avoid any questions corresponding to skipped material. Again, restudy the objectives in the text that correspond to each question you miss.
4. **Attend a final-exam review session if one is available.**
5. **If you are still having difficulty, use the supplements for extra review.** You might try the videotapes, *The Prealgebra Book of Problems*, or the InterAct Math Tutorial Software.
6. **For any remaining difficulties, see your instructor, go to a tutoring session, or participate in a study group.**
7. **See if previous final exams are available.** If they are, use them for practice, being alert to trouble spots.
8. **Take the Final Examination in the text during the last couple of days before the final.** See how much of the final exam you can complete under test-like conditions.

Moderate Scenario: Three Days to Two Weeks of Study Time

1. **Begin by browsing through each chapter, reviewing the highlighted or boxed information regarding important formulas in both the text and the Summary and Review.** There may be some formulas that you will need to memorize.
2. **Retake all tests that your instructor has returned.** Restudy the objectives in the text that correspond to each question you miss.
3. **Then work the Chapter Tests and Cumulative Reviews in the portion of the text that you covered.** Avoid any questions corresponding to skipped material. Again, restudy the objectives in the text that correspond to each question you miss.
4. **Attend a final-exam review session if one is available.**
5. **For any remaining difficulties, see your instructor, go to a tutoring session, or participate in a study group.**
6. **Take the Final Examination in the text during the last couple of days before the final.** See how much of the final exam you can complete under test-like conditions.

Worst Scenario: One or Two Days of Study Time

1. **Begin by browsing through each chapter, reviewing the highlighted or boxed information regarding important formulas in both the text and the Summary and Review.** There may be some formulas that you will need to memorize.
2. **Then work the last Cumulative Review in the portion of the text that you covered.** Avoid any questions corresponding to skipped material. Restudy the objectives in the text that correspond to each question you miss.
3. **Attend a final-exam review session if one is available.**
4. **Take the Final Examination in the text as preparation for the final.** See how much of the final exam you can complete under test-like conditions.

Promise yourself that next semester you will allow more time for final exam preparation.

2.9

EXERCISE SET

For Extra Help

Digital Video
Tutor CD 2
Videotape 2

InterAct
Math

Math Tutor
Center

MathXL

MyMathLab

a   Add.

1. $(3x + 7) + (-7x + 3)$

2. $(6x + 1) + (-7x + 2)$

3. $(-9x + 7) + (x^2 + x - 2)$

4. $(x^2 - 5x + 4) + (8x - 9)$

5. $(x^2 - 7) + (x^2 + 7)$

6. $(x^3 + x^2) + (2x^3 - 5x^2)$

7. $(6t^4 + 4t^3 - 1) + (5t^2 - t + 1)$

8. $(5t^2 - 3t + 12) + (2t^2 + 8t - 30)$

9. $(2 + 4x + 6x^2 + 7x^3) + (5 - 4x + 6x^2 - 7x^3)$

10. $(3x^4 - 6x - 5x^2 + 5) + (6x^2 - 4x^3 - 1 + 7x)$

11. $(9x^8 - 7x^4 + 2x^2 + 5) + (8x^7 + 4x^4 - 2x)$

12. $(4x^5 - 6x^3 - 9x + 1) + (6x^3 + 9x^2 + 9x)$

13. $(8t^4 + 6t^3 - t^2 + 3t) + (5t^4 - 2t^3 + t - 3)$

14. $(7t^5 - 3t^4 - 2t^2 + 5) + (3t^5 - 2t^4 + 4t^3 - t^2)$

15. $(-5x^4y^3 + 7x^3y^2 - 4xy^2) + (2x^3y^3 - 3x^3y^2 - 5xy)$

16. $(-9a^5b^4 + 7a^3b^3 + 2a^2b^2) + (2a^4b^4 - 5a^3b^3 - a^2b^2)$

17. $(8a^3b^2 + 5a^2b^2 + 6ab^2) + (5a^3b^2 - a^2b^2 - 4a^2b)$

18. $(6x^3y^3 - 4x^2y^2 + 3xy^2) + (x^3y^3 + 7x^3y^2 - 2xy^2)$

19. $(17.5abc^3 + 4.3a^2bc) + (-4.9a^2bc - 5.2abc)$

20. $(23.9x^3yz - 19.7x^2y^2z) + (-14.6x^3yz - 8x^2yz)$

b Find two equivalent expressions for the opposite of each polynomial.

21. $-5x$

22. $x^2 - 3x$

23. $-x^2 + 13x - 7$

24. $-7x^3 - x^2 - x$

25. $12x^4 - 3x^3 + 3$

26. $4x^3 - 6x^2 - 8x + 1$

Simplify.

27. $-(3x - 5)$

28. $-(-2x + 4)$

29. $-(4x^2 - 3x + 2)$

30. $-(-6a^3 + 2a^2 - 9a + 1)$

31. $-\left(-4x^4 + 6x^2 + \frac{3}{4}x - 8\right)$

32. $-(-5x^4 + 4x^3 - x^2 + 0.9)$

c Subtract.

33. $(3x + 2) - (-4x + 3)$

34. $(6x + 1) - (-7x + 2)$

35. $(9t^2 + 7t + 5) - (5t^2 + t - 1)$

36. $(8t^2 - 5t + 7) - (3t^2 - 2t + 1)$

37. $(-8x + 2) - (x^2 + x - 3)$

38. $(x^2 - 5x + 4) - (8x - 9)$

39. $(7a^2 + 5a - 9) - (2a^2 + 7)$

40. $(8u^2 - 6u + 5) - (2a^2 - 19a)$

41. $(8x^4 + 3x^3 - 1) - (4x^2 - 3x + 5)$

42. $(-4x^2 + 2x) - (3x^3 - 5x^2 + 3)$

43. $(1.2x^3 + 4.5x^2 - 3.8x) - (-3.4x^3 - 4.7x^2 + 23)$

44. $(0.5x^4 - 0.6x^2 + 0.7) - (2.3x^4 + 1.8x - 3.9)$

45. $\left(\frac{5}{8}x^3 - \frac{1}{4}x - \frac{1}{3}\right) - \left(-\frac{1}{8}x^3 + \frac{1}{4}x - \frac{1}{3}\right)$

46. $\left(\frac{1}{5}x^3 + 2x^2 - 0.1\right) - \left(-\frac{2}{5}x^3 + 2x^2 + 0.01\right)$

47. $(9x^3y^3 + 8x^2y^2 + 7xy) - (3x^3y^3 - 2x^2y + 3xy)$

48. $(3x^4y + 2x^3y - 7x^2y) - (5x^4y + 2x^2y^2 - 2x^2y)$

d Evaluate each polynomial for $x = 4$.

49. $-7x + 5$

50. $-3x + 1$

51. $2x^2 - 5x + 7$

52. $3x^2 + x + 7$

53. $x^3 - 5x^2 + x$

54. $7 - x + 3x^2$

Evaluate each polynomial for $x = -1$.

55. $2x + 9$

56. $6 - 2x$

57. $x^2 - 2x + 1$

58. $5x - 6 + x^2$

59. $-3x^3 + 7x^2 - 3x - 2$

60. $-2x^3 - 5x^2 + 4x + 3$

Falling Distance. The distance, in feet, traveled by a body falling freely from rest in t seconds is approximated by the polynomial $16t^2$.

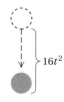
$16t^2$

61. A stone is dropped from a cliff and takes 8 sec to hit the ground. How high is the cliff?

62. A brick is dropped from a building and takes 3 sec to hit the ground. How high is the building?

Minutes of Daylight. The number of minutes of daylight in Chicago, on a date n days after December 21, can be approximated by

$$-0.01096n^2 + 4n + 548.$$

63. ▦ Determine the number of minutes of daylight in Chicago 92 days after December 21.

64. ▦ Determine the number of minutes of daylight in Chicago 123 days after December 21.

Daily Accidents.   The average number of accidents per day involving drivers who are a years old is approximated by the polynomial
$$0.4a^2 - 40a + 1039.$$

65. Evaluate the polynomial for $a = 18$ to find the daily number of accidents involving 18-year-old drivers.

66. Evaluate the polynomial for $a = 20$ to find the daily number of accidents involving 20-year-old drivers.

Total Revenue.   Cutting Edge Electronics is marketing a new kind of stereo. *Total revenue* is the total amount of money taken in. The firm determines that when it sells x stereos, it takes in
$$280x - 0.4x^2 \text{ dollars}.$$

67. What is the total revenue from the sale of 75 stereos?

68. What is the total revenue from the sale of 100 stereos?

Total Cost.   Cutting Edge Electronics determines that the total cost of producing x stereos is given by
$$5000 + 0.6x^2 \text{ dollars}.$$

69. What is the total cost of producing 500 stereos?

70. What is the total cost of producing 650 stereos?

71. ^{D}W Is every term a monomial? Why or why not?

72. ^{D}W Suppose that two polynomials, each containing 3 terms, are added. Is it possible for the sum to contain more than 3 terms? fewer than 3 terms? exactly 3 terms? Explain.

(SYNTHESIS)

73. ^{D}W Is it possible for the quotient of two polynomials to be a polynomial? Why or why not?

74. ^{D}W Explain, in your own words, how the distributive law is used when subtracting polynomials.

Minutes of Daylight.   The number of minutes of daylight in Los Angeles, on a date n days after December 21, can be approximated by
$$-0.0085n^2 + 3.1014n + 593.$$

75. ▦ Determine the number of minutes of daylight in Los Angeles on "Ground Hog Day."

76. ▦ How much more daylight is available in Chicago than in Los Angeles on July 4? (See Exercises 63 and 64.)

77. ^D**W** 🔲 While using the formulas for number of minutes of daylight, Alicia argues that instead of replacing n with 360, she can get nearly the same result using 5 instead. What do you think her reasoning is?

78. ^D**W** Explain how the associative and commutative laws can be used when adding polynomials.

79. 🔲 *Medicine.* When a person swallows 400 mg of ibuprofen, the number of milligrams in the bloodstream t hours later can be approximated by the polynomial

$$0.5t^4 + 3.45t^3 - 96.65t^2 + 347.7t,$$

with $0 \le t \le 6$. Determine the amount of ibuprofen in the bloodstream **(a)** 1 hr after swallowing 400 mg; **(b)** 2 hr after swallowing 400 mg; **(c)** 6 hr after swallowing 400 mg.

80. 🔲 *Cellular Phone Sales.* The polynomial

$$0.04x^3 - 0.23x^2 + 0.94x - 0.05$$

can be used to estimate the number of cellular phones in use, in millions, x years after 1985. Estimate the number of cellular phones in use in 2004.

Perform the indicated operations and simplify.

81. $(7y^2 - 5y + 6) - (3y^2 + 8y - 12) + (8y^2 - 10y + 3)$

82. $(3x^2 - 4x + 6) - (-2x^2 + 4) + (-5x - 3)$

83. $(-y^4 - 7y^3 + y^2) + (-2y^4 + 5y - 2) - (-6y^3 + y^2)$

84. $(-4 + x^2 + 2x^3) - (-6 - x + 3x^3) - (-x^2 - 5x^3)$

85. Complete: $9x^4 +$ _____ $+ 5x^2 - 7x^3 +$ _____ $- 9 +$ _____ $= 12x^4 - 5x^3 + 5x^2 - 16.$

86. Complete: $8t^4 +$ _____ $- 2t^3 +$ _____ $- 2t^2 + t -$ _____ $- 3 +$ _____ $= 8t^4 + 7t^3 - 3t + 4.$

Summary and Review

The review that follows is meant to prepare you for a chapter exam. It consists of two parts. The first part is a checklist of some of the Study Tips referred to in this and preceding chapters, as well as a list of important properties and formulas. The second part is the Review Exercises. These provide practice exercises for the exam, together with references to section objectives so you can go back and review. Before beginning, stop and look back over the skills you have obtained. What skills in mathematics do you have now that you did not have before studying this chapter?

STUDY TIPS CHECKLIST

The foundation of all your study skills is TIME!	☐ Are you making use of the many supplements that exist for this textbook?
	☐ Are you consistently working in pencil, with an eraser nearby?
	☐ Have you prepared in advance for any help sessions you are attending?
	☐ Are you getting enough sleep to work at the peak of your powers?
	☐ Are you making sure that you understand everything you read before moving forward?
	☐ Are you avoiding over-reliance on the answers listed in the back of the book?

IMPORTANT PROPERTIES AND FORMULAS

For any integers a, b, and c: $a + (-a) = 0$; $a - b = a + (-b)$;
$a \cdot 0 = 0$; $a(b + c) = ab + ac$

Perimeter of a Rectangle: $P = 2l + 2w$, or $P = 2(l + w)$

Perimeter of a Square: $P = 4s$

The Addition Principle: $a = b$ is equivalent to $a + c = b + c$.

The Division Principle: For $c \neq 0$, $a = b$ is equivalent to $\dfrac{a}{c} = \dfrac{b}{c}$.

REVIEW EXERCISES

1. Tell which integers correspond to this situation: [2.1a]
Bonnie has $527 in her campus account and Roger is $53 in debt.

Use either $<$ or $>$ for ☐ to form a true statement. [2.1b]

2. 0 ☐ -5 3. -7 ☐ 6 4. -4 ☐ -19

Find the absolute value.   [2.1c]

5. $|-39|$ **6.** $|23|$ **7.** $|0|$

8. Find $-x$ when $x = -72$.   [2.1d]

9. Find $-(-x)$ when $x = 59$.   [2.1d]

Compute and simplify.   [2.2a], [2.3a], [2.4a, b], [2.5a, b]

10. $-14 + 5$

11. $-5 + (-6)$

12. $14 + (-8)$

13. $0 + (-24)$

14. $17 - 29$

15. $9 - (-14)$

16. $-8 - (-7)$

17. $-3 - (-10)$

18. $-3 + 7 + (-8)$

19. $8 - (-9) - 7 + 2$

20. $-23 \cdot (-4)$

21. $7(-12)$

22. $2(-4)(-5)(-1)$

23. $15 \div (-5)$

24. $\dfrac{-55}{11}$

25. $\dfrac{0}{7}$

26. $7 \div 1^2 \cdot (-3) - 4$ **27.** $(-3)|4 - 3^2| - 5$

28. Evaluate $3a + b$ for $a = 4$ and $b = -5$.   [2.6a]

29. Evaluate $\dfrac{-x}{y}$, $\dfrac{x}{-y}$, and $-\dfrac{x}{y}$ for $x = 30$ and $y = 5$.   [2.6a]

Multiply.   [2.6b]

30. $4(5x + 9)$ **31.** $3(2a - 4b + 5)$

Combine like terms.   [2.7a]

32. $5a + 12a$ **33.** $-7x + 13x$

34. $9m + 14 - 12m - 8$

35. Find the perimeter of a frame that is 8 in. by 10 in.
   [2.7b]

36. Find the perimeter of a square pane of glass that is
   25 cm on each side.   [2.7b]

CHAPTER 2: Introduction to Integers
and Algebraic Expressions

Solve. [2.8a, b, c, d]

37. $x - 9 = -17$

38. $-4t = 36$

39. $56 = 6x - 10$

40. ^DW Explain the difference between equivalent expressions and equivalent equations.

41. ^DW Is a number's absolute value ever less than the number itself? Why or why not?

Perform the indicated operation. [2.9a, c]

42. $(-4x + 9) + (7x - 15)$

43. $(7x^4 - 5x^3 + 3x - 5) + (x^3 - 4x + 2)$

44. $(9a^5 + 8a^3 + 4a + 7) - (a^5 - 4a^3 + a^2 - 2)$

45. $(8a^3b^3 + 9a^2b^3) - (3a^3b^3 - 2a^2b^3 + 7)$

46. Find two equivalent expressions for the opposite of
$12x^3 - 4x^2 + 9x - 3$. [2.9b]

Evaluate.

47. $5t^3 + t$, for $t = -2$ [2.9d]

48. The altitude, in feet, of a falling golf ball t seconds after it reaches the peak of its flight, can be estimated by $-16t^2 + 200$. Find the ball's altitude 3 seconds after it has reached its peak. [2.9d]

49. Write a word name for 386,451. [1.1c]

50. Estimate by rounding to the nearest ten. Show your work. [1.4b]

$$\begin{array}{r} 7\ 2\ 9\ 6 \\ -\ 2\ 7\ 4\ 1 \\ \hline \end{array}$$

51. Estimate by rounding to the nearest hundred. Show your work. [1.4b]

$$2481 - 1729$$

52. In 2001, Barry Bonds hit a record-setting 73 home runs and Sammy Sosa hit 64. How many did they hit altogether that year? [1.8a]

Multiply. [1.5a]

53. $3 \cdot 8495$

54. $\begin{array}{r} 7\ 3\ 4 \\ \times\ \ \ 2\ 9 \\ \hline \end{array}$

55. ^DW A classmate insists on reading $-x$ as "negative x." When asked why, the response is "because $-x$ is negative." What mistake is this student making? [2.1d]

56. ^DW Are $(a - b)^2$ and $(b - a)^2$ equivalent for all choices of a and b? Why or why not? Experiment with different replacements for a and b. [2.6a]

Simplify. [2.5b]

57. ▦ $87 \div 3 \cdot 29^3 - (-6)^6 + 1957$

58. ▦ $1969 + (-8)^5 - 17 \cdot 15^3$

59. ▦ $\dfrac{113 - 17^3}{15 + 8^3 - 507}$

60. For what values of x will $8 + x^3$ be negative? [2.6a]

61. For what values of x is $|x| > x$? [2.1b, c]

1. Tell which integers correspond to this situation: The Tee Shop sold 542 fewer muscle shirts than expected in January and 307 more than expected in February.

2. Use either $<$ or $>$ for $\square$ to form a true statement.
$$-14 \ \square \ -21$$

3. Find the absolute value: $|-739|$

4. Find $-(-x)$ when $x = -19$.

Compute and simplify.

5. $6 + (-17)$

6. $-9 + (-12)$

7. $-8 + 17$

8. $0 - 12$

9. $7 - 22$

10. $-5 - 19$

11. $-8 - (-27)$

12. $31 - (-3) - 5 + 9$

13. $(-4)^3$

14. $27(-10)$

15. $-9 \cdot 0$

16. $-72 \div (-9)$

17. $\dfrac{-56}{7}$

18. $8 \div 2 \cdot 2 - 3^2$

19. $29 - (3 - 5)^2$

20. Jeannie rewound a tape in her video camera from the 8 minute mark to the -15 minute mark. How many minutes of tape were rewound?

21. Evaluate $\dfrac{a-b}{6}$ for $a = -8$ and $b = 10$.

22. Multiply: $7(2x + 3y - 1)$.

23. Combine like terms:
$9x - 14 - 5x - 3$.

Solve.

24. $-7x = -35$

25. $a + 9 = -3$

26. Add: $(12a^3 - 9a^2 + 8) + (6a^3 + 4a^2 - a)$.

27. Find two equivalent expressions for the opposite of $-9a^4 + 7b^2 - ab + 3$.

28. Subtract: $(12x^4 + 7x^2 - 6) - (9x^4 + 8x^2 + 5)$.

29. The height, in meters, of a ball t seconds after it has been thrown is approximated by $-4.9t^2 + 15t + 2$. How high is the ball 2 sec after it has been thrown?

SKILL MAINTENANCE

30. Write a word name for 2,308,451.

31. Estimate by rounding to the nearest ten. Show your work.
$$\begin{array}{r} 3\ 2\ 0\ 4 \\ -\ 1\ 9\ 1\ 5 \end{array}$$

32. Estimate the difference by rounding to the nearest hundred. Show your work.
$$9247 - 2879$$

33. Maurice shoveled snow from 9 driveways while Phyllis shoveled snow from 12. How many driveways did they shovel altogether?

Multiply.

34. $8 \cdot 706$

35.
$$\begin{array}{r} 3\ 0\ 2 \\ \times\ \ \ 6\ 8 \end{array}$$

SYNTHESIS

36. Monty plans to attach trim around the doorway and along the base of the walls in a 12-ft by 14-ft room. If the doorway is 3 ft by 7 ft, how many feet of trim are needed? (Only three sides of a doorway get trim.)

Simplify.

37. $9 - 5[x + 2(3 - 4x)] + 14$

38. $15x + 3(2x - 7) - 9(4 + 5x)$

39. $49 \cdot 14^3 \div 7^4 + 1926^2 \div 6^2$

40. $3487 - 16 \div 4 \cdot 4 \div 2^8 \cdot 14^4$

1-2 Cumulative Review

1. Write standard notation for the number written in words in the following sentence: In 2002 there were over one hundred thirty-one million, four hundred fifty-one thousand automobiles in the United States.

2. Write a word name for 5,380,001,437.

Add.

3.
$$
\begin{array}{r}
1\,5{,}8\,9\,2 \\
+\ \ 2{,}9\,3\,5 \\
\hline
\end{array}
$$

4.
$$
\begin{array}{r}
7\,9\,8\,9 \\
7\,8\,9 \\
+\ \ \ \ \ 7\,9 \\
\hline
\end{array}
$$

Subtract.

5.
$$
\begin{array}{r}
8\,2\,7\,6 \\
-\ \ \ 4\,3\,0 \\
\hline
\end{array}
$$

6.
$$
\begin{array}{r}
3\,0\,0\,6 \\
-\ \ \ 5\,7\,8 \\
\hline
\end{array}
$$

Multiply.

7.
$$
\begin{array}{r}
6\,2\,1 \\
\times\ \ \ 2\,7 \\
\hline
\end{array}
$$

8.
$$
\begin{array}{r}
2\,5\,0\,5 \\
\times\ 3\,3\,0\,0 \\
\hline
\end{array}
$$

9. $43 \cdot (-8)$

10. $-12(-6)$

Divide.

11. $6\,3\,\overline{)\,6\,5\,5\,2}$

12. $6\,2\,\overline{)\,3\,8\,4\,4}$

13. $0 \div (-67)$

14. $60 \div (-12)$

15. Round 427,931 to the nearest thousand.

16. Round 5309 to the nearest hundred.

Estimate each sum or product by rounding to the nearest hundred. Show your work.

17.
$$
\begin{array}{r}
7\,4\,9{,}5\,5\,9 \\
+\ 3\,0\,1{,}3\,6\,2 \\
\hline
\end{array}
$$

18.
$$
\begin{array}{r}
7\,4\,9 \\
\times\ 5\,3\,1 \\
\hline
\end{array}
$$

19. Use < or > for ☐ to form a true sentence:
$-26\ \boxed{}\ 19.$

20. Find the absolute value: $|-279|$.

Simplify.

21. $35 - 25 \div 5 + 2 \times 3$

22. $\{17 - [8 - (5 - 2 \times 2)]\} \div (3 + 12 \div 6)$

23. $10 \div 1(-5) - 6^2$

24. 5^3

25. Evaluate $\dfrac{x + y}{5}$ for $x = 11$ and $y = 4$.

26. Evaluate $7x^2$ for $x = -2$.

Use the distributive law to write an equivalent expression.

27. $-2(x + 5)$

28. $6(3x - 2y + 4)$

Simplify.

29. $-12 + (-14)$

30. $-17 - 14$

31. $23 - 38$

32. $-12 - (-25)$

Solve.

33. $x + 8 = 35$

34. $-12t = 36$

35. $-6 + x = 9$

36. $-39 = 4x - 7$

Solve.

37. In the movie *Little Big Man*, Dustin Hoffman plays a character who ages from 17 to 121. This represents the greatest age range depicted by one actor in one film. How many years did Hoffman's character age?
Source: Guinness Book of World Records

38. Four of the largest hotels in the United States are in Las Vegas. One has 3174 rooms, the second has 2920 rooms, the third has 2832 rooms, and the fourth has 5005 rooms. What is the total number of rooms in these four hotels?

39. Amanda is offered a part-time job paying $4940 a year. How much is each weekly paycheck?

40. Eastside Appliance sells a refrigerator for $600 and $30 tax with no delivery charge. Westside Appliance sells the same model for $560 and $28 tax plus a $25 delivery charge. Which is the better buy?

41. Write an equivalent expression by combining like terms: $7x - 9 + 3x - 5$.

42. $(4x^5 + 7x^4 - 3x^2 + 9) + (6x^5 - 8x^4 + 2x^3 - 7)$

(SYNTHESIS)

43. A soft drink distributor has 166 loose cans of cola. The distributor wishes to form as many 24-can cases as possible and then, with any remaining cans, as many six-packs as possible. How many cases will be filled? How many six-packs? How many loose cans will remain?

44. Simplify: $a - \{3a - [4a - (2a - 4a)]\}$.

45. ▦ Simplify: $37 \cdot 64 \div 4^2 \cdot 2 - (7^3 - (-4)^5)$

46. Find two solutions of $5|x| - 2 = 13$.

Fraction Notation: Multiplication and Division

Gateway to Chapter 3

We consider multiplication and division using fraction notation in this chapter. To aid our study, the chapter begins with factorizations and rules for divisibility. After multiplication and division have been discussed, those skills are used to solve equations and real-world problems.

Real-World Application

Green Season Gardening uses about $\frac{2}{3}$ yd of bark mulch per customer each spring. How many customers can they accommodate with one 30-yd batch of bark mulch?

This problem appears as Exercise 49 in Section 3.8.

1. Determine whether 165 is divisible by 3. Do not use long division.   [3.1b]

2. Determine whether 1645 is divisible by 5. Do not use long division.   [3.1b]

3. Determine whether 67 is prime, composite, or neither.   [3.2b]

4. Find the prime factorization of 280.   [3.2c]

Simplify.   [3.3b]

5. $\dfrac{75}{75}$

6. $\dfrac{9t}{1}$

7. $\dfrac{0}{50}$

8. $\dfrac{-8}{32}$

9. $\dfrac{10a}{35a}$

10. Find an equivalent expression for $\dfrac{3}{7}$ with a denominator of 28.   [3.5a]

Multiply and, if possible, simplify.   [3.6a]

11. $\dfrac{1}{6} \cdot \dfrac{15}{7}$

12. $\dfrac{5}{6} \cdot (-24)$

13. $\dfrac{2a}{5} \cdot \dfrac{25}{8}$

Find the reciprocal.   [3.7a]

14. $\dfrac{9}{13}$

15. 11

Divide and, if possible, simplify.   [3.7b]

16. $20 \div \dfrac{5}{9}$

17. $\dfrac{2}{3} \div \left(-\dfrac{8}{9}\right)$

18. $\dfrac{14}{9} \div (7x)$

Solve.   [3.8a]

19. $-\dfrac{8}{7} = 4x$

20. $\dfrac{7}{10} \cdot x = 21$

21. $\dfrac{5}{12} = \dfrac{2}{3} \cdot a$

Solve.   [3.8b]

22. Heather earns \$72 for working a full day. How much will she earn for working $\frac{3}{4}$ of a day?

23. A piece of licorice $\frac{5}{8}$ m long is to be cut into 15 pieces of the same length. What is the length of each piece?

24. A triangular sign with a base of 3 ft and a height of 4 ft is cut from a 4-ft by 8-ft sheet of plywood. Find the area of the leftover plywood.

3.1

MULTIPLES AND DIVISIBILITY

Before we can begin our work with fractions, certain concepts that pertain to integers must be discussed. For example, before we can develop a method for simplifying a fraction like $\frac{285}{357}$, we will first need to learn about *multiples* and *divisibility*.

a Multiples

A **multiple** of a number is a product of that number and an integer. For example, some multiples of 2 are:

2   (because $2 = 1 \cdot 2$);
4   (because $4 = 2 \cdot 2$);
6   (because $6 = 3 \cdot 2$);
8   (because $8 = 4 \cdot 2$);
10   (because $10 = 5 \cdot 2$).

We can also find multiples of 2 by counting by twos: 2, 4, 6, 8, and so on.

EXAMPLE 1 Show that each of the numbers 3, 6, 9, and 15 is a multiple of 3.

We show that each of 3, 6, 9, and 15 can be expressed as a product of 3 and some integer:

$$3 - 1 \cdot 3; \quad 6 - 2 \cdot 3; \quad 9 = 3 \cdot 3; \quad 15 = 5 \cdot 3.$$

Do Exercises 1 and 2.

EXAMPLE 2 Multiply by 1, 2, 3, and so on, to find eight multiples of six.

$1 \cdot 6 - 6$ $5 \cdot 6 = 30$
$2 \cdot 6 = 12$ $6 \cdot 6 = 36$
$3 \cdot 6 = 18$ $7 \cdot 6 = 42$
$4 \cdot 6 = 24$ $8 \cdot 6 = 48$

Do Exercise 3.

DIVISIBILITY

A number b is said to be **divisible** by another number a if b is a multiple of a.

Thus,

6 is divisible by 2 because 6 is a multiple of 2 ($6 = 3 \cdot 2$);
27 is divisible by 3 because 27 is a multiple of 3 ($27 = 9 \cdot 3$);
100 is divisible by 25 because 100 is a multiple of 25 ($100 = 4 \cdot 25$).

Objectives

a Find some multiples of a number, and determine whether a number is divisible by another number.

b Test to see if a number is divisible by 2, 3, 5, 6, 9, or 10.

1. Show that each of the numbers 5, 45, and 100 is a multiple of 5.

2. Show that each of the numbers 10, 60, and 110 is a multiple of 10.

3. Multiply by 1, 2, 3, and so on, to find ten multiples of 5.

Answers on page A-9

Study Tips

CREATE YOUR OWN GLOSSARY

Understanding the meaning of mathematical terminology is essential for success in any math course. To assist with this, try writing your own glossary of important words toward the back of your notebook. Often, just the act of writing out a word's definition can help you remember what the word means.

4. Determine whether 16 is divisible by 2.

5. Determine whether 125 is divisible by 5.

6. Determine whether 125 is divisible by 6.

Determine whether each of the following numbers is divisible by 2.

7. 84   **8.** 59

9. 998   **10.** 2225

Answers on page A-9

Saying that b is divisible by a means that $b \div a$ results in a remainder of zero. When this happens, we sometimes say that a divides b "evenly."

EXAMPLE 3   Determine whether 24 is divisible by 3.

We divide 24 by 3:

$$\begin{array}{r} 8 \\ 3\overline{)24} \\ \underline{24} \\ 0 \end{array}$$

The remainder of 0 indicates that 24 is divisible by 3.

EXAMPLE 4   Determine whether 98 is divisible by 4.

We divide 98 by 4:

$$\begin{array}{r} 24 \\ 4\overline{)98} \\ \underline{8} \\ 18 \\ \underline{16} \\ 2 \end{array} \leftarrow \text{Not } 0$$

Since the remainder is not 0 we know that 98 is *not* divisible by 4.

Do Exercises 4–6.

b   Tests for Divisibility by 2, 3, or 5

We now learn quick ways of checking for divisibility by 2, 3, and 5 without actually performing long division. Remembering these tests will be especially helpful in Section 3.2.

DIVISIBILITY BY 2

You may already know the test for divisibility by 2.

> **BY 2**
>
> A number is **divisible by 2** (is *even*) if it has a ones digit of 0, 2, 4, 6, or 8 (that is, it has an even ones digit).

To see why this test works, start counting by 2's: 2, 4, 6, 8, 10, 12, 14, 16, 18, 20, 22, ... Note that the ones digit will always be 0, 2, 4, 6, or 8, no matter how high we count.

EXAMPLES   Determine whether each of the following numbers is divisible by 2.

5.   355   *is not* divisible by 2; 5 is not even.

6. 4786   *is* divisible by 2; 6 is even.

7. 8990   *is* divisible by 2; 0 is even.

8. 4261   *is not* divisible by 2; 1 is not even.

Do Exercises 7–10.

DIVISIBILITY BY 3

> ### BY 3
>
> A number is **divisible by 3** if the sum of its digits is divisible by 3.

An explanation of why this test works is outlined in Exercise 67 at the end of this section.

EXAMPLES Determine whether each of the following numbers is divisible by 3.

9. 84 $8 + 4 = 12$ The sum of the digits, 12, *is* divisible by 3, so 84 is divisible by 3.

10. 201 $2 + 0 + 1 = 3$ The sum of the digits, 3, *is* divisible by 3, so 201 is divisible by 3.

11. 526 $5 + 2 + 6 = 13$ The sum of the digits, 13, *is not* divisible by 3, so 526 is not divisible by 3.

Do Exercises 11–13.

DIVISIBILITY BY 5

To determine the test for divisibility by 5, we start counting by 5's: 5, 10, 15, 20, 25, 30, 35, ... Note that the ones digit will always be 5 or 0, no matter how high we count.

> ### BY 5
>
> A number is **divisible by 5** if its ones digit is 0 or 5.

EXAMPLES Determine whether each of the following numbers is divisible by 5.

12. 220   *is* divisible by 5 because its ones digit is 0.

13. 475   *is* divisible by 5 because its ones digit is 5.

14. 6514   *is not* divisible by 5 because its ones digit is neither 0 nor 5.

Do Exercises 14–17.

DIVISIBILITY BY 4, 6, 7, 8, 9, AND 10

For our work with fractions, the tests for divisibility by 2, 3, and 5 are most useful. Although tests exist for divisibility by 4, 7, and 8, they are often more difficult to perform than the actual long division and are rarely used.

Determining whether a number is divisible by 6 or 10, on the other hand, is relatively simple. Because $6 = 2 \cdot 3$, any number that is a multiple of 6 is also a multiple of 2 and 3. Thus, for a number to be divisible by 6, it must be both even and divisible by 3. Similarly, for a number to be divisible by 10, it must be both even and divisible by 5 (since $10 = 2 \cdot 5$)—that is to say it must have a ones digit of 0.

Determine whether each of the following numbers is divisible by 3.

11. 111

12. 1111

13. 309

Determine whether each of the following numbers is divisible by 5.

14. 5780

15. 3427

16. 34,678

17. 7775

Answers on page A-9

Determine whether each of the
following numbers is divisible by 6.

18. 810

19. 106

20. 321

21. 474

Determine whether each of the
following numbers is divisible by 10.

22. 305

23. 300

24. 847

25. 8760

Determine whether each of the
following numbers is divisible by 9.

26. 16

27. 126

28. 930

29. 29,223

Answers on page A-9

EXAMPLES Determine whether each of the following numbers is divisible by 6.

15. 720

Because 720 is even, it is divisible by 2. Since $7 + 2 + 0 = 9$ and 9 is divisible by 3, we know that 720 is also divisible by 3.

$$720 \qquad 7 + 2 + 0 = 9$$

   ↑   ↑

Even   Divisible by 3

Since 720 is divisible by both 2 and 3, we know that 720 *is* divisible by 6.

16. 531

Because 531 is not even, we know that 531 *is not* divisible by 6.

17. 478

Because the sum of its digits is not divisible by 3, we know that 478 is not divisible by 3.

$$4 + 7 + 8 = 19$$

                ↑

Not divisible by 3

Since 478 is not divisible by 3, we know that 478 *is not* divisible by 6.

Do Exercises 18–21.

EXAMPLES Determine whether each of the following numbers is divisible by 10.

18. 3440   *is* divisible by 10 because its ones digit is 0.

19. 3447   *is not* divisible by 10 because its ones digit is not 0.

Do Exercises 22–25.

The test for divisibility by 9 is similar to the test for 3—if the sum of a number's digits is divisible by 9, then the number itself is as well. An explanation of why this works is outlined in Exercise 67.

EXAMPLE 20 Are the numbers 6984 and 322 divisible by 9?

The number 6984 *is* divisible by 9 because

$$6 + 9 + 8 + 4 = 27$$

and 27 is divisible by 9.

The number 322 *is not* divisible by 9 because

$$3 + 2 + 2 = 7$$

and 7 is not divisible by 9.

Do Exercises 26–29.

3.1 EXERCISE SET

Digital Video Tutor CD 2 Videotape 3 | InterAct Math | Math Tutor Center | MathXL | MyMathLab

a Multiply by 1, 2, 3, and so on, to find ten multiples of each number.

1. 7   **2.** 4   **3.** 20   **4.** 50   **5.** 3   **6.** 8

7. 13   **8.** 17   **9.** 10   **10.** 12   **11.** 9   **12.** 11

13. Determine whether 61 is divisible by 3.

14. Determine whether 29 is divisible by 2.

15. Determine whether 1880 is divisible by 5.

16. Determine whether 4227 is divisible by 3.

17. Determine whether 206 is divisible by 2.

18. Determine whether 196 is divisible by 7.

19. Determine whether 5127 is divisible by 9.

20. Determine whether 200 is divisible by 5.

21. Determine whether 8650 is divisible by 8.

22. Determine whether 4143 is divisible by 9.

b To answer Exercises 23–28, consider the following numbers.

84	150	235	567
4740	467	3609	6390
179	19,458	2004	1775
492	97	671,500	4007

23. Which of the above are divisible by 3?

24. Which of the above are divisible by 7?

25. Which of the above are divisible by 2?

26. Which of the above are divisible by 6?

27. Which of the above are divisible by 5?

28. Which of the above are divisible by 10?

To answer Exercises 29–34, consider the following numbers. Use the tests for divisibility.

46	300	85	256
224	36	711	8064
19	45,270	13,251	1867
555	4444	254,765	21,568

29. Which of the above are divisible by 3?

30. Which of the above are divisible by 2?

31. Which of the above are divisible by 10?

32. Which of the above are divisible by 5?

33. Which of the above are divisible by 6?

34. Which of the above are divisible by 9?

To answer Exercises 35–40, consider the following numbers.

56	200	75	35
324	42	812	402
784	501	2345	111,111
55,555	3009	2001	1005

35. Which of the above are divisible by 2?

36. Which of the above are divisible by 3?

37. Which of the above are divisible by 5?

38. Which of the above are divisible by 10?

39. Which of the above are divisible by 9?

40. Which of the above are divisible by 6?

41. **D$_W$** Describe a test that can be used to determine whether a number is divisible by 25.

42. **D$_W$** Is every counting number a multiple of 1? Why or why not?

Solve.

43. $16 \cdot t = 848$ [1.7b], [2.8b]

44. $m + 9 = 14$ [1.7b], [2.8a]

45. $23 + x = 15$ [1.7b], [2.8a]

46. $24 \cdot m = -576$ [1.7b], [2.8b]

47. Find the total cost of 12 sweaters at $37 each and 4 jackets at $59 each.   [1.8a]

48. Add: $-34 + 76$.   [2.2a]

Evaluate.   [1.9b]

49. 5^3

50. 7^3

51. 4^5

52. 3^6

Write in exponential notation.   [1.9a]

53. $9 \cdot 9 \cdot 9 \cdot 9 \cdot 9$

54. $7 \cdot 7 \cdot 7 \cdot 7 \cdot 7 \cdot 7$

55. D_W Describe a test that can be used to determine whether a number is divisible by 18.

56. D_W Describe a test for determining whether a number is divisible by 30.

57. ▦ Find the largest five-digit number that is divisible by 47.

58. ▦ Find the largest six-digit number that is divisible by 53.

Find the smallest number that is simultaneously a multiple of the given numbers.

59. 2, 3, and 5

60. 3, 5, and 7

61. 4, 6, and 10

62. 6, 10, and 14

63. ▦ 17, 43, and 85

64. ▦ 26, 57, and 130

65. 30, 70, and 120

66. 25, 100, and 175

67. D_W To help see why the tests for division by 3 and 9 work, note that any four-digit number $abcd$ can be rewritten as $1000 \cdot a + 100 \cdot b + 10 \cdot c + d$, or $999a + 99b + 9c + a + b + c + d$.

a) Explain why $999a + 99b + 9c$ is divisible by both 9 and 3 for all choices of a, b, c, and d.

b) Explain why the four-digit number $abcd$ is divisible by 9 if $a + b + c + d$ is divisible by 9 and is divisible by 3 if $a + b + c + d$ is divisible by 3.

68. A passenger in a taxicab asks for the driver's company number. The driver says abruptly, "Sure—it's the smallest multiple of 11 that, when divided by 2, 3, 4, 5, or 6, has a remainder of 1." What is the number?

Objectives

a Find the factors of a number.

b Given a number from 1 to 100, tell whether it is prime, composite, or neither.

c Find the prime factorization of a composite number.

List all the factors of each number. (*Hint*: Find some factorizations of the number.)

1. 14

2. 10

3. 8

4. 32

In Section 3.1, we saw that both 28 and 35 are multiples of 7. This is the same as saying that 7 is a *factor* of both 28 and 35. When a number is expressed as a product of factors, we say that we have *factored* the original number. Thus, "factor" can be used as either a noun or a verb. Being able to factor is an important skill needed for a solid understanding of fractions.

a **Factoring Numbers**

From the equation $3 \cdot 4 = 12$, we can say that 3 and 4 are *factors* of 12. Since $12 = 12 \cdot 1$, we know that 12 and 1 are also factors of 12.

FACTORS AND FACTORIZATIONS

A number c is a **factor** of a if a is divisible by c.

A **factorization** of a expresses a as a product of two or more numbers.

For example, each of the following gives a factorization of 12.

$12 = 4 \cdot 3$ ← This factorization shows that 4 and 3 are factors of 12.

$12 = 12 \cdot 1$ ← This factorization shows that 12 and 1 are factors of 12.

$12 = 6 \cdot 2$ ← This factorization shows that 6 and 2 are factors of 12.

$12 = 2 \cdot 3 \cdot 2$ ← This factorization shows that 2 and 3 are factors of 12.

Thus, 1, 2, 3, 4, 6, and 12 are all factors of 12. Note that since $n = n \cdot 1$, every number has a factorization, and every number has itself and 1 as factors.

EXAMPLE 1 Find all the factors of 24.

To get started, we can use some of the tests for divisibility. For example, since 24 is even, we know that 2 is a factor. Since the sum of the digits in 24 is 6 and 6 is divisible by 3, we know that 3 is a factor. We can use trial and error to determine that 4 is also a factor, but that 5 is not. A list of factorizations can then be used to make a complete list of factors.

Factorizations: $1 \cdot 24;\ 2 \cdot 12;\ 3 \cdot 8;\ 4 \cdot 6;$

Factors: 1, 2, 3, 4, 6, 8, 12, 24

It is useful to note that when two different numbers are factors of a number, the product of those numbers is also a factor. For instance, in Example 1, since 2 and 3 are both factors of 24, their product, 6, is also a factor.

EXAMPLE 2 Find all the factors of 105.

Since 105 is odd, 2 is not a factor. Because the sum of the digits is 6 and 6 is divisible by 3, we know that 3 is a factor. Since the ones digit is 5, we also know that 5 is a factor.

Factorizations: $1 \cdot 105;\ 3 \cdot 35;\ 5 \cdot 21;\ 7 \cdot 15$

Factors: 1, 3, 5, 7, 15, 21, 35, 105

Do Exercises 1–4.

Answers on page A-9

b   Prime and Composite Numbers

5. Tell whether each number is prime, composite, or neither.

1, 2, 6, 12, 13, 19, 41, 65, 73, 99

> ### PRIME AND COMPOSITE NUMBERS
>
> A natural number that has exactly two different factors is called a **prime number.**
>
> - The number 1 is *not* prime.
> - A natural number, other than 1, that is not prime is **composite.**

To see if a number is prime or composite, we can check to see if it is divisible by a number other than itself or 1. If such a number exists, then the original number is composite.

EXAMPLE 3   Determine whether the numbers 2, 3, 4, 5, 7, 9, 10, 11, 27, and 63 are prime, composite, or neither.

Because 2, 3, 5, 7, and 11 are each divisible only by 1 and the number itself, they are *prime*.

Because 4 and 10 are each divisible by 2 (as well as 1 and the number itself), they are *composite*.

Because 9, 27, and 63 are each divisible by 3 (as well as 1 and the number itself), they are *composite*.

Thus we have:

Prime: 2, 3, 5, 7, 11;

Composite: 4, 9, 10, 27, 63.

Because 0 is not a natural number, it is neither prime nor composite. Note that 1 is not prime because it does not have two different factors. The number 2 is the smallest prime, as well as the only even prime.

Do Exercise 5.

The following is a table of the prime numbers from 2 to 157. There are more extensive tables, but these prime numbers will be the most helpful to you in this text. At present, the largest known prime is $2^{6972593} - 1$. This number has over 2 million digits!
Source: *The New York Times 2002 Almanac*

In August of 2002, three Indian computer scientists made history by devising a quick and definitive way for a computer to tell whether a number is prime. Although earlier methods existed, none were as quick and reliable.
Source: *New York Times, 8/8/02*

Answers on page A-9

> ### A TABLE OF PRIMES FROM 2 TO 157
>
> 2, 3, 5, 7, 11, 13, 17, 19, 23, 29, 31, 37, 41, 43, 47, 53, 59, 61, 67, 71, 73, 79, 83, 89, 97, 101, 103, 107, 109, 113, 127, 131, 137, 139, 149, 151, 157

Although you need not memorize this entire list, remembering at least the first nine or ten is important.

Study Tips

PACE YOURSELF

Most instructors agree that it is better for a student to study for one hour four days in a week, than to study once a week for four hours. Of course, the total weekly study time will vary from student to student. It is common to expect an average of two hours of homework for each hour of class time.

C   Prime Factorizations

To express a composite number as a product of primes is to find the **prime factorization** of the number. To do this, we first consider the primes

2, 3, 5, 7, 11, 13, 17, 19, 23, and so on,

and determine whether a given number is divisible by any of them.

EXAMPLE 4   Find the prime factorization of 39.

a) We check for divisibility by the first prime, 2. Since 39 is not even, 2 is not a factor of 39.

b) Since the sum of the digits in 39 is 12 and 12 is divisible by 3, we know that 39 is divisible by 3. We then perform the division.

$$\frac{13}{3)39} \quad R = 0 \qquad \text{A remainder of 0 confirms that 3 is a factor of 39.}$$

Because 13 is a prime, we are finished. The prime factorization is

$$39 = 3 \cdot 13.$$

EXAMPLE 5   Find the prime factorization of 76.

a) Since 76 is even, it must have 2 as a factor.

$$\frac{38}{2)76} \qquad \text{We can write } 76 = 2 \cdot 38.$$

b) Because 38 is also even, we see that 76 contains a second factor of 2.

$$\frac{19}{2)38} \qquad \text{Note that } 38 = 2 \cdot 19, \text{ so } 76 = 2 \cdot 2 \cdot 19.$$

Because 19 is prime, we can factor no further. The complete factorization is

$$76 = 2 \cdot 2 \cdot 19. \qquad \text{All factors are prime.}$$

We abbreviate our procedure as follows.

$$\frac{19}{2)38} \longleftarrow \text{We stop dividing when the quotient is prime.}$$
$$2)76 \longleftarrow \text{We begin here and work upward.}$$
$$76 = 2 \cdot 2 \cdot 19$$

A factorization like $2 \cdot 2 \cdot 19$ can be written as $2^2 \cdot 19$ or $2 \cdot 19 \cdot 2$ or $19 \cdot 2 \cdot 2$ or $19 \cdot 2^2$. In any case, the prime factors are the same. For this reason, we agree that any of these may be considered "the" prime factorization of 76.

> Each composite number is uniquely determined by its prime factorization.

This last result is sometimes called the Fundamental Theorem of Arithmetic.

EXAMPLE 6 Find the prime factorization of 72.

$$
\begin{array}{r}
3 \leftarrow \text{3 is prime, so we stop dividing.} \\
3\overline{)9} \\
2\overline{)18} \\
2\overline{)36} \\
2\overline{)72} \leftarrow \text{Begin here and work upward.}
\end{array}
$$

$72 = 2 \cdot 2 \cdot 2 \cdot 3 \cdot 3$

Another way to find a prime factorization is by using a **factor tree** as follows:

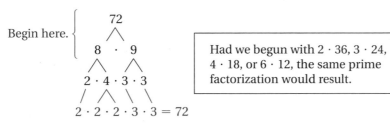

Begin here.
$$
\begin{array}{c}
72 \\
\wedge \\
8 \quad \cdot \quad 9 \\
\wedge \quad \wedge \\
2 \cdot 4 \cdot 3 \cdot 3 \\
/ \wedge \backslash \backslash \\
2 \cdot 2 \cdot 2 \cdot 3 \cdot 3 = 72
\end{array}
$$

> Had we begun with $2 \cdot 36$, $3 \cdot 24$, $4 \cdot 18$, or $6 \cdot 12$, the same prime factorization would result.

EXAMPLE 7 Find the prime factorization of 189.

We can use a string of successive divisions.

$$
\begin{array}{r}
7 \leftarrow \text{7 is prime, so we stop dividing.} \\
3\overline{)\;21} \\
3\overline{)\;63} \\
3\overline{)189} \leftarrow \text{Begin here. Since 189 is odd, 2 will not be a factor. We}
\end{array}
$$
start with 3.

$189 = 3 \cdot 3 \cdot 3 \cdot 7$

We can also use a factor tree.

$$
\begin{array}{c}
189 \\
\wedge \\
3 \cdot 63 \\
/ \quad \wedge \\
3 \cdot 7 \cdot 9 \\
/ \; / \; \wedge \\
3 \cdot 7 \cdot 3 \cdot 3 = 189
\end{array}
$$

> **CAUTION!**
>
> Keep in mind the difference between finding all the factors of a number and finding the prime factorization. In Example 7, the prime factorization is $3 \cdot 3 \cdot 3 \cdot 7$. The factors of 189 are 1, 3, 7, 9, 21, 27, 63, and 189.

EXAMPLE 8 Find the prime factorization of 130 and list all factors of 130.

To find the prime factorization, we can use a string of divisions or a factor tree.

$$
\begin{array}{r}
13 \\
5\overline{)\;65} \\
2\overline{)130}
\end{array}
\qquad
\begin{array}{c}
130 \\
\wedge \\
10 \quad \cdot \quad 13 \\
\wedge \quad \backslash \\
130 = 2 \cdot 5 \cdot 13
\end{array}
$$

From the prime factorization we can easily identify 2, 5, and 13 as factors. We can form the products $2 \cdot 5$, $2 \cdot 13$, and $5 \cdot 13$ to find that 10, 26, and 65 are also factors. A complete list of factors is 1, 2, 5, 10, 13, 26, 65, and 130.

Do Exercises 6–11.

Finding a number's prime factorization can be quite challenging, especially when the prime factors themselves are large. This difficulty is used worldwide as a way of securing transactions over the Internet.

Write the prime factorization of each number.

6. 6

7. 12

8. 45

9. 98

10. 126

11. 144

Answers on page A-9

a   List all the factors of each number.

1. 18	**2.** 16	**3.** 54	**4.** 48
5. 9	**6.** 4	**7.** 13	**8.** 11

b   State whether each number is prime, composite, or neither.

9. 17	**10.** 24	**11.** 22	**12.** 31
13. 48	**14.** 43	**15.** 53	**16.** 54
17. 1	**18.** 2	**19.** 81	**20.** 37
21. 47	**22.** 51	**23.** 29	**24.** 49

c   Find the prime factorization of each number.

25. 27	**26.** 16	**27.** 14	**28.** 15
29. 80	**30.** 32	**31.** 25	**32.** 40
33. 62	**34.** 169	**35.** 140	**36.** 50
37. 121	**38.** 170	**39.** 175	**40.** 196
41. 99	**42.** 77	**43.** 86	**44.** 78
45. 217	**46.** 497	**47.** 7000	**48.** 5000

a , **c**   List all the factors of each number.

49. 100	**50.** 135	**51.** 385	**52.** 110
53. 81	**54.** 196	**55.** 225	**56.** 441

57. **D**$_W$ Is it possible for two consecutive natural numbers other than 2 and 3 to both be prime? Why or why not?

58. **D**$_W$ Is it necessary to try dividing 41 by all primes through 37 in order to demonstrate that 41 is prime?

Multiply.

59. $-2 \cdot 13$ [2.4a] **60.** $(-8)(-32)$ [2.4a]

Add.

61. $-17 + 25$ [2.2a] **62.** $-9 + (-14)$ [2.2a]

Divide.

63. $53 \div 53$ [1.6c] **64.** $73 \div 1$ [1.6c] **65.** $0 \div 22$ [2.5a]

66. $22 \div 22$ [1.6c] **67.** $-42 \div 1$ [2.5a] **68.** $0 \div (-42)$ [2.5a]

SYNTHESIS

69. $^\mathbf{D}\mathbf{w}$ Is it possible for the sum or product of two prime numbers to be prime? Why or why not?

70. $^\mathbf{D}\mathbf{w}$ It was mentioned that the largest known prime is $2^{6972593} - 1$. How can you tell that it is not even?

71. $^\mathbf{D}\mathbf{w}$ If a and b are both factors of c, does it follow that $a \cdot b$ is also a factor of c? Why or why not?

Find the prime factorization of each number.

72. 15,125 **73.** 2035 **74.** 136,097

75. 102,971 **76.** 473,073,361 **77.** 168,840

78. Describe an arrangement of 54 objects that corresponds to the factorization $54 = 6 \times 9$.

79. Describe an arrangement of 24 objects that corresponds to the factorization $24 = 2 \cdot 3 \cdot 4$.

80. Two numbers are **relatively prime** if there is no prime number that is a factor of both numbers. For example, 10 and 21 are relatively prime but 15 and 18 are not. List five pairs of composite numbers that are relatively prime.

81. *Factors and Sums.* In the table below, the top number in each column has been factored in such a way that the sum of the factors is the bottom number in the column. For example, in the first column, 56 has been factored as $7 \cdot 8$, and $7 + 8 = 15$, the bottom number. Such thinking will be important in understanding the meaning of a factor and in algebra.

Product	56	63	36	72	140	96	48	168	110	90	432	63
Factor	7											
Factor	8											
Sum	15	16	20	38	24	20	14	29	21	19	42	24

Find the missing numbers in the table.

3.3 FRACTIONS AND FRACTION NOTATION

Objectives

a Identify the numerator and the denominator of a fraction and write fraction notation for part of an object or part of a set of objects.

b Simplify fraction notation like n/n to 1, $0/n$ to 0, and $n/1$ to n.

Identify the numerator and the denominator of each fraction.

1. $\dfrac{5}{7}$

2. $\dfrac{5a}{7b}$

3. $\dfrac{-22}{3}$

The study of arithmetic begins with the set of whole numbers

0, 1, 2, 3, 4, 5, 6, 7, 8, 9, 10, 11, and so on.

The need soon arises for fractional parts of numbers such as halves, thirds, fourths, and so on. Here are some examples:

- $\frac{1}{25}$ of the parking spaces in a commercial area in the state of Indiana must be marked for the handicapped.
- For $\frac{9}{10}$ of the people in the United States, English is the primary language.
- $\frac{1}{11}$ of all women develop breast cancer at some point in their lives.
  - About $\frac{1}{5}$ of the earth's surface is frozen.
  - $\frac{43}{200}$ of the world's population is in China.

a Identifying Numerators and Denominators

The following are some additional examples of fractions:

$$\frac{1}{2}, \quad \frac{13}{41}, \quad \frac{-8}{5}, \quad \frac{x}{y}, \quad -\frac{4}{25}, \quad \frac{2a}{7b}.$$

This way of writing number names is called **fraction notation.** The top number is called the **numerator** and the bottom number is called the **denominator.**

EXAMPLE 1 Identify the numerator and the denominator.

$\dfrac{7}{8}$ $\leftarrow$ Numerator
$\phantom{\dfrac{7}{8}}$ $\leftarrow$ Denominator

Do Exercises 1–3.

Let's look at various situations that involve fractions.

FRACTIONS AS A PARTITION OF AN OBJECT DIVIDED INTO EQUAL PARTS

Consider a candy bar divided into 5 equal sections. If you eat 2 sections, you have eaten $\frac{2}{5}$ of the candy bar.

The denominator 5 tells us the unit, $\frac{1}{5}$. The numerator 2 tells us the number of equal parts we are considering, 2.

Answers on page A-10

EXAMPLE 2 The circle below represents $1. What part is shaded?

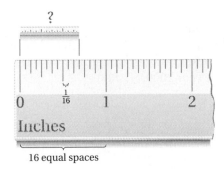

$\frac{1}{4}$ of a dollar

$1

When an object is divided into 4 parts of the same size, each of these parts is $\frac{1}{4}$ of the object. Thus, $\frac{1}{4}$ (*one-fourth* or *one-quarter*) of a dollar is shaded.

Do Exercises 4–7.

The markings on a ruler use fractions.

EXAMPLE 3 What part of an inch is indicated?

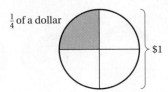

?

$\frac{1}{16}$

0   1   2

Inches

16 equal spaces

Each inch on the ruler shown above is divided into 16 equal parts. The measured length extends to the 11th mark. Thus, $\frac{11}{16}$ is indicated.

EXAMPLE 4 What part of a cup is filled?

The measuring cup is divided into 3 parts of the same size, and 2 of them are filled. This is $2 \cdot \frac{1}{3}$, or $\frac{2}{3}$. Thus, $\frac{2}{3}$ (read *two-thirds*) of a cup is filled.

Do Exercises 8–10.

What part is shaded?

4.

$1

5. 1 mile

6.

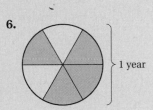

1 year

7. 1 mile

What part is shaded or indicated?

8.

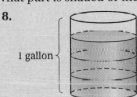

1 gallon

9.

0   1   2

Inches

10.

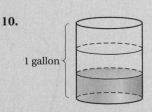

1 gallon

Answers on page A-10

233

3.3 Fractions and Fraction Notation

11. What part of this set, or collection, of tools are wrenches? hammers?

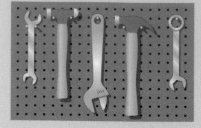

Answer on page A-10

234

CHAPTER 3: Fraction Notation: Multiplication and Division

Study Tips

UNDERSTAND YOUR MISTAKES

When you receive a graded quiz, test, or assignment back from your instructor, it is important to review and understand what your mistakes were. Too often students simply file away old papers without first making an effort to learn from their mistakes.

EXAMPLE 5 What part of this set, or collection, of people are pop stars? U.S. presidents?

| Connie Chung | Abraham Lincoln | Christina Aguilera | Ricky Martin | George W. Bush | Janet Jackson |

There are 6 people in the set. We know that 3 of them, Christina Aguilera, Ricky Martin, and Janet Jackson, are pop stars. Thus, 3 of 6, or $\frac{3}{6}$, are pop stars. Lincoln and Bush are U.S. presidents, so $\frac{2}{6}$ are U.S. presidents.

We will simplify such fraction notation in Section 3.5.

Do Exercise 11.

The diagram in Example 2 is an example of a *circle graph*, or *pie chart*. Circle graphs are often used to illustrate the relationships of fractional parts of a whole. The following graph shows how the world's population was distributed in the year 2000.

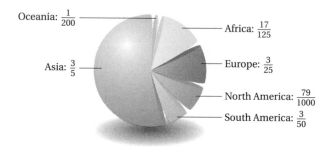

Oceania: $\frac{1}{200}$ Africa: $\frac{17}{125}$

Asia: $\frac{3}{5}$ Europe: $\frac{3}{25}$

North America: $\frac{79}{1000}$

South America: $\frac{3}{50}$

Fractions greater than 1 correspond to situations like the following.

EXAMPLE 6 What part is shaded?

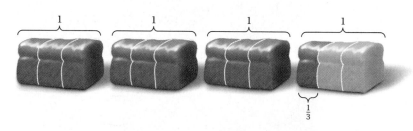

1   1   1   1

$\frac{1}{3}$

Each loaf of bread is divided into 3 equal parts. The unit is $\frac{1}{3}$. The *denominator* is 3. We have 10 of the units shaded. This tells us the *numerator* is 10. Thus, $\frac{10}{3}$ is shaded.

EXAMPLE 7 What part is shaded?

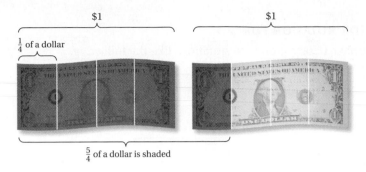

$1 $1

$\frac{1}{4}$ of a dollar

$\frac{5}{4}$ of a dollar is shaded

We can regard this as two objects of 4 parts each and take 5 of those parts. We have more than one whole object. Thus, $5 \cdot \frac{1}{4}$, or $\frac{5}{4}$ (also, 5 quarters) is shaded.

Do Exercises 12 and 13.

FRACTIONS AS RATIOS

A **ratio** is a quotient of two quantities. We can express a ratio with fraction notation. (We will consider ratios in more detail in Chapter 5.)

EXAMPLE 8 *Baseball Standings.* The following are the final standings in the National League West for 2002, when the division was won by the Arizona Diamondbacks. Find the ratio of Arizona's wins to losses, wins to total games, and losses to total games.
Source: Major League Baseball

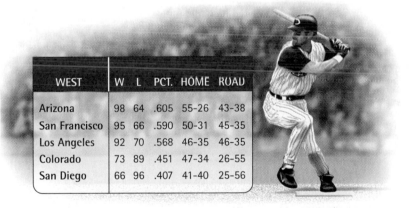

WEST	W	L	PCT.	HOME	ROAD
Arizona	98	64	.605	55-26	43-38
San Francisco	95	66	.590	50-31	45-35
Los Angeles	92	70	.568	46-35	46-35
Colorado	73	89	.451	47-34	26-55
San Diego	66	96	.407	41-40	25-56

Arizona won 98 games and lost 64 games. They played a total of 98 + 64, or 162 games. Thus we have the following.

The ratio of wins to losses is $\dfrac{98}{64}$.

The ratio of wins to total games is $\dfrac{98}{162}$.

The ratio of losses to total games is $\dfrac{64}{162}$.

Do Exercise 14.

What part is shaded?

12.

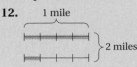

1 mile

2 miles

13.

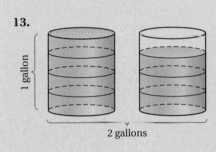

1 gallon

2 gallons

14. Baseball Standings. Refer to the table in Example 8. The San Francisco Giants finished second in the National League West in 2002. Find the ratio of Giant wins to losses, wins to total games, and losses to total games.
Source: Major League Baseball

Answers on page A-10

Simplify. Assume that $a \neq 0$.

15. $\dfrac{8}{8}$

16. $\dfrac{a}{a}$

17. $\dfrac{-52}{-52}$

18. $\dfrac{1}{1}$

19. $\dfrac{-2347}{-2347}$

20. $\dfrac{54a}{54a}$

b Some Fraction Notation for Integers

FRACTION NOTATION FOR 1

The number 1 corresponds to situations like the following.

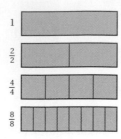

If we divide an object into n parts and take n of them, we get all of the object (1 whole object). Since a negative divided by a negative is a positive, the following is stated for *all* nonzero integers.

> **WRITING 1 AS A FRACTION**
>
> $\dfrac{n}{n} = 1$, for any integer n that is not 0.

EXAMPLE 9 Simplify: **a)** $\dfrac{5}{5}$; **b)** $\dfrac{-9}{-9}$; **c)** $\dfrac{17x}{17x}$ (assume $x \neq 0$).

a) $\dfrac{5}{5} = 1$ 　　　　**b)** $\dfrac{-9}{-9} = 1$ 　　　　**c)** $\dfrac{17x}{17x} = 1$

Do Exercises 15–20.

FRACTION NOTATION FOR 0

Consider $\frac{0}{4}$. This corresponds to dividing an object into 4 parts and taking none of them. We get 0. This result also extends to all nonzero integers.

> **THE NUMBER 0 AS A FRACTION**
>
> $\dfrac{0}{n} = 0$, for any integer n that is not 0.

EXAMPLE 10 Simplify: **a)** $\dfrac{0}{9}$; **b)** $\dfrac{0}{1}$; **c)** $\dfrac{0}{5a}$ (assume that $a \neq 0$); **d)** $\dfrac{0}{-23}$.

a) $\dfrac{0}{9} = 0$ 　　　　　　　　　　**b)** $\dfrac{0}{1} = 0$

c) $\dfrac{0}{5a} = 0$ 　　　　　　　　　　**d)** $\dfrac{0}{-23} = 0$

Answers on page A-10

Fraction notation with a denominator of 0, such as $n/0$, does not represent a number because we cannot divide an object into *zero* parts. (If it is not divided at all, then we say that it is undivided and remains in one part.)

DIVISION BY 0

$\dfrac{n}{0}$ is not defined.

$\left(\text{When asked to simplify } \dfrac{n}{0}, \text{ we write } \textit{undefined.}\right)$

Do Exercises 21–26.

OTHER INTEGERS

Consider $\frac{4}{1}$. This corresponds to dividing an object into one part (leaving it whole) and taking four of them. We have 4 objects.

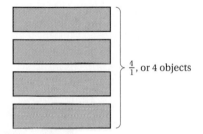
$\frac{4}{1}$, or 4 objects

DIVISION BY 1

Any integer divided by 1 is the original integer. That is,

$$\dfrac{n}{1} = n, \quad \text{for any integer } n.$$

EXAMPLE 11 Simplify: **a)** $\dfrac{2}{1}$; **b)** $\dfrac{-9}{1}$; **c)** $\dfrac{3x}{1}$.

a) $\dfrac{2}{1} = 2$ **b)** $\dfrac{-9}{1} = -9$ **c)** $\dfrac{3x}{1} = 3x$

Do Exercises 27–30.

Answers on page A-10

3.3
EXERCISE SET

For Extra Help

Digital Video   InterAct   Math Tutor   MathXL   MyMathLab
Tutor CD 2   Math   Center
Videotape 3

a   Identify the numerator and the denominator of each fraction.

1. $\dfrac{3}{4}$ 2. $\dfrac{-9}{10}$ 3. $\dfrac{7}{-9}$ 4. $\dfrac{15}{8}$ 5. $\dfrac{2x}{3z}$ 6. $\dfrac{9a}{2b}$

What part of the object or set of objects is shaded? In Exercises 17–20, what part of an inch is indicated?

7. $1

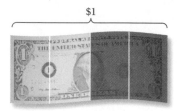

8. $1

9.

1 yard

10.

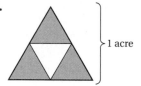

1 mile

11.

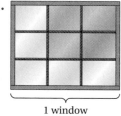

1 window

12.

1 square yard

13.

1 acre

14.

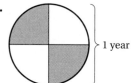

1 year

15.

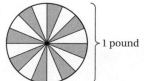

1 pound

16.

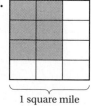

1 square mile

17.

18.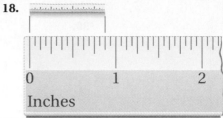

19.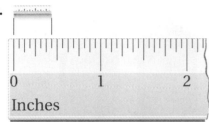

20.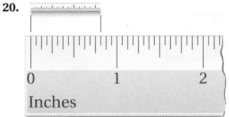

21.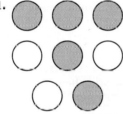

22.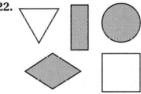

23.

24.

For each of Exercises 25–28, give fraction notation for the amount of gas (a) in the tank and (b) used from a full tank.

25.

26.

27.

28.

What part is shaded?

29.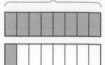
1 gold bar

30.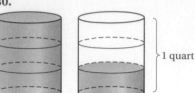
1 quart

31.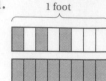
1 foot

32.
1 window

33.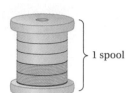
1 spool

34.
1 quart

35. *Police-Resident Ratio.* Washington, D.C., has the highest ratio of police to residents in the United States, 67 police officers for every 10,000 residents. What is the ratio of police to residents?

36. *Moviegoers.* Of every 1000 people who attend movies, 340 are in the 18–24 age group. What is the ratio of moviegoers in the 18–24 age group to all moviegoers?
Source: American Demographics

37. *Gas Mileage.* Ruth's 2002 Honda Civic can go 721 mi on 14 gal of gasoline. What is the ratio of:
a) miles driven to gasoline burned?
b) gasoline burned to miles driven?

38. Russ delivers car parts to auto service centers. On Thursday he had 15 deliveries. By noon he had delivered only 4 orders. What is the ratio of:
a) orders delivered to total number of orders?
b) orders delivered to orders not delivered?
c) orders not delivered to total number of orders?

39. For the following set of people, what is the ratio of:
a) women to the total number of people?
b) women to men?
c) men to the total number of people?
d) men to women?

40. For the following set of nuts and bolts, what is the ratio of:
a) nuts to bolts?
b) bolts to nuts?
c) nuts to the total number of elements?
d) total number of elements to nuts?

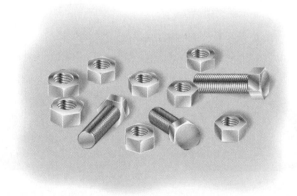

b Simplify, if possible. Assume that all variables are nonzero.

41. $\dfrac{0}{17}$

42. $\dfrac{19}{19}$

43. $\dfrac{15}{1}$

44. $\dfrac{10}{1}$

45. $\dfrac{20}{20}$

46. $\dfrac{-20}{1}$

47. $\dfrac{-14}{-14}$

48. $\dfrac{4a}{1}$

49. $\dfrac{0}{-234}$

50. $\dfrac{37a}{37a}$

51. $\dfrac{3n}{3n}$

52. $\dfrac{0}{-1}$

53. $\dfrac{9x}{9x}$

54. $\dfrac{-12a}{1}$

55. $\dfrac{-63}{1}$

56. $\dfrac{-3x}{-3x}$

57. $\dfrac{0}{2u}$

58. $\dfrac{0}{8}$

59. $\dfrac{52}{0}$

60. $\dfrac{8-8}{1247}$

61. $\dfrac{7n}{1}$

62. $\dfrac{247}{0}$

63. $\dfrac{6}{7-7}$

64. $\dfrac{15}{9-9}$

65. **Dw** Explain in your own words why $n/1 - n$, for any integer n.

66. **Dw** Explain in your own words why $0/n = 0$, for any nonzero integer n.

SKILL MAINTENANCE

Multiply.

67. $-7(30)$ [2.4a]

68. $23 \cdot (-14)$ [2.4a]

69. $(-71)(-12)0$ [2.4b]

70. $32(-29)0$ [2.4b]

71. Recently, the average annual income of people living in Connecticut was $40,600 per person. In Mississippi, the average annual income was $20,993. How much more do people in Connecticut make, on average, than those living in Mississippi?   [1.8a]
Source: *The New York Times 2002 Almanac*

72. Sandy can type 62 words per minute. How long will it take Sandy to type 12,462 words?   [1.8a]

SYNTHESIS

73. **Dw** Explain in your own words why $\dfrac{n}{0}$ is undefined for any integer n.

74. **Dw** What is the ratio of negative integers to positive integers? Why?

75. The year 2003 began on a Wednesday. What fractional part of 2003 were Thursdays?

76. The year 2002 began on a Tuesday. What fractional part of 2002 were Tuesdays?

77. Rayona earned $2700 one summer. During the following semester, she spent $1200 for tuition, $540 for rent, and $360 for food. The rest went for miscellaneous expenses. What part of the income went for tuition? rent? food? miscellaneous expenses?

78. The surface of Earth is 3 parts water and 1 part land. What fractional part of Earth is water? land?

79. A couple had 3 daughters, each of whom had 2 sons. If each son fathered 4 daughters, what fractional part of the couple's descendants is male?

80. A couple had 3 sons, each of whom had 3 daughters. If each daughter gave birth to 3 sons, what fractional part of the couple's descendants is female?

81. During the 1990s the U.S. population grew by nearly 33,000,000. Of this growth, $\frac{17}{200}$ occurred in the Northeast, $\frac{7}{50}$ occurred in the Midwest, $\frac{9}{25}$ occurred in the South, and $\frac{83}{200}$ in the West. Label each sector of the graph with the most appropriate geographical location.

U.S. Growth in 1990s

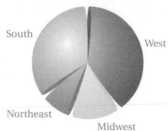

What part of each object is shaded?

82.

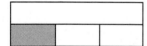

83.

84.

85.

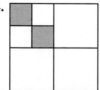

3.4 MULTIPLICATION OF FRACTIONS

Objectives

a Multiply an integer and a fraction.

b Multiply using fraction notation.

c Solve problems involving multiplication of fractions.

Before discussing how to simplify fraction notation (Section 3.5), it is essential that we study multiplication of fractions.

a Multiplication by an Integer

We can find $3 \cdot \frac{1}{4}$ by thinking of repeated addition. We add three $\frac{1}{4}$'s.

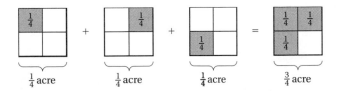

$\frac{1}{4}$ acre $\frac{1}{4}$ acre $\frac{1}{4}$ acre $\frac{3}{4}$ acre

We see that $3 \cdot \frac{1}{4} = \frac{1}{4} + \frac{1}{4} + \frac{1}{4} = \frac{3}{4}$.

Do Exercises 1 and 2.

> To multiply a fraction by an integer,
> **a)** multiply the top number (the numerator) by the integer and
>
> $$6 \cdot \frac{4}{5} = \frac{6 \cdot 4}{5} = \frac{24}{5}$$
>
> **b)** keep the same denominator.

EXAMPLES Multiply.

1. $5 \times \frac{3}{8} = \frac{5 \times 3}{8} = \frac{15}{8}$ We generally replace the $\times$ symbol with $\cdot$

> Skip this step when you feel comfortable doing so.

2. $\frac{2}{5} \cdot 13 = \frac{2 \cdot 13}{5} = \frac{26}{5}$

3. $-10 \cdot \frac{1}{3} = \frac{-10}{3}$, or $-\frac{10}{3}$ Recall that $\frac{-a}{b} = -\frac{a}{b}$.

4. $a \cdot \frac{4}{7} = \frac{4a}{7}$ Recall that $a \cdot 4 = 4 \cdot a$.

Do Exercises 3–6.

1. Find $2 \cdot \frac{1}{3}$.

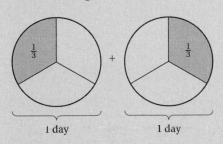

1 day   1 day

2. Find $5 \cdot \frac{1}{8}$.

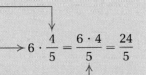

Multiply.

3. $7 \times \frac{2}{3}$

4. $(-11) \cdot \frac{3}{10}$

5. $34 \cdot \frac{2}{5}$

6. $x \cdot \frac{4}{9}$

Answers on page A-10

7. Draw diagrams to illustrate $\frac{1}{4}$ and $\frac{1}{2} \cdot \frac{1}{4}$.

8. Draw diagrams to illustrate $\frac{1}{3}$ and $\frac{4}{5} \cdot \frac{1}{3}$.

Multiply.

9. $\dfrac{3}{8} \cdot \dfrac{5}{7}$

10. $\dfrac{4}{3} \cdot \dfrac{8}{5}$

11. $\left(-\dfrac{3}{10}\right)\left(-\dfrac{1}{10}\right)$

12. $(-7)\dfrac{a}{b}$

Answers on page A-10

CHAPTER 3: Fraction Notation:
Multiplication and Division

---

b   Multiplication Using Fraction Notation

To illustrate the meaning of an expression like $\frac{1}{2} \cdot \frac{1}{3}$, we first represent $\frac{1}{3}$, and then shade half of that region. Note that $\frac{1}{2} \cdot \frac{1}{3}$ is the same as $\frac{1}{2}$ of $\frac{1}{3}$.

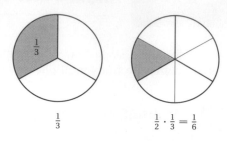

$\frac{1}{3}$ $\frac{1}{2} \cdot \frac{1}{3} = \frac{1}{6}$

Do Exercise 7.

To visualize $\frac{2}{5} \cdot \frac{3}{4}$, we first represent $\frac{3}{4}$, and then shade $\frac{2}{5}$ of that region,

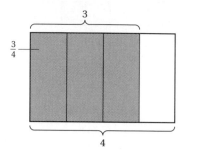

Since 6 of the 20 sections are now shaded, we have

$$\frac{2}{5} \cdot \frac{3}{4} = \frac{6}{20} \quad \begin{array}{l}\leftarrow \text{This is the product of the numerators.} \\ \leftarrow \text{This is the product of the denominators.}\end{array}$$

Do Exercise 8.

Notice that the product of two fractions is the product of the numerators over the product of the denominators.

To multiply a fraction by a fraction,

a) multiply the numerators and

b) multiply the denominators. ———

$$\frac{9}{7} \cdot \frac{3}{4} = \frac{9 \cdot 3}{7 \cdot 4} = \frac{27}{28}$$

EXAMPLES Multiply.

5. $\dfrac{5}{6} \cdot \dfrac{7}{4} = \dfrac{5 \cdot 7}{6 \cdot 4} = \dfrac{35}{24}$

Skip this step when you feel comfortable doing so.

6. $\dfrac{3}{5} \cdot \dfrac{7}{8} = \dfrac{3 \cdot 7}{5 \cdot 8} = \dfrac{21}{40}$

7. $\dfrac{4}{x} \cdot \dfrac{y}{9} = \dfrac{4y}{9x}$

8. $(-6)\left(-\dfrac{4}{5}\right) = \dfrac{-6}{1} \cdot \dfrac{-4}{5} = \dfrac{24}{5}$ Recall that $\dfrac{n}{1} = n$.

Do Exercises 9–12.

C   Applications and Problem Solving

Most problems that can be solved by multiplying fractions can be thought of in terms of rectangular arrays.

 EXAMPLE 9 A dude ranch owns a square mile of land. The owner gives $\frac{4}{5}$ of it to her daughter who, in turn, gives $\frac{2}{3}$ of her share to her son. How much land goes to the daughter's son?

1. **Familiarize.** We first make a drawing to help solve the problem. The land may not be square. It could be in a shape like A or B below, or it could even be in more than one piece. But to think about the problem, we can visualize a square, as shown by shape C.

1 square mile   1 square mile   1 square mile

The daughter gets $\frac{4}{5}$ of the land. We shade $\frac{4}{5}$.

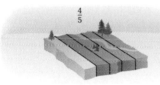

Her son gets $\frac{2}{3}$ of her part. We "raise" that.

2. **Translate.** We let $n =$ the part of the land that goes to the daughter's son. We are taking "two-thirds of four-fifths." The word "of" corresponds to multiplication. Thus, the following multiplication sentence corresponds to the situation:

$$\frac{2}{3} \cdot \frac{4}{5} = n.$$

3. **Solve.** The number sentence tells us what to do. We have

$$\frac{2}{3} \cdot \frac{4}{5} = n, \quad \text{or} \quad \frac{8}{15} = n.$$

4. **Check.** We can check this in the figure above, where we see that 8 of 15 equally sized parts will go to the daughter's son.

5. **State.** The daughter's son gets $\frac{8}{15}$ of a square mile of land.

Do Exercise 13.

13. Camp Mohawk uses $\frac{3}{4}$ of its extra land for recreational purposes. Of that, $\frac{1}{2}$ is used for swimming pools. What part of the extra land is used for swimming pools?

Answer on page A-10

Study Tips

ADD YOUR VOICE TO THE AUTHOR'S

If you own your text, consider using it as a notebook. Since many instructors closely parallel the book, it is often useful to make notes on the appropriate page as he or she is lecturing.

14. The length of a button on a fax machine is $\frac{9}{10}$ cm. The width is $\frac{7}{10}$ cm. What is the area?

We have seen that the area of a rectangular region is found by multiplying length by width. That is true whether length and width are whole numbers or not. Remember, the area of a rectangular region is given by the formula

$$A = l \cdot w \quad (Area = length \cdot width).$$

EXAMPLE 10 The length of a computer's Delete key is $\frac{9}{16}$ in. The width is $\frac{3}{8}$ in. What is the area?

1. **Familiarize.** Recall that area is length times width. We make a drawing, letting $A =$ the area of the computer key.

2. **Translate.** Next, we translate.

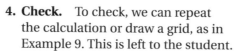

$$A = \frac{9}{16} \cdot \frac{3}{8}$$

3. **Solve.** The sentence tells us what to do. We multiply:

$$\frac{9}{16} \cdot \frac{3}{8} = \frac{9 \cdot 3}{16 \cdot 8} = \frac{27}{128}.$$

4. **Check.** To check, we can repeat the calculation or draw a grid, as in Example 9. This is left to the student.

5. **State.** The area of the key is $\frac{27}{128}$ square inches, or $\frac{27}{128}$ in^2.

Do Exercise 14.

15. Of the students at Overton Junior College, $\frac{1}{8}$ participate in sports and $\frac{3}{5}$ of these play football. What fractional part of the students play football?

EXAMPLE 11 A muffin recipe calls for $\frac{3}{4}$ cup of cornmeal. A chef is making $\frac{1}{2}$ of the recipe. How much cornmeal should the chef use?

1. **Familiarize.** We first make a drawing or at least visualize the situation. We let $n =$ the amount of cornmeal the chef should use.

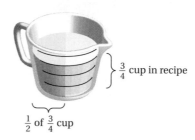

$\frac{3}{4}$ cup in recipe

$\frac{1}{2}$ of $\frac{3}{4}$ cup

2. **Translate.** The multiplication sentence $\frac{1}{2} \cdot \frac{3}{4} = n$ corresponds to the situation.

3. **Solve.** We carry out the multiplication:

$$\frac{1}{2} \cdot \frac{3}{4} = \frac{1 \cdot 3}{2 \cdot 4} = \frac{3}{8}.$$

4. **Check.** We check by repeating the calculation. This is left to the student.

5. **State.** The chef should use $\frac{3}{8}$ cup of cornmeal.

Do Exercise 15.

Answers on page A-10

3.4

EXERCISE SET

For Extra Help

Digital Video   InterAct   Math Tutor   MathXL   MyMathLab
Tutor CD 2   Math   Center
Videotape 3

a Multiply.

1. $3 \cdot \frac{1}{8}$

2. $2 \cdot \frac{1}{5}$

3. $(-5) \times \frac{1}{6}$

4. $(-4) \times \frac{1}{7}$

5. $\frac{2}{3} \cdot 7$

6. $\frac{2}{5} \cdot 7$

7. $(-1)\frac{7}{9}$

8. $(-1)\frac{4}{11}$

9. $\frac{5}{6} \cdot x$

10. $\frac{5}{6} \cdot y$

11. $\frac{2}{5}(-3)$

12. $\frac{3}{5}(-4)$

13. $a \cdot \frac{2}{7}$

14. $b \cdot \frac{3}{8}$

15. $17 \times \frac{m}{6}$

16. $\frac{n}{7} \cdot 30$

17. $-3 \cdot \frac{-2}{5}$

18. $-4 \cdot \frac{-5}{7}$

19. $\frac{2}{7}(\ x)$

20. $-\frac{3}{4}(-a)$

b Multiply.

21. $\frac{1}{3} \cdot \frac{1}{5}$

22. $\frac{1}{4} \cdot \frac{1}{2}$

23. $\left(-\frac{1}{4}\right) \times \frac{1}{10}$

24. $\left(-\frac{1}{3}\right) \times \frac{1}{10}$

25. $\frac{2}{3} \times \frac{1}{5}$

26. $\frac{3}{5} \times \frac{1}{5}$

27. $\frac{2}{y} \cdot \frac{x}{9}$

28. $\left(-\frac{3}{4}\right)\left(-\frac{3}{5}\right)$

29. $\left(-\frac{3}{4}\right)\left(-\frac{3}{4}\right)$

30. $\frac{3}{b} \cdot \frac{a}{7}$

31. $\frac{2}{3} \cdot \frac{7}{13}$

32. $\frac{3}{11} \cdot \frac{4}{5}$

33. $\frac{1}{10}\left(\frac{-3}{5}\right)$

34. $\frac{3}{10}\left(\frac{-7}{5}\right)$

35. $\frac{7}{8} \cdot \frac{a}{8}$

36. $\frac{4}{5} \cdot \frac{7}{x}$

37. $\frac{1}{y} \cdot \frac{1}{100}$

38. $\frac{b}{10} \cdot \frac{13}{100}$

39. $\frac{-14}{15} \cdot \frac{13}{19}$

40. $\frac{-12}{13} \cdot \frac{12}{13}$

C   Solve.

41. A rectangular table top measures $\frac{4}{5}$ m long by $\frac{3}{5}$ m wide. What is its area?

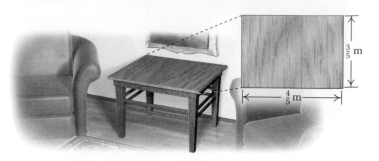

42. If each slice of pie is $\frac{1}{6}$ of a pie, how much of the pie is $\frac{1}{2}$ of a slice?

43. *Football: High School to Pro.* One of 39 high school football players plays college football. One of 39 college players plays professional football. What fractional part of high school players play professional football?
Source: National Football League

44. A gasoline can holds $\frac{7}{8}$ liter (L). How much will the can hold when it is $\frac{1}{2}$ full?

45. It takes $\frac{2}{3}$ yd of ribbon to make a bow. How much ribbon is needed to make 5 bows?

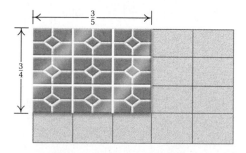

46. *Cooking.* The Red River Cafe's recipe for blueberry crisp calls for $\frac{3}{4}$ cup of maple syrup–coated rolled oats. How much is needed to make $\frac{1}{2}$ of a recipe?

47. *Floor Tiling.* A bathroom floor is being tiled. An area $\frac{3}{5}$ of the length and $\frac{3}{4}$ of the width is covered. What fraction of the floor has been tiled?

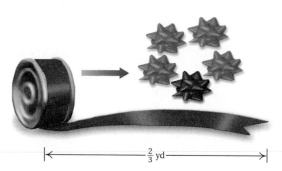

48. *Basement Carpet.* A basement floor is being carpeted. An area $\frac{7}{8}$ of the length and $\frac{3}{4}$ of the width is covered by lunch time. What fraction of the floor has been completed?

49. *Municipal Waste.* Four-fifths of all municipal waste is landfill and one-tenth of all municipal waste is landscape trimmings. What fractional part of municipal waste is landscape trimmings that are landfill?
Source: Based on information from The Statistical Abstract of the United States and the Chittenden, VT, Solid Waste District.

50. *Municipal Waste.* About $\frac{19}{50}$ of all municipal waste is paper and paperboard. Of this, approximately $\frac{2}{5}$ is recycled. What fractional part of municipal waste is paper and paperboard that will be recycled?
Source: Statistical Abstract of the United States

CHAPTER 3: Fraction Notation:
Multiplication and Division

51. $\mathbf{D_W}$ Following Example 4, we explained, using words and pictures, why $\frac{2}{5} \cdot \frac{3}{4}$ equals $\frac{6}{20}$. Present a similar explanation of why $\frac{2}{3} \cdot \frac{4}{7}$ equals $\frac{8}{21}$.

52. $\mathbf{D_W}$ Write a problem for a classmate to solve. Design the problem so that the solution is "About $\frac{1}{30}$ of the students are left-handed women."

SKILL MAINTENANCE

Divide.

53. $180 \div 20$ [1.6c]

54. $280 \div 40$ [1.6c]

55. $450 \div (-9)$ [2.5a]

56. $540 \div (-6)$ [2.5a]

57. $\dfrac{-35}{5}$ [2.5a]

58. $\dfrac{-60}{12}$ [2.5a]

59. $\dfrac{-65}{-5}$ [2.5a]

60. $\dfrac{-42}{-7}$ [2.5a]

What does the digit 8 mean in each number?   [1.1a]

61. 4,678,952

62. 8,473,901

63. 7148

64. 23,803

SYNTHESIS

65. $\mathbf{D_W}$ Is multiplication of fractions commutative? Why or why not?

66. $\mathbf{D_W}$ Is multiplication of fractions associative? Why or why not?

67. *Forestry.* A chain saw holds $\frac{1}{5}$ gal of fuel. Chain saw fuel is $\frac{1}{16}$ two-cycle oil and $\frac{15}{16}$ unleaded gasoline. How much two-cycle oil is in a freshly filled chain saw?

Multiply. Write each answer using fraction notation.

68. ▦ $\dfrac{341}{517} \cdot \dfrac{209}{349}$

69. ▦ $\left(-\dfrac{57}{61}\right)^3$

70. $\left(\dfrac{2}{5}\right)^3\left(-\dfrac{7}{9}\right)$

71. $\left(-\dfrac{1}{2}\right)^5\left(\dfrac{3}{5}\right)$

72. $\left(-\dfrac{3}{4}\right)^2\left(-\dfrac{5}{7}\right)^2$

73. Evaluate $-\dfrac{2}{3}xy$ for $x = \dfrac{2}{5}$ and $y = -\dfrac{1}{7}$.

74. Evaluate $-\dfrac{3}{4}ab$ for $a = \dfrac{2}{5}$ and $b = \dfrac{7}{5}$.

75. ▦ Evaluate $-\dfrac{4}{7}ab$ for $a = \dfrac{93}{107}$ and $b = \dfrac{13}{41}$.

76. ▦ Evaluate $-\dfrac{19}{73}xy$ for $x = \dfrac{103}{105}$ and $y = \dfrac{47}{61}$.

Objectives

a Multiply by 1 to find an equivalent expression using a different denominator.

b Simplify fraction notation.

c Test to determine whether two fractions are equivalent.

Multiply.

1. $\dfrac{1}{2} \cdot \dfrac{8}{8}$

2. $\dfrac{3}{7} \cdot \dfrac{a}{a}$

3. $-\dfrac{8}{25} \cdot \dfrac{4}{4}$

4. $\dfrac{8}{3}\left(\dfrac{-2}{-2}\right)$

Answers on page A-10

CONNECTING THE CONCEPTS

We have already pointed out that much of our work in mathematics—and in this text in particular—is concerned with writing either equivalent expressions or equivalent equations. When new topics arise, these tasks are often postponed because attention must be given to terminology and notation. This is precisely what we have done with regard to fraction notation and multiplication of fractions. In the rest of this chapter we put these preliminaries to work. First we will use multiplication and different notations for 1 to write equivalent, "simplified" expressions. Then we will use multiplication of fractions as a tool for solving equations.

a Multiplying by 1

Recall the following:

$$1 = \frac{1}{1} = \frac{2}{2} = \frac{3}{3} = \frac{4}{4} = \frac{-13}{-13} = \frac{45}{45} = \frac{100}{100} = \frac{n}{n}.$$

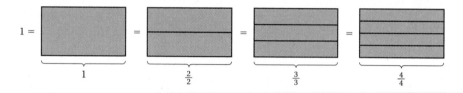

Any nonzero number divided by itself is 1. (See Section 1.6.)

Now recall that for any whole number a, we have $1 \cdot a = a \cdot 1 = a$. This holds for fractions as well.

> **MULTIPLICATIVE IDENTITY FOR FRACTIONS**
>
> When we multiply a number by 1, we get the same number:
>
> $$\frac{3}{5} = \frac{3}{5} \cdot 1 = \frac{3}{5} \cdot \frac{4}{4} = \frac{12}{20}.$$

Since $\frac{3}{5} = \frac{12}{20}$, we know that $\frac{3}{5}$ and $\frac{12}{20}$ are two names for the same number. We also say that $\frac{3}{5}$ and $\frac{12}{20}$ are **equivalent.** (See Section 2.6).

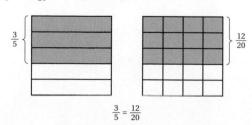

$$\frac{3}{5} = \frac{12}{20}$$

Do Exercises 1–4.

Suppose we want to rename $\frac{2}{3}$, using a denominator of 15. We can multiply by 1 to find a number equivalent to $\frac{2}{3}$:

$$\frac{2}{3} = \frac{2}{3} \cdot \frac{5}{5} = \frac{2 \cdot 5}{3 \cdot 5} = \frac{10}{15}.$$

We chose $\frac{5}{5}$ for 1 because $15 \div 3$ is 5.

EXAMPLE 1   Find a number equivalent to $\frac{1}{4}$ with a denominator of 24.

Since $24 \div 4 = 6$, we multiply by 1, using $\frac{6}{6}$:

$$\frac{1}{4} = \frac{1}{4} \cdot \frac{6}{6} = \frac{1 \cdot 6}{4 \cdot 6} = \frac{6}{24}.$$

EXAMPLE 2   Find a number equivalent to $\frac{2}{5}$ with a denominator of -35.

Since $-35 \div 5 = -7$, we multiply by 1, using $\frac{-7}{-7}$:

$$\frac{2}{5} = \frac{2}{5}\left(\frac{-7}{-7}\right) = \frac{2(-7)}{5(-7)} = \frac{-14}{-35}.$$

EXAMPLE 3   Find an expression equivalent to $\frac{9}{8}$ with a denominator of $8a$.

Since $8a \div 8 = a$, we multiply by 1, using $\frac{a}{a}$:

$$\frac{9}{8} \cdot \frac{a}{a} = \frac{9a}{8a}.$$

Do Exercises 5–9.

b   Simplifying Fraction Notation

All of the following are names for eight-ninths:

$$\frac{8}{9}, \frac{-8}{-9}, \frac{16}{18}, \frac{80}{90}, \frac{-24}{-27}.$$

We say that $\frac{8}{9}$ is **simplest** because it has the smallest positive denominator. Note that 8 and 9 have no factor in common other than 1.

To simplify, we reverse the process of multiplying by 1. This is accomplished by removing any factors (other than 1) that the numerator and the denominator have in common.

$$\frac{12}{18} = \frac{2 \cdot 6}{3 \cdot 6} \longleftarrow \text{Factoring the numerator}$$
$$\qquad\qquad \longleftarrow \text{Factoring the denominator}$$

$$= \frac{2}{3} \cdot \frac{6}{6} \qquad \text{Factoring the fraction}$$

$$= \frac{2}{3} \cdot 1 \qquad \frac{6}{6} = 1$$

$$= \frac{2}{3} \qquad\qquad \text{Removing the factor 1: } \frac{2}{3} \cdot 1 = \frac{2}{3}$$

Find an equivalent expression for each number, using the denominator indicated. Use multiplication by 1.

5. $\dfrac{4}{3} = \dfrac{?}{9}$

6. $\dfrac{3}{4} = \dfrac{?}{-24}$

7. $\dfrac{9}{10} = \dfrac{?}{10x}$

8. $\dfrac{7}{15} = \dfrac{?}{45}$

9. $\dfrac{-8}{7} = \dfrac{?}{49}$

Answers on page A-10

Study Tips

TWO BOOKS ARE BETTER THAN ONE

Many students find it helpful to use a second book as a reference when studying. Perhaps you or a friend own a text from a previous math course that can serve as a resource. Often professors have older texts that they will happily give away. Library book sales and thrift shops can also be excellent sources for extra books. Saving your text when you finish a math course can provide you with an excellent aid for your next course.

Simplify.

10. $\dfrac{8}{14}$

11. $\dfrac{-10}{12}$

12. $\dfrac{40}{8}$

13. $\dfrac{4a}{3a}$

14. $-\dfrac{50}{30}$

■ **EXAMPLES** Simplify.

4. $\dfrac{-8}{20} = \dfrac{-2 \cdot 4}{5 \cdot 4} = \dfrac{-2}{5} \cdot \dfrac{4}{4} = \dfrac{-2}{5}$ Removing a factor equal to 1: $\dfrac{4}{4} = 1$

5. $\dfrac{2}{6} = \dfrac{1 \cdot 2}{3 \cdot 2} = \dfrac{1}{3} \cdot \dfrac{2}{2} = \dfrac{1}{3}$

> Writing 1 allows for pairing of factors in the numerator and the denominator.

6. $\dfrac{30}{6} = \dfrac{5 \cdot 6}{1 \cdot 6} = \dfrac{5}{1} \cdot \dfrac{6}{6} = \dfrac{5}{1} = 5$ ◄

> We could also simplify $\frac{30}{6}$ by doing the division $30 \div 6$. That is, $\frac{30}{6} = 30 \div 6 = 5$.

7. $-\dfrac{15}{10} = -\dfrac{3 \cdot 5}{2 \cdot 5}$

$\qquad = -\dfrac{3}{2} \cdot \dfrac{5}{5}$ Removing a factor equal to 1: $\dfrac{5}{5} = 1$

$\qquad = -\dfrac{3}{2}$

8. $\dfrac{4x}{15x} = \dfrac{4 \cdot x}{15 \cdot x}$

$\qquad = \dfrac{4}{15} \cdot \dfrac{x}{x}$ Removing a factor equal to 1: $\dfrac{x}{x} = 1$

$\qquad = \dfrac{4}{15}$

Note that $\frac{4}{15}$ is considered simplified—the numbers 4 and 15 have no factors in common.

Do Exercises 10–14.

The tests for divisibility can be very helpful when simplifying.

■ **EXAMPLE 9**   Simplify: $\dfrac{105}{135}$.

Since both 105 and 135 end in 5, we know that 5 is a factor of both the numerator and the denominator:

$$\dfrac{105}{135} = \dfrac{21 \cdot 5}{27 \cdot 5} = \dfrac{21}{27} \cdot \dfrac{5}{5} = \dfrac{21}{27}.$$ To find the 21, we divided 105 by 5.
To find the 27, we divided 135 by 5.

A fraction is not "simplified" if common factors of the numerator and the denominator remain. Because 21 and 27 are both divisible by 3, we must simplify further:

$$\dfrac{105}{135} = \dfrac{21}{27} = \dfrac{7 \cdot 3}{9 \cdot 3} = \dfrac{7}{9} \cdot \dfrac{3}{3} = \dfrac{7}{9}.$$ To find the 7, we divided 21 by 3.
To find the 9, we divided 27 by 3.

EXAMPLE 10 Simplify: $\frac{90}{84}$.

Since 90 and 84 are both even, we know that 2 is a common factor:

$$\frac{90}{84} = \frac{2 \cdot 45}{2 \cdot 42}$$

$$= \frac{2}{2} \cdot \frac{45}{42} = \frac{45}{42}. \quad \text{Removing a factor equal to 1: } \frac{2}{2} = 1$$

Before stating that $\frac{45}{42}$ represents simplified form, we must check to see whether 45 and 42 share a common factor. Since the sum of the digits in 45 is 9 and 9 is divisible by 3, we know that 45 is divisible by 3. Similarly, it can be shown that 42 is divisible by 3. Thus, 3 is a common factor and we can simplify further:

$$\frac{45}{42} = \frac{3 \cdot 15}{3 \cdot 14}$$

$$= \frac{3}{3} \cdot \frac{15}{14} = \frac{15}{14}. \quad \text{Removing a factor equal to 1: } \frac{3}{3} = 1$$

Thus $\frac{90}{84}$ simplifies to $\frac{15}{14}$.

Do Exercises 15–18.

CANCELING

Canceling is a shortcut that you may have used for removing a factor that equals 1 when working with fraction notation. With *great* concern, we mention it as a possibility for speeding up your work. Canceling may be done only when removing common factors in numerators and denominators. Each common factor allows us to remove a factor equal to 1 in a product.

Our concern is that canceling be done with care and understanding. In effect, slashes are used to indicate factors equal to 1 that have been removed. For instance, Example 10 might have been done faster as follows:

$$\frac{90}{84} = \frac{2 \cdot 45}{2 \cdot 42} \quad \text{Factoring the numerator and the denominator}$$

$$= \frac{\cancel{2} \cdot 45}{\cancel{2} \cdot 42} \quad \begin{array}{l}\text{When a factor equal to 1 is noted,} \\ \text{it is "canceled" as shown: } \frac{2}{2} = 1.\end{array}$$

$$= \frac{45}{42} = \frac{\cancel{3} \cdot 15}{\cancel{3} \cdot 14} = \frac{15}{14}.$$

> **CAUTION!**
>
> The difficulty with canceling is that it is often applied incorrectly in situations like the following:
>
> $$\frac{\cancel{2} + 3}{\cancel{2}} = 3; \qquad \frac{\cancel{4} + 1}{\cancel{4} + 2} = \frac{1}{2}; \qquad \frac{1\cancel{5}}{\cancel{5}4} = \frac{1}{4}.$$
> $$\text{Wrong!} \qquad\qquad \text{Wrong!} \qquad\qquad \text{Wrong!}$$
>
> The correct answers are
>
> $$\frac{2 + 3}{2} = \frac{5}{2}; \qquad \frac{4 + 1}{4 + 2} = \frac{5}{6}; \qquad \frac{15}{54} = \frac{\cancel{3} \cdot 5}{\cancel{3} \cdot 18} = \frac{5}{18}.$$
>
> In each of the incorrect cancellations, the numbers canceled did not form a factor equal to 1. Factors are parts of products. For example, in $2 \cdot 3$, the numbers 2 and 3 are factors, but in $2 + 3$, the numbers 2 and 3 are terms, not factors.

Simplify.

15. $\frac{35}{40}$

16. $\frac{801}{702}$

17. $\frac{-24}{21}$

18. Simplify each fraction in this circle graph.

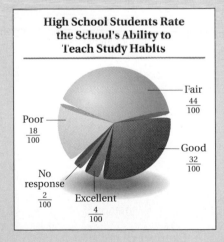

High School Students Rate the School's Ability to Teach Study Habits

Fair $\frac{44}{100}$

Poor $\frac{18}{100}$

Good $\frac{32}{100}$

No response $\frac{2}{100}$

Excellent $\frac{4}{100}$

Answers on page A-10

- If you cannot factor, do not cancel! If in doubt, do not cancel!
- Only factors can be canceled and factors are never separated by + or − signs.

C · A Test for Equality

When denominators are the same, we say that fractions have a **common denominator.** One way to compare fractions like $\frac{2}{4}$ and $\frac{3}{6}$ is to find a common denominator and compare numerators. One way to do this is to multiply each fraction by 1, using the other denominator to write 1:

The denominator is 6

$$\frac{3}{6} = \frac{3}{6} \cdot \frac{4}{4} = \frac{3 \cdot 4}{6 \cdot 4} = \frac{12}{24}$$

$$\frac{2}{4} = \frac{2}{4} \cdot \frac{6}{6} = \frac{2 \cdot 6}{4 \cdot 6} = \frac{12}{24}$$

Both denominators are 24

The denominator is 4

Because $\dfrac{12}{24} = \dfrac{12}{24}$ is true, it follows that $\dfrac{3}{6} = \dfrac{2}{4}$ is also true.

The "key" to the above work is that $3 \cdot 4$ and $2 \cdot 6$ are equal. Had these products differed, we would have shown that $\frac{3}{6}$ and $\frac{2}{4}$ were *not* equal. Note where the numbers 3, 4, 2, and 6 appear in the fractions $\frac{3}{6}$ and $\frac{2}{4}$.

A TEST FOR EQUALITY

We multiply these two numbers: $3 \cdot 4$.

We multiply these two numbers: $6 \cdot 2$.

$$\frac{3}{6} \quad \frac{2}{4}$$

We call $3 \cdot 4$ and $6 \cdot 2$ **cross products.** Since the cross products are the same ($3 \cdot 4 = 6 \cdot 2$), we know that

$$\frac{3}{6} = \frac{2}{4}.$$

In the examples that follow, the symbol $\neq$ is used to denote when two expressions are *not* equal.

EXAMPLE 11 Use $=$ or $\neq$ for $\square$ to write a true sentence:

$$\frac{6}{7} \, \square \, \frac{7}{8}.$$

We multiply these two numbers: $6 \cdot 8 = 48$.   We multiply these two numbers: $7 \cdot 7 = 49$.

$$\frac{6}{7} \quad \frac{7}{8}$$

Because $48 \neq 49$ (read "48 is not equal to 49"), $\frac{6}{7} = \frac{7}{8}$ is not a true sentence. Thus,

$$\frac{6}{7} \neq \frac{7}{8}.$$

EXAMPLE 12 Use $=$ or $\neq$ for $\square$ to write a true sentence:

$$\frac{6}{10} \, \square \, \frac{3}{5}.$$

We multiply these two numbers: $6 \cdot 5 = 30$.   We multiply these two numbers: $10 \cdot 3 = 30$.

$$\frac{6}{10} \quad \frac{3}{5}$$

Because the cross products are the same, we have

$$\frac{6}{10} = \frac{3}{5}.$$

Remembering that $\dfrac{-a}{b}$, $\dfrac{a}{-b}$, and $-\dfrac{a}{b}$ all represent the same number can be helpful when checking for equality.

EXAMPLE 13 Use $=$ or $\neq$ for $\square$ to write a true sentence:

$$\frac{-6}{8} \, \square \, -\frac{9}{12}.$$

We rewrite $-\frac{9}{12}$ as $\frac{-9}{12}$ and then check cross products:

$-6 \cdot 12 = -72$ $-9 \cdot 8 = -72$

$$\frac{-6}{8} \quad \frac{-9}{12}.$$

Because the cross products are the same, we have $\frac{-6}{8} = -\frac{9}{12}$.

Do Exercises 19–21.

Use $=$ or $\neq$ for $\square$ to write a true sentence.

19. $\dfrac{2}{6} \, \square \, \dfrac{3}{9}$

20. $\dfrac{7}{4} \, \square \, \dfrac{3}{2}$

21. $-\dfrac{10}{15} \, \square \, \dfrac{8}{-12}$

Answers on page A-10

3.5 EXERCISE SET

a Find an equivalent expression for each number, using the denominator indicated. Use multiplication by 1.

1. $\dfrac{1}{2} = \dfrac{?}{10}$

2. $\dfrac{1}{6} = \dfrac{?}{12}$

3. $\dfrac{3}{4} = \dfrac{?}{-48}$

4. $\dfrac{2}{9} = \dfrac{?}{-18}$

5. $\dfrac{7}{10} = \dfrac{?}{50}$

6. $\dfrac{3}{8} = \dfrac{?}{48}$

7. $\dfrac{11}{5} = \dfrac{?}{5t}$

8. $\dfrac{5}{3} = \dfrac{?}{3a}$

9. $\dfrac{5}{12} = \dfrac{?}{48}$

10. $\dfrac{7}{8} = \dfrac{?}{56}$

11. $-\dfrac{17}{18} = -\dfrac{?}{54}$

12. $-\dfrac{11}{16} = -\dfrac{?}{256}$

13. $\dfrac{3}{-8} = \dfrac{?}{-40}$

14. $\dfrac{7}{-8} = \dfrac{?}{-32}$

15. $\dfrac{-7}{22} = \dfrac{?}{132}$

16. $\dfrac{-10}{21} = \dfrac{?}{126}$

17. $\dfrac{5}{8} = \dfrac{?}{8x}$

18. $\dfrac{2}{3} = \dfrac{?}{3a}$

19. $\dfrac{10}{7} = \dfrac{?}{7a}$

20. $\dfrac{4}{3} = \dfrac{?}{3n}$

21. $\dfrac{4}{9} = \dfrac{?}{9ab}$

22. $\dfrac{8}{11} = \dfrac{?}{11xy}$

23. $\dfrac{4}{9} = \dfrac{?}{27b}$

24. $\dfrac{8}{11} = \dfrac{?}{55y}$

b Simplify.

25. $\dfrac{2}{4}$

26. $\dfrac{3}{6}$

27. $-\dfrac{6}{9}$

28. $\dfrac{-9}{12}$

29. $\dfrac{10}{25}$

30. $\dfrac{8}{10}$

31. $\dfrac{27}{-3}$

32. $\dfrac{28}{-4}$

33. $\dfrac{27}{36}$

34. $\dfrac{30}{40}$

35. $-\dfrac{24}{14}$

36. $-\dfrac{16}{10}$

37. $\dfrac{16n}{48n}$

38. $\dfrac{150a}{25a}$

39. $\dfrac{-17}{51}$

40. $\dfrac{-425}{525}$

41. $\dfrac{420}{480}$

42. $\dfrac{180}{240}$

43. $\dfrac{153}{136}$

44. $\dfrac{117}{91}$

45. $\dfrac{3ab}{8ab}$

46. $\dfrac{6xy}{7xy}$

47. $\dfrac{9xy}{6x}$

48. $\dfrac{10ab}{15a}$

49. $\dfrac{21rt}{28t}$

50. $\dfrac{25mn}{30n}$

51. $\dfrac{-18a}{20ab}$

52. $\dfrac{-19x}{38xy}$

Use = or ≠ for ☐ to write a true sentence.

53. $\dfrac{3}{4}$ ☐ $\dfrac{9}{12}$ **54.** $\dfrac{4}{8}$ ☐ $\dfrac{3}{6}$ **55.** $\dfrac{1}{5}$ ☐ $\dfrac{2}{9}$ **56.** $\dfrac{1}{4}$ ☐ $\dfrac{2}{9}$

57. $\dfrac{3}{8}$ ☐ $\dfrac{6}{16}$ **58.** $\dfrac{2}{6}$ ☐ $\dfrac{6}{18}$ **59.** $\dfrac{2}{5}$ ☐ $\dfrac{3}{7}$ **60.** $\dfrac{1}{3}$ ☐ $\dfrac{1}{4}$

61. $\dfrac{-3}{10}$ ☐ $\dfrac{-4}{12}$ **62.** $\dfrac{-2}{9}$ ☐ $\dfrac{-8}{36}$ **63.** $-\dfrac{12}{9}$ ☐ $\dfrac{-8}{6}$ **64.** $\dfrac{-8}{7}$ ☐ $-\dfrac{16}{14}$

65. $\dfrac{5}{-2}$ ☐ $-\dfrac{17}{7}$ **66.** $-\dfrac{10}{3}$ ☐ $\dfrac{24}{-7}$ **67.** $\dfrac{305}{145}$ ☐ $\dfrac{122}{58}$ **68.** $\dfrac{425}{165}$ ☐ $\dfrac{130}{66}$

69. D_W Explain in your own words when it *is* possible to "cancel" and when it *is not* possible to "cancel."

70. D_W Can fraction notation be simplified if the numerator and denominator are two different prime numbers? Why or why not?

SKILL MAINTENANCE

Solve.

71. The East Dorchester soccer field is 90 yd long and 40 yd wide. What is its area? [1.8a]

72. Yardbird Landscaping buys 13 maple saplings and 17 oak saplings for a project. A maple costs $23 and an oak costs $37. How much is spent altogether for the saplings? [1.8a]

Multiply. [2.4a]

73. $-12(-5)$ **74.** $-5(-13)$ **75.** $-9 \cdot 7$ **76.** $-8 \cdot 8$

Solve. [1.7b]

77. $30 \cdot x = 150$ **78.** $10{,}947 = 123 \cdot y$ **79.** $5280 = 1760 + t$ **80.** $x + 2368 = 11{,}369$

SYNTHESIS

81. D_W Sometimes a fraction can be simplified more than once. What determines whether or not this can occur?

82. D_W Why is multiplication of fractions (Section 3.4) discussed before simplification of fractions (Section 3.5)?

Simplify. Use the list of prime numbers on p. 181.

83. $\dfrac{221}{247}$ **84.** $\dfrac{209ab}{247ac}$ **85.** $-\dfrac{253x}{143y}$

86. $-\dfrac{187a}{289b}$ **87.** ▦ $\dfrac{2603}{2831}$ **88.** ▦ $\dfrac{3473}{3197}$

89. Sociologists have found that 4 of 10 people are shy. Write fraction notation for the part of the population that is shy; the part that is not shy. Simplify.

90. Sociologists estimate that 3 of 20 people are left-handed. In a crowd of 460 people, how many would you expect to be left-handed?

91. ▦ *Batting Averages.* For the 2002 season, Barry Bonds of the San Francisco Giants won the National League batting title with 149 hits in 403 times at bat. Manny Ramirez of the Boston Red Sox won the American League title with 152 hits in 436 times at bat. Did they have the same fraction of hits in times at bat (batting average)? Why or why not?
Source: Major League Baseball

92. ▦ On a test of 82 questions, Penny got 63 correct. On another test of 100 questions, she got 77 correct. Did she get the same portion of each test correct? Why or why not?

a Simplifying When Multiplying

We usually want a simplified answer when we multiply (in Chapter 4 there will be times we don't). To make such simplifying easier, it is generally best not to calculate the products in the numerator and the denominator until we have first factored and simplified. Consider

$$\frac{5}{6} \cdot \frac{14}{15}.$$

We proceed as follows:

$$\frac{5}{6} \cdot \frac{14}{15} = \frac{5 \cdot 14}{6 \cdot 15}$$ We do not yet carry out the multiplication. Note that 2 is a factor of 6 and 14. Also, note that 5 is a factor of 5 and 15.

$$= \frac{5 \cdot 2 \cdot 7}{2 \cdot 3 \cdot 5 \cdot 3}$$ Factoring and identifying common factors

$$= \frac{5 \cdot 2}{5 \cdot 2} \cdot \frac{7}{3 \cdot 3}$$ Factoring the fraction

$$\left. \begin{array}{l} = 1 \cdot \dfrac{7}{3 \cdot 3} \\[2mm] = \dfrac{7}{3 \cdot 3} \end{array} \right\}$$ Removing a factor equal to 1: $\dfrac{5 \cdot 2}{5 \cdot 2} = 1$

$$= \frac{7}{9}.$$

To multiply and simplify:

a) Write the products in the numerator and the denominator, but do not calculate the products.

b) Identify any common factors of the numerator and the denominator.

c) Factor the fraction to remove any factors that equal 1.

d) Calculate the remaining products.

EXAMPLES Multiply and simplify.

1. $\dfrac{2}{3} \cdot \dfrac{5}{4} = \dfrac{2 \cdot 5}{3 \cdot 4}$ Note that 2 is a common factor of 2 and 4.

$$= \frac{2 \cdot 5}{3 \cdot 2 \cdot 2}$$ Try to go directly to this step.

$$\left. \begin{array}{l} = \dfrac{2}{2} \cdot \dfrac{5}{3 \cdot 2} \\[2mm] = 1 \cdot \dfrac{5}{3 \cdot 2} = \dfrac{5}{6} \end{array} \right\}$$ Removing a factor equal to 1: $\dfrac{2}{2} = 1$

2. $\dfrac{6}{7} \cdot \dfrac{-5}{3} = \dfrac{3 \cdot 2 \cdot (-5)}{7 \cdot 3}$ Note that 3 is a common factor of 6 and 3.

$$= \frac{3}{3} \cdot \frac{2(-5)}{7} = \frac{-10}{7}, \text{ or } -\frac{10}{7}$$ Removing a factor equal to 1: $\dfrac{3}{3} = 1$

3. $\dfrac{10}{21} \cdot \dfrac{14a}{15} = \dfrac{5 \cdot 2 \cdot 7 \cdot 2a}{7 \cdot 3 \cdot 5 \cdot 3}$ Note that 5 is a common factor of 10 and 15.
Note that 7 is a common factor of 21 and 14a.

$\qquad = \dfrac{5 \cdot 7}{5 \cdot 7} \cdot \dfrac{2 \cdot 2a}{3 \cdot 3}$ ⎫
$\qquad = \dfrac{4a}{9}$ ⎭   Removing a factor equal to 1: $\dfrac{5 \cdot 7}{5 \cdot 7} = 1$

4. $32 \cdot \dfrac{7}{8} = \dfrac{8 \cdot 4 \cdot 7}{8 \cdot 1}$ Note that 8 is a common factor of 32 and 8.

$\qquad = \dfrac{8}{8} \cdot \dfrac{4 \cdot 7}{1} = 28$ Removing a factor equal to 1: $\dfrac{8}{8} = 1$

> **CAUTION!**
>
> Canceling can be used as follows for these examples.
>
> **1.** $\dfrac{2}{3} \cdot \dfrac{5}{4} = \dfrac{\cancel{2} \cdot 5}{3 \cdot \cancel{2} \cdot 2} = \dfrac{5}{6}$ Removing a factor equal to 1: $\dfrac{2}{2} = 1$
>
> **2.** $\dfrac{6}{7} \cdot \dfrac{-5}{3} = \dfrac{\cancel{3} \cdot 2(-5)}{7 \cdot \cancel{3}} = \dfrac{-10}{7}$ Removing a factor equal to 1: $\dfrac{3}{3} = 1$
>
> **3.** $\dfrac{10}{21} \cdot \dfrac{14a}{15} = \dfrac{\cancel{5} \cdot 2 \cdot \cancel{7} \cdot 2a}{\cancel{7} \cdot 3 \cdot \cancel{5} \cdot 3} = \dfrac{4a}{9}$ Removing a factor equal to 1: $\dfrac{5 \cdot 7}{5 \cdot 7} = 1$
>
> **4.** $32 \cdot \dfrac{7}{8} = \dfrac{\cancel{8} \cdot 4 \cdot 7}{\cancel{8} \cdot 1} = 28$ Removing a factor equal to 1: $\dfrac{8}{8} = 1$
>
> **Remember, only factors can be canceled!**

Do Exercises 1–4.

b   Solving Problems

■ **EXAMPLE 5**   Common Ground Catering anticipates 48 couples eating salmon at a year-end banquet. Allowing $\frac{2}{3}$ pound of salmon per couple, how many pounds of salmon should be prepared?

1. Familiarize.   We first make a drawing or at least visualize the situation. Repeated addition will work here.

⎫
⎬ 48 couples
⎭

$\frac{2}{3}$ of a pound for each couple

We let $n =$ the number of pounds of salmon.

2. Translate.   The problem translates to the following equation:

Rephrase: Number of pounds of salmon   is   number of couples   times   number of pounds per couple

Translate: n $=$ 48 $\cdot$ $\dfrac{2}{3}$

Multiply and simplify.

1. $\dfrac{2}{3} \cdot \dfrac{7}{8}$

2. $\dfrac{4}{5} \cdot \dfrac{-5}{12}$

3. $16 \cdot \dfrac{3}{8}$

4. $\dfrac{5}{2x} \cdot 6$

Answers on page A-11

5. Yardbird Landscaping uses $\frac{2}{5}$ lb of peat moss for a rosebush. How much will be needed for 30 rosebushes?

3. Solve. To solve the equation, we carry out the multiplication:

$$n = 48 \cdot \frac{2}{3} = \frac{48 \cdot 2}{3} \qquad \text{Multiplying}$$

$$= \frac{3 \cdot 16 \cdot 2}{3 \cdot 1} \qquad \text{Note that 48 is divisible by 3.}$$

$$= \frac{3}{3} \cdot \frac{16 \cdot 2}{1} = 32 \qquad \text{Removing the factor } \frac{3}{3} \text{ and simplifying}$$

4. Check. We could repeat the calculation but this check is left to the student. We can also think about the reasonableness of the answer. Since each couple requires less than 1 pound, it makes sense that 48 couples require fewer than 48 pounds. This provides a partial check of the answer.

A second partial check can be performed using the units:

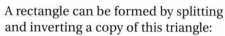

$$48 \text{ couples} \cdot \frac{2}{3} \text{ pounds per couple}$$

$$= 48 \cdot \frac{2}{3} \cdot \cancel{\text{couples}} \cdot \frac{\text{pounds}}{\cancel{\text{couple}}}$$

$$= 32 \text{ pounds.}$$

Since the resulting unit is pounds, the unit in which an answer was expected, we have another partial check.

5. State. Common Ground Catering should prepare 32 pounds of salmon.

Do Exercise 5.

AREA

Multiplication of fractions can arise in geometry problems involving the area of a triangle. Consider a triangle with a base of length b and a height of h:

A rectangle can be formed by splitting and inverting a copy of this triangle:

The rectangle's area, $b \cdot h$, is exactly twice the area of the triangle. We have the following result.

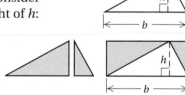

AREA OF A TRIANGLE

The **area A of a triangle** is half the length of the base b times the height h:

$$A = \frac{1}{2} \cdot b \cdot h.$$

EXAMPLE 6 Find the area of this triangle.

$$A = \frac{1}{2} \cdot b \cdot h$$

$$= \frac{1}{2} \cdot 9 \text{ yd} \cdot 6 \text{ yd}$$

$$= \frac{9 \cdot 6}{2} \text{ yd}^2$$

$$= 27 \text{ yd}^2$$

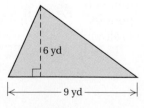

Answer on page A-11

EXAMPLE 7 Find the area of this triangle.

$$A = \frac{1}{2} \cdot b \cdot h$$

$$= \frac{1}{2} \cdot \frac{10}{3} \text{ cm} \cdot 4 \text{ cm}$$

$$= \frac{1 \cdot 10 \cdot 4}{2 \cdot 3} \text{ cm}^2$$

$$= \frac{1 \cdot 2 \cdot 5 \cdot 4}{2 \cdot 3} \text{ cm}^2 \qquad \text{Removing a factor equal to 1: } \frac{2}{2} = 1$$

$$= \frac{20}{3} \text{ cm}^2$$

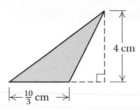
4 cm

$\frac{10}{3}$ cm

Do Exercises 6 and 7.

EXAMPLE 8 Find the area of this kite.

8 in.   8 in.

27 in.

1. **Familiarize.** We look for figures with areas we can calculate using area formulas that we already know. We let $K =$ the kite's area.

2. **Translate.** The kite consists of two triangles, each with a base of 27 in. and a height of 8 in. We can apply the formula $A = \frac{1}{2} \cdot b \cdot h$ for the area of a triangle and then multiply by 2.

Rephrase:	$\underbrace{\text{Kite's area}}$	is	twice	$\underbrace{\text{Area of long triangle}}$
Translate:	K	$=$	2	$\cdot \quad \frac{1}{2}(27 \text{ in.}) \cdot (8 \text{ in.})$

3. **Solve.** We have

$$K = 2 \cdot \frac{1}{2} \cdot (27 \text{ in.}) \cdot (8 \text{ in.})$$

$$= 1 \cdot 27 \text{ in.} \cdot 8 \text{ in.} = 216 \text{ in}^2.$$

4. **Check.** We can check by repeating the calculations. The unit, in^2, is appropriate for area.

5. **State.** The area of the kite is 216 in^2.

Do Exercise 8.

Find the area.

6.

12 m

16 m

7.

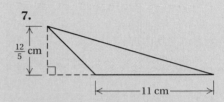
$\frac{12}{5}$ cm

11 cm

8. Find the area.

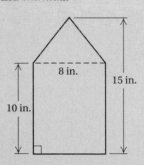
8 in.

10 in.

15 in.

Answers on page A-11

3.6

EXERCISE SET

For Extra Help

Digital Video
Tutor CD 2
Videotape 3

InterAct
Math

Math Tutor
Center

MathXL

MyMathLab

a   Multiply. Don't forget to simplify, if possible.

1. $\dfrac{3}{8} \cdot \dfrac{7}{3}$

2. $\dfrac{4}{5} \cdot \dfrac{1}{4}$

3. $\dfrac{7}{8} \cdot \dfrac{-1}{7}$

4. $\dfrac{5}{6} \cdot \dfrac{-1}{5}$

5. $\dfrac{1}{8} \cdot \dfrac{6}{7}$

6. $\dfrac{2}{5} \cdot \dfrac{1}{10}$

7. $\dfrac{1}{6} \cdot \dfrac{4}{3}$

8. $\dfrac{3}{6} \cdot \dfrac{1}{6}$

9. $\dfrac{12}{-5} \cdot \dfrac{9}{8}$

10. $\dfrac{16}{-15} \cdot \dfrac{5}{4}$

11. $\dfrac{5x}{9} \cdot \dfrac{4}{5}$

12. $\dfrac{25}{4a} \cdot \dfrac{4}{3}$

13. $\dfrac{1}{4} \cdot 12$

14. $\dfrac{1}{6} \cdot 12$

15. $21 \cdot \dfrac{1}{3}$

16. $18 \cdot \dfrac{1}{2}$

17. $-16\left(-\dfrac{3}{4}\right)$

18. $-24\left(-\dfrac{5}{6}\right)$

19. $\dfrac{3}{8} \cdot 8a$

20. $\dfrac{2}{9} \cdot 9x$

21. $\left(-\dfrac{3}{8}\right)\left(-\dfrac{8}{3}\right)$

22. $\left(-\dfrac{7}{9}\right)\left(-\dfrac{9}{7}\right)$

23. $\dfrac{a}{b} \cdot \dfrac{b}{a}$

24. $\dfrac{n}{m} \cdot \dfrac{m}{n}$

25. $\dfrac{1}{26} \cdot 143a$

26. $\dfrac{1}{28} \cdot 105n$

27. $176\left(\dfrac{1}{-6}\right)$

28. $135\left(\dfrac{1}{-10}\right)$

29. $-8x \cdot \dfrac{1}{-8x}$

30. $-5a \cdot \dfrac{1}{-5a}$

31. $\dfrac{2x}{9} \cdot \dfrac{27}{2x}$

32. $\dfrac{10a}{3} \cdot \dfrac{3}{5a}$

33. $\dfrac{7}{10} \cdot \dfrac{34}{150}$

34. $\dfrac{8}{10} \cdot \dfrac{45}{100}$

35. $\dfrac{36}{85} \cdot \dfrac{25}{-99}$

36. $\dfrac{-70}{45} \cdot \dfrac{50}{49}$

37. $\dfrac{-98}{99} \cdot \dfrac{27a}{175a}$

38. $\dfrac{70}{-49} \cdot \dfrac{63}{300x}$

39. $\dfrac{110}{33} \cdot \dfrac{-24}{25x}$

40. $\dfrac{-19}{130} \cdot \dfrac{65}{38x}$

41. $\left(-\dfrac{11}{24}\right)\dfrac{3}{5}$

42. $\left(\dfrac{15}{22}\right)\dfrac{4}{7}$

43. $\dfrac{10a}{21} \cdot \dfrac{3}{8b}$

44. $\dfrac{17}{21y} \cdot \dfrac{3x}{5}$

 Solve.

The *pitch* of a screw is the distance between its threads. With each complete rotation, the screw goes in or out a distance equal to its pitch. Use this information to answer Exercises 45 and 46.

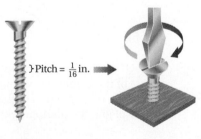

}Pitch = $\frac{1}{16}$ in.

Each rotation moves the screw in or out $\frac{1}{16}$ in.

45. The pitch of a screw is $\frac{1}{16}$ in. How far will it go into a piece of oak when it is turned 10 complete rotations clockwise?

46. The pitch of a screw is $\frac{3}{32}$ in. How far will it come out of a piece of plywood when it is turned 10 complete rotations counterclockwise?

47. *Swimming Speeds.* The swimming speed of a killer whale is about 30 mph. The swimming speed of a dolphin is about $\frac{3}{5}$ that of a killer whale. Find the swimming speed of a dolphin.

Source: G. Cafiero and M. Jahoda, *Whales and Dolphins.* New York: Barnes & Noble Books, 1994

48. After Jack completes 60 hr of teacher training at college, he can earn $95 for working a full day as a substitute teacher. How much will he receive for working $\frac{1}{5}$ of a day?

49. *Mailing-List Addresses.* Business people have determined that $\frac{1}{4}$ of the addresses on a mailing list will change in one year. A business has a mailing list of 2500 people. After one year, how many addresses on that list will be incorrect?

50. *Shy People.* Sociologists have determined that $\frac{2}{5}$ of the people in the world are shy. A sales manager is interviewing 650 people for an aggressive sales position. How many of these people might be shy?

51. LeGrand Chocolate Shop is preparing Valentine boxes. How many pounds of truffles will be needed to fill 75 boxes if each box contains $\frac{2}{5}$ lb?

52. For their annual pancake breakfast, the Colchester Boy Scouts need $\frac{2}{3}$ cup of Bisquick® per person. If at most 135 guests are expected, how much Bisquick do the scouts need?

53. A recipe for piecrust calls for $\frac{2}{3}$ cup of flour. A chef is making $\frac{1}{2}$ of the recipe. How much flour should the chef use?

54. Of the students in an entering class, $\frac{2}{5}$ have cameras and $\frac{1}{4}$ of these students will join the college photography club. What fraction of the students in the entering class will join the photography club?

55. A house worth $154,000 is assessed for $\frac{3}{4}$ of its value. What is the assessed value of the house?

56. Roxanne's tuition was $2800. A loan was obtained for $\frac{3}{4}$ of the tuition. How much was the loan?

57. *Map Scaling.* On a map, 1 in. represents 240 mi. How much does $\frac{3}{8}$ in. represent?

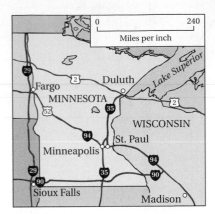

58. *Map Scaling.* On a map, 1 in. represents 120 mi. How much does $\frac{3}{4}$ in. represent?

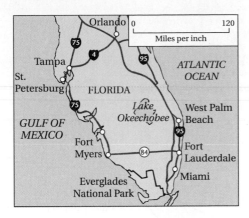

59. *Household Budgets.* A family has an annual income of $36,000. Of this, $\frac{1}{4}$ is spent for food, $\frac{1}{5}$ for housing, $\frac{1}{10}$ for clothing, $\frac{1}{9}$ for savings, $\frac{1}{4}$ for taxes, and the rest for other expenses. How much is spent for each?

60. *Household Budgets.* A family has an annual income of $29,700. Of this, $\frac{1}{4}$ is spent for food, $\frac{1}{5}$ for housing, $\frac{1}{10}$ for clothing, $\frac{1}{9}$ for savings, $\frac{1}{4}$ for taxes, and the rest for other expenses. How much is spent for each?

Family Income

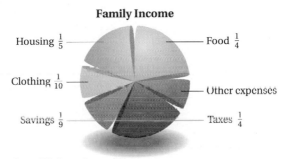

Housing $\frac{1}{5}$

Clothing $\frac{1}{10}$

Savings $\frac{1}{9}$

Food $\frac{1}{4}$

Other expenses

Taxes $\frac{1}{4}$

Source: U.S. Census Bureau

Find the area.

61.

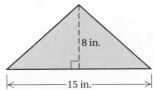

8 in.

15 in.

62.

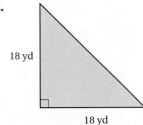

18 yd

18 yd

63.

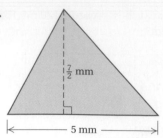

$\frac{7}{2}$ mm

5 mm

64.

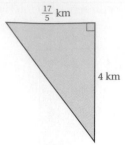

$\frac{17}{5}$ km

4 km

65.

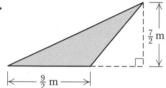

$\frac{7}{2}$ m

$\frac{9}{2}$ m

66.

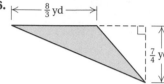

$\frac{8}{3}$ yd

$\frac{7}{4}$ yd

67.

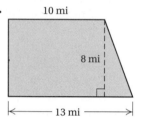

10 mi

8 mi

13 mi

68.

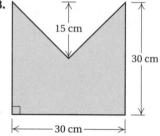

15 cm

30 cm

30 cm

69. *Jewelry Making.* A Zuni bolo tie is made by soldering together two identically kite-shaped pieces of sterling silver, as shown below. Determine the surface area of the front of the bolo tie.

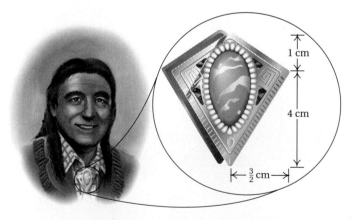

1 cm

4 cm

$\frac{3}{2}$ cm

70. *Construction.* Find the total area of the sides and ends of the town office building shown. Do not subtract for any windows, doors, or steps.

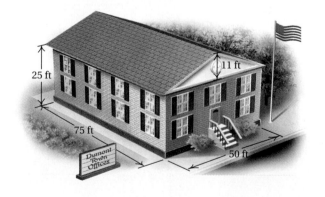

25 ft

11 ft

75 ft

50 ft

Dumont Town Offices

71. D_W When multiplying using fraction notation, we form products in the numerator and the denominator, but do not immediately calculate the products. Why?

72. D_W If a fraction's numerator and denominator have no factors (other than 1) in common, can the fraction be simplified? Why or why not?

─────(**SKILL MAINTENANCE**)─────

Solve. [1.7b]

73. $48 \cdot t = 1680$

74. $74 \cdot x = 6290$

75. $3125 = 25 \cdot t$

76. $2880 = 24 \cdot y$

77. $t + 28 = 5017$

78. $456 + x = 9002$

79. $8797 = y + 2299$

80. $10{,}000 = 3593 + m$

─────(**SYNTHESIS**)─────

81. D_W Why is it useful to remember which numbers are prime when simplifying fractions?

82. D_W Is the product of two fractions always a fraction? Why or why not?

Simplify. Use the list of prime numbers on p. 181.

83. ▦ $\dfrac{201}{535} \cdot \dfrac{4601}{6499}$

84. ▦ $\dfrac{5767}{3763} \cdot \dfrac{159}{395}$

85. ▦ $\dfrac{667}{899} \cdot \dfrac{558}{621}$

86. *College Profile.* Of students entering a college, $\frac{7}{8}$ have completed high school and $\frac{2}{3}$ are older than 20. If $\frac{1}{7}$ of all students are left-handed, what fraction of students entering the college are left-handed high school graduates over the age of 20?

87. *College Profile.* Refer to the information in Exercise 86. If 480 students are entering the college, how many of them are left-handed high school graduates 20 yr old or younger?

88. *College Profile.* Refer to Exercise 86. What fraction of students entering the college did not graduate high school, are 20 yr old or younger, and are left-handed?

89. ▦ *Manufacturing.* A TriMint candy box is triangular at each end, as shown below. Find the surface area of the box.

90. ▦ *Painting.* Shoreline Painting needs to determine the surface area of an octagonal steeple. Find the total area, if the dimensions are as shown below.

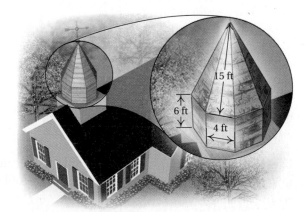

91. (See Exercise 70). If both sides and both ends of the town office building are identical, and if the windows are each 3 ft by 4 ft, and the entrances 6 ft by 8 ft, how many square feet of siding does the building require?

Find the reciprocal.

1. $\dfrac{7}{8}$

2. $\dfrac{-6}{x}$

3. 2

4. $\dfrac{1}{5}$

5. $-\dfrac{3}{10}$

Answers on page A-11

CALCULATOR CORNER

Most calculators are now equipped with a "reciprocal key," which is labeled $\boxed{1/x}$ or $\boxed{x^{-1}}$.

To use this key with fraction notation, first make sure that you can display fraction notation (see p. 208 in Section 3.5). Once a fraction is displayed, simply press the reciprocal key and the fraction's reciprocal will appear. On graphing calculators that have an $\boxed{x^{-1}}$ key, it is necessary to also press $\boxed{\text{ENTER}}$ and then use the Frac option of the $\boxed{\text{MATH}}$ menu.

Exercises: Use a calculator to display the reciprocal of each number.

1. $\dfrac{7}{10}$ 2. $-\dfrac{9}{4}$

3. 29   4. $\dfrac{1}{25}$

a   Reciprocals

Look at these products:

$$8 \cdot \frac{1}{8} = \frac{8}{8} = 1; \qquad \frac{-2}{3} \cdot \frac{3}{-2} = \frac{-6}{-6} = 1.$$

RECIPROCALS

If the product of two numbers is 1, we say that they are **reciprocals** of each other.* To find the reciprocal of a fraction, interchange the numerator and the denominator.

The numbers $\dfrac{3}{4}$ and $\dfrac{4}{3}$ are reciprocals of each other.

EXAMPLES   Find the reciprocal.

1. The reciprocal of $\dfrac{4}{5}$ is $\dfrac{5}{4}$.   Note that $\dfrac{4}{5} \cdot \dfrac{5}{4} = \dfrac{20}{20} = 1$.

2. The reciprocal of $\dfrac{a}{b}$ is $\dfrac{b}{a}$.   Note that $\dfrac{a}{b} \cdot \dfrac{b}{a} = \dfrac{ab}{ba} = 1$.

3. The reciprocal of 8 is $\dfrac{1}{8}$.   Think of 8 as $\dfrac{8}{1}$: $\dfrac{8}{1} \cdot \dfrac{1}{8} = \dfrac{8}{8} = 1$.

4. The reciprocal of $\dfrac{1}{3}$ is 3.   Note that $\dfrac{1}{3} \cdot 3 = \dfrac{3}{3} = 1$.

5. The reciprocal of $-\dfrac{5}{9}$ is $-\dfrac{9}{5}$.   Negative numbers have negative reciprocals: $\left(-\dfrac{5}{9}\right)\left(-\dfrac{9}{5}\right) = \dfrac{45}{45} = 1$.

Do Exercises 1–5.

Does 0 have a reciprocal? If it did, it would have to be a number x such that

$$0 \cdot x = 1.$$

But 0 times any number is 0. Thus, 0 has no reciprocal.

b   Division

Consider the division $\frac{3}{4} \div \frac{1}{8}$. This asks how many $\frac{1}{8}$'s are in $\frac{3}{4}$. We can answer this by looking at the figure below.

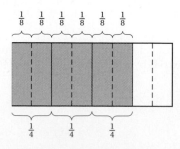

*A reciprocal is also called a multiplicative inverse.

We see that there are six $\frac{1}{8}$'s in $\frac{3}{4}$. Thus,

$$\frac{3}{4} \div \frac{1}{8} = 6.$$

This can be checked by multiplying:

$$6 \cdot \frac{1}{8} = \frac{6}{8} = \frac{3}{4}.$$

Here is a faster way to divide. An explanation of why it works appears on the next page.

DIVISION OF FRACTIONS

To divide a fraction, multiply by its reciprocal:

Multiply by the reciprocal of the divisor.

$$\frac{a}{b} \div \frac{c}{d} = \frac{a}{b} \cdot \frac{d}{c}.$$

Recall that when two numbers with unlike signs are multiplied or divided, the result is negative. When both numbers have the same sign, the result is positive.

EXAMPLES Divide and simplify.

6. $\dfrac{5}{6} \div \dfrac{2}{3} = \dfrac{5}{6} \cdot \dfrac{3}{2}$ Multiplying by the reciprocal of the divisor

$\qquad\qquad = \dfrac{5 \cdot 3}{3 \cdot 2 \cdot 2}$ Factoring and identifying a common factor

$\qquad\qquad = \dfrac{3}{3} \cdot \dfrac{5}{2 \cdot 2}$ Removing a factor equal to 1: $\dfrac{3}{3} = 1$

$\qquad\qquad = \dfrac{5}{4}$

7. $\dfrac{-3}{5} \div \dfrac{1}{2} = \dfrac{-3}{5} \cdot 2$ The reciprocal of $\dfrac{1}{2}$ is 2.

$\qquad\qquad = \dfrac{-3 \cdot 2}{5} = \dfrac{-6}{5}$

8. $\dfrac{2a}{5} \div 7 = \dfrac{2a}{5} \cdot \dfrac{1}{7}$ The reciprocal of 7 is $\dfrac{1}{7}$.

$\qquad\qquad = \dfrac{2a \cdot 1}{5 \cdot 7} = \dfrac{2a}{35}$

9. $\dfrac{\frac{7}{10}}{-\frac{14}{15}} = \dfrac{7}{10} \div \left(-\dfrac{14}{15}\right)$ The fraction bar indicates division.

$\qquad\qquad = \dfrac{7}{10} \cdot \left(-\dfrac{15}{14}\right)$ Multiplying by the reciprocal of the divisor

$\qquad\qquad = \dfrac{7 \cdot 5(-3)}{2 \cdot 5 \cdot 7 \cdot 2}$ Factoring and identifying common factors

$\qquad\qquad = \dfrac{7 \cdot 5}{7 \cdot 5} \cdot \dfrac{-3}{4}$ Removing a factor equal to 1: $\dfrac{7 \cdot 5}{7 \cdot 5} = 1$

$\qquad\qquad = -\dfrac{3}{4}$

Divide and simplify.

6. $\dfrac{2}{7} \div \dfrac{6}{5}$

7. $\left(-\dfrac{2}{3}\right) \div \dfrac{1}{4}$

8. $\dfrac{5}{4} \div 10$

9. $60 \div \dfrac{3a}{5}$

10. $\dfrac{\frac{-6}{7}}{\frac{3}{5}}$

11. To remember *why* fractions are divided as they are, multiply by 1 to perform the following division, using the reciprocal of $\frac{4}{5}$ to write 1.

$$\dfrac{\frac{6}{7}}{\frac{4}{5}}$$

CAUTION!

Canceling can be used as follows for Examples 6 and 9.

6. $\dfrac{5}{6} \div \dfrac{2}{3} = \dfrac{5}{6} \cdot \dfrac{3}{2} = \dfrac{5 \cdot 3}{6 \cdot 2} = \dfrac{5 \cdot \cancel{3}}{\cancel{3} \cdot 2 \cdot 2} = \dfrac{5}{2 \cdot 2} = \dfrac{5}{4}$ Removing a factor equal to 1: $\frac{3}{3} = 1$

9. $\dfrac{7}{10} \div \left(-\dfrac{14}{15}\right) = \dfrac{7}{10} \cdot \left(-\dfrac{15}{14}\right) = \dfrac{\cancel{7} \cdot \cancel{5}(-3)}{2 \cdot \cancel{5} \cdot \cancel{7} \cdot 2} = \dfrac{-3}{4}, \text{ or } -\dfrac{3}{4}$

   Removing a factor equal to 1: $\frac{7 \cdot 5}{7 \cdot 5} = 1$

Remember, if you can't factor, you can't cancel!

Do Exercises 6–10.

Why do we multiply by a reciprocal when dividing? To see why, consider $\frac{2}{3} \div \frac{7}{5}$. We will multiply by 1 to find an equivalent expression. To write 1 we use $(5/7)/(5/7)$; it comes from the reciprocal of $\frac{7}{5}$.

$$\dfrac{2}{3} \div \dfrac{7}{5} = \dfrac{\frac{2}{3}}{\frac{7}{5}} \qquad \text{Writing fraction notation for the division}$$

$$= \dfrac{\frac{2}{3}}{\frac{7}{5}} \cdot 1 \qquad \text{Multiplying by 1}$$

$$= \dfrac{\frac{2}{3}}{\frac{7}{5}} \cdot \dfrac{\frac{5}{7}}{\frac{5}{7}} \qquad \text{Multiplying by 1; } \tfrac{5}{7} \text{ is the reciprocal of } \tfrac{7}{5} \text{ and } \dfrac{\frac{5}{7}}{\frac{5}{7}} = 1$$

$$= \dfrac{\frac{2}{3} \cdot \frac{5}{7}}{\frac{7}{5} \cdot \frac{5}{7}} \qquad \text{Multiplying the numerators and the denominators}$$

$$= \dfrac{\frac{2}{3} \cdot \frac{5}{7}}{1} = \dfrac{2}{3} \cdot \dfrac{5}{7} = \dfrac{10}{21}$$

After we multiplied, we got 1 for the denominator. The numerator (in color) shows the multiplication by the reciprocal of $\frac{7}{5}$.

Thus,

$$\dfrac{2}{3} \div \dfrac{7}{5} = \dfrac{2}{3} \cdot \dfrac{5}{7} = \dfrac{10}{21}.$$

Expressions of the form $\dfrac{\frac{a}{b}}{\frac{c}{d}}$ are examples of *complex fractions*.

Do Exercise 11.

3.7

EXERCISE SET

For Extra Help

Digital Video
Tutor CD 2
Videotape 3

InterAct
Math

Math Tutor
Center

MathXL

MyMathLab

a Find the reciprocal.

1. $\dfrac{7}{3}$

2. $\dfrac{6}{5}$

3. 9

4. 3

5. $\dfrac{1}{7}$

6. $\dfrac{1}{4}$

7. $-\dfrac{10}{3}$

8. $-\dfrac{12}{5}$

9. $\dfrac{3}{17}$

10. $\dfrac{9}{28}$

11. $\dfrac{-3n}{m}$

12. $\dfrac{8t}{-7r}$

13. $\dfrac{8}{-15}$

14. $\dfrac{-6}{25}$

15. $7m$

16. $5n$

17. $\dfrac{1}{4a}$

18. $\dfrac{1}{9t}$

19. $-\dfrac{1}{3z}$

20. $-\dfrac{1}{2x}$

b Divide. Don't forget to simplify when possible.

21. $\dfrac{3}{7} \div \dfrac{3}{4}$

22. $\dfrac{2}{3} \div \dfrac{2}{5}$

23. $\dfrac{7}{6} \div \dfrac{5}{-3}$

24. $\dfrac{5}{3} \div \dfrac{4}{-9}$

25. $\dfrac{4}{3} \div \dfrac{1}{3}$

26. $\dfrac{10}{9} \div \dfrac{1}{2}$

27. $\left(-\dfrac{1}{3}\right) \div \dfrac{1}{6}$

28. $\left(-\dfrac{1}{4}\right) \div \dfrac{1}{5}$

29. $\left(-\dfrac{10}{21}\right) \div \left(-\dfrac{2}{15}\right)$

30. $-\dfrac{15}{28} \div \left(-\dfrac{9}{20}\right)$

31. $\dfrac{3}{8} \div 24$

32. $\dfrac{5}{6} \div 45$

33. $\dfrac{12}{7} \div (4x)$

34. $\dfrac{18}{5} \div (2y)$

35. $(-12) \div \dfrac{3}{2}$

36. $(-24) \div \dfrac{3}{8}$

37. $28 \div \dfrac{4}{5a}$

38. $40 \div \dfrac{2}{3m}$

39. $\left(-\dfrac{5}{8}\right) \div \left(-\dfrac{5}{8}\right)$

40. $\left(-\dfrac{2}{5}\right) \div \left(-\dfrac{2}{5}\right)$

41. $\dfrac{-8}{15} \div \dfrac{4}{5}$

42. $\dfrac{6}{-13} \div \dfrac{3}{26}$

43. $\dfrac{77}{64} \div \dfrac{49}{18}$

44. $\dfrac{81}{42} \div \dfrac{33}{56}$

45. $120a \div \dfrac{45}{14}$

46. $360n \div \dfrac{27n}{8}$

47. $\dfrac{\frac{2}{5}}{\frac{3}{7}}$

48. $\dfrac{\frac{5}{6}}{\frac{2}{7}}$

49. $\dfrac{\dfrac{7}{20}}{\dfrac{8}{5}}$

50. $\dfrac{\dfrac{8}{21}}{\dfrac{6}{5}}$

51. $\dfrac{-\dfrac{15}{8}}{\dfrac{9}{10}}$

52. $\dfrac{-\dfrac{27}{10}}{\dfrac{21}{20}}$

53. $\dfrac{-\dfrac{9}{16}}{-\dfrac{6}{5}}$

54. $\dfrac{-\dfrac{35}{18}}{-\dfrac{14}{27}}$

55. $\mathbf{D_W}$ Without performing the division, explain why $5 \div \frac{1}{7}$ is a larger number than $5 \div \frac{2}{3}$.

56. $\mathbf{D_W}$ Carl incorrectly insists that $\frac{2}{5} \div \frac{3}{4}$ is $\frac{15}{8}$. What mistake is he probably making?

SKILL MAINTENANCE

Divide.   [1.6c]

57. $268 \div 4$

58. $268 \div 8$

59. $6842 \div 24$

60. $8765 \div 85$

Solve.

61. $4 \cdot x = 268$ [1.7b]

62. $4 + x = 268$ [1.7b]

63. $y + 502 = 9001$ [1.7b]

64. $56 \cdot 78 = T$ [1.7b]

65. $-8t = 72$ [2.8b]

66. $-8 + r = -5$ [2.8a]

67. $12t = -48$ [2.8b]

68. $15x = -60$ [2.8b]

SYNTHESIS

69. $\mathbf{D_W}$ Is division of fractions associative? Why or why not?

70. $\mathbf{D_W}$ Under what conditions is division of fractions commutative?

Simplify.

71. $\left(\dfrac{4}{15} \div \dfrac{2}{25}\right)^2$

72. $\left(\dfrac{9}{10} \div \dfrac{12}{25}\right)^2$

73. $\left(\dfrac{9}{10} \div \dfrac{2}{5} \div \dfrac{3}{8}\right)^2$

74. $\dfrac{\left(-\dfrac{3}{7}\right)^2 \div \dfrac{12}{5}}{\left(\dfrac{-2}{9}\right)\left(\dfrac{9}{2}\right)}$

75. $\left(\dfrac{14}{15} \div \dfrac{49}{65} \cdot \dfrac{77}{260}\right)^2$

76. $\left(\dfrac{10}{9}\right)^2 \div \dfrac{35}{27} \cdot \dfrac{49}{44}$

Simplify. Use the list of prime numbers on p. 181.

77. 🖩 $\dfrac{711}{1957} \div \dfrac{10,033}{13,081}$

78. 🖩 $\dfrac{8633}{7387} \div \dfrac{485}{581}$

79. 🖩 $\dfrac{451}{289} \div \dfrac{123}{340}$

80. 🖩 $\dfrac{530}{490} \div \dfrac{1060}{980}$

CHAPTER 3: Fraction Notation:
Multiplication and Division

3.8

SOLVING EQUATIONS: THE MULTIPLICATION PRINCIPLE

Objectives

a Use the multiplication principle to solve equations.

b Solve problems by using the multiplication principle.

In Sections 1.7 and 2.8, we learned to solve an equation involving multiplication by dividing on both sides. With fraction notation, we can solve the same type of equation by using multiplication.

a The Multiplication Principle

We have seen that to divide by a fraction, we multiply by the reciprocal of that fraction. This suggests that we restate the division principle in its more common form—the multiplication principle.

THE MULTIPLICATION PRINCIPLE

For any numbers a, b, and c, with $c \neq 0$,

$$a = b \quad \text{is equivalent to} \quad a \cdot c = b \cdot c.$$

EXAMPLE 1 Solve: $\frac{3}{4}x = 15$.

We can multiply by any nonzero number on both sides to produce an equivalent equation. Since we are looking for an equation of the form $1x = \square$, we multiply both sides of the equation by the reciprocal of $\frac{3}{4}$.

$$\frac{3}{4}x = 15$$

$$\frac{4}{3} \cdot \frac{3}{4}x = \frac{4}{3} \cdot 15 \qquad \text{Using the multiplication principle;}$$
note that $\frac{4}{3}$ is the reciprocal of $\frac{3}{4}$.

$$\left(\frac{4}{3} \cdot \frac{3}{4}\right)x = \frac{4 \cdot 15}{3} \qquad \text{Using an associative law;}$$
try to do this mentally.

$$1x = 20 \qquad \text{Multiplying; note that } \frac{4 \cdot 15}{3} = \frac{4 \cdot \cancel{3} \cdot 5}{\cancel{3}}.$$

$$x = 20 \qquad \text{Remember that } 1x \text{ is } x.$$

To confirm that 20 is the solution, we perform a check.

CHECK: $$\frac{3}{4}x = 15$$

$$\frac{\frac{3}{4} \cdot 20 \;?\; 15}{}$$

$$\frac{3 \cdot \cancel{4} \cdot 5}{\cancel{4}} \qquad \text{Removing a factor equal to 1: } \frac{4}{4} = 1$$

$$3 \cdot 5 \;\big|\; 15 \quad \text{TRUE}$$

The solution is 20.

Note that using the multiplication principle to multiply by $\frac{4}{3}$ on both sides is the same as using the division principle to divide by $\frac{3}{4}$ on both sides.

Do Exercises 1 and 2.

Solve.

1. $\frac{2}{3}x = 8$

2. $\frac{2}{7}a = -6$

Answers on page A-11

Study Tips

WHEN ONE JUST ISN'T ENOUGH

When an exercise gives you difficulty, it is usually wise to practice solving some other exercises that are very similar to the one that gave you trouble. Usually, if the troubling exercise is odd, the next (even) exercise is quite similar. Checking the Chapter Review and Test for similar problems is also a good idea.

Solve.

3. $-\dfrac{9}{8} = 4x$

In an expression like $\frac{3}{4}x$, the constant factor—in this case, $\frac{3}{4}$—is called the **coefficient.** In Example 1, we multiplied on both sides by $\frac{4}{3}$, the reciprocal of the coefficient of x.

■ **EXAMPLE 2** Solve: $5a = -\dfrac{7}{3}$.

We have

$$5a = -\frac{7}{3}$$

$$\frac{1}{5} \cdot 5a = \frac{1}{5} \cdot \left(-\frac{7}{3}\right) \qquad \text{Multiplying both sides by } \tfrac{1}{5}, \text{ the reciprocal of 5}$$

$$1a = -\frac{1 \cdot 7}{5 \cdot 3}$$

$$a = -\frac{7}{15}.$$

CHECK:

$$\begin{array}{c|c} 5a = -\dfrac{7}{3} \\ \hline 5\left(-\dfrac{7}{15}\right) \ ? \ -\dfrac{7}{3} \\ -\dfrac{5 \cdot 7}{5 \cdot 3} \\ -\dfrac{7}{3} \ \bigg| \ -\dfrac{7}{3} \quad \textbf{TRUE} \end{array}$$

4. $-\dfrac{6}{7}a = \dfrac{9}{14}$

The solution is $-\dfrac{7}{15}$.

■ **EXAMPLE 3** Solve: $\dfrac{10}{3} = -\dfrac{4}{9}x$.

We have

$$\frac{10}{3} = -\frac{4}{9}x$$

$$-\frac{9}{4} \cdot \frac{10}{3} = -\frac{9}{4} \cdot \left(-\frac{4}{9}\right)x \qquad \begin{array}{l}\text{Multiplying both sides by } -\tfrac{9}{4}, \text{ the} \\ \text{reciprocal of } -\tfrac{4}{9}\end{array}$$

$$-\frac{3 \cdot 3 \cdot 2 \cdot 5}{2 \cdot 2 \cdot 3} = x$$

$$-\frac{15}{2} = x. \qquad \text{Removing a factor equal to 1: } \frac{3 \cdot 2}{2 \cdot 3} = 1$$

We leave the check to the student. The solution is $-\dfrac{15}{2}$.

Do Exercises 3 and 4.

b Problem Solving

Equations involving multiplication of fractions arise frequently in problem-solving situations.

EXAMPLE 4 *Herbal Remedies.* At Sunshine Herbs, Sue needs to fill as many tea bags as possible with $\frac{3}{5}$ g of chamomile. If she begins with 51 g of chamomile, how many tea bags can she fill?

1. **Familiarize.** We first make a drawing or at least visualize the situation. Repeated subtraction, or division, will work here.

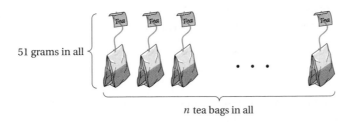

$\frac{3}{5}$ of a gram in each tea bag

51 grams in all

n tea bags in all

We let $n = $ the number of tea bags that can be filled.

2. **Translate.** The problem can be translated to the following equation:

$$\frac{3}{5} \cdot n = 51.$$

3. **Solve.** To solve the equation, we use the multiplication principle:

$$\frac{5}{3} \cdot \frac{3}{5} \cdot n = \frac{5}{3} \cdot 51 \qquad \text{Multiplying both sides by } \frac{5}{3}$$

$$1n = \frac{5 \cdot 51}{3}$$

$$\left.\begin{array}{l} n = \dfrac{5 \cdot 3 \cdot 17}{1 \cdot 3} \\[2ex] n = \dfrac{3}{3} \cdot \dfrac{5 \cdot 17}{1} \end{array}\right\} \quad \text{Identifying a factor equal to 1}$$

$$n = 85. \qquad \text{Simplifying}$$

4. **Check.** If each of 85 tea bags took $\frac{3}{5}$ g of chamomile, we would know that

$$85 \cdot \frac{3}{5} = \frac{85 \cdot 3}{5} = \frac{\cancel{5} \cdot 17 \cdot 3}{\cancel{5}} = 17 \cdot 3,$$

or 51 g of chamomile is used. Since the problem states that Sue begins with 51 g, our answer checks. Note too that *tea bags · grams/bag = grams*, so the units also check.

5. **State.** Sue can fill 85 tea bags with 51 g of chamomile.

Do Exercises 5 and 6.

---

5. Each loop in a spring uses $\frac{3}{8}$ in. of wire. How many loops can be made from 120 in. of wire?

6. For a party, Jana made an 8-foot submarine sandwich. If one serving is $\frac{2}{3}$ ft, how many servings does Jana's sub contain?

Answers on page A-11

7. The Rozzis' oil tank had 175 gal of oil when it was $\frac{7}{8}$ full. How much could the tank hold altogether?

EXAMPLE 5 Melissa Esplanah sells pharmaceutical supplies. After she had driven 210 mi, $\frac{5}{6}$ of her sales trip was completed. How long was the total trip?

1. Familiarize. We think: 210 mi is $\frac{5}{6}$ of the trip. We make a drawing to help visualize the situation. We let n = the length of the trip.

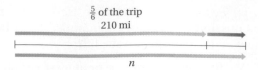
$\frac{5}{6}$ of the trip
210 mi

n

2. Translate. We translate to an equation.

$$\underbrace{\text{Fraction completed}}_{\frac{5}{6}} \quad \text{of} \quad \underbrace{\begin{array}{c}\text{Total} \\ \text{length} \\ \text{of trip}\end{array}}_{n} \quad \text{is} \quad \underbrace{\begin{array}{c}\text{Amount} \\ \text{already} \\ \text{traveled}\end{array}}_{210}$$

$$\frac{5}{6} \cdot n = 210$$

3. Solve. The equation that corresponds to the situation is $\frac{5}{6} \cdot n = 210$. To solve, we use the multiplication principle:

$$\frac{6}{5} \cdot \frac{5}{6} \cdot n = \frac{6}{5} \cdot 210 \qquad \text{Multiplying both sides by } \frac{6}{5}$$

$$1n = \frac{6 \cdot 210}{5}$$

$$\left.\begin{array}{l} n = \dfrac{6 \cdot 5 \cdot 42}{1 \cdot 5} \\[2mm] n = \dfrac{5}{5} \cdot \dfrac{6 \cdot 42}{1} \end{array}\right\} \quad \text{Identifying a factor equal to 1}$$

$$n = 252.$$

4. Check. If the total trip was 252 miles, then $\frac{5}{6}$ of 252 is

$$\frac{5 \cdot 252}{6} = \frac{5 \cdot \cancel{6} \cdot 42}{1 \cdot \cancel{6}} = 210 \text{ mi.}$$

Our answer checks.

5. State. The total trip was 252 mi.

Do Exercise 7.

Answer on page A-11

3.8
EXERCISE SET

For Extra Help

Digital Video
Tutor CD 3
Videotape 3

InterAct
Math

Math Tutor
Center

MathXL

MyMathLab

a   Use the multiplication principle to solve each equation. Don't forget to check!

1. $\dfrac{4}{5}x = 12$

2. $\dfrac{4}{3}x = 20$

3. $\dfrac{7}{3}a = 21$

4. $\dfrac{4}{5}a = 24$

5. $\dfrac{2}{9}x = -10$

6. $\dfrac{3}{8}x = -21$

7. $6a = \dfrac{12}{17}$

8. $3a = \dfrac{15}{14}$

9. $\dfrac{1}{4}x = \dfrac{3}{5}$

10. $\dfrac{1}{6}x = \dfrac{2}{7}$

11. $\dfrac{3}{2}t = -\dfrac{8}{7}$

12. $\dfrac{4}{3}t = -\dfrac{5}{2}$

13. $\dfrac{4}{5} = -10a$

14. $\dfrac{6}{5} = -12a$

15. $\dfrac{9}{5}x = \dfrac{3}{10}$

16. $\dfrac{10}{3}x = \dfrac{8}{15}$

17. $-\dfrac{9}{10}x = 8$

18. $-\dfrac{2}{11}x = 5$

19. $a \cdot \dfrac{9}{7} = -\dfrac{3}{14}$

20. $a \cdot \dfrac{9}{4} = -\dfrac{3}{10}$

21. $-x = \dfrac{7}{13}$

22. $-x = \dfrac{7}{11}$

23. $-x = -\dfrac{27}{31}$

24. $-x = -\dfrac{35}{39}$

25. $7t = 6$

26. $-6t = 1$

27. $-24 = -10a$

28. $-18 = -20a$

29. $-\dfrac{14}{9} = \dfrac{10}{3}t$

30. $-\dfrac{15}{7} = \dfrac{3}{2}t$

31. $n \cdot \dfrac{4}{15} = \dfrac{12}{25}$

32. $n \cdot \dfrac{5}{16} = \dfrac{15}{14}$

33. $-\dfrac{7}{20}x = -\dfrac{21}{10}$

34. $-\dfrac{7}{15}x = -\dfrac{21}{10}$

35. $-\dfrac{25}{17} = -\dfrac{35}{34}a$

36. $-\dfrac{49}{45} = -\dfrac{28}{27}a$

 b   Solve.

37. Benny uses $\frac{2}{5}$ gram (g) of toothpaste each time he brushes his teeth. If Benny buys a 30-g tube, how many times will he be able to brush his teeth?

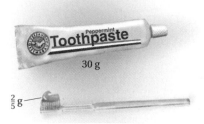

30 g

$\frac{2}{5}$ g

38. A piece of coaxial cable $\frac{4}{5}$ meter (m) long is to be cut into 8 pieces of the same length. What is the length of each piece?

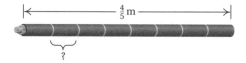

39. *Daily Driving.*   Toshiko makes insurance estimates when claims are filed. After driving 180 kilometers (km), she completes $\frac{5}{8}$ of a daily route. How long is the route? How much driving remains?

40. *Highway Maintenance.*   Alicia Simon and her road crew paint the lines in the middle and on the sides of a highway. They average about $\frac{5}{16}$ of a mile each hour. How long will it take to paint the lines on 70 mi of highway?

41. *Knitting.*   Gene is knitting a pair of socks in which each stitch is $\frac{5}{32}$ in. long. How many stitches will Gene need for a row that is 10 in. long?

42. *Knitting.*   Brianna is knitting a sweater in which each stitch is $\frac{3}{8}$ in. long. How many stitches will Brianna need for a row that is 12 in. long?

43. *Packaging.* The South Shore Co-op prepackages cheddar cheese in $\frac{3}{4}$-lb packages. How many packages can be made from a 15-lb wheel of cheese?

44. *Meal Planning.* Ian purchased 6 lb of cold cuts for a luncheon. If Ian is to allow $\frac{3}{8}$ lb per person, how many people can attend the luncheon?

45. *Art Supplies.* The Ferristown School District purchased $\frac{3}{4}$ T (ton) of clay. The clay is to be shared equally among the district's 6 art departments. How much will each art department receive?

46. *Gardening.* The Bingham community garden is to be split into 16 equally sized plots. If the garden occupies $\frac{3}{4}$ acre of land, how large will each plot be?

Large quantities of soil, gravel, or loam are normally sold by the *yard* (yd). Although technically the unit for this type of volume should be *cubic yard* (yd^3), in practice only the word *yard* is used. Exercises 47–50 make use of this terminology.

47. *Landscaping.* To cover a walkway at a summer cottage with fresh gravel, $\frac{3}{4}$ yd of gravel is needed. Eric's dump truck has a 6 yd capacity. How many cottage walkways can be covered with one dump truck load?

48. *Landscaping.* To freshly cover a driveway in Surf City with crushed stone requires $\frac{4}{5}$ yd of stone. How many driveways can be freshly covered with one load of a 12-yd dump truck?

49. *Gardening.* Green Season Gardening uses about $\frac{2}{3}$ yd of bark mulch per customer every spring. How many customers can they accommodate with one 30-yd batch of bark mulch?

50. *Gardening.* Bright Moments Greenhouse sells topsoil by the yard. If the typical customer purchases $\frac{2}{5}$ yd, how many customers will it take to use up a 30-yd batch of topsoil?

51. *Sewing.* A pair of basketball shorts requires $\frac{3}{4}$ yd of nylon. How many pairs of shorts can be made from 24 yd of the fabric?

52. *Sewing.* A child's shirt requires $\frac{5}{6}$ yd of cotton fabric. How many shirts can be made from 25 yd of the fabric?

Pitch of a Screw. Refer to Exercises 45 and 46 in Exercise Set 3.6.

53. After a screw has been turned 8 complete rotations, it is extended $\frac{1}{2}$ in. into a piece of wallboard. What is the pitch of the screw?

54. The pitch of a screw is $\frac{3}{32}$ in. How many complete rotations are necessary to drive the screw $\frac{3}{4}$ in. into a piece of pine wood?

55. **D_W** Does the multiplication principle enable us to solve any questions that could not have been solved with the division principle? Why or why not?

56. **D_W** Can the multiplication principle be used to solve equations like $7x = 63$? Why or why not?

SKILL MAINTENANCE

Simplify.

57. $-23 + 49$ [2.2a]

58. $-69 + 27$ [2.2a]

59. $-38 - 29$ [2.3a]

60. $-47 - 18$ [2.3a]

61. $36 \div (-3)^2 \times (7 - 2)$ [2.5b]

62. $(-37 - 12 + 1) \div (-2)^3$ [2.5b]

Form an equivalent expression by combining like terms. [2.7a]

63. $13x + 4x$

64. $9a - 5a$

65. $2a + 3 + 5a$

66. $3x - 7 + x$

SYNTHESIS

67. **D_W** Write a problem for a classmate to solve. Devise the problem so that the solution requires the classmate to divide by a fraction. Arrange for the solution to be "The contents of the barrel will fill 40 bags with $\frac{3}{4}$ lb in each bag."

68. **D_W** To solve $\frac{3}{4}x = 15$, James multiplies each side of the equation by 4. Is there anything wrong with this? Why or why not?

Solve.

69. $2x - 7x = -\dfrac{10}{9}$

70. $\left(-\dfrac{4}{7}\right)^2 = \left(\dfrac{2^3 - 9}{3}\right)^3 x$

Solve using the five-step problem-solving approach.

71. A package of coffee beans weighed $\frac{21}{32}$ lb when it was $\frac{3}{4}$ full. How much could the package hold when completely filled?

72. After swimming $\frac{2}{7}$ mi, Katie had swum $\frac{3}{4}$ of the race. How long a race was Katie competing in?

73. A block of Swiss cheese is 12 in. long. How many slices will it yield if half of the brick is cut by a slicer set for $\frac{3}{32}$-in. slices and half is cut by a slicer set for $\frac{5}{32}$-in. slices?

74. See Exercise 48. If each driveway required $\frac{3}{5}$ yd of stone and the stone cost $90 a yard, how much would the landscaper receive for a full load?

75. See Exercise 47. If each cottage required $\frac{3}{5}$ yd of gravel and the gravel cost $85 a yard, how much would Eric receive for a full load?

76. ▦ If each customer at Bright Moments Greenhouse bought $\frac{7}{8}$ yd of topsoil and the topsoil cost $95 a yard, how much would Bright Moments receive for a 30-yd batch?

77. ▦ If each customer at Green Season Gardening used $\frac{3}{4}$ yd of mulch and the mulch cost $65 a yard, how much would Green Season receive for a 25-yd batch?

3 Summary and Review

The review that follows is meant to prepare you for a chapter exam. It consists of two parts. The first part is a checklist of the Study Tips referred to so far in this text. The second part is the Review Exercises. These provide practice exercises for the exam, together with references to section objectives so you can go back and review. Before beginning, stop and look back over the skills you have obtained. What skills in mathematics do you have now that you did not have before studying this chapter?

STUDY TIPS CHECKLIST

The foundation of all your study skills is TIME!	☐ Have you started your own glossary of terms in your notebook?
	☐ Are you spreading your study time over several days rather than cramming it all into one day?
	☐ Are you inspecting papers that your instructor returns so that you can learn from your mistakes?
	☐ Are you writing helpful notes to yourself in your text?
	☐ Have you tried using a second book as a reference text?
	☐ Have you located a suitable study partner?
	☐ Have you identified those exercises that gave you difficulty and are worth revisiting?

REVIEW EXERCISES

1. Determine whether 3920 is divisible by 6. Do not use long division.   [3.1b]

2. Determine whether 673 is divisible by 5. Do not use long division.   [3.1b]

3. Determine whether 5238 is divisible by 9. Do not use long division.   [3.1b]

Find the prime factorization of each number.   [3.2c]

4. 70   **5.** 72   **6.** 150

7. Determine whether 57 is prime, composite, or neither.   [3.2b]

8. Identify the numerator and the denominator of $\frac{9}{7}$.   [3.3a]

What part is shaded?   [3.3a]

9. 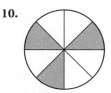   **10.**

Simplify, if possible. Assume that all variables are nonzero.

11. $\dfrac{0}{6}$ [3.3b]

12. $\dfrac{74}{74}$ [3.3b]

13. $\dfrac{48}{1}$ [3.3b]

14. $\dfrac{7x}{7x}$ [3.3b]

15. $-\dfrac{10}{15}$ [3.5b]

16. $\dfrac{7}{28}$ [3.5b]

17. $\dfrac{-42}{42}$ [3.5b]

18. $\dfrac{9m}{12m}$ [3.5b]

19. $\dfrac{12}{30}$ [3.5b]

20. $\dfrac{-27}{0}$ [3.3b]

21. $\dfrac{6x}{1}$ [3.3b]

22. $\dfrac{-9}{-27}$ [3.5b]

Find an equivalent expression for each number, using the denominator indicated. Use multiplication by 1.   [3.5a]

23. $\dfrac{5}{7} = \dfrac{?}{21}$

24. $\dfrac{-6}{11} = \dfrac{?}{55}$

Find the reciprocal of each number.   [3.7a]

25. $\dfrac{2}{13}$

26. -7

27. $\dfrac{1}{8}$

28. $\dfrac{3x}{5y}$

Perform the indicated operation and, if possible, simplify.

29. $\dfrac{2}{9} \cdot \dfrac{7}{5}$ [3.4b]

30. $\dfrac{3}{x} \cdot \dfrac{y}{7}$ [3.4b]

31. $\dfrac{3}{4} \cdot \dfrac{8}{9}$ [3.6a]

32. $-\dfrac{5}{7} \cdot \dfrac{1}{10}$ [3.6a]

33. $\dfrac{3a}{10} \cdot \dfrac{2}{15a}$ [3.6a]

34. $\dfrac{4a}{7} \cdot \dfrac{7}{4a}$ [3.6a]

35. $9 \div \dfrac{5}{3}$ [3.7b]

36. $\dfrac{3}{14} \div \dfrac{6}{7}$ [3.7b]

37. $120 \div \dfrac{3}{5}$ [3.7b]

38. $-\dfrac{5}{36} \div \left(-\dfrac{25}{12}\right)$ [3.7b]

39. $21 \div \dfrac{7}{2a}$ [3.7b]

40. $-\dfrac{23}{25} \div \dfrac{23}{25}$ [3.7b]

41. $\dfrac{\tfrac{21}{30}}{\tfrac{14}{15}}$ [3.7b]

42. $\dfrac{-\tfrac{3}{40}}{-\tfrac{54}{35}}$ [3.7b]

CHAPTER 3: Fraction Notation:
Multiplication and Division

Find the area. [3.6b]

43.

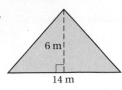

6 m
14 m

44.

10 ft

$\frac{7}{2}$ ft

Solve. [3.8a]

45. $\frac{2}{3}x = 160$

46. $\frac{3}{8} = -\frac{5}{4}t$

47. $-\frac{1}{7}n = -4$

Solve.

48. The Mulligans have driven $\frac{4}{5}$ of a 275-mi trip. How far have they driven? [3.6b]

49. A chocolate chip cookie recipe calls for $\frac{3}{4}$ cup of sugar. In making $\frac{1}{2}$ of this recipe, how much sugar should be used? [3.6b]

50. The Winchester swim team has 4 swimmers in a $\frac{2}{3}$-mi relay race. How far will each person swim? [3.8b]

51. How many $\frac{2}{3}$-cup cereal bowls can be filled from 12 cups of cornflakes? [3.8b]

52. **D**_W A student claims that $\frac{2}{8}$ is simplified form of $\frac{20}{80}$. Is the student correct? Why or why not? [3.5b]

53. **D**_W Write in your own words a series of steps that can be used when simplifying fraction notation. [3.5b]

54. Solve: $17 \cdot x = 408$. [1.7b], [2.8b]

55. Simplify: $20 \div 2 \cdot 2 - 3^2$. [1.9c]

56. Add: $(-798) + 812$. [2.2a]

57. Multiply: $-3 \cdot (-9)$. [2.4a]

Solve. [1.8a]

58. The balance in your checking account is $789. After purchases of $78, $97, and $102 and a deposit of $400, what is your new balance?

59. A new MINI Cooper gets 43 mpg on the highway. How far can the car be driven on a full tank of 13 gal of gasoline?
Source: carlist.com

60. Add: $(3x^2 + 5x - 6) + (7x^3 - 2x)$ [2.9a]

61. Simplify: $\frac{15x}{14z} \cdot \frac{17yz}{35xy} \div \left(-\frac{3}{7}\right)^2$. [3.6a], [3.7b]

62. What digit(s) could be inserted in the ones place to make 574__ divisible by 6? [3.1b]

63. A prime number that becomes a prime number when its digits are reversed is called a **palindrome prime.** For example, 17 is a palindrome prime because both 17 and 71 are primes. Which of the following numbers are palindrome primes? [3.2b]

13, 91, 16, 11, 15, 24, 29, 101, 201, 37

64. ▦ In the division below, find a and b. Assume a/b is in simplified form. [3.7b]

$$\frac{19}{24} \div \frac{a}{b} = \frac{187,853}{268,224}$$

65. ▦ Use a calculator and the list of prime numbers on p. 181 to find simplified fraction notation for the solution of [3.8a]

$$\frac{1751}{267}x = \frac{3193}{2759}.$$

283

1. Determine whether 5682 is divisible by 3. Do not use long division.

2. Determine whether 7018 is divisible by 5. Do not use long division.

Find the prime factorization of each number.

3. 36

4. 60

5. Determine whether 93 is prime, composite, or neither.

6. Identify the numerator and the denominator of $\frac{4}{9}$.

7. What part is shaded?

Simplify, if possible. Assume that all variables are nonzero.

8. $\dfrac{32}{1}$

9. $\dfrac{-12}{-12}$

10. $\dfrac{0}{16}$

11. $\dfrac{-8}{24}$

12. $\dfrac{9x}{45x}$

13. $\dfrac{7}{63}$

14. Find an equivalent expression for $\dfrac{3}{8}$ with a denominator of 40.

Find the reciprocal.

15. $\dfrac{a}{42}$

16. -9

Perform the indicated operation. Simplify, if possible.

17. $\dfrac{5}{7} \cdot \dfrac{7}{2}$

18. $\dfrac{2}{11} \div \dfrac{3}{4}$

19. $3 \cdot \dfrac{x}{8}$

20. $\dfrac{\dfrac{4}{7}}{-\dfrac{8}{3}}$

21. $\dfrac{4a}{13} \cdot \dfrac{9b}{30ab}$

Solve.

22. A $\frac{3}{4}$-lb slab of cheese is shared equally by 5 people. How much does each person receive?

23. Monroe weighs $\frac{5}{7}$ of his dad's weight. If his dad weighs 175 lb, how much does Monroe weigh?

24. $\dfrac{7}{8} \cdot x = 56$

25. $\dfrac{7}{10} = \dfrac{-2}{5} \cdot t$

26. Find the area.

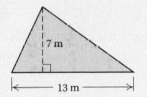

27. Simplify: $3^2 + 2(1 + 3)^2$.

28. Solve: $47 \cdot t = 4747$.

29. Add: $(-93) + (-74)$.

30. Simplify: $(-9)(-7)$.

31. A recipe for a batch of buttermilk pancakes calls for $\frac{3}{4}$ teaspoon (tsp) of salt. Jacqueline plans to cut the amount of salt in half for each of 5 batches of pancakes. How much salt will she need altogether?

32. Grandma Phyllis left $\frac{2}{3}$ of her $\frac{7}{8}$-acre tree farm to Karl. Karl gave $\frac{1}{4}$ of his share to his oldest daughter, Irene. How much land did Irene receive?

33. Simplify: $\left(-\dfrac{3}{8}\right)^2 \div \dfrac{6}{7} \cdot \dfrac{2}{9} \div (-5)$.

34. Solve: $\dfrac{33}{38} \cdot \dfrac{34}{55} = \dfrac{17}{35} \cdot \dfrac{15}{19}x$.

1. Write a word name: 2,056,783.

Add.

2.
$$
\begin{array}{r}
2\ 7\ 4\ 3 \\
+\ 8\ 2\ 3\ 9 \\
\hline
\end{array}
$$

3. $-29 + (-14)$

4. $-45 + 12$

Subtract.

5.
$$
\begin{array}{r}
6\ 3\ 2\ 4 \\
-\ 4\ 1\ 9\ 5 \\
\hline
\end{array}
$$

6. $27 - 50$

7. $-12 - (-4)$

Multiply and, if possible, simplify.

8.
$$
\begin{array}{r}
7\ 3\ 5 \\
\times\ \ \ 2\ 3 \\
\hline
\end{array}
$$

9. $-52 \cdot 6$

10. $\dfrac{6}{7} \cdot (-35x)$

11. $\dfrac{2}{9} \cdot \dfrac{21}{10}$

Divide and, if possible, simplify.

12. $1\ 3\ \overline{)\ 3\ 0\ 5\ 8}$

13. $-85 \div 5$

14. $-16 \div \dfrac{4}{7}$

15. $\dfrac{3}{7} \div \dfrac{9}{14}$

16. Round 4509 to the nearest ten.

17. Estimate the product by rounding to the nearest hundred. Show your work.
$$
\begin{array}{r}
9\ 2\ 1 \\
\times\ 4\ 5\ 3 \\
\hline
\end{array}
$$

18. Find the absolute value: $|-479|$.

19. Simplify: $10^2 \div 5(-2) - 8(2 - 8)$.

20. Determine whether 98 is prime, composite, or neither.

21. Evaluate $a - b^2$ for $a = -5$ and $b = 4$.

Solve.

22. $a + 24 = 49$

23. $7x = 49$

24. $\dfrac{2}{9} \cdot a = -10$

25. A 1996 van that gets 25 miles per gallon is traded in toward a 2003 truck that gets 17 miles per gallon. How many more miles per gallon did the older vehicle get?

26. A 48-oz coffee pot is poured into 6 mugs. How much will each mug hold if the coffee is poured out evenly?

Combine like terms.

27. $8 - 4x - 13 + 9x$

28. $-12x + 7y + 15x$

Simplify, if possible.

29. $\dfrac{97}{97}$

30. $\dfrac{0}{81}$

31. $\dfrac{63}{1}$

32. $\dfrac{-10}{54}$

Find the reciprocal.

33. $\dfrac{2}{5}$

34. 57

35. Find an equivalent expression for $\frac{3}{10}$ with a denominator of 70. Use multiplying by 1.

36. A babysitter earns $60 for working a full day. How much is earned for working $\frac{3}{5}$ of a day?

37. How many $\frac{3}{4}$-lb servings can be made from a 9-lb roast?

38. Tony has jogged $\frac{2}{3}$ of a course that is $\frac{9}{10}$ of a mile long. How far has Tony gone?

39. Subtract: $(6x^5 + 9x^2 - 10) - (2x^5 + 4x^3 + 3)$

40. Evaluate the polynomial $9x^2 - 5x$ for $x = 3$

41. Evaluate $\dfrac{ab}{c}$ for $a = -\dfrac{2}{5}$, $b = \dfrac{10}{13}$, and $c = \dfrac{26}{27}$.

42. Evaluate $-|xy|^2$ for $x = -\dfrac{3}{5}$ and $y = \dfrac{1}{2}$.

43. Wayne and Patty each earn $85 a day, while Janet earns $90 a day. They decide to pool their earnings from three days and spend $\frac{2}{5}$ of that on entertainment and save the rest. How much will Wayne, Patty, and Janet end up saving?

Fraction Notation: Addition and Subtraction

Gateway to Chapter 4

In this chapter, we consider addition and subtraction using fraction notation. Also discussed are addition, subtraction, multiplication, and division using mixed numerals. These operations are then used to solve equations and real-world applications.

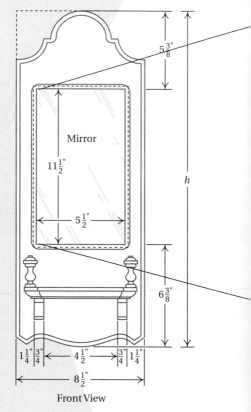

Front View

Real-World Application

The mirror-backed candle shelf, shown above with a carpenter's diagram, was designed and built by Harry Cooper. Such shelves were popular in Colonial times because the mirror provided extra lighting from the candle. A rectangular walnut board is used to make the back of the shelf. Find the area of the original board and the amount left over after the space for the mirror has been cut out.

Source: Popular Science Woodworking Projects

This problem appears as Example 11 in Section 4.7.

1. Find the least common multiple of 25 and 30. [4.1a]

2. Use < or > for ☐ to write a true sentence. [4.2c]

$$\frac{7}{9} \,\square\, \frac{4}{5}.$$

Perform the indicated operation and, if possible, simplify.

3. $\dfrac{-3}{8} + \dfrac{5}{8}$ [4.2a]

4. $\dfrac{5}{6} + \dfrac{-7}{9} + \dfrac{1}{15}$ [4.2b]

5. $\dfrac{1}{7} - \dfrac{2}{5}$ [4.3a]

6. Convert to fraction notation: $5\dfrac{3}{8}$. [4.5a]

7. Convert to a mixed numeral: $\dfrac{17}{5}$. [4.5b]

8. Divide. Write a mixed numeral for the answer.

$$1\,2\,\overline{)\,4\,7\,6\,5}\quad[4.5c]$$

9. Subtract. Write a mixed numeral for the answer.

$$13\dfrac{1}{5}\quad[4.6b]$$
$$-\ 8\dfrac{5}{6}$$

Solve.

10. $\dfrac{2}{3} + x = \dfrac{8}{9}$ [4.3b]

11. $14 = \dfrac{2}{3}x + 20$ [4.4a]

Perform the indicated operations. Write a mixed numeral for each answer.

12. $(-5)\left(-3\dfrac{8}{11}\right)$ [4.7a]

13. $6\dfrac{1}{3} \cdot 5\dfrac{3}{4}$ [4.7a]

14. $45 \div \left(-5\dfrac{5}{6}\right)$ [4.7b]

15. $4\dfrac{5}{12} \div 3\dfrac{1}{4}$ [4.7b]

16. Evaluate $xy \div z$ for $x = 3\dfrac{2}{5}$, $y = 6$, and $z = 2\dfrac{1}{3}$. [4.7c]

Solve.

17. At Sunny Hollow Camp, the cook bought 100 lb of potatoes and used $12\frac{1}{2}$ lb. How many pounds were left over? [4.6c]

18. The weight of water is $62\frac{1}{2}$ lb per cubic foot. How many cubic feet would be occupied by $265\frac{5}{8}$ lb of water? [4.7d]

19. On a trip, Janet averaged $315\frac{1}{2}$ miles per day for 5 days. How far did she travel altogether in those 5 days? [4.7d]

20. Uri is baking a birthday cake that requires $3\frac{3}{4}$ cups of flour and a batch of biscotti that requires $2\frac{1}{2}$ cups. How much flour is required altogether? [4.6c]

4.1

LEAST COMMON MULTIPLES

Before discussing addition or subtraction of fractions, it is essential that we be able to find the **least common multiple** of two or more numbers.

a Finding Least Common Multiples

> **LEAST COMMON MULTIPLE, LCM**
>
> The **least common multiple,** or LCM, of two natural numbers is the smallest number that is a multiple of both.

EXAMPLE 1 Find the LCM of 20 and 30.

a) First list some multiples of 20 by multiplying 20 by 1, 2, 3, and so on:

   20, 40, 60, 80, 100, 120, 140, 160, 180, 200, 220, 240, ...

b) Then list some multiples of 30 by multiplying 30 by 1, 2, 3, and so on:

   30, 60, 90, 120, 150, 180, 210, 240, ...

c) Now list the numbers *common* to both lists, the common multiples:

   60, 120, 180, 240, ...

d) These are the common multiples of 20 and 30. Which is the smallest? The LCM of 20 and 30 is 60.

Do Exercises 1 and 2.

Next we develop two highly efficient methods for finding LCMs. You may choose to learn only one method (consult your instructor). However, if you intend to study algebra, you should definitely learn method 2.

METHOD 1: FINDING LCMS USING ONE LIST OF MULTIPLES

The first method works especially well when the numbers are relatively small.

> *Method 1.* To find the LCM of two numbers (say, 9 and 12), first determine whether the larger number is a multiple of the other.
>
> **1.** If it *is*, it is the LCM.
>
>   (Since 12 is not a multiple of 9, the LCM is not 12.)
>
> **2.** If the larger number *is not* a multiple of the other, check each consecutive multiple of the larger number until you find one that *is* a multiple of the other number. That number is the LCM.
>
>   ($2 \cdot 12 = 24$, but 24 *is not* a multiple of 9.
>
> $3 \cdot 12 = 36$, and 36 *is* a multiple of 9, so the LCM of 9 and 12 is 36.)

1. By examining lists of multiples, find the LCM of 9 and 15.

2. By examining lists of multiples, find the LCM of 8 and 14.

Answers on page A-12

Find the LCM using one list of multiples.

3. 6, 9

4. 6, 8

5. 7, 14

Find the LCM using lists of multiples.

6. 20, 40, 50

Answers on page A-12

Study Tips

FILL IN YOUR BLANKS

Don't hesitate to write out any missing steps that you'd like to see included. For instance, in Example 5, it is stated (in red) that 60 is a multiple of 4. To solidify your understanding, you may want to write in "60 ÷ 4 = 15."

EXAMPLE 2   Find the LCM of 8 and 10.

1. 10 is the larger number, but it is not a multiple of 8.
2. Check multiples of 10:

$2 \cdot 10 = 20,$ Not a multiple of 8
$3 \cdot 10 = 30,$ Not a multiple of 8
$4 \cdot 10 = 40.$ A multiple of both 8 and 10

The LCM = 40.

EXAMPLE 3   Find the LCM of 4 and 14.

1. 14 is the larger number, but it is not a multiple of 4.
2. Check multiples of 14:

$2 \cdot 14 = 28.$ A multiple of 4

The LCM = 28.

EXAMPLE 4   Find the LCM of 8 and 32.

1. 32 is the larger number and 32 is a multiple of 8, so it is the LCM.

The LCM = 32.

Do Exercises 3–5.

To find the least common multiple of three numbers, we find the LCM of two of the numbers and then find the LCM of that number and the third number.

EXAMPLE 5   Find the LCM of 4, 10, and 15. We can start by finding the LCM of any two of the numbers. Let's use 10 and 15:

1. 15 is the larger number, but it is not a multiple of 10.
2. Check multiples of 15:

$2 \cdot 15 = 30.$ A multiple of 10

Note now that any multiple of 30 will automatically be a multiple of 10 and 15. Thus, to find the LCM of 10, 15, and 4, we need only find the LCM of 30 and 4:

1. 30 is not a multiple of 4.
2. Check multiples of 30:

$2 \cdot 30 = 60.$ Since it is a multiple of 4, we know
                        that 60 is the LCM of 30 and 4.

The LCM of 4, 10, and 15 is 60.

Do Exercise 6.

METHOD 2: FINDING LCMS USING FACTORIZATIONS

A second method for finding LCMs uses prime factorizations and is usually the best method when the numbers are large. Consider again 20 and 30. Their prime factorizations are

$$20 = 2 \cdot 2 \cdot 5 \quad \text{and} \quad 30 = 2 \cdot 3 \cdot 5.$$

The least common multiple must include the factors of each number, so it must include each prime factor the greatest number of times that it appears in either of the factorizations. To find the LCM for 20 and 30, we select one factorization, say,

$$2 \cdot 2 \cdot 5,$$

and observe that since it lacks the factor 3, it does not contain the entire factorization of 30. If we multiply $2 \cdot 2 \cdot 5$ by 3, every prime factor occurs just often enough to have both 20 and 30 as factors.

$$\text{LCM} = 2 \cdot 2 \cdot 5 \cdot 3$$

— 20 is a factor of the LCM.

— 30 is a factor of the LCM.

Note that each prime factor is used the greatest number of times that it occurs in either of the individual factorizations.

> *Method 2.* To find the LCM of two numbers (say, 9 and 12):
>
> **1.** Write the prime factorization of each number.
>
> $(9 = 3 \cdot 3; \qquad 12 = 2 \cdot 2 \cdot 3)$
>
> **2.** Select one of the factorizations and see whether it contains the other.
>
> $(2 \cdot 2 \cdot 3 \text{ does not contain } 3 \cdot 3.)$
>
> a) If it does, it is the LCM.
>
> b) If it does not, multiply that factorization by those prime factors of the other number that it lacks. The final product is the LCM.
>
> $(2 \cdot 2 \cdot 3 \cdot 3 \text{ is the LCM.})$
>
> **3.** As a check, make sure that the LCM includes each factor the greatest number of times that it occurs in either factorization.

EXAMPLE 6 Find the LCM of 18 and 21.

1. We begin by writing the prime factorization of each number:

$$18 = 2 \cdot 3 \cdot 3 \quad \text{and} \quad 21 = 3 \cdot 7.$$

2. a) We note that $2 \cdot 3 \cdot 3$ does not contain the other factorization, $3 \cdot 7$.

  b) To find the LCM of 18 and 21, we multiply $2 \cdot 3 \cdot 3$ by the factor of 21 that it lacks, 7:

$$\text{LCM} = 2 \cdot 3 \cdot 3 \cdot 7.$$

— 18 is a factor.

— 21 is a factor.

3. The greatest number of times that 2 occurs as a factor of 18 or 21 is **one** time; the greatest number of times that 3 occurs as a factor of 18 or 21 is **two** times, and the greatest number of times that 7 occurs as a factor of 18 or 21 is **one** time. To check, note that the LCM has exactly **one** 2, **two** 3s, and **one** 7. The LCM is $2 \cdot 3 \cdot 3 \cdot 7$, or 126.

Use prime factorizations to find the LCM.

7. 8, 10

8. 18, 40

9. 5, 30

Find the LCM.

10. 8, 18, 30

11. 10, 20, 25

Answers on page A-12

■ EXAMPLE 7 Find the LCM of 24 and 36.

1. We begin by writing the prime factorization of each number:

$$24 = 2 \cdot 2 \cdot 2 \cdot 3 \quad \text{and} \quad 36 = 2 \cdot 2 \cdot 3 \cdot 3.$$

2. **a)** Neither factorization contains the other.

   b) To find the LCM of 24 and 36, we multiply the factorization of 24, $2 \cdot 2 \cdot 2 \cdot 3$, by any prime factors of 36 that are lacking. In this case, a second factor of 3 is needed. We have

   ———— 24 is a factor.

   $$\text{LCM} = 2 \cdot 2 \cdot 2 \cdot 3 \cdot 3.$$

   ———— 36 is a factor.

3. To check, note that 2 and 3 appear in the LCM the greatest number of times that each appears as a factor of either 24 or 36. The LCM is

   $$2 \cdot 2 \cdot 2 \cdot 3 \cdot 3 \quad \text{or} \quad 72.$$

■ EXAMPLE 8 Find the LCM of 7 and 21.

1. Because 7 is prime, we think of $7 = 7$ as a "factorization" in order to carry out our procedure:

   $$7 = 7 \quad \text{and} \quad 21 = 3 \cdot 7.$$

2. One factorization, $3 \cdot 7$, contains the other. Thus the LCM is $3 \cdot 7$, or 21.

Do Exercises 7–9.

We can use the same approach to find the LCM of three numbers.

■ EXAMPLE 9 Find the LCM of 27, 90, and 84.

1. We first find the prime factorization of each number:

   $$27 = 3 \cdot 3 \cdot 3, \quad 90 = 2 \cdot 3 \cdot 3 \cdot 5, \quad \text{and} \quad 84 = 2 \cdot 2 \cdot 3 \cdot 7.$$

2. **a)** No one factorization contains the other two.

   b) We consider first 27 and 90 (any two of the three can be used). The factorization of 90 is $2 \cdot 3 \cdot 3 \cdot 5$. Since 27 contains a third factor of 3, we multiply by another factor of 3:

   ———— 90 is a factor.

   $$2 \cdot 3 \cdot 3 \cdot 5 \cdot 3.$$

   ———— 27 is a factor.

   Next, we multiply $2 \cdot 3 \cdot 3 \cdot 5 \cdot 3$ by the factors of 84 that are still missing, $2 \cdot 7$:

   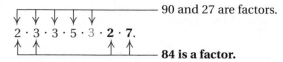

   ———— 90 and 27 are factors.

   $$2 \cdot 3 \cdot 3 \cdot 5 \cdot 3 \cdot \mathbf{2 \cdot 7}.$$

   ———— **84 is a factor.**

   The LCM is $2 \cdot 3 \cdot 3 \cdot 5 \cdot 3 \cdot 2 \cdot 7$, or 3780.

3. The check is left to the student.

Do Exercises 10 and 11.

Exponential notation is often helpful when writing least common multiples. Let's reconsider Example 7:

$$24 = 2 \cdot 2 \cdot 2 \cdot 3 = 2^3 \cdot 3^1 \qquad 2^3 \text{ is the greatest power of 2 and}$$
$$36 = 2 \cdot 2 \cdot 3 \cdot 3 = 2^2 \cdot 3^2 \qquad 3^2 \text{ is the greatest power of 3}$$
$$\text{LCM} = 2 \cdot 2 \cdot 2 \cdot 3 \cdot 3 = 2^3 \cdot 3^2, \text{ or } 72.$$

Note that the greatest power of each factor is used to construct the LCM. The same method works perfectly with variables.

EXAMPLE 10 Find the LCM of $7a^2b$ and ab^3.

1. We have the following factorizations:

   $$7a^2b = 7 \cdot a \cdot a \cdot b \quad \text{and} \quad ab^3 = a \cdot b \cdot b \cdot b.$$

2. **a)** No one factorization contains the other.

   b) Consider the factorization of $7a^2b$, which is $7 \cdot a \cdot a \cdot b$. Since ab^3 contains two more factors of b, we multiply by $b \cdot b$:

   $7 \cdot a \cdot a \cdot b \cdot b \cdot b$ — $7a^2b$ is a factor.

   — ab^3 is a factor.

   The LCM is $7 \cdot a \cdot a \cdot b \cdot b \cdot b$, or $7a^2b^3$.

3. To check, note that the greatest power of 7 is 7^1, or just 7. The greatest power of a is a^2, and the greatest power of b is b^3, so the LCM is $7a^2b^3$.

Do Exercises 12 and 13.

Find the LCM.

12. xy, yz

13. $5a^2, a^3b$

Answers on page A-12

a   Find the LCM of each set of numbers or expressions.

1. 5, 10

2. 4, 12

3. 10, 25

4. 10, 15

5. 20, 40

6. 8, 12

7. 18, 27

8. 9, 11

9. 30, 50

10. 8, 36

11. 30, 40

12. 21, 27

13. 18, 24

14. 12, 18

15. 60, 70

16. 35, 45

17. 16, 36

18. 24, 32

19. 18, 20

20. 36, 48

21. 2, 3, 7

22. 2, 5, 9

23. 3, 6, 15

24. 6, 12, 18

25. 24, 36, 12

26. 8, 16, 22

27. 5, 12, 15

28. 12, 18, 40

29. 9, 12, 6

30. 8, 16, 12

31. 180, 100, 450

32. 18, 30, 50, 48

33. 75, 100

34. 81, 90

35. ab, bc

36. $7x, xy$

37. $3x, 9x^2$

38. $10x^4, 5x^3$

39. $4x^3, x^2y$

40. $6ab^2, a^3b$

41. $2r^3st^4, 8rs^2t$

42. $3m^2n^4p^5, 9mn^2p^4$

43. a^3b, b^2c, ac^2

44. x^2z^3, x^3y, y^2z

Applications of LCMs: Planet Orbits. Earth, Jupiter, Saturn, and Uranus all revolve around the sun. Earth takes 1 yr, Jupiter 12 yr, Saturn 30 yr, and Uranus 84 yr to make a complete revolution. One night, you look at those three distant planets and wonder how many years it will take before they have the same position again. To determine this, you find the LCM of 12, 30, and 84. It will be that number of years.

45. How often will Jupiter and Saturn appear in the same position in the night sky as seen from Earth tonight?

46. How often will Jupiter, Saturn, and Uranus appear in the same direction in the night sky as seen from Earth?

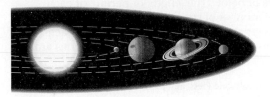

47. ^{D}**W** Are the rules for divisibility useful when looking for LCMs? Why or why not?

48. ^{D}**W** What is the difference between a common multiple and a least common multiple?

Perform the indicated operation and, if possible, simplify.

49. $-38 + 52$ [2.2a]

50. $-18 \div \left(\dfrac{2}{3} \right)$ [3.7b]

51. $23 \cdot 345$ [1.5a]

52. $\dfrac{4}{5} \cdot \dfrac{10}{12}$ [3.6a]

53. $\dfrac{4}{5} \div \left(-\dfrac{7}{10} \right)$ [3.7b]

54. $382 - 549$ [2.3a]

55. ^{D}**W** Under what conditions is the LCM of two composite numbers simply the product of the two numbers?

56. ^{D}**W** Is the LCM of two prime numbers always their product? Why or why not?

57. ^{D}**W** Is the LCM of two numbers always at least twice as large as the larger of the two numbers? Why or why not?

Use a calculator and the multiples method to find the LCM of each pair of numbers.

58. 288; 324

59. 2700; 7800

60. 7719; 18,011

61. 17,385; 24,339

62. The tables at a flea market are either 6 ft long or 8 ft long. If one row is all 6-ft tables and one row is all 8-ft tables, what is the shortest common row length?

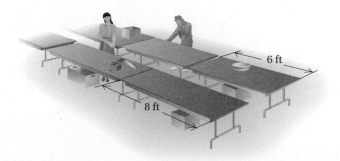

6 ft

8 ft

South African Artistry. In South Africa, the design of every woven handbag, or *gipatsi* (plural *sipatsi*), is created by repeating two or more geometric patterns. Each pattern encircles the bag, sharing the strands of fabric with any pattern above or below. The length, or period, of each pattern is the number of strands required to construct the pattern. For a gipatsi to be considered beautiful, each individual pattern must fit a whole number of times around the bag.

Source: Gerdes, Paulus. *Women, Art and Geometry in Southern Africa.* Asmara, Eritrea: Africa World Press, Inc., p. 5.

63. A weaver is using two patterns to create a gipatsi. Pattern A is 10 strands long, and pattern B is 3 strands long. What is the smallest number of strands that can be used to complete the gipatsi?

64. A weaver is using a four-strand pattern, a six-strand pattern, and an eight-strand pattern. What is the smallest number of strands that can be used to complete the gipatsi?

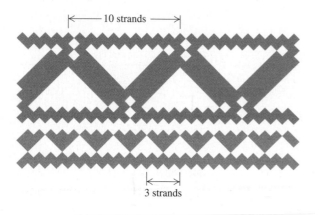

65. Use Example 9 to help find the LCM of 27, 90, 84, 210, 108, and 50.

66. Use Examples 6 and 7 to help find the LCM of 18, 21, 24, 36, 63, 56, and 20.

67. Consider a^3b^2 and a^2b^5. Determine whether each of the following is the LCM of a^3b^2 and a^2b^5. Tell why or why not.
   a) a^3b^3
   b) a^2b^5
   c) a^3b^5

68. Find three different pairs of numbers for which 56 is the LCM. Do not use 56 itself in any of the pairs.

69. Find three different pairs of numbers for which 54 is the LCM. Do not use 54 itself in any of the pairs.

4.2

ADDITION, ORDER, AND APPLICATIONS

a Like Denominators

Addition using fraction notation corresponds to combining or putting like things together, just as when we combined like terms in Section 2.7. For example,

We combine two sets, each of which consists of equally sized parts of one object.

This is the resulting set.

1   1   1

$\frac{2}{8}$ + $\frac{3}{8}$ = $\frac{5}{8}$

2 eighths + 3 eighths = 5 eighths,

or $\quad 2 \cdot \frac{1}{8} + 3 \cdot \frac{1}{8} = 5 \cdot \frac{1}{8}$,

or $\quad \frac{2}{8} + \frac{3}{8} = \frac{5}{8}$.

Do Exercise 1.

To add when denominators are the same,
a) add the numerators,
b) keep the denominators, and
c) if possible, simplify.

$$\frac{2}{6} + \frac{5}{6} = \frac{2+5}{6} = \frac{7}{6}$$

EXAMPLES Add and, if possible, simplify.

1. $\dfrac{2}{4} + \dfrac{1}{4} = \dfrac{2+1}{4} = \dfrac{3}{4}$ No simplifying is possible.

2. $\dfrac{3}{12} + \dfrac{5}{12} = \dfrac{3+5}{12} = \dfrac{8}{12}$ Adding numerators; the denominator remains unchanged.

   $= \dfrac{4}{4} \cdot \dfrac{2}{3} = \dfrac{2}{3}$ Simplifying by removing a factor equal to 1: $\frac{4}{4} = 1$

3. $\dfrac{-11}{6} + \dfrac{3}{6} = \dfrac{-11+3}{6} = \dfrac{-8}{6}$

   $= \dfrac{2}{2} \cdot \dfrac{-4}{3} = \dfrac{-4}{3}$, or $-\dfrac{4}{3}$ Removing a factor equal to 1: $\frac{2}{2} = 1$

4. $-\dfrac{2}{a} + \left(-\dfrac{3}{a}\right) = \dfrac{-2}{a} + \dfrac{-3}{a}$ Recall that $-\dfrac{m}{n} = \dfrac{-m}{n}$.

   $= \dfrac{-2 + (-3)}{a} = \dfrac{-5}{a}$, or $-\dfrac{5}{a}$

Do Exercises 2–5.

Objectives

a Add using fraction notation when denominators are the same.

b Add using fraction notation when denominators are different.

c Use < or > to form a true statement using fraction notation.

d Solve problems involving addition with fraction notation.

1. Find $\dfrac{1}{5} + \dfrac{3}{5}$.

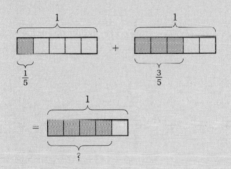

1   1

$\frac{1}{5}$ + $\frac{3}{5}$

1

$= $

?

Add and, if possible, simplify.

2. $\dfrac{1}{3} + \dfrac{2}{3}$

3. $\dfrac{5}{12} + \dfrac{1}{12}$

4. $\dfrac{-9}{16} + \dfrac{3}{16}$

5. $\dfrac{3}{x} + \dfrac{-7}{x}$

Answers on page A-12

Simplify by combining like terms.

6. $\frac{3}{10}a + \frac{1}{10}a$

7. $\frac{2}{19} + \frac{3}{19}x + \frac{5}{19} + \frac{7}{19}x$

Answers on page A-12

Study Tips

LEAVE A TRAIL

Students sometimes make the mistake of viewing their supporting work as "scrap" work. Most instructors regard your reasoning as more important than your final answer. Try to organize your supporting work so that your instructor (and you as well) can follow your steps.

We may need to add fractions when combining like terms.

■ **EXAMPLE 5** Simplify by combining like terms: $\frac{2}{7}x + \frac{3}{7}x$.

$$\frac{2}{7}x + \frac{3}{7}x = \left(\frac{2}{7} + \frac{3}{7}\right)x \qquad \text{Try to do this step mentally.}$$

$$= \frac{5}{7}x.$$

Do Exercises 6 and 7.

b Addition Using the Least Common Denominator

> **CONNECTING THE CONCEPTS**
>
> When adding, subtracting, multiplying, or dividing, we form equivalent expressions. For example, $\frac{1}{2} \cdot \frac{1}{3}$ is equivalent to $\frac{1}{6}$, and $\frac{2}{7}x + \frac{3}{7}x$ is equivalent to $\frac{5}{7}x$.
>
> We have also seen that a fraction like $\frac{3}{4}$ can be written in many equivalent forms $\left(\frac{6}{8}, \frac{9}{12}, \frac{15}{20}, \text{etc.}\right)$. Which of these many forms of $\frac{3}{4}$ will be most useful when adding $\frac{3}{4} + \frac{1}{6}$? This is where the concept of least common multiple becomes important.
>
> The least common multiple of 4 and 6 can be used as the denominator of one fraction that is equivalent to $\frac{3}{4}$ and of a second fraction that is equivalent to $\frac{1}{6}$. Once the sum $\frac{3}{4} + \frac{1}{6}$ is rewritten as an equivalent expression in which both denominators are the same number, we can perform the addition and write one fraction for the result. By using the *least* common multiple instead of just any common multiple, we make our calculations as easy as possible.
>
> Now that least common multiples, multiplication of fractions, and addition of fractions with like denominators are understood, we have all the background required for a thorough understanding of how to add (or subtract) any two fractions.

Let's now add $\frac{1}{2} + \frac{1}{3}$:

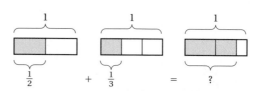

By rewriting $\frac{1}{2}$ as $\frac{1}{2} \cdot \frac{3}{3} = \frac{3}{6}$ and $\frac{1}{3}$ as $\frac{1}{3} \cdot \frac{2}{2} = \frac{2}{6}$, we can determine the sum.

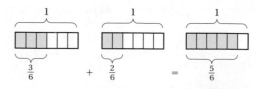

Thus, when denominators differ, before adding we must multiply by a form of 1 to get a common denominator. There is always more than one common denominator that can be used. Consider the addition $\frac{3}{4} + \frac{1}{6}$:

A. $\frac{3}{4} + \frac{1}{6} = \frac{3}{4} \cdot 1 + \frac{1}{6} \cdot 1$

$= \frac{3}{4} \cdot \frac{6}{6} + \frac{1}{6} \cdot \frac{4}{4}$

Here 24 is the common denominator.

$= \frac{18}{24} + \frac{4}{24} = \frac{22}{24} = \frac{11}{12}$;

B. $\frac{3}{4} + \frac{1}{6} = \frac{3}{4} \cdot 1 + \frac{1}{6} \cdot 1$

$= \frac{3}{4} \cdot \frac{3}{3} + \frac{1}{6} \cdot \frac{2}{2}$

Here 12 is the common denominator.

$= \frac{9}{12} + \frac{2}{12} = \frac{11}{12}$

We had to simplify at the end of (A), but not in (B). In (B), we used the *least* common multiple of the denominators, 12. That number is called the **least common denominator**, or **LCD**.

> To add when denominators are different:
>
> a) Find the least common multiple of the denominators. That number is the least common denominator, LCD.
>
> b) Multiply by 1, writing 1 in the form of n/n, to find an equivalent sum in which the LCD appears in each fraction.
>
> c) Add and, if possible, simplify.

EXAMPLE 6 Add: $\frac{1}{8} + \frac{3}{4}$.

a) Since 4 is a factor of 8, the LCM of 4 and 8 is 8. Thus the LCD is 8.

b) We need to find a fraction equivalent to $\frac{3}{4}$ with a denominator of 8:

$\frac{1}{8} + \frac{3}{4} = \frac{1}{8} + \frac{3}{4} \cdot \frac{2}{2}$.   *Think:* $4 \times \square = 8$. The answer is 2, so we multiply by 1, using $\frac{2}{2}$.

c) We add: $\frac{1}{8} + \frac{6}{8} = \frac{7}{8}$. $\frac{7}{8}$ cannot be simplified.

Do Exercise 8.

In Examples 7–10, we follow the same steps without spelling them out.

EXAMPLE 7 Add: $\frac{5}{6} + \frac{1}{9}$.

The LCD is 18. $6 = 2 \cdot 3$ and $9 = 3 \cdot 3$, so the LCM of 6 and 9 is $2 \cdot 3 \cdot 3$, or 18.

$\frac{5}{6} + \frac{1}{9} = \frac{5}{6} \cdot 1 + \frac{1}{9} \cdot 1$

$= \frac{5}{6} \cdot \frac{3}{3} + \frac{1}{9} \cdot \frac{2}{2}$ *Think:* $9 \times \square = 18$. The answer is 2, so we multiply by 1, using $\frac{2}{2}$.

Think: $6 \times \square = 18$. The answer is 3, so we multiply by 1, using $\frac{3}{3}$.

$= \frac{15}{18} + \frac{2}{18} = \frac{17}{18}$

Do Exercise 9.

8. Add using the least common denominator.

$$\frac{2}{3} + \frac{1}{6}$$

9. Add: $\frac{3}{8} + \frac{5}{6}$.

Answers on page A-12

4.2   Addition, Order, and Applications

10. Add: $\dfrac{1}{-6} + \dfrac{7}{18}$.

11. Add: $7 + \dfrac{3}{5}$.

Add.

12. $\dfrac{4}{10} + \dfrac{1}{100} + \dfrac{3}{1000}$

13. $\dfrac{7}{10} + \dfrac{-2}{21} + \dfrac{1}{7}$

Answers on page A-12

CHAPTER 4: Fraction Notation:
Addition and Subtraction

■ **EXAMPLE 8**   Add: $\dfrac{3}{-5} + \dfrac{11}{10}$.

$$\dfrac{3}{-5} + \dfrac{11}{10} = \dfrac{-3}{5} + \dfrac{11}{10}$$

Recall that $\dfrac{m}{-n} = \dfrac{-m}{n}$. We generally avoid negative signs in the denominator. The LCD is 10.

$$= \dfrac{-3}{5} \cdot \dfrac{2}{2} + \dfrac{11}{10}$$

$$= \dfrac{-6}{10} + \dfrac{11}{10}$$

$$= \dfrac{5}{10}$$

$$= \dfrac{1}{2}$$

> We may still have to simplify, but simplifying is almost always easier if the LCD has been used.

Do Exercise 10.

■ **EXAMPLE 9**   Add: $\dfrac{5}{8} + 2$.

$$\dfrac{5}{8} + 2 = \dfrac{5}{8} + \dfrac{2}{1}$$ Rewriting 2 in fraction notation

$$= \dfrac{5}{8} + \dfrac{2}{1} \cdot \dfrac{8}{8}$$ The LCD is 8.

$$= \dfrac{5}{8} + \dfrac{16}{8} = \dfrac{21}{8}$$

Do Exercise 11.

■ **EXAMPLE 10**   Add: $\dfrac{9}{70} + \dfrac{11}{21} + \dfrac{-6}{15}$.

We need to determine the LCM of 70, 21, and 15:

$$70 = 2 \cdot 5 \cdot 7,$$
$$21 = 3 \cdot 7,$$ The LCM is $2 \cdot 3 \cdot 5 \cdot 7$, or 210.
$$15 = 3 \cdot 5$$

$$\dfrac{9}{70} + \dfrac{11}{21} + \dfrac{-6}{15} = \dfrac{9}{70} \cdot \dfrac{3}{3} + \dfrac{11}{21} \cdot \dfrac{2 \cdot 5}{2 \cdot 5} + \dfrac{-6}{15} \cdot \dfrac{7 \cdot 2}{7 \cdot 2}$$

> In each case, we multiply by 1 to obtain the LCD. To form 1, look at the prime factorization of the LCD and use the factor(s) missing from each denominator.

$$= \dfrac{9 \cdot 3}{70 \cdot 3} + \dfrac{11 \cdot 10}{21 \cdot 10} + \dfrac{-6 \cdot 14}{15 \cdot 14}$$

$$= \dfrac{27}{210} + \dfrac{110}{210} + \dfrac{-84}{210}$$

$$= \dfrac{137 + (-84)}{210}$$

$$= \dfrac{53}{210}.$$ Since 53 is prime and not a factor of 210, we cannot simplify.

Do Exercises 12 and 13.

C. Order

Common denominators are also important for determining the larger of two fractions. When two fractions share a common denominator, the larger number can be found by comparing numerators. For example, 4 is greater than 3, so $\frac{4}{5}$ is greater than $\frac{3}{5}$.

$$\frac{4}{5} > \frac{3}{5}$$

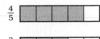

Similarly, because -6 is less than -2, we have

$$\frac{-6}{7} < \frac{-2}{7}, \quad \text{or} \quad -\frac{6}{7} < -\frac{2}{7}.$$

Do Exercises 14–16.

EXAMPLE 11 Use $<$ or $>$ for $\Box$ to form a true sentence:

$$\frac{5}{8} \ \Box \ \frac{2}{3}.$$

You can confirm that the LCD is 24. We multiply by 1 to find two fractions equivalent to $\frac{5}{8}$ and $\frac{2}{3}$ with denominators the same:

$$\frac{5}{8} \cdot \frac{3}{3} = \frac{15}{24}; \qquad \frac{2}{3} \cdot \frac{8}{8} = \frac{16}{24}.$$

Since $15 < 16$, it follows that $\frac{15}{24} < \frac{16}{24}$. Thus,

$$\frac{5}{8} < \frac{2}{3}.$$

EXAMPLE 12 Use $<$ or $>$ for $\Box$ to form a true sentence:

$$-\frac{89}{100} \ \Box \ -\frac{9}{10}.$$

The LCD is 100.

$$\frac{-9}{10} \cdot \frac{10}{10} = \frac{-90}{100} \qquad \text{We multiply by } \tfrac{10}{10} \text{ to get the LCD.}$$

Since $-89 > -90$, it follows that $-\frac{89}{100} > -\frac{90}{100}$, so

$$-\frac{89}{100} > -\frac{9}{10}.$$

Do Exercises 17–19.

d. Applications and Problem Solving

EXAMPLE 13 *Carpentry.* Dick Bonewitz, a master carpenter, makes special pieces of furniture for his family and friends. To cut expenses, he sometimes glues two kinds of plywood together. He glues a $\frac{1}{4}$-in. $\left(\frac{1}{4}''\right)$ piece of walnut plywood to a $\frac{3}{8}$-in. $\left(\frac{3}{8}''\right)$ piece of less expensive plywood. What is the total thickness of these pieces?

Use $<$ or $>$ for $\Box$ to form a true sentence.

14. $\dfrac{3}{8} \ \Box \ \dfrac{5}{8}$

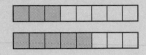

15. $\dfrac{7}{10} \ \Box \ \dfrac{6}{10}$

16. $\dfrac{-2}{9} \ \Box \ \dfrac{-5}{9}$

Use $<$ or $>$ for $\Box$ to form a true sentence.

17. $\dfrac{2}{3} \ \Box \ \dfrac{3}{4}$

18. $\dfrac{-3}{4} \ \boxed{<} \ \dfrac{-8}{12}$

19. $\dfrac{5}{6} \ \Box \ \dfrac{7}{8}$

Answers on page A-12

20. Sally jogs for $\frac{4}{5}$ mi, rests, and then jogs for another $\frac{1}{10}$ mi. How far does she jog in all?

$\frac{1}{10}$ mi

$\frac{4}{5}$ mi

D

Answer on page A-12

1. Familiarize. We first make a drawing. We let T = the total thickness of the plywood.

$\frac{1}{4}''$

$\frac{3}{8}''$

2. Translate. The problem can be translated to an equation as follows.

Thickness of less expensive plywood	plus	Thickness of walnut plywood	is	Total thickness
↓	↓	↓	↓	↓
$\frac{3}{8}$	$+$	$\frac{1}{4}$	$=$	T

3. Solve. To solve the equation, we carry out the addition. The LCD is 8 because 4 is a factor of 8. We multiply by 1 in order to obtain the LCD:

$$\frac{3}{8} + \frac{1}{4} = T$$

$$\frac{3}{8} + \frac{1}{4} \cdot \frac{2}{2} = T$$

$$\frac{3}{8} + \frac{2}{8} = T$$

$$\frac{5}{8} = T.$$

4. Check. We check by repeating the calculation. We also note that the sum should be larger than either of the individual measurements, which it is. This gives us a partial check on the reasonableness of the answer.

5. State. The total thickness of the plywood is $\frac{5}{8}$ in.

Do Exercise 20.

CALCULATOR CORNER

Many calculators now have a key labeled $\boxed{a^{b/c}}$, that allows for computations with fraction notation. To calculate

$$\frac{2}{3} + \frac{4}{5}$$

with such a calculator, the following keystrokes can be used (note that the key $\boxed{a^{b/c}}$ usually doubles as the $\boxed{d/c}$ key):

$\boxed{2}\ \boxed{a^{b/c}}\ \boxed{3}\ \boxed{+}\ \boxed{4}\ \boxed{a^{b/c}}\ \boxed{5}\ \boxed{=}\ \boxed{SHIFT}\ \boxed{d/c}$.

The display that appears,

$\boxed{22 \rfloor 15}$,

represents the fraction $\frac{22}{15}$.

Note that we used the keystrokes $\boxed{SHIFT}\ \boxed{d/c}$ to convert from a mixed numeral (see Section 4.5) to fraction notation.

Graphing calculators can also perform computations with fraction notation. To do the above addition on a graphing calculator, we use the $\boxed{MATH}$ key as follows:

$\boxed{2}\ \boxed{\div}\ \boxed{3}\ \boxed{+}\ \boxed{4}\ \boxed{\div}\ \boxed{5}\ \boxed{MATH}\ \boxed{1}\ \boxed{ENTER}$.

CAUTION!

Although it is possible to add on a calculator using fraction notation, it is still very important for you to understand how such addition is performed longhand. For this reason, your instructor may disallow the use of calculators on this chapter's test.

Exercises: Calculate.

1. $\frac{3}{8} + \frac{1}{4}$ **2.** $\frac{5}{12} + \frac{7}{10}$ **3.** $\frac{15}{7} + \frac{1}{3}$

4. $\frac{19}{20} + \frac{17}{35}$ **5.** $\frac{29}{30} + \frac{18}{25}$ **6.** $\frac{17}{23} + \frac{13}{29}$

a , b   Add and, if possible, simplify.

1. $\dfrac{4}{9} + \dfrac{1}{9}$

2. $\dfrac{1}{4} + \dfrac{1}{4}$

3. $\dfrac{4}{7} + \dfrac{3}{7}$

4. $\dfrac{7}{8} + \dfrac{1}{8}$

5. $\dfrac{7}{10} + \dfrac{3}{-10}$

6. $\dfrac{1}{-6} + \dfrac{5}{6}$

7. $\dfrac{9}{a} + \dfrac{4}{a}$

8. $\dfrac{2}{t} + \dfrac{3}{t}$

9. $\dfrac{-7}{11} + \dfrac{3}{11}$

10. $\dfrac{7}{12} + \dfrac{-5}{12}$

11. $\dfrac{2}{9}x + \dfrac{5}{9}x$

12. $\dfrac{3}{11}a + \dfrac{2}{11}a$

13. $\dfrac{3}{32}t + \dfrac{13}{32}t$

14. $\dfrac{3}{25}x + \dfrac{12}{25}x$

15. $-\dfrac{2}{x} + \left(-\dfrac{7}{x}\right)$

16. $-\dfrac{7}{a} + \dfrac{5}{a}$

17. $\dfrac{1}{8} + \dfrac{1}{6}$

18. $\dfrac{1}{9} + \dfrac{1}{6}$

19. $\dfrac{-4}{5} + \dfrac{7}{10}$

20. $\dfrac{-3}{4} + \dfrac{1}{12}$

21. $\dfrac{7}{12} + \dfrac{3}{8}$

22. $\dfrac{7}{8} + \dfrac{1}{16}$

23. $\dfrac{3}{20} + 4$

24. $\dfrac{2}{15} + 3$

25. $\dfrac{5}{-8} + \dfrac{5}{6}$

26. $\dfrac{5}{-6} + \dfrac{7}{9}$

27. $\dfrac{3}{10}x + \dfrac{7}{100}x$

28. $\dfrac{9}{20}a + \dfrac{3}{40}a$

29. $\dfrac{5}{12} + \dfrac{8}{15}$

30. $\dfrac{3}{16} + \dfrac{1}{12}$

31. $\dfrac{-7}{10} + \dfrac{-29}{100}$

32. $\dfrac{-3}{10} + \dfrac{-27}{100}$

33. $2 + \dfrac{5}{12}$

34. $7 + \dfrac{3}{8}$

35. $-5t + \dfrac{2}{7}t$

36. $-4x + \dfrac{3}{5}x$

37. $-\dfrac{5}{12} + \dfrac{7}{-24}$

38. $-\dfrac{1}{18} + \dfrac{5}{-12}$

39. $\dfrac{4}{10} + \dfrac{3}{100} + \dfrac{7}{1000}$

40. $\dfrac{7}{10} + \dfrac{2}{100} + \dfrac{9}{1000}$

41. $\dfrac{3}{10} + \dfrac{5}{12} + \dfrac{8}{15}$

42. $\dfrac{1}{2} + \dfrac{3}{8} + \dfrac{1}{4}$

43. $\dfrac{5}{6} + \dfrac{25}{52} + \dfrac{7}{4}$

44. $\dfrac{15}{24} + \dfrac{7}{36} + \dfrac{91}{48}$

45. $\dfrac{2}{9} + \dfrac{7}{10} + \dfrac{-4}{15}$

46. $\dfrac{5}{12} + \dfrac{-3}{8} + \dfrac{1}{10}$

C   Use < or > for ☐ to form a true sentence.

47. $\frac{3}{8} \square \frac{2}{8}$ **48.** $\frac{7}{9} \square \frac{5}{9}$ **49.** $\frac{2}{3} \square \frac{5}{6}$ **50.** $\frac{11}{18} \square \frac{5}{9}$

51. $\frac{-2}{3} \square \frac{-5}{7}$ **52.** $\frac{-3}{5} \square \frac{-4}{7}$ **53.** $\frac{9}{15} \square \frac{7}{10}$ **54.** $\frac{5}{14} \square \frac{8}{21}$

55. $\frac{3}{4} \square -\frac{1}{5}$ **56.** $\frac{3}{8} \square -\frac{13}{16}$ **57.** $\frac{-7}{20} \square \frac{-6}{15}$ **58.** $\frac{-7}{12} \square \frac{-9}{16}$

Arrange each group of fractions from smallest to largest.

59. $\frac{3}{10}, \frac{5}{12}, \frac{4}{15}$ **60.** $\frac{5}{6}, \frac{19}{21}, \frac{11}{14}$

d   Solve.

61. Mitch bought $\frac{1}{4}$ lb of gumdrops and $\frac{1}{2}$ lb of caramels. How many pounds of candy did Mitch buy altogether?

62. Rose bought $\frac{1}{3}$ lb of orange pekoe tea and $\frac{1}{2}$ lb of English cinnamon tea. How many pounds of tea did Rose buy altogether?

63. Ola walked $\frac{7}{8}$ mi to the student union, and then $\frac{2}{5}$ mi to class. How far did Ola walk?

64. Ruwanda walked $\frac{3}{8}$ mi to Juan's dormitory, and then $\frac{3}{4}$ mi to class. How far did Ruwanda walk?

65. *Baking.* A recipe for bread calls for $\frac{2}{3}$ cup of water, $\frac{1}{4}$ cup of milk, and $\frac{1}{8}$ cup of oil. How many cups of liquid ingredients does the recipe call for?

66. *Baking.* A recipe for muffins calls for $\frac{1}{2}$ qt (quart) of buttermilk, $\frac{1}{3}$ qt of skim milk, and $\frac{1}{16}$ qt of oil. How many quarts of liquid ingredients does the recipe call for?

67. *Meteorology.* On Monday, April 15, it rained $\frac{1}{2}$ in. in the morning and $\frac{3}{8}$ in. in the afternoon. How much did it rain altogether?

68. *Nursing.* Janine took $\frac{1}{5}$ gram (g) of ibuprofen before lunch and $\frac{1}{2}$ g after lunch. How much did she take altogether?

69. A park naturalist hikes $\frac{3}{5}$ mi to a lookout, another $\frac{3}{10}$ mi to an osprey's nest, and finally, $\frac{3}{4}$ mi to a campsite. How far does the naturalist hike?

70. A triathlete runs $\frac{7}{8}$ mi, canoes $\frac{1}{3}$ mi, and swims $\frac{1}{6}$ mi. How many miles does the triathlete cover?

71. A tile $\frac{5}{8}$ in. thick is cemented to subflooring that is $\frac{7}{8}$ in. thick. The cement is $\frac{3}{32}$ in. thick. How thick is the result?

72. A baker used $\frac{1}{2}$ lb of flour for rolls, $\frac{1}{4}$ lb for donuts, and $\frac{1}{3}$ lb for cookies. How much flour was used?

73. *Masonry.* A cubic meter of concrete mix contains 420 kg of cement, 150 kg of stone, and 120 kg of sand. What is the total weight of the cubic meter of concrete mix? What fractional part is cement? stone? sand? Add these amounts. What is the result?

74. *Entertaining.* A recipe for cherry punch calls for $\frac{1}{5}$ L of ginger ale and $\frac{3}{5}$ L of black cherry soda. How much liquid is needed? If the recipe is doubled, how much liquid is needed? If the recipe is halved, how much liquid is needed?

75. ^{D}W Explain why $\frac{3}{2000}$ is greater than $\frac{3}{2002}$. Are common denominators required for an explanation? Why or why not?

76. ^{D}W To add numbers with different denominators, Chris is consistently using the product of the denominators as a common denominator. Is this correct? Why or why not?

SKILL MAINTENANCE

Subtract. [2.3a]

77. $-7 - 6$

78. $-5 - (-9)$

79. $9 - 17$

80. $-8 - 23$

Evaluate. [2.6a]

81. $\dfrac{x - y}{3}$, for $x = 7$ and $y = -3$

82. $3(x + y)$ and $3x + 3y$, for $x = 5$ and $y = 9$

Holiday Expenditures. The following chart shows average expenditures per person of consumers during the Christmas holidays of 1999 and 2000. Use these data for Exercises 83–88. [1.8a]

HOLIDAY EXPENDITURES	1999	2000
Gifts	$1088	$1161
Entertainment	188	197
Travel	151	154
Decorations / cards	77	88
Other holiday expenses	54	84
Total	?	?

Source: 2000 American Express Retail Index

83. How much more was spent on gifts in 2000 than in 1999?

84. How much more was spent on decorations and cards in 2000 than in 1999?

85. How much more was spent on travel in 2000 than in 1999?

86. How much more was spent on entertainment in 2000 than in 1999?

87. What was the total expenditure in 1999?

88. What was the total expenditure in 2000?

SYNTHESIS

89. $\mathbf{D_W}$ Suppose that a classmate believes, incorrectly, that $\frac{2}{5} + \frac{4}{5} = \frac{6}{10}$. How could you convince the classmate that he or she is mistaken?

90. $\mathbf{D_W}$ Explain how pictures could be used to convince someone that $\frac{5}{7}$ is larger than $\frac{13}{21}$.

Add and, if possible, simplify.

91. $\dfrac{3}{10}t + \dfrac{2}{7} + \dfrac{2}{15}t + \dfrac{3}{5}$

92. $\dfrac{2}{9} + \dfrac{4}{21}x + \dfrac{4}{15} + \dfrac{3}{14}x$

93. $5t^2 + \dfrac{6}{a}t + 2t^2 + \dfrac{3}{a}t$

Use $<$, $>$, or $=$ for $\square$ to form a true sentence.

94. ⊞ $\dfrac{10}{97} + \dfrac{67}{137} \;\square\; \dfrac{8123}{13,289}$

95. ⊞ $\dfrac{12}{169} + \dfrac{53}{103} \;\square\; \dfrac{10,192}{17,407}$

96. ⊞ $\dfrac{37}{157} + \dfrac{20}{107} \;\square\; \dfrac{6942}{16,799}$

97. A guitarist's band is booked for Friday and Saturday nights at a local club. The guitarist's group is a trio on Friday and expands to a quintet on Saturday. Thus the guitarist is paid one-third of one-half the weekend's pay for Friday and one-fifth of one-half the weekend's pay for Saturday. What fractional part of the total pay did the guitarist receive for the weekend's work? If the band was paid $1200, how much did the guitarist receive?

98. ⊞ In the sum below, a and b are digits (so $1b$ is a two-digit number and $35a$ is a three-digit number). Find a and b. *Hint*: $a < 4$ and $b > 6$.

$$\frac{a}{17} + \frac{1b}{23} = \frac{35a}{391}$$

99. ⊞ Consider only the numbers 3, 4, 5, and 6. Assume each can be placed in only one blank in the following.

$$\square + \frac{\square}{\square} \cdot \square = ?$$

What placement of the numbers in the blanks yields the largest number?

100. ⊞ Consider only the numbers 2, 3, 4, and 5. Assume each is placed in a blank in the following.

$$\frac{\square}{\square} + \frac{\square}{\square} = ?$$

What placement of the numbers in the blanks yields the largest sum?

101. ⊞ Use a standard calculator. Arrange the following in order from smallest to largest.

$$\frac{3}{4}, \frac{17}{21}, \frac{13}{15}, \frac{7}{9}, \frac{15}{17}, \frac{13}{12}, \frac{19}{22}$$

Objectives

a   Subtract using fraction notation.

b   Solve equations of the type $x + a = b$ and $a + x = b$, where a and b may be fractions.

c   Solve applied problems involving subtraction with fraction notation.

Subtract and simplify.

1. $\dfrac{7}{8} - \dfrac{3}{8}$

2. $\dfrac{5}{9a} - \dfrac{1}{9a}$

3. $\dfrac{7}{10} - \dfrac{13}{10}$

4. $-\dfrac{2}{x} - \dfrac{4}{x}$

Answers on page A-12

a   **Subtraction**

LIKE DENOMINATORS

We can consider the difference $\frac{4}{8} - \frac{3}{8}$ as we did before, as either "take away" or "how much more." Let's consider "take away."

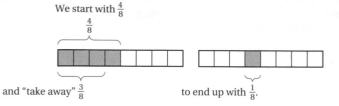

We start with $\frac{4}{8}$

and "take away" $\frac{3}{8}$ to end up with $\frac{1}{8}$.

We start with 4 eighths and take away 3 eighths:

$$4 \text{ eighths} - 3 \text{ eighths} = 1 \text{ eighth},$$

or $\quad 4 \cdot \dfrac{1}{8} - 3 \cdot \dfrac{1}{8} = \dfrac{1}{8}, \quad$ or $\quad \dfrac{4}{8} - \dfrac{3}{8} = \dfrac{1}{8}.$

> To subtract when denominators are the same,
>
> a) subtract the numerators,
>
> b) keep the denominator, and
>
> $$\dfrac{7}{10} - \dfrac{4}{10} = \dfrac{7 - 4}{10} = \dfrac{3}{10}$$
>
> c) simplify, if possible.

EXAMPLES   Subtract and, if possible, simplify.

1. $\dfrac{8}{13} - \dfrac{3}{13} = \dfrac{8 - 3}{13} = \dfrac{5}{13}$

2. $\dfrac{3}{35} - \dfrac{13}{35} = \dfrac{3 - 13}{35} = \dfrac{-10}{35} = \dfrac{5}{5} \cdot \dfrac{-2}{7} = \dfrac{-2}{7},$ or $-\dfrac{2}{7}$ Removing a factor equal to 1: $\frac{5}{5} = 1$

3. $\dfrac{13}{2a} - \dfrac{5}{2a} = \dfrac{13 - 5}{2a} = \dfrac{8}{2a} = \dfrac{2}{2} \cdot \dfrac{4}{a} = \dfrac{4}{a}$ Removing a factor equal to 1: $\frac{2}{2} = 1$

4. $-\dfrac{7}{t} - \dfrac{2}{t} = \dfrac{-7 - 2}{t} = \dfrac{-9}{t},$ or $-\dfrac{9}{t}$

Do Exercises 1–4.

DIFFERENT DENOMINATORS

> To subtract when denominators are different:
>
> a) Find the least common multiple of the denominators. That number is the least common denominator, LCD.
>
> b) Multiply by 1, using an appropriate notation, n/n, to express each fraction in an equivalent form that contains the LCD.
>
> c) Subtract and, if possible, simplify.

EXAMPLE 5 Subtract: $\dfrac{2}{5} - \dfrac{3}{8}$.

a) The LCM of 5 and 8 is 40, so the LCD is 40.

b) We need to find numbers equivalent to $\frac{2}{5}$ and $\frac{3}{8}$ with denominators of 40:

$$\dfrac{2}{5} - \dfrac{3}{8} = \dfrac{2}{5} \cdot \dfrac{8}{8} - \dfrac{3}{8} \cdot \dfrac{5}{5} \longleftarrow$$

Think: $8 \times ? = 40$. The answer is 5, so we multiply by 1, using $\frac{5}{5}$.

Think: $5 \times ? = 40$. The answer is 8, so we multiply by 1, using $\frac{8}{8}$.

c) We subtract: $\dfrac{16}{40} - \dfrac{15}{40} = \dfrac{16 - 15}{40} = \dfrac{1}{40}$.

d) Since $\frac{1}{40}$ cannot be simplified, we are finished. The answer is $\frac{1}{40}$.

Do Exercise 5.

EXAMPLE 6 Subtract: $\dfrac{7}{12} - \dfrac{5}{6}$.

Since 6 is a factor of 12, the LCM of 6 and 12 is 12. The LCD is 12.

$$\dfrac{7}{12} - \dfrac{5}{6} = \dfrac{7}{12} - \dfrac{5}{6} \cdot \dfrac{2}{2} \longleftarrow$$

Think: $6 \times ? = 12$. The answer is 2, so we multiply by 1, using $\frac{2}{2}$.

$$= \dfrac{7}{12} - \dfrac{10}{12}$$

$$= \dfrac{7 - 10}{12} = \dfrac{-3}{12} \qquad \text{If we prefer, we can add the opposite: } 7 + (-10).$$

$$= \dfrac{3}{3} \cdot \dfrac{-1}{4} = \dfrac{-1}{4}, \text{ or } -\dfrac{1}{4} \qquad \text{Simplifying by removing a factor equal to 1: } \frac{3}{3} = 1$$

EXAMPLE 7 Subtract: $\dfrac{17}{24} - \dfrac{4}{15}$.

We need to find the LCM of 24 and 15.

$$\left. \begin{array}{l} 24 = 2 \cdot 2 \cdot 2 \cdot 3, \\ 15 = 3 \cdot 5 \end{array} \right\} \quad \text{The LCM is } 2 \cdot 2 \cdot 2 \cdot 3 \cdot 5, \text{ or } 120.$$

$$\dfrac{17}{24} - \dfrac{4}{15} = \dfrac{17}{24} \cdot \dfrac{5}{5} - \dfrac{4}{15} \cdot \dfrac{8}{8}$$

Multiplying by 1 to obtain the LCD. To form 1, use the factors of the LCM that each denominator lacks. Note that $2 \cdot 2 \cdot 2 = 8$.

$$= \dfrac{85}{120} - \dfrac{32}{120} = \dfrac{85 - 32}{120} = \dfrac{53}{120}.$$

Do Exercises 6–9.

EXAMPLE 8 Simplify by combining like terms: $\dfrac{7}{8}x - \dfrac{3}{4}x$.

$$\dfrac{7}{8}x - \dfrac{3}{4}x = \left(\dfrac{7}{8} - \dfrac{3}{4} \right)x \qquad \text{Try to do this step mentally.}$$

$$= \left(\dfrac{7}{8} - \dfrac{6}{8} \right)x = \dfrac{1}{8}x \qquad \text{Multiplying } \dfrac{3}{4} \text{ by } \dfrac{2}{2} \text{ and subtracting}$$

Do Exercise 10.

5. Subtract: $\dfrac{3}{4} - \dfrac{2}{3}$.

Subtract.

6. $\dfrac{5}{6} - \dfrac{2}{3}$

7. $\dfrac{2}{5} - \dfrac{7}{10}$

8. $\dfrac{2}{3} - \dfrac{5}{6}$

9. $\dfrac{11}{28} - \dfrac{5}{16}$

10. Simplify: $\dfrac{9}{10}x - \dfrac{3}{5}x$.

Answers on page A-12

Solve.

11. $x - \dfrac{2}{5} = \dfrac{1}{5}$

12. $x + \dfrac{2}{3} = \dfrac{5}{6}$

13. $\dfrac{3}{5} + t = -\dfrac{7}{8}$

Answers on page A-12

Study Tips

CHAPTER 4: Fraction Notation:
Addition and Subtraction

b Solving Equations

In Section 2.8, we introduced the addition principle as one way to form equivalent equations. We can use that principle here to solve equations containing fractions.

EXAMPLE 9 Solve: $x - \dfrac{1}{3} = -\dfrac{2}{7}$.

$$x - \frac{1}{3} = -\frac{2}{7}$$

$$x - \frac{1}{3} + \frac{1}{3} = -\frac{2}{7} + \frac{1}{3}$$ Using the addition principle: adding $\frac{1}{3}$ to both sides

$$x + 0 = -\frac{2}{7} + \frac{1}{3}$$ Adding $\frac{1}{3}$ "undid" the subtraction of $\frac{1}{3}$ in the previous step.

$$x = -\frac{2}{7} \cdot \frac{3}{3} + \frac{1}{3} \cdot \frac{7}{7}$$ Multiplying by 1 to obtain the LCD, 21

$$x = -\frac{6}{21} + \frac{7}{21} = \frac{1}{21}$$ The solution appears to be $\frac{1}{21}$.

CHECK:

$$\frac{x - \dfrac{1}{3} = -\dfrac{2}{7}}{\begin{array}{c|c} \dfrac{1}{21} - \dfrac{1}{3} \;\overset{?}{\;} & -\dfrac{2}{7} \\[2mm] \dfrac{1}{21} - \dfrac{1}{3} \cdot \dfrac{7}{7} & \\[2mm] \dfrac{1}{21} - \dfrac{7}{21} & \\[2mm] \dfrac{-6}{21} & \\[2mm] -\dfrac{2}{7} \cdot \dfrac{3}{3} & -\dfrac{2}{7} \quad \text{TRUE} \end{array}}$$

Our answer checks. The solution is $\frac{1}{21}$.

Recall that since subtraction can be regarded as adding the opposite of the number being subtracted, the addition principle allows us to subtract the same number on both sides of an equation.

EXAMPLE 10 Solve: $x + \dfrac{1}{4} = \dfrac{3}{5}$.

$$x + \frac{1}{4} - \frac{1}{4} = \frac{3}{5} - \frac{1}{4}$$ Using the addition principle: adding $-\frac{1}{4}$ to, or subtracting $\frac{1}{4}$ from, both sides

$$x + 0 = \frac{3}{5} \cdot \frac{4}{4} - \frac{1}{4} \cdot \frac{5}{5}$$ The LCD is 20. We multiply by 1 to get the LCD.

$$x = \frac{12}{20} - \frac{5}{20} = \frac{7}{20}$$

The solution is $\frac{7}{20}$. We leave the check to the student.

Do Exercises 11–13.

C ‖ Applications and Problem Solving

EXAMPLE 11 *Jewelry Making.* Coldwater Creek offers the pendant necklace illustrated at right. The sterling silver capping at the top measures $\frac{11}{32}$ in. and the total length of the pendant is $\frac{7}{8}$ in. Find the length, or diameter, of the pearl ball on the pendant.

1. **Familiarize.** Using a sketch—or a photo, if one is available—we write in the given measurements. We let d represent the pearl's diameter, in inches.

2. **Translate.** We see that this is a "missing addend" situation. We can translate to an equation.

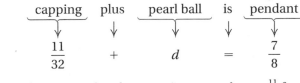

$$\frac{11}{32} \quad + \quad d \quad = \quad \frac{7}{8}$$

Source: ©Coldwater Creek Inc. www.coldwatercreek.com

3. **Solve.** To solve the equation, we subtract $\frac{11}{32}$ from both sides:

$$\frac{11}{32} + d = \frac{7}{8}$$

$$\frac{11}{32} + d - \frac{11}{32} = \frac{7}{8} - \frac{11}{32} \qquad \text{Subtracting } \frac{11}{32} \text{ from both sides}$$

$$d + 0 = \frac{7}{8} \cdot \frac{4}{4} - \frac{11}{32} \qquad \text{The LCD is 32. We multiply by 1 to obtain the LCD.}$$

$$d = \frac{28}{32} - \frac{11}{32}$$

$$= \frac{17}{32}.$$

4. **Check.** To check, we return to the original problem and add:

$$\frac{11}{32} + \frac{17}{32} = \frac{28}{32} = \frac{7}{8} \cdot \frac{4}{4} = \frac{7}{8}.$$

Since the overall length of the pendant is $\frac{7}{8}$", our answer checks.

5. **State.** The diameter of the pearl is $\frac{17}{32}$ in.

Do Exercise 14.

14. Kelly has run for $\frac{2}{3}$ mi and will stop when she has run for $\frac{7}{8}$ mi. How much farther does she have to go?

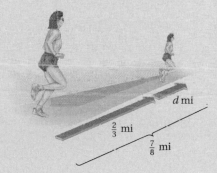

Answer on page A-12

4.3 EXERCISE SET

For Extra Help

Digital Video Tutor CD 3 Videotape 4 | InterAct Math | Math Tutor Center | MathXL | MyMathLab

a   Subtract and, if possible, simplify.

1. $\dfrac{5}{6} - \dfrac{1}{6}$

2. $\dfrac{7}{5} - \dfrac{2}{5}$

3. $\dfrac{9}{16} - \dfrac{13}{16}$

4. $\dfrac{5}{12} - \dfrac{7}{12}$

5. $\dfrac{8}{a} - \dfrac{6}{a}$

6. $\dfrac{4}{t} - \dfrac{9}{t}$

7. $-\dfrac{2}{9} - \dfrac{5}{9}$

8. $-\dfrac{3}{11} - \dfrac{4}{11}$

9. $-\dfrac{3}{8} - \dfrac{1}{8}$

10. $-\dfrac{3}{10} - \dfrac{1}{10}$

11. $\dfrac{10}{3t} - \dfrac{4}{3t}$

12. $\dfrac{9}{2a} - \dfrac{5}{2a}$

13. $\dfrac{3}{5a} - \dfrac{7}{5a}$

14. $\dfrac{2}{7t} - \dfrac{10}{7t}$

15. $\dfrac{7}{8} - \dfrac{1}{16}$

16. $\dfrac{4}{3} - \dfrac{5}{6}$

17. $\dfrac{7}{15} - \dfrac{4}{5}$

18. $\dfrac{3}{4} - \dfrac{3}{28}$

19. $\dfrac{3}{4} - \dfrac{1}{20}$

20. $\dfrac{3}{4} - \dfrac{4}{16}$

21. $\dfrac{2}{15} - \dfrac{5}{12}$

22. $\dfrac{11}{16} - \dfrac{9}{10}$

23. $\dfrac{7}{10} - \dfrac{23}{100}$

24. $\dfrac{9}{10} - \dfrac{3}{100}$

25. $\dfrac{7}{15} - \dfrac{3}{25}$

26. $\dfrac{18}{25} - \dfrac{4}{35}$

27. $\dfrac{69}{100} - \dfrac{9}{10}$

28. $\dfrac{42}{100} - \dfrac{11}{20}$

29. $\dfrac{1}{8} - \dfrac{2}{3}$

30. $\dfrac{3}{4} - \dfrac{1}{2}$

31. $-\dfrac{3}{10} - \dfrac{7}{25}$

32. $-\dfrac{5}{18} - \dfrac{2}{27}$

33. $\dfrac{2}{3} - \dfrac{4}{5}$

34. $\dfrac{1}{2} - \dfrac{3}{5}$

35. $\dfrac{-5}{18} - \dfrac{7}{24}$

36. $\dfrac{-7}{25} - \dfrac{2}{15}$

37. $\dfrac{13}{90} - \dfrac{17}{120}$

38. $\dfrac{8}{25} - \dfrac{29}{150}$

39. $\dfrac{2}{3}x - \dfrac{4}{9}x$

40. $\dfrac{7}{4}x - \dfrac{5}{12}x$

41. $\dfrac{2}{5}a - \dfrac{3}{4}a$

42. $\dfrac{4}{7}a - \dfrac{1}{3}a$

b Solve.

43. $x - \dfrac{4}{9} = \dfrac{3}{9}$

44. $x - \dfrac{3}{11} = \dfrac{7}{11}$

45. $a + \dfrac{2}{11} = \dfrac{6}{11}$

46. $a + \dfrac{4}{15} = \dfrac{13}{15}$

47. $x + \dfrac{1}{3} = \dfrac{7}{9}$

48. $x + \dfrac{1}{2} = \dfrac{7}{8}$

49. $a - \dfrac{3}{8} = \dfrac{3}{4}$

50. $x - \dfrac{3}{10} = \dfrac{2}{5}$

51. $\dfrac{2}{3} + x = \dfrac{4}{5}$

52. $\dfrac{4}{5} + x = \dfrac{6}{7}$

53. $\dfrac{3}{8} + a = \dfrac{1}{12}$

54. $\dfrac{5}{6} + a = \dfrac{2}{9}$

55. $n - \dfrac{3}{10} = -\dfrac{1}{6}$

56. $n - \dfrac{3}{4} = -\dfrac{5}{12}$

57. $x + \dfrac{3}{4} = -\dfrac{1}{2}$

58. $x + \dfrac{5}{6} = -\dfrac{11}{12}$

c Solve.

59. *Fitness.*   As part of a fitness program, Deb swims $\frac{1}{2}$ mi every day. She has already swum $\frac{1}{5}$ mi today. How much farther should Deb swim?

60. *Exercise.*   As part of an exercise program, Hugo walks $\frac{7}{8}$ mi each day. He has already walked $\frac{1}{3}$ mi today. How much farther should Hugo walk?

61. *Tire Tread.* A new long-life tire has a tread depth of $\frac{3}{8}$ in. instead of a more typical $\frac{11}{32}$ in. How much deeper is the new tread depth?
Source: *Popular Science*

$\frac{3}{8}$ in.

$\frac{11}{32}$ in.

62. From a $\frac{4}{5}$-lb wheel of cheese, a $\frac{1}{4}$-lb piece was served. How much cheese remained on the wheel?

63. *Woodworking.* Celeste is replacing a $\frac{3}{4}$-in. thick shelf in her bookcase. If her replacement board is $\frac{15}{16}$ in. thick, how much should it be planed down before the repair can be completed?

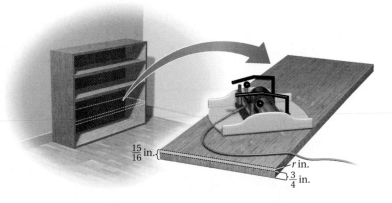

$\frac{15}{16}$ in.

r in.

$\frac{3}{4}$ in.

64. *Culinary Arts.* A $\frac{4}{5}$-cup batch of Vera's Vinaigrette consists of olive oil and balsamic vinegar. If the recipe calls for $\frac{2}{3}$ cup of oil, how much vinegar is required?

65. A server has a bottle containing $\frac{11}{12}$ cup of garlic-infused olive oil. He serves $\frac{1}{4}$ cup on a plate to a large party for bread dipping. How much remains in the bottle?

66. *Furniture Cleaner.* A $\frac{2}{3}$-cup mixture of lemon juice and olive oil makes an excellent cleaner for wood furniture. If the mixture contains $\frac{1}{4}$ cup of lemon juice, how much olive oil is in the cleaner?

67. Mandy just finished listening to a $\frac{3}{4}$-hr tape of "The Greatest Country-Western Vocalists." If $\frac{1}{3}$ hr was devoted to male vocalists, how much time was reserved for female vocalists?

68. Jorge's $\frac{3}{4}$-hr drive to a job was a mixture of city and country driving. If $\frac{2}{5}$ hr was city driving, how much time was spent on country driving?

69. Blake used $\frac{1}{4}$ cup of maple syrup in preparing the batter for a batch of maple oatbran muffins. Sheila pointed out that the recipe actually calls for $\frac{2}{3}$ cup of syrup. How much more syrup should Blake add to the batter?

70. Amber added $\frac{1}{3}$ quart of two-cycle oil to a fuel mixture for her lawn mower. She then noticed that the owner's manual indicates $\frac{1}{2}$ quart should have been added. How much more two-cycle oil should Amber add to the mixture?

71. **D$_W$** To solve $x - \frac{1}{2} = -\frac{7}{8}$, Steffen adds $\frac{7}{8}$ to both sides of the equation. Is this correct? Has he formed an equivalent equation? Explain.

72. **D$_W$** Florence incorrectly writes $\frac{7}{12} - \frac{7}{8} = \frac{7}{4}$. How could you convince her that this subtraction is incorrect?

SKILL MAINTENANCE

Divide and, if possible, simplify. [3.7b]

73. $\dfrac{3}{7} \div \dfrac{9}{4}$

74. $\dfrac{9}{10} \div \dfrac{3}{5}$

75. $7 \div \dfrac{1}{3}$

76. $\dfrac{1}{4} \div 8$

Solve. [3.6h], [2.8d]

77. A small box of Kellogg's cornflakes weighs $\frac{3}{4}$ lb. How much do 8 small boxes of cornflakes weigh?

78. A batch of fudge requires $\frac{3}{4}$ cup of sugar. How much sugar is needed to make 12 batches?

79. $3x - 8 = 25$

80. $5x + 9 = 24$

SYNTHESIS

81. **D$_W$** If a negative fraction is subtracted from another negative fraction, is the result always negative? Why or why not?

82. **D$_W$** Without performing the actual computation, explain how you can tell that $\frac{3}{7} - \frac{5}{9}$ is negative.

Simplify.

83. $\dfrac{7}{8} - \dfrac{3}{4} - \dfrac{1}{16}$

84. $\dfrac{9}{10} - \dfrac{1}{2} - \dfrac{2}{15}$

85. $\dfrac{2}{5} - \dfrac{1}{6}(-3)^2$

86. $\dfrac{7}{8} - \dfrac{1}{10}\left(-\dfrac{5}{6}\right)^2$

87. $-4 \cdot \dfrac{3}{7} - \dfrac{1}{7} \cdot \dfrac{4}{5}$

88. $\left(\dfrac{5}{6}\right)^2 + \left(\dfrac{3}{4}\right)^2$

89. $\left(-\dfrac{2}{5}\right)^3 - \left(-\dfrac{3}{10}\right)^3$

90. $\dfrac{3}{17} - \dfrac{2}{19} - \left(\dfrac{3}{17} - \dfrac{2}{19}\right)$

91. Herm's stamp collection was left to his three children. Jake received $\frac{1}{4}$ of the collection, Pam received $\frac{1}{16}$ of the collection, and the rest went to Belinda. What fractional piece of the collection did Belinda receive?

92. A new Chevrolet Prizm costs $14,400. Pam will pay $\frac{1}{2}$ of the cost, Sam will pay $\frac{1}{4}$ of the cost, Jan will pay $\frac{1}{6}$ of the cost, and Nan will pay the rest.

   a) How much will Nan pay?
   b) What fractional part will Nan pay?

93. The circle graph below shows how long shoppers stay when visiting a mall. What portion of shoppers stay for 0–2 hr?

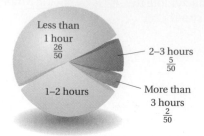

Less than 1 hour $\frac{26}{50}$

2–3 hours $\frac{5}{50}$

1–2 hours

More than 3 hours $\frac{2}{50}$

94. As part of a rehabilitation program, an athlete must swim and then walk a total of $\frac{9}{10}$ km each day. If one lap in the swimming pool is $\frac{3}{80}$ km, how far must the athlete walk after swimming 10 laps?

95. A VCR can record up to 6 hr on one tape. It can also fill that same tape in either 4 hr or 2 hr when running at faster speeds. A tape is placed in the machine, which records for $\frac{1}{2}$ hr at the 4-hr speed and $\frac{3}{4}$ hr at the 2-hr speed. How much time is left on the tape to record at the 6-hr speed?

96. Mazzi's meat slicer cut 8 slices of turkey and 3 slices of Vermont cheddar. If each turkey slice was $\frac{1}{16}$-in. thick and each cheddar slice was $\frac{5}{32}$-in. thick, how tall was the pile of cold cuts?

97. Mark Romano owns $\frac{7}{12}$ of Romano-Chrenka Chevrolet and Lisa Romano owns $\frac{1}{6}$. If Paul and Ella Chrenka own the remaining share of the dealership equally, what fractional piece does Paul own?

98. The Fullerton estate was left to four children. One received $\frac{1}{4}$ of the estate, one received $\frac{3}{8}$, and the twins split the rest. What fractional piece did each twin receive?

Solve.

99. $x + \dfrac{16}{323} = \dfrac{10}{187}$

100. $x + \dfrac{7}{253} = \dfrac{12}{299}$

101. Determine what whole number a must be in order for the following to be true:

$$\frac{10 + a}{23} = \frac{330}{391} - \frac{a}{17}$$

102. A mountain climber, beginning at sea level, climbs $\frac{3}{5}$ km, descends $\frac{1}{4}$ km, climbs $\frac{1}{3}$ km, and then descends $\frac{1}{7}$ km. At what elevation does the climber finish?

103. *Microsoft Interview.* The following is a question taken from an employment interview with Microsoft. Try to answer it. "Given a gold bar that can be cut exactly twice and a contractor who must be paid one-seventh of a gold bar every day for seven days, how should the bar be cut?"
Source: *Fortune Magazine,* January 22, 2001

CHAPTER 4: Fraction Notation:
Addition and Subtraction

4.4 SOLVING EQUATIONS: USING THE PRINCIPLES TOGETHER

Objectives

a Solve equations that involve fractions and require use of both the addition principle and the multiplication principle.

b Solve equations by using the multiplication principle to clear fractions.

In Section 3.8 we used the multiplication principle to solve equations like

$$\frac{2}{3}x = \frac{5}{6} \quad \text{and} \quad 7 = \frac{5}{4}t.$$

In Section 4.3 we used the addition principle to solve equations like

$$\frac{4}{5} + x = \frac{1}{2} \quad \text{and} \quad \frac{7}{3} = t - \frac{2}{9}.$$

We are now ready to solve equations in which both principles are required. Equations of this sort were first encountered in Section 2.8, but at that time no fractions appeared.

a   Using the Principles Together

Recall that equations are most commonly solved by producing a sequence of equivalent equations. Thus, the equations $5x + 2 = 47$ and $x = 9$ are equivalent:

$$5x + 2 = 47$$
$$5x + 2 - 2 = 47 - 2 \qquad \text{Using the addition principle}$$
$$5x = 45$$
$$\frac{1}{5} \cdot 5x = \frac{1}{5} \cdot 45 \qquad \text{Using the multiplication principle}$$
$$x = 9 \qquad \text{It appears that the solution is 9.}$$

As a check, note that $5 \cdot 9 + 2 = 45 + 2 = 47$, as desired. The solution is 9.

EXAMPLE 1   Solve: $\dfrac{2}{3}x - \dfrac{1}{9} = \dfrac{4}{9}$.

We first isolate $\frac{2}{3}x$ by adding $\frac{1}{9}$ to both sides:

$$\frac{2}{3}x - \frac{1}{9} = \frac{4}{9}$$
$$\frac{2}{3}x - \frac{1}{9} + \frac{1}{9} = \frac{4}{9} + \frac{1}{9} \qquad \text{Using the addition principle}$$
$$\frac{2}{3}x + 0 = \frac{5}{9} \qquad \text{Try to perform this step mentally.}$$
$$\frac{2}{3}x = \frac{5}{9}$$

Next, we isolate x by multiplying both sides by $\frac{3}{2}$:

$$\frac{2}{3}x = \frac{5}{9} \qquad \text{Note that the reciprocal of } \tfrac{2}{3} \text{ is } \tfrac{3}{2}.$$
$$\frac{3}{2} \cdot \frac{2}{3}x = \frac{3}{2} \cdot \frac{5}{9} \qquad \text{Using the multiplication principle}$$
$$1x = \frac{15}{18}, \text{ or } \frac{5}{6} \qquad \text{Simplifying; the solution appears to be } \tfrac{5}{6}.$$

Study Tips

PLUG IT IN

Every solution of an equation can be checked by substituting that value in the original equation. Take advantage of the opportunity to determine (without consulting the back of the text) if your answers are correct on quizzes and tests.

1. Solve: $\frac{3}{5}t - \frac{8}{15} = \frac{2}{15}$.

2. Solve: $3 + \frac{14}{5}t = -\frac{21}{5}$.

CHECK:

$$\frac{2}{3}x - \frac{1}{9} = \frac{4}{9}$$

$$\frac{2}{3} \cdot \frac{5}{6} - \frac{1}{9} \overset{?}{|} \frac{4}{9}$$

$$\frac{2 \cdot 5}{3 \cdot 2 \cdot 3} - \frac{1}{9} \qquad \text{Removing a factor equal to 1: } \frac{2}{2} = 1$$

$$\frac{4}{9} \left| \frac{4}{9} \right. \quad \textbf{TRUE}$$

The solution is $\frac{5}{6}$.

Do Exercise 1.

■ **EXAMPLE 2** Solve: $5 + \frac{9}{2}t = -\frac{7}{2}$.

We first isolate $\frac{9}{2}t$ by subtracting 5 from both sides:

$$5 + \frac{9}{2}t = -\frac{7}{2}$$

$$5 + \frac{9}{2}t - 5 = -\frac{7}{2} - 5 \qquad \text{Subtracting 5 from both sides}$$

$$\frac{9}{2}t = -\frac{7}{2} - \frac{10}{2} \qquad \text{Writing 5 as } \frac{10}{2} \text{ to use the LCD}$$

$$\frac{9}{2}t = -\frac{17}{2} \qquad \text{Note that the reciprocal of } \frac{9}{2} \text{ is } \frac{2}{9}.$$

$$\frac{2}{9} \cdot \frac{9}{2}t = \frac{2}{9}\left(-\frac{17}{2}\right) \qquad \text{Multiplying both sides by } \frac{2}{9}$$

$$1t = -\frac{2 \cdot 17}{9 \cdot 2} \qquad \text{Removing a factor equal to 1: } \frac{2}{2} = 1$$

$$t = -\frac{17}{9}$$

CHECK:

$$5 + \frac{9}{2}t = -\frac{7}{2}$$

$$5 + \frac{\cancel{9}}{2}\left(-\frac{17}{\cancel{9}}\right) \overset{?}{|} -\frac{7}{2} \qquad \text{Removing a factor equal to 1: } \frac{9}{9} = 1$$

$$5 + \left(-\frac{17}{2}\right)$$

$$\frac{10}{2} + \left(\frac{-17}{2}\right)$$

$$\frac{10 - 17}{2}$$

$$\frac{-7}{2} \left| -\frac{7}{2} \right. \quad \textbf{TRUE}$$

The solution is $-\frac{17}{9}$.

Do Exercise 2.

Sometimes the variable appears on the right side of the equation. The strategy for solving the equation remains the same.

EXAMPLE 3 Solve: $20 = 6 - \dfrac{2}{3}x$.

3. Solve: $9 - \dfrac{3}{4}x = 21$.

Our plan is to first use the addition principle to isolate $-\frac{2}{3}x$ and then to use the multiplication principle to isolate x.

$$20 = 6 - \frac{2}{3}x$$

$$20 - 6 = 6 - \frac{2}{3}x - 6 \qquad \text{Subtracting 6 (or adding } -6\text{) on both sides}$$

$$14 = -\frac{2}{3}x$$

$$\left(-\frac{3}{2}\right)14 = \left(-\frac{3}{2}\right)\left(-\frac{2}{3}x\right) \qquad \text{Multiplying both sides by } -\frac{3}{2}$$

$$-\frac{3 \cdot 14}{2} = 1x$$

$$-\frac{3 \cdot 7 \cdot \cancel{2}}{\cancel{2}} = 1x \qquad \text{Removing a factor equal to 1: } \frac{2}{2} = 1$$

$$-21 = x.$$

CHECK:

$$20 = 6 - \frac{2}{3}x$$

$$\overline{20 \overset{?}{\ } 6 - \frac{2}{3}(-21)}$$

$$6 + \frac{42}{3}$$

$$20 \ \Big| \ 6 + 14 \qquad \textbf{TRUE}$$

The solution is -21.

Do Exercise 3.

b Clearing Fractions

With some hesitancy, we now show an alternative approach for solving Examples 1–3. The advantage of this approach is that it minimizes calculations involving fractions. The disadvantage is that it requires an extra step and careful use of the distributive law. Key to this approach is using the multiplication principle in the *first* step to produce an equivalent equation that is "cleared of fractions."

To "clear fractions" in Example 1, we identify the LCD, 9, and use the multiplication principle. Because the LCD is a common multiple of the denominators, when that number is used to multiply the numerator of each fraction, the resulting fractions can then be simplified. An equivalent equation can then be written without using fractions. We demonstrate this approach on the top of the next page.

Answer on page A-12

4. Solve Example 3 by clearing fractions:

$$20 = 6 - \frac{2}{3}x.$$

5. Solve Margin Exercise 1 by clearing fractions:

$$\frac{3}{5}t - \frac{8}{15} = \frac{2}{15}.$$

$$\frac{2}{3}x - \frac{1}{9} = \frac{4}{9}$$

$$9\left(\frac{2}{3}x - \frac{1}{9}\right) = 9 \cdot \frac{4}{9} \qquad \text{Multiplying both sides by the LCD, 9}$$

$$\frac{9 \cdot 2}{3}x - 9 \cdot \frac{1}{9} = \frac{9 \cdot 4}{9} \qquad \text{Using the distributive law}$$

$$\left. \begin{array}{l} \dfrac{3 \cdot 3 \cdot 2}{3}x - \dfrac{9}{9} = \dfrac{9 \cdot 4}{9} \\[2ex] 6x - 1 = 4 \end{array} \right\} \quad \begin{array}{l} \text{Factoring and simplifying. The equation} \\ \text{is now cleared of fractions.} \end{array}$$

$$6x - 1 + 1 = 4 + 1 \qquad \text{Adding 1 to both sides}$$

$$6x = 5$$

$$\frac{6x}{6} = \frac{5}{6} \qquad \begin{array}{l} \text{Dividing both sides by 6 or multiplying} \\ \text{both sides by } \frac{1}{6} \end{array}$$

$$x = \frac{5}{6} \qquad \text{Simplifying}$$

Since $\frac{5}{6}$ was indeed the solution in Example 1, we have a check.

EXAMPLE 4 Solve Example 2 by clearing fractions:

$$5 + \frac{9}{2}t = -\frac{7}{2}.$$

The LCD is 2, so we begin by multiplying both sides of the equation by 2:

$$2\left(5 + \frac{9}{2}t\right) = 2\left(-\frac{7}{2}\right) \qquad \text{Using the multiplication principle}$$

$$2 \cdot 5 + \frac{2 \cdot 9}{2}t = -\frac{2 \cdot 7}{2} \qquad \text{Using the distributive law}$$

$$10 + 9t = -7 \qquad \begin{array}{l} \text{Simplifying and removing a factor} \\ \text{equal to 1: } \frac{2}{2} = 1. \text{ The equation is} \\ \text{now cleared of fractions.} \end{array}$$

$$10 + 9t - 10 = -7 - 10 \qquad \text{Subtracting 10 from both sides}$$

$$9t = -17 \qquad \text{Simplifying}$$

$$\frac{9t}{9} = -\frac{17}{9} \qquad \begin{array}{l} \text{Dividing both sides by 9 or multiplying} \\ \text{both sides by } \frac{1}{9} \end{array}$$

$$t = -\frac{17}{9} \qquad \text{Simplifying}$$

Since the solution in Example 2 is also $-\frac{17}{9}$, we have a check. The solution is $-\frac{17}{9}$.

Do Exercises 4 and 5.

Either of the methods discussed in this section can be used to solve equations that contain fractions, but for students planning to continue in algebra, it is important that *both* methods be thoroughly understood.

Answers on page A-12

a   Solve using the addition principle and/or the multiplication principle. Don't forget to check!

1. $6x - 3 = 15$ *3*

2. $7x - 6 = 22$

3. $3a + 9 = 24$ *5*

4. $19 = 2x - 7$

5. $4a + 9 = 37$

6. $2a - 9 = -7$

7. $31 = 3x - 5$

8. $5x + 7 = -8$

9. $\dfrac{3}{2}t - \dfrac{1}{4} = \dfrac{1}{2}$

10. $\dfrac{1}{4}t + \dfrac{1}{8} = \dfrac{1}{2}$

11. $\dfrac{2}{5}x + \dfrac{3}{10} = \dfrac{3}{5}$

12. $\dfrac{4}{3}x - \dfrac{2}{15} = \dfrac{2}{15}$

13. $5 - \dfrac{3}{4}x = 3$

14. $3 - \dfrac{2}{5}x = 6$

15. $-1 + \dfrac{2}{5}t = -\dfrac{4}{5}$

16. $-2 + \dfrac{1}{6}t = -\dfrac{7}{4}$

17. $12 = 8 + \dfrac{7}{2}t$

18. $7 = 5 + \dfrac{3}{2}t$

19. $-4 = \dfrac{2}{3}x - 7$

20. $-3 = \dfrac{2}{5}x - 4$

21. $7 = a + \dfrac{14}{5}$

22. $9 = a + \dfrac{47}{10}$

23. $\dfrac{2}{5}t - 1 = \dfrac{7}{5}$

24. $-\dfrac{53}{4} = \dfrac{3}{2}a + 2$

25. $\dfrac{39}{8} = \dfrac{11}{4} + \dfrac{1}{2}x$

26. $\dfrac{17}{2} = \dfrac{2}{7}t - \dfrac{3}{2}$

27. $\dfrac{13}{3}s + \dfrac{11}{2} = \dfrac{35}{4}$

28. $\dfrac{11}{5}t + \dfrac{36}{5} = \dfrac{7}{2}$

b Solve by using the multiplication principle to clear fractions.

29. $\frac{1}{2}x - \frac{1}{4} = \frac{1}{2}$

30. $\frac{1}{3}x - \frac{1}{6} = \frac{2}{3}$

31. $7 = \frac{4}{9}t + 5$

32. $5 = \frac{4}{7}t + 3$

33. $-3 = \frac{3}{4}t - \frac{1}{2}$

34. $-2 = \frac{4}{3}t - \frac{5}{6}$

35. $\frac{4}{3} - \frac{5}{6}x = \frac{3}{2}$

36. $\frac{3}{2} - \frac{5}{3}x = \frac{5}{6}$

37. $-\frac{3}{4} = -\frac{5}{6} - \frac{1}{2}x$

38. $-\frac{1}{4} = -\frac{2}{3} - \frac{1}{6}x$

39. $\frac{4}{3} - \frac{1}{5}t = \frac{3}{4}$

40. $\frac{2}{5} - \frac{3}{4}t = \frac{4}{3}$

41. $\mathbf{D_W}$ Describe a procedure that a classmate could use to solve the equation $\frac{a}{b}x + c = d$ for x.

42. $\mathbf{D_W}$ Nathan begins solving the equation $-\frac{2}{3}x + 7 = -9$ by adding 9 to both sides. Is this a wise thing to do? Why or why not?

<hr>

SKILL MAINTENANCE

Divide. [2.5a]

43. $39 \div (-3)$

44. $56 \div (-7)$

45. $(-72) \div (-4)$

46. $(-81) \div (-3)$

Solve. [2.3b]

47. Jeremy withdraws $200 from his bank's ATM (automated teller machine), makes a $90 deposit, and then withdraws another $40. How much has Jeremy's account balance changed?

48. Animal Instinct, a pet supply store, makes a profit of $850 on Friday, and $375 on Saturday, but suffers a loss of $45 on Sunday. Find the total profit or loss for the three days.

Divide and simplify. [3.7b]

49. $\frac{10}{7} \div 2m$

50. $45n \div \frac{9}{4}$

51. $^\mathbf{D}_\mathbf{W}$ Emma begins solving the equation $\frac{2}{3}x - \frac{1}{5} = \frac{4}{7}$ by multiplying both sides by $\frac{3}{2}$. Is this a wise thing to do? Why or why not?

52. $^\mathbf{D}_\mathbf{W}$ Andrew begins solving the equation $\frac{2}{3}x + 1 = \frac{5}{6}$ by multiplying both sides by 24. Is this a wise thing to do? Why or why not?

Solve.

53. ▦ $\dfrac{553}{2451}a - \dfrac{13}{57} = \dfrac{29}{43}$

54. ▦ $\dfrac{1081}{3599}x - \dfrac{17}{61} = \dfrac{19}{59}$

55. ▦ $\dfrac{71}{73} = \dfrac{19}{47} - \dfrac{53}{91}t$

56. ▦ $\dfrac{23}{79} - \dfrac{41}{67}x = \dfrac{37}{83}$

57. $-\dfrac{a}{5} + \dfrac{31}{4} = \dfrac{16}{3}$

58. $\dfrac{47}{5} - \dfrac{a}{4} = \dfrac{44}{7}$

59. $\dfrac{49}{8} + \dfrac{2x}{9} = 4$

60. The perimeter of the figure shown is 15 cm. Solve for x.

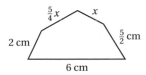

61. The perimeter of the figure is 21 cm. Solve for x.

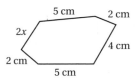

62. The perimeter of the figure is 6 ft. Solve for x.

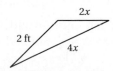

63. The perimeter of the figure is 15 cm. Solve for n.

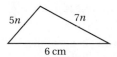

4.5 MIXED NUMERALS

Objectives

a Convert from mixed numerals to fraction notation.

b Convert from fraction notation to mixed numerals.

c Divide, writing a mixed numeral for the quotient.

1. $1 + \dfrac{2}{3} = \square$ ——— Convert to a mixed numeral.

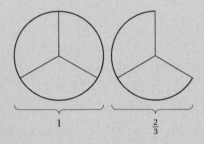

Convert to a mixed numeral.

2. $7 + \dfrac{1}{4}$ **3.** $15 + \dfrac{2}{9}$

Answers on page A-13

Study Tips

VISUALIZE

When studying for a quiz or test, don't feel that you need to redo every assigned problem. A more productive use of your time would be simply to reread the assigned problems, making certain that you can visualize the steps that lead to a solution. When you are unsure of how to solve a problem, redo that problem in its entirety, seeking outside help as needed.

a   What is a Mixed Numeral?

A symbol like $2\frac{3}{8}$ is called a **mixed numeral.**

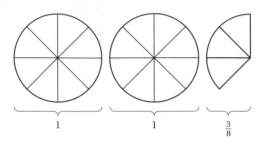

$$2\frac{3}{8} \quad \text{means} \quad 2 + \frac{3}{8}$$

This is a whole number.   This is a fraction less than 1.

The following figure illustrates one use of a mixed numeral in daily life. The bolt shown is $2\frac{3}{8}$ in. long. The length is given as a whole-number part, 2, and a fraction part, $\frac{3}{8}$. We can represent the measurement as $\frac{19}{8}$, but $2\frac{3}{8}$ makes the length easier to visualize and is thus more descriptive.

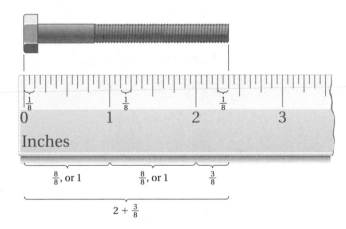

EXAMPLES   Convert to a mixed numeral.

1. $7 + \dfrac{2}{5} = 7\dfrac{2}{5}$ **2.** $4 + \dfrac{3}{10} = 4\dfrac{3}{10}$

Do Exercises 1–3.

The notation $2\frac{3}{4}$ has a plus sign left out. To aid in understanding, we sometimes write the missing plus sign: $2 + \frac{3}{4}$. Similarly, the notation $-5\frac{2}{3}$ has a minus sign left out since $-5\frac{2}{3} = -\left(5 + \frac{2}{3}\right) = -5 - \frac{2}{3}$.

Mixed numerals can be displayed easily on a number line, as shown here.

EXAMPLES Convert to fraction notation.

3. $2\frac{3}{4} = 2 + \frac{3}{4}$ Inserting the missing plus sign

$= \frac{2}{1} + \frac{3}{4}$ $2 = \frac{2}{1}$

$= \frac{2}{1} \cdot \frac{4}{4} + \frac{3}{4}$ Finding a common denominator

$= \frac{8}{4} + \frac{3}{4}$

$= \frac{11}{4}$ Adding

4. $4\frac{3}{10} = 4 + \frac{3}{10} = \frac{4}{1} + \frac{3}{10} = \frac{4}{1} \cdot \frac{10}{10} + \frac{3}{10} = \frac{40}{10} + \frac{3}{10} = \frac{43}{10}$

Do Exercises 4 and 5.

Using Example 4, we can develop a faster way to convert.

To convert from a mixed numeral like $4\frac{3}{10}$ to fraction notation:

(a) Multiply: $4 \cdot 10 = 40$.
(b) Add: $40 + 3 = 43$.
(c) Keep the denominator.

(b) ↗
(a) $4\frac{3}{10} = \frac{43}{10}$ ↖

EXAMPLES Convert to fraction notation.

5. $6\frac{2}{3} = \frac{20}{3}$ $6 \cdot 3 = 18$; $18 + 2 = 20$; keep the denominator.

6. $8\frac{2}{9} = \frac{74}{9}$ $9 \cdot 8 = 72$; $72 + 2 = 74$; keep the denominator.

7. $10\frac{7}{8} = \frac{87}{8}$ $8 \cdot 10 = 80$; $80 + 7 = 87$; keep the denominator.

Do Exercises 6–8.

To find the opposite of the number in Example 5, we can write either $-6\frac{2}{3}$ or $-\frac{20}{3}$. Thus, to convert a negative mixed numeral to fraction notation, we remove the negative sign for purposes of computation and then include it in the answer.

EXAMPLES Convert to fraction notation.

8. $-5\frac{1}{3} = -\left(5 + \frac{1}{3}\right) = -\frac{16}{3}$ $3 \cdot 5 = 15$; $15 + 1 = 16$; include the negative sign

9. $-7\frac{5}{6} = -\left(7 + \frac{5}{6}\right) = -\frac{47}{6}$ $6 \cdot 7 = 42$; $42 + 5 = 47$

Do Exercises 9 and 10.

Convert to fraction notation.

4. $4\frac{2}{5}$ 5. $6\frac{1}{10}$

Convert to fraction notation. Use the faster method.

6. $3\frac{2}{7}$

7. $9\frac{1}{8}$

8. $20\frac{2}{3}$

Convert to fraction notation.

9. $-6\frac{2}{5}$

10. $-7\frac{2}{9}$

Answers on page A-13

Convert to a mixed numeral.

11. $\dfrac{7}{3}$

12. $\dfrac{16}{15}$

Convert to a mixed numeral.

13. $\dfrac{110}{6}$

Convert to a mixed numeral.

14. $\dfrac{-12}{5}$

15. $-\dfrac{134}{12}$

16. Divide. Write a mixed numeral for the answer.

$$6\overline{)4\ 8\ 4\ 6}$$

17. Over the last 4 yr, Roland Thompson's raspberry patch has yielded 48, 35, 65, and 75 qt of berries. Find the average yield for the four years.

Answers on page A-13

---

b Writing Mixed Numerals

We can find a mixed numeral for $\frac{5}{3}$ as follows:

$$\frac{5}{3} = \frac{3}{3} + \frac{2}{3} = 1 + \frac{2}{3} = 1\frac{2}{3}.$$

We can also visualize $\frac{5}{3}$ as one-third of 5 objects, as shown below.

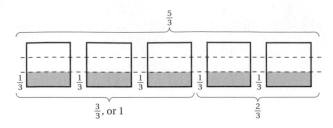

Note that one third of 5 is the same as 5 divided by 3.

> To convert from fraction notation to a mixed numeral, divide.
>
> $$\frac{19}{7}; \qquad 7\overline{)19} \quad \begin{array}{r} 2 \\ \hline 19 \\ 14 \\ \hline 5 \end{array} \rightarrow \text{The quotient}$$
>
> $\rightarrow$ The remainder
>
> $2\dfrac{5}{7} \qquad \dfrac{19}{7} = 2\dfrac{5}{7}$

■ **EXAMPLES** Convert to a mixed numeral.

10. $\dfrac{8}{5}$ $\quad 5\overline{)8}\ \begin{array}{r}1\\ 5\\ \hline 3\end{array}$ $\quad \dfrac{8}{5} = 1\dfrac{3}{5}$

> A fraction larger than 1, such as $\frac{8}{5}$, is sometimes referred to as an "improper" fraction. We have intentionally avoided such terminology. The use of notation such as $\frac{8}{5}$, $\frac{69}{10}$, and so on, is quite proper and very common in algebra.

11. $\dfrac{69}{10}$ $\quad 10\overline{)69}\ \begin{array}{r}6\\ 60\\ \hline 9\end{array}$ $\quad \dfrac{69}{10} = 6\dfrac{9}{10}$

Do Exercises 11 and 12.

Whenever the fraction part of the mixed numeral can be simplified, it is important to do so.

■ **EXAMPLE 12** Convert to a mixed numeral: $\dfrac{122}{8}$.

$$8\overline{)122}\ \begin{array}{r}15\\ 80\\ \hline 42\\ 40\\ \hline 2\end{array} \qquad \frac{122}{8} = 15\frac{2}{8} = 15\frac{1}{4}$$

Do Exercise 13.

The same procedure also works with negative numbers. Of course, the result will be a negative mixed numeral.

EXAMPLE 13 Convert $\dfrac{-9}{4}$ to a mixed numeral.

Since $\quad 4\overline{)9}$, $\quad$ we have $\quad \dfrac{9}{4} = 2\dfrac{1}{4}.$ $\quad$ Thus, $\quad \dfrac{-9}{4} = -2\dfrac{1}{4}.$
$$\begin{array}{r} 2 \\ 4\overline{)9} \\ \underline{8} \\ 1 \end{array}$$

Do Exercises 14 and 15 on the opposite page.

C Finding Quotients and Averages

It is quite common when performing long division to express the quotient as a mixed numeral. As in Examples 10–13, the remainder becomes the numerator of the fraction part of the mixed numeral.

EXAMPLE 14 Divide. Write a mixed numeral for the quotient.

$$7\overline{)6\ 3\ 4\ 1}$$

We first divide as usual.

$$\begin{array}{r} 9\ 0\ 5 \\ 7\overline{)6\ 3\ 4\ 1} \\ \underline{6\ 3\ 0\ 0} \\ 4\ 1 \\ \underline{3\ 5} \\ 6 \end{array}$$

The answer is 905 R 6, or $905\dfrac{6}{7}$. Using fraction notation, we write $\dfrac{6341}{7} = 905\dfrac{6}{7}$.

Do Exercise 16 on the opposite page.

EXAMPLE 15 *Charities.* The American Institute of Philanthropy monitors how much charitable organizations spend in order to raise $100. Five of the best organizations in this respect are listed below. How much did they spend, on average, to raise $100?
Source: *AIP Charity Rating Guide & Watchdog Report* 7/02, American Institute of Philanthropy, St. Louis, MO 63108

American Indian Graduate Center	$6
AIDS Research Alliance	$8
Guide Dogs for the Blind	$5
NAACP	$7
Sierra Club Foundation	$3

Recall from Section 1.9 that to find the *average* of a set of values, we add the values and divide that sum by the number of values being added.

$$\text{Average spent} = \frac{\$6 + \$8 + \$5 + \$7 + \$3}{5} = \frac{\$29}{5} = \$5\frac{4}{5}.$$

On average, these groups spent $5\dfrac{4}{5}$ (or $5.80) to raise $100.

Do Exercise 17 on the opposite page.

CALCULATOR CORNER

When using a calculator to divide whole numbers, we can express the result as a mixed numeral. One way to do this is to use a $\boxed{a^{b/c}}$ key if your calculator is so equipped. To use this key for 36 ÷ 5, we press 36 $\boxed{a^{b/c}}$ 5 $\boxed{=}$. The display

$$\boxed{7 \lrcorner 1 \lrcorner 5}$$

represents $7\dfrac{1}{5}$.

Another approach, which works on all calculators, is to press 36 ÷ 5 and then examine the result, 7.2. The whole-number part of our answer is 7. The fraction part of the answer is formed by writing the remainder from 36 ÷ 5 over 5. To find the remainder, we multiply the whole-number part of our answer, 7, by 5 and subtract that result from 36:

$$36 \boxed{-} 7 \boxed{\times} 5 \boxed{=} 1.$$

Thus, the desired fraction is $\dfrac{1}{5}$ and we have $36 \div 5 = 7\dfrac{1}{5}$.

Exercises: Use a calculator to divide. Write each result as a mixed numeral.

1. $7\overline{)39}$
2. $5\overline{)42}$
3. $6\overline{)8857}$
4. $9\overline{)6088}$
5. $11\overline{)567,895}$
6. $32\overline{)234,567}$
7. $45\overline{)6033}$
8. $213\overline{)567,988}$
9. $112\overline{)400,003}$
10. $908\overline{)11,234}$

a Convert to fraction notation.

1. $7\frac{2}{3}$

2. $6\frac{2}{5}$

3. $6\frac{1}{4}$

4. $8\frac{1}{2}$

5. $-20\frac{1}{8}$

6. $-10\frac{1}{3}$

7. $5\frac{1}{10}$

8. $8\frac{1}{10}$

9. $20\frac{3}{5}$

10. $30\frac{4}{5}$

11. $-8\frac{2}{7}$

12. $-8\frac{7}{8}$

13. $6\frac{9}{10}$

14. $1\frac{3}{5}$

15. $-12\frac{3}{4}$

16. $-15\frac{2}{3}$

17. $5\frac{7}{10}$

18. $7\frac{3}{100}$

19. $-5\frac{7}{100}$

20. $-6\frac{4}{15}$

b Convert to a mixed numeral.

21. $\frac{16}{3}$

22. $\frac{19}{8}$

23. $\frac{45}{6}$

24. $\frac{30}{9}$

25. $\frac{57}{10}$

26. $\frac{-89}{10}$

27. $\frac{65}{9}$

28. $\frac{65}{8}$

29. $\frac{-33}{6}$

30. $\frac{-50}{8}$

31. $\frac{46}{4}$

32. $\frac{39}{9}$

33. $\frac{-12}{8}$

34. $-\frac{57}{6}$

35. $\frac{307}{5}$

36. $\frac{227}{4}$

37. $-\frac{413}{50}$

38. $\frac{467}{100}$

c Divide. Write a mixed numeral for the answer.

39. $8\,\overline{)\,8\ 6\ 9}$

40. $3\,\overline{)\,2\ 1\ 2\ 6}$

41. $7\,\overline{)\,6\ 3\ 4\ 5}$

42. $9\,\overline{)\,9\ 1\ 1\ 0}$

43. $2\ 1\,\overline{)\,8\ 5\ 2}$

44. $8\ 5\,\overline{)\,7\ 6\ 7\ 2}$

45. $-302 \div 15$

46. $-475 \div 13$

47. $471 \div (-21)$

48. $542 \div (-25)$

Nutrition. For Exercises 49–52, consider the list at right of the 20 least fatty fast foods.

Source: Mark Green, *The Consumer Bible.* New York: Workman, 1995, p. 25.

49. What is the average number of grams (g) of fat in the foods from Boston Market?

50. What is the average number of grams of fat in the foods from Arby's and Jack-in-the-Box taken together?

51. What is the average number of grams of fat for the entire list?

52. What is the average number of grams of fat for the last 10 items on the list?

53. $\mathbf{D_W}$ Describe in your own words a method for rewriting a mixed numeral as a fraction.

54. $\mathbf{D_W}$ Describe in your own words a method for rewriting a fraction as a mixed numeral.

CHAIN	FOOD	FAT
Boston Market	Fruit salad side dish	0 g
Boston Market	Steamed vegetables	0 g
Hardee's	Mashed potatoes and gravy side	0 g
KFC	Garden rice side dish	1 g
KFC	Mashed potatoes with gravy side dish	1 g
KFC	Green beans side dish	1 g
Arby's	Chicken Noodle Soup	2 g
Jack-in-the-Box	Chicken Teriyaki Bowl	2 g
KFC	Baked Beans side dish	2 g
KFC	Mean Greens side dish	2 g
Boston Market	Chicken Soup	3 g
Church's	Potatoes & Gravy	3 g
Jack-in-the-Box	Beef Teriyaki Bowl	3 g
KFC	Red Beans & Rice	3 g
Popeye's	Corn on the cob	3 g
Arby's	Mixed Vegetable Soup	4 g
Boston Market	Chicken breast sandwich, no mayo or mustard	4 g
Boston Market	White meat chicken quarter, no skin or wing	4 g
Dairy Queen/Brazier	BBQ Beef sandwich	4 g
KFC	Vegetable Medley Salad	4 g

SKILL MAINTENANCE

Multiply and simplify. [3.6a]

55. $\dfrac{7}{9} \cdot \dfrac{24}{21}$

56. $\dfrac{5}{12} \cdot \dfrac{9}{10}$

57. $\dfrac{7}{10} \cdot \dfrac{5}{14}$

58. $\dfrac{21}{35} \cdot \dfrac{25}{12}$

59. $-\dfrac{17}{25} \cdot \dfrac{15}{34}$

60. $\dfrac{7}{20} \cdot \left(\dfrac{45}{49} \right)$

SYNTHESIS

61. $\mathbf{D_W}$ Toni claims that $3\frac{1}{5}$ is the reciprocal of $5\frac{1}{3}$. How can you convince her that she is mistaken?

62. $\mathbf{D_W}$ Are the numbers $2\frac{1}{3}$ and $2 \cdot \frac{1}{3}$ equal? Why or why not?

Write a mixed numeral for each number or sum listed.

63. 🖩 $\dfrac{128{,}236}{541}$

64. 🖩 $\dfrac{103{,}676}{349}$

65. $\dfrac{56}{7} + \dfrac{2}{3}$

66. $\dfrac{72}{12} + \dfrac{5}{6}$

67. $\dfrac{12}{5} + \dfrac{19}{15}$

68. How many weeks are in a leap year?

69. How many weeks are in a year?

70. *Athletics.* At a track and field meet, the hammer that is thrown has a wire length ranging from 3 ft, $10\frac{1}{4}$ in. to 3 ft, $11\frac{3}{4}$ in., a $4\frac{1}{8}$-in. grip, and a 16-lb ball with a diameter of $4\frac{3}{8}$ in. to $5\frac{1}{8}$ in. Give specifications for the wire length and diameter of an "average" hammer.

1. Add.

$$2\frac{3}{10}$$
$$+\,7\frac{1}{10}$$

2. Add.

$$8\frac{2}{5}$$
$$+\,3\frac{7}{10}$$

3. Add.

$$5\frac{3}{4}$$
$$+\,8\frac{5}{6}$$

Answers on page A-13

a Addition Using Mixed Numerals

To find the sum $1\frac{5}{8} + 3\frac{1}{8}$, we first add the fractions. Then we add the whole numbers and, if possible, simplify the fraction part.

$$
\begin{array}{r}
1\dfrac{5}{8} = \\[4pt]
+\,3\dfrac{1}{8} = \\[4pt]
\hline
\dfrac{6}{8}
\end{array}
\qquad
\begin{array}{r}
1\dfrac{5}{8} \\[4pt]
+\,3\dfrac{1}{8} \\[4pt]
\hline
4\dfrac{6}{8} = 4\dfrac{3}{4}
\end{array}
$$

— Simplifying

↑ Add the fractions.   ↑ Add the whole numbers.

Do Exercise 1.

Recall that the fraction part of a mixed numeral should always be less than 1.

EXAMPLE 1 Add: $5\frac{2}{3} + 3\frac{5}{6}$. Write a mixed numeral for the answer.

The LCD is 6.

$$
\begin{array}{r}
5\dfrac{2}{3}\cdot\dfrac{2}{2} = 5\dfrac{4}{6} \\[6pt]
+\,3\dfrac{5}{6} = +\,3\dfrac{5}{6} \\[6pt]
\hline
8\dfrac{9}{6} = 8 + \dfrac{9}{6} \\[6pt]
= 8 + 1\dfrac{1}{2} \\[6pt]
= 9\dfrac{1}{2}
\end{array}
$$

To find a mixed numeral for $\frac{9}{6}$, we divide:

$$
\begin{array}{r}
1 \\
6\overline{)9} \\
6 \\
\hline
3
\end{array}
\qquad \frac{9}{6} = 1\frac{3}{6} = 1\frac{1}{2}
$$

$\frac{19}{2}$ is also a correct answer, but it is not a mixed numeral, which is what we are working with in Sections 4.5, 4.6, and 4.7.

Do Exercise 2.

EXAMPLE 2 Add: $10\frac{5}{6} + 7\frac{3}{8}$.

The LCD is 24.

$$
\begin{array}{r}
10\dfrac{5}{6}\cdot\dfrac{4}{4} = 10\dfrac{20}{24} \\[6pt]
+\,7\dfrac{3}{8}\cdot\dfrac{3}{3} = +\,7\dfrac{9}{24} \\[6pt]
\hline
17\dfrac{29}{24} = 18\dfrac{5}{24}
\end{array}
$$

Do Exercise 3.

b Subtraction Using Mixed Numerals

EXAMPLE 3 Subtract: $7\frac{3}{4} - 2\frac{1}{4}$.

$$
\begin{array}{r}
7\,\dfrac{3}{4} = \\[2mm]
-\;2\,\dfrac{1}{4} = \\[2mm]
\hline
\dfrac{2}{4}
\end{array}
\qquad
\begin{array}{r}
7\,\dfrac{3}{4} \\[2mm]
-\;2\,\dfrac{1}{4} \\[2mm]
\hline
5\,\dfrac{2}{4} = 5\frac{1}{2}
\end{array}
$$

↑ Simplify.

↑ Subtract the fractions.

↑ Subtract the whole numbers.

EXAMPLE 4 Subtract: $9\frac{4}{5} - 3\frac{1}{2}$.

The LCD is 10.

$$
\begin{array}{r}
9\,\dfrac{4}{5} \cdot \dfrac{2}{2} = 9\,\dfrac{8}{10} \\[3mm]
-\;3\,\dfrac{1}{2} \cdot \dfrac{5}{5} = -\,3\,\dfrac{5}{10} \\[3mm]
\hline
6\,\dfrac{3}{10}
\end{array}
$$

Do Exercises 4 and 5.

To subtract fractions, we may need to "borrow" from the whole number. This enables us to write an equivalent expression in which the fractions are more easily subtracted.

EXAMPLE 5 Subtract: $13 - 9\frac{3}{8}$.

$$
\begin{array}{r}
13 \;=\; 12\,\dfrac{8}{8} \\[3mm]
-\;9\,\dfrac{3}{8} = -\;9\,\dfrac{3}{8} \\[3mm]
\hline
3\,\dfrac{5}{8}
\end{array}
$$

$13 = 12 + 1 = 12 + \dfrac{8}{8} = 12\dfrac{8}{8}$

EXAMPLE 6 Subtract: $7\frac{1}{6} - 2\frac{1}{4}$.

The LCD is 12.

$$
\left.
\begin{array}{r}
7\,\dfrac{1}{6} \cdot \dfrac{2}{2} = 7\,\dfrac{2}{12} \\[3mm]
-\;2\,\dfrac{1}{4} \cdot \dfrac{3}{3} = -\,2\,\dfrac{3}{12} \\[3mm]
\hline
\end{array}
\right\}
$$

To subtract $\frac{3}{12}$ from $\frac{2}{12}$, we borrow 1, or $\frac{12}{12}$, from 7:
$7\frac{2}{12} = 6 + 1 + \frac{2}{12} = 6 + \frac{12}{12} + \frac{2}{12} = 6\frac{14}{12}.$

Subtract.

4. $10\dfrac{7}{8}$
$-\ 9\dfrac{3}{8}$

5. $8\dfrac{2}{3}$
$-\ 5\dfrac{1}{2}$

Subtract.

6. 5
$-\ 1\dfrac{1}{3}$

7. $8\dfrac{1}{9}$
$-\ 4\dfrac{5}{6}$

Answers on page A-13

Combine like terms.

8. $7\dfrac{1}{6}t + 5\dfrac{2}{3}t$

9. $7\dfrac{11}{12}x - 5\dfrac{2}{3}x$

10. $5\dfrac{11}{15}x + 8\dfrac{3}{10}x$

Answers on page A-13

We can write this as

$$
\begin{array}{rcl}
7\dfrac{2}{12} & = & 6\dfrac{14}{12} \\[2mm]
-2\dfrac{3}{12} & = & -2\dfrac{3}{12} \\[2mm]
\hline
 & & 4\dfrac{11}{12}
\end{array}
$$

Do Exercises 6 and 7 on the previous page.

To combine like terms, we use the distributive law and add or subtract.

■ **EXAMPLE 7** Combine like terms: **(a)** $9\frac{3}{4}x - 4\frac{1}{2}x$; **(b)** $4\frac{5}{6}t + 2\frac{7}{9}t$.

a) $9\dfrac{3}{4}x - 4\dfrac{1}{2}x = \left(9\dfrac{3}{4} - 4\dfrac{1}{2}\right)x$ Using the distributive law;
this is often done mentally.

$\qquad = \left(9\dfrac{3}{4} - 4\dfrac{2}{4}\right)x$ The LCD is 4.

$\qquad = 5\dfrac{1}{4}x$ Subtracting

b) $4\dfrac{5}{6}t + 2\dfrac{7}{9}t = \left(4\dfrac{5}{6} + 2\dfrac{7}{9}\right)t$ This step is often performed mentally.

$\qquad = \left(4\dfrac{15}{18} + 2\dfrac{14}{18}\right)t$ The LCD is 18.

$\qquad = 6\dfrac{29}{18}t = 7\dfrac{11}{18}t$

Do Exercises 8–10.

C **Applications and Problem Solving**

■ **EXAMPLE 8** *Travel Distance.* To satisfy her physical education requirement, Penny mountain biked $5\frac{1}{4}$ mi on Tuesday and $4\frac{9}{10}$ mi on Thursday. What was the total distance Penny rode?

1. **Familiarize.** We let d = the total distance traveled in miles.

2. **Translate.** We translate as follows.

Distance biked Tuesday		Distance biked Thursday		Total distance biked
$5\dfrac{1}{4}$	$+$	$4\dfrac{9}{10}$	$=$	d

3. **Solve.** The sentence tells us what to do. We add. The LCD is 20.

$$
\begin{array}{rcccl}
5\dfrac{1}{4} & = & 5\dfrac{1}{4}\cdot\dfrac{5}{5} & = & 5\dfrac{5}{20} \\[3mm]
+\,4\dfrac{9}{10} & = & +\,4\dfrac{9}{10}\cdot\dfrac{2}{2} & = & +\,4\dfrac{18}{20} \\[2mm]
\hline
 & & & & 9\dfrac{23}{20} = 10\dfrac{3}{20}
\end{array}
$$

Thus, $d = 10\frac{3}{20}$ mi.

4. Check. We check by repeating the calculation. We also note that the sum is approximately 5 + 5, or 10, so our answer is reasonable.

5. State. Penny biked a total of $10\frac{3}{20}$ mi.

Do Exercise 11.

EXAMPLE 9 *Carpentry.* The following illustration shows the layout for the construction of a desk drawer. Find a, the width of the slot.

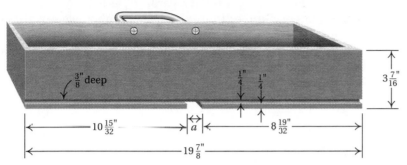

Middle Drawer / Back Layout

1. Familiarize. Measurement a is shown in the drawing. It is part of a length totaling $19\frac{7}{8}$".

2. Translate. We rephrase and translate as follows.

Rephrase: The total length is the sum of three measurements

Translate: $19\frac{7}{8} = 10\frac{15}{32} + a + 8\frac{19}{32}$

3. Solve. We solve for a:

$$19\frac{7}{8} = 10\frac{15}{32} + a + 8\frac{19}{32}$$

$$19\frac{7}{8} = a + 10\frac{15}{32} + 8\frac{19}{32} \qquad \text{Using a commutative law}$$

$$19\frac{7}{8} = a + 18\frac{34}{32}$$

$$19\frac{7}{8} = a + 19\frac{1}{16} \qquad \frac{34}{32} = 1\frac{2}{32} = 1\frac{1}{16}$$

$$19\frac{7}{8} - 19\frac{1}{16} = a + 19\frac{1}{16} - 19\frac{1}{16} \qquad \text{Subtracting } 19\frac{1}{16} \text{ from both sides}$$

$$\frac{13}{16} = a. \qquad \frac{7}{8} - \frac{1}{16} = \frac{14}{16} - \frac{1}{16} = \frac{13}{16}$$

4. Check. We check by repeating the calculation, or adding the three measures:

$$10\frac{15}{32} + 8\frac{19}{32} + \frac{13}{16} = 19\frac{7}{8}.$$

5. State. The length a in the diagram is $\frac{13}{16}$".

Do Exercise 12.

---

11. Executive Car Care sold two pieces of synthetic leather, one $6\frac{1}{4}$ yd long and the other $10\frac{5}{6}$ yd long. What was the total length of the leather?

12. There are $20\frac{1}{3}$ gal of water in a rainbarrel; $5\frac{3}{4}$ gal are poured out and $8\frac{2}{3}$ gal are returned after a heavy rainfall. How many gallons of water are then in the barrel?

Answers on page A-13

13. Subtract: $7 - 7\dfrac{3}{4}$.

Subtract.

14. $5\dfrac{1}{2} - 9\dfrac{3}{4}$

15. $4\dfrac{2}{3} - 7\dfrac{1}{6}$

Answer on page A-13

---

d   Negative Mixed Numerals

Consider the numbers $5\dfrac{3}{4}$ and $-5\dfrac{3}{4}$ on a number line.

Note that just as $5\dfrac{3}{4}$ means $5 + \dfrac{3}{4}$, we can regard $-5\dfrac{3}{4}$ as $-5 - \dfrac{3}{4}$.

To subtract a larger number from a smaller number, we must modify the approach of Examples 3–6. To see why, consider the subtraction $4 - 4\dfrac{1}{2}$. We know that if we have \$4 and make a \$$4\dfrac{1}{2}$ purchase, we will owe half a dollar. Thus,

$$4 - 4\dfrac{1}{2} = -\dfrac{1}{2}.$$

The following is *not* correct:

$$
\begin{array}{rr}
4 & 3\dfrac{2}{2} \\[4pt]
-\,4\dfrac{1}{2} & -\,4\dfrac{1}{2} \\[4pt]
\hline
& -1\dfrac{1}{2}
\end{array}
\left. \rule{0pt}{50pt}\right\} \ \text{Wrong!}
$$

The correct answer can be found by *adding* the results of $3 - 4$ and $\dfrac{2}{2} - \dfrac{1}{2}$: $-1 + \dfrac{1}{2} = -\dfrac{1}{2}$ (see below.)

The correct answer, $-\dfrac{1}{2}$, can be obtained by rewriting the subtraction as addition (see Section 2.3):

$$4 - 4\dfrac{1}{2} = 4 + \left(-4\dfrac{1}{2}\right).$$

Because $-4\dfrac{1}{2}$ has the greater absolute value, the answer will be negative. The difference in absolute value is $4\dfrac{1}{2} - 4 = \dfrac{1}{2}$, so

$$4 - 4\dfrac{1}{2} = -\dfrac{1}{2}.$$

Do Exercise 13.

EXAMPLE 10   Subtract: $3\dfrac{2}{7} - 4\dfrac{2}{5}$.

Since $4\dfrac{2}{5}$ is greater than $3\dfrac{2}{7}$, the answer will be negative. We can also see this by rewriting the subtraction as $3\dfrac{2}{7} + \left(-4\dfrac{2}{5}\right)$. The difference in absolute values is

$$
\begin{array}{rcccr}
4\dfrac{2}{5} & = & 4\dfrac{2}{5} \cdot \dfrac{7}{7} & = & 4\dfrac{14}{35} \\[10pt]
-\,3\dfrac{2}{7} & = & -\,3\dfrac{2}{7} \cdot \dfrac{5}{5} & = & -\,3\dfrac{10}{35} \\[6pt]
\hline
& & & & 1\dfrac{4}{35}.
\end{array}
$$

Because $-4\dfrac{2}{5}$ has the larger absolute value, we make the answer negative.

Thus, $3\dfrac{2}{7} - 4\dfrac{2}{5} = -1\dfrac{4}{35}$.

Do Exercises 14 and 15.

EXAMPLE 11 Subtract: $-6\frac{4}{5} - \left(-9\frac{3}{10}\right)$.

We write the subtraction as addition:

$$-6\frac{4}{5} - \left(-9\frac{3}{10}\right) = -6\frac{4}{5} + 9\frac{3}{10}.$$ Instead of subtracting, we add the opposite.

Since $9\frac{3}{10}$ has the greater absolute value, the answer will be positive. The difference in absolute values is

$$
\begin{array}{rcccc}
9\dfrac{3}{10} = & 9\ \dfrac{3}{10} & = & 9\dfrac{3}{10} = & 8\dfrac{13}{10} \\[2ex]
-\,6\dfrac{4}{5} = & -\,6\ \boxed{\dfrac{4}{5}\cdot\dfrac{2}{2}} & = & -\,6\dfrac{8}{10} = & -\,6\dfrac{8}{10} \\[2ex]
\hline
& & & & 2\dfrac{5}{10} = 2\dfrac{1}{2}.
\end{array}
$$

Thus, $-6\frac{4}{5} - \left(-9\frac{3}{10}\right) = 2\frac{1}{2}$.

Do Exercises 16 and 17.

In Section 2.2, we saw that to add two negative numbers we add absolute values and make the answer negative. The same approach is used with mixed numerals.

EXAMPLE 12 Subtract: $-4\frac{1}{6} - 5\frac{2}{9}$.

We rewrite the subtraction as addition:

$$
\begin{aligned}
-4\frac{1}{6} - 5\frac{2}{9} &= -4\frac{1}{6} + \left(-5\frac{2}{9}\right) && \text{Instead of subtracting,}\\
&&& \text{we add the opposite.}\\
&= -\left(4\frac{1}{6} + 5\frac{2}{9}\right) && \text{The LCD is 18.}\\
&&& \tfrac{1}{6}\cdot\tfrac{3}{3} = \tfrac{3}{18};\ \tfrac{2}{9}\cdot\tfrac{2}{2} = \tfrac{4}{18}\\
&= -\left(4\frac{3}{18} + 5\frac{4}{18}\right)\\
&= -9\frac{7}{18}.
\end{aligned}
$$

Thus, $-4\frac{1}{6} - 5\frac{2}{9} = -9\frac{7}{18}$.

Do Exercise 18.

Subtract.

16. $-7\frac{1}{3} - \left(-5\frac{1}{2}\right)$

17. $-4\frac{1}{10} - \left(-7\frac{2}{5}\right)$

18. Subtract: $-7\frac{1}{10} - 6\frac{2}{15}$.

Answers on page A-13

CALCULATOR CORNER

To add mixed numerals, we use the $\boxed{a^{b/c}}$ key on a scientific calculator or the FRAC option of the $\boxed{\text{MATH}}$ key on a graphing calculator.

To find $4\frac{2}{5} + 8\frac{1}{3}$ on a scientific calculator, we press

$4 \boxed{a^{b/c}} 2 \boxed{a^{b/c}} 5 \boxed{+} 8 \boxed{a^{b/c}} 1 \boxed{a^{b/c}} 3 \boxed{=}.$

The display

12 ⌐ 11 ⌐ 15

indicates that the sum is $12\frac{11}{15}$.

Some calculators are capable of displaying mixed numerals in the way in which we write them, as shown below.

Keystrokes for a graphing calculator vary slightly. Consult your owner's manual or an instructor if you need help with your particular model.

Exercises: Perform each calculation. Give the answer as a mixed numeral.

1. $4\frac{1}{3} + 5\frac{4}{5}$

2. $9\frac{2}{7} - 8\frac{1}{4}$

3. $7\frac{2}{9} - 5\frac{1}{7}$

4. $5\frac{3}{20} + 2\frac{11}{12}$

5. $8\frac{17}{19} - 9\frac{2}{11}$

6. $6\frac{13}{15} - 9\frac{2}{17}$

4.6 EXERCISE SET

a , **b**   Perform the indicated operation. Write a mixed numeral for each answer.

1. $2\dfrac{7}{8}$
$+\ 6\dfrac{5}{8}$

2. $2\dfrac{5}{6}$
$+\ 5\dfrac{5}{6}$

3. $4\dfrac{1}{4}$
$+\ 1\dfrac{2}{3}$

4. $4\dfrac{1}{3}$
$+\ 5\dfrac{2}{9}$

5. $7\dfrac{3}{4}$
$+\ 5\dfrac{5}{6}$

6. $4\dfrac{3}{8}$
$+\ 6\dfrac{5}{12}$

7. $3\dfrac{2}{5}$
$+\ 8\dfrac{7}{10}$

8. $5\dfrac{1}{2}$
$+\ 3\dfrac{7}{10}$

9. $6\dfrac{3}{8}$
$+\ 10\dfrac{5}{6}$

10. $\dfrac{5}{8}$
$+\ 1\dfrac{5}{6}$

11. $18\dfrac{4}{5}$
$+\ \ 2\dfrac{7}{10}$

12. $15\dfrac{5}{8}$
$+\ 11\dfrac{3}{4}$

13. $14\dfrac{5}{8}$
$+\ 13\dfrac{1}{4}$

14. $16\dfrac{1}{4}$
$+\ 15\dfrac{7}{8}$

15. $4\dfrac{1}{5}$
$-\ 2\dfrac{3}{5}$

16. $5\dfrac{1}{8}$
$-\ 2\dfrac{3}{8}$

17. $9\dfrac{3}{5}$
$-\ 3\dfrac{1}{2}$

18. $8\dfrac{2}{3}$
$-\ 7\dfrac{1}{2}$

19. $34\dfrac{1}{3}$
$-\ 12\dfrac{5}{8}$

20. $23\dfrac{5}{16}$
$-\ 16\dfrac{3}{4}$

21. 19
$-\ 5\dfrac{3}{4}$

22. 17
$-\ 3\dfrac{7}{8}$

23. 34
$-\ 18\dfrac{5}{8}$

24. 23
$-\ 19\dfrac{3}{4}$

25. $21\dfrac{1}{6}$
$-\ 13\dfrac{3}{4}$

26. $42\dfrac{1}{10}$
$-\ 23\dfrac{7}{12}$

27. $25\dfrac{1}{9}$
$-\ 13\dfrac{5}{6}$

28. $23\dfrac{5}{16}$
$-\ 14\dfrac{7}{12}$

b Combine like terms.

29. $1\frac{3}{14}t + 7\frac{2}{21}t$

30. $6\frac{1}{2}x + 8\frac{3}{4}x$

31. $9\frac{1}{2}x - 7\frac{3}{8}x$

32. $7\frac{3}{4}x - 2\frac{3}{8}x$

33. $5\frac{9}{10}t + 2\frac{7}{8}t$

34. $9\frac{2}{7}x + 2\frac{3}{8}x$

35. $37\frac{5}{9}t - 25\frac{4}{5}t$

36. $23\frac{1}{6}t - 19\frac{2}{5}t$

37. $2\frac{5}{6}x + 3\frac{1}{3}x$

38. $7\frac{3}{20}t + 1\frac{2}{15}t$

39. $1\frac{3}{11}x + 8\frac{2}{3}x$

40. $6\frac{11}{12}t + 3\frac{7}{10}t$

c Solve.

41. *Sewing from a Pattern.* Nanao wants to make an outfit in size 8. Using 45-in. fabric, she needs $1\frac{3}{8}$ yd for the dress, $\frac{5}{8}$ yd of contrasting fabric for the band at the bottom, and $3\frac{3}{8}$ yd for the jacket. How many yards in all of 45-in. fabric are needed to make the outfit?

42. *Sewing from a Pattern.* Negar wants to make an outfit in size 12. Using 45-in. fabric, she needs $2\frac{3}{4}$ yd for the dress and $3\frac{1}{2}$ yd for the jacket. How many yards in all of 45-in. fabric are needed to make the outfit?

43. For a family barbecue, Jason bought packages of hamburger weighing $1\frac{2}{3}$ lb and $5\frac{3}{4}$ lb. What was the total weight of the meat?

44. Marsha's Butcher Shop sold packages of sliced turkey breast weighing $1\frac{1}{3}$ lb and $4\frac{3}{5}$ lb. What was the total weight of the meat?

45. *Heights.* Rocky is $187\frac{1}{10}$ cm tall and his daughter is $180\frac{3}{4}$ cm tall. How much taller is Rocky?

46. *Heights.* Aunt Louise is $168\frac{1}{4}$ cm tall and her son is $150\frac{7}{10}$ cm tall. How much taller is Aunt Louise?

47. Tara is $4\frac{1}{2}$ in. taller than her son, who is $62\frac{3}{4}$ in. tall. How tall is Tara?

48. Nicholas is $8\frac{3}{4}$ in. taller than his daughter, who is $59\frac{1}{2}$ in. tall. How tall is Nicholas?

49. A plumber uses pipes of lengths $10\frac{5}{16}$ in. and $8\frac{3}{4}$ in. in the installation of a sink. How much pipe is used?

50. *Writing Supplies.* The standard pencil is $6\frac{7}{8}$ in. wood and $\frac{1}{2}$ in. eraser. What is the total length of the standard pencil?
Source: Eberhard Faber American

51. *Carpentry.* When cutting wood with a saw, a carpenter must take into account the thickness of the saw blade. Suppose that from a piece of wood 36 in. long, a carpenter cuts a $15\frac{3}{4}$-in. length with a saw blade that is $\frac{1}{8}$ in. in thickness. How long is the piece that remains?

52. *NCAA Football Goalposts.* In college football, the distance between goalposts was reduced from $23\frac{1}{3}$ ft to $18\frac{1}{2}$ ft. By how much was it reduced?

Source: NCAA

53. *Running.* Angela is preparing to run the San Diego marathon. Recently she ran a 10-km "Fun Run." A marathon is $26\frac{7}{32}$ mi and 10 km is $6\frac{1}{5}$ mi. How much farther will Angela run in the marathon?

54. *Running.* Harvey successfully ran both the Spring Lake 5-mi race and the Boys & Girls Club 10-km "Dog Day Race." Given that 5 mi is about $8\frac{1}{20}$ km, how much farther did Harvey run in the Dog Day Race?

55. *Cooking.* Among the ingredients in a recipe for black bean and corn salsa are the following:
Source: Based on Jane Butel's *Southwestern Grill*, HPBooks, 1996, p. 206

$1\frac{1}{2}$ cups onion
$1\frac{1}{3}$ cups diced jalapeño
$2\frac{1}{2}$ cups cooked black beans
$1\frac{1}{2}$ cups cooked whole-kernel corn
$\frac{3}{4}$ cups chopped cilantro

How many cups of ingredients are listed?

56. *Cooking.* A recipe for boniato bread includes the following ingredients:
Source: Based on *Miami Spice* by Steven Raichlen, Workman Publishing, 1993, p. 93

$\frac{1}{4}$ cup water
$\frac{1}{3}$ cup sugar
$5\frac{1}{2}$ cups unbleached all-purpose flour

How many cups of ingredients are listed?

57. *Interior Design.* Sue, an interior designer, worked $10\frac{1}{2}$ hr over a three-day period. If Sue worked $2\frac{1}{2}$ hr on the first day and $4\frac{1}{5}$ hr on the second, how many hours did Sue work on the third day?

58. *Painting.* Geri had $3\frac{1}{2}$ gal of paint. It took $2\frac{3}{4}$ gal to paint the family room. She estimated that it would take $2\frac{1}{4}$ gal to paint the living room. How much more paint was needed?

Find the perimeter of (distance around) the figure.

59.

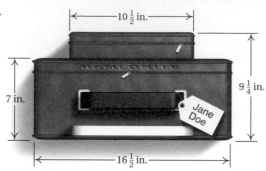

60.

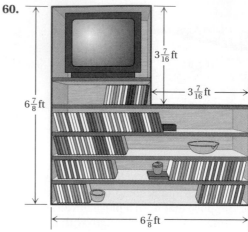

61.

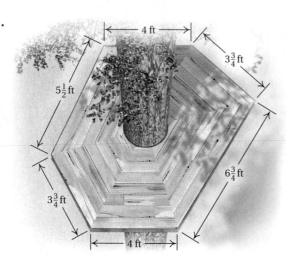

62.

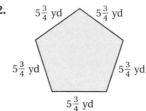

63.

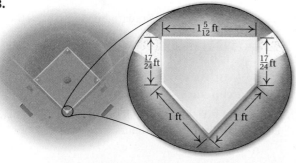

64.

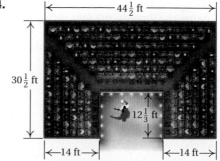

Find the length d in the figure.

65.

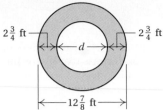

$2\frac{3}{4}$ ft — d — $2\frac{3}{4}$ ft

$12\frac{7}{8}$ ft

66.

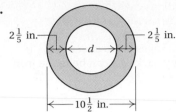

$2\frac{1}{5}$ in. — d — $2\frac{1}{5}$ in.

$10\frac{1}{2}$ in.

67. Find the smallest length of a bolt that will pass through a piece of tubing with an outside diameter of $\frac{1}{2}$ in., a washer $\frac{1}{16}$ in. thick, a piece of tubing with a $\frac{3}{4}$-in. outside diameter, another washer $\frac{1}{16}$ in. thick, and a nut $\frac{3}{16}$ in. thick.

68. The front of the stage at the Steel Pony Coffee House is $6\frac{1}{2}$ yd long. If renovation work succeeds in adding $2\frac{3}{4}$ yd in length, how long is the renovated stage?

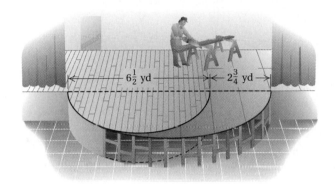

$6\frac{1}{2}$ yd $2\frac{3}{4}$ yd

d Subtract.

69. $8\frac{3}{5} - 9\frac{2}{5}$

70. $4\frac{5}{7} - 8\frac{3}{7}$

71. $3\frac{1}{2} - 6\frac{3}{4}$

72. $5\frac{1}{2} - 7\frac{3}{4}$

73. $3\frac{4}{5} - 7\frac{2}{3}$

74. $2\frac{3}{7} - 5\frac{1}{2}$

75. $-3\frac{1}{5} - 4\frac{2}{5}$

76. $-5\frac{3}{8} - 4\frac{1}{8}$

77. $-4\frac{2}{5} - 6\frac{3}{7}$

78. $-2\frac{3}{4} - 3\frac{3}{8}$

79. $-6\frac{1}{9} - \left(-4\frac{2}{9}\right)$

80. $-2\frac{3}{5} - \left(-1\frac{1}{5}\right)$

81. **D**_{**W**} Write a problem for a classmate to solve. Design the problem so the solution is "The larger package holds $4\frac{1}{2}$ oz more than the smaller package."

82. **D**_{**W**} Is the sum of two mixed numerals always a mixed numeral? Why or why not?

Solve.

83. Rick's Market prepackages Swiss cheese in $\frac{3}{4}$-lb packages. How many packages can be made from a 12-lb slab of cheese? [3.8b]

84. The Thompson Dairy produced 4578 oz of milk one morning. How many 16-oz cartons would this have filled? How much milk would have been left over? [1.8a]

Determine whether the first number is divisible by the second.

85. 9993 by 3 [3.1b]

86. 9993 by 9 [3.1b]

87. 2345 by 9 [3.1b]

88. 2345 by 5 [3.1b]

89. 2335 by 10 [3.1b]

90. 7764 by 6 [3.1b]

91. 18,888 by 6 [3.1b]

92. 18,888 by 4 [3.1a]

93. Multiply and simplify: $\dfrac{15}{9} \cdot \dfrac{18}{39}$. [3.6a]

94. Divide and simplify: $\dfrac{12}{25} \div \dfrac{24}{5}$. [3.7b]

95. $\mathbf{D_W}$ Explain how the "borrowing" that is used in this section compares with the borrowing used in Section 1.3.

96. $\mathbf{D_W}$ Ryan insists that since $\frac{5}{7} - \frac{2}{7}$ is $\frac{3}{7}$, and $4 - 5$ is -1, it follows that $4\frac{5}{7} - 5\frac{2}{7}$ is $-1\frac{3}{7}$. How could you convince him that he is mistaken?

Calculate each of the following. Write the result as a mixed numeral.

97. ▦ $3289\frac{1047}{1189} + 5278\frac{32}{41}$

98. ▦ $5798\frac{17}{53} - 3909\frac{1957}{2279}$

99. ▦ $4230\frac{19}{73} - 5848\frac{17}{29}$

100. ▦ $57{,}825\frac{13}{79} - 64{,}200\frac{1}{43}$

Solve.

101. $35\dfrac{2}{3} + n = 46\dfrac{1}{4}$

102. $42\dfrac{7}{9} = x - 13\dfrac{2}{5}$

103. $-15\dfrac{7}{8} = 12\dfrac{1}{2} + t$

104. A post for a pier is 29 ft long. Half of the post extends above the water's surface and $8\frac{3}{4}$ ft of the post is buried in mud. How deep is the water at that location?

105. An algebra text is $1\frac{1}{8}$ in. thick, $9\frac{3}{4}$ in. long, and $8\frac{1}{2}$ in. wide. If the front, back, and spine of the book were unfolded, they would form a rectangle. What would the perimeter of that rectangle be?

$1\frac{1}{8}$ in.

$9\frac{3}{4}$ in.

$8\frac{1}{2}$ in.

4.7 MULTIPLICATION AND DIVISION OF MIXED NUMERALS; APPLICATIONS

Objectives

a Multiply using mixed numerals.

b Divide using mixed numerals.

c Evaluate expressions using mixed numerals.

d Solve problems involving multiplication and division with mixed numerals.

Whereas addition and subtraction of mixed numerals can be performed by leaving the numbers as mixed numerals, multiplication and division are most easily performed by first converting the numbers to fraction notation.

a Multiplication

MULTIPLICATION USING MIXED NUMERALS

To multiply using mixed numerals, first convert to fraction notation. Then multiply with fraction notation and, if appropriate, rewrite the answer as an equivalent mixed numeral.

EXAMPLE 1 Multiply: $6 \cdot 2\frac{1}{2}$.

$$6 \cdot 2\frac{1}{2} = \frac{6}{1} \cdot \frac{5}{2} = \frac{6 \cdot 5}{1 \cdot 2} = \frac{2 \cdot 3 \cdot 5}{2 \cdot 1} = 15$$

Removing a factor equal to 1: $\frac{2}{2} = 1$.

Here we write fraction notation.

Do Exercise 1.

1. Multiply: $8 \cdot 3\frac{1}{2}$.

EXAMPLE 2 Multiply: $3\frac{1}{2} \cdot \frac{3}{4}$.

$$3\frac{1}{2} \cdot \frac{3}{4} = \frac{7}{2} \cdot \frac{3}{4} = \frac{21}{8} = 2\frac{5}{8}$$

Although fraction notation is needed, *common denominators are not required.*

Do Exercise 2.

2. Multiply: $5\frac{1}{2} \cdot \frac{3}{7}$.

EXAMPLE 3 Multiply: $-10 \cdot 5\frac{2}{3}$.

$$-10 \cdot 5\frac{2}{3} = -\frac{10}{1} \cdot \frac{17}{3} = -\frac{170}{3} = -56\frac{2}{3}$$

3. Multiply: $-2 \cdot 6\frac{2}{5}$.

EXAMPLE 4 Multiply: $2\frac{1}{4} \cdot 3\frac{2}{5}$.

$$2\frac{1}{4} \cdot 3\frac{2}{5} = \frac{9}{4} \cdot \frac{17}{5} = \frac{153}{20} = 7\frac{13}{20}$$

4. Multiply: $3\frac{1}{3} \cdot 2\frac{1}{2}$.

Answers on page A-13

> **CAUTION!**
>
> $2\frac{1}{4} \cdot 3\frac{2}{5} \neq 6\frac{2}{20}$. A common error is to multiply the whole numbers and then the fractions. The correct answer, $7\frac{13}{20}$, is found only after converting to fraction notation.

Do Exercises 3 and 4.

Study Tips

USE WHAT YOU KNOW

An excellent strategy for solving any new type of problem is to rewrite the problem in an equivalent form that we already know how to solve. Although this is not always feasible, when it is—as in Examples 1–7 of this section—it can make a new topic much easier to learn.

5. Divide: $63 \div 5\frac{1}{4}$.

b Division

The division $1\frac{1}{2} \div \frac{1}{6}$ is shown here.

We see that $\frac{1}{6}$ goes into $1\frac{1}{2}$ nine times.

$$1\frac{1}{2} \div \frac{1}{6} = \frac{3}{2} \div \frac{1}{6}$$

$$= \frac{3}{2} \cdot 6 = \frac{3 \cdot 6}{2} = \frac{3 \cdot 3 \cdot 2}{2 \cdot 1} = \frac{3 \cdot 3}{1} \cdot \frac{2}{2} = \frac{3 \cdot 3}{1} \cdot 1 = 9$$

DIVISION USING MIXED NUMERALS

To divide using mixed numerals, first write an equivalent expression using fraction notation. Then divide and, if appropriate, convert the answer back to an equivalent mixed numeral.

Divide.

6. $2\frac{1}{4} \div 1\frac{1}{5}$

EXAMPLE 5 Divide: $32 \div 3\frac{1}{5}$.

$$32 \div 3\frac{1}{5} = \frac{32}{1} \div \frac{16}{5} \qquad \text{Converting to fraction notation}$$

$$= \frac{32}{1} \cdot \frac{5}{16} = \frac{32 \cdot 5}{1 \cdot 16} = \frac{2 \cdot \cancel{16} \cdot 5}{1 \cdot \cancel{16}} = 10 \qquad \begin{array}{l}\text{Removing a factor} \\ \text{equal to 1: } \frac{16}{16} = 1\end{array}$$

$\underset{\text{Remember to multiply by the reciprocal of the divisor.}}{\uparrow}$

CAUTION!

The reciprocal of $3\frac{1}{5}$ is neither $5\frac{1}{3}$ nor $3\frac{5}{1}$!

Do Exercise 5.

7. $1\frac{3}{4} \div \left(-2\frac{1}{2}\right)$

EXAMPLE 6 Divide: $2\frac{1}{3} \div 1\frac{3}{4}$.

$$2\frac{1}{3} \div 1\frac{3}{4} = \frac{7}{3} \div \frac{7}{4} = \frac{7}{3} \cdot \frac{4}{7} = \frac{7 \cdot 4}{7 \cdot 3} = \frac{4}{3} = 1\frac{1}{3} \qquad \begin{array}{l}\text{Removing a factor} \\ \text{equal to 1: } \frac{7}{7} = 1\end{array}$$

EXAMPLE 7 Divide: $-1\frac{3}{5} \div \left(-3\frac{1}{3}\right)$.

$$-1\frac{3}{5} \div \left(-3\frac{1}{3}\right) = -\frac{8}{5} \div \left(-\frac{10}{3}\right) = \frac{8}{5} \cdot \frac{3}{10} \qquad \begin{array}{l}\text{The product or quotient of} \\ \text{two negatives is positive.}\end{array}$$

$$= \frac{\cancel{2} \cdot 4 \cdot 3}{5 \cdot \cancel{2} \cdot 5} = \frac{12}{25} \qquad \begin{array}{l}\text{Removing a factor} \\ \text{equal to 1: } \frac{2}{2} = 1\end{array}$$

Do Exercises 6 and 7.

Answers on page A-13

C Evaluating Expressions

Mixed numerals can appear in algebraic expressions just as the integers of Section 2.6 did.

EXAMPLE 8 A train traveling r miles per hour for t hours travels a total of rt miles. (*Remember*: Distance = Rate · Time.)

a) Find the distance traveled by a 60-mph train in $2\frac{3}{4}$ hr.

b) Find the distance traveled if the speed of the train is $26\frac{1}{2}$ mph and the time is $2\frac{2}{3}$ hr.

a) We evaluate rt for $r = 60$ and $t = 2\frac{3}{4}$:

$$rt = 60 \cdot 2\frac{3}{4}$$

$$= \frac{60}{1} \cdot \frac{11}{4}$$

$$= \frac{15 \cdot \cancel{4} \cdot 11}{1 \cdot \cancel{4}} = 165. \qquad \text{Removing a factor equal to 1: } \frac{4}{4} = 1$$

In $2\frac{3}{4}$ hr, a 60-mph train travels 165 mi.

b) We evaluate rt for $r = 26\frac{1}{2}$ and $t = 2\frac{2}{3}$:

$$rt = 26\frac{1}{2} \cdot 2\frac{2}{3}$$

$$= \frac{53}{2} \cdot \frac{8}{3} = \frac{53 \cdot \cancel{2} \cdot 4}{\cancel{2} \cdot 3} \qquad \text{Removing a factor equal to 1: } \frac{2}{2} = 1$$

$$= \frac{212}{3} = 70\frac{2}{3}.$$

In $2\frac{2}{3}$ hr, a $26\frac{1}{2}$-mph train travels $70\frac{2}{3}$ mi.

EXAMPLE 9 Evaluate $x + yz$ for $x = 7\frac{1}{3}$, $y = \frac{1}{3}$, and $z = 5$.

We substitute and follow the rules for order of operations:

$$x + yz = 7\frac{1}{3} + \frac{1}{3} \cdot 5$$

$$= 7\frac{1}{3} + \frac{1}{3} \cdot \frac{5}{1} \qquad \text{Multiply first; then add.}$$

$$= 7\frac{1}{3} + \frac{5}{3}$$

$$\left. \begin{array}{l} = 7\frac{1}{3} + 1\frac{2}{3} \\[2mm] = 8\frac{3}{3} = 9. \end{array} \right\} \qquad \text{Adding mixed numerals}$$

Do Exercises 8–10.

Evaluate.

8. rt, for $r = 78$ and $t = 2\frac{1}{4}$

9. $7xy$, for $x = 9\frac{2}{5}$ and $y = 2\frac{3}{7}$

10. $x - y \div z$, for $x = 5\frac{7}{8}$, $y = \frac{1}{4}$, and $z = 2$

Answers on page A-13

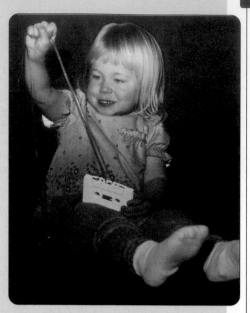

Margaret Grace Bittinger, age 2

11. Kyle's Ford pickup truck travels on an interstate highway at 65 mph for $3\frac{1}{2}$ hr. How far does it travel?

12. Holly's Villager minivan traveled 302 mi on $15\frac{1}{10}$ gal of gas. How many miles per gallon did it get?

Answers on page A-13

---

d **Applications and Problem Solving**

■ **EXAMPLE 10** *Cassette Tape Music.* The tape in an audio cassette is played at a rate of $1\frac{7}{8}$ in. per second. A child has destroyed 30 in. of tape. How many seconds of music have been lost?

1. **Familiarize.** We can make a drawing to help us visualize the situation.

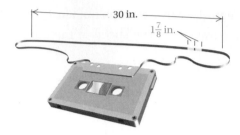

Since each $1\frac{7}{8}$ in. of tape represents 1 sec of lost music, the question can be regarded as asking how many $1\frac{7}{8}$-in. segments are in 30 in. of tape. We let t = the number of seconds of music lost.

2. **Translate.** The situation corresponds to a division sentence:

$$t = 30 \div 1\frac{7}{8}. \qquad \text{Note that in.} \div \text{in./sec} = \text{in.} \cdot \text{sec/in.} = \text{sec.}$$

3. **Solve.** To solve the equation, we perform the division:

$$t = 30 \div 1\frac{7}{8}$$

$$= \frac{30}{1} \div \frac{15}{8} \qquad \text{Writing } 1\frac{7}{8} \text{ as an equivalent fraction}$$

$$= \frac{30}{1} \cdot \frac{8}{15} \qquad \text{Multiplying by the reciprocal of } \frac{15}{8}$$

$$= \frac{15 \cdot 2 \cdot 8}{1 \cdot 15} \qquad \text{Removing a factor equal to 1: } \frac{15}{15} = 1$$

$$= 16. \qquad \text{This represents the number of seconds lost.}$$

4. **Check.** We check by multiplying. If 16 sec of music were lost, then

$$16 \cdot 1\frac{7}{8} = \frac{16}{1} \cdot \frac{15}{8} \qquad \text{Note that sec} \cdot \text{in./sec} = \text{in.}$$

$$= \frac{8 \cdot 2 \cdot 15}{1 \cdot 8} \qquad \text{Removing a factor equal to 1: } \frac{8}{8} = 1$$

$$= \frac{2 \cdot 15}{1}$$

$$= 30 \text{ in.}$$

of tape were destroyed. A quicker, but less precise, check can be made by noting that $1\frac{7}{8} \approx 2$. Then $16 \cdot 1\frac{7}{8} \approx 16 \cdot 2 = 32 \approx 30$. Our answer checks.

5. **State.** The cassette has lost 16 sec of music.

Do Exercises 11 and 12.

EXAMPLE 11 *Mirror Area.* The mirror-backed candle shelf, shown below with a carpenter's diagram, was designed and built by Harry Cooper. Such shelves were popular in Colonial times because the mirror provided extra lighting from the candle. A rectangular walnut board is used to make the back of the shelf. Find the area of the original board and the amount left over after the opening for the mirror has been cut out.
Source: *Popular Science* Woodworking Projects

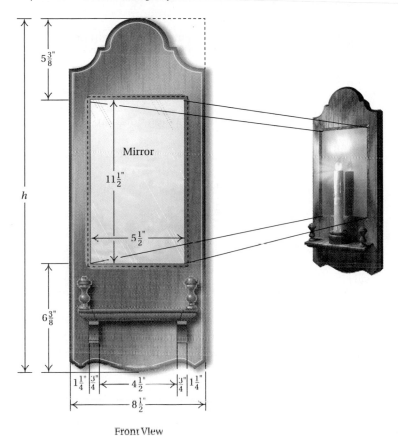

Front View

1. **Familiarize.** Note that there are two rectangles in the diagram: one representing the original board and one representing the mirror. Note too that we can determine the area of the mirror from the given information, but to determine the area of the original board, we must first find its height in inches. This height can be found by adding the vertical measurements, $6\frac{3}{8}''$, $11\frac{1}{2}''$, and $5\frac{3}{8}''$. We let R = the area, in square inches, of the original board after the mirror opening has been removed.

2. **Translate.** We rephrase and translate as follows:

Rephrase: $\underbrace{\text{Area of board after opening is cut}}$ is $\underbrace{\text{Area of original board}}$ minus $\underbrace{\text{Area of mirror.}}$

Translate: $R \quad = \quad 8\frac{1}{2}\left(6\frac{3}{8} + 11\frac{1}{2} + 5\frac{3}{8}\right) \quad - \quad 5\frac{1}{2} \cdot 11\frac{1}{2}$

13. A room measures $22\frac{1}{2}$ ft by $15\frac{1}{2}$ ft. A 9-ft by 12-ft Oriental rug is placed in the center of the room. How much area is not covered by the rug?

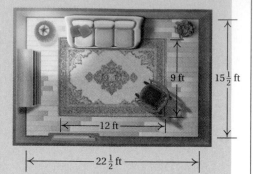

9 ft

$15\frac{1}{2}$ ft

12 ft

$22\frac{1}{2}$ ft

3. Solve. We calculate as follows:

$$R = 8\frac{1}{2}\left(6\frac{3}{8} + 11\frac{1}{2} + 5\frac{3}{8}\right) - 5\frac{1}{2} \cdot 11\frac{1}{2}$$

$$= 8\frac{1}{2}\left(6\frac{3}{8} + 11\frac{4}{8} + 5\frac{3}{8}\right) - 5\frac{1}{2} \cdot 11\frac{1}{2} \quad \text{Finding a common denominator}$$

$$= 8\frac{1}{2} \cdot 22\frac{10}{8} - 5\frac{1}{2} \cdot 11\frac{1}{2}$$

$$= 8\frac{1}{2} \cdot 22\frac{5}{4} - 5\frac{1}{2} \cdot 11\frac{1}{2} \quad \left.\right\} \quad \begin{array}{l}\text{Finding the height of}\\\text{the original board}\end{array}$$

$$= 8\frac{1}{2} \cdot 23\frac{1}{4} - 5\frac{1}{2} \cdot 11\frac{1}{2}$$

$$= \frac{17}{2} \cdot \frac{93}{4} - \frac{11}{2} \cdot \frac{23}{2} \quad \text{Writing fraction notation}$$

$$= \frac{1581}{8} - \frac{253}{4} \quad \text{Multiplying}$$

This is the area of the mirror.

$$= 197\frac{5}{8} - 63\frac{1}{4}$$

This is the area of the original board.

$$= 197\frac{5}{8} - 63\frac{2}{8} \quad \left.\right\}$$

$$= 134\frac{3}{8}. \quad \left.\right\} \quad \text{Subtracting}$$

4. Check. To check, we can separately calculate the two rectangular areas and then subtract. This is almost the same as repeating the calculations. We leave this for the student.

5. State. The area of the original board is $197\frac{5}{8}$ in². The area left over is $134\frac{3}{8}$ in².

Do Exercise 13.

CALCULATOR CORNER

Mixed numerals are multiplied or divided on a fraction calculator or a graphing calculator in much the same way that addition or subtraction is performed. For example, to find $3\frac{2}{3} \cdot 4\frac{1}{5}$, we press

$$\boxed{3}\ \boxed{a^{b}/_{c}}\ \boxed{2}\ \boxed{a^{b}/_{c}}\ \boxed{3}\ \boxed{\times}\ \boxed{4}\ \boxed{a^{b}/_{c}}\ \boxed{1}\ \boxed{a^{b}/_{c}}\ \boxed{5}\ \boxed{=}.$$

The calculator displays

$$\boxed{15\ \lrcorner 2\ \lrcorner 5},$$

so the product is $15\frac{2}{5}$.

Exercises: Perform each calculation. Give the answer as a mixed numeral.

1. $2\frac{1}{3} \cdot 4\frac{3}{5}$

2. $10\frac{7}{10} \div 3\frac{5}{6}$

3. $-7\frac{2}{9} \div 4\frac{1}{5}$

4. $-7\frac{9}{16} \cdot 3\frac{4}{7}$

5. $4\frac{12}{13} \cdot 6\frac{4}{11}$

6. $2\frac{10}{17} \cdot 9\frac{11}{13}$

Answer on page A-13

CHAPTER 4: Fraction Notation: Addition and Subtraction

EXAMPLE 12 Melody has had three children. Their birth weights were $7\frac{1}{2}$ lb, $7\frac{3}{4}$ lb, and $6\frac{3}{4}$ lb. What was the average weight of her babies?

1. **Familiarize.** Recall that to compute an *average*, we add the values and then divide the sum by the number of values. We let $w =$ the average weight, in pounds.

2. **Translate.** We have

$$w = \frac{7\frac{1}{2} + 7\frac{3}{4} + 6\frac{3}{4}}{3}.$$

3. **Solve.** We first add:

$$7\frac{1}{2} + 7\frac{3}{4} + 6\frac{3}{4} = 7\frac{2}{4} + 7\frac{3}{4} + 6\frac{3}{4} \qquad \text{Finding the LCD}$$

$$= 20\frac{8}{4}$$

$$= 22. \qquad 20\frac{8}{4} = 20 + \frac{8}{4} = 20 + 2$$

Then we divide:

$$w = \frac{7\frac{1}{2} + 7\frac{3}{4} + 6\frac{3}{4}}{3} = \frac{22}{3} = 7\frac{1}{3}. \qquad \text{Dividing by 3}$$

4. **Check.** As a partial check, we note that the average is smaller than the largest individual value and larger than the smallest individual value. We could also repeat our calculations.

5. **State.** The average weight of the three babies was $7\frac{1}{3}$ lb.

Do Exercise 14.

14. After two weeks, Kurt's tomato seedlings measure $9\frac{1}{2}$ in., $10\frac{3}{4}$ in., $10\frac{1}{4}$ in., and 9 in. tall. Find their average height.

Answer on page A-13

4.7

EXERCISE SET

For Extra Help

Digital Video
Tutor CD 3
Videotape 4

InterAct
Math

Math Tutor
Center

MathXL

MyMathLab

a Multiply. Write a mixed numeral for each answer.

1. $16 \cdot 1\frac{2}{5}$

2. $5 \cdot 3\frac{3}{4}$

3. $6\frac{2}{3} \cdot \frac{1}{4}$

4. $-9 \cdot 2\frac{3}{5}$

5. $20\left(-2\frac{5}{6}\right)$

6. $7\frac{3}{8} \cdot 4\frac{1}{3}$

7. $3\frac{1}{2} \cdot 4\frac{2}{3}$

8. $4\frac{1}{5} \cdot 5\frac{1}{4}$

9. $-2\frac{3}{10} \cdot 4\frac{2}{5}$

10. $4\frac{7}{10} \cdot 5\frac{3}{10}$

11. $\left(-6\frac{3}{10}\right)\left(-5\frac{7}{10}\right)$

12. $-20\frac{1}{2} \cdot \left(-10\frac{1}{5}\right)$

b Divide. Write a mixed numeral for each answer whenever possible.

13. $30 \div 2\frac{3}{5}$

14. $18 \div 2\frac{1}{4}$

15. $8\frac{2}{5} \div 7$

16. $3\frac{3}{8} \div 3$

17. $5\frac{1}{4} \div 2\frac{3}{5}$

18. $5\frac{4}{5} \div 2\frac{1}{2}$

19. $-5\frac{1}{4} \div 2\frac{3}{7}$

20. $-4\frac{3}{8} \div 2\frac{5}{6}$

21. $5\frac{1}{10} \div 4\frac{3}{10}$

22. $4\frac{1}{10} \div 2\frac{1}{10}$

23. $20\frac{1}{4} \div (-90)$

24. $12\frac{1}{2} \div (-50)$

c Evaluate.

25. lw, for $l = 2\frac{3}{5}$ and $w = 9$

26. mv, for $m = 7$ and $v = 3\frac{2}{5}$

27. rs, for $r = 5$ and $s = 3\frac{1}{7}$

28. rt, for $r = 5\frac{2}{3}$ and $t = -2\frac{3}{8}$

29. mt, for $m = 6\frac{2}{9}$ and $t = -4\frac{3}{5}$

30. $M \div NP$, for $M = 2\frac{1}{4}$, $N = -5$, and $P = 2\frac{1}{3}$

31. $R \cdot S \div T$, for $R = 4\frac{2}{3}$, $S = 1\frac{3}{7}$, and $T = -5$

32. $a - bc$, for $a = 18$, $b = 2\frac{1}{5}$, and $c = 3\frac{3}{4}$

33. $r + ps$, for $r = 5\frac{1}{2}$, $p = 3$, and $s = 2\frac{1}{4}$

34. $s + rt$, for $s = 3\frac{1}{2}$, $r = 5\frac{1}{2}$, and $t = 7\frac{1}{2}$

35. $m + n \div p$, for $m = 7\frac{2}{5}$, $n = 4\frac{1}{2}$, and $p = 6$

36. $x - y \div z$, for $x = 9$, $y = 2\frac{1}{2}$, and $z = 3\frac{3}{4}$

 Solve.

37. *Exercise.* At one point during a spinning class at Rhonda's health club, her bicycle wheel was completing $96\frac{2}{3}$ revolutions per minute. How many revolutions did the wheel complete in 6 min?

38. *Home Furnishings.* Each shelf in June's entertainment center is 27 in. long. A videocassette is $1\frac{1}{8}$ in. thick. How many cassettes can she place on each shelf?

39. *Sodium Consumption.* The average American woman consumes $1\frac{1}{3}$ tsp of sodium each day. How much sodium do 10 average American women consume in one day?
Source: *Nutrition Action Health Letter*, March 1994, p. 6. 1875 Connecticut Ave., N.W., Washington, DC 20009-5728.

40. *Aeronautics.* Most space shuttles orbit the earth once every $1\frac{1}{2}$ hr. How many orbits are made every 24 hr?

41. *Cookie Sheet Apple Pie.* Listed below is the recipe for cookie sheet apple pie. What are the ingredients for $\frac{1}{2}$ recipe? for 5 recipes?
Source: Reprinted with permission from Taste of Home, Greendale, WI, www.tasteofhome.com

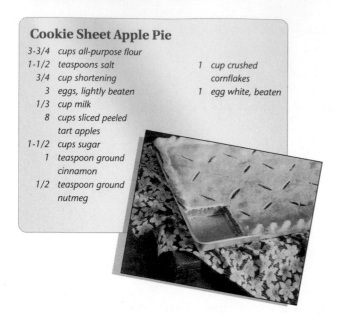

Cookie Sheet Apple Pie

3-3/4　cups all-purpose flour
1-1/2　teaspoons salt
3/4　cup shortening
3　eggs, lightly beaten
1/3　cup milk
8　cups sliced peeled tart apples
1-1/2　cups sugar
1　teaspoon ground cinnamon
1/2　teaspoon ground nutmeg

1　cup crushed cornflakes
1　egg white, beaten

42. *Fruit Cocktail Bars.* Listed below is the recipe for fruit cocktail bars. What are the ingredients for $\frac{1}{2}$ recipe? for 3 recipes?
Source: Reprinted with permission from Taste of Home, Greendale, WI, www.tasteofhome.com

Fruit Cocktail Bars

1-1/2　cups sugar
2　eggs
1　can (17 ounces) fruit cocktail, undrained
1　teaspoon vanilla extract
2-1/4　cups all-purpose flour
1-1/2　teaspoons baking soda
1　teaspoon salt
1-1/3　cups flaked coconut
1　cup chopped walnuts

Glaze:
1/2　cup sugar
1/4　cup butter **or** margarine
2　tablespoons milk
1/4　teaspoon vanilla extract

43. *Temperatures.* Fahrenheit temperature can be obtained from Celsius (centigrade) temperature by multiplying by $1\frac{4}{5}$ and adding 32°. What Fahrenheit temperature corresponds to a Celsius temperature of 20°?

44. *Temperature.* Fahrenheit temperature can be obtained from Celsius (centigrade) temperature by multiplying by $1\frac{4}{5}$ and adding 32°. What Fahrenheit temperature corresponds to the Celsius temperature of boiling water, which is 100°?

45. *Word Processing.* Kelly wants to create a table using Microsoft® Word software for word processing. She needs to have two columns, each $1\frac{1}{2}$ in. wide, and five columns, each $\frac{3}{4}$ in. wide. Will this table fit on a piece of standard paper that is $8\frac{1}{2}$ in. wide? If so, how wide will each margin be if her margins on each side are to be of equal width?

46. *Construction.* A rectangular lot has dimensions of $302\frac{1}{2}$ ft by $205\frac{1}{4}$ ft. A building with dimensions of 100 ft by $25\frac{1}{2}$ ft is built on the lot. How much area is left over?

47. Rick's Honda Odyssey traveled 385 mi on $15\frac{4}{10}$ gal of gas. How many miles per gallon did it get?

48. Lois's Ford Explorer traveled 213 mi on $14\frac{2}{10}$ gal of gas. How many miles per gallon did it get?

49. A serving of filleted fish is generally considered to be about $\frac{1}{3}$ lb. How many servings can be prepared from $5\frac{1}{2}$ lb of salmon fillet?

50. A serving of fish steak (cross section) is generally $\frac{1}{2}$ lb. How many salmon steak servings can be prepared from a cleaned $18\frac{3}{4}$-lb salmon?

51. The weight of water is $62\frac{1}{2}$ lb per cubic foot. What is the weight of $5\frac{1}{2}$ cubic feet of water?

52. The weight of water is $62\frac{1}{2}$ lb per cubic foot. What is the weight of $2\frac{1}{4}$ cubic feet of water?

53. *Video Recording.* The tape in a VCR operating in the short-play mode travels at a rate of $1\frac{3}{8}$ in. per second. How many inches of tape are used to record for 60 sec in the short-play mode?

54. *Audio Recording.* The tape in an audio cassette is played at the rate of $1\frac{7}{8}$ in. per second. How many inches of tape are used when a cassette is played for $5\frac{1}{2}$ sec?

55. *Weightlifting.* In 1997, weightlifter Gao Shihong of China snatched $103\frac{1}{2}$ kg. This amount was about $1\frac{1}{2}$ times her body weight. How much did Shihong weigh?
Source: *The Guinness Book of Records*, 1998

56. *Weightlifting.* In 1983, weightlifter Stefan Topurov of Bulgaria hoisted $396\frac{3}{4}$ lb over his head. This amount was about three times his body weight. How much did Topurov weigh?
Source: *The Guinness Book of Records*, 1998

57. *Birth Weights.* The Piper quadruplets of Great Britain weighed $2\frac{9}{16}$ lb, $2\frac{9}{32}$ lb, $2\frac{1}{0}$ lb, and $2\frac{5}{16}$ lb at birth. Find their average birth weight.
Source: *The Guinness Book of Records*, 1990

58. *Vertical Leaps.* Eight-year-old Zachary registered vertical leaps of $12\frac{3}{4}$ in., $13\frac{3}{4}$ in., $13\frac{1}{2}$ in., and 14 in. Find his average vertical leap.

59. *Manufacturing.* A test of five light bulbs showed that they burned for the lengths of time given on the graph below. For how many days, on average, did the bulbs burn?

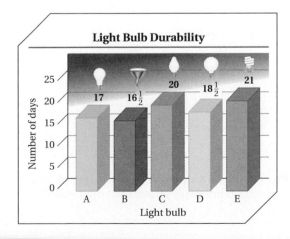

60. *Packaging.* A sample of four bags of beef jerky showed the weights given on the graph below. What was the average weight?

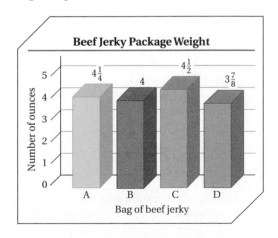

61. *Home Furnishings.* An L-shaped room consists of a rectangle that is $8\frac{1}{2}$ ft by 11 ft adjacent to one that is $6\frac{1}{2}$ by $7\frac{1}{2}$ ft. What is the total area of a carpet that covers the floor?

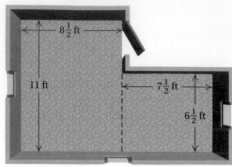

62. *Home Furnishings.* An L-shaped sun room consists of a rectangle that is $9\frac{1}{2}$ ft by 12 ft adjacent to one that is $9\frac{1}{2}$ ft by 8 ft. What is the total area of a carpet that covers the floor?

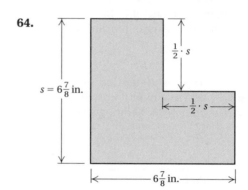

Find the area of each shaded region.

63.

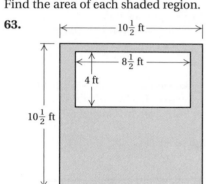

64.

65.

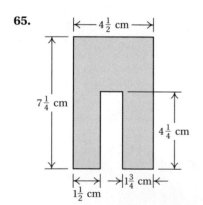

66.

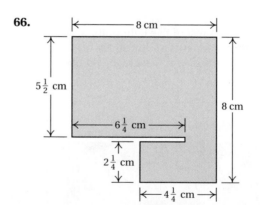

67. DW Under what circumstances is a pair of mixed numerals more easily multiplied than added?

68. DW Under what circumstances is a pair of mixed numerals more easily added than multiplied?

Multiply or divide, as indicated, and, if possible, simplify.

69. $\dfrac{7}{10} \cdot \dfrac{3}{10}$ [3.6a]

70. $\dfrac{9}{10} \div \dfrac{21}{100}$ [3.7b]

71. $-\dfrac{63}{100} \div \dfrac{7}{10}$ [3.7b]

72. $\begin{array}{r} 6\ 7\ 0\ 9 \\ \times\quad 2\ 1\ 3 \end{array}$ [1.5a]

73. $\begin{array}{r} 5\ 2\ 8\ 9 \\ \times\quad\ \ 7\ 6\ 8 \end{array}$ [1.5a]

74. $\begin{array}{r} 8\ 9\ 7\ 4 \\ \times\quad\ \ 8\ 5\ 7 \end{array}$ [1.5a]

75. Round to the nearest ten: 45,765.   [1.4a]

76. Round to the nearest hundred: 45,765.   [1.4a]

77. $\mathbf{D_W}$ A turntable for long-playing records (LPs) typically turns $33\frac{1}{3}$ revolutions per minute. Write a problem that involves a turntable and has "The turntable spins $181\frac{1}{3}$ times" as the solution.

78. $\mathbf{D_W}$ If Kate and Jessie are both less than 5 ft, $6\frac{1}{2}$ in. tall, but Dot is over 5 ft, $6\frac{1}{2}$ in. tall, is it possible that the average height of the three exceeds 5 ft, $6\frac{1}{2}$ in.? Why or why not?

Simplify. Write each answer as a mixed numeral whenever possible.

79. 🖩 $15\dfrac{2}{11} \cdot 23\dfrac{31}{43}$

80. 🖩 $17\dfrac{23}{31} \cdot 19\dfrac{13}{15}$

81. $8 \div \dfrac{1}{2} + \dfrac{3}{4} + \left(-5 - \dfrac{5}{8}\right)^2$

82. $\left(\dfrac{5}{9} - \dfrac{1}{4}\right)(-12) + \left(-4 - \dfrac{3}{4}\right)^2$

83. $\dfrac{1}{3} \div \left(\dfrac{1}{2} - \dfrac{1}{5}\right) \times \dfrac{1}{4} + \dfrac{1}{6}$

84. $\dfrac{7}{8} - 1\dfrac{1}{8} \times \dfrac{2}{3} + \dfrac{9}{10} \div \dfrac{3}{5}$

85. $4\dfrac{1}{2} \div 2\dfrac{1}{2} + 8 - 4 \div \dfrac{1}{2}$

86. $6 - 2\dfrac{1}{3} \times \dfrac{3}{4} + \dfrac{5}{8} \div \dfrac{2}{3}$

87. Find r if

$$\dfrac{1}{r} = \dfrac{1}{40} + \dfrac{1}{60} + \dfrac{1}{80}.$$

88. *Heights.*   Find the average height of the following NBA players:

Kevin Garnett	6 ft, 11 in.
Ray Allen	6 ft, 5 in.
Travis Best	5 ft, 11 in.
Kobe Bryant	6 ft, 7 in.
Shaquille O'Neal	7 ft, 1 in.

89. *Water Consumption.*   According to the *Consumer Guide to Home Energy Savings* (7th edition, by Alex Wilson et al., 1999, published by American Council for an Energy-Efficient America), washing one load of clothes uses $1\frac{3}{5}$ times the amount of hot water required for the average shower. If the average shower uses 20 gallons of hot water, how much hot water will two showers and two loads of wash require?

The review that follows is meant to prepare you for a chapter exam. It consists of two parts. The first part is a checklist of some of the Study Tips referred to in this chapter. The second part is the Review Exercises. These provide practice exercises for the exam, together with references to section objectives so you can go back and review. Before beginning, stop and look back over the skills you have obtained. What skills in mathematics do you have now that you did not have before studying this chapter?

STUDY TIPS CHECKLIST

The foundation of all your study skills is TIME!	☐ Are you writing in any missing steps while reading the examples?
	☐ Are you keeping your supporting work organized and legible?
	☐ Are you contacting your instructor *in advance* of planned absences?
	☐ Are you checking your solutions in the original equation?
	☐ Are you redoing only those problems that give you difficulty?
	☐ Have you considered e-mailing questions to your instructor?
	☐ Are you looking for similarities between new problems and those you already can solve?

REVIEW EXERCISES

Find the LCM. [4.1a]

1. 16 and 20   **2.** 18 and 45   **3.** 3, 6, and 30

Perform the indicated operation and, if possible, simplify.
[4.2a, b], [4.3a]

4. $\dfrac{2}{9} + \dfrac{5}{9}$

5. $\dfrac{7}{x} + \dfrac{2}{x}$

6. $-\dfrac{6}{5} + \dfrac{11}{15}$

7. $\dfrac{5}{16} + \dfrac{3}{24}$

8. $\dfrac{7}{9} - \dfrac{5}{9}$

9. $\dfrac{1}{4} - \dfrac{3}{8}$

10. $\dfrac{10}{27} - \dfrac{2}{9}$

11. $\dfrac{5}{6} - \dfrac{2}{9}$

Use < or > for ☐ to form a true sentence. [4.2c]

12. $\dfrac{4}{7} \ \square \ \dfrac{5}{9}$

13. $-\dfrac{8}{9} \ \square \ -\dfrac{11}{13}$

Solve. [4.3b], [4.4a]

14. $x + \dfrac{2}{5} = \dfrac{7}{8}$

15. $7a - 3 = 25$

16. $5 + \dfrac{16}{3}x = \dfrac{5}{9}$

17. $\dfrac{22}{5} = \dfrac{16}{5} + \dfrac{5}{2}x$

Solve by using the multiplication principle to clear fractions. [4.4b]

18. $\frac{5}{3}x + \frac{5}{6} = \frac{3}{2}$

Convert to fraction notation. [4.5a]

19. $7\frac{1}{2}$

20. $30\frac{4}{9}$

21. $-9\frac{2}{7}$

Convert to a mixed numeral. [4.5b]

22. $\frac{13}{5}$

23. $\frac{-27}{4}$

24. $\frac{57}{8}$

25. $\frac{7}{2}$

26. Divide. Write a mixed numeral for the answer. [4.5c]

$7896 \div (-9)$

27. Gina's golf scores were 80, 82, and 85. What was her average score? [4.5c]

Perform the indicated operation. Write a mixed numeral for each answer. [4.6a, b, d]

28. $\quad 7\frac{3}{5}$
$+ \ 2\frac{4}{5}$
$\overline{}$

29. $\quad 6\frac{1}{3}$
$+ \ 5\frac{2}{5}$
$\overline{}$

30. $-3\frac{5}{6} + \left(-5\frac{1}{6}\right)$

31. $-2\frac{3}{4} + 4\frac{1}{2}$

32. $\quad 14$
$- \ 6\frac{2}{9}$
$\overline{}$

33. $\quad 9\frac{3}{5}$
$- \ 4\frac{13}{15}$
$\overline{}$

34. $4\frac{5}{8} - 9\frac{3}{4}$

35. $-7\frac{1}{2} - 6\frac{3}{4}$

Combine like terms. [4.2a], [4.6b]

36. $\frac{4}{9}x + \frac{1}{3}x$

37. $8\frac{3}{10}a - 5\frac{1}{8}a$

Perform the indicated operation. Write a mixed numeral or integer for each answer. [4.7a, b]

38. $6 \cdot 2\frac{2}{3}$

39. $-5\frac{1}{4} \cdot \frac{2}{3}$

40. $2\frac{1}{5} \cdot 1\frac{1}{10}$

41. $2\frac{2}{5} \cdot 2\frac{1}{2}$

42. $-54 \div 2\frac{1}{4}$

43. $2\frac{2}{5} \div \left(-1\frac{7}{10}\right)$

44. $3\frac{1}{4} \div 26$

45. $4\frac{1}{5} \div 4\frac{2}{3}$

Evaluate. [4.7c]

46. $5x - y$, for $x = 3\frac{1}{5}$ and $y = 2\frac{2}{7}$

47. $2a \div b$, for $a = 5\frac{2}{11}$ and $b = 3\frac{4}{5}$

Solve.

48. A curtain requires $2\frac{3}{5}$ m of material. How many such curtains can be made from 39 m of material? [4.7d]

49. The San Diaz drama club had $\frac{3}{8}$ of a vegetarian pizza, $1\frac{1}{2}$ plain pizzas, and $1\frac{1}{4}$ pepperoni pizzas remaining after a cast party. How many pizzas remained altogether? [4.6c]

50. Mica pedals up a $\frac{1}{10}$-mi hill and then coasts for $\frac{1}{2}$ mi down the other side. How far has she traveled? [4.2d]

51. A wedding-cake recipe requires 12 cups of shortening. Being calorie-conscious, the wedding couple decides to reduce the shortening by $3\frac{5}{8}$ cups and replace it with prune purée. How many cups of shortening are used in their new recipe? [4.6c]

52. What is the sum of the areas in the figure below? [4.6c], [4.7d]

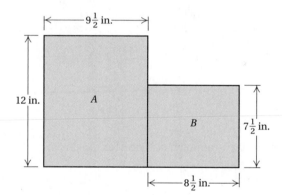

53. In the figure in Exercise 52, how much larger is the area of rectangle A than the area of rectangle B? [4.6c], [4.7d]

54. Multiply and simplify: $\frac{9}{10} \cdot \left(-\frac{7}{10}\right)$. [3.6a]

55. Divide and simplify: $\frac{3}{10} \div \left(-\frac{17}{100}\right)$. [3.7b]

56. Bright Sunshine Landscaping made $230 Monday but lost $150 on Tuesday and $110 on Wednesday. Find the total profit or loss. [2.3b]

57. Multiply: $7(a - 9)$. [2.6b]

58. **Dw** Rachel insists that $3\frac{2}{5} \cdot 1\frac{3}{7} = 3\frac{6}{35}$. What mistake is she probably making and how should she have proceeded instead? [4.7a]

59. **Dw** Do least common multiples play any role in the addition or subtraction of mixed numerals? Why or why not? [4.6a, b]

60. ▦ Find the LCM of 141, 2419, and 1357. [4.1a]

61. Find r if
$$\frac{1}{r} = \frac{1}{100} + \frac{1}{150} + \frac{1}{200}.$$ [4.2b], [4.4b]

62. Find the smallest integer for which each fraction is greater than $\frac{1}{2}$. [4.2c]

a) $\dfrac{\square}{11}$ b) $\dfrac{\square}{8}$

c) $\dfrac{\square}{23}$ d) $\dfrac{\square}{35}$

e) $\dfrac{-51}{\square}$ f) $\dfrac{-78}{\square}$

g) $\dfrac{-2}{\sqcap}$ h) $\dfrac{-1}{\square}$

63. Find the largest integer for which each fraction is greater than 1. [4.2c]

a) $\dfrac{7}{\square}$ b) $\dfrac{11}{\square}$

c) $\dfrac{47}{\square}$ d) $\dfrac{\frac{9}{8}}{\square}$

e) $\dfrac{\square}{-13}$ f) $\dfrac{\square}{-27}$

g) $\dfrac{\square}{-1}$ h) $\dfrac{\square}{-\frac{1}{2}}$

1. Find the LCM of 12 and 16.

Perform the indicated operation and, if possible, simplify.

2. $\dfrac{1}{2} + \dfrac{5}{2}$

3. $-\dfrac{7}{8} + \dfrac{2}{3}$

4. $\dfrac{5}{t} - \dfrac{3}{t}$

5. $\dfrac{5}{6} - \dfrac{3}{4}$

6. $\dfrac{5}{8} - \dfrac{17}{24}$

7. Use $<$ or $>$ for $\square$ to form a true sentence.

$\dfrac{6}{7} \ \square \ \dfrac{21}{25}$

Solve.

8. $x + \dfrac{2}{3} = \dfrac{11}{12}$

9. $-5x - 3 = 9$

10. $\dfrac{3}{4} = \dfrac{1}{2} + \dfrac{5}{3}x$

Convert to fraction notation.

11. $3\dfrac{1}{2}$

12. $-9\dfrac{3}{8}$

13. Convert to a mixed numeral:

$-\dfrac{74}{9}$

14. Divide. Write a mixed numeral for the answer.

$1\ 1\ \overline{)\ 1\cdot 7\ 8\ 9}$

Perform the indicated operation. Write a mixed numeral for each answer.

15. $\quad 6\dfrac{2}{5}$

$\quad + \ 7\dfrac{4}{5}$

16. $\quad 3\dfrac{1}{4}$

$\quad + \ 9\dfrac{1}{6}$

17. $\quad 10\dfrac{1}{6}$

$\quad - \ 5\dfrac{7}{8}$

18. $14 + \left(-5\dfrac{3}{7}\right)$

19. $3\dfrac{4}{5} - 9\dfrac{1}{2}$

Combine like terms.

20. $\dfrac{3}{8}x - \dfrac{1}{2}x$

21. $5\dfrac{2}{11}a - 3\dfrac{1}{5}a$

Perform the indicated operation. Write a mixed numeral for each answer.

22. $9 \cdot 4\frac{1}{3}$

23. $6\frac{3}{4} \cdot \left(-2\frac{2}{3}\right)$

24. $33 \div 5\frac{1}{2}$

25. $2\frac{1}{3} \div 1\frac{1}{6}$

Evaluate.

26. $\frac{2}{3}ab$, for $a = 7$ and $b = 4\frac{1}{5}$

27. $4 + mn$, for $m = 7\frac{2}{5}$ and $n = 3\frac{1}{4}$

Solve.

28. One batch of low-cholesterol turkey chili calls for $1\frac{1}{2}$ lb of roasted turkey breast. How much turkey is needed for 5 batches?

29. An order of books for a math course weighs 220 lb. Each book weighs $2\frac{3}{4}$ lb. How many books are in the order?

30. Marilyn weighs $123\frac{1}{2}$ lb. Her brother Mike weighs $173\frac{1}{2}$ lb. What is the average of their weights?

31. A standard piece of paper is $\frac{43}{200}$ m by $\frac{7}{25}$ m. By how much does the length exceed the width?

SKILL MAINTENANCE

32. Multiply: $-3(x - 4)$.

33. Divide and simplify:
$$\left(-\frac{19}{10}\right) \div \left(\frac{21}{100}\right).$$

34. Round 5347 to the nearest hundred.

35. A rock climber descended from an altitude of 720 ft to a depth of 470 ft below sea level. How many feet did the climber descend?

SYNTHESIS

36. Yuri and Olga are orangutans who perform in a circus by riding bicycles around a circular track. It takes Yuri $\frac{6}{25}$ min and Olga $\frac{8}{25}$ min to complete one lap. They start their act together at one point and complete their act when they are next together at that point. How long does the act last?

37. Dolores runs 17 laps at her health club. Terence runs 17 laps at his health club. If the track at Dolores's health club is $\frac{1}{7}$ mi long, and the track at Terence's is $\frac{1}{8}$ mi long, who runs farther? How much farther?

38. The students in a math class can be organized into study groups of 8 each such that no students are left out. The same class of students can also be organized into groups of 6 such that no students are left out.

a) Find some class sizes for which this will work.
b) Find the smallest such class size.

39. Simplify each of the following, using fraction notation. Try to answer part (e) by recognizing a pattern in parts (a) through (d).

a) $\dfrac{1}{1 \cdot 2}$

b) $\dfrac{1}{1 \cdot 2} + \dfrac{1}{2 \cdot 3}$

c) $\dfrac{1}{1 \cdot 2} + \dfrac{1}{2 \cdot 3} + \dfrac{1}{3 \cdot 4}$

d) $\dfrac{1}{1 \cdot 2} + \dfrac{1}{2 \cdot 3} + \dfrac{1}{3 \cdot 4} + \dfrac{1}{4 \cdot 5}$

e) $\dfrac{1}{1 \cdot 2} + \dfrac{1}{2 \cdot 3} + \dfrac{1}{3 \cdot 4} + \dfrac{1}{4 \cdot 5} + \dfrac{1}{5 \cdot 6} + \dfrac{1}{6 \cdot 7} + \dfrac{1}{7 \cdot 8} + \dfrac{1}{8 \cdot 9} + \dfrac{1}{9 \cdot 10}$

1. In the number 2753, what digit names tens?

2. Write expanded notation for 6075.

3. Write a word name for the number in the following sentence: The diameter of Uranus is 29,500 miles.

Add and, if possible, simplify.

4. $\begin{array}{r} 3\ 7\ 5 \\ +\ 2\ 4\ 8 \\ \hline \end{array}$

5. $29 + (-37)$

6. $\dfrac{3}{8} + \dfrac{1}{24}$

7. $\begin{array}{r} 2\dfrac{3}{4} \\ +\ 5\dfrac{1}{2} \\ \hline \end{array}$

Subtract and, if possible, simplify.

8. $\begin{array}{r} 7\ 4\ 6\ 9 \\ -\ 2\ 3\ 4\ 5 \\ \hline \end{array}$

9. $-9 - (-25)$

10. $\dfrac{4}{t} - \dfrac{9}{t}$

11. $\begin{array}{r} 2\dfrac{1}{3} \\ -\ 1\dfrac{1}{6} \\ \hline \end{array}$

Multiply and, if possible, simplify.

12. $\begin{array}{r} 2\ 7\ 8 \\ \times\ \ 1\ 8 \\ \hline \end{array}$

13. $29(-5)$

14. $\dfrac{9}{10} \cdot \dfrac{5}{3}$

15. $18\left(-\dfrac{5}{6}\right)$

16. $2\dfrac{1}{3} \cdot 3\dfrac{1}{7}$

Divide. Write the answer with the remainder in the form 34 R 7.

17. $731 \div 15$

18. $4\ 5\ )\overline{\ 2\ 5\ 3\ 1\ }$

19. In Question 18, write a mixed numeral for the answer.

Divide and, if possible, simplify.

20. $\dfrac{2}{5} \div \left(-\dfrac{7}{10}\right)$

21. $2\dfrac{1}{5} \div \dfrac{3}{10}$

22. Round 38,478 to the nearest hundred.

23. Find the LCM of 24 and 36.

24. Without performing the division, determine whether 4296 is divisible by 6.

25. Find all factors of 16.

26. What part is shaded?

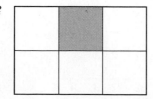

Use $<$, $>$, or $=$ for $\square$ to form a true sentence.

27. $\dfrac{4}{5} \ \square\ \dfrac{4}{6}$

28. $-\dfrac{3}{7} \ \square\ -\dfrac{5}{12}$

Simplify.

29. $\dfrac{36}{45}$

30. $-\dfrac{420}{30}$

31. Convert to fraction notation: $7\dfrac{3}{10}$.

32. Convert to a mixed numeral: $-\dfrac{17}{3}$.

Solve.

33. $x + 37 = 92$

34. $x + \dfrac{7}{9} = \dfrac{4}{3}$

35. $\dfrac{7}{9} \cdot t = -\dfrac{4}{3}$

36. $\dfrac{5}{7} = \dfrac{1}{3} + 4a$

37. Evaluate $\dfrac{t + p}{3}$ for $t = -4$ and $p = 16$.

38. Multiply: $7(b - 5)$.

39. Multiply: $-3(x - 2 + z)$.

40. Combine like terms: $x - 5 - 7x - 4$.

Solve.

41. A jacket costs $87 and a coat costs $148. How much does it cost to buy both?

42. The emergency soup kitchen fund contains $978. From this fund, $148 and $167 are withdrawn for expenses. How much is left in the fund?

43. A rectangular lot measures 27 ft by 11 ft. What is its area?

44. How many people can get equal $16 shares from a total of $496?

45. A recipe calls for $\frac{4}{5}$ tsp of salt. How much salt should be used in $\frac{1}{2}$ recipe?

46. A book weighs $2\frac{3}{5}$ lb. How much do 15 books weigh?

47. How many pieces, each $2\frac{3}{8}$ cm long, can be cut from a piece of wire 38 cm long?

48. How long is the shortest bolt that will pass through a $\frac{1}{16}$-in. thick washer, a $\frac{3}{4}$-in. thick backboard, and a $\frac{3}{8}$-in. thick nut? Disregard the head of the bolt.

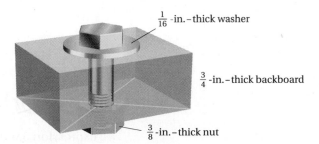

$\frac{1}{16}$ -in.–thick washer

$\frac{3}{4}$ -in.–thick backboard

$\frac{3}{8}$ -in.–thick nut

SYNTHESIS

49. Solve: $7x - \dfrac{2}{3}(x - 6) = 6\dfrac{5}{7}$.

50. Each floor of a seven-story office building is 25 m by $22\frac{1}{2}$ m, with a 5-m by $4\frac{1}{2}$-m elevator/stairwell. How many square meters of office space are in the building?

Decimal Notation

Gateway to Chapter 5

In this chapter, we consider the meaning of decimal
notation. This will enable us to study addition, subtraction,
multiplication, and division using decimals. Also discussed
are rounding, estimating, equation solving, and problem
solving using decimals.

Real–World Application

The expression $5.06x + 9.7$ can be used to predict the average daily number
of e-mail messages, in billions, in North America x years after 2000. Predict
the average daily volume of e-mail messages in 2008.

Source: Pitney Bowes

This problem appears as Example 19 in Section 5.3.

1. Write a word name for 17.369. [5.1a]

2. Write $625.27 in words, as on a check. [5.1a]

Write each number as a fraction and, if possible, a mixed numeral. [5.1b]

3. 0.89

4. 5.407

Write decimal notation for each number. [5.1b]

5. $\dfrac{287}{100}$

6. $-\dfrac{79}{10,000}$

7. Round 32.0447 to the nearest tenth. [5.1d]

Perform the indicated operation.

8. $\begin{array}{r} 7\ 0\ 4.2 \\ 5.8\ 1 \\ +\quad 0.3\ 0\ 8 \\ \hline \end{array}$ [5.2a]

9. $\begin{array}{r} 3\ 4.0\ 6\ 1 \\ -\quad 2.3\ 2\ 9 \\ \hline \end{array}$ [5.2b]

10. $\begin{array}{r} 7.3\ 2\ 5 \\ \times\quad 0.6\ 4 \\ \hline \end{array}$ [5.3a]

11. $91.6851 - 344.6788$ [5.2b]

12. $-6.6\,\overline{)\,2\ 0\ 0.6\ 4}$ [5.4a]

13. Combine like terms: $8.3a + 4.6a$. [5.2d]

14. Combine like terms: $-2.7x + 5.1 - 4.2x + 1.7$. [5.2d]

15. Simplify: $(2 - 1.7)^2 - 4.1 \times 3.1$. [5.4b]

16. Estimate the sum $3.649 + 4.038$ by rounding to the nearest tenth. [5.6a]

17. Multiply by 1 to find decimal notation for $\frac{7}{5}$. [5.5c]

18. Use division to find decimal notation for $\frac{29}{7}$. [5.5a]

19. Calculate: $\frac{3}{4} \times 2.378$. [5.5d]

20. Find the area of a triangular sail that is 2.8 m wide at the base and 3.1 m tall. [5.5d]

Solve.

21. $x + 4.87 = 9.21$ [5.7a]

22. $-9.6y = 808.896$ [5.7a]

23. $4.2x - 3.8 = 18.88$ [5.7a]

24. $4.7a - 1.9 = 3.2a + 7.1$ [5.7b]

25. $2.3(t + 4) - 0.5t = 5.8t - 9$ [5.7b]

Solve. [5.8a]

26. A checking account contained $434.19. After a $148.24 check was drawn, how much was left in the account?

27. On a three-day trip, Sara drove the following distances: 432.6 mi, 179.2 mi, and 469.8 mi. What was the total number of miles driven?

28. Estimate the cost of 6 compact discs at $14.95 each.

29. Dunkel Construction paid $47,567.89 for 14 acres of land. How much did 1 acre of land cost? Round to the nearest cent.

30. Jorge filled the gas tank of his Ford Focus and noted that the odometer read 52,091.7. At the next fill-up, when the odometer read 52,338.1, it took 8 gal to fill the tank. How many miles per gallon did Jorge's Focus get?

The set of **rational numbers** consists of the **integers**

$$\dots, -3, -2, -1, 0, 1, 2, 3, \dots,$$

and fractions like

$$\frac{1}{2}, \frac{2}{3}, \frac{-7}{8}, \frac{17}{-10}, \text{ and so on.}$$

We used fraction notation for rational numbers in Chapters 3 and 4. Here in Chapter 5, we will use *decimal notation* to represent the set of rational numbers. For example, $\frac{3}{4}$ will be written as 0.75, and $9\frac{1}{2}$ will be written as 9.5. A number written in decimal notation is often simply referred to as a *decimal*.

The word *decimal* comes from the Latin word *decima*, meaning a *tenth part*. Since our usual counting system is based on tens, we will find decimal notation to be a natural extension of a system with which we are already familiar.

CONNECTING THE CONCEPTS

Decimal notation is a method for writing numbers that offers several advantages over fraction or mixed numeral notation. Chief among these advantages is the fact that addition, subtraction, multiplication, and division are performed in much the same way that these operations are performed with whole numbers.

As with fraction and mixed numeral notation, decimal notation can appear in a variety of algebraic expressions and equations. In this chapter we will repeat the pattern used in earlier chapters: First we will master the basics and then, as our skills develop, focus on algebraic expressions and equations.

---

a ## Decimal Notation and Word Names

The Razor Kick Scooter® costs $148.97. The dot in $148.97 is called a **decimal point.** Since $0.97, or 97¢, is $\frac{97}{100}$ of a dollar, it follows that

$$\$148.97 = 148 + \frac{97}{100} \text{ dollars.}$$

Also, since $0.97, or 97¢, has the same value as

9 dimes + 7 cents

and 1 dime is $\frac{1}{10}$ of a dollar and 1 cent is $\frac{1}{100}$ of a dollar, we can write

$$148.97 = 1 \cdot 100 + 4 \cdot 10 + 8 \cdot 1 + 9 \cdot \frac{1}{10} + 7 \cdot \frac{1}{100}.$$

This is an extension of the expanded notation for whole numbers that we used in Chapter 1. The place values are 100, 10, 1, $\frac{1}{10}$, $\frac{1}{100}$, and so on. We can see this on a **place-value chart.** The value of each place is $\frac{1}{10}$ as large as the one to its left.

$148.97

Source: Razor USA

Write a word name for the decimal in each sentence.

1. On average, each person in the United States consumed 15.3 lb of seafood in a recent year.
   Source: National Oceanographic and Atmospheric Administration

2. The average speed during the Homestead, FL, NASCAR race of November 17, 2002, was 116.462 mph.
   Source: *The Daytona Beach News-Journal*, 11/18/02

3. 245.89

4. 34.00647

5. 31,079.764

Let's see how to understand decimal notation using a place-value chart:

PLACE-VALUE CHART							
Hundreds	Tens	Ones	Ten*ths*	Hundred*ths*	Thousand*ths*	Ten-Thousand*ths*	Hundred-Thousand*ths*
100	10	1	$\frac{1}{10}$	$\frac{1}{100}$	$\frac{1}{1000}$	$\frac{1}{10,000}$	$\frac{1}{100,000}$

| | | 2 | 9 | . 5 | 2 | 9 | 7 |

The women's record, held by Junxia Wang of China, in the 10,000-meter run is 29.5297 min.

The decimal notation 29.5297 means

2 tens + 9 ones + 5 tenths + 2 hundredths + 9 thousandths + 7 ten-thousandths

or $\quad 29 + \dfrac{5}{10} + \dfrac{2}{100} + \dfrac{9}{1000} + \dfrac{7}{10,000}.$

Using 10,000 as the least common denominator, we have

$$29.5297 = 29 + \frac{5000}{10,000} + \frac{200}{10,000} + \frac{90}{10,000} + \frac{7}{10,000} = 29\frac{5297}{10,000}.$$

We read both 29.5297 and $29\frac{5297}{10,000}$ as

"Twenty-nine and five thousand two hundred ninety-seven ten-thousandths."

We read the decimal point as "and." Note that the word names to the right of the decimal point always end in *th*. We can also read 29.5297 as "Two nine *point* five two nine seven," or "Twenty-nine point five two nine seven."

To write a word name from decimal notation,

a) write a word name for the whole number (the number named to the left of the decimal point),

397.685
→ Three hundred ninety-seven

b) write the word "and" for the decimal point, and

397.685
Three hundred ninety-seven and

c) write a word name for the number named to the right of the decimal point, followed by the place value of the last digit.

397.685
Three hundred ninety-seven and six hundred eighty-five *thousandths*

EXAMPLE 1 Write a word name for the number in this sentence: The most recent earthquake to shake New England measured 5.2.

Five and two tenths

EXAMPLE 2 Write a word name for the number in this sentence: The world record in the women's pole vault is 4.81 meters, set by Stacy Dragila of the U.S.
Source: *CNN Sports News 2002*

> Four and eighty-one hundredths

EXAMPLE 3 Write a word name for the number in this sentence: The world record in the men's 800-meter run is 1.6852 min, held by Wilson Kipketer of Denmark.
Source: *Guinness World Records 2002*

> One and six thousand eight hundred fifty-two ten-thousandths

EXAMPLE 4 Write a word name for the number in this sentence: The current one-mile land speed record of 763.035 mph is held by Andy Green.
Source: *Guinness World Records 2001*

> Seven hundred sixty-three and thirty-five thousandths

Do Exercises 1–5 on the previous page.

Decimal notation is also used with money. It is common on a check to write "and ninety-five cents" as "and $\frac{95}{100}$ dollars."

EXAMPLE 5 Write $5876.95 in words, as on a check.

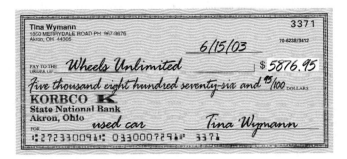

> Five thousand, eight hundred seventy-six and $\frac{95}{100}$ dollars

Do Exercises 6 and 7.

b Converting Between Decimal Notation and Fraction Notation

We can find fraction notation as follows:

$$9.875 = 9 + \frac{875}{1000} = \frac{9000}{1000} + \frac{875}{1000} = \frac{9875}{1000}$$

Decimal notation ──────── Fraction notation

$$9.\underbrace{875}_{\text{3 decimal places}} \qquad \frac{9\underbrace{875}_{}}{1\underbrace{000}_{\text{3 zeros}}}$$

Write in words, as on a check.

6. $4217.56

7. $13.98

Answers on page A-14

Write fraction notation. Do not
simplify.
8. 0.549

To convert from decimal to fraction notation,

a) count the number of decimal places,

4.98
↑
└── 2 places

b) move the decimal point that many
places to the right, and

4.98,   Move
⤷   2 places.

c) write the answer over a denominator
of 1 followed by that number of zeros.

$\dfrac{498}{100}$ 2 zeros

For a number like 0.876, we write a 0 to call attention to the presence of a
decimal point.

EXAMPLE 6   Write fraction notation for 0.876. Do not simplify.

$$0.876 \qquad 0.876. \qquad 0.876 = \frac{876}{1000}$$

3 places   3 zeros

Write as a fraction and as a mixed
numeral.

9. 75.069

Decimals greater than 1 or less than −1 can be written either as fractions
or mixed numerals.

EXAMPLE 7   Write 56.23 as a fraction and as a mixed numeral.

To write as a fraction, we follow the procedure outlined above:

$$56.23 \qquad 56.23. \qquad 56.23 = \frac{5623}{100}$$

2 places   2 zeros

To write 56.23 as a mixed numeral, we rewrite the whole number part and
express the rest in fraction form:

$$56.23 = 56\frac{23}{100}$$

10. −312.9

EXAMPLE 8   Write −2.6073 as a fraction and as a mixed numeral.

We have

$$-2.6073 = -\frac{26,073}{10,000}, \qquad \text{and} \qquad -2.6073 = -2\frac{6073}{10,000}.$$

4 places   4 zeros

Do Exercises 8–10.

To write $\frac{5328}{10}$ as a decimal we can first divide to find an equivalent mixed
numeral:

$$\frac{5328}{10} = 532\frac{8}{10}.$$

Next note that

$$532\frac{8}{10} = 532 + \frac{8}{10}$$

$$= 532.8.$$

$$
\begin{array}{r}
5\ 3\ 2 \\
1\ 0\ \overline{)\ 5\ 3\ 2\ 8} \\
5\ 0 \\ \hline
3\ 2 \\
3\ 0 \\ \hline
2\ 8 \\
2\ 0 \\ \hline
8
\end{array}
$$

Answers on page A-14

This procedure can be generalized. It is the reverse of the procedure used in Examples 6–8.

> To convert from fraction notation to decimal notation when the denominator is 10, 100, 1000, and so on,
>
> a) count the number of zeros, and
>
> $$\frac{8679}{1000}$$
>
> └── 3 zeros
>
> b) move the decimal point that number of places to the left. Leave off the denominator.
>
> 8.679. Move 3 places.
>
> $$\frac{8679}{1000} = 8.679$$

EXAMPLE 9   Write decimal notation for $\frac{47}{10}$.

$$\frac{47}{10}$$

└── 1 zero

4.7.

$$\frac{47}{10} = 4.7$$ The decimal point is moved 1 place.

EXAMPLE 10   Write decimal notation for $\frac{123,067}{10,000}$.

$$\frac{123,067}{10,000}$$

└── 4 zeros

12.3067.

$$\frac{123,067}{10,000} = 12.3067$$ The decimal point is moved 4 places.

To move the decimal point to the left, we may need to write extra 0's.

EXAMPLE 11   Write decimal notation for $-\frac{9}{100}$.

$$-\frac{9}{100}$$

└── 2 zeros

−0.09.

$$-\frac{9}{100} = -0.09$$ The decimal point is moved 2 places.

Do Exercises 11–14.

For denominators other than 10, 100, and so on, we will usually perform long division. This is examined in Section 5.5.

If a mixed numeral has a fraction part with a denominator that is a power of ten, such as 10, 100, or 1000, and so on, we first write the mixed numeral as a sum of a whole number and a fraction. Then we convert to decimal notation.

EXAMPLE 12   Write decimal notation for $23\frac{59}{100}$.

$$23\frac{59}{100} = 23 + \frac{59}{100} = 23 \text{ and } \frac{59}{100} = 23.59$$

Do Exercises 15 and 16.

Write decimal notation for each number.

11. $\frac{743}{100}$

12. $-\frac{73}{1000}$

13. $\frac{67,089}{10,000}$

14. $-\frac{9}{10}$

Write decimal notation for each number.

15. $-7\frac{3}{100}$

16. $23\frac{47}{1000}$

Answers on page A-14

17. 2.04,   2.039

18. 0.06,   0.008

19. 0.5,   0.58

20. 1,   0.9999

Which number is larger?

21. 0.8989,   0.09898

22. 21.006,   21.05

23. −34.01,   −34.008

24. −9.12,   −8.98

Answers on page A-14

C Order

To compare numbers in decimal notation, consider 0.85 and 0.9. First note that $0.9 = 0.90$ because $\frac{9}{10} = \frac{90}{100}$. Since $0.85 = \frac{85}{100}$, it follows that $\frac{85}{100} < \frac{90}{100}$ and $0.85 < 0.9$. This leads us to a quick way to compare two numbers in decimal notation.

> To compare two positive numbers in decimal notation, start at the left and compare corresponding digits. When two digits differ, the number with the larger digit is the larger of the two numbers. To ease the comparison, extra zeros can be written to the right of the last decimal place.

EXAMPLE 13   Which is larger: 2.109 or 2.1?

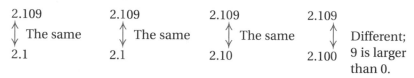

Thus, 2.109 is larger. In symbols, 2.109 > 2.1.

EXAMPLE 14   Which is larger: 0.09 or 0.108?

0.09	0.09
↕ The same	↕ Different; 1 is larger than 0.
0.108	0.108

Thus, 0.108 is larger. In symbols, 0.108 > 0.09.

Do Exercises 17–20.

As before, we can use a number line to visualize order. We illustrate Examples 13 and 14 below. Larger numbers are always to the right.

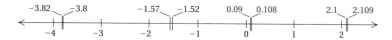

Note from the number line that $-2 < -1$. Similarly, $-1.57 < -1.52$.

> To compare two negative numbers in decimal notation, start at the left and compare corresponding digits. When two digits differ, the number with the smaller digit is the larger of the two numbers.

EXAMPLE 15   Which is larger: −3.8 or −3.82?

−3.8	−3.80
↕↕ The same	↕ Different; 0 is smaller than 2.
−3.82	−3.82

Thus, −3.8 is larger. In symbols, −3.8 > −3.82. (See the number line above.)

Do Exercises 21–24.

d   Rounding

We round decimals in much the same way that we round whole numbers. To see how, we use a number line.

EXAMPLE 16   Round 0.37 to the nearest tenth.

Here is part of a number line, magnified.

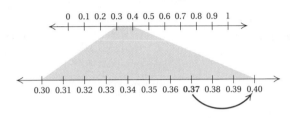

We see that 0.37 is closer to 0.40 than to 0.30. Thus, when 0.37 is rounded to the nearest tenth, we round *up* to 0.4 .

> To round to a certain place:
>
> a) Locate the digit in that place.
> b) Consider the next digit to the right.
> c) If the digit to the right is 5 or greater, add one to the original digit. If the digit to the right is 4 or less, round down. In either case, drop all numbers to the right of the original digit. Rounding down is sometimes called *rounding off*.

EXAMPLE 17   Round 72.3846 to the nearest hundredth.

a) Locate the digit in the hundredths place.

$$7\ 2.3\ 8\ 4\ 6$$

b) Consider the next digit to the right.

c) Since that digit, 4, is less than 5, we round *down* from 72.3846 to 72.38 .

CAUTION!

72.39 is not a correct answer to Example 17. It is incorrect to round sequentially from right to left as follows: 72.3846, 72.385, 72.39 .

72.38   72.3846   72.39
Correct   Incorrect

EXAMPLE 18   Round −0.064 to the nearest tenth.

a) Locate the digit in the tenths place.

$$-0.0\ 6\ 4$$

b) Consider the next digit to the right.

c) Since that digit, 6, is greater than 5, round from −0.064 to −0.1 .

The answer is −0.1 . Since −0.1 < −0.064, we actually rounded *down*.

Do Exercises 25–43.

Round to the nearest tenth.

25. 2.76   **26.** 13.85

27. −234.448   **28.** 7.009

Round to the nearest hundredth.

29. 0.6362   **30.** −7.8348

31. 34.69514   **32.** −0.02521

Round to the nearest thousandth.

33. 0.94347   **34.** −8.00382

35. −43.111943   **36.** 37.400526

Round 7459.35981 to the nearest:

37. Thousandth.

38. Hundredth.

39. Tenth.

40. One.

41. Ten. (*Caution*: "Tens" are not "tenths.")

42. Hundred.

43. Thousand.

Answers on page A-14

a   Write a word name for the number in the sentence.

1. *MP3.* The MP3 audio format is changing the way we obtain and listen to music, allowing us to download digital music from the Internet. The cost of a Creative Labs NOMAD Jukebox Zen Digital Audio Player® is $249.94.
Source: Creative Labs

2. *Microsoft.* Recently, the stock of Microsoft sold for $55.74 per share.

NASDAQ			
NASDAQ COMPOSITE INDEX			
MOST ACTIVE: SHARE VOLUME			
	Vol.(000s)	Last	Change
Intel	48,185	19.11	−.63
Cisco	33,203	14.17	−.26
SunMicro s	25,027	3.70	−.06
Oracle s	19,106	10.81	−.24
Microsft	18,809	55.74	−.80
Applied m	17,270	15.08	−.03
JDS Uniph	16,144	3.05	−.07
Millennium	10,781	11.25	+.44
DellCptr	10,614	28.49	−.26
Atmel	10,142	3.20	+.20

3. *Quaker Oats.* Recently, the stock of Quaker Oats sold for $96.4375 per share.

4. *Water Weight.* One gallon of water weighs 8.35 lb.

5. *Smallest Seed.* Epiphytic orchids have the smallest seeds of any plant, with over 28.13029 billion per ounce.
Source: Guinness Book of Records, 2002

6. The largest bookstore—the midtown Barnes and Noble in Manhattan—has 12.87 mi of shelves.
Source: Guinness Book of Records, 2001

7. The average loss of daylight in October in Anchorage, Alaska, is 5.63 min per day.

8. Recently, one British pound was worth about $1.57079 in U.S. currency.
Source: Bloomberg.com

Write in words, as on a check.

9. $524.95   **10.** $149.99   **11.** $36.72   **12.** $0.67

b   Write each number as a fraction and, if possible, as a mixed numeral. Do not simplify.

13. 7.3   **14.** 4.9   **15.** 203.6   **16.** −57.32   **17.** −2.703

18. 0.00013   **19.** 0.0109   **20.** 1.0008   **21.** −4.0003   **22.** −9.012

23. −0.0207   **24.** −0.00104   **25.** 70.00105   **26.** 60.0403

Write decimal notation for each number.

27. $\dfrac{3}{10}$

28. $\dfrac{73}{10}$

29. $-\dfrac{59}{100}$

30. $-\dfrac{67}{100}$

31. $\dfrac{3798}{1000}$

32. $\dfrac{780}{1000}$

33. $\dfrac{78}{10,000}$

34. $\dfrac{56,788}{100,000}$

35. $\dfrac{-18}{100,000}$

36. $\dfrac{-2347}{100}$

37. $\dfrac{486,197}{1,000,000}$

38. $\dfrac{8,953,074}{1,000,000}$

39. $7\dfrac{13}{1000}$

40. $4\dfrac{909}{1000}$

41. $-8\dfrac{431}{1000}$

42. $-49\dfrac{32}{1000}$

43. $2\dfrac{1739}{10,000}$

44. $9243\dfrac{1}{10}$

45. $8\dfrac{953,073}{1,000,000}$

46. $2256\dfrac{3059}{10,000}$

c   Which number is larger?

47. 0.06,   0.58

48. 0.008,   0.8

49. 0.403,   0.410

50. 42.06,   42.1

51. -5.046, -5.043

52. -324.19, -325.19

53. 234.07,   235.07

54. 0.99999,   1

55. 0.007, $\dfrac{7}{100}$

56. $\dfrac{73}{10}$,   0.73

57. -0.872, -0.873

58. -0.8437, -0.84384

d   Round to the nearest tenth.

59. 0.23

60. 0.85

61. -0.372

62. -0.261

63. 2.951

64. 7.532

65. -327.2347

66. -8.7493

Round to the nearest hundredth.

67. 0.893

68. 0.675

69. -0.6666

70. -7.5252

71. 0.9952

72. 207.9976

73. -0.03488

74. -9.27481

Round to the nearest thousandth.

75. 0.5724

76. 0.6666

77. 17.0015

78. 123.4562

79. -20.20202

80. -0.10346

81. 9.98487

82. 67.100602

Round 809.47321 to the nearest:

83. Tenth.

84. Thousandth.

85. Hundredth.

86. One.

87. $\mathbf{D_W}$ Brian rounds 536.447 to the nearest one and, incorrectly, gets 537. How might he have made this mistake?

88. $\mathbf{D_W}$ Describe in your own words a procedure for converting from decimal notation to fraction notation.

Add or subtract, as indicated.

89.   6 8 1
       + 1 4 9   [1.2b]

90. $\dfrac{681}{1000} + \dfrac{149}{1000}$ [4.2a]

91.   2 6 7
       −   8 5   [1.3d]

92. $\dfrac{267}{100} - \dfrac{85}{100}$ [4.3a]

93. $\dfrac{37}{55} - \dfrac{49}{55}$ [4.3a]

94. $-\dfrac{29}{34} + \dfrac{14}{34}$ [4.2a]

95.   3 4 , 9 0 3
       −   1 , 9 4 5   [1.3d]

96.   4 9 3 7
       + 5 7 8 9   [1.2b]

97. **D**w Describe a series of steps that could be used to write fractions like $\frac{3}{4}, \frac{2}{5}, \frac{7}{20}$, or $\frac{19}{25}$ in decimal form.

98. **D**w Why is it preferable to *not* use the word "and" when reading a number like 457?

99. Arrange the following numbers in order from smallest to largest.

$$-0.989, \ -0.898, \ -1.009, \ -1.09, \ -0.098$$

100. Arrange the following numbers in order from smallest to largest.

$$-2.018, \ -2.1, \ -2.109, \ -2.0119, \ -2.108,$$
$$-2.000001$$

Truncating. There are other methods of rounding decimal notation. A computer often uses a method called **truncating.** To truncate we drop off decimal places right of the rounding place, which is the same as changing all digits to the right of the rounding place to zeros. For example, rounding 6.78093456285102 to the ninth decimal place, using truncating, gives us 6.780934562. Use truncating to round each of the following to the fifth decimal place, that is, the hundred-thousandth.

101. 6.78346123

102. 6.783461902

103. 99.999999999

104. 0.030303030303

Global Warming. The graph below is based on the average global temperatures for January through May of 1910 through 2002. Each bar indicates, in Fahrenheit degrees, how much above or below average the temperature was for the year.

105. For what year(s) was the yearly temperature more than 0.4 degree above average?

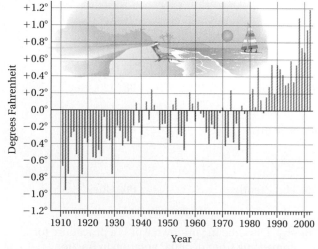

A Warming Trend

Degrees above or below the average global temperature between 1910 and 2002 for January through May. In degrees Fahrenheit.

Sources: Council on Environmental Quality, *The New York Times*, and NASA Goddard Institute for Space Studies.

106. What was the last year in which the yearly temperature was more than 0.6 degree below average?

107. What was the last year in which the yearly temperature was below average?

108. For what year(s) was the yearly temperature more than 1.0 degree above average?

5.2

ADDITION AND SUBTRACTION OF DECIMALS

a   Addition

Adding with decimal notation is similar to adding whole numbers. First we line up the decimal points so that we can add corresponding place-value digits. Then we add digits from the right. For example, we add the thousandths, then the hundredths, and so on, carrying if necessary. If desired, we can write extra zeros to the far right of the decimal point so that the number of places is the same.

EXAMPLE 1   Add: $56.314 + 17.78$.

$$
\begin{array}{r}
5\ 6\ .\ 3\ 1\ 4 \\
+\ 1\ 7\ .\ 7\ 8\ 0 \\
\hline
\end{array}
$$
Lining up the decimal points in order to add
Writing an extra zero to the far right of the decimal point

$$
\begin{array}{r}
5\ 6\ .\ 3\ 1\ \boxed{4} \\
+\ 1\ 7\ .\ 7\ 8\ \boxed{0} \\
\hline
\boxed{4}
\end{array}
$$
Adding thousandths

$$
\begin{array}{r}
5\ 6\ .\ 3\ \boxed{1}\ 4 \\
1\ 7\ .\ 7\ \boxed{8}\ 0 \\
\hline
\boxed{9}\ 4
\end{array}
$$
Adding hundredths

$$
\begin{array}{r}
\overset{1}{}\ \ \ \ \ \\
5\ 6\ .\ \boxed{3}\ 1\ 4 \\
+\ 1\ 7\ .\ \boxed{7}\ 8\ 0 \\
\hline
.\ \boxed{0}\ 9\ 4
\end{array}
$$
Adding tenths
Write a decimal point in the answer.
We get 10 tenths = 1 one + 0 tenths, so we carry the 1 to the ones column.

$$
\begin{array}{r}
\overset{1}{}\ \overset{1}{}\ \ \ \\
5\ \boxed{6}\ .\ 3\ 1\ 4 \\
+\ 1\ \boxed{7}\ .\ 7\ 8\ 0 \\
\hline
\boxed{4}\ .\ 0\ 9\ 4
\end{array}
$$
Adding ones
We get 14 ones = 1 ten + 4 ones, so we carry the 1 to the tens column.

$$
\begin{array}{r}
\overset{1}{}\ \overset{1}{}\ \ \ \\
\boxed{5}\ 6\ .\ 3\ 1\ 4 \\
+\ \boxed{1}\ 7\ .\ 7\ 8\ 0 \\
\hline
\boxed{7}\ 4\ .\ 0\ 9\ 4
\end{array}
$$
Adding tens

Do Exercises 1 and 2.

EXAMPLE 2   Add: $3.42 + 0.237 + 14.1$.

$$
\begin{array}{r}
3.4\ 2\ 0 \\
0.2\ 3\ 7 \\
+\ 1\ 4.1\ 0\ 0 \\
\hline
1\ 7.7\ 5\ 7
\end{array}
$$
Lining up the decimal points and writing extra zeros

Adding

Do Exercises 3–5.

Add.

1.
$$
\begin{array}{r}
0.8\ 4\ 7 \\
+\ 1\ 0.0\ 7 \\
\hline
\end{array}
$$

2.
$$
\begin{array}{r}
2.1 \\
0.7\ 3\ 9 \\
+\ 3\ 1.3\ 6\ 8\ 9 \\
\hline
\end{array}
$$

Add.

3. $0.02 + 4.3 + 0.649$

4. $0.37 + 6.291 + 0.1372$

5. $0.7438 + 9.10864 + 0.3519$

Answers on page A-14

Add.
6. 789 + 123.67

7. 45.78 + 2467 + 1.993

Subtract.
8. 37.428 − 26.674

9. 0.3 4 7
  − 0.0 0 8

Answers on page A-14

Consider the addition $3456 + 19.347$. Keep in mind that any whole number has an "unwritten" decimal point at the far right, with 0 fractional parts. For example, 3456 can also be written 3456.000. When adding, it is often helpful to write in that decimal point and extra zeros.

EXAMPLE 3 Add: $3456 + 19.347$.

$$
\begin{array}{r}
\overset{1}{}\\
3\,4\,5\,6.0\,0\,0\\
+\quad 1\,9.3\,4\,7\\
\hline
3\,4\,7\,5.3\,4\,7
\end{array}
$$

Writing in the decimal point and extra zeros
Lining up the decimal points
Adding

Do Exercises 6 and 7.

b Subtraction

Subtracting with decimal notation is similar to subtracting whole numbers. First we line up the decimal points so that we can subtract corresponding place-value digits. Then we subtract digits from the right. In the example below, we first subtract the thousandths, then the hundredths, the tenths, and so on, borrowing if necessary.

EXAMPLE 4 Subtract: $56.314 − 17.78$.

$$
\begin{array}{r}
5\,6.3\,1\,4\\
-\,1\,7.7\,8\,0\\
\hline
\end{array}
$$

Lining up the decimal points in order to subtract
Writing an extra 0

$$
\begin{array}{r}
5\,6.3\,1\,4\\
-\,1\,7.7\,8\,0\\
\hline
4
\end{array}
$$

Subtracting thousandths

$$
\begin{array}{r}
\overset{2\;\;11}{}\\
5\,6.3\,\cancel{1}\,4\\
-\,1\,7.7\,8\,0\\
\hline
3\,4
\end{array}
$$

Borrowing a tenth to subtract hundredths

$$
\begin{array}{r}
\overset{12}{\overset{5\;\;\cancel{2}\;\;11}{}}\\
5\,\cancel{6}.\cancel{3}\,\cancel{1}\,4\\
-\,1\,7.7\,8\,0\\
\hline
.5\,3\,4
\end{array}
$$

Borrowing a one to subtract tenths
Writing a decimal point

$$
\begin{array}{r}
\overset{15\;\;12}{\overset{4\;\;\cancel{5}\;\;\cancel{2}\;\;11}{}}\\
\cancel{5}\,\cancel{6}.\cancel{3}\,\cancel{1}\,4\\
-\,1\,7.7\,8\,0\\
\hline
8.5\,3\,4
\end{array}
$$

Borrowing a ten to subtract ones

$$
\begin{array}{r}
\overset{15\;\;12}{\overset{4\;\;\cancel{5}\;\;\cancel{2}\;\;11}{}}\\
\cancel{5}\,\cancel{6}.\cancel{3}\,\cancel{1}\,4\\
-\,1\,7.7\,8\,0\\
\hline
3\,8.5\,3\,4
\end{array}
$$

Subtracting tens

CHECK:
$$
\begin{array}{r}
\overset{1\;\;1\;\;1}{}\\
3\,8.5\,3\,4\\
+\,1\,7.7\,8\,0\\
\hline
5\,6.3\,1\,4
\end{array}
$$

Do Exercises 8 and 9.

Study Tips

NEATNESS COUNTS

When working with decimals, make an extra effort to write neatly. Lining up decimal places, and clearly distinguishing decimal points from commas will help avert mistakes that could result from sloppiness.

EXAMPLE 5 Subtract: 23.08 − 5.0053 .

$$\begin{array}{r} \overset{1}{\cancel{2}} \overset{13}{\cancel{3}}.0 \overset{7}{\cancel{8}} \overset{9}{\cancel{0}} \overset{10}{\cancel{0}} \\ - \quad 5.0\ 0\ 5\ 3 \\ \hline 1\ 8.0\ 7\ 4\ 7 \end{array}$$
Writing two extra zeros to the right of the last digit

Subtracting

Do Exercises 10–12.

As with addition, when subtraction involves an integer, there is an "un-written" decimal point that can be written in. Extra zeros can then be written in to the right of the decimal point.

EXAMPLE 6 Subtract: 456 − 2.467 .

$$\begin{array}{r} \overset{5}{\cancel{4}}\ \overset{9}{5}\ \overset{9}{\cancel{6}}.\overset{10}{\cancel{0}}\ \cancel{0}\ \cancel{0} \\ - \qquad 2.4\ 6\ 7 \\ \hline 4\ 5\ 3.5\ 3\ 3 \end{array}$$
Writing in the decimal point and extra zeros

Subtracting

Do Exercises 13 and 14.

C Adding and Subtracting with Negatives

Negative decimals are added or subtracted just like integers.

> To add a negative number and a positive number:
>
> a) Determine the sign of the number with the greater absolute value.
> b) Subtract the smaller absolute value from the larger one.
> c) The answer is the difference from part (b) with the sign from part (a).

EXAMPLE 7 Add: −13.82 + 4.69 .

a) Since $|-13.82| > |4.69|$, the sign of the number with the greater absolute value is negative.

b)
$$\begin{array}{r} 1\ 3.\overset{7}{\cancel{8}}\ \overset{12}{\cancel{2}} \\ - \quad 4.6\ 9 \\ \hline 9.1\ 3 \end{array}$$
Finding the difference of the absolute values

c) Finally, we combine the results of steps (a) and (b): $-13.82 + 4.69 = -9.13$.

Do Exercises 15 and 16.

> To add two negative numbers:
>
> a) Add the absolute values.
> b) Make the answer negative.

EXAMPLE 8 Add: −2.306 + (−3.125).

a)
$$\left.\begin{array}{r} 2.3\ 0\ 6 \\ + \ 3.1\ 2\ 5 \end{array}\right\}$$
Note that $|-2.306| = 2.306$ and $|-3.125| = 3.125$.

$5.4\ 3\ 1$ Adding the absolute values

b) $-2.306 + (-3.125) = -5.431$ The sum of two negatives is negative.

Do Exercise 17.

Subtract.

10. 2.9 − 0.36

11. 0.43 − 0.18762

12. 5.27 − 0.00008

Subtract.

13. 1277 − 82.78

14. 5 − 0.0089

Add.

15. 7.42 + (−9.38)

16. −4.201 + 7.36

17. Add: −7.49 + (−5.8)

Answers on page A-14

Subtract.
18. $9.25 - 13.41$

19. $-5.72 - 4.19$

20. $9.8 - (-2.6)$

21. $-5.9 - (-3.2)$

Combine like terms.
22. $5.8x - 2.1x$

23. $-5.9a + 7.6a$

24. $-4.8y + 7.5 + 2.1y - 2.1$

Answers on page A-14

382

CHAPTER 5: Decimal Notation

To subtract, we add the opposite of the number being subtracted.

EXAMPLE 9 Subtract: $-3.1 - 4.8$.

$$-3.1 - 4.8 = -3.1 + (-4.8) \qquad \text{Adding the opposite of 4.8}$$
$$= -7.9 \qquad \text{The sum of two negatives is negative.}$$

EXAMPLE 10 Subtract: $-7.9 - (-8.5)$.

$$-7.9 - (-8.5) = -7.9 + 8.5 \qquad \text{Adding the opposite of } -8.5$$
$$= 0.6 \qquad \text{Subtracting absolute values. The answer is positive since 8.5 has the larger absolute value.}$$

Do Exercises 18–21.

d   Combining Like Terms

Recall that like, or similar, terms have exactly the same variable factors. To combine like terms, we add or subtract coefficients to form an equivalent expression.

EXAMPLE 11 Combine like terms: $3.2x + 4.6x$.

These are the coefficients.

$$3.2x + 4.6x = (3.2 + 4.6)x \qquad \text{Using the distributive law— try to do this step mentally.}$$
$$= 7.8x \qquad \text{Adding}$$

A similar procedure is used when subtracting like terms.

EXAMPLE 12 Combine like terms: $4.13a - 7.56a$.

$$4.13a - 7.56a = (4.13 - 7.56)a \qquad \text{Using the distributive law}$$
$$= (4.13 + (-7.56))a \qquad \text{Adding the opposite of 7.56}$$
$$= -3.43a \qquad \text{Subtracting absolute values. The coefficient is negative since } |-7.56| > |4.13|.$$

When more than one pair of like terms is present, we can rearrange the terms and then simplify.

EXAMPLE 13 Combine like terms: $5.7x - 3.9y - 2.4x + 4.5y$.

$$5.7x - 3.9y - 2.4x + 4.5y$$
$$= 5.7x + (-3.9y) + (-2.4x) + 4.5y \qquad \text{Rewriting as addition}$$
$$= 5.7x + (-2.4x) + 4.5y + (-3.9y) \qquad \text{Using the commutative law to rearrange}$$
$$= 3.3x + 0.6y \qquad \text{Combining like terms}$$

With practice, you will be able to perform many of the above steps mentally.

Do Exercises 22–24.

a Add.

1. 4 2 6.2 5
    +   3 8.1 2

2.   4 1.8 2 3
    + 6 1 4.9 1 5

3. 6 5 9.4 0 3
    + 9 1 6.8 1 2

4. 8 7 5.7 9 5
    + 3 2 4.8 6 2

5.   9.1 0 4
    + 1 2 3.4 5 6

6. 4.1 5 2 3
    + 3.2 7 7 8

7. 2.006 + 5.817

8. 0.8096 + 0.7856

9. 20.0124 + 30.0124

10. 0.263 + 0.8

11. 0.83 + 0.005

12. 0.347 + 10.04

13. 0.34 + 3.5 + 0.127 + 768

14. 2.3 + 0.729 + 23

15. 17 + 3.24 + 0.256 + 0.3689

16.   4 7.8
    2 1 9.8 5 2
      4 3.5 9
    + 6 6 6.7 1 3

17.   2.7 0 3
      7 8.3 3
      2 8.0 0 0 9
    + 1 1 8.4 3 4 1

18.   1 3.7 2
          9.1 1 2
      6 5 4 2.7 9 0 8
    +   2 3.9 0 1

b Subtract.

19. 4 7.5 9 6
    −   6.2 1 5

20. 1 1.3 4 5
    −   2.1 0 5

21. 5 1.3 1
    −   2.2 9

22. 3 7.4 5
    −   6.3 2

23.
```
    3.6
 - 0.0 3 6
```

24.
```
  2 8.0
 -   0.2 8
```

25.
```
  9 2.3 4 1
 -   6.4 2
```

26.
```
  0.3 4 6
 - 0.0 3 4 6
```

27.
```
    3.0 0 7 4
 - 1.3 4 0 8
```

28.
```
  3 2.7 9 7 8
 -   0.0 5 9 2
```

29.
```
    6.0 7
 - 2.0 0 7 8
```

30.
```
    1.0
 - 0.9 9 9 9
```

31. $30.24 - 0.241$

32. $100.12 - 0.112$

33. $34.07 - 30.7$

34. $36.2 - 16.28$

35. $8.45 - 7.405$

36. $3.801 - 2.81$

37. $6.003 - 2.3$

38. $1 - 0.0098$

39. $2 - 1.0908$

40. $100 - 0.34$

41. $624 - 18.79$

42. $7.48 - 2.6$

43. $57.803 - 4.6$

44. $25.008 - 12.4$

45. $263.7 - 102.08$

46. $19 - 1.198$

47. $45 - 0.999$

48. $10.056 - 0.392$

C   Add or subtract, as indicated.

49. $-5.02 + 1.73$

50. $-4.31 + 7.66$

51. $12.9 - 15.4$

52. $27.2 - 31.9$

53. $-2.9 + (-4.3)$

54. $-7.49 - 1.82$

55. $-4.301 + 7.68$

56. $-5.952 + 7.98$

57. $-12.9 - 3.7$

58. $-8.7 - 12.4$

59. $-2.1 - (-4.6)$

60. $-4.3 - (-2.5)$

61. $14.301 + (-17.82)$

62. $13.45 + (-18.701)$

63. $7.201 - (-2.4)$

64. $2.901 - (-5.7)$

65. $96.9 + (-21.4)$

66. $43.2 + (-10.9)$

67. $-8.9 - (-12.7)$

68. $-4.5 - (-7.3)$

69. $-4.9 - 5.392$

70. $89.3 - 92.1$

71. $14.7 - 23.5$

72. $-7.201 - 1.9$

d Combine like terms.

73. $1.8x + 3.9x$

74. $7.9x + 1.3x$

75. $17.59a - 12.73a$

76. $23.28a - 15.79a$

77. $15.2t + 7.9 + 5.9t$

78. $29.5t - 4.8 + 7.6t$

79. $5.217x - 8.134x$

80. $6.317t - 9.429t$

81. $4.906y - 7.1 + 3.2y$

82. $9.108y + 4.2 + 3.7y$

83. $4.8x + 1.9y - 5.7x + 1.2y$

84. $3.2r - 4.1t + 5.6t + 1.9r$

85. $4.9 - 3.9t + 2.3 - 4.5t$

86. $5.8 + 9.7x - 7.2 - 12.8x$

87. $\mathbf{D_W}$ Boris claims he can add negative numbers but not subtract them. What advice would you give him?

88. $\mathbf{D_W}$ Explain the error in the following: Subtract.

$$\begin{array}{r} 7\,3.0\,8\,9 \\ -\ 5.0\,0\,6\,1 \\ \hline 2.3\,0\,2\,8 \end{array}$$

Multiply. [3.4b]

89. $\dfrac{3}{5} \cdot \dfrac{4}{7}$

90. $\dfrac{2}{9} \cdot \dfrac{7}{5}$

91. $\dfrac{3}{10} \cdot \dfrac{21}{100}$

Evaluate. [2.6a]

92. $8 - 2x^2$, for $x = 3$

93. $5 - 3x^2$, for $x = 2$

94. $7 + 2x^2 \div 3$, for $x = 6$

95. **D_W** In what sense is balancing a checkbook (see Exercise 102 below) or determining the perimeter of a shape similar to combining like terms?

96. **D_W** Although the step in which it is used may not always be written out, the commutative law is often used when combining like terms. Under what circumstances would the commutative law *not* be needed for combining like terms?

Combine like terms.

97. ▦ $-3.928 - 4.39a + 7.4b - 8.073 + 2.0001a - 9.931b - 9.8799a + 12.897b$

98. ▦ $79.02x + 0.0093y - 53.14z - 0.02001y - 37.987z - 97.203x - 0.00987y$

99. ▦ $39.123a - 42.458b - 72.457a + 31.462b - 59.491 + 37.927a$

100. Fred presses the wrong key when using a calculator and adds 235.7 instead of subtracting it. The incorrect answer is 817.2. What is the correct answer?

101. Millie presses the wrong key when using a calculator and subtracts 349.2 instead of adding it. The incorrect answer is −836.9. What is the correct answer?

102. ▦ Find the errors, if any, in the balances in this checkbook.

20___		RECORD ALL CHARGES OR CREDITS THAT AFFECT YOUR ACCOUNT						
DATE	CHECK NUMBER	TRANSACTION DESCRIPTION	√ T	(−) PAYMENT/ DEBIT	(+ OR −) OTHER	(+) DEPOSIT/ CREDIT	BALANCE FORWARD	
							2767	73
8/16	432	Burch Laundry		23 56			2744	16
8/19	433	Rogers TV		20 49			2764	65
8/20		Deposit				85 00	2848	65
8/21	434	Galaxy Records		48 60			2801	05
8/22	435	Electric Works		267 95			2533	09

Find *a*.

103.
```
  9 3.a 4 3
- 8 7.9 6 9
-----------
    5.2 7 4
```

104.
```
  4 8 1.a 2 4
-   7 2.9 7 8
-------------
  4 0 8.3 4 6
```

5.3

MULTIPLICATION OF DECIMALS

a | Multiplication

To develop an understanding of how decimals are multiplied, consider

2.3×1.12 .

One way to find this product is to first convert each factor to fraction notation:

$$2.3 \times 1.12 = \frac{23}{10} \times \frac{112}{100}.$$

Next, we multiply the fractions and then return to decimal notation:

$$\frac{23}{10} \times \frac{112}{100} = \frac{2576}{1000} = 2.576 \ .$$

Note that the number of decimal places in the product is the sum of the number of decimal places in the factors.

$$
\begin{array}{r r}
1.1\ 2 & \text{(2 decimal places)} \\
\times \quad 2.3 & \text{(1 decimal place)} \\
\hline
2.5\ 7\ 6 & \text{(3 decimal places)}
\end{array}
$$

Now consider 0.02×3.412:

$$0.02 \times 3.412 = \frac{2}{100} \times \frac{3412}{1000}$$

$$= \frac{6824}{100,000} = 0.06824 \ .$$

Again, note that the number of decimal places in the product is the sum of the number of decimal places in the factors.

$$
\begin{array}{r r}
3.4\ 1\ 2 & \text{(3 decimal places)} \\
\times \quad 0.0\ 2 & \text{(2 decimal places)} \\
\hline
0.0\ 6\ 8\ 2\ 4 & \text{(5 decimal places)}
\end{array}
$$

It is important to write in this zero.

We have the following rule for multiplying decimals.

> To multiply using decimal notation: 0.8×0.43
>
> **a)** Ignore the decimal points, for the moment, and multiply as though both factors are integers.
>
> $$
> \begin{array}{r}
> \overset{2}{0.4}\ 3 \\
> \times \quad 0.8 \\
> \hline
> 3\ 4\ 4
> \end{array}
> $$
> Ignore the decimal points for now.
>
> **b)** Locate the decimal point so that the number of decimal places in the product is the sum of the number of places in the factors.
>
> $$
> \begin{array}{r r}
> 0.4\ 3 & \text{(2 decimal places)} \\
> \times \quad 0.8 & \text{(1 decimal place)} \\
> \hline
> 0.3\ 4\ 4 & \text{(3 decimal places)}
> \end{array}
> $$
>
> Count off the number of decimal places by starting at the far right and moving the decimal point to the left.

Objectives

a Multiply using decimal notation.

b Convert from dollars to cents and cents to dollars, and from notation like 45.7 million to standard notation.

c Evaluate algebraic expressions using decimal notation.

Study Tips

IF A QUESTION STUMPS YOU

Unless you know the material "cold," don't be surprised if a quiz or test includes a question for which you feel unprepared. Should this happen, do not get rattled—simply skip the question and continue with the quiz or test, returning to the trouble spot after the other questions have been answered.

1. Multiply.

$$\begin{array}{r} 7\ 6.3 \\ \times\quad 8.2 \\ \hline \end{array}$$

Multiply.

2.
$$\begin{array}{r} 4\ 2\ 1\ 3 \\ \times\ 0.0\ 0\ 5\ 1 \\ \hline \end{array}$$

3. 2.3×0.0041

4. $5.2014 \times (-2.41)$

Answers on page A-15

■ **EXAMPLE 1** Multiply: 8.3×74.6 .

a) Ignore the decimal points and multiply as if both factors are integers:

$$\begin{array}{r} \overset{3}{\underset{1}{}}\ \overset{4}{\underset{1}{}} \\ 7\ 4.6 \\ \times\qquad 8.3 \\ \hline 2\ 2\ 3\ 8 \\ 5\ 9\ 6\ 8\ 0 \\ \hline 6\ 1\ 9\ 1\ 8 \qquad \text{We are not yet finished.} \end{array}$$

b) Place the decimal point in the result. The number of decimal places in the product is the sum, $1 + 1$, of the number of decimal places in the factors.

$$\begin{array}{rl} 7\ 4.6 & \text{(1 decimal place)} \\ \times\qquad 8.3 & \text{(1 decimal place)} \\ \hline 2\ 2\ 3\ 8 & \\ 5\ 9\ 6\ 8\ 0 & \\ \hline 6\ 1\ 9.1\ 8 & \text{(2 decimal places)} \end{array}$$

Do Exercise 1.

As we catch on to the skill, we can combine the two steps.

■ **EXAMPLE 2** Multiply: 0.0032×2148.

$$\begin{array}{rl} 2\ 1\ 4\ 8 & \text{(0 decimal places)} \\ \times\ 0.0\ 0\ 3\ 2 & \text{(4 decimal places)} \\ \hline 4\ 2\ 9\ 6 & \\ 6\ 4\ 4\ 4\ 0 & \\ \hline 6.8\ 7\ 3\ 6 & \text{(4 decimal places)} \end{array}$$

■ **EXAMPLE 3** Multiply: -0.14×0.867 .

Multiplying the absolute values, we have

$$\begin{array}{rl} 0.8\ 6\ 7 & \text{(3 decimal places)} \\ \times\qquad 0.1\ 4 & \text{(2 decimal places)} \\ \hline 3\ 4\ 6\ 8 & \\ 8\ 6\ 7\ 0 & \\ \hline 0.1\ 2\ 1\ 3\ 8 & \text{(5 decimal places)} \end{array}$$

Since the product of a negative and a positive is negative, the answer is -0.12138 .

Do Exercises 2–4.

Suppose that a product involves multiplication by a tenth, hundredth, thousandth, and so on. From the following products, a pattern emerges.

$$\begin{array}{rrrr} 4\ 5.6 & 4\ 5.6 & 4\ 5.6 & 4\ 5.6 \\ \times\quad 0.1 & \times 0.0\ 1 & \times 0.0\ 0\ 1 & \times 0.0\ 0\ 0\ 1 \\ \hline 4.5\ 6 & 0.4\ 5\ 6 & 0.0\ 4\ 5\ 6 & 0.0\ 0\ 4\ 5\ 6 \end{array}$$

Note the location of the decimal point in each product. In each case, the product is *smaller* than 45.6 and contains the digits 456.

To multiply any number by a tenth, hundredth, or thousandth, and so on,

a) count the number of decimal places in the tenth, hundredth, or thousandth, and

$$0.001 \times 34.45678$$
$$\qquad \longrightarrow 3 \text{ places}$$

b) move the decimal point that many places to the left. Use zeros as placeholders when necessary.

$$0.001 \times 34.45678 = 0.034.45678$$
Move 3 places to the left.

$$0.001 \times 34.45678 = 0.03445678$$

EXAMPLES Multiply.

4. $0.1 \times 45 = 4.5$ Moving the decimal point one place to the left

5. $0.01 \times 243.7 = 2.437$ Moving the decimal point two places to the left

6. $0.001 \times (-8.2) = -0.0082$ Moving the decimal point three places to the left. This requires writing two extra zeros.

7. $0.0001 \times 536.9 = 0.05369$ Moving the decimal point four places to the left. This requires writing one extra zero.

Do Exercises 5–8.

Next we consider multiplication of a decimal by a power of ten such as 10, 100, 1000, and so on. From the following products, a pattern emerges.

```
  5.2 3 7          5.2 3 7              5.2 3 7
×     1 0        ×   1 0 0          ×   1 0 0 0
  0 0 0 0          0 0 0 0              0 0 0 0
5 2 3 7          0 0 0 0              0 0 0 0
5 2.3 7 0        5 2 3 7              0 0 0 0
                 5 2 3.7 0 0          5 2 3 7
                                    5 2 3 7.0 0 0
```

Note the location of the decimal point in each product. In each case, the product is *larger* than 5.237 and contains the digits 5237.

To multiply any number by a power of ten, such as 10, 100, 1000, and so on,

a) count the number of zeros, and

$$1000 \times 34.45678$$
$$\qquad \longrightarrow 3 \text{ zeros}$$

b) move the decimal point that many places to the right. Use zeros as placeholders when necessary.

$$1000 \times 34.45678 = 34.456.78$$
Move 3 places to the right.

$$1000 \times 34.45678 = 34,456.78$$

EXAMPLES Multiply.

8. $10 \times 32.98 = 329.8$ Moving the decimal point one place to the right

9. $100 \times 4.7 = 470$ Moving the decimal point two places to the right. The 0 in 470 is a placeholder.

Multiply.

5. 0.1×746

6. 0.001×732.4

7. $(-0.01) \times 6.2$

8. 0.0001×723.6

Multiply.

9. 10×53.917

10. $100 \times (-62.417)$

11. 1000×83.9

12. $10,000 \times 57.04$

Answers on page A-15

Convert the number in each sentence to standard notation.

13. In a recent year, there were more than 24.1 million in-line roller bladers in the United States.
Source: *Statistical Abstract of the United States, 2001*

14. By 2010, there will be approximately 1.4 billion people living in China.
Source: *Statistical Abstract of the United States, 2001*

Answers on page A-15

CALCULATOR CORNER

To use a calculator to multiply with decimal notation, we use the $\boxed{.}$, $\boxed{\times}$, and $\boxed{=}$ keys. To find 4.78 × 0.34, for example, we press $\boxed{4}$ $\boxed{.}$ $\boxed{7}$ $\boxed{8}$ $\boxed{\times}$ $\boxed{.}$ $\boxed{3}$ $\boxed{4}$ $\boxed{=}$. The display reads $\boxed{\quad 1.6252 \quad}$, so 4.78 × 0.34 = 1.6252.

Exercises: Use a calculator to multiply.

1.   5.4
     ×   9

2.   4 1 5
     × 1 6.7

3.   1 7.6 3
     ×   8.1

4. 0.04 × 12.69

5. 586.4 × 13.5

6. 4.003 × 5.1

EXAMPLES Multiply.

10. 1000 × (−2.4167) = −2416.7   Moving the decimal point three places to the right

11. 10,000 × 7.52 = 75,200   Moving the decimal point four places to the right and using two zeros as placeholders

Do Exercises 9–12 on the previous page.

b   Applications Using Multiplication with Decimal Notation

NAMING LARGE NUMBERS

We often see notation like the following in newspapers, magazines, and on television.

In 2000, approximately 16.3 million U.S. workers belonged to unions.
Source: U.S. Dept. of Labor

In 1999, the last year for which data is available, U.S. healthcare expenses totaled approximately $1.2 trillion.
Source: *The New York Times Almanac 2002*

Recently, a total of 103.5 billion pieces of mail were shipped in the United States in one year.
Source: *The New York Times Almanac 2002*

To understand such notation, it helps to consider the following table.

NAMING LARGE NUMBERS	
1 hundred = 100 = 10^2 → 2 zeros	1 billion = 1,000,000,000 = 10^9 → 9 zeros
1 thousand = 1000 = 10^3 → 3 zeros	1 trillion = 1,000,000,000,000 = 10^{12} → 12 zeros
1 million = 1,000,000 = 10^6 → 6 zeros	

EXAMPLE 12 Convert the number in this sentence to standard notation: O'Hare International Airport handles approximately 55.9 million passengers per year.
Source: Chicago Department of Aviation

$$55.9 \text{ million} = 55.9 \times 1 \text{ million}$$
$$= 55.9 \times 1,000,000 \quad \text{→ 6 zeros}$$
$$= 55,900,000 \quad \text{→ Moving the decimal point six places to the right}$$

Do Exercises 13 and 14.

MONEY CONVERSION

Converting from dollars to cents is like multiplying by 100. To see why, consider $19.43 .

$$\$19.43 = 19.43 \times \$1 \qquad \text{We think of } \$19.43 \text{ as } 19.43 \times 1 \text{ dollar,}$$
$$\text{or } 19.43 \times \$1.$$
$$= 19.43 \times 100¢ \qquad \text{Substituting } 100¢ \text{ for } \$1: \ \$1 = 100¢$$
$$= 1943¢ \qquad \text{Multiplying}$$

> ### DOLLARS TO CENTS CONVERSIONS
> To convert from dollars to cents, move the decimal point two places to the right and change from the $ sign in front to a ¢ sign at the end.

EXAMPLES Convert from dollars to cents.

13. $189.64 = 18,964¢   **14.** $0.75 = 75¢

Do Exercises 15 and 16.

Converting from cents to dollars is like multiplying by 0.01 . To see why, consider 65¢.

$$65¢ = 65 \times 1¢ \qquad \text{We think of } 65¢ \text{ as } 65 \times 1 \text{ cent,}$$
$$\text{or } 65 \times 1¢.$$
$$= 65 \times \$0.01 \qquad \text{Substituting } \$0.01 \text{ for } 1¢: \ 1¢ = \$0.01$$
$$= \$0.65 \qquad \text{Multiplying}$$

> ### CENTS TO DOLLARS CONVERSIONS
> To convert from cents to dollars, move the decimal point two places to the left and change the ¢ sign at the end to a $ sign in front.

EXAMPLES Convert from cents to dollars.

15. 395¢ = $3.95   **16.** 8503¢ = $85.03

Do Exercises 17 and 18.

C   Evaluating

Algebraic expressions are often evaluated using numbers written in decimal notation.

EXAMPLE 17 Evaluate Prt for $P = 780$, $r = 0.12$, and $t = 0.5$.

We will see in Chapter 8 that this product could be used to determine the interest paid on $780, borrowed at 12 percent simple interest, for half a year. We substitute as follows:

$$Prt = 780 \cdot 0.12 \cdot 0.5 = 780 \cdot 0.06 = 46.8 \qquad \text{This would represent}$$
$$\$46.80 .$$

Do Exercise 19.

Convert from dollars to cents.

15. $15.69

16. $0.17

Convert from cents to dollars.

17. 35¢

18. 577¢

19. Evaluate lwh for $l = 3.2$, $w = 2.6$, and $h = 0.8$. (This is the formula for the volume of a rectangular box.)

Answers on page A-15

20. Find the area of the stamp in Example 18.

EXAMPLE 18   Find the perimeter of a stamp that is 3.25 cm long and 2.5 cm wide.

Recall that the perimeter, P, of a rectangle of length l and width w is given by the formula

$$P = 2l + 2w.$$

Thus, we evaluate $2l + 2w$ for $l = 3.25$ and $w = 2.5$:

$$
\begin{aligned}
2l + 2w &= 2 \cdot 3.25 + 2 \cdot 2.5 \\
&= 6.5 + 5.0 \\
&= 11.5.
\end{aligned}
$$

Remember the rules for order of operations.

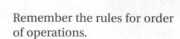

The perimeter is 11.5 cm.

EXAMPLE 19   The expression $5.06t + 9.7$ can be used to predict the average number of e-mail messages, in billions, each day, in North America t years after 2000. Predict the average number of North American e-mails in 2008.
Source: Pitney Bowes

21. Evaluate $6.28rh + 3.14r^2$ for $r = 1.5$ and $h = 5.1$. (This is the formula for the area of an open can.)

2008 is 8 years after 2000, so we evaluate $5.06t + 9.7$ for $t = 8$:

$$
\begin{aligned}
5.06t + 9.7 &= 5.06 \cdot 8 + 9.7 \\
&= 40.48 + 9.7 \\
&= 50.18 .
\end{aligned}
$$

In 2008 there will be approximately 50.18 billion e-mails each day in North America.

Do Exercises 20 and 21.

Answers on page A-15

5.3
EXERCISE SET

For Extra Help

Digital Video
Tutor CD 4
Videotape 5

InterAct
Math

Math Tutor
Center

MathXL

MyMathLab

a Multiply.

1. 6.8
  × 7

2. 5.7
  × 0.9

3. 0.8 4
  ×   8

4. 7.3
  × 0.6

5.   6.3
  × 0.0 4

6.   7.8
  × 0.0 9

7. 2 8.6
  × 0.0 9

8. 2 5.9
  × 0.0 7

9. 10 × 42.63

10. 100 × 2.8793

11. −1000 × 783.686852

12. −0.34 × 1000

13. −7.8 × 100

14. 0.00238 × (−10)

15. 0.1 × 79.18

16. 0.01 × 789.235

17. 0.001 × 97.68

18. 8976.23 × 0.001

19. 28.7 × (−0.01)

20. 0.0325 × (−0.1)

21. 2.7 3
  × 1 6

22. 8.2 7
  × 5.4

23. 0.9 8 4
  ×   3.3

24. 7.4 8 9
  ×   8.2

25. (−37.4)(−2.4)

26. 569(−1.05)

27. 749(−0.43)

28. (−876)(−20.4)

29. 0.8 7
  × 6 4

30. 7.2 5
  × 6 0

31. 4 6.5 0
  ×   7 5

32. 8.2 4
  × 7 0 3

33. (−0.231)(−0.5)

34. (−12.3)(−1.08)

35. 9.42 × (−1000)

36. −7.6 × (−1000)

37. −95.3 × (−0.0001)

38. −4.23 × (−0.001)

b Convert from dollars to cents.

39. $57.06

40. $49.85

41. $0.95

42. $0.49

43. $0.01

44. $0.09

Convert from cents to dollars.

45. 72¢

46. 52¢

47. 2¢

48. 5¢

49. 6399¢

50. 5238¢

Convert the number in each sentence to standard notation.

51. A century is approximately 3.156 billion seconds.

52. Stonehenge was completed approximately 2.104 billion minutes ago.
Source: Based on information in *The Cambridge Factfinder*, 4th ed.

53. Approximately 63.1 trillion seconds have passed since the continents assumed their present shapes.
Source: Based on information in *The Cambridge Factfinder*, 4th ed.

54. In 2000, dealer sales of automobiles totaled $713.3 billion.
Source: U.S. Census Bureau, and Population Division, Population Estimates Program

55. In 2000, the average pay for the CEO of an S&P 500 company was $13.1 million.
Source: Institute for Policy Studies

56. The total surface area of Earth is 196.8 million square miles.

  Evaluate.

57. $P + Prt$, for $P = 10,000$, $r = 0.04$, and $t = 2.5$
(*A formula for adding interest*)

58. $6.28r(h + r)$, for $r = 10$ and $h = 17.2$
(*Surface area of a cylinder*)

59. $vt + 0.5at^2$, for $v = 10$, $t = 1.5$, and $a = 9.8$
(*A physics formula*)

60. $4lh + 2h^2$, for $l = 3.5$ and $h = 1.2$
(*Surface area of a rectangular prism*)

Find **(a)** the perimeter and **(b)** the area of a rectangular room with the given dimensions.

61. 12.5 ft long, 9.5 ft wide

62. 10.25 ft long, 8 ft wide

63. 8.4 m wide, 10.5 m long

64. 8.2 yd long, 6.4 yd wide

Evaluate the expression in Example 19 to predict the average daily number of e-mails in North America in the year indicated.

65. 2010

66. 2009

67. $\mathbf{D_W}$ If two rectangles have the same perimeter, will they also have the same area? Why?

68. $\mathbf{D_W}$ Is it easier to multiply numbers written in decimal notation or fraction notation? Why?

SKILL MAINTENANCE

Divide. [2.5a]

69. $-162 \div 6$

70. $-216 \div (-6)$

71. $-1035 \div (-15)$

72. $-423 \div 3$

73. $-525 \div (25)$

74. $675 \div (-25)$

75. $-7050 \div 50$

76. $575 \div (-25)$

77. **D_W** In your own words, explain why the decimal point in a product is located by adding the number of decimal places in the numbers being multiplied.

78. **D_W** Is it possible for the product of two numbers to contain fewer decimal places than either of the numbers being multiplied?

79. One light-year (LY) is 9.46×10^{12} km. The star Regulus is 85 LY from Earth. How many billions of kilometers (km) from Earth is Regulus?
Source: *The Cambridge Factfinder*, 4th ed.

80. The star Deneb is 1600 LY from Earth. How many billions of kilometers from Earth is Deneb (see Exercise 79)?
Source: *The Cambridge Factfinder*, 4th ed.

Evaluate using a calculator.

81. $d + vt + at^2$, for $d = 79.2$, $v = 3.029$, $t = 7.355$, and $a = 4.9$ (*A physics formula for distance traveled*)

82. $3.14r^2 + 6.28rh$, for $r = 5.756$ in. and $h = 9.047$ in. (*Surface area of a toy silo, including bottom*)

83. $0.5(b_1 + b_2)h$, for $b_1 = 9.7$ cm, $b_2 = 13.4$ cm, and $h = 6.32$ cm (*A geometry formula for the area of a trapezoid*)

84. $0.5bh$, for $b = 12.59$ cm, and $h = 13.72$ cm (*A formula for the area of a triangle*)

Express as a power of 10.

85. (1 trillion) · (1 billion)

86. (1 million) · (1 billion)

87. In Great Britain, France, and Germany, a billion means a million millions. Write standard notation for the British number 6.6 billion.

88. A quadrillion is 10^{15}. Write standard notation for 5.2 quadrillion.

Electric Bills. Recently, electric bills from the Central Vermont Public Service Corporation consisted of a "customer charge" of $0.374 per day plus an "energy charge" of $0.1174 per kilowatt-hour (kWh) for the first 250 kWh used and $0.09079 per kilowatt-hour for each kilowatt-hour in excess of 250.
Source: 2002 CVPS monthly statement

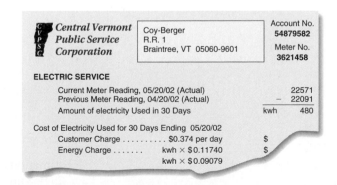

89. From April 20 to May 20, the Coy-Bergers used 480 kWh of electricity. What was their bill for the period?

90. From June 20 to July 20, the D'Amicos used 430 kWh of electricity. What was their bill for the period?

DIVISION OF DECIMALS

a Division

WHOLE-NUMBER DIVISORS

Now that we have studied multiplication of decimals, we can develop a procedure for division. The following divisions are justified by the multiplication in each *check*:

This is the dividend. ⟶ 651
This is the divisor. ⟶ 7

This is the quotient.

$$\frac{651}{7} = 93 \qquad Check: \ 7 \cdot 93 = 651 \ .$$

$$\frac{65.1}{7} = 9.3 \qquad Check: \ 7 \cdot 9.3 = 65.1 \ .$$

$$\frac{6.51}{7} = 0.93 \qquad Check: \ 7 \cdot 0.93 = 6.51 \ .$$

$$\frac{0.651}{7} = 0.093 \qquad Check: \ 7 \cdot 0.093 = 0.651 \ .$$

Note that the number of decimal places in each quotient is the same as the number of decimal places in the dividend.

> To perform long division by a whole number,
>
> a) place the decimal point directly above the decimal point in the dividend, and
> b) divide as though dividing whole numbers.
>
> $$\begin{array}{r} 0.8\ 4 \leftarrow \text{Quotient} \\ 7 \overline{)\ 5.8\ 8} \leftarrow \text{Dividend} \\ 5\ 6\ 0 \\ \hline 2\ 8 \\ 2\ 8 \\ \hline 0 \leftarrow \text{Remainder} \end{array}$$
>
> Divisor

EXAMPLE 1 Divide: $82.08 \div 24$.

We have

Place the decimal point.

$$\begin{array}{r} 3.4\ 2 \\ 2\ 4 \overline{)\ 8\ 2.0\ 8} \\ 7\ 2\ 0\ 0 \\ \hline 1\ 0\ 0\ 8 \\ 9\ 6\ 0 \\ \hline 4\ 8 \\ 4\ 8 \\ \hline 0 \end{array}$$

Divide as though dividing whole numbers.

Estimation can be used as a partial check: $24 \approx 25$ and $82.08 \approx 75$; since $75 \div 25 = 3$ and $3 \approx 3.42$, we have a quick partial check. Our answer is 3.42 .

Do Exercises 1–3.

Divide.

1. $9 \overline{)\ 5.4}$

2. $1\ 5 \overline{)\ 2\ 5.5}$

3. $8\ 2 \overline{)\ 3\ 8.5\ 4}$

Sometimes it helps to write some extra zeros to the right of the dividend's right-most decimal place. This doesn't change the value of the number since adding 0 tenths, or hundredths, or thousandths, and so on, does not change a number.

EXAMPLE 2 Divide: $30 \div 8$.

$$
\begin{array}{r}
3. \\
8 \overline{) 3\ 0.} \\
\underline{2\ 4} \\
6
\end{array}
$$
Place the decimal point and divide to find how many ones.

$$
\begin{array}{r}
3. \\
8 \overline{) 3\ 0.0} \\
\underline{2\ 4} \downarrow \\
6\ 0
\end{array}
$$
Write an extra zero. This does not change the number.

$$
\begin{array}{r}
3.7 \\
8 \overline{) 3\ 0.0} \\
\underline{2\ 4} \\
6\ 0 \\
\underline{5\ 6} \\
4
\end{array}
$$
Divide to find how many tenths.

$$
\begin{array}{r}
3.7 \\
8 \overline{) 3\ 0.0\ 0} \\
\underline{2\ 4} \\
6\ 0 \\
\underline{5\ 6} \downarrow \\
4\ 0
\end{array}
$$
Write an extra zero.

$$
\begin{array}{r}
3.7\ 5 \\
8 \overline{) 3\ 0.0\ 0} \\
\underline{2\ 4} \\
6\ 0 \\
\underline{5\ 6} \\
4\ 0 \\
\underline{4\ 0} \\
0
\end{array}
$$
Repeat the procedure: Divide to find how many hundredths are in the quotient.

Since the remainder is 0, we are finished.

To check, the student can confirm that $3.75 \cdot 8 = 30$.
We have $30 \div 8 = 3.75$.

EXAMPLE 3 Divide: $-4 \div 25$.

We first consider $4 \div 25$:

$$
\begin{array}{r}
0.1\ 6 \\
2\ 5 \overline{) 4.0\ 0} \\
\underline{2\ 5} \\
1\ 5\ 0 \\
\underline{1\ 5\ 0} \\
0
\end{array}
$$
← We can write as many extra zeros as needed.

← Since the remainder is 0, we are finished.

Since a negative number divided by a positive number is negative, the answer is -0.16 . To check, note that $(-0.16)25 = -4$.

Do Exercises 4–6.

Divide.
4. $2\ 5 \overline{)\ 8}$

5. $-23 \div 4$

6. $8\ 6 \overline{)\ 2\ 1.5}$

Answers on page A-15

Study Tips

KNOW YOUR CALCULATOR

When using a calculator on a quiz or test (assuming you are permitted to do so), be sure that you are already familiar with the device. Usually it is better to replace dead batteries than to borrow a calculator with which you are not familiar.

It is possible to use a calculator to find whole-number remainders when doing division. To see how one method works, consider the quotient 17 ÷ 8. We know that

$$17 \div 8 = 2.125.$$

To check, we can multiply:

$$8 \times 2.125 = 17,$$

or, using the distributive law, we can write

$$8 \times (2 + 0.125) = 8 \times 2 + 8 \times 0.125$$
$$= 16 + 1 = 17.$$

Note that 17 ÷ 8 = 2 R 1. Thus, we can find a whole-number remainder by multiplying the decimal portion of a quotient by the divisor.

To find the quotient and the whole-number remainder for 567 ÷ 13, we can use a calculator to find that

$$567 \div 13 \approx 43.61538462 \qquad$$ To isolate the portion to the right of the decimal point, we can subtract 43.

When the decimal part of the quotient is multiplied by the divisor, we have

$$0.61538462 \times 13 = 8.00000006.$$

The rounding error in the result may vary, depending on the calculator used. We see that 567 ÷ 13 = 43 R 8.

Exercises: Find the quotient and the whole-number remainder for each of the following.

1. 478 ÷ 17   3. 824 ÷ 11
2. 815 ÷ 7   4. 7888 ÷ 19

DIVISORS THAT ARE NOT WHOLE NUMBERS

Note that division like

$$0.2\,4\,\overline{)\,8.2\,0\,8}$$

can be written as $\frac{8.208}{0.24}$. Multiplying by a form of 1, we can find an equivalent division with a whole-number divisor, as in Examples 1–3:

$$\frac{8.208}{0.24} = \frac{8.208}{0.24} \times \frac{100}{100} = \frac{820.8}{24}. \qquad$$ We used $\frac{100}{100}$ in order to move the decimal point in 0.24 two places.

Since the divisor is now a whole number, we have effectively traded the "new" problem

$$0.2\,4\,\overline{)\,8.2\,0\,8}$$

for an equivalent problem that is more familiar:

$$2\,4\,\overline{)\,8\,2\,0.8}.$$

This provides motivation for the following procedure.

To divide when the divisor is not a whole number,

a) move the decimal point (multiply by 10, 100, and so on) to make the divisor a whole number;

$$0.2\,4\,\overline{)\,8.2\,0\,8}$$
Move 2 places to the right.

b) move the decimal point the same number of places (multiply the same way) in the dividend; and

$$0.2\,4\,\overline{)\,8.2\,0\,8}$$
Move 2 places to the right.

c) place the decimal point for the answer directly above the new decimal point in the dividend and divide as if dividing by a whole number.

$$\begin{array}{r} 3\ 4.2 \\ 2\,4\,\overline{)\,8\,2\,0.8} \\ 7\,2\,0\,0 \\ \hline 1\,0\,0\,8 \\ 9\,6\,0 \\ \hline 4\,8 \\ 4\,8 \\ \hline 0 \end{array}$$

EXAMPLE 4 Divide: $6.708 \div (-8.6)$.

We first consider $6.708 \div 8.6$:

$$8.6 \overline{)6.7\,0\,8}$$

Multiply the divisor by 10 (move the decimal point 1 place). Multiply the same way in the dividend (move the decimal point 1 place).

$$
\begin{array}{r}
.7\ 8 \\
86 \overline{)6\ 7.0\ 8} \\
\underline{6\ 0\ 2\ 0} \\
6\ 8\ 8 \\
\underline{6\ 8\ 8} \\
0
\end{array}
$$

Then divide.
Note: $\frac{6.708}{8.6} = \frac{6.708}{8.6} \cdot \frac{10}{10} = \frac{67.08}{86}$.

Check: $(0.78)8.6 = 6.708$

Since a positive number divided by a negative number is negative, we have
$6.708 \div (-8.6) = -0.78$.

Do Exercises 7–9.

EXAMPLE 5 Divide: $-12 \div (-0.64)$.

Note first that a negative number divided by a negative number is positive. To find the quotient, we consider $12 \div 0.64$:

$$0.64 \overline{)1\ 2.}$$

Put a decimal point at the end of the whole number.

$$0.64 \overline{)1\ 2.0\ 0}$$

Multiply the divisor by 100 (move the decimal point 2 places). Multiply the same way in the dividend (move 2 places). Write additional zeros as needed.

$$
\begin{array}{r}
1\ 8.7\ 5 \\
64 \overline{)1\ 2\ 0\ 0.0\ 0} \\
\underline{6\ 4\ 0} \\
5\ 6\ 0 \\
\underline{5\ 1\ 2} \\
4\ 8\ 0 \\
\underline{4\ 4\ 8} \\
3\ 2\ 0 \\
\underline{3\ 2\ 0} \\
0
\end{array}
$$

Then divide.

Since the remainder is 0, we are finished.
Check: $18.75(-0.64) = -12$

We have $-12 \div (-0.64) = 18.75$.

Do Exercises 10 and 11.

To divide quickly by a thousandth, hundredth, tenth, ten, hundred, and so on, consider

$$\frac{43.9}{100} \quad \text{and} \quad \frac{43.9}{0.001}.$$

$$
\begin{array}{r}
.4\ 3\ 9 \\
100 \overline{)4\ 3.9\ 0\ 0} \\
\underline{4\ 0\ 0} \\
3\ 9\ 0 \\
\underline{3\ 0\ 0} \\
9\ 0\ 0 \\
\underline{9\ 0\ 0} \\
0
\end{array}
\qquad
\begin{array}{r}
4\ 3\ 9\ 0\ 0. \\
0.0\ 0\ 1 \overline{)4\ 3.9\ 0\ 0} \\
\end{array}
$$

7. a) Complete.

$$\frac{3.75}{0.25} = \frac{3.75}{0.25} \times \frac{100}{100}$$
$$= \frac{(\quad)}{25}$$

b) Divide.

$$0.2\ 5 \overline{)3.7\ 5}$$

Divide.

8. $4.067 \div (-0.83)$

9. $-44.8 \div (-3.5)$

Divide.

10. $1.6 \overline{)2\ 5}$

11. $-36 \div 0.75$

Answers on page A-15

Divide.

12. $\dfrac{0.1278}{0.01}$

13. $\dfrac{0.1278}{100}$

14. $\dfrac{98.47}{1000}$

15. $\dfrac{6.7832}{-0.1}$

Division of 43.9 by a number greater than 1 results in a quotient *smaller* than 43.9, whereas division by a positive number less than 1 results in a quotient that is *larger* than 43.9. Keeping this in mind can help you remember how to move the decimal point.

To divide by a power of ten, such as 10, 100, or 1000, and so on,

a) count the number of zeros in the divisor, and

$$\dfrac{713.495}{100}$$
$$\hookrightarrow 2 \text{ zeros}$$

b) move the decimal point that number of places to the left.

$$\dfrac{713.495}{100}, \quad 7.13.495 \quad \dfrac{713.495}{100} = \dfrac{7.13495}{1.00} = 7.13495$$
$$2 \text{ places to the left}$$

To divide by a tenth, hundredth, or thousandth, and so on,

a) count the number of decimal places in the divisor, and

$$\dfrac{89.12}{0.001}$$
$$\hookrightarrow 3 \text{ zeros}$$

b) move the decimal point that number of places to the right.

$$\dfrac{89.12}{0.001}, \quad 89.120. \quad \dfrac{89.12}{0.001} = \dfrac{89120}{1.0} = 89,120$$
$$3 \text{ places to the right}$$

EXAMPLE 6 Divide: $\dfrac{0.0732}{10}$.

$$\dfrac{0.0732}{10}, \quad 0.0.0732, \quad \dfrac{0.0732}{10} = 0.00732$$
$$1 \text{ zero} \qquad 1 \text{ place to the left to change 10 to 1}$$

The answer is 0.00732 .

EXAMPLE 7 Divide: $\dfrac{-23.738}{0.001}$.

$$\dfrac{-23.738}{0.001}, \quad -23.738. \quad \dfrac{-23.738}{0.001} = -23,738$$
$$3 \text{ places} \qquad 3 \text{ places to the right to change 0.001 to 1}$$

The answer is $-23,738$.

Do Exercises 12–15.

b   Order of Operations: Decimal Notation

The rules for order of operations apply when simplifying expressions involving decimal notation.

Answers on page A-15

RULES FOR ORDER OF OPERATIONS

1. Do all calculations within grouping symbols first.
2. Evaluate all exponential expressions.
3. Do all multiplications and divisions in order from left to right.
4. Do all additions and subtractions in order from left to right.

EXAMPLE 8 Simplify: $(5 - 0.06) \div 2 + 3.42 \times 0.1$.

$$(5 - 0.06) \div 2 + 3.42 \times 0.1 = 4.94 \div 2 + 3.42 \times 0.1 \quad \text{Working inside the parentheses}$$

$$= 2.47 + 0.342 \quad \text{Multiplying and dividing in order from left to right}$$

$$= 2.812$$

EXAMPLE 9 Simplify: $13 - [5.4(1.3^2 + 0.21) \div 0.6]$.

$$13 - [5.4(1.3^2 + 0.21) \div 0.6]$$

$$= 13 - [5.4(1.69 + 0.21) \div 0.6] \quad\Big\} \quad \text{Working in the innermost parentheses first}$$

$$= 13 - [5.4 \times 1.9 \div 0.6]$$

$$= 13 - [10.26 \div 0.6] \quad \text{Multiplying}$$

$$= 13 - 17.1 \quad \text{Dividing}$$

$$= -4.1$$

Do Exercises 16 and 17.

EXAMPLE 10 *Home Entertainment.* The graph below shows U.S. sales of VCRs, in billions of dollars, from 1997 to 2001. Find the average yearly sales for the period.

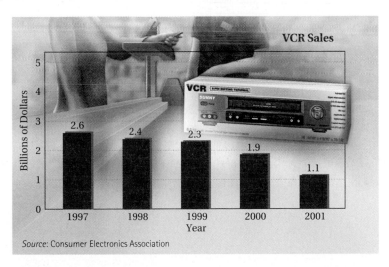

Source: Consumer Electronics Association

To find the average of a set of numbers, we add and then divide by the number of addends. The average of 2.6, 2.4, 2.3, 1.9, and 1.1 is given by

$$(2.6 + 2.4 + 2.3 + 1.9 + 1.1) \div 5 = 10.3 \div 5 = 2.06 \,.$$

The average yearly sales of VCRs in the U.S. from 1997 to 2001 were $2.06 billion.

Do Exercise 18.

Simplify.

16. $0.25 \cdot (1 + 0.08) - 0.0274$

17. $[(19.7 - 17.2)^2 + 3] \div (-1.25)$

18. Home Entertainment. The bar graph below shows U.S. sales of camcorders, in billions of dollars, from 1998 to 2002. Find the average sales for the period.

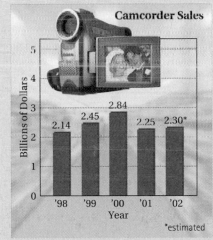

Source: Consumer Electronics Association

Answers on page A-15

a   Divide.

1. $5 \overline{)\ 6\ 3}$

2. $5 \overline{)\ 6\ 2}$

3. $4 \overline{)\ 9\ 5.1\ 2}$

4. $8 \overline{)\ 2\ 5.9\ 2}$

5. $1\ 2 \overline{)\ 8\ 9.7\ 6}$

6. $2\ 3 \overline{)\ 2\ 5.0\ 7}$

7. $3\ 3 \overline{)\ 2\ 3\ 7.6}$

8. $12.4 \div (-4)$

9. $5.4 \div (-6)$

10. $3.6 \div 4$

11. $-9.144 \div 8$

12. $-7.254 \div 6$

13. $0.0\ 6 \overline{)\ 8.4}$

14. $0.0\ 4 \overline{)\ 1.6\ 8}$

15. $2.6 \overline{)\ 1\ 0\ 4}$

16. $6 \div (-15)$

17. $1.8 \div (-12)$

18. $3\ 6 \overline{)\ 1\ 4.7\ 6}$

19. $2.7 \overline{)\ 1\ 2\ 9.6}$

20. $6.2 \overline{)\ 4\ 6.5}$

21. $8.5 \overline{)\ 2\ 7.2}$

22. $39.06 \div (-4.2)$

23. $-5 \div (-8)$

24. $-7 \div (-8)$

25. $0.4\ 7 \overline{)\ 0.1\ 2\ 2\ 2}$

26. $0.5\ 4 \overline{)\ 0.2\ 7}$

27. $0.0\ 3\ 2 \overline{)\ 0.0\ 7\ 4\ 8\ 8}$

28. $0.0\ 1\ 7 \overline{)\ 1.5\ 8\ 1}$

29. $-24.969 \div 82$

30. $-25.221 \div 42$

31. $\dfrac{-213.4567}{100}$ **32.** $\dfrac{-213.4567}{10}$ **33.** $\dfrac{1.0237}{0.001}$ **34.** $\dfrac{1.0237}{-0.01}$ **35.** $\dfrac{92.36}{-0.01}$ **36.** $\dfrac{56.78}{-0.001}$

37. $\dfrac{0.8172}{10}$ **38.** $\dfrac{0.5678}{1000}$ **39.** $\dfrac{0.97}{0.1}$ **40.** $\dfrac{0.97}{0.001}$ **41.** $\dfrac{52.7}{-1000}$ **42.** $\dfrac{8.9}{-100}$

43. $\dfrac{75.3}{-0.001}$ **44.** $\dfrac{63.47}{-0.1}$ **45.** $\dfrac{-75.3}{1000}$ **46.** $\dfrac{23{,}001}{100}$

b   Simplify.

47. $14 \times (82.6 + 67.9)$ **48.** $(26.2 - 14.8) \times 12$ **49.** $0.003 + 3.03 \div (-0.01)$

50. $42 \times (10.6 + 0.024)$ **51.** $(4.9 - 18.6) \times 13$ **52.** $4.2 \times 5.7 + 0.7 \div 3.5$

53. $210.3 - 4.24 \times 1.01$ **54.** $-7.32 + 0.04 \div 0.1^2$ **55.** $12 \div (-0.03) - 12 \times 0.03^2$

56. $(5 - 0.04)^2 \div 4 + 8.7 \times 0.4$ **57.** $(4 - 2.5)^2 \div 100 + 0.1 \times 6.5$ **58.** $4 \div 0.4 - 0.1 \times 5 + 0.1^2$

59. $6 \times 0.9 - 0.1 \div 4 + 0.2^3$ **60.** $5.5^2 \times [(6 - 7.8) \div 0.06 + 0.12]$

61. $12^2 \div (12 + 2.4) - [(2 - 2.4) \div 0.8]$ **62.** $0.01 \times \{[(4 - 0.25) \div 2.5] - (4.5 - 4.025)\}$

63. *Uninsured U.S. Citizens.* The information in the graph below indicates the number of U.S. citizens with no healthcare insurance. Find the average number of uninsured citizens for the period shown.

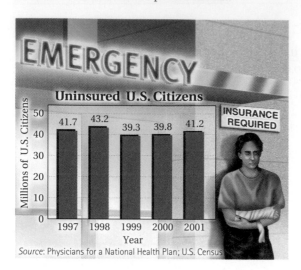

Source: Physicians for a National Health Plan; U.S. Census

64. *Home Office Equipment.* The information in the graph below shows U.S. sales of home computers. Find the average sales for the period.

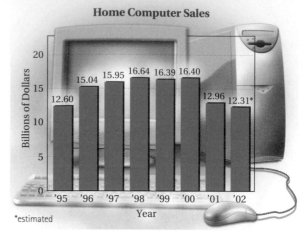

*estimated

Source: Consumer Electronics Association

65. *Gasoline Consumption.* The information in the graph below shows the average number of miles per gallon for U.S. vehicles. Find the average for the entire period.

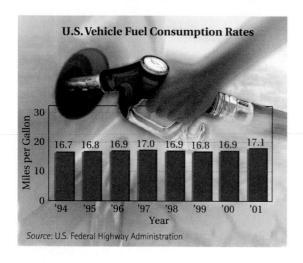

Source: U.S. Federal Highway Administration

66. *World Population.* Using the information in the following bar graph, determine the average population of the world for the years 1950 through 2000.

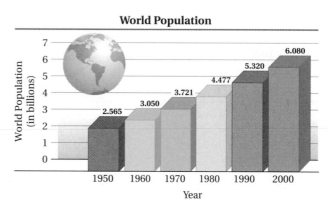

Sources: Francis Urban and Philip Rose. *World Population by Country and Region, 1950–86,* and *Projections to 2050,* U.S. Dept. of Agriculture.

The following table lists the global average temperature for the years 1991 through 2002. Use the table for Exercises 67 and 68.

YEAR	1991	1992	1993	1994	1995	1996	1997	1998	1999	2000	2001	2002
Global Temperature (in degrees Fahrenheit)	59.74°	59.23°	59.36°	59.56°	59.72°	59.58°	59.74°	60.26°	59.99°	59.93°	60.19°	60.43°

Source: Based on information from Lester R. Brown et al., *Vital Signs 1997,* the Council of Environmental Quality, and NASA Goddard Institute for Space Studies.

67. Find the average temperature for the years 1998 through 2002.

68. Find the average temperature for the years 1992 through 1996.

69. $\mathbf{D_W}$ Mel insists that $53 \div 0.1$ is 5.3. Give a "common sense" argument that could convince him that he is mistaken.

70. $\mathbf{D_W}$ Gilda insists that $7.9 \div 10$ is 79. Give a "common sense" argument that could convince her that she is mistaken.

SKILL MAINTENANCE

Simplify to form an equivalent expression.   [3.5b]

71. $\dfrac{33}{44}$

72. $\dfrac{49}{56}$

73. $-\dfrac{27}{18}$

74. $-\dfrac{18}{60}$

75. $\dfrac{9a}{27}$

76. $\dfrac{12x}{30}$

77. $\dfrac{4r}{20r}$

78. $\dfrac{10t}{15t}$

SYNTHESIS

79. $\mathbf{D_W}$ Which is easier and why: Dividing a decimal by a decimal or dividing a fraction by a fraction?

80. $\mathbf{D_W}$ In Exercise 64, the number 12.60 was used. Why do you think the number 12.6 was not used instead?

Calculate each of the following.

81. $\boxplus$ $7.434 \div (-1.2) \times 9.5 + 1.47^2$

82. $\boxplus$ $-9.46 \times 2.1^2 \div 3.5 + 4.36$

83. $\boxplus$ $9.0534 - 2.041^2 \times 0.731 \div 1.043^2$

84. $\boxplus$ $23.042(7 - 4.037 \times 1.46 - 0.932^2)$

Solve.

85. $439.57 \times 0.01 \div 1000 \cdot x = 4.3957$

86. $5.2738 \div 0.01 \times 1000 \div t = 52.738$

87. $0.0329 \div 0.001 \times 10^4 \div x - 3290$

88. $-4.302 \times 0.1^2 \div 0.001 \cdot t = -430.2$

89. *Men's and Women's Salaries.* The 30 highest-paid women in the world average $8.7 million a year in earnings, while the 30 highest-paid men average $112.9 million a year. The men's figure is how many times the women's figure? Round to the nearest whole number.
Source: Institute for Policy Studies

90. *Television Ratings.* A television rating point represents 980,000 households. The 1998 NBA Finals was viewed in approximately 18.5 million households, a record for the NBA. How many rating points did the finals receive? Round to the nearest tenth.
Source: *Burlington Free Press*

$\boxplus$ *Electric Bills.* Recently, electric bills from the Central Vermont Public Service Corporation consisted of a "customer charge" of $0.374 per day plus an "energy charge" of $0.1174 per kilowatt-hour (kWh) for the first 250 kWh used and $0.09079 per kWh for each kWh in excess of 250.

91. From August 20 to September 20, the Kaufmans' bill was $59.10. How many kilowatt-hours of electricity did they use (round to the nearest kilowatt-hour)?

92. From July 20 to August 20, the McGuires' bill was $70. How many kilowatt-hours of electricity did they use (round to the nearest kilowatt-hour)?

MORE WITH FRACTION NOTATION AND DECIMAL NOTATION

Objectives

a Use division to convert fraction notation to decimal notation.

b Round numbers named by repeating decimals.

c Convert certain fractions to decimal notation by using equivalent fractions.

d Simplify expressions that contain both fraction and decimal notation.

Find decimal notation.

1. $\dfrac{2}{5}$

2. $\dfrac{-5}{8}$

Answers on page A-15

Study Tips

IDENTIFY THE HIGHLIGHTS

If you haven't already tried one, consider using a highlighter as you read. By highlighting sentences or phrases that you find especially important, you will make it easier to review important material in the future. Highlighters are only helpful when used, so be sure to keep your highlighter with you whenever you study.

Now that we know how to divide using decimal notation, we can express *any* fraction as a decimal. This means that any *rational* number (ratio of integers) can be written as a decimal.

a Using Division to Find Decimal Notation

Recall that $\dfrac{a}{b}$ means $a \div b$. This gives us one way of converting fraction notation to decimal notation.

EXAMPLE 1 Find decimal notation for $\dfrac{3}{20}$.

Because $\dfrac{3}{20}$ means $3 \div 20$, we can perform long division:

$$
\begin{array}{r}
0.1\,5 \\
2\,0 \overline{)\,3.0\,0} \\
\underline{2\,0} \\
1\,0\,0 \\
\underline{1\,0\,0} \\
0
\end{array}
$$

We are finished when the remainder is 0.

We have $\dfrac{3}{20} = 0.15$.

EXAMPLE 2 Find decimal notation for $\dfrac{-7}{8}$.

Since $\dfrac{-7}{8}$ means $-7 \div 8$ and a negative divided by a positive is negative, we know that the decimal will be negative. We divide 7 by 8 and make the result negative:

$$
\begin{array}{r}
0.8\,7\,5 \\
8 \overline{)\,7.0\,0\,0} \\
\underline{6\,4} \\
6\,0 \\
\underline{5\,6} \\
4\,0 \\
\underline{4\,0} \\
0
\end{array}
$$

Thus $\dfrac{-7}{8} = -0.875$.

Do Exercises 1 and 2.

When division with decimals ends, or *terminates*, as in Examples 1 and 2, the result is called a *terminating decimal*. If the division does *not* lead to a remainder of 0, but instead leads to a repeating pattern of nonzero remainders, we have what is called a *repeating decimal*.

EXAMPLE 3 Find decimal notation for $\frac{5}{6}$.

Since $\frac{5}{6}$ means $5 \div 6$, we have

$$
\begin{array}{r}
0.8\ 3\ 3 \\
6\ )\ \overline{5.0\ 0\ 0} \\
\underline{4\ 8} \\
2\ 0 \\
\underline{1\ 8} \\
2\ 0 \\
\underline{1\ 8} \\
2
\end{array}
$$

Since 2 keeps reappearing as a remainder, the digits repeat and will continue to do so; therefore,

$$
\frac{5}{6} = 0.83333\ldots.
$$

The dots indicate an endless sequence of digits in the quotient. When there is a repeating pattern, the dots are often replaced by a bar to indicate the repeating part, in this case, only the 3:

$$
\frac{5}{6} = 0.8\overline{3}\ .
$$

Do Exercises 3 and 4.

EXAMPLE 4 Find decimal notation for $-\frac{4}{11}$.

Since $-\frac{4}{11}$ is negative, we divide 4 by 11 and make the result negative.

$$
\begin{array}{r}
0.3\ 6\ 3\ 6 \\
1\ 1\ )\ \overline{4.0\ 0\ 0\ 0} \\
\underline{3\ 3} \\
7\ 0 \\
\underline{6\ 6} \\
4\ 0 \\
\underline{3\ 3} \\
7\ 0 \\
\underline{6\ 6} \\
4
\end{array}
$$

Since 7 and 4 keep reappearing as remainders, the sequence of digits "36" repeats in the quotient, and

$$
\frac{4}{11} = 0.363636\ldots, \quad \text{or} \quad 0.\overline{36}\ .
$$

Thus, $-\frac{4}{11} = -0.\overline{36}$.

Do Exercises 5 and 6.

Find decimal notation for each number.

3. $\dfrac{1}{6}$

4. $\dfrac{2}{3}$

Find decimal notation for each number.

5. $\dfrac{5}{11}$

6. $-\dfrac{12}{11}$

Answers on page A-15

5.5 More with Fraction Notation and Decimal Notation

7. Find decimal notation for $\frac{5}{7}$.

Is there a way to know which fractions represent terminating decimals and which represent repeating decimals? The answer is "yes, provided the fraction is written in simplified form." As illustrated in Examples 1 and 2, when the denominator of a simplified fraction has no prime factor other than 2 or 5, the decimal terminates. When, as in Examples 3 and 4, the denominator of the simplified fraction has a prime factor other than 2 or 5, the decimal repeats.

EXAMPLE 5 Find decimal notation for $\frac{3}{7}$.

Because 7 is not a product of 2's and/or 5's, we expect a repeating decimal:

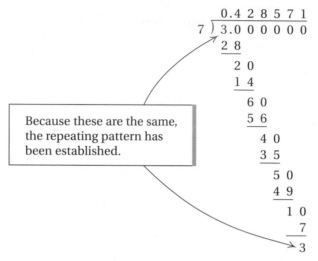

Because these are the same, the repeating pattern has been established.

Since we have already divided 7 into 3, the sequence of digits "428571" repeats in the quotient. We have

$$\frac{3}{7} = 0.428571428571\ldots, \quad \text{or} \quad 0.\overline{428571}.$$

Do Exercise 7.

b   Rounding Repeating Decimals

The repeating part of a decimal can be so long that it will not fit on a calculator. For example, when $\frac{5}{97}$ is written as a decimal, its repeating part is 96 digits long! Most calculators round off repeating decimals to 9 or 10 decimal places. In applied problems, repeating decimals are generally rounded to a predetermined degree of accuracy.

Answer on page A-15

EXAMPLE 6 Round $4.\overline{27}$ to the nearest thousandth.

We first rewrite the decimal without the bar. The repeating part is rewritten until we have passed the thousandths place:

$$4.\overline{27} = 4.2727\ldots.$$

Now we round as in Section 5.1.

a) Locate the digit in the thousandths place.   4.2 7 2 7...
                                                              ↑

b) Consider the next digit to the right.   4.2 7 2 7...
                                                              └↑

c) Since that digit, 7, is greater than or equal to 5, round up.

   4.273   This is the answer.

Round each to the nearest tenth, hundredth, and thousandth.

8. $0.\overline{6}$

9. $0.6\overline{08}$

10. $-7.3\overline{49}$

11. $2.689\overline{1}$

EXAMPLES Round each to the nearest tenth, hundredth, and thousandth.

	Nearest tenth	Nearest hundredth	Nearest thousandth
7. $0.8\overline{3} = 0.83333\ldots$	0.8	0.83	0.833
8. $3.\overline{09} = 3.090909\ldots$	3.1	3.09	3.091
9. $-4.1\overline{763} = -4.1763763\ldots$	−4.2	−4.18	4.176

Do Exercises 8–11.

C More with Conversions

Recall that fractions like $\frac{3}{10}$ or $-\frac{71}{1000}$ can be converted to decimal notation, without using long division. When a denominator is a factor of 10, 100, and so on, we can convert to decimal notation by finding (perhaps mentally) an equivalent fraction in which the denominator is a power of 10.

EXAMPLE 10 Find decimal notation for $-\frac{7}{500}$.

Since $500 \cdot 2 = 1000$, and 1000 is a power of 10, we use $\frac{2}{2}$ as an expression for 1:

$$-\frac{7}{500} = -\frac{7}{500} \cdot \frac{2}{2} = -\frac{14}{1000} = -0.014 .$$ *Think*: $1000 \div 500 = 2$, and $7 \cdot 2 = 14$.

EXAMPLE 11 Find decimal notation for $\frac{9}{25}$.

$$\frac{9}{25} = \frac{9}{25} \cdot \frac{4}{4} = \frac{36}{100} = 0.36$$ Using $\frac{4}{4}$ for 1 to get a denominator of 100

As a check, we can divide:

```
        0.3 6
 2 5 ) 9.0 0
        7 5        Note that multiplication by 1 is much faster.
        1 5 0
        1 5 0
            0
```

Answers on page A-15

Multiply by a form of 1 to find decimal notation for each number.

12. $\dfrac{4}{5}$

13. $-\dfrac{9}{20}$

14. $\dfrac{7}{200}$

15. $\dfrac{33}{25}$

Calculate.

16. $\dfrac{5}{6} \times 0.864$

17. $\dfrac{1}{3} \times 0.384 + \dfrac{5}{8} \times 0.6784$

Answers on page A-15

■ **EXAMPLE 12** Find decimal notation for $\frac{7}{4}$.

$$\frac{7}{4} = \frac{7}{4} \cdot \frac{25}{25} = \frac{175}{100} = 1.75$$

Using $\frac{25}{25}$ for 1 to get a denominator of 100. You might also note that 7 quarters is $1.75.

Do Exercises 12–15.

d Calculations with Fraction and Decimal Notation Together

In certain kinds of calculations, fraction and decimal notation might occur together. In such cases, there are at least three ways in which we can proceed.

■ **EXAMPLE 13** Calculate: $\frac{2}{3} \times 0.576$.

METHOD 1 Perhaps the quickest method is to treat 0.576 as $\frac{0.576}{1}$. Then we multiply 0.576 by 2, and divide the result by 3.

$$\frac{2}{3} \times 0.576 = \frac{2}{3} \times \frac{0.576}{1}$$

$$= \frac{2 \times 0.576}{3} = \frac{1.152}{3}$$

$$= 0.384$$

$$
\begin{array}{r}
0.3\ 8\ 4 \\
3\ )\ \overline{1.1\ 5\ 2} \\
\underline{9} \\
2\ 5 \\
\underline{2\ 4} \\
1\ 2 \\
\underline{1\ 2} \\
0
\end{array}
$$

METHOD 2 A second way to do this calculation is to convert the fraction to decimal notation so that both numbers are decimals. Since $\frac{2}{3}$ is a repeating decimal, it is first rounded to some chosen decimal place. We choose three decimal places. Then, using decimal notation, we multiply. Note that the answer is not as accurate as that found by Method 1, due to the rounding.

$$\frac{2}{3} \times 0.576 = 0.\overline{6} \times 0.576$$

$$\approx 0.667 \times 0.576 = 0.384192 \qquad \text{This is } less \text{ accurate than the result in Method 1.}$$

METHOD 3 A third method is to convert the decimal to a fraction so that both numbers are in fraction notation. The answer can be left in fraction notation and simplified, or we can convert back to decimal notation and, if appropriate, round.

$$\frac{2}{3} \times 0.576 = \frac{2}{3} \cdot \frac{576}{1000} = \frac{2 \cdot 576}{3 \cdot 1000}$$

$$= \frac{2 \cdot 2 \cdot 2 \cdot 2 \cdot 2 \cdot 2 \cdot 2 \cdot 3 \cdot 3}{2 \cdot 2 \cdot 2 \cdot 3 \cdot 5 \cdot 5 \cdot 5} \qquad \text{Factoring}$$

$$= \frac{2 \cdot 2 \cdot 2 \cdot 3}{2 \cdot 2 \cdot 2 \cdot 3} \cdot \frac{2 \cdot 2 \cdot 2 \cdot 2 \cdot 3}{5 \cdot 5 \cdot 5} \qquad \begin{array}{l}\text{Removing a factor equal} \\ \text{to 1: } \frac{2 \cdot 2 \cdot 2 \cdot 3}{2 \cdot 2 \cdot 2 \cdot 3} = 1\end{array}$$

$$= \frac{2 \cdot 2 \cdot 2 \cdot 2 \cdot 3}{5 \cdot 5 \cdot 5} = \frac{48}{125}, \text{ or } 0.384$$

Do Exercises 16 and 17.

■ **EXAMPLE 14** *Boating.* A triangular sail from a single-sail day cruiser is 3.4 m wide and 4.2 m tall. Find the area of the sail.

1. **Familiarize.** We first make a drawing and recall that the formula for the area, A, of a triangle with base b and height h is $A = \frac{1}{2}bh$.

2. **Translate.** We substitute 3.4 for b and 4.2 for h:

$$A = \frac{1}{2}bh = \frac{1}{2}(3.4)(4.2) \qquad \text{Evaluating}$$

3. **Solve.** We simplify as follows:

$$A = \frac{1}{2}(3.4)(4.2)$$

$$-\frac{3.4}{2}(4.2) \qquad \text{Multiplying } \tfrac{1}{2} \text{ and } \tfrac{3.4}{1}$$

$$= 1.7(4.2) \qquad \text{Dividing}$$

$$= 7.14 \ . \qquad \text{Multiplying}$$

4. **Check.** To check, we repeat the calculations using the commutative law to multiply in a different order. We also rewrite $\frac{1}{2}$ as 0.5:

$$\frac{1}{2}(4.2)(3.4) = 0.5(4.2)(3.4)$$

$$= (2.1)(3.4) = 7.14.$$

Our answer checks.

5. **State.** The area of the sail is 7.14 m² (square meters).

Do Exercise 18.

18. Find the area of a triangular window that is 3.25 ft wide and 2.6 ft tall.

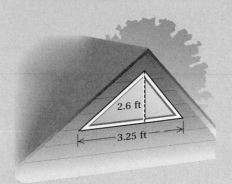

2.6 ft

3.25 ft

CALCULATOR CORNER

Many geometric applications of decimal notation involve the number π (see Exercises 99–102 of this section).

Most calculators now have a key that provides an approximation of π to at least six decimal places. Often a key labeled ⎡SHIFT⎤ or ⎡2nd⎤ must be pressed first.

To calculate the value of an expression like $2\pi(7.5)$, on most calculators we simply press

⎡2⎤ ⎡×⎤ ⎡2nd⎤ ⎡π⎤ ⎡×⎤ ⎡7⎤ ⎡.⎤ ⎡5⎤

and then ⎡=⎤ or ⎡ENTER⎤.

Exercises:

1. Calculate $4\pi(9.8)$.

2. Evaluate $2\pi r$ for $r = 8.37$.

Answer on page A-15

5.5

EXERCISE SET

For Extra Help

Digital Video
Tutor CD 4
Videotape 5

InterAct
Math

Math Tutor
Center

MathXL

MyMathLab

a , **c**   Find decimal notation for each number.

1. $\dfrac{3}{8}$

2. $\dfrac{3}{5}$

3. $\dfrac{-1}{2}$

4. $\dfrac{-1}{4}$

5. $\dfrac{3}{25}$

6. $\dfrac{7}{20}$

7. $\dfrac{9}{40}$

8. $\dfrac{3}{40}$

9. $\dfrac{13}{25}$

10. $\dfrac{17}{25}$

11. $\dfrac{-17}{20}$

12. $\dfrac{-13}{20}$

13. $-\dfrac{9}{16}$

14. $-\dfrac{5}{16}$

15. $\dfrac{7}{5}$

16. $\dfrac{3}{2}$

17. $\dfrac{28}{25}$

18. $\dfrac{31}{20}$

19. $\dfrac{11}{-8}$

20. $\dfrac{17}{-10}$

21. $-\dfrac{39}{40}$

22. $-\dfrac{17}{40}$

23. $\dfrac{121}{200}$

24. $\dfrac{32}{125}$

25. $\dfrac{8}{15}$

26. $\dfrac{7}{9}$

27. $\dfrac{1}{3}$

28. $\dfrac{1}{9}$

29. $\dfrac{-4}{3}$

30. $\dfrac{-8}{9}$

31. $\dfrac{7}{6}$

32. $\dfrac{7}{11}$

33. $-\dfrac{14}{11}$ **34.** $-\dfrac{7}{11}$ **35.** $\dfrac{-5}{12}$ **36.** $\dfrac{-11}{12}$

37. $\dfrac{127}{500}$ **38.** $\dfrac{83}{500}$ **39.** $\dfrac{4}{33}$ **40.** $\dfrac{5}{33}$

41. $\dfrac{-12}{55}$ **42.** $\dfrac{-5}{22}$ **43.** $\dfrac{35}{111}$ **44.** $\dfrac{27}{111}$

45. $\dfrac{4}{7}$ **46.** $\dfrac{2}{7}$ **47.** $\dfrac{-37}{25}$ **48.** $\dfrac{-31}{250}$

b   For Exercises 49–60, round each number to the nearest tenth, hundredth, and thousandth.

49. $\dfrac{4}{11}$ **50.** $\dfrac{3}{11}$ **51.** $-\dfrac{5}{3}$ **52.** $-\dfrac{19}{16}$

53. $\dfrac{-8}{17}$ **54.** $\dfrac{-7}{13}$ **55.** $\dfrac{7}{12}$ **56.** $\dfrac{2}{15}$

57. $\dfrac{29}{-150}$ **58.** $\dfrac{37}{-150}$ **59.** $\dfrac{7}{-9}$ **60.** $\dfrac{5}{-13}$

Calculate and write the result as a decimal.

61. $\dfrac{7}{8}(10.84)$

62. $\dfrac{4}{5}(264.8)$

63. $\dfrac{47}{9}(-79.95)$

64. $\dfrac{7}{11}(-2.7873)$

65. $\left(\dfrac{1}{6}\right)0.0765 + \left(\dfrac{3}{4}\right)0.1124$

66. $\left(\dfrac{2}{5}\right)6384.1 - \left(\dfrac{5}{8}\right)156.56$

67. $\dfrac{3}{4} \times 2.56 - \dfrac{7}{8} \times 3.94$

68. $\dfrac{2}{5} \times 3.91 - \dfrac{7}{10} \times 4.15$

69. $5.2 \times 1\dfrac{7}{8} \div 0.4$

70. $4\dfrac{3}{4} \times 0.5 \div 0.1$

Solve.

71. Find the area of a triangular shawl that is 1.8 m long and 1.2 m wide.

72. Find the area of a triangular sign that is 1.5 m wide and 1.5 m tall.

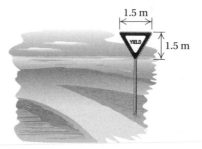

73. Find the area of a triangular stamp that is 3.4 cm wide and 3.4 cm tall.

74. Find the area of a triangular reflector that is 7.4 cm wide and 9.1 cm tall.

75. Find the area of the kite shown.

76. Find the area of the kite shown.

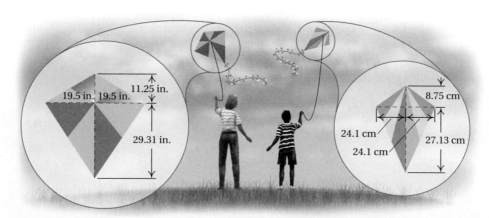

77. $\mathbf{D_W}$ When is long division *not* the fastest way of converting a fraction to decimal notation?

78. $\mathbf{D_W}$ Examine Example 13 of this section. How could the problem be changed so that method 2 would give a result that is completely accurate?

SKILL MAINTENANCE

79. Round 3572 to the nearest ten. [1.4a]

80. Round 3572 to the nearest thousand. [1.4a]

81. Round 78,951 to the nearest hundred. [1.4a]

82. Round 19,829,996 to the nearest ten. [1.4a]

83. Simplify: $\dfrac{95}{-1}$. [3.3b]

84. Solve: $5x - 9 = 7x + 11$. [4.4a]

85. Simplify: $9 - 4 + 2 \div (-1) \cdot 6$. [2.5b]

86. Simplify: $\dfrac{-9}{-9}$. [3.3b]

SYNTHESIS

87. $\mathbf{D_W}$ Are the numbers $5.1\overline{47}$ and $5.14\overline{747}$ equal? Why or why not?

88. $\mathbf{D_W}$ 🖩 A scientific calculator indicates that

$$\frac{5}{6} = 0.833333333 \quad \text{and} \quad \frac{4{,}999{,}999{,}998}{6{,}000{,}000{,}000} = 0.833333333.$$

a) Is it true that $\frac{5}{6} = \frac{4{,}999{,}999{,}998}{6{,}000{,}000{,}000}$? Why or why not?
b) Should decimal notation for $\frac{4{,}999{,}999{,}998}{6{,}000{,}000{,}000}$ repeat? Why or why not?

🖩 Find decimal notation. Save the answers for Exercise 94.

89. $\dfrac{1}{7}$

90. $\dfrac{2}{7}$

91. $\dfrac{3}{7}$

92. $\dfrac{4}{7}$

93. $\dfrac{5}{7}$

94. 🖩 From the pattern of answers to Exercises 89–93, predict the decimal notation for $\frac{6}{7}$. Check your answer on a calculator.

Find decimal notation. Save the answers for Exercise 98.

95. $\dfrac{1}{9}$

96. $\dfrac{1}{99}$

97. $\dfrac{1}{999}$

98. 🖩 From the pattern of Exercises 95–97, predict the decimal notation for $\frac{1}{9999}$. Check your answer on a calculator.

The formula $A = \pi r^2$ is used to find the area, A, of a circle with radius r. For Exercises 99 and 100 find the area of a circle with the given radius, using $\frac{22}{7}$ for π. For Exercises 101 and 102, use 3.14 for π or a calculator with a π key.

99. $r = 2.1$ cm

100. $r = 1.4$ cm

101. 🖩 $r = \dfrac{3}{4}$ ft

102. 🖩 $r = 4\dfrac{1}{2}$ yd

103. $\mathbf{D_W}$ Classify each equation as True or False and provide an explanation for each answer.

a) $0.3333 = \dfrac{1}{3}$ **b)** $0.\overline{3} = \dfrac{1}{3}$ **c)** $0.\overline{6} = \dfrac{2}{3}$ **d)** $0.\overline{9} = 1$

ESTIMATING

1. Estimate to the nearest ten the total cost of one digital phone and one TV.

2. About how much more does the computer cost than the TV?

Answers on page A-15

Study Tips

PUTTING MATH TO USE

One excellent way to study math is to use it in your everyday life. The concepts of this section can be easily reinforced if you use estimating when you next go shopping.

a Estimating Sums, Differences, Products, and Quotients

Estimating has many uses. It can be done before a problem is even attempted and it can be done afterward as a check, even when we are using a calculator. Often, an estimate is all we need. We usually estimate by rounding the numbers so that there are one or two nonzero digits. Consider the following advertisements while reading Examples 1–4.

$399.97 — Anson Processor 1.2Ghz Computer
$69.92 — Tilco Digital Phone with Caller ID
$139.99 — Panton 19" TV

EXAMPLE 1 Estimate to the nearest ten the total cost of one computer and one TV.

We are estimating the sum

$399.97 + $139.99 = Total cost.

The estimate to the nearest ten is

$400 + $140 = $540.   (Estimated total cost)

We rounded $399.97 to the nearest ten and $139.99 to the nearest ten. The estimated sum is $540.

Do Exercise 1.

EXAMPLE 2 About how much more does the computer cost than the phone? Estimate to the nearest ten.

The word "About" indicates estimation. We have

$399.97 − $69.92 = Price difference.

The estimate to the nearest ten is

$400 − $70 = $330.   (Estimated price difference)

Do Exercise 2.

EXAMPLE 3 Estimate the total cost of three TVs.

We are estimating the product

$$3 \times \$139.99 = \text{Total cost.}$$

The estimate is found by rounding $139.99 to the nearest ten:

$$3 \times \$140 = \$420.$$

Do Exercise 3.

EXAMPLE 4 About how many computers can be bought with $1300?

To estimate $1300 \div 399.97$, we mentally search for a number near 1300 that is a multiple of a number near 399.97. Rounding 399.97 to the nearest hundred, we get 400. Since 1300 is close to 1200, which is a multiple of 400, we have

$$1300 \div 399.97 \approx 1200 \div 400 = 3,$$

so the answer is 3.

Do Exercise 4.

When estimating, we usually look for numbers that are easy to work with. For example, if multiplying, we might round 0.43 to 0.5 and 8.9 to 10, because 0.5 and 10 are convenient numbers to multiply.

EXAMPLE 5 Estimate: 4.8×62. Do not find the actual product.

We round 4.8 to the nearest one and 62 to the nearest ten. This gives us two easy numbers with which to work, 5 and 60. Since

$$4.8 \times 62 \approx 5 \times 60$$

and

$$5 \times 60 = 300$$

the estimated product is 300.

Compare these estimates for the product 4.94×38:

$$5 \times 40 = 200, \quad 5 \times 38 = 190, \quad 4.9 \times 40 = 196, \quad 4.9 \times 38 = 186.2.$$

The first estimate was the easiest. You could probably do it mentally. The others had more nonzero digits and were more accurate, but required more work.

Do Exercises 5–10.

3. Estimate the total cost of five phones.

4. About how many TVs can be bought with $550?

Estimate each product. Do not find the actual product.

5. 2.1×8.02

6. 36×0.54

7. 0.93×472

8. 0.72×0.1

9. 0.12×180.3

10. 24.359×5.2

Answers on page A-15

Select the most appropriate estimate for each quotient.

11. 59.78 ÷ 29.1

    a) 200   **b)** 20
    c) 2   **d)** 0.2

12. 82.08 ÷ 2.4

    a) 40   **b)** 4.0
    c) 400   **d)** 0.4

13. 0.1768 ÷ 0.08

    a) 8   **b)** 10
    c) 2   **d)** 20

14. Which of the following is an appropriate estimate of 0.0069 ÷ 0.15?

    a) 0.5   **b)** 50
    c) 0.05 **d)** 23.4

■ **EXAMPLE 6** Which of the following is the best estimate of 82.08 ÷ 24?

    a) 400   **b)** 16   **c)** 40   **d)** 4

This is about 80 ÷ 20, so the answer is about 4. We could also estimate the division as 75 ÷ 25, or 3. In any case, of the choices listed, (d) is the most appropriate.

■ **EXAMPLE 7** Which of the following is the best estimate of 94.18 ÷ 3.2?

    a) 30   **b)** 300   **c)** 3   **d)** 60

This is about 90 ÷ 3, so the answer is about 30. Thus the most appropriate choice is (a).

■ **EXAMPLE 8** Which of the following is the best estimate of 0.0156 ÷ 1.3?

    a) 0.2   **b)** 0.002   **c)** 0.02   **d)** 20

This is about 0.02 ÷ 1, so the answer is about 0.02. Thus the most appropriate choice is (c).

Do Exercises 11–13.

In some cases, it is easier to estimate a quotient by checking products than by rounding the divisor and the dividend.

■ **EXAMPLE 9** Which of the following is the best estimate of 0.0074 ÷ 0.23?

    a) 0.3   **b)** 0.03   **c)** 300   **d)** 3

Note that 0.23 is close to 0.25 and that it is easier to multiply than divide by 0.25. Thus we use 0.25 to check some products.

We first try 3:

$$0.23 \times 3 \approx 0.25 \times 3 = 0.75 .$$ This is too large.

We try a smaller estimate, 0.3:

$$0.23 \times 0.3 \approx 0.25 \times 0.3 = 0.075 .$$ This is also too large.

We make the estimate smaller still, 0.03:

$$0.23 \times 0.03 \approx 0.25 \times 0.03 = 0.0075 .$$

This is close to 0.0074, so the quotient is close to 0.03. Thus, the most appropriate choice is (b).

Do Exercise 14.

Answers on page A-15

a   Consider the following advertisements for Exercises 1–8. Estimate the sums, differences, products, or quotients involved in these problems. Answers will vary, so show all steps.

$59 00
Phelps Personal CD Player

Ciesta Grillmeister 450 Gas Grill
$169 92

Kent Washer
$249 99

$29 95
Carco Booster Car Seat

1. Estimate the total cost of one gas grill and one booster seat.

2. Estimate the total cost of one CD player and one washer.

3. About how much more does the washer cost than the CD player?

4. About how much more does the grill cost than the booster seat?

5. Estimate the cost of five booster seats.

6. Estimate the cost of four CD players.

7. About how many washers can be bought with $1700?

8. About how many grills can be bought with $1750?

Estimate by rounding as directed.

9. $0.02 + 1.31 + 0.34$; nearest tenth

10. $0.88 + 2.07 + 1.54$; nearest one

11. $6.03 + 0.007 + 0.214$; nearest one

12. $1.11 + 8.888 + 99.94$;
nearest one

13. $52.367 + 1.307 + 7.324$;
nearest one

14. $12.9882 + 1.0115$;
nearest tenth

15. $2.678 - 0.445$; nearest tenth

16. $12.9882 - 1.0115$; nearest one

17. $198.67432 - 24.5007$; nearest ten

Choose a rounding digit that gives one or two nonzero digits and select the most appropriate estimate.

18. $234.12321 - 200.3223$
   a) 600   **b)** 60
   c) 300   **d)** 30

19. 49×7.89
   a) 400   **b)** 40
   c) 4   **d)** 0.4

20. 7.4×8.9
   a) 95   **b)** 63
   c) 124   **d)** 6

21. 98.4×0.083
   a) 80   **b)** 12
   c) 8   **d)** 0.8

22. 78×5.3
   a) 400   **b)** 800
   c) 40   **d)** 8

23. $3.6 \div 4$
   a) 10   **b)** 1
   c) 0.1   **d)** 0.01

24. $0.0713 \div 1.94$
   a) 4   **b)** 0.4
   c) 0.04   **d)** 40

25. $74.68 \div 24.7$
   a) 9   **b)** 3
   c) 12   **d)** 120

26. $914 \div 0.921$
   a) 10   **b)** 100
   c) 1000   **d)** 1

27. *Palm VIIxe and the Sears Tower.* The Palm VIIxe PDA (Personal Digital Assistant) is 4.7 in. (about 0.39167 ft) high. Estimate how many PDAs it would take, if placed end to end, to reach from the ground to the top of the Sears Tower, which is 1454 ft tall. Round to one or two nonzero digits.
Source: www.yahoo.com

1454 ft

4.7 in. = 0.39167 ft

28. *Paint.* Recently the Home Depot sold BEHR semi-gloss exterior house paint for $22.97 a gallon. Estimate how many gallons could be bought with $4500.

29. **Dw** Describe a situation in which an estimate is made by rounding to the nearest 10,000 and then multiplying.

30. **Dw** A roll of fiberglass insulation costs $21.95. Describe two situations involving estimating and the cost of fiberglass insulation. Devise one situation so that $21.95 is rounded to $22. Devise the other situation so that $21.95 is rounded to $20.

SKILL MAINTENANCE

Solve.   [2.8d], [4.4a]

31. $5x + 4 = 39$

32. $9x + 3 = -15$

33. $-4t + 10 = 30$

34. $7t - 8 = -29$

35. $18 = 6 - 2x$

36. $20 - 8 + 4x$

37. $\frac{3}{4}t + 5 = 17$

38. $\frac{2}{5}t - 9 = 7$

Find the perimeter.   [2.7b]

39.

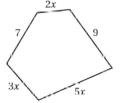

40.

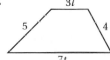

SYNTHESIS

41. **Dw** Rather than charge $30 for an item, stores often price the item at $29.99, or $29.95, or sometimes even $29.97 . Why does this practice exist?

42. **Dw** Rick rounded -305.281 to -305.3 . Did he round up or down? Explain.

The following were done on a calculator and then rewritten. Estimate to determine whether the decimal point was placed correctly.

43. $178.9462 \times 61.78 = 11{,}055.29624$

44. $14{,}973.35 \div 298.75 = 501.2$

45. $19.7236 - 1.4738 \times 4.1097 = 1.366672414$

46. $28.46901 \div 4.9187 - 2.5081 = 3.279813473$

47. ▦ Use one of $+, -, \times, \div$ in each blank to make a true sentence.
  a) $(0.37 \,\square\, 18.78) \,\square\, 2^{13} = 156{,}876.8$
  b) $2.56 \,\square\, 6.4 \,\square\, 51.2 \,\square\, 17.4 = 312.84$

48. ▦ In the subtraction below, a and b are digits. Find a and b.

$$
\begin{array}{r}
b876.a4321 \\
-\,1234.a678b \\
\hline
8641.b7a32
\end{array}
$$

SOLVING EQUATIONS

5.7

Objectives

a Solve equations containing decimals and one variable term.

b Solve equations containing decimals and two or more variable terms.

Solve.

1. $7.4t + 1.25 = 27.89$

2. $-5.7 + 4.8x = -14.82$

Answers on page A-16

In Section 4.4, we used a combination of the addition and multiplication principles to solve equations like $5x + 7 = -3$. We now use those same properties to solve similar equations involving decimals.

a Equations with One Variable Term

Recall that equations like $5x + 7 = -3$ are normally solved by first "undoing" the addition and then "undoing" the multiplication. This reverses the order of operations in which we add last and multiply first.

EXAMPLE 1 Solve: $4.2x + 3.7 = -26.12$.

$$4.2x + 3.7 = -26.12$$

$$4.2x + 3.7 - 3.7 = -26.12 - 3.7 \qquad \text{Subtracting 3.7 from, or adding } -3.7 \text{ to, both sides}$$

$$4.2x = -29.82 \qquad \text{Simplifying}$$

$$\frac{4.2x}{4.2} = \frac{-29.82}{4.2} \qquad \text{Multiplying by } \frac{1}{4.2} \text{ or dividing by 4.2 on both sides}$$

$$x = -7.1 \qquad \text{Simplifying}$$

CHECK:

$$\begin{array}{c|c} \hline 4.2x + 3.7 = -26.12 \\ \hline 4.2(-7.1) + 3.7 \ ? \ -26.12 \\ -29.82 + 3.7 \ \big| \\ -26.12 \ \big| \ -26.12 \quad \textbf{TRUE} \end{array}$$

The solution is -7.1.

Do Exercises 1 and 2.

Study Tips

KEEP YOUR FOCUS

When studying with someone else, it can be very tempting to prolong conversation that has little to do with the mathematics that you need to study. If you see that this may happen, explain to your partner(s) that you enjoy the nonmathematical conversation, but would enjoy it more later— after the math work is completed.

CALCULATOR CORNER

To check the solution of Example 1 with a scientific calculator, we press the following sequence of keys:

[4] [.] [2] [×] [7] [.] [1] [+/−] [+] [3] [.] [7] [=].

On a graphing calculator we press

[4] [.] [2] [×] [(−)] [7] [.] [1] [+] [3] [.] [7] [ENTER].

In both cases, the result, -26.12, shows that -7.1 *is* a solution of $4.2x + 3.7 = -26.12$.

Exercises:

1. Use a calculator to check the solution of Margin Exercises 1 and 2.

2. Use a calculator to show that -3.6 is *not* a solution of $7.4t + 1.25 = 27.89$ (Margin Exercise 1).

3. Use a calculator to show that 1.9 is *not* a solution of $-5.7 + 4.8x = -14.82$.

b Equations with Two or More Variable Terms

Some equations have variable terms on both sides. To solve such an equation, we use the addition principle to get all variable terms on one side of the equation and all constant terms on the other side.

EXAMPLE 2 Solve: $10x - 7 = 2x + 13$.

We begin by subtracting $2x$ from (or adding $-2x$ to) each side. This will group all variable terms on one side of the equation:

$$10x - 7 - 2x = 2x + 13 - 2x \qquad \text{Adding } -2x \text{ to both sides}$$
$$8x - 7 = 13. \qquad\qquad\qquad \text{Combining like terms}$$

This last equation is similar to Example 1. As in that example, we use the addition principle to isolate all constant terms on one side:

$$8x - 7 = 13$$
$$8x - 7 + 7 = 13 + 7 \qquad \text{Adding 7 to both sides}$$
$$8x = 20 \qquad\qquad \text{Simplifying (combining like terms)}$$
$$\frac{8x}{8} = \frac{20}{8} \qquad\qquad \text{Dividing both sides by 8}$$
$$x = 2.5 .$$

CHECK:
$$\begin{array}{c|c}
\multicolumn{2}{c}{10x - 7 = 2x + 13} \\
\hline
10(2.5) - 7 \ ? \ 2(2.5) + 13 \\
25 - 7 \ \big| \ 5 + 13 \\
18 \ \big| \ 18 \qquad \textbf{TRUE}
\end{array}$$

The solution is 2.5 .

CONNECTING THE CONCEPTS

In Example 2 we used a very common, but useful problem-solving technique: we performed one or more steps that effectively turned a "new" problem into an equivalent form with which we were already familiar. Most mathematicians are primarily interested in solving new problems and rapidly lose interest in problems that offer no new "twist." An old joke makes this point—a mathematician, in a psychology experiment, walks into a room with a trash can on fire and a bucket of water next to it. The mathematician promptly douses the fire. Next, a new experiment is arranged in which the water bucket is now in a corner of the room. This time, after entering the room, the mathematician simply moves the bucket of water next to the flaming trash can. When asked, "Why not douse the fire?" the mathematician replies, "After I turned the new problem into a problem I already solved, I lost interest." Think of this when you encounter a new type of problem.

Sometimes it may be easier to combine all variable terms on the right side and all constant terms on the left side.

Solve.

3. $10t - 3 = 4t + 18$

4. $8 + 4x = 9x - 3$

5. $2.1x - 45.3 = 17.3x + 23.1$

6. Solve: $3(x + 5) = 20 - x$.

Answers on page A-16

■ **EXAMPLE 3** Solve: $11 - 3t = 7t + 8$.

We can combine all variable terms on the right side by adding $3t$ to both sides:

$$11 - 3t = 7t + 8$$
$$11 - 3t + 3t = 7t + 8 + 3t \qquad \text{Adding } 3t \text{ to both sides}$$
$$11 = 10t + 8 \qquad \text{Combining like terms}$$
$$11 - 8 = 10t + 8 - 8 \qquad \text{Subtracting 8 from both sides}$$
$$3 = 10t$$
$$\frac{3}{10} = \frac{10t}{10} \qquad \text{Dividing both sides by 10}$$
$$0.3 = t.$$

CHECK:
$$\frac{11 - 3t = 7t + 8}{11 - 3(0.3) \; ? \; 7(0.3) + 8}$$
$$11 - 0.9 \;\bigg|\; 2.1 + 8$$
$$10.1 \;\bigg|\; 10.1 \qquad \textbf{TRUE}$$

The solution is 0.3 .

Note that in Example 3 the variable appears on the right side of the last equation. It does not matter whether the variable is isolated on the right or left side. What is important is that you have a clear direction to your work as you proceed from step to step.

Do Exercises 3–5.

■ **EXAMPLE 4** Solve: $5(x + 1) = 3x + 12$.

By using the distributive law, we can find an equivalent equation:

$$5(x + 1) = 3x + 12$$
$$5 \cdot x + 5 \cdot 1 = 3x + 12 \qquad \text{Using the distributive law to remove parentheses}$$
$$5x + 5 = 3x + 12. \qquad \text{Simplifying}$$

We now solve as we did in Examples 2 and 3:

$$5x + 5 - 3x = 3x + 12 - 3x \qquad \text{Subtracting } 3x \text{ from both sides}$$
$$2x + 5 = 12 \qquad \text{Simplifying}$$
$$2x + 5 - 5 = 12 - 5 \qquad \text{Subtracting 5 from both sides}$$
$$2x = 7$$
$$\frac{2x}{2} = \frac{7}{2} \qquad \text{Dividing both sides by 2}$$
$$x = 3.5 .$$

CHECK:
$$\frac{5(x + 1) = 3x + 12}{5(3.5 + 1) \; ? \; 3(3.5) + 12}$$
$$5(4.5) \;\bigg|\; 10.5 + 12$$
$$22.5 \;\bigg|\; 22.5 \qquad \textbf{TRUE}$$

The solution is 3.5 .

Do Exercise 6.

5.7
EXERCISE SET

For Extra Help

Digital Video
Tutor CD 4
Videotape 5

InterAct
Math

Math Tutor
Center

MathXL

MyMathLab

a Solve. Remember to check.

1. $5x = 27$

2. $36 \cdot y = 14.76$

3. $x + 15.7 = 3.1$

4. $x + 13.9 = 4.2$

5. $5x - 8 = 22$

6. $4x - 7 = 13$

7. $6.9x - 8.4 = 4.02$

8. $7.1x - 9.3 = 8.45$

9. $21.6 + 4.1t = 6.43$

10. $12.4 + 3.7t = 2.04$

11. $-26.05 = 7.5x + 9.2$

12. $-43.42 = 8.7x + 5.3$

13. $-4.2x + 3.04 = -4.1$

14. $-2.9x - 2.24 = -17.9$

15. $-3.05 = 7.24 - 3.5t$

16. $-4.62 = 5.68 - 2.5t$

b Solve. Remember to check.

17. $9x - 2 = 5x + 34$

18. $8x - 5 = 6x + 9$

19. $2x + 6 = 7x - 10$

20. $3x + 4 = 11x - 6$

21. $5y - 3 = 4 + 9y$

22. $6y - 5 = 8 + 10y$

23. $5.9x + 67 = 7.6x + 16$

24. $2.1x + 42 = 5.2x - 20$

25. $7.8a + 2 = 2.4a + 19.28$

26. $7.5a - 5.16 = 3.1a + 12$

27. $6(x + 2) = 4x + 30$

28. $5(x + 3) = 3x + 23$

29. $5(x + 3) = 15x - 6$

30. $2(x + 3) = 4x - 11$

31. $7a - 9 = 15(a - 3)$

32. $2a - 7 = 12(a - 3)$

33. $2.9(x + 8.1) = 7.8x - 3.95$

34. $2(x + 7.3) = 6x - 0.83$

35. $-6.21 - 4.3t = 9.8(t + 2.1)$

36. $-7.37 - 3.2t = 4.9(t + 6.1)$

37. $4(x - 2) - 9 = 2x + 9$

38. $9(x - 4) + 13 = 4x + 12$

39. $43(7 - 2x) + 34 = 50(x - 4.1) + 744$

40. $34(5 - 3.5x) = 12(3x - 8) + 653.5$

41. **D_W** Which equation do you consider more challenging to solve and why:

$$4.2x + 3.7 = -26.12 \quad \text{or} \quad 10x - 7 = 2x + 13?$$

42. **D_W** Is it "incorrect" to begin solving $5x + 9 = x + 12$ by dividing both sides by 5? Why or why not?

Find the area of each figure. [3.6b]

43.

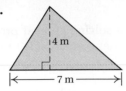
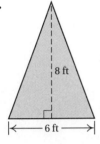

4 m

7 m

44.

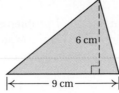

6 cm

9 cm

45.

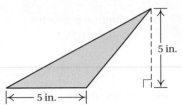

5 in.

5 in.

46.

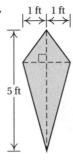

8 ft

6 ft

47.

1 ft   1 ft

5 ft

48.

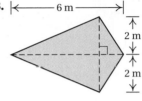

6 m

2 m

2 m

49. Subtract: $\dfrac{3}{25} - \dfrac{7}{10}$.   [4.3a]

50. Simplify: $\dfrac{0}{-18}$.   [3.3b]

51. Add: $-17 + 24 + (-9)$.   [2.2a]

52. Solve: $3x - 10 = 14$.   [2.8d]

53. ^{D}W Is it possible for an equation like $x + 3 = x + 5$ to have a solution? Why or why not?

54. ^{D}W Is it possible for an equation like $4x - 1 = 4(x - 2) + 4$ to have a solution? Why or why not?

Solve.

55. $7.035(4.91x - 8.21) + 17.401 = 23.902x - 7.372815$

56. $8.701(3.4 - 5.1x) - 89.321 = 5.401x + 74.65787$

57. $5(x - 4.2) + 3[2x - 5(x + 7)] = 39 + 2(7.5 - 6x) + 3x$

58. $14(2.5x - 3) + 9x + 5 = 4(3.25 - x) + 2[5x - 3(x + 1)]$

59. $3.5(4.8x - 2.9) + 4.5 = 9.4x - 3.4(x - 1.9)$

60. $4.19 - 1.8(4.5x - 6.4) = 3.1(9.8 + x)$

APPLICATIONS AND PROBLEM SOLVING

a Solve applied problems involving decimals.

1. Body Temperature. Normal body temperature is 98.6°F. When fevered, most people will die if their bodies reach 107°F. This is a rise of how many degrees?

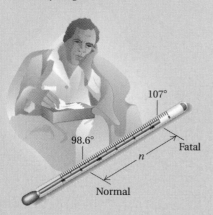

107°

98.6°

Fatal

n

Normal

a Solving applied problems with decimals is like solving applied problems with integers. We translate first to an equation that corresponds to the situation. Then we solve the equation.

■ **EXAMPLE 1** *Car Mileage.* In a 2002 Sierra Club test drive, Darden Rice averaged 44.5 mpg (miles per gallon) in her Toyota Prius while Joe Murphy averaged 16.3 mpg in his GMC Yukon. How many more miles per gallon did the Prius achieve?
Source: *Sierra Magazine*, May/June 2002

Sierra Club organizers Darden Rice (left) and Joe Murphy (right) traveled from Tampa to Tallahassee to promote climate-friendly cars.

1. **Familiarize.** We could draw or visualize a bar graph to show the two mileages. Instead, we let *d* represent the difference, in miles per gallon.

2. **Translate.** This is a "how-much-more" situation. We translate as follows, using the data given.

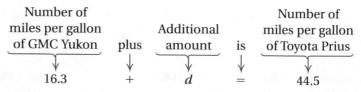

Number of miles per gallon of GMC Yukon	plus	Additional amount	is	Number of miles per gallon of Toyota Prius
↓	↓	↓	↓	↓
16.3	+	*d*	=	44.5

3. **Solve.** We solve the equation by subtracting 16.3 from both sides:

$$16.3 + d - 16.3 = 44.5 - 16.3$$
$$d = 28.2$$

4. **Check.** We can check by adding 28.2 to 16.3 to get 44.5 .

5. **State.** The Toyota Prius achieved 28.2 miles per gallon more than the GMC Yukon.

Answer on page A-16

Do Exercise 1.

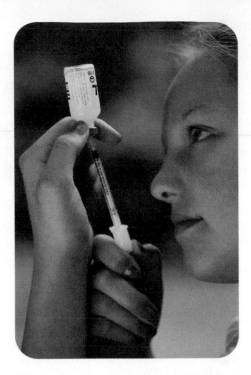

2. At Copylot Printing, the cost of copying is 8 cents per page. How much, in dollars, would it cost to make 466 copies?

EXAMPLE 2 A 100-unit syringe is often used by diabetics and nurses to administer insulin. Each unit on the syringe represents 0.01 cc (cubic centimeter). Each day Wendy averages 42 units of insulin. How many cc's will Wendy use in a typical week?

1. **Familiarize.** We make a drawing or at least visualize the situation. We let a = the amount of insulin used.

2. **Translate.** We translate as follows.

Amount used each day	times	Number of days in a week	is	Total amount injected
↓	↓	↓	↓	↓
0.42 cc	×	7	=	a

3. **Solve.** To solve the equation, we carry out the multiplication.

$$\begin{array}{r} 0.4\,2 \\ \times \quad\quad 7 \\ \hline 2.9\,4 \end{array}$$

Thus, a = 2.94 cc.

4. **Check.** We can check using approximation:

0.42 cc × 7 ≈ 0.4 cc × 7 = 2.8 cc ≈ 2.94 cc.

Note too that 2.94 is bigger than 0.42, so our answer makes sense.

5. **State.** Wendy uses 2.94 cc's of insulin in a typical week.

Do Exercise 2.

Answer on page A-16

3. Car Payments. Kevin's car loan totals $11,370 and is to be paid over 5 yr in monthly payments of equal size. Find the amount of each payment.

MULTISTEP PROBLEMS

EXAMPLE 3 *Student Loans.*
Upon graduation from college, Jannette will be faced with repaying a Stafford loan that totals $23,334. The loan is to be paid back over 10 yr in equal monthly payments. Find the amount of each payment.

1. **Familiarize.** We imagine the situation as one in which borrowed money is repaid in monthly checks that are always the same size. Since we are not told how many checks there will be, part of solving will be to determine how many months there are in 10 yr. We let m = the size of each monthly payment.

2. **Translate.** To find the amount of the monthly payment, we note that the amount owed is split up, or *divided*, into payments of equal size. The size of each payment will depend on how many payments there are. To find the number of payments, we first determine that in 10 yr there are

    $$10 \cdot 12 = 120 \text{ months.} \qquad \text{There are 12 months in a year.}$$

    We have

Amount of monthly payment	is	Total amount owed	divided by	Number of payments
↓	↓	↓	↓	↓
m	=	$23,334	÷	120.

3. **Solve.** To solve, we carry out the division.

    $$
    \begin{array}{r}
    194.45 \\
    120 \overline{)\ 23{,}334.00} \\
    \underline{120} \\
    1133 \\
    \underline{1080} \\
    534 \\
    \underline{480} \\
    540 \\
    \underline{480} \\
    600 \\
    \underline{600} \\
    0
    \end{array}
    \qquad m = 194.45
    $$

4. **Check.** To check, we first verify that there are 120 months in 10 years. We can do this with division:

    $$120 \text{ months} \div 12 \text{ months per year} = 10 \text{ years.}$$

    To check that the amount of the monthly payment is correct, we can estimate the product:

    $$\$194.45 \cdot 120 \approx \$200 \cdot 120 = \$24{,}000 \approx \$23{,}334.$$

5. **State.** Jannette's monthly payments will be $194.45.

Do Exercise 3.

Answer on page A-16

Study Tips

FINISHING A CHAPTER

Try to be aware of when you reach the end of a chapter. Sometimes the end of a chapter signals the arrival of a quiz or test. Almost always, the end of a chapter indicates the end of a particular area of study. Because future work will likely rely upon your mastery of the chapter completed, make use of the chapter review and test to solidify your understanding before moving onward.

EXAMPLE 4 *Gas Mileage.* Emma filled her Pontiac Vibe with gas and noted that the odometer read 67,507.8 . After the next filling, the odometer read 67,890.3 . It took 12.5 gal to fill the tank. How many miles per gallon did Emma's Vibe get?

1. **Familiarize.** We make a drawing.

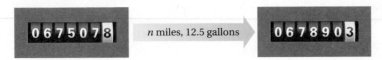

n miles, 12.5 gallons

This is a two-step problem. First, we find the number of miles driven between fill-ups. We let n = the number of miles driven.

2., 3. **Translate** and **Solve.** To find the number of miles driven, we translate and solve as follows.

Second odometer reading	minus	First odometer reading	is	Number of miles driven
↓	↓	↓	↓	↓
67,890.3	−	67,507.8	=	n

To solve the equation, we simplify on the left side:

$$67,890.3 - 67,507.8 = n$$
$$382.5 - n.$$

$$\begin{array}{r} 6\ 7,8\ 9\ 0.3 \\ -\ 6\ 7,5\ 0\ 7.8 \\ \hline 3\ 8\ 2.5 \end{array}$$

Next, we divide the number of miles driven by the number of gallons used. This gives us m = the number of miles per gallon—that is, the gas mileage. The division that corresponds to the situation is

$$382.5 \div 12.5 = m.$$ Note that miles ÷ gallons = miles per gallon.

To find the number m, we divide.

$$\begin{array}{r} 3\ 0.6 \\ 1\ 2.5.\ \overline{)\ 3\ 8\ 2.5{\scriptstyle\wedge}0} \\ \underline{3\ 7\ 5\ 0} \\ 7\ 5\ 0 \\ \underline{7\ 5\ 0} \\ 0 \end{array}$$

Thus, $m = 30.6$.

4. **Check.** To check, we first multiply the number of miles per gallon times the number of gallons:

$$12.5\ \text{gal} \times 30.6\ \text{mpg} = 382.5\ \text{mi}.$$ 12.5 gal would take Emma 382.5 mi.

Then we add 382.5 to 67,507.8:

$$67,507.8 + 382.5 = 67,890.3 .$$

The number 30.6 mpg checks.

5. **State.** Emma's Pontiac Vibe got 30.6 miles per gallon.

Do Exercise 4.

4. Gas Mileage.   Ivan filled his Ford Focus and noted that the odometer read 38,320.8 . After the next filling, the odometer read 38,649.7 . It took 11.5 gal to fill the tank. How many miles per gallon (mpg) did Ivan's Ford get?

Answer on page A-16

5. Suppose that an 8-in.-wide disc is punched out of an 8-in. by 8-in. sheet of metal. How much material is left over?

Some problems may require us to recall important formulas. Example 5 involves a formula from geometry that is worth remembering.

In any circle, a **diameter** is a segment that passes through the center of the circle with endpoints on the circle. A **radius** is a segment with one endpoint on the center and the other endpoint on the circle. The area, A, of a circle with radius of length r is given by

$$A = \pi \cdot r^2,$$

where $\pi \approx 3.14$.

EXAMPLE 5   The Northfield Tap and Die Company stamps 6-cm-wide discs out of metal squares that are 6 cm by 6 cm. How much metal remains after the disc has been punched out?

1. **Familiarize.**   We make, and label, a drawing. The question deals with discs, squares, and leftover material, so we list the relevant area formulas.
   For a square with sides of length s,

   $$Area = s^2.$$

   For a circle with radius of length r,

   $$Area = \pi \cdot r^2,$$

   where $\pi \approx 3.14$.

   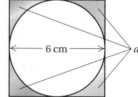

2. **Translate.**   To find the amount left over, we subtract the area of the disc from the area of the square. Note that a circle's radius is half of its diameter, or width.

Area of square in square centimeters	minus	Area of disc in square centimeters	is	Area left over in square centimeters
6^2	$-$	$3.14 \times \left(\dfrac{6}{2}\right)^2$	$=$	a

3. **Solve.**   We simplify as follows:

$$6^2 - 3.14\left(\frac{6}{2}\right)^2 = a$$

$$36 - 3.14(3)^2 = a$$

$$36 - 3.14 \cdot 9 = a$$

$$36 - 28.26 = a$$

$$7.74 = a.$$

4. **Check.**   We can repeat our calculation as a check. Note that 7.74 is less than the area of the disc, which in turn is less than the area of the square. This agrees with the impression given by our drawing.

5. **State.**   The amount of material left over is 7.74 cm^2.

Do Exercise 5.

Answer on page A-16

EXAMPLE 6 *Truck Rentals.* Yardbird Landscaping has rented a 22-ft truck at a daily rate of $49.95 plus 35 cents a mile. They have budgeted $125 for renting a truck to deliver trees to customers around the county. How many miles can a one-day rental truck be driven without exceeding the budget?

6. Yardbird Landscaping charges customers $25 plus $20 per hour to rototill a garden. For how many hours can Emily hire Yardbird if she has budgeted $50 for rototilling?

1. **Familiarize.** Suppose that the landscapers drive 100 mi. Then the cost would be

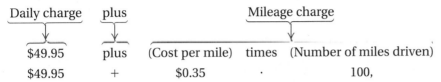

Daily charge   plus   Mileage charge

$49.95   plus   (Cost per mile)   times   (Number of miles driven)

$49.95   + $0.35   ·   100,

which is $49.95 + $35, or $84.95. This familiarizes us with the way in which a calculation is made. Note that we convert 35 cents to $0.35 so that only one unit, dollars, is used. Note also that the landscapers can exceed 100 mi and still be within budget. To see just how many miles the budget allows for, we could make and check more guesses, but this would be very time-consuming. Instead, we let m = the number of miles that can be driven within a $125 budget.

2. **Translate.** The problem can be rephrased and translated as follows.

                                     Number of

Daily rate   plus   Cost per mile   times   miles driven   is   Cost

   $49.95   + $0.35   · m = $125

3. **Solve.** We solve the equation:

$$49.95 + 0.35m = 125$$

$$0.35m = 75.05 \qquad \text{Subtracting 49.95 from both sides}$$

$$m = \frac{75.05}{0.35} \qquad \text{Dividing both sides by 0.35}$$

$$m \approx 214.4 \ . \qquad \text{Rounding to the nearest tenth}$$

4. **Check.** We check in the original problem. We multiply 214.4 by $0.35, getting $75.04. Then we add $75.04 to $49.95 and get $124.99, which is just about the $125 allotted. Our answer is not exact because we rounded.

5. **State.** Yardbird Landscaping can drive the truck about 214.4 mi without exceeding the budget.

Do Exercise 6.

Answer on page A-16

5.8

EXERCISE SET

For Extra Help

 Digital Video Tutor CD 4 Videotape 5

 InterAct Math

 Math Tutor Center

 MathXL

MyMathLab

a Solve using the five-step problem-solving procedure.

1. What is the cost of 7 jackets at $32.98 each?

2. What is the cost of 8 pairs of socks at $4.95 each?

3. *Gasoline Cost.* What is the cost, in dollars, of 20.4 gal of gasoline at 174.9 cents per gallon? (174.9 cents = $1.749) Round the answer to the nearest cent.

4. *Gasoline Cost.* What is the cost, in dollars, of 15.3 gal of gasoline at 172.9 cents per gallon? (172.9 cents = $1.729) Round the answer to the nearest cent.

5. *Body Temperature.* Normal body temperature is 98.6°F. During an illness, a patient's temperature rose 4.2°. What was the new temperature?

6. *Gasoline Cost.* What is the cost, in dollars, of 13.8 gal of gasoline at 169.9 cents per gallon? Round the answer to the nearest cent.

7. *Lottery Winnings.* In Texas, one of the state lotteries is called "Cash 5." In a recent weekly game, the lottery prize of $127,315 was shared equally by 6 winners. How much was each winner's share? Round to the nearest cent.
Source: Texas Lottery

8. *Lunch Costs.* A group of 5 students pays $37.45 for lunch and splits the cost equally. What is each person's share?

9. *Stamp.* Find the area and the perimeter of the stamp shown here.

2.5 cm

3.25 cm

10. *Pole Vault Pit.* Find the area and the perimeter of the landing area of the pole vault pit shown here.

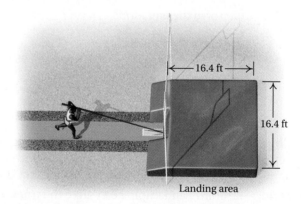

16.4 ft

16.4 ft

Landing area

11. *Odometer Reading.* The Levines checked the odometer before starting a trip. It read 22,456.8 and they know that they will be driving 234.7 mi. What will the odometer read at the end of the trip?

12. *Miles Driven.* Petra bought gasoline when the odometer read 14,296.3 . At the next gasoline purchase, the odometer read 14,515.8 . How many miles had been driven?

13. Roberto bought a CD for $16.99 and paid with a $20 bill. How much change was there?

14. Madeleine buys a book for $44.68 and pays with a $50 bill. How much change does she receive?

15. *Medicine.* After taking aspirin, Wanda's temperature dropped from 103.2°F to 99.7°F. How much did her temperature drop?

16. *Nursing.* A nurse draws 17.85 mg of blood and uses 9.68 mg in a blood test. How much is left?

17. *Culinary Arts.* One pound of crabmeat makes three servings at the Key West Seafood Restaurant. If the crabmeat costs $16.95 per pound, what is the cost per serving?

18. *Finance.* A car loan totaling $4425 is to be paid off in 12 monthly payments of equal size. How much is each payment?

19. *Beverage Consumption.* Each year, the average U.S. citizen drinks about 49.0 gal of soft drinks, 41.2 gal of water, 25.3 gal of milk, 24.8 gal of coffee, and 7.8 gal of fruit juice. What is the total amount that the average U.S. citizen drinks?

20. *Medicine.* After being tested for allergies, Mike was given allergy shots of 0.25 mL, 0.4 mL, 0.5 mL, and 0.5 mL over a 7-week period. What was the total amount of the injections?

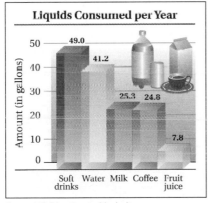

Source: U.S. Department of Agriculture

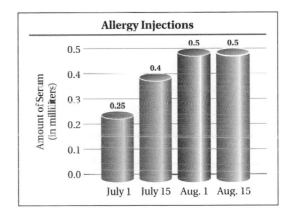

21. *Gas Mileage.* Peggy filled her van's gas tank and noted that the odometer read 26,342.8 . After the next filling, the odometer read 26,736.7 . It took 19.5 gal to fill the tank. How many miles per gallon did the van get?

22. *Gas Mileage.* Peter filled his Honda's gas tank and noted that the odometer read 18,943.2 . After the next filling, the odometer read 19,306.2 . It took 13.2 gal to fill the tank. How many miles per gallon did the car get?

23. *Nursing.* Phil injects a total of 38 units of insulin, each day for a week (see Example 2). How many cc's of insulin does he use in a week?

24. *Nursing.* Carlie averages 49 units of insulin per day, for 15 days (see Example 2). How many cc's of insulin has she used during those 15 days?

25. *Jackie Robinson Poster.*   A special limited-edition poster was painted by sports artist Leroy Neiman. Commissioned by Barton L. Kaufman, it commemorates the entrance of the first African-American, Jackie Robinson, into major league baseball in 1947. The dimensions of the poster are as shown. How much area is not devoted to the painting?
Source: Barton L. Kaufman, private collection

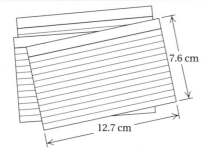

26. *Earth Day Poster.*   An Earth Day poster that is 61.8 cm by 73.2 cm includes a 2-cm border. What is the area of the poster inside the border?

27. *Study Cards.*   An instructor allows her students to bring one 7.6-cm by 12.7-cm index card to the final exam, with notes of any sort written on the card. If both sides of the card are used, how much area is available for notes?

28. *Stamps.*   Find the total area of the stamps shown.

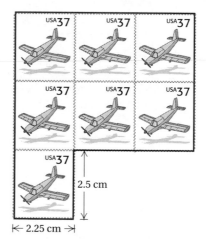

29. *Cost of Video Game.*   A certain video game costs 25 cents and runs for 1.5 min. Assuming a player does not win any free games and plays continuously, how much money, in dollars, does it cost to play the video game for 1 hr?

30. *Property Taxes.*   The Colavitos own a house with an assessed value of $184,500. For every $1000 of assessed value, they pay $7.68 in taxes. How much do they pay in taxes?

Find the length d in each figure.

31.

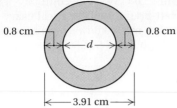

0.8 cm — — 0.8 cm

d

3.91 cm

32.

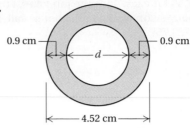

0.9 cm — — 0.9 cm

d

4.52 cm

33. *Carpentry.* A round, 6-ft-wide hot tub is being built into a 12-ft by 30-ft rectangular deck. How much decking is needed for the surface of the deck?

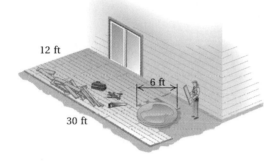

12 ft

6 ft

30 ft

34. *Landscaping.* A rectangular yard is 20 ft by 15 ft. The yard is covered with grass except for a circular flower garden with an 8-ft diameter. Find the area of grass in the yard.

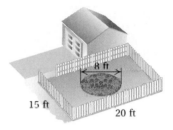

8 ft

15 ft

20 ft

35. A 4-ft by 6-ft table top is cut from a round table top that is 9 ft wide. How much wood will be left over?

36. A 4-ft by 4-ft tablecloth is cut from a round tablecloth that is 6 ft wide. Find the area of the cloth left over.

37. Zachary worked 53 hr during a week one summer. He earned $8.50 per hour for the first 40 hr and $12.75 per hour for overtime. How much did Zachary earn during the week?

38. It costs $24.95 a day plus 27 cents per mile to rent a compact car at Shuttles Rent-A-Car. How much, in dollars, would it cost to drive the car 120 mi in 1 day?

39. *Bike Rentals.* Mike's Bikes rents mountain bikes. The shop charges $4.00 insurance for each rental plus $6.00 per hour. For how many hours can a person rent a bike with $25.00?

40. *Phone Bills.* Auritech Communication charges 50¢ for the first minute and 32¢ for each additional minute for a third-party-billed phone call. For how long could two parties speak if the bill for the call cannot exceed $5.30?

41. *Service Calls.* JoJo's Service Center charges $30 for a house call plus $37.50 for each hour the job takes. For how long has a repairperson worked on a house call if the bill comes to $123.75?

42. *Electric Rates.* Southeast Electric charges 9¢ per kilowatt-hour for the first 200 kWh. The company charges 11¢ per kilowatt-hour for all electrical usage in excess of 200 kWh. How many kilowatt-hours were used if a monthly electric bill was $57.60?

43. *Field Dimensions.* The dimensions of a World Cup soccer field are 114.9 yd by 74.4 yd. The dimensions of a standard football field are 120 yd by 53.3 yd. How much greater is the area of a World Cup soccer field?

44. *Overtime Pay.* A construction worker earned $17 per hour for the first 40 hr of work and $25.50 per hour for work in excess of 40 hr. One week she earned $896.75. How much overtime did she work?

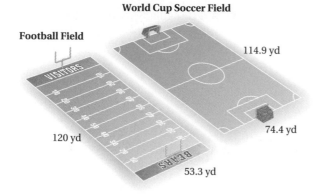

45. Frank has been sent to the store with $40 to purchase 6 lb of cheese at $4.79 a pound and as many bottles of seltzer, at $0.64 a bottle, as possible. How many bottles of seltzer should Frank buy?

46. Janice has been sent to the store with $30 to purchase 5 pt of strawberries at $2.49 a pint and as many bags of chips, at $1.39 a bag, as possible. How many bags of chips should Janice buy?

47. $\mathbf{D_W}$ Write a problem for a classmate to solve. Design the problem so that the solution is "Mona's Buick got 23.5 mpg."

48. $\mathbf{D_W}$ Write a problem for a classmate to solve. Design the problem so that the solution is "The larger field is 200 m² bigger."

SKILL MAINTENANCE

49. Simplify: $\dfrac{0}{-13}$. [3.3b]

50. Add: $-\dfrac{4}{5} + \dfrac{7}{10}$. [4.2b]

51. Subtract: $\dfrac{8}{11} - \dfrac{4}{3}$. [4.3a]

52. Solve: $4x - 7 = 9x + 13$. [5.7b]

53. Add: $4\dfrac{1}{3} + 2\dfrac{1}{2}$. [4.6a]

54. Simplify: $\dfrac{-72}{-72}$. [3.3b]

55. $\mathbf{D_W}$ Which is a better deal and why: a 14-in. pizza that costs $9.95 or a 16-in. pizza that costs $11.95?

56. $\mathbf{D_W}$ To determine the average amount that each U.S. citizen drinks per year, Alison obtained the following graph and found the average of the numbers listed. Was Alison's approach correct? Why or why not?

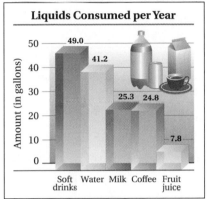

Source: U.S. Department of Agriculture

57. A "French Press" coffee pot requires no filters, but costs $34.95. Kenny can also buy a plastic drip cone for $4.49, but the cone requires filters which cost $0.04 per pot dripped. How many pots of coffee must Kenny make for the French Press pot to be the more economical purchase?

58. You can drive from home to work using either of two routes:

> *Route A*: Via interstate highway, 7.6 mi, with a speed limit of 65 mph.
> *Route B*: Via a country road, 5.6 mi, with a speed limit of 50 mph.

Assuming you drive at the posted speed limit, how much time can you save by taking the faster route?

59. A 25-ft by 30-ft yard contains an 8-ft wide, round fountain. How many 1-lb bags of grass seed should be purchased to seed the lawn if 1 lb of seed covers 300 ft^2?

60. If the daily rental for a car is $18.90 plus a certain price per mile, and Lindsey must drive 190 mi in one day and still stay within a $55.00 budget, what is the highest price per mile that Lindsey can afford?

61. Find the shaded area. What assumptions must you make?

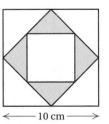

$\longleftarrow$ 10 cm $\longrightarrow$

62. *Fast-Food Meals.* In 1995, the average fast-food meal cost $9.42; in 1996, it was $10.06; in 1997, it was $10.56; and in 1998, it was $11.01. Determine the average yearly increase in the cost of a fast-food meal.
Source: Sandelman and Associates, Brea, California

63. *Family Dining.* In 1995, the average cost of a family's dinner outside the home was $25.39; in 1996, it was $27.40; in 1997, it was $27.00; and in 1998, it was $29.35. Determine the average yearly increase in what it costs a family to eat out.
Source: Sandelman and Associates, Brea, California

The review that follows is meant to prepare you for a chapter exam. It consists of two parts. The first part is a checklist of some of the Study Tips referred to in this text. The second part is the Review Exercises. These provide practice exercises for the exam, together with references to section objectives so you can go back and review. Before beginning, stop and look back over the skills you have obtained. What powers in mathematics do you have now that you did not have before studying this chapter?

STUDY TIPS CHECKLIST

The foundation of all your study skills is TIME!	☐ Have you found ways (in class, on-line, or by phone) to get your questions answered?
	☐ Are you making a conscious effort to keep your work legible and well organized?
	☐ Are you familiar with the operation of your calculator—if one is permitted?
	☐ Do you use a highlighter to help you study important concepts?
	☐ Are you alert to opportunities to put your math to work in your everyday life?

REVIEW EXERCISES

Convert the number in the sentence to standard notation.

1. Russia has the largest total area of any country in the world, at 6.59 million square miles.   [5.3b]

2. The total weight of the turkeys consumed by Americans during the Thanksgiving holidays is about 6.9 million pounds.   [5.3b]

3. Write a word name for 5.206.   [5.1a]

4. Write $597.25 in words, as on a check.   [5.1a]

Write each number as a fraction and, if possible, as a mixed numeral.   [5.1b]

5. 0.09

6. −3.0227

Write decimal notation for each number.   [5.1b]

7. $-\dfrac{34}{1000}$

8. $\dfrac{2791}{100}$

Which number is larger?   [5.1c]

9. 0.034,   0.0185

10. −0.67,   −0.19

Round 39.4287 to the nearest: [5.1d]

11. Tenth.

12. Hundredth.

Perform the indicated operation.

13.
$$\begin{array}{r} 2\ 3\ 6.2\ 3\ 1 \\ 2\ 6\ 3.4 \\ +\quad 0.1\ 9\ 8 \\ \hline \end{array}$$ [5.2a]

14.
$$\begin{array}{r} 3\ 7.6\ 4\ 5 \\ -\quad 8.4\ 9\ 7 \\ \hline \end{array}$$ [5.2b]

15. $219.3 + 2.8 + 7$ [5.2a]

16. $745.0109 - 59.959$ [5.2b]

17. $-37.8 + (-19.5)$ [5.2c]

18. $-7.52 - (-9.89)$ [5.2c]

19.
$$\begin{array}{r} 4\ 8 \\ \times\ 0.2\ 7 \\ \hline \end{array}$$ [5.3a]

20. $-3.7(0.29)$ [5.3a]

21.
$$\begin{array}{r} 2\ 4.6\ 8 \\ \times\ 1\ 0\ 0\ 0 \\ \hline \end{array}$$ [5.3a]

22. $25\overline{)80}$ [5.4a]

23. $11.52 \div (-7.2)$ [5.4a]

24. $\dfrac{276.3}{1000}$ [5.4a]

Combine like terms. [5.2d]

25. $3.7x - 5.2y - 1.5x - 3.9y$

26. $7.94 - 3.89a + 4.63 + 1.05a$

27. Evaluate $P - Prt$ for $P = 1000$, $r = 0.05$, and $t = 1.5$. (*A formula for depreciation*) [5.3c]

28. Simplify: $9 - 3.2(-1.5) + 5.2^2$. [5.4b]

29. Estimate the sum $7.298 + 3.961$ to the nearest tenth. [5.6a]

30. About how many videotapes, at $2.45 each, can be purchased with $49.95? [5.6a]

31. Convert 1549 cents to dollars. [5.3b]

32. Round $248.\overline{27}$ to the nearest hundredth. [5.5b]

Multiply by a form of 1 to find decimal notation for each number. [5.5c]

33. $\dfrac{13}{5}$

34. $\dfrac{32}{25}$

Use division to find decimal notation for each number. [5.5a]

35. $\dfrac{13}{4}$

36. $-\dfrac{7}{6}$

37. Calculate: $\dfrac{4}{15} \times 79.05$. [5.5d]

Solve. Remember to check.

38. $t - 4.3 = -7.5$ [5.7a]

39. $4.1x + 5.6 = -6.7$ [5.7a]

40. $6x - 11 = 8x + 4$ [5.7b]

41. $3(x + 2) = 5x - 7$ [5.7b]

Solve. [5.8a]

42. In the United States, there are 51.81 telephone poles for every 100 people. In Canada, there are 40.65 . How many more telephone poles for every 100 people are there in the United States?

43. Stacia, a coronary intensive care nurse, earned $620.74 during a recent 40-hr week. What was her hourly wage? Round to the nearest cent.

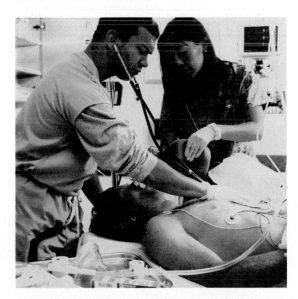

44. Worldwide, the average person drinks 3.48 cups of tea per day. How many cups of tea does the average person drink in a week? in a month (30 days)?

45. Derek had $6274.35 in his checking account. He used $485.79 to buy a Palm Digital Assistant with his debit card. How much was left in his account?

46. *CellularOne® Rates.* In the late 1990s, one plan for cellular phones in Indiana was called "Indiana 1600." The charge was $124.99 per month, and included up to 1600 min of calling time. Minutes over 1600 were charged at a rate of $0.25 per minute. One month, under this plan, Maria used her cell phone for 2000 min. What was the charge?
Source: CellularOne® from Bell South

47. *Gas Mileage.* Inge wants to estimate gas mileage per gallon. With an odometer reading 36,057.1, she fills up. At 36,217.6 mi, the tank is refilled with 11.1 gal. Find the mileage per gallon. Round to the nearest tenth.

48. Zack's times in the quarter-mile run were 89.3 sec, 88.9 sec, and 90.0 sec. What was his average time?

49. A taxi driver charges $7.25 plus 95 cents a mile for out-of-town fares. How far can an out-of-towner travel on $15.23?

50. $\mathbf{D_W}$ Stacy claims that to convert $\frac{3}{20}$ to decimal notation, she thinks of money—nickels in particular. How do you think she does this?

51. $\mathbf{D_W}$ Why is $\frac{1}{3} \cdot \frac{1}{6}$ more easily computed in fraction notation than decimal notation? What would be the best way to express this product as a decimal?

52. Simplify: $\dfrac{-29}{-29}$. [3.3b]

53. Add and simplify: $-\dfrac{1}{9} + \dfrac{1}{6}$. [4.2b]

54. Subtract and simplify: $\dfrac{4}{5} - \dfrac{1}{2}$. [4.3a]

55. Simplify: $\dfrac{1}{2}x + \dfrac{3}{4}y - \dfrac{3}{4}x - y$. [4.3a]

56. Find the opposite of the polynomial:

$$14x^5 - 8x^3 + 5. \quad [2.9b]$$

57. ▦ In each of the following, use $+$, $-$, $\times$, or $\div$ in each blank to make a true sentence. [5.4b]
a) $2.56 - 6.4 \;\square\; 51.2 - 17.4 + 89.7 = 119.66$
b) $(11.12 \;\square\; 0.29)3^4 = 877.23$

58. Arrange from smallest to largest: [5.1c], [5.5a]

$$-\dfrac{2}{3}, \quad -\dfrac{15}{19}, \quad -\dfrac{11}{13}, \quad \dfrac{-5}{7}, \quad \dfrac{-13}{15}, \quad \dfrac{-17}{20}.$$

59. The Fit Fiddle Health Club generally charges a $79 membership fee and $42.50 a month. Alayn has a coupon that will allow her to join the club for $299 for six months. How much will Alayn save if she uses the coupon? [5.8a]

60. $\mathbf{D_W}$ ▦ Sal's sells Sicilian pizza as a 17-in. by 20-in. pie for $15 or as an 18-in.–diameter round pie for $14. Which is a better buy and why? [5.8a]

1. Write a word name for 6.0401.

2. Write $1234.78 in words, as on a check.

Write fraction notation for each number. Do not simplify.

3. −0.2

4. 7.308

Write decimal notation for each number.

5. $\dfrac{284}{10,000}$

6. $-\dfrac{528}{100}$

Which number is larger?

7. 0.07, 0.162

8. −0.173, −0.25

Round 9.4523 to the nearest:

9. Tenth.

10. Thousandth.

Perform the indicated operation.

11.
```
   4 0 2.3
       2.8 1
 +     0.1 0 9
```

12.
```
     0.1 2 5
 ×     0.2 4
```

13.
```
   2 1 3.4 5
 ×     0.0 0 1
```

14.
```
   5 2.0 9 1
 −     7.3 4 5
```

15. $342.9 + 8.1 + 5.37$

16. $-9.5 + 7.3$

17. $2 - 0.0054$

18. $2\,5\,\overline{)\,1\,1}$

19. $3.3\,\overline{)\,1\,0\,0.3\,2}$

20. $\dfrac{-346.82}{1000}$

21. Convert $179.82 to cents.

22. Combine like terms:
$$4.1x + 5.2 - 3.9y + 5.7x - 9.8.$$

23. Evaluate $2l + 4w + 2h$ for $l = 2.4$, $w = 1.3$, and $h = 0.8$. (*The total girth of a postal package*)

24. Simplify: $20 \div 5(-2)^2 - 8.4$.

25. About how many gallons of gasoline, at $1.749 per gallon, can be bought with $20? Round to the nearest gallon.

26. Round $48.\overline{74}$ to the nearest tenth.

Multiply by a form of 1 to find decimal notation for each number.

27. $\dfrac{8}{5}$

28. $\dfrac{21}{4}$

Use division to find decimal notation for each number.

29. $-\dfrac{7}{16}$

30. $\dfrac{11}{9}$

31. Calculate: $\dfrac{3}{8} \times 45.6 - \dfrac{1}{5} \times 36.9$.

Solve. Remember to check.

32. $17y - 3.12 = -58.2$

33. $9t - 4 = 6t + 26$

34. $4 + 2(x - 3) = 7x - 9$

Solve.

35. *MP3 Players.*   Matt buys 6 Compaq iPAQ 64 Mb Personal Audio Players at $199.99 each. What is the total cost?
Source: Compaq

36. In 1896, Alfred Hajos set the world record in the 100-m freestyle swim with a time of 82.2 sec. A hundred years later, Aleksandr Popov set a new record of 48.74 sec. How much better was Popov's time?

37. *CellularOne® Rates.*   In the late 1990s, one plan for cellular phones in Indiana was called "Indiana 1000." The charge was $84.99 per month, and included up to 1000 min of calling time. Minutes over 1000 were charged at a rate of $0.25 per minute. One month, under this plan, Ramon used his cell phone for 1142 min. What was the charge?
Source: CellularOne® from Bell South

38. *Gas Mileage.*   Tina wants to estimate the gas mileage per gallon in her economy car. At 76,843 mi, the tank is filled with 14.3 gal of gasoline. At 77,310 mi, the tank is filled with 16.5 gal of gasoline. Find the mileage per gallon. Round to the nearest tenth.

39. *Airport Passengers.*   The following graph shows the number of passengers in a recent year who traveled through the country's busiest airports. Find the average number of passengers passing through these airports.

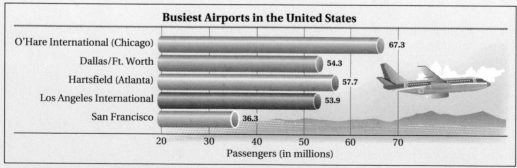

Busiest Airports in the United States

O'Hare International (Chicago) 67.3
Dallas/Ft. Worth 54.3
Hartsfield (Atlanta) 57.7
Los Angeles International 53.9
San Francisco 36.3

Passengers (in millions)

Source: Air Transport Association of America

40. Simplify: $\dfrac{0}{57}$.

41. Add and simplify: $\dfrac{2}{7} + \dfrac{3}{21}$.

42. Subtract and simplify: $\dfrac{2}{3} - \dfrac{7}{10}$.

43. Simplify: $\dfrac{4}{5}x + \dfrac{2}{3}y - \dfrac{1}{10}x - \dfrac{3}{5}y$.

44. Evaluate the polynomial
$x^4 + x^3 + x^2$ at $x = -1$

45. Use one of the words *sometimes*, *never*, or *always* to complete each of the following.

a) The product of two numbers greater than 0 and less than 1 is _____ less than 1.

b) The product of two numbers greater than 1 is _____ less than 1.

c) The product of a number greater than 1 and a number less than 1 is _____ equal to 1.

d) The product of a number greater than 1 and a number less than 1 is _____ equal to 0.

46. *Seafood Consumption.* The following graph shows the annual consumption, in pounds, of seafood per person in the United States in recent years. From 1970 to 1999, by how much, on average, did per person consumption of seafood increase yearly?

47. *Travel Costs.* Roundtrip airfare between Burlington, VT and Newark, NJ often costs $189. The cost of driving (gas and general wear and tear) is about 32¢ per mile. Is it more economical to fly or drive the 320 miles for (a) an individual; (b) a couple; (c) a family of 3?

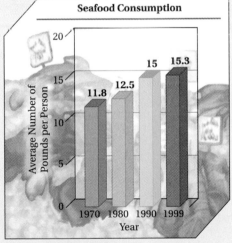

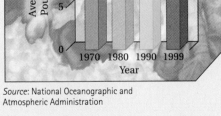

Seafood Consumption

Average Number of Pounds per Person

1970: 11.8
1980: 12.5
1990: 15
1999: 15.3

Year

Source: National Oceanographic and Atmospheric Administration

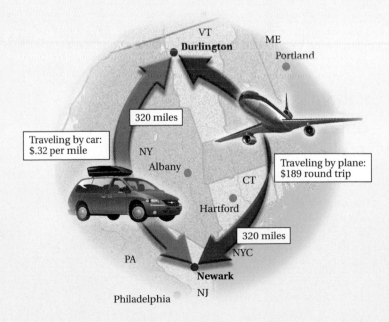

Traveling by car: $.32 per mile

Traveling by plane: $189 round trip

320 miles

VT
Burlington
ME
Portland
NY
Albany
CT
Hartford
NYC
Newark
NJ
PA
Philadelphia

320 miles

1. Write expanded notation: 207,491.

2. Write $802.53 in words, as on a check.

3. Write fraction notation: 10.09.

4. Convert to fraction notation: $4\dfrac{3}{8}$.

5. Write decimal notation: $\dfrac{-35}{1000}$.

6. List all the factors of 66.

7. Find the prime factorization of 154.

8. Find the LCM of 28 and 35.

9. Round 6962.4721 to the nearest hundred.

10. Round 6962.4721 to the nearest hundredth.

Add and, if possible, simplify.

11. $3\dfrac{2}{3}$
$+\ 2\dfrac{5}{9}$

12.
```
  1 1 0.8 6 3
        0.7 3
    1 2 1.9
+       1.9 0 4
```

13.
```
    5 2 4 9
        2 1 5
+         3 1
```

14. $-\dfrac{4}{15}+\dfrac{7}{30}$

Subtract.

15. $-23-48$

16. $9010-563.47$

17. $\dfrac{8}{9}-\dfrac{7}{8}$

18. $7\dfrac{1}{5}-3\dfrac{4}{5}$

Multiply and, if possible, simplify.

19.
```
  2 3.9
× 0.2
```

20. $-\dfrac{3}{5}\times\dfrac{10}{21}$

21. $3\dfrac{2}{11}\cdot 4\dfrac{2}{7}$

22. $5\cdot\dfrac{3}{10}$

Divide and, if possible, simplify.

23. $2\dfrac{4}{5}\div 1\dfrac{13}{15}$

24. $\dfrac{6}{5}\div\dfrac{7}{8}$

25. $-43.795\div 0.001$

26. $2.1\,\overline{)4\,3.2\,6}$

Use $<$, $>$, or $=$ for $\square$ to write a true sentence.

27. $\dfrac{2}{3}\ \square\ \dfrac{5}{7}$

28. $-7\ \square\ -4$

29. Evaluate $a \div 3 \cdot b$, for $a = 18$ and $b = 2$.

30. Multiply: $4(x - y + 3)$.

Combine like terms.

31. $-4p + 9 + 11p - 17$

32. $x - 9 + 13x - 2$

Solve. Remember to check.

33. $8.32 + x = 9.1$

34. $-75 \cdot x = 2100$

35. $y \cdot 9.47 = 81.6314$

36. $1062 - y = -368{,}313$

37. $t + \dfrac{5}{6} = \dfrac{8}{9}$

38. $\dfrac{7}{8} \cdot t = \dfrac{7}{16}$

39. $2.4x - 7.1 = 2.05$

40. $2(x - 3) = 5x - 13$

Solve.

41. In 2000 there were 2219 heart transplants, 14,168 kidney transplants, 4816 liver transplants, 1330 pancreas transplants, and 1002 lung transplants. How many transplants of these five organs were performed?
Source: Based on information from U.S. transplant.org

42. After making a $450 down payment on a motorcycle, $\frac{3}{10}$ of the total cost was paid. How much did the motorcycle cost?

43. There are 60 seconds in a minute and 60 minutes in an hour. How many seconds are in a day?

44. Claude's college tuition was $4200. A loan was obtained for $\frac{2}{3}$ of the tuition. For how much was the loan?

45. The balance in a checking account is $314.79. After a check is written for $56.02, what is the balance in the account?

46. A clerk in a deli sold $1\frac{1}{2}$ lb of cheese, $2\frac{3}{4}$ lb of turkey, and $2\frac{1}{4}$ lb of roast beef. How many pounds of cold cuts were sold altogether?

47. A triangular sail has a height of 16 ft and a base of 11 ft. Find its area.

48. A movie screen measures 19.8 ft by 23.6 ft. Find its area.

SYNTHESIS

49. A carton of Luna™ Bar boxes weighs about 320 oz. If each box of Luna Bars weighs 25.4 oz, what is the greatest number of boxes that could be inside the carton?

50. In the Newton Market, Brenda used a manufacturer's coupon to buy juice. With the coupon, if 3 cartons of juice were purchased, the fourth carton was free. The price of each carton was $1.89. What was the cost per carton with the coupon? Round to the nearest cent.

Introduction to Graphing and Statistics

Gateway to Chapter 6

There are many ways in which data can be represented and analyzed. One way is to use graphs. In this chapter, we examine several kinds of graphs: pictographs, bar graphs, line graphs, and graphs drawn from equations in two variables. Another way to analyze data is to study certain numbers, or *statistics*, that are related to the data. We will consider three statistics in this chapter: the *mean*, the *median*, and the *mode*.

Real-World Application

The Toyota Prius, a gas/electric hybrid car, averages 52 miles per gallon in city driving and has an 11.9-gallon gas tank. How much city driving can be done on $\frac{4}{5}$ of a tank of gas?

Source: Based on information from the EPA and Toyota Corp.

This problem appears as Exercise 46 in Section 6.5.

CHAPTER

6

1. **Cost of Life Insurance.** The following table shows the comparison of the cost of a $100,000 life insurance policy for female smokers and nonsmokers at certain ages. [6.1a]
   a) How much does it cost a female nonsmoker, age 32, for insurance?
   b) How much more does it cost a female smoker, age 35, than a nonsmoker of the same age?

LIFE INSURANCE: FEMALE		
Age	Cost (Smoker)	Cost (Nonsmoker)
31	$294	$170
32	298	172
33	302	176
34	310	178
35	316	182

Source: State Farm Insurance

2. **Study Times vs. Grades.** An English instructor asked his students to keep track of how much time each spent studying for a chapter test. He collected the information together with the test scores. The data are given in the table below. Draw a line graph of the data. [6.2d]

STUDY TIME (in hours)	TEST GRADE (in percent)
2	75
3	83
4	80
5	85
6	90
7	97
8	93

3. Using the data in Question 1, draw a vertical bar graph showing the cost of insurance for a female nonsmoker, age 31–35. Use age on the horizontal scale and cost on the vertical scale. [6.2b]

The line graph at right shows the relationship between blood cholesterol level and risk of coronary heart disease.

4. Which of the cholesterol levels listed has the highest risk? [6.2c]

5. About how much higher is the risk at 260 than at 200? [6.2c]

Source: American Heart Association

6. Plot these points: [6.3a]

   $(-2, 4), (5, -3), (0, 6), (3, 0), (-4, -1), (2, 4)$.

7. In which quadrant is the point $(-5, 7)$ located? [6.3b]

8. Determine whether the ordered pair $(-2, 4)$ is a solution of the equation $2x - y = 0$. [6.3c]

Graph on a plane. [6.4b]

9. $y = -x$

10. $x + 2y = 9$

11. $y = \frac{2}{3}x - 1$

In Questions 12–14, find (a) the mean, (b) the median, and (c) any modes that exist. [6.5a, b, c]

12. 46, 50, 53, 55

13. 5, 5, 3, 1, 1

14. 4, 17, 4, 18, 4, 17, 18, 20

15. Wynton drove 660 mi in 12 hr. What was his average rate of travel? [6.5a]

16. To get a B in chemistry, Delores must average 80 (or better) on four tests. Scores on the first three tests were 78, 81, and 75. What is the lowest score that she can receive on the last test and still get a B? [6.5a]

17. Use the graph from Question 4 to estimate the frequency of occurrence of heart disease among people whose blood cholesterol level is 207. [6.6a]

18. A die is about to be rolled. Find the probability that a 3 will be rolled. [6.6b]

6.1

TABLES AND PICTOGRAPHS

a Reading and Interpreting Tables

A **table** is often used to present data in rows and columns.

Objectives

a Extract and interpret data from tables.

b Extract and interpret data from pictographs.

c Draw pictographs.

■ **EXAMPLE 1**   The table below lists the average charges for a full-time student at different types of schools.

Institutions of Higher Education—Charges: 1995 to 2001

[In dollars. Estimated. For the entire academic year ending in year shown. Figures are average charges per full-time equivalent student. Room and board are based on full-time students.]

ACADEMIC CONTROL AND YEAR	TUITION AND REQUIRED FEES[1]		MEAL COSTS		DORMITORY CHARGES	
	2-yr. Colleges	4-yr. Colleges	2-yr. Colleges	4-yr. Colleges	2-yr. Colleges	4-yr. Colleges
Public:						
1995	1,192	2,977	1,712	2,108	1,232	1,992
1996	1,239	3,151	1,681	2,192	1,297	2,104
1997	1,276	3,323	1,789	2,282	1,339	2,187
1998	1,314	3,486	1,795	2,438	1,401	2,285
1999	1,327	3,640	1,828	2,576	1,450	2,408
2000	1,338	3,768	1,834	2,628	1,549	2,516
2001	1,359	3,983	1,900	2,687	1,603	2,656
Private:						
1995	6,914	14,537	2,023	3,035	2,233	3,469
1996	7,094	15,605	2,090	3,218	2,371	3,680
1997	7,236	16,552	2,181	3,142	2,537	3,826
1998	7,464	17,229	2,785	3,132	2,672	3,756
1999	7,854	18,340	2,884	3,188	2,581	3,914
2000	8,235	19,307	2,922	3,157	2,808	4,070
2001	8,961	20,143	2,962	3,303	2,768	4,265

[1]For in-state students.

Source: U.S. National Center for Education Statistics, *Digest of Education Statistics*, annual.

a) What is the most expensive charge on the table? In what year, and at what type of school, did it occur?

b) In what year did meal costs at public 2-yr colleges drop?

c) Lea went to—and lived at—a private 4-yr college in 1999. Assuming that the college's rates were average for private 4-yr colleges, how much did she pay?

d) From 1997 to 2001, what was the average tuition at a public 2-yr college?

Careful examination of the table will give the answers.

a) To identify the most expensive charge, we inspect the entries in the table. Doing so, we find that the largest charge was $20,143. This was the tuition at a private 4-yr college in 2001.

b) Again we inspect the table. This time we note that meal costs at a public 2-yr college dropped in 1996.

Use the table in Example 1 to answer each of the following.

1. What is the smallest fee on the table and what was it for?

2. In what year did tuition at public 2-yr colleges first exceed $1300?

3. Find the average tuition at a public 4-yr college from 1997 to 2001.

Answers on page A-17

c) We locate the columns for 4-yr colleges and look down the left-hand column for the year 1999 and "Private" subheading. We find that Lea paid $18,340 for tuition and fees, $3188 for meals, and $3914 for dormitory charges. Lea's total charges were $18,340 + $3188 + $3914 = $25,442.

d) To find the average tuition at a public 2-yr college, we locate the 2-yr college column under "Tuition and Required Fees" and use the "Public" figures for 1997–2001:

$$\frac{\$1276 + \$1314 + \$1327 + \$1338 + \$1359}{5} = \$1322.80.$$

The average tuition at a public 2-yr college, for the years 1997–2001, was $1322.80.

Do Exercises 1–3 on the previous page.

b | Reading and Interpreting Pictographs

Pictographs (or *picture graphs*) are another way to show information. Instead of actually listing the amounts to be considered, a **pictograph** uses symbols to represent the amounts. In addition, a *key* is given telling what each symbol represents.

EXAMPLE 2 *Drinking and Driving.* Motor vehicle accidents remain the leading cause of death among Americans under the age of 35. The following pictograph shows approximately how many alcohol-related motor vehicle deaths occurred from 1991 to 2001. A key indicates that each symbol 🚗 represents 2000 deaths.

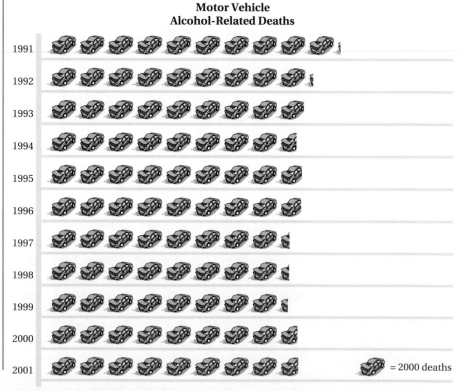

Motor Vehicle Alcohol-Related Deaths

🚗 = 2000 deaths

Source: National Highway Safety Administration, Center for Disease Control, and laurushealth.com

a) Determine the approximate number of alcohol-related motor vehicle deaths in 1996.

b) In which year did the number of alcohol-related motor vehicle deaths first drop below 18,000?

We use the information in the pictograph as follows.

a) The number of alcohol-related motor vehicle fatalities in 1996 is represented by about $8\frac{3}{4}$ symbols. Since $8\frac{3}{4} \cdot 2000$ is 17,500, there were about 17,500 such fatalities in 1996.

b) To determine when the number of fatalities first fell below 18,000, note that each symbol represents 2000 deaths. Since $18,000 \div 2000 = 9$, we look for the first year in which fewer than 9 full symbols appear. This occurs in 1993 since not quite 9 complete autos appear on that line.

Do Exercises 4 and 5.

C   Drawing Pictographs

EXAMPLE 3   *North American Concert Revenue.*   The following is a list of the gross revenue (money taken in) during one year by the five top-grossing acts for the years 1995–2000.
Source: *The World Almanac*

Draw a pictograph to represent the data. Let the symbol ▨ represent $10,000,000.

The Rolling Stones	$89.3 million	(1997)
Tina Turner	$80.2 million	(2000)
U2	$79.9 million	(1997)
'N Sync	$76.4 million	(2000)
Dave Matthews Band	$68.2 million	(2000)

Some computation is necessary before we can draw the pictograph.

The Rolling Stones: Note that $89.3 \div 10 = 8.93$. Thus we need 8 whole symbols and 0.93 of another symbol. Now 0.93 is hard to draw, but we estimate it to be about $\frac{9}{10}$ of a symbol.

Tina Turner: Note that $80.2 \div 10 = 8.02$. Thus we need 8 whole symbols and 0.02 of another symbol. We round this to 8 symbols.

U2: Note that $79.9 \div 10 = 7.99$. Thus we need 7 whole symbols and 0.99 of another symbol. We round this to 8 symbols.

'N Sync: Note that $76.4 \div 10 = 7.64$. Thus we need 7 whole symbols and a bit more than half of another symbol.

Dave Matthews Band: Note that $68.2 \div 10 = 6.82$. Thus we need 6 whole symbols and 0.82 or about $\frac{4}{5}$ of another symbol.

4. Approximately how many alcohol-related motor vehicle deaths occurred in 2001?

5. In which year did the number of alcohol-related motor vehicle deaths first drop below 20,000? (Inspect the pictograph carefully.)

Answers on page A-17

6. Concert Revenue. The following is a list of three other high-grossing acts during the same time and their total gross revenues. Draw a pictograph to represent the data.

Tim McGraw/Faith Hill
$48.8 million (2000)

The Eagles
$63.3 million (1995)

Bruce Springsteen
$61.4 million (1999)

The pictograph can now be drawn as follows. We list the concert act in one column, draw the monetary amounts using symbols, indicate the key, and title the overall graph "Total Gross Revenue." Note that a different choice for the symbol in the key will result in a different pictograph.

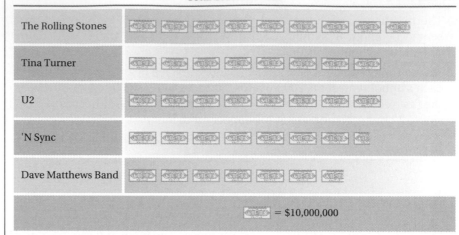

Total Gross Revenue

Do Exercise 6.

Answer on page A-17

a *Nutrition Information.* The following table lists nutrition information for a 1-cup serving of five name-brand cereals (it does not consider the use of milk or sweetener). Use the table for Exercises 1–6.

CEREAL	CALORIES	FAT (in grams)	TOTAL CARBOHYDRATES (in grams)	SODIUM (in milligrams)
Cinnamon Life®	160	1.3	34.7	200
Life® (Regular)	160	2.0	33.3	213.3
Lucky Charms®	120	1.0	25.0	210
Kellogg's Complete®	120	0.7	30.7	280
Wheaties®	110	1.0	24.0	220

Sources: Quaker Oats; General Mills; Kellogg's

1. Which cereal has the least amount of sodium?

2. Which cereal has the greatest amount of fat?

3. Which cereal has the least amount of fat?

4. Find the average total carbohydrates in the cereals listed.

5. Find the average amount of fat in the cereals listed.

6. Find the average amount of sodium in the cereals listed.

Planets. Use the following table, which lists information about the planets, for Exercises 7–12.

PLANET	AVERAGE DISTANCE FROM SUN (in miles)	DIAMETER (in miles)	LENGTH OF PLANET'S DAY IN EARTH TIME (in days)	TIME OF REVOLUTION IN EARTH TIME (in years)
Mercury	35,983,000	3,031	58.82	0.24
Venus	67,237,700	7,520	224.59	0.62
Earth	92,955,900	7,926	1.00	1.00
Mars	141,634,800	4,221	1.03	1.88
Jupiter	483,612,200	88,846	0.41	11.86
Saturn	888,184,000	74,898	0.43	29.46
Uranus	1,782,000,000	31,763	0.45	84.01
Neptune	2,794,000,000	31,329	0.66	164.78
Pluto	3,666,000,000	1,423	6.41	248.53

Source: The Handy Science Answer Book, Gale Research, Inc.

7. Find the average distance from the sun to Jupiter.

8. How long is a day on Venus?

9. Which planet has a time of revolution of 164.78 yr?

10. Which planet has a diameter of 4221 mi?

11. Which planets have an average distance from the sun that is greater than 500,000,000 mi?

12. Which planets have a diameter that is less than 5000 mi?

Heat Index. In warm weather, a person can feel hotter due to reduced heat loss from the skin caused by higher humidity. The **temperature–humidity index,** or **apparent temperature,** is the temperature with no humidity that gives the same heat effect. The following table lists the apparent temperatures for various actual temperatures and relative humidities. Use this table for Exercises 13–22.

ACTUAL TEMPERATURE (°F)	RELATIVE HUMIDITY									
	10%	20%	30%	40%	50%	60%	70%	80%	90%	100%
	APPARENT TEMPERATURE (°F)									
75°	75	77	79	80	82	84	86	88	90	92
80°	80	82	85	87	90	92	94	97	99	102
85°	85	88	91	94	97	100	103	106	108	111
90°	90	93	97	100	104	107	111	114	118	121
95°	95	99	103	107	111	115	119	123	127	131
100°	100	105	109	114	118	123	127	132	137	141
105°	105	110	115	120	125	131	136	141	146	151

In Exercises 13–16, find the apparent temperature for each actual temperature and humidity combination given.

13. 80°, 60% **14.** 90°, 70% **15.** 85°, 90% **16.** 95°, 80%

17. How many listed temperature–humidity combinations give an apparent temperature of 100°?

18. How many listed temperature–humidity combinations give an apparent temperature of 111°?

19. At a relative humidity of 50%, what actual temperatures give an apparent temperature above 100°?

20. At a relative humidity of 90%, what actual temperatures give an apparent temperature above 100°?

21. At an actual temperature of 95°, what relative humidities give an apparent temperature above 100°?

22. At an actual temperature of 85°, what relative humidities give an apparent temperature above 100°?

Global Warming. Scientists are increasingly concerned about global warming, the trend of average global temperatures rising over time. One possible effect is the melting of the polar icecaps. Use the following table for Exercises 23–26.

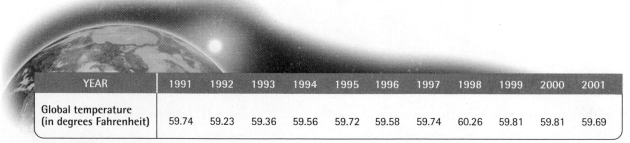

YEAR	1991	1992	1993	1994	1995	1996	1997	1998	1999	2000	2001
Global temperature (in degrees Fahrenheit)	59.74	59.23	59.36	59.56	59.72	59.58	59.74	60.26	59.81	59.81	59.69

Sources: Based on data from Lester R. Brown et al., *Vital Signs*; the Council of Environmental Quality, Goddard Institute for Space Studies, National Climatic Data Center, and the Natural Resources Defense Council

23. Find the average global temperatures in 2000 and 2001.

24. Find the average global temperatures in 1998 and 1999.

25. Find the four-year average of the average global temperatures for the years 1991 to 1994. Find the four-year average of the average global temperatures for the years 1998 to 2001. By how many degrees does the latter average exceed the former?

26. Find the average of the average global temperatures for the years 1994 to 1996. Find the ten-year average of the average global temperatures for the years 1992 to 2001. By how many degrees does the ten-year average exceed the average for the years 1994 to 1996?

Phone Rates. The following table shows the rates for several popular long-distance calling plans during a recent year. (Plans may vary by state.) Use the table for Exercises 27–34.

COMPANY	PLAN	PEAK RATE	OFF-PEAK RATE	MONTHLY FEES	INFO NUMBER
AT&T	One Rate 7 Cent Plus	7 cents/min	7 cents/min	$3.95	800-222-0300
Verizon	Best Times*	8 cents/min	5 cents/min	$4.95	800-483-7988
Sprint	Sprint Nickel AnyTime	5 cents/min	5 cents/min	$8.95	800-877-4646
Total Call Intl.	Connect for Less	4.9 cents/min	4.9 cents/min	$0	800-605-3949
Excel	Three-Penny Plan	10 cents/min	3 cents/min	$5.95	800-875-9235
Earth Tones	Green Saver	8 cents/min	8 cents/min	$4.95	888-327-8486
MCI	Anytime Advantage	7 cents/min	7 cents/min	$2.95	800-444-3333

*Plans may vary by state

27. Of the plans listed, which company has the least expensive peak rate?

28. Of the plans listed, which company has the least expensive off-peak rate?

29. Shannon has the Best Times plan. She spoke for 50 min at the peak rate and for 75 min at the off-peak rate. What was the total cost for these calls?

30. For the plans listed, what is the average peak rate? Round to the nearest tenth of a cent.

31. Which plan has the highest off-peak rate?

32. Which plan has a peak rate of 10 cents/min?

33. Find the average off-peak rate for the seven companies.

34. What is the average of the three most expensive off-peak rates? Round to the nearest tenth of a cent.

b *World Population Growth.* The following pictograph shows world population in various years. Use the pictograph for Exercises 35–42.

World Population

Year		
1650	ᶤ	
1850	𝖎	
1930	𝖎 𝖎	
1975	𝖎 𝖎 𝖎	
2000	𝖎 𝖎 𝖎 𝖎 𝖎 ᶤ	
2012 (projected)	𝖎 𝖎 𝖎 𝖎 𝖎 𝖎	
2070 (projected)	𝖎 𝖎 𝖎 𝖎 𝖎 𝖎 𝖎 𝖎	

𝖎 = 1 billion people

Source: U.S. Census Bureau, International Database

35. What was the world population in 1850?

36. What was the world population in 1975?

37. In which year will the population be the greatest?

38. In which year was the population the least?

39. Between which two of the years listed was the amount of growth the least?

40. Between which two of the years listed was the amount of growth the greatest?

41. How much greater will the world population be in 2012 than in 1975?

42. How much greater was the world population in 2000 than in 1930?

Birth Rate. The following pictograph shows the number of births per 100 citizens in various countries in 2001. Use the pictograph for Exercises 43–48.

43. What was the approximate birth rate in Mexico in 2001?

44. What was the approximate birth rate in Sudan in 2001?

45. Which country had a birth rate of about 1.6 births per 100 people?

46. Which country had a birth rate of about 4.1 births per 100 people?

47. Which country had a birth rate of about 1.5 births per 100 people?

48. Which country's birth rate is approximately twice that of Canada?

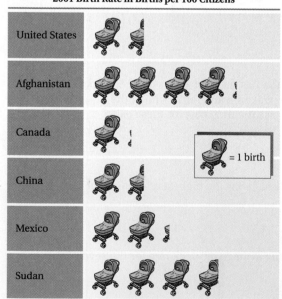

2001 Birth Rate in Births per 100 Citizens

Sources: U.S. Census Bureau, International Database

49. *Coffee Consumption.* The following chart lists approximately how many cups of coffee each person (per capita) drinks annually in several countries. Draw a pictograph that reflects this data. Use the symbol ☕ to represent 100 cups.

Source: Based on information from the Beverage Marketing Corporation

COUNTRY	COFFEE CONSUMPTION PER CAPITA
Germany	1113
United States	615
Switzerland	1220
France	790
Italy	730

Coffee Consumption

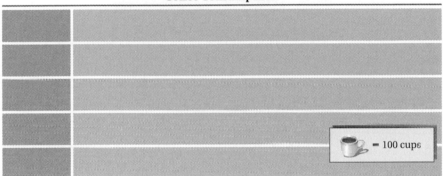

50. Redo Exercise 49, using the symbol ☕ to represent 200 cups.

Coffee Consumption

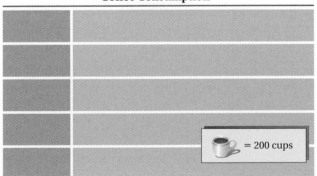

51. *Elephant Population.* The following chart shows the elephant population of various countries in Africa. Draw a pictograph that represents the data. Let the symbol 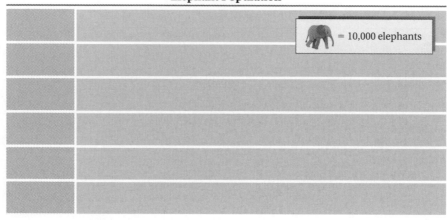 represent 10,000 elephants.

COUNTRY	ELEPHANT POPULATION
Cameroon	20,050
Zimbabwe	49,800
Sudan	19,800
Zaire	110,120
Tanzania	60,070
Botswana	69,105

Source: Based on information from *National Geographic*

Elephant Population

= 10,000 elephants

Source: National Geographic

52. Redo Exercise 51, using the symbol 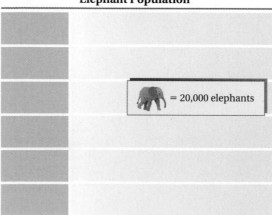 to represent 20,000 elephants.

Elephant Population

= 20,000 elephants

53. **D**_W Loreena is drawing a pictograph in which dollar bills are used as symbols to represent the tuition at various private colleges. Should each dollar bill represent $20,000, $2000, or $200? Why?

54. **D**_W What advantage(s) does a table have over a pictograph?

SKILL MAINTENANCE

Perform the indicated operation and, if possible, simplify.

55. $-\dfrac{3}{8} + \dfrac{5}{16}$ [4.2b]

56. $-\dfrac{2}{7} - \dfrac{3}{5}$ [4.3a]

Solve.

57. $9x - 5 = -23$ [2.8d]

58. $3x - 2 = 7x + 10$ [5.7b]

59. $-4x = 3x - 7$ [5.7b]

Convert to decimal notation. [5.5a]

60. $\dfrac{3}{8}$

61. $\dfrac{29}{25}$

62. $\dfrac{5}{6}$

SYNTHESIS

63. **D**_W Suppose you are drawing a pictograph to represent the number of hours each of three students spends on-line each month. What would be an appropriate symbol to use and what exactly would the symbol represent? Explain how you arrived at your answer.

64. **D**_W Since information is lost when converting a chart into a pictograph (we lose precision), why would anyone want to draw a pictograph to replace a chart?

For Exercises 65–68, consider again the chart of phone rates.

COMPANY	PLAN	PEAK RATE	OFF-PEAK RATE	MONTHLY FEES	INFO NUMBER
AT&T	One Rate 7 Cent Plus	7 cents/min	7 cents/min	$3.95	800-222-0300
Verizon	Best Times*	8 cents/min	5 cents/min	$4.95	800-483-7988
Sprint	Sprint Nickel AnyTime	5 cents/min	5 cents/min	$8.95	800-877-4646
Total Call Intl.	Connect for Less	4.9 cents/min	4.9 cents/min	$0	800-605-3949
Excel	Three-Penny Plan	10 cents/min	3 cents/min	$5.95	800-875-9235
Earth Tones	Green Saver	8 cents/min	8 cents/min	$4.95	888-327-8486
MCI	Anytime Advantage	7 cents/min	7 cents/min	$2.95	800-444-3333

*Plans may vary by state

65. Bridget spoke the same number of minutes at the peak rate as she did at the off-peak rate. If her Best Times bill was for $42, for how many minutes did she speak at each rate?

66. Brad has $50 budgeted for his long-distance phone bill and wants to speak on the phone for as many minutes as possible. Which plan should he select and for how many minutes can he speak?

67. **D**_W Under what circumstances is Excel a better deal than Sprint?

68. **D**_W Under what circumstances is Verizon a better deal than AT&T?

6.2

BAR GRAPHS AND LINE GRAPHS

Beginning in Chapter 1, we have used *bar graphs* to convey information (see pages 8, 39, and 309). In this section, we make further use of bar graphs and also introduce *line graphs*.

Objectives

a Extract and interpret data from bar graphs.

b Draw bar graphs.

c Extract and interpret data from line graphs.

d Draw line graphs.

a Reading and Interpreting Bar Graphs

EXAMPLE 1 *Fat Content in Fast Foods.* For many Americans, fast food is a regular part of their diet. The following bar graph shows the fat content of several popular items sold by national chains.

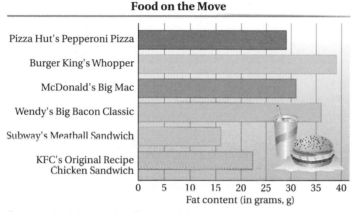

Food on the Move

Source: Based on information from Olen.com and the Minnesota Attorney General's Office

a) About how much fat is in a Big Mac?

b) Which item contains the least amount of fat?

c) Which item contains about 29 g of fat?

We look at the graph to answer the questions.

a) We move to the right along the bar representing McDonald's Big Mac. We can read, fairly accurately, that there is a bit more than 30 g of fat in the Big Mac.

b) The shortest bar is for Subway's Meatball Sandwich. Thus, that sandwich contains the least amount of fat.

c) We locate the line representing 30 g and then go up until we reach a bar that ends just short of there. We then go across to the left and read the name of the item. Pizza Hut's Pepperoni Pizza contains about 29 g of fat.

Do Exercises 1–3.

Use the bar graph in Example 1 to answer Margin Exercises 1–3.

1. About how much fat is in the Wendy's Big Bacon Classic?

2. Which item contains the greatest amount of fat?

3. Which items contain less than 25 g of fat?

Answers on page A-17

Use the bar graph in Example 2 to answer each of the following.

4. Approximately how many women, per 100,000, develop breast cancer between the ages of 35 and 39?

5. In what age group is the mortality rate the highest?

6. In what age group do about 350 out of every 100,000 women develop breast cancer?

7. Does the breast-cancer mortality rate seem to increase from the youngest to the oldest age group?

Answers on page A-17

Bar graphs are often drawn vertically and sometimes a double bar graph is used to make comparisons.

EXAMPLE 2 *Breast Cancer.* The following graph indicates the incidence and mortality rates of breast cancer for women of various age groups.

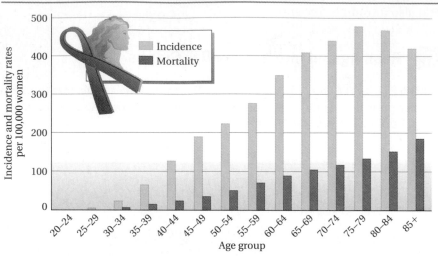

When Breast Cancer Strikes

Source: National Cancer Institute

a) Approximately how many women, per 100,000, develop breast cancer between the ages of 40 and 44?

b) In what age range is the mortality rate for breast cancer approximately 100 for every 100,000 women?

c) In what age range is the incidence of breast cancer the highest?

d) Does the incidence of breast cancer always increase from the younger to the older age groups?

We look at the graph to answer the questions.

a) To determine the rate of incidence for women ages 40–44, we go to the right, across the bottom, to the green bar above the age group 40–44. Next, we go up to the top of that bar and, from there, back to the left to read approximately 130 on the vertical scale. About 130 out of every 100,000 women develop breast cancer between the ages of 40 and 44.

b) To find which age group has a mortality rate of nearly 100 per 100,000, we read up the vertical scale to the number 100. From there we move to the right until we come to the top of a red bar. Moving down that bar, we find that in the 65–69 age group, about 100 out of every 100,000 women die of breast cancer.

c) To determine which age group has the highest rate of incidence, we look for the tallest green bar and read the age range below it. The incidence of breast cancer is highest for women in the 75–79 age group.

d) Looking at the heights of the bars, we see that the incidence of breast cancer actually *decreases* after ages 75–79. Thus, the incidence of breast cancer does not always increase from the younger to older age groups.

Do Exercises 4–7.

b   Drawing Bar Graphs

EXAMPLE 3   *Centenarians.*   The number of centenarians—that is, people 100 yr or older—is growing rapidly. Projections from the U.S. Bureau of the Census and the National Center for Health Statistics are shown below. Use the projections to form a bar graph.

YEAR	PROJECTED NUMBER OF CENTENARIANS
2000	96,000
2010	129,000
2020	235,000
2030	381,000
2040	551,000
2050	1,095,000

Source: U.S. Census Bureau, "National Population Projections—Summary Tables," 1/13/00.

First, we draw a horizontal scale with six equally spaced intervals and the different years listed. We title that scale "Year." (See the figure on the left below.) Next, we label the vertical scale "Projected Number (in thousands)." Note that the largest number (in thousands) is 1095 and the smallest is 96. If we count by 100's, we can range from 0 to 1100 with 11 marks. Finally, we draw vertical bars to represent the number of centenarians projected for each year and title the graph. (See the figure on the right below.)

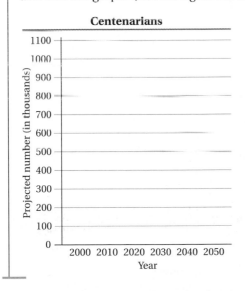

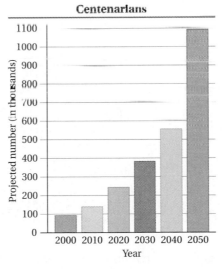

Do Exercise 8.

When drawing bar graphs, be careful to use a consistent scale, even when no unit markings are shown. Failure to do so can create misleading images, as in the newspaper article on the next page.

---

8. Planetary Moons. Make a horizontal bar graph to show the number of moons orbiting the various planets.

PLANET	MOONS
Earth	1
Mars	2
Jupiter	17
Saturn	28
Uranus	21
Neptune	8
Pluto	1

Source: National Aeronautics and Space Administration

Answer on page A-18

Study Tips

KEEPING MATH RELEVANT

We have already stated that finding applications of math in your everyday life is a great study aid. Try to extend this idea to the newspapers, periodicals, and books that you read. Look with a critical eye at graphs and their labels. Not only will this help with your math, it will make you a more informed citizen.

9. What is wrong with the following graph?

Air Pollutant Emissions of Carbon Dioxide, in Tons per Person

United States	20
Australia	17

Note that $\frac{103}{109} \approx 0.94$, yet the the shorter bar is considerably less than 0.94 of the longer bar. A ruler can be used to show that it is drawn so that it is about $\frac{8}{10}$ of the longer bar.

Do Exercise 9.

It's About Time

Although this summer's hits "Star Wars: Attack of the Clones" and "Minority Report" clocked at two hours-plus, "Men in Black II" at 82 minutes reflects a Hollywood trend: Movies are getting shorter.

Source: Gannett News Service, 7/11/02

Average movie length, in minutes:

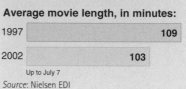

1997	109
2002	103

Up to July 7
Source: Nielsen EDI

C Reading and Interpreting Line Graphs

Line graphs are often used to show a change over time as well as to indicate patterns or trends.

EXAMPLE 4 *New Home Sales.* The following line graph shows the number of new home sales, in thousands, over a recent twelve-month period. The jagged line at the base of the vertical scale indicates an unnecessary portion of the scale. Note that the vertical scale differs from the horizontal scale so that the data can be easily shown.

New Home Sales

Source: U.S. Department of Commerce

a) For which month were new home sales the greatest?

b) Between which months did new home sales increase?

c) For which months were new home sales about 700 thousand?

We look at the graph to answer the questions.

a) The greatest number of new home sales was about 825 thousand in month 1.

b) Reading the graph from left to right, we see that new home sales increased from month 2 to month 3, from month 3 to month 4, from month 5 to month 6, from month 7 to month 8, from month 8 to month 9, from month 9 to month 10, and from month 10 to month 11.

c) We look from left to right along the line at 700.

Answer on page A-18

New Home Sales

We see that points are closest to 700 thousand at months 3, 6, 10, 11, and 12.

Do Exercises 10–12.

EXAMPLE 5 *Monthly Loan Payment.* Suppose that you borrow $110,000 at an interest rate of 9% to buy a home. The following graph shows how the size of the monthly payment depends on the length of the loan. (Note that the smaller the monthly payment, the longer the duration of the loan.)

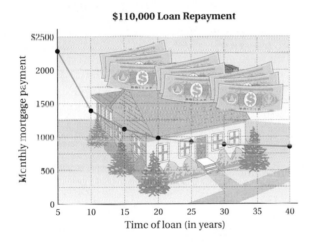

$110,000 Loan Repayment

a) Estimate the monthly payment for a loan of 15 yr.

b) What time period corresponds to a monthly payment of about $1400?

c) By how much does the monthly payment decrease when the loan period is increased from 10 yr to 20 yr?

We look at the graph to answer the questions.

a) We find the time period labeled "15" on the bottom scale and move up from that point to the line. We then go straight across to the left and find that the monthly payment is about $1100.

b) We locate $1400 on the vertical axis. Then we move to the right until we hit the line. The point $1400 is on the line at the 10-yr time period.

c) The graph shows that the monthly payment for 10 yr is about $1400; for 20 yr, it is about $990. Thus the monthly payment is decreased by about $1400 − $990, or $410. (It should be noted that you will pay back $990 · 20 · 12 − $1400 · 10 · 12, or $69,600, more in interest for a 20-yr loan.)

Do Exercises 13–15.

Use the line graph in Example 4 to answer each of the following.

10. For which month were new home sales lowest?

11. Between which months did new home sales decrease?

12. For which months were new home sales below 700 thousand?

Use the line graph in Example 5 to answer Margin Exercises 13–15.

13. Estimate the monthly payment for a loan of 25 yr.

14. What time period corresponds to a monthly payment of about $850?

15. By how much does the monthly payment decrease when the loan period is increased from 5 yr to 20 yr?

Answers on page A-18

16. Cell Phones. Listed below are projections on the use of cell phones with or without access to the Internet. Make a line graph of the data.

YEAR	NUMBER OF CELL PHONES (in millions)
2001	119.8
2002	135.3
2003	150.2
2004	163.8
2005	176.9

Source: Forrester Research

d | Drawing Line Graphs

■ EXAMPLE 6 *Cell Phones with Internet Access.* Listed below are projections on the use of cell phones with access to the Internet. Make a line graph of the data.

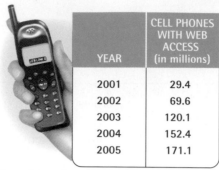

YEAR	CELL PHONES WITH WEB ACCESS (in millions)
2001	29.4
2002	69.6
2003	120.1
2004	152.4
2005	171.1

Source: Forrester Research

First, we indicate the different years on the horizontal scale and give the horizontal scale the title "Year." (See the figure on the left below.) Next, we scale the vertical axis by 25's to show the number of phones, in millions, and give the vertical scale the title "Number of cell phones (in millions)." We also give the graph the overall title "Cell Phones with Web Access."

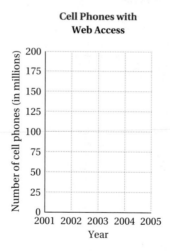

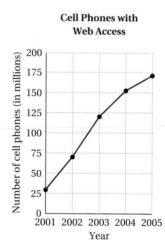

Next, we mark the number of phones at the appropriate level above each year. Then we draw line segments connecting the points. The dramatic change over time can now be observed easily from the graph.

Do Exercise 16.

Answer on page A-18

a *Chocolate Desserts.* The following horizontal bar graph shows the average caloric content of various kinds of chocolate foods or beverages. Use the bar graph for Exercises 1–8.

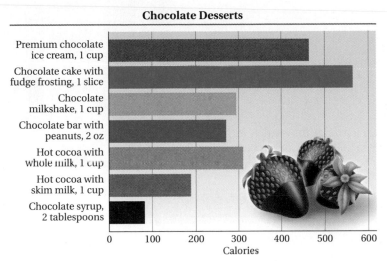

Chocolate Desserts

Source: *Better Homes and Gardens*, December 1996

1. Estimate how many calories there are in 1 cup of hot cocoa with skim milk.

2. Estimate how many calories there are in 1 cup of premium chocolate ice cream.

3. Which dessert contains about 460 calories?

4. Which desserts contain about 300 calories?

5. How many more calories are there in 1 cup of hot cocoa made with whole milk than in 1 cup of hot cocoa made with skim milk?

6. Fred occasionally drinks a 4-cup chocolate milkshake. How many calories does he consume?

7. Duane likes to eat 2 cups of premium chocolate ice cream on his birthday. How many calories does he consume?

8. Bernice likes to eat a 6-oz chocolate bar with peanuts as a snack. How many calories does she consume?

Education, Earnings, and Gender. Side-by-side bar graphs allow for comparisons. The one shown at right provides data on the effect of education on earning power for men and women from 1970 to 2000. Use the bar graph in Exercises 9–16.

9. How much were the average earnings for men with bachelor's degrees in 1970? in 2000? How much had they increased?

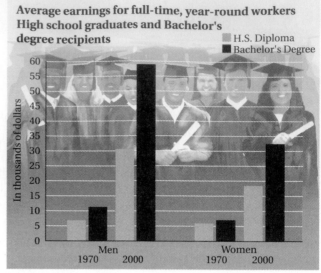

Average earnings for full-time, year-round workers
High school graduates and Bachelor's degree recipients

Source: USA Group Foundation

10. How much were the average earnings for women with bachelor's degrees in 1970? in 2000? How much had they increased?

11. How much were the average earnings for women who had ended their education at high school graduation in 1970? in 2000? How much had they increased?

12. How much were the average earnings for men who had ended their education at high school graduation in 1970? in 2000? How much had they increased?

13. In 1970, how much more did men with bachelor's degrees earn than men who ended their education at high school graduation?

14. In 2000, how much more did men with bachelor's degrees earn than men who ended their education at high school graduation?

15. In 2000, how much more did women with bachelor's degrees earn than women who ended their education at high school graduation?

16. In 1970, how much more did women with bachelor's degrees earn than women who ended their education at high school graduation?

CHAPTER 6: Introduction to Graphing and Statistics

Deforestation.   The world is gradually losing its tropical forests. The following triple bar graph shows the amount of forested land of three tropical regions in the years 1980, 1990, and 2000. Use the bar graph for Exercises 17–24.

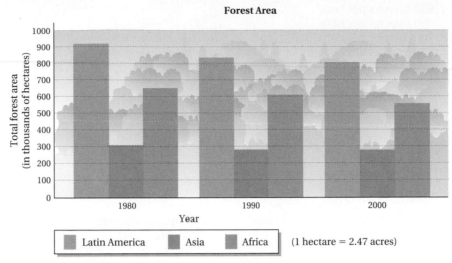

Forest Area

(1 hectare = 2.47 acres)

Source: World Resources Institute and United Nations Johannesburg Summit 2002

17. What was the forest area of Latin America in 1980?

18. What was the forest area of Africa in 1990?

19. Which region experienced the greatest loss of forest area from 1980 to 2000?

20. Which region experienced the smallest loss of forest area from 1980 to 2000?

21. Which region had a forest area of about 802 thousand hectares in 2000?

22. Which region had a forest area of about 300 thousand hectares in 1980?

23. What was the average forest area in Latin America for the three years listed?

24. What was the average forest area in Asia for the three years listed?

b

25. *Commuting Time.*   The following table lists the average commuting time in six metropolitan areas with more than 1 million people. Make a vertical bar graph to illustrate the data.

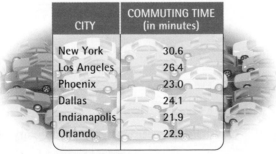

CITY	COMMUTING TIME (in minutes)
New York	30.6
Los Angeles	26.4
Phoenix	23.0
Dallas	24.1
Indianapolis	21.9
Orlando	22.9

Source: U.S. Census Bureau

Use the data and the bar graph in Exercise 25 for Exercises 26–29.

26. Which city has the greatest commuting time?

27. Which city has the least commuting time?

28. What is the difference between the greatest and least commuting times for the six cities?

29. What is the average commuting time for the six cities?

30. *Calorie Expenditure.* Use the following information to make a horizontal bar graph showing the number of calories burned during each activity by a person weighing 152 lb.

Tennis:	420 calories per hour
Jogging:	650 calories per hour
Hiking:	590 calories per hour
Office work:	180 calories per hour
Sleeping:	70 calories per hour

Use the data and the bar graph in Exercise 30 for Exercises 31–34.

31. What is the difference in the number of calories burned per hour between sleeping and jogging?

32. Suppose you were trying to lose weight by exercising and had to choose one of these exercises. If your doctor told you not to jog, what would be the most beneficial exercise?

33. Ryan works at the office for 8 hr and then sleeps for 7 hr. How many calories does Ryan burn doing this?

34. Nancy hiked for 6 hr and then slept for 8 hr. How many calories did she burn doing this?

C *Average Salary of Major League Baseball Players.* The following graph shows the average salary of Major League baseball players over a recent 12-yr period. Use the graph for Exercises 35–40.

Average Salary of Major League Baseball Players

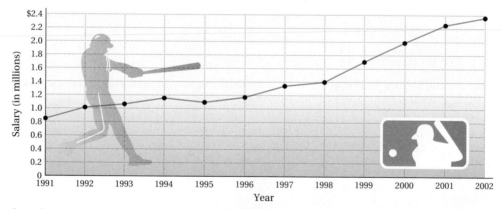

Source: Based on information from the Associated Press and Paul Kagan Associates

35. In which year was the average salary the highest?

36. In which year was the average salary the lowest?

37. What was the difference in salary between the highest and lowest salaries?

38. Between which two years was the increase in salary the greatest?

39. Between which two years did the salary decrease?

40. In what year was the average salary about $1.2 million?

d

41. *Ozone Layer.* Make a line graph of the data, listing years on the horizontal scale.

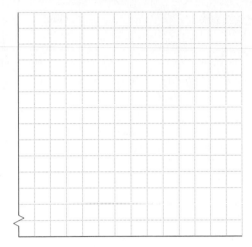

YEAR	OZONE LEVEL (in Dobson Units)
1996	290
1997	293
1998	294
1999	293
2000	292
2001	290.5
2002	290

Source: johnstonsarchive.net

Use the data and the line graph in Exercise 41 for Exercises 42–45.

42. Between which two years was the decrease in the ozone level the greatest?

43. Between which two years was the increase in the ozone level the greatest?

44. What was the average ozone level over the 7-yr period?

45. What was the average ozone level from 1999 through 2002?

46. *Motion Picture Expense.* Make a line graph of the data, listing years on the horizontal scale.

YEAR	AVERAGE EXPENSE PER PICTURE (in millions)
1995	54.1
1996	61.0
1997	53.4
1998	52.7
1999	51.5
2000	54.8
2001	47.7

Source: Motion Picture Association of America

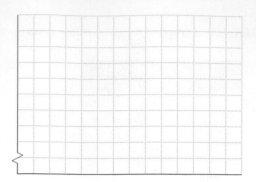

Use the data and the line graph in Exercise 46 for Exercises 47–50.

47. Between which two years was the increase in motion-picture expense the greatest?

48. Between which two years was the decrease in motion-picture expense the greatest?

49. What was the average motion-picture expense over the 7-yr period?

50. What was the average motion-picture expense from 1999 through 2001? Round to the nearest tenth of a million dollars.

51. **Dw** Can bar graphs always, sometimes, or never be converted to line graphs? Why?

52. **Dw** Explain how the information in Exercises 47 and 48 can be used to estimate the cost of producing a motion picture in 2006.

SKILL MAINTENANCE

53. How many 12-oz bottles can be filled from a vat containing 408 oz of catsup? [1.8a]

54. It is known to operators of pizza restaurants that if 50 pizzas are ordered in an evening, people will request extra cheese on 9 of them. Find the ratio of pizzas ordered with extra cheese to pizzas ordered. [3.3a]

55. A can of Cola-Cola contains 12 fluid ounces. How many fluid ounces are in a six-pack? [1.8a]

56. 24 is $\frac{3}{4}$ of what number? [3.8b]

57. $\frac{2}{3}$ of 75 is what number? [3.4c]

58. $\frac{3}{5}$ of 30 is what number? [3.4c]

59. Solve: $-9 = -2x + 3$. [2.8d]

60. Solve: $17 = -3x - 4$. [2.8d]

61. **D**_W In his groundbreaking book, *The Visual Display of Quantitative Information*, Edward Tufte cites the following graph as a misleading representation of data. In what way is the graph misleading?

IN THE BARREL...
Price per bbl. of light crude, leaving Saudi Arabia on Jan. 1

April 1
$14.55

$13.34

$12.70

$12.09

$11.51

$10.46

$10.95

$2.41

'73 '74 '75 '76 1977 1978 1979

©1979 Time Inc. Reprinted by Permission

62. **D**_W Tufte (see Exercise 61) also cites the following as a misleading presentation of information. In what way is it misleading?

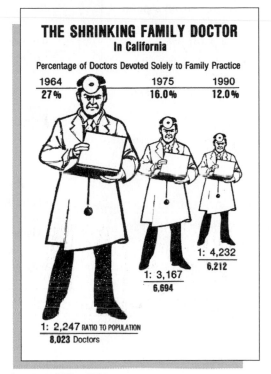

THE SHRINKING FAMILY DOCTOR
In California

Percentage of Doctors Devoted Solely to Family Practice

1964	1975	1990
27%	16.0%	12.0%

1: 4,232
6,212

1: 3,167
6,694

1: 2,247 RATIO TO POPULATION
8,023 Doctors

©1979 Los Angeles Times

63. 🖩 Bonnie eats a 700-cal breakfast, jogs for 45 min, works in her office for $2\frac{1}{2}$ hr, and eats a 615-cal lunch. She then works for another $5\frac{1}{2}$ hr before eating a 235-cal snack and playing tennis for 40 min. If Bonnie weighs 152 lb (see Exercise 30), how many calories has she lost or gained in the course of the day?

64. 🖩 Use the information in Example 2 to approximate the average rate of incidence of breast cancer for all women above the age of 24.

65. **D**_W Consider the graph in Example 4. Sam states that the initial drop shows that sales were nearly cut in half over the first month of the year. What mistake is Sam making?

ORDERED PAIRS AND EQUATIONS IN TWO VARIABLES

Objectives

a   Plot a point, given its coordinates. Find coordinates, given a point.

b   Determine the quadrant in which a point lies.

c   Determine whether an ordered pair is a solution of an equation with two variables.

Plot these points on the graph below.

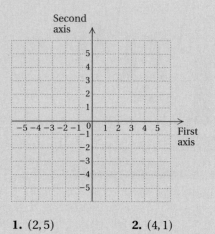

1. $(2, 5)$ **2.** $(4, 1)$

Answers on page A-18

Study Tips

AND NOW FOR SOMETHING COMPLETELY DIFFERENT

When a brand-new topic, like graphing ordered pairs, arises, try to master that new skill when it first appears. By staying in command of this new material, you will ultimately save yourself time and build a solid foundation that will breed confidence as you move forward.

Bar graphs and line graphs are used to illustrate relationships between the items or quantities listed along the bottom and the side of the graph. The horizontal and vertical sides of a bar graph or line graph are often called the **axes** (pronounced ăk sēź; singular: **axis**). By using two perpendicular number lines as axes, we will find that we can use points to represent solutions of certain equations. First, however, we must learn to graph points.

a   Points and Ordered Pairs

When two number lines are used as axes, a grid can be formed. The grid provides a helpful way of locating any point on the plane. Just as a location in a city might be given as the intersection of an avenue and a side street, a point on a plane can be regarded as the intersection of a vertical line and a horizontal line. In the figure below, these lines pass through 3 on the horizontal axis and 4 on the vertical axis. Thus the **first coordinate** of this point is 3 and the **second coordinate** is 4. **Ordered pair** notation, $(3, 4)$, provides a quick way of stating this.

> **CAUTION!**
>
> When writing an ordered pair, you should *always* list the coordinate from the horizontal axis first.

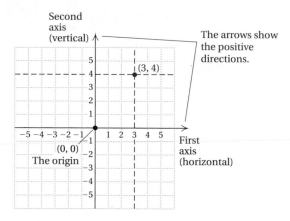

The point $(0, 0)$, where the axes cross each other, is called the **origin.** To graph, or *plot*, the point $(3, 4)$, we can begin at the origin and move horizontally (along the first axis) to the number 3. From there, we move up 4 units vertically and make a "dot."

It is important to always make sure that the first coordinate matches the number that would be below (or above) the point on the horizontal axis. Similarly, the second coordinate should always match the number that would be to the left (or right) of the point on the vertical axis.

Do Exercises 1 and 2.

EXAMPLE 1 Plot the points $(-5, 2)$ and $(2, -5)$.

To plot $(-5, 2)$, we locate -5 on the first, or horizontal, axis. From there we go up 2 units and make a dot.

To plot $(2, -5)$, we locate 2 on the first, or horizontal, axis. Then we go down 5 units and make a dot. Note that the order of the numbers within a pair is important: $(2, -5) \neq (-5, 2)$.

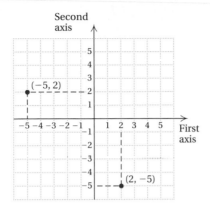

Do Exercises 3–8.

To determine the coordinates of a given point, we first look directly above or below the point to find the point's horizontal coordinate. Then we look to the left (or right) of the point to identify the vertical coordinate.

EXAMPLE 2 Determine the coordinates of points A, B, C, D, E, F, and G.

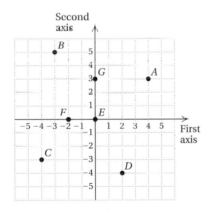

We look below point A to see that its first coordinate is 4. Looking to the left of point A, we find that its second coordinate is 3. Thus the coordinates of point A are $(4, 3)$. The coordinates of the other points are

$B: (-3, 5);$ $C: (-4, -3);$ $D: (2, -4);$

$E: (0, 0);$ $F: (-2, 0);$ $G: (0, 3).$

Do Exercise 9.

Plot these points on the graph below.

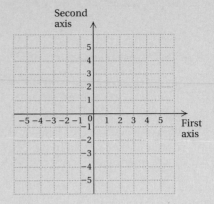

3. $(-2, 5)$

4. $(-3, -4)$

5. $(5, -3)$

6. $(-2, -1)$

7. $(0, -3)$

8. $(2, 0)$

9. Determine the coordinates of points A, B, C, D, E, F, and G on the graph below.

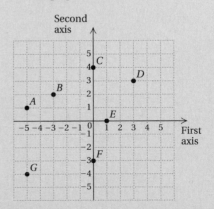

Answers on page A-18

6.3 Ordered Pairs and Equations in Two Variables

10. What can you say about the coordinates of a point in the third quadrant?

11. What can you say about the coordinates of a point in the fourth quadrant?

In which quadrant is each point located?

12. $(5, 3)$

13. $(-6, -4)$

14. $(10, -14)$

15. $(-13, 9)$

Answers on page A-18

b | Quadrants

The axes divide the plane into four regions, or **quadrants.** For any point in region I (the *first quadrant*), both coordinates are positive. For any point in region II (the *second quadrant*), the first coordinate is negative and the second coordinate is positive. In region III (the *third quadrant*), both coordinates are negative. In region IV (the *fourth quadrant*), the first coordinate is positive and the second coordinate is negative.

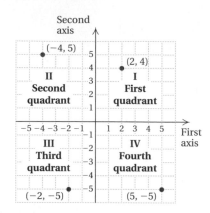

As the figure above illustrates, the point $(2, 4)$ is in the first quadrant, $(-4, 5)$ is in the second quadrant, $(-2, -5)$ is in the third quadrant, and $(5, -5)$ is in the fourth quadrant.

Do Exercises 10–15.

c | Solutions of Equations

The coordinate system we have just introduced is called the **Cartesian** coordinate system, in honor of the great mathematician and philosopher René Descartes (1596–1650). Legend has it that Descartes hit upon the idea of the coordinate system after watching a fly stop several times on the ceiling over his bed. Descartes used this coordinate system as a method of presenting solutions of equations containing two variables. Equations like $3x + 2y = 8$ have ordered pairs as solutions. In Section 6.4, we will find solutions and graph them. Here we simply practice checking to see if an ordered pair is a solution.

To determine whether an ordered pair is a solution of an equation, we normally substitute the first coordinate for the variable that comes first alphabetically and the second coordinate for the variable that is last alphabetically. The letters x and y are used most often.

EXAMPLE 3 Determine whether the ordered pair $(2, 1)$ is a solution of the equation $3x + 2y = 8$.

$$\begin{array}{c|c} 3x + 2y = 8 \\ \hline 3 \cdot 2 + 2 \cdot 1 \; ? \; 8 \\ 6 + 2 \\ 8 \; \big| \; 8 \quad \text{TRUE} \end{array}$$

Substituting 2 for x and 1 for y (alphabetical order of variables)

Since the equation becomes true, $(2, 1)$ is a solution.

In a similar manner, we can show that $(0, 4)$ and $(4, -2)$ are also solutions of $3x + 2y = 8$. In fact, there is an infinite number of solutions of $3x + 2y = 8$.

EXAMPLE 4 Determine whether the ordered pair $(-2, 3)$ is a solution of the equation $2t = 4s - 8$.

We substitute:

$$\begin{array}{c|c}
\multicolumn{2}{c}{2t = 4s - 8} \\
\hline
2 \cdot 3 \ ? \ 4(-2) - 8 & \text{Substituting } -2 \text{ for } s \text{ and } 3 \text{ for } t \\
6 \ \vert \ -8 - 8 & \\
6 \ \vert \ -16 & \textbf{FALSE}
\end{array}$$

Since the equation becomes false, $(-2, 3)$ is not a solution.

Do Exercises 16 and 17.

CALCULATOR CORNER

Solutions of equations in two variables can be easily checked on a calculator. For instance, to demonstrate that $(5.1, -3.65)$ is a solution of $3x + 2y = 8$, on most scientific calculators we press

$$\boxed{3} \ \boxed{\times} \ \boxed{5} \ \boxed{.} \ \boxed{1} \ \boxed{+} \ \boxed{2} \ \boxed{\times} \ \boxed{3} \ \boxed{.} \ \boxed{6} \ \boxed{5} \ \boxed{+/-} \ \boxed{=} .$$

On most graphing calculators we press $\boxed{3} \ \boxed{\times} \ \boxed{5} \ \boxed{.} \ \boxed{1} \ \boxed{+} \ \boxed{2} \ \boxed{\times} \ \boxed{+/-}$ $\boxed{3} \ \boxed{.} \ \boxed{6} \ \boxed{5} \ \boxed{\text{ENTER}}$. The result, 8, shows that $(5.1, -3.65)$ is a solution.

Most calculators now have memory keys. These keys enable us to store and recall a number as needed. Any number being displayed can be stored by pressing a particular key. On most calculators, this key is labeled $\boxed{\text{STO}}$, $\boxed{\text{M}}$, or $\boxed{\text{Min}}$. Once a number has been stored, we can retrieve or recall the number by pressing a key labeled $\boxed{\text{RCL}}$ or $\boxed{\text{MR}}$.

To show that $(7.35, 10.7)$ is a solution of $2t = 4s - 8$, we can first evaluate and store the right side of the equation:

$$\boxed{4} \ \boxed{\times} \ \boxed{7} \ \boxed{.} \ \boxed{3} \ \boxed{5} \ \boxed{-} \ \boxed{8} \ \boxed{=} \ \boxed{\text{STO}} .$$

The result, 21.4, has been stored in the calculator's memory, so we need not worry about writing it down. To complete the check, we clear the calculator and evaluate the left side of the equation:

$$\boxed{2} \ \boxed{\times} \ \boxed{1} \ \boxed{0} \ \boxed{.} \ \boxed{7} \ \boxed{=} .$$

To show that this result matches the number stored earlier, we do not clear the display, but instead subtract the number stored:

$$\boxed{-} \ \boxed{\text{RCL}} \ \boxed{=} .$$

The result, 0, indicates that 2×10.7 and $4 \times 7.35 - 8$ are equal. A result other than 0 would indicate that the ordered pair in question does not check.

As always, keystrokes may vary, so consult your owner's manual if the above keystrokes do not work for your calculator.

Exercises: Determine whether each point is a solution of the given equation.

1. $(7.9, 3.2)$; $5x + 4y = 52.3$
2. $(1.9, 2.3)$; $7x - 8y = 5.1$
3. $(4.3, 4.75)$; $5y = 6x - 7$
4. $(3.8, \ 4.3)$; $9a - 17 = 4b$
5. $(9.4, -3.9)$; $3a - 15 = 29 + 4b$
6. $(5.6, 8.8)$; $4y + 23 = 7x + 19$
7. $(-2.4, 8.5625)$;
   $3.5x + 17.4 = 3.2y - 18.4$
8. $(1.8, 2.6)$;
   $9.2x - 15.3 = 4.8y - 13.7$

---

16. Determine whether $(5, 1)$ is a solution of $y = 2x + 3$.

17. Determine whether $(4, -1)$ is a solution of $3x + 2y = 10$.

Answers on page A-18

6.3

EXERCISE SET

For Extra Help

Digital Video
Tutor CD 4
Videotape 6

InterAct
Math

Math Tutor
Center

MathXL

MyMathLab

a Plot each group of points on the given graph below.

1. $(4, 4)$ $(-2, 4)$ $(5, -3)$ $(-5, -5)$ $(0, 4)$ $(0, -4)$
$(3, 0)$ $(-4, 0)$

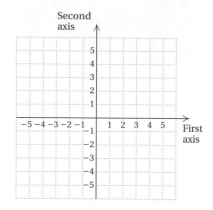

2. $(2, 5)$ $(-1, 3)$ $(3, -2)$ $(-2, -4)$ $(0, 4)$ $(0, -5)$
$(5, 0)$ $(-5, 0)$

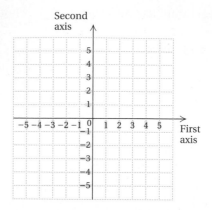

3. $(-2, -4)$ $(5, -4)$ $\left(0, 3\frac{1}{2}\right)$ $\left(4, 3\frac{1}{2}\right)$ $(-1, -3)$ $(-1, 5)$
$(4, -1)$ $(-2, 0)$

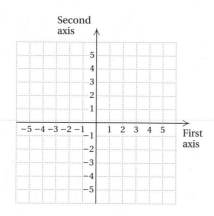

4. $(-3, -1)$ $(5, 1)$ $(-1, -5)$ $(0, 0)$ $(0, 1)$ $(-4, 0)$
$\left(2, 3\frac{1}{2}\right)$ $\left(4\frac{1}{2}, -2\right)$

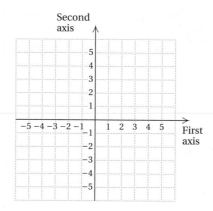

Determine the coordinates of points A, B, C, D, E, and F.

5.

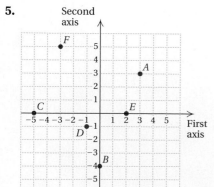

6.

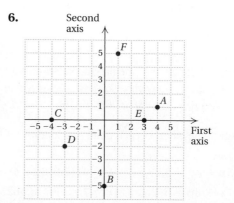

7.

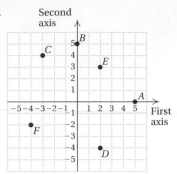

8.

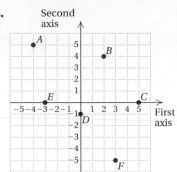

b In which quadrant is each point located?

9. $(-5, 3)$

10. $(-12, 1)$

11. $(100, -1)$

12. $\left(35\frac{1}{2}, -2\frac{1}{2}\right)$

13. $(-6.5, -1.9)$

14. $(-3.4, -5.9)$

15. $\left(3\frac{7}{10}, 9\frac{1}{11}\right)$

16. $(1895, 1492)$

Complete each sentence using the words *positive* or *negative* or the numerals I, II, III, or IV.

17. In quadrant IV, first coordinates are always _____ and second coordinates are always _____.

18. In quadrant III, first coordinates are always _____ and second coordinates are always _____.

19. In quadrant _____, both coordinates are always negative.

20. In quadrant _____, both coordinates are always positive.

21. In quadrants I and _____, the first coordinate is always _____.

22. In quadrants II and _____, the second coordinate is always _____.

c Determine whether each ordered pair is a solution of the given equation.

23. $(4, 3)$; $y = 2x - 5$

24. $(1, 7)$; $y = 2x + 5$

25. $(2, -3)$; $3x - y = 4$

26. $(-1, 4)$; $2x + y = 6$

27. $(-2, -1)$; $3c + 2d = -8$

28. $(0, -4)$; $4p + 2q = -9$

29. $(5, -4)$; $\quad 3x + y = 19$

30. $(-1, 7)$; $\quad x - y = -8$

31. $\left(2\dfrac{1}{3}, 6\right)$; $\quad 2q - 3p = 3$

32. $\left(3, 1\dfrac{1}{4}\right)$; $\quad 2p - 4q = 1$

33. $(2.4, 0.7)$; $\quad y = 5x - 11.3$

34. $(1.8, 7.4)$; $\quad y = 3x + 2$

35. D_W Under what conditions will the points (a, b) and (b, a) be in the same quadrant?

36. D_W Describe in your own words how to plot the point (a, b).

SKILL MAINTENANCE

Solve.

37. $3x - 4 = 17$ [2.8d]

38. $7 + 2x = 25$ [2.8d]

39. $5(x - 2) = 3x - 4$ [5.7b]

40. $\dfrac{3}{7}t - 4 = 2$ [4.4a]

41. $-\dfrac{1}{9}t = \dfrac{2}{3}t$ [5.7b]

42. Simplify: $\dfrac{90}{51}$. [3.5b]

43. Combine like terms: [4.6b]

$$7\dfrac{2}{11}a - 5\dfrac{1}{3}a.$$

44. Simplify: [2.7a]

$$3(x - 5) + 4x - 9.$$

SYNTHESIS

45. D_W Write an equation for which $(-2, 5)$ is a solution and explain how you found the equation.

46. D_W In which quadrant, if any, is the point $(5, 0)$? Why?

Determine whether each ordered pair is a solution of the given equation.

47. $(-2.37, 1.23)$; $\quad 5.2x + 6.1y = -4.821$

48. $(4.16, -9.35)$; $\quad 6.5x - 7.2y = -94.35$

CHAPTER 6: Introduction to Graphing and Statistics

In Exercises 49–52, determine quadrant(s) in which the point could be located.

49. The first coordinate is positive.

50. The second coordinate is negative.

51. The first and second coordinates are equal.

52. The first coordinate is the opposite of the second coordinate.

53. The points $(-1, 1)$, $(4, 1)$, and $(4, -5)$ are three vertices of a rectangle. Find the coordinates of the fourth vertex.

54. A parallelogram is a four-sided polygon with two pairs of parallel sides (two examples are shown below). Three parallelograms share the vertices $(-2, -3)$, $(-1, 2)$, and $(4, -3)$. Find the fourth vertex of each parallelogram.

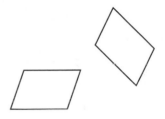

55. Graph eight points such that the sum of the coordinates in each pair is 7.

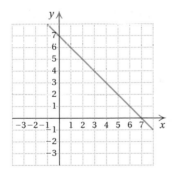

56. Graph eight points such that for each point the first coordinate minus the second coordinate is 3.

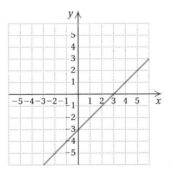

57. Find the perimeter of a rectangle with vertices at $(5, 3)$, $(5, -2)$, $(-3, -2)$, and $(-3, 3)$.

58. Find the area of a rectangle with vertices at $(0, 9)$, $(0, -4)$, $(5, -4)$, and $(5, 9)$.

Objectives

a Find solutions of equations in two variables.

b Graph linear equations in two variables.

c Graph equations for horizontal or vertical lines.

1. Find a solution of $x - y = 3$. Let $y = 5$.

2. Complete these solutions of $5x + y = 10$: $(1, \square)$; $(\square, -5)$.

Answers on page A-19

Study Tips

DOES MORE THAN ONE SOLUTION EXIST?

Keep in mind that many problems—in math and elsewhere—have more than one solution. When asked to find *a* solution of an equation containing two variables, there is usually more than one solution.

In Section 6.3, we saw how to determine whether an ordered pair is a solution of an equation in two variables. We now develop a way of finding such solutions on our own. Once we can find a few ordered pairs that solve an equation, we will be able to graph the equation.

a Finding Solutions

To solve an equation with one variable, like $3x + 2 = 8$, we isolate the variable, x, on one side of the equation. To solve an equation with two variables, we will first replace one variable with some number choice and then solve the resulting equation.

EXAMPLE 1 Find solutions of $x + y = 7$ for $x = 5$ and for $x = -1$.

If x is 5, then $x + y = 7$ can be rewritten as

$$5 + y = 7.$$

We solve as follows:

$$5 + y = 7$$
$$5 + y - 5 = 7 - 5 \qquad \text{Subtracting 5 from both sides}$$
$$y = 2.$$

The ordered pair $(5, 2)$ is a solution of $x + y = 7$. We leave it for the student to show that $(-1, 8)$ is another solution of $x + y = 7$.

Do Exercise 1.

EXAMPLE 2 Complete these solutions of $2x + 3y = 8$: $(\square, 2)$; $(-2, \square)$.

To complete the pair $(\square, 2)$, we replace y with 2 and solve for x:

$$2x + 3y = 8$$
$$2x + 3 \cdot 2 = 8 \qquad \text{Substituting 2 for } y$$
$$2x + 6 = 8$$
$$2x + 6 - 6 = 8 - 6 \qquad \text{Subtracting 6 from both sides}$$
$$2x = 2$$
$$\tfrac{1}{2} \cdot 2x = \tfrac{1}{2} \cdot 2 \qquad \text{Multiplying both sides by } \tfrac{1}{2}$$
$$x = 1.$$

Thus, $(1, 2)$ is a solution of $2x + 3y = 8$. The check is left for the student.

To complete the pair $(-2, \square)$, we replace x with -2 and solve for y:

$$2x + 3y = 8$$
$$2(-2) + 3y = 8 \qquad \text{Substituting } -2 \text{ for } x$$
$$-4 + 3y = 8$$
$$3y = 12 \qquad \text{Adding 4 to both sides}$$
$$y = 4. \qquad \text{Dividing both sides by 3}$$

Thus, $(-2, 4)$ is also a solution of $2x + 3y = 8$. Again we leave the check for the student.

Do Exercise 2.

EXAMPLE 3 Find three solutions of $2x - y = 5$.

We are free to use *any* number as a replacement for either x or y. To find one solution, we select 1 as a replacement for x. We then solve for y:

$$2x - y = 5$$
$$2 \cdot 1 - y = 5 \qquad \text{Substituting 1 for } x. \text{ Other choices are possible.}$$
$$2 - y = 5$$
$$-y = 3 \qquad \text{Subtracting 2 from both sides}$$
$$-1y = 3 \qquad \text{Recall that } -a = -1 \cdot a.$$
$$y = -3. \qquad \text{Dividing both sides by } -1$$

Thus, $(1, -3)$ is one solution of $2x - y = 5$.

To find a second solution, we choose to replace y with 2 and solve for x:

$$2x - y = 5$$
$$2x - 2 = 5 \qquad \text{Substituting 2 for } y. \text{ Other choices are possible.}$$
$$2x = 7 \qquad \text{Adding 2 to both sides}$$
$$x = 3.5. \qquad \text{Dividing both sides by } 2$$

Thus, $(3.5, 2)$ is a second solution of $2x - y = 5$.

To find a third solution, we can replace x with 0 and solve for y:

$$2x - y = 5$$
$$2 \cdot 0 - y = 5 \qquad \text{Substituting 0 for } x. \text{ Other choices are possible.}$$
$$0 - y = 5$$
$$-y = 5$$
$$-1y = 5 \qquad \text{Try to do this step mentally.}$$
$$y = -5. \qquad \text{Dividing both sides by } -1$$

The pair $(0, -5)$ is a third solution of $2x - y = 5$.

Note that three different choices for x or y would have given three different solutions. There is an infinite number of ordered pairs that are solutions, so it is unlikely for two students to have solutions that match entirely.

Do Exercises 3 and 4.

b Graphing Equations

Equations like those considered in Examples 1–3 are in the form $Ax + By = C$. All equations that can be written this way are said to be **linear** because the solutions of each equation, when graphed, form a straight line. When the appropriate line is drawn, we say that we have *graphed* the equation.

EXAMPLE 4 Graph: $2x - y = 5$.

In Example 3, we found that $(1, -3)$, $(3.5, 2)$, and $(0, -5)$ are solutions of $2x - y = 5$. Had we not known that, before graphing we would need to calculate two or three solutions, just as we did in Example 3.

3. Find three solutions of $x + 2y = 7$. Answers may vary.

4. Find three solutions of $y = -2x + 7$. Answers may vary.

Answers on page A-19

5. Graph $x + 2y = 7$. Use the results from Margin Exercise 3.

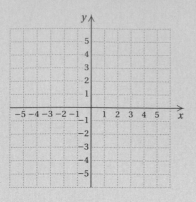

Graph.

6. $y = 3x$

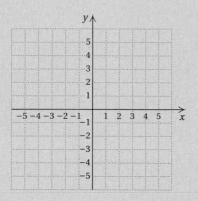

7. $y = \frac{1}{2}x$

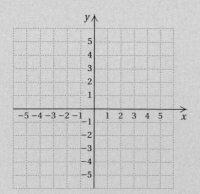

Next, we plot the points and look for a pattern. As expected, the points describe a straight line. We draw the line, as shown on the right below.

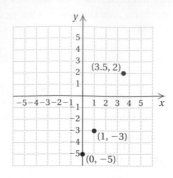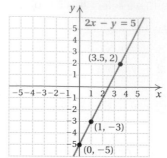

Note that two points are enough to determine a line, but if either point is calculated incorrectly, an incorrect line will be drawn. For this reason, we generally calculate and graph at least three ordered pairs before drawing each line. If the points do not all line up, we know that a mistake has been made.

Do Exercise 5.

Equations like $y = 2x$ or $y = x + 2$ are also linear. To find pairs that solve such equations, it is usually best to substitute for x and then calculate y.

EXAMPLE 5 Graph: $y = 2x$.

First, we find some ordered pairs that are solutions. The ordered pairs that are solutions are commonly listed in a table, as shown below. Suppose we choose 3 for x. Then

$$y = 2x = 2 \cdot 3 = 6,$$

so $(3, 6)$ is one solution.

To find a second solution, we can replace x with -2:

$$y = 2x = 2(-2) = -4.$$

Thus, $(-2, -4)$ is a solution.

To find a third solution, we can replace x with 0:

$$y = 2x = 2 \cdot 0 = 0.$$

Thus, $(0, 0)$ is a solution.

We can compute additional pairs if we wish and form a table.

x	y $y = 2x$	(x, y)
3	6	$(3, 6)$
-2	-4	$(-2, -4)$
0	0	$(0, 0)$
1	2	$(1, 2)$

Substitute for x.
Compute the value of y.
Form the ordered pair (x, y).
Plot the points.
Draw and label the graph.

Next, we plot these points. We draw the line, or graph, with a ruler and label it $y = 2x$.

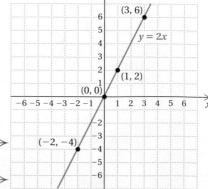

Do Exercises 6 and 7 on the preceding page.

EXAMPLE 6 Graph: $y = -3x$.

We make a table of solutions. Then we plot the points, draw the line with a ruler, and label the line $y = -3x$.

If x is 0, then $y = -3 \cdot 0 = 0$.
If x is 1, then $y = -3 \cdot 1 = -3$.
If x is -2, then $y = -3(-2) = 6$.
If x is 2, then $y = -3 \cdot 2 = -6$.

x	y $y = -3x$	(x, y)
0	0	$(0, 0)$
1	-3	$(1, -3)$
-2	6	$(-2, 6)$
2	-6	$(2, -6)$

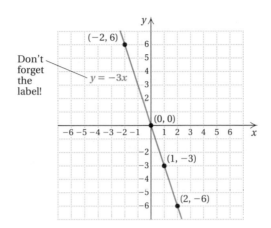

Don't forget the label!

Do Exercises 8 and 9.

EXAMPLE 7 Graph: $y = x + 2$.

We make a table of solutions. Then we plot the points, draw the line with a ruler, and label it.

If x is 0, then $y = 0 + 2 = 2$.
If x is 1, then $y = 1 + 2 = 3$.
If x is -1, then $y = -1 + 2 = 1$.
If x is 3, then $y = 3 + 2 = 5$.

x	y $y = x + 2$	(x, y)
0	2	$(0, 2)$
1	3	$(1, 3)$
-1	1	$(-1, 1)$
3	5	$(3, 5)$

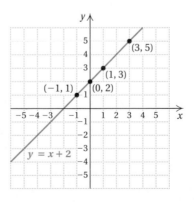

Graph.

8. $y = -x$ (or $y = -1 \cdot x$)

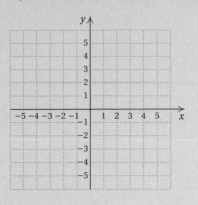

9. $y = -2x$

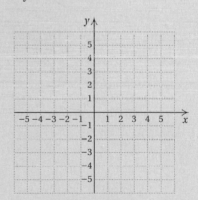

Answers on page A-19

Graph.

10. $y = x + 1$

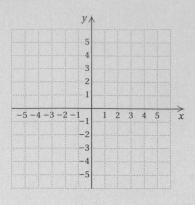

11. $y = -2x + 1$

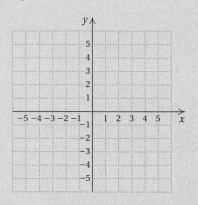

12. $y = \dfrac{3}{5}x$

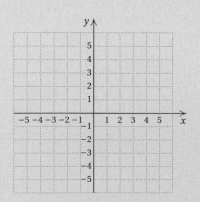

EXAMPLE 8 Graph: $y = \frac{2}{3}x$.

We make a table of solutions, plot the points, and draw and label the line. It is important to note that by selecting multiples of 3 as x-values, we avoid fraction values for y.

If x is 6, then $y = \frac{2}{3} \cdot 6 = 4$.
If x is 3, then $y = \frac{2}{3} \cdot 3 = 2$.
If x is 0, then $y = \frac{2}{3} \cdot 0 = 0$.
If x is -3, then $y = \frac{2}{3}(-3) = -2$.

x	$y = \frac{2}{3}x$	(x, y)
6	4	$(6, 4)$
3	2	$(3, 2)$
0	0	$(0, 0)$
-3	-2	$(-3, -2)$

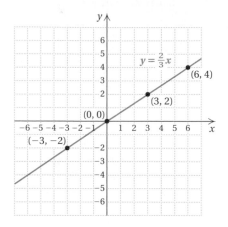

Do Exercises 10–12.

C Graphing Horizontal or Vertical Lines

We have already stated that any equation in the form $Ax + By = C$ is linear, provided A and B are not both zero. If A is 0 and B is nonzero, there is no x-term and the graph is a horizontal line. If B is 0 and A is nonzero, there is no y-term and the graph is a vertical line. In Examples 9 and 10, we consider both of these possibilities.

EXAMPLE 9 Graph: $y = 3$.

We regard $y = 3$ as $0 \cdot x + y = 3$. No matter what number we choose for x, we find that y must be 3 if the equation is to be solved.

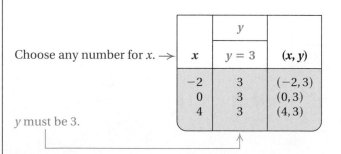

Choose any number for x. →

x	$y = 3$	(x, y)
-2	3	$(-2, 3)$
0	3	$(0, 3)$
4	3	$(4, 3)$

y must be 3.

All pairs will have 3 as the y-coordinate.

When we plot $(-2, 3)$, $(0, 3)$, and $(4, 3)$ and connect the points, we obtain a horizontal line. Any ordered pair of the form $(x, 3)$ is a solution, so the line is 3 units above the x-axis.

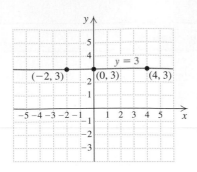

EXAMPLE 10 Graph: $x = -4$.

We regard $x = -4$ as $x + 0 \cdot y = -4$ and make a table with all -4's in the x-column.

x must be -4. →

x		
$x = -4$	y	(x, y)
-4	-5	$(-4, -5)$
-4	1	$(-4, 1)$
-4	3	$(-4, 3)$

All pairs will have -4 as the x-coordinate.

Choose any number for y.

When we plot $(-4, -5)$, $(-4, 1)$, and $(-4, 3)$ and connect them, we obtain a vertical line. Any ordered pair of the form $(-4, y)$ is a solution, so the line is 4 units left of the y-axis.

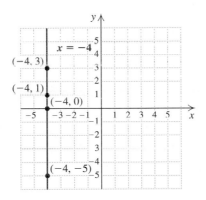

Do Exercises 13 and 14.

13. $y = 4$

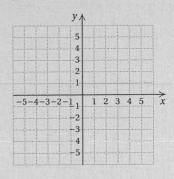

14. $x = 5$

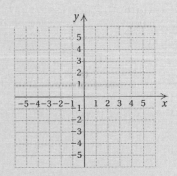

Answers on page A-19

CALCULATOR CORNER

Calculators or computers with graphing capability have become increasingly common. This technology is generally used for graphing equations that are more complicated than $y = x + 2$ and $y = \frac{2}{3}x$ (Examples 7 and 8) and *in no way decreases the importance of understanding how such equations are graphed by hand*. The purpose of the following discussion is to show how a graphing calculator can be used to check your work and how it might enable you to handle more challenging problems.

All graphing calculators utilize a window, the rectangular portion of the screen in which a graph appears. For now, the "Standard" window extending from -10 to 10 on both the x- and y-axes will suffice. The standard window is usually selected from the Zoom menu.

To graph $y = x + 2$, we press a key (usually labeled $\boxed{Y=}$) and then

$$\boxed{(X,T,\theta)} \ \boxed{+} \ \boxed{2} \ \boxed{\text{GRAPH}}$$

(keystrokes may vary with the calculator used). A graph similar to that shown on the left below should appear. To view some of the ordered pairs that are solutions, a TRACE key can be used to move a cursor along the line. Near the bottom of the window the cursor's coordinates appear (see the graph on the right below).

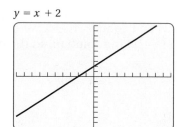

$y = x + 2$

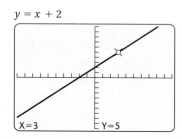

$y = x + 2$

Exercises: Use graphing technology to graph each of the following.

1. $y = \frac{2}{3}x$ (Example 8)
2. $y = x + 1$ (Margin Exercise 10)
3. $y = -2x + 1$ (Margin Exercise 11)
4. $y = \frac{3}{5}x$ (Margin Exercise 12)

6.4

EXERCISE SET

For Extra Help

Digital Video
Tutor CD 4
Videotape 6

InterAct
Math

Math Tutor
Center

MathXL

MyMathLab

a For each equation, use the indicated value to find an ordered pair that is a solution.

1. $x + y = 8$; let $x = 5$

2. $x + y = 5$; let $x = 4$

3. $2x + y = 7$; let $x = 3$

4. $x + 2y = 9$; let $y = 4$

5. $y = 3x - 1$; let $x = 5$

6. $y = 2x + 7$; let $x = 3$

7. $x + 3y = 1$; let $x = 10$

8. $5x + y = 7$; let $y = -8$

9. $2x + 5y = 17$; let $x = 1$

10. $5x + 2y = 19$; let $x = 1$

11. $3x - 2y = 8$; let $y = -1$

12. $2x - 5y = 12$; let $y = -2$

For each equation, complete the given ordered pairs.

13. $x + y = 4$; $(\Box, 3)$; $(-1, \Box)$

14. $x - y = 6$; $(\Box, 2)$; $(9, \Box)$

15. $x - y = 4$; $(\Box, 3)$; $(10, \Box)$

16. $x + y = 10$; $(\Box, 8)$; $(3, \Box)$

17. $2x + 3y = 15$; $(3, \Box)$; $(\Box, 1)$

18. $3x + 2y = 16$; $(4, \Box)$; $(\Box, -1)$

19. $3x + 5y = 14$; $(3, \square)$; $(\square, 4)$

20. $4x + 3y = 11$; $(5, \square)$; $(\square, 2)$

21. $y = 4x$; $(\square, 4)$; $(-2, \square)$

22. $y = 6x$; $(\square, 6)$; $(-2, \square)$

23. $2x + 5y = 3$; $(0, \square)$; $(\square, 0)$

24. $5x + 7y = 9$; $(0, \square)$; $(\square, 0)$

For each equation, find three solutions. Answers may vary.

25. $x + y = 9$

26. $x + y = 19$

27. $y = 4x$

28. $y = 5x$

29. $3x + y = 13$

30. $x + 5y = 12$

31. $y = 3x - 1$

32. $y = 2x + 5$

33. $y = -7x$

34. $y = -4x$

35. $4 + y = x$

36. $3 + y = x$

37. $3x + 2y = 12$

38. $2x + 3y = 18$

39. $y = \frac{1}{3}x + 2$

40. $y = \frac{1}{2}x + 5$

CHAPTER 6: Introduction to Graphing
and Statistics

b Graph each equation.

41. $x + y = 6$

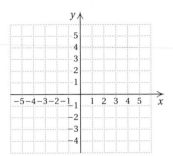

42. $x + y = 4$

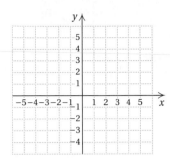

43. $x - 1 = y$

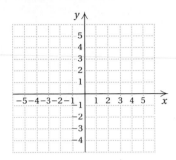

44. $x - 2 = y$

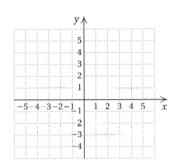

45. $y = x - 4$

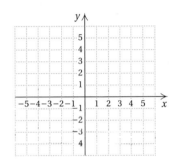

46. $y = x - 5$

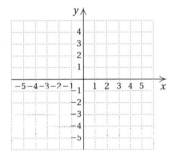

47. $y = \frac{1}{3}x$

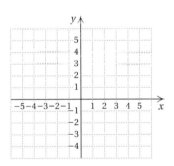

48. $y = -\frac{1}{3}x$

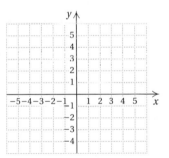

49. $y = x$

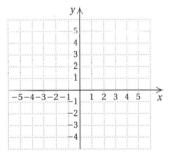

50. $y = x - 3$

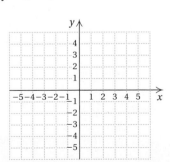

51. $y = 2x - 1$

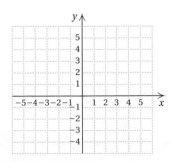

52. $y = 2x - 3$

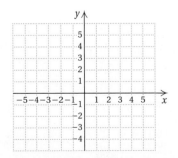

53. $y = 2x + 1$

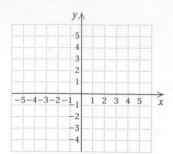

54. $y = 3x + 1$

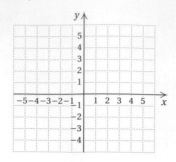

55. $y = \frac{2}{5}x$

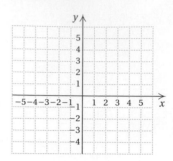

56. $y = \frac{3}{4}x$

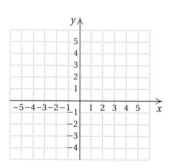

57. $y = -x + 4$

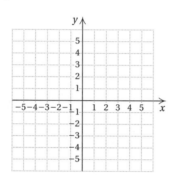

58. $y = -x + 5$

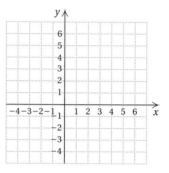

59. $y = \frac{2}{3}x + 1$

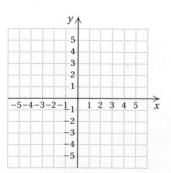

60. $y = \frac{2}{5}x - 1$

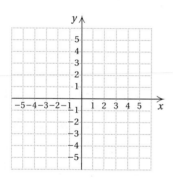

C Graph.

61. $y = 2$

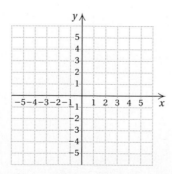

62. $y = 1$

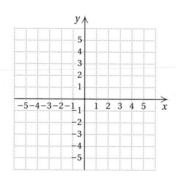

63. $x = 2$

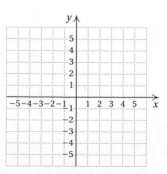

64. $x = 3$

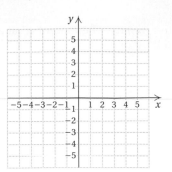

65. $x = -3$

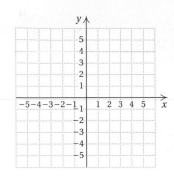

66. $x = -1$

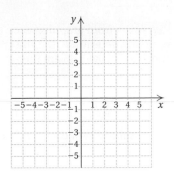

67. $y = -4$

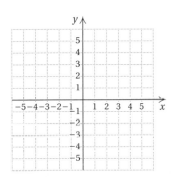

68. $y = -2$

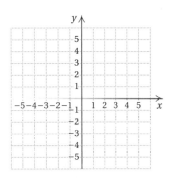

69. D_W To graph a linear equation, a student plots three points and discovers that the points do not line up with each other. What should the student do next?

70. D_W In Example 8, we found that by choosing multiples of 3 for x, we could avoid fractions. What is the advantage of avoiding fractions? Would it have been incorrect to substitute values for x that are *not* multiples of 3? Why or why not?

SKILL MAINTENANCE

71. The tunes on Miles Davis's classic *Kind of Blue* album are approximately 9 min, $9\frac{1}{2}$ min, $5\frac{1}{2}$ min, $11\frac{1}{2}$ min, and $9\frac{1}{2}$ min long. Find the average length of a tune on that album. [4.6c]

72. The books on Sherry's nightstand are 243, 410, 352, and 274 pages long. What is the average length of a book on the nightstand? [1.9c]

73. A recipe for a batch of chili calls for $\frac{3}{4}$ cup of red wine vinegar. How much vinegar is needed to make $2\frac{1}{2}$ batches of chili? [4.7d]

Simplify.

74. $-\dfrac{49}{77}$ [3.5b]

75. $-8 - 5^2 \cdot 2(3 - 4)$ [2.5b]

76. $\dfrac{3}{10}\left(-\dfrac{25}{12}\right)$ [3.4b]

Solve.

77. $4.8 - 1.5x = 0.9$ [5.7a]

78. $3x - 8 = 5x - 12$ [5.7b]

79. ^{D}**W** Apart from graphing each equation, how can someone determine that the graphs of $14x + 21y = 63$ and $10x + 15y = 45$ are the same?

80. ^{D}**W** What is the greatest number of quadrants that a line can pass through? Why?

Find three solutions of each equation. Then graph the equation.

81. 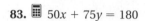 $21x - 70y = -14$

82. $25x + 80y = 100$

83. $50x + 75y = 180$

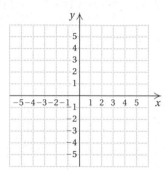

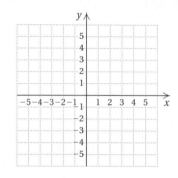

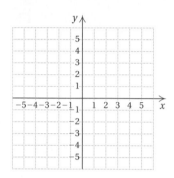

84. Use the graph in Example 4 to find three solutions of $2x - y = 5$. Do not use the ordered pairs already listed.

85. Use the graph in Example 7 to find three solutions of $y = x + 2$. Do not use the ordered pairs already listed.

86. List all solutions of $x + y = 6$ that use only whole numbers.

87. Graph three solutions of $y = |x|$ in the second quadrant and another three solutions in the first quadrant.

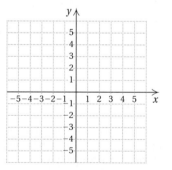

If a graphing calculator is available, use it to graph each of the following.

88. $y = -0.63x + 2.8$

89. $y = 2.3x - 4.1$

6.5
MEANS, MEDIANS, AND MODES

Pictographs, bar graphs, and line graphs provide three ways of representing a collection of data *visually*. Sometimes it is useful to describe a set of data *numerically*, using *statistics*. A **statistic** is simply a number that is derived from a set of data. There are three statistics used as *center points* or *measures of central tendency*. These are numbers that serve to represent the entire data set. Let's examine all three.

a Means

The most commonly used center point is the *average* of the set of numbers. We have already computed an average several times in this book (see pages 92, 305, and 355). Although the word "average" is often used in everyday speech, in math we generally use the word *mean* instead.

> ### MEAN
>
> To find the **mean** of a set of numbers, add the numbers and then divide by the number of items of data.

EXAMPLE 1 *Golfing.* In 1997, Tiger Woods set the record for the lowest total score in a golf tournament consisting of four rounds. His scores were 70, 66, 65, and 69. Find his mean score per round.

To find the mean, we add the scores together and then divide by the number of scores, 4:

$$\frac{70 + 66 + 65 + 69}{4} = \frac{270}{4} = 67.5.$$

Tiger Woods's mean score was 67.5.

Do Exercises 1–4.

EXAMPLE 2 *Food Waste.* Courtney is a typical American consumer. In the course of 1 yr, she discards 100 lb of food waste. What is the average number of pounds of food waste discarded each week? Round to the nearest tenth.

We already know the total amount of food waste for the year. Since there are 52 weeks in a year, we divide by 52 and round:

$$\frac{100}{52} \approx 1.9.$$

On average, Courtney discards 1.9 lb of food waste per week.

Do Exercise 5.

Objectives

a Find the mean of a set of numbers and solve applied problems involving means.

b Find the median of a set of numbers and solve applied problems involving medians.

c Find the mode of a set of numbers and solve applied problems involving modes.

d Compare two sets of data using their means.

Find the mean.

1. 14, 175, 36

2. 75, 36.8, 95.7, 12.1

3. Wendy scored the following on five tests: 96, 85, 82, 74, 68. What is her mean score?

4. In a five-game series, Antonio scored 26, 21, 13, 14, and 23 points. Find the mean number of points scored per game.

5. **Food Waste.** Courtney also composts (converts to dirt) 5 lb of food waste each year. How much, on average, does Courtney compost per month? Round to the nearest tenth of a pound.

Answers on page A-20

6. GPA. Alex earned the following grades one semester.

COURSE	GRADE	NUMBER OF CREDIT HOURS IN COURSE
Jazz Studies	B	3
Astronomy	C	4
Elements of Writing	C	4
Survey of Math	A	2

What was Alex's grade point average? Assume that the grade point values are 4.0 for an A, 3.0 for a B, and so on. Round to the nearest tenth.

EXAMPLE 3 *GPA.* In most colleges, students are assigned grade point values for grades awarded. The **grade point average**, or **GPA**, is the average of the grade point values for each credit hour taken. At most colleges, grade point values are assigned as follows:

A: 4.0, B: 3.0, C: 2.0, D: 1.0, F: 0.0

Meg earned the following grades for one semester. What was her grade point average?

COURSE	GRADE	NUMBER OF CREDIT HOURS IN COURSE
Economics	B	3
Basic Mathematics	A	4
Creative Writing	A	3
French	C	4
Physical Education	D	1

Because some of Meg's courses carried more credit than others, the grades in those courses carry more weight mathematically. We could regard Meg's B in Economics as three B's (since it is a three-credit course), her A in Math as four A's, and so on for all 15 credits. Rather than add 15 single-credit grades, we will multiply and then add before finally dividing by the total number of credits:

Economics $\quad 3.0 \cdot 3 = 9$
Basic Mathematics $\quad 4.0 \cdot 4 = 16$
Creative Writing $\quad 4.0 \cdot 3 = 12$ Multiplying grade point values by the number of credits for
French $\quad 2.0 \cdot 4 = 8$ each course
Physical Education $\quad 1.0 \cdot 1 = \underline{1}$
$46 \quad$ (Total)

The total number of credit hours taken is $3 + 4 + 3 + 4 + 1$, or 15. We divide 46 by 15 and round to the nearest tenth:

$$\text{GPA} = \frac{46}{15} \approx 3.1.$$

Meg's grade point average was 3.1.

Do Exercise 6.

CALCULATOR CORNER

Means can be easily computed on a calculator if we remember the order in which operations are performed. For example, to calculate

$$\frac{85 + 92 + 79}{3}$$

on most calculators, we press

[8] [5] [+] [9] [2] [+] [7] [9] [=] [÷] [3] [=],
or [(] [8] [5] [+] [9] [2] [+] [7] [9] [)] [÷] [3] [=].

Exercises

1. What would the result have been if we had not used parentheses in the latter sequence of keystrokes?

2. Use a calculator to solve Examples 1–4.

Answer on page A-20

EXAMPLE 4 To earn a B in math, Geraldo must have a mean test score of at least 80. On the first four tests, his scores were 79, 88, 64, and 78. What is the lowest score that Geraldo can get on the last test and still get a B?

We can find the total of the five scores needed as follows:

$$80 + 80 + 80 + 80 + 80 = 5 \cdot 80, \quad \text{or} \quad 400.$$

The total of the scores on the first four tests is

$$79 + 88 + 64 + 78 = 309.$$

Thus Geraldo needs to get at least

$$400 - 309, \quad \text{or} \quad 91$$

in order to get a B. We can check this as follows:

$$\frac{79 + 88 + 64 + 78 + 91}{5} = \frac{400}{5}, \quad \text{or} \quad 80.$$

Do Exercise 7.

b Medians

Another measure of central tendency is the *median*. Medians are useful when we wish to de-emphasize unusually extreme scores. For example, suppose a small class scored as follows on an exam.

| Phil: | 78 | Pat: | 56 | Matt: | 82 |
| Jill: | 81 | Olga: | 84 | | |

Let's first list the scores in order from smallest to largest:

56, 78, 81, 82, 84.
↑
Middle score

The middle score—in this case, 81—is called the **median.** Note that because of the extremely low score of 56, the average of the scores is 76.2. In this example, the median may be more indicative of how the class as a whole performed.

EXAMPLE 5 What is the median of this set of numbers?

99, 870, 91, 98, 106, 90, 98

We first rearrange the numbers in order from smallest to largest. Then we locate the middle number, 98.

90, 91, 98, 98, 99, 106, 870
↑
Middle number

The median is 98.

Do Exercises 8–10.

> ### MEDIAN
>
> Once a set of data is listed in order, from smallest to largest, the **median** is the middle number if there is an odd number of values. If there is an even number of values, the median is the number that is the average of the two middle numbers.

7. To receive an A in math, Rosa must have a mean test grade of at least 90 on four tests. On the first three tests, her scores were 80, 100, and 86. What is the lowest score that Rosa can get on the last test and still get an A?

Find the median.

8. 17, 13, 18, 14, 19

9. 20, 14, 13, 19, 16, 18, 17

10. 78, 81, 83, 91, 103, 102, 122, 119, 88

Answers on page A-20

Study Tips

AVOID OVERCONFIDENCE

Sometimes a topic that seems familiar—for example, averaging—reappears and students take a vacation from their studies, thinking they "know it already." Try to avoid this tendency. Often a new wrinkle is included that will catch the unsuspecting student by surprise.

Find the median.

11. $1300, $2000, $3900, $1600, $1800, $1400

12. 68, 34, 67, 69, 58, 70

Find any modes that exist.

13. 23, 45, 45, 45, 78

14. 34, 34, 67, 67, 68, 70

15. 13, 24, 27, 28, 67, 89

16. In a lab, Gina determined the mass, in grams, of each of five eggs:

15 g, 19 g, 19 g, 14 g, 18 g.

a) What is the mean?

b) What is the median?

c) What is the mode?

Answers on page A-20

EXAMPLE 6 The salaries of the six instructors (one of whom is the owner) of the Belmont Ridge School are as follows:

$35,000, $29,000, $32,000, $31,000, $93,000, $30,000.

What is the median salary at the school?

We rearrange the numbers in order from smallest to largest. The two middle numbers are $31,000 and $32,000. Thus the median is halfway between $31,000 and $32,000 (the average of $31,000 and $32,000):

$29,000, $30,000, $31,000, $32,000, $35,000, $93,000.

$$\text{Median} = \frac{\$31,000 + \$32,000}{2} = \frac{\$63,000}{2} = \$31,500.$$

The average of the middle numbers is 31,500.

The median salary is $31,500.

Do Exercises 11 and 12.

In Example 6, the mean salary is $41,666.67, whereas the median salary is $31,500. If you were interviewing for a teaching job at Belmont Ridge and given a choice between being told the mean or the median salary, the median would probably give a better indication of what you would likely earn.

C Modes

The final type of center-point statistic is the **mode.**

> **MODE**
>
> The **mode** of a set of data is the number or numbers that occur most often. If each number occurs the same number of times, there is no mode.

EXAMPLE 7 Find the mode of these data.

13,   14,   17,   17,   18,   19

The number that occurs most often is 17. Thus the mode is 17.

A set of data has just one mean and just one median, but it can have more than one mode. It may also have no mode—when all numbers are equally represented. For example, the set of data 5, 7, 11, 13, 19 has no mode.

EXAMPLE 8 Find the modes of these data.

33,   34,   34,   34,   35,   36,   37,   37,   37,   38,   39,   40

There are two numbers that occur most often, 34 and 37. Thus the modes are 34 and 37.

Do Exercises 13–16.

Which statistic is best for a particular situation? If someone is bowling, the *mean* from several games is a good indicator of that person's ability. If someone is buying a home, the *median* price for a neighborhood is often most indicative of what homes sell for there. Finally, if someone is reordering for a clothing store, the *mode* of the waist sizes sold is probably the most important statistic.

d Comparing Two Sets of Data

Sometimes there is a need to make comparisons between two sets of data. Most often the mean is used, as is the case in the next example and the corresponding exercises.

■ **EXAMPLE 9** *Battery Testing.* An experiment is performed to compare battery quality. Two kinds of batteries were tested to see how long, in hours, they kept a portable CD player running. On the basis of this test, which battery is better?

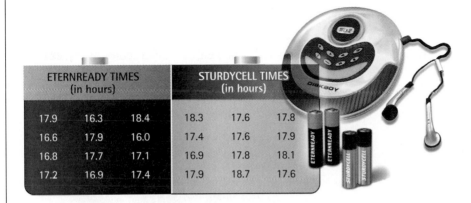

ETERNREADY TIMES (in hours)			STURDYCELL TIMES (in hours)		
17.9	16.3	18.4	18.3	17.6	17.8
16.6	17.9	16.0	17.4	17.6	17.9
16.8	17.7	17.1	16.9	17.8	18.1
17.2	16.9	17.4	17.9	18.7	17.6

Note that it is difficult to analyze the data at a glance because the numbers are close together. We need a way to compare the two groups. Let's compute the mean of each set of data.

Eternready: Mean

$$= \frac{17.9 + 16.3 + 18.4 + 16.6 + 17.9 + 16.0 + 16.8 + 17.7 + 17.1 + 17.2 + 16.9 + 17.4}{12}$$

$$= \frac{206.2}{12} \approx 17.2$$

Sturdycell: Mean

$$= \frac{18.3 + 17.6 + 17.8 + 17.4 + 17.6 + 17.9 + 16.9 + 17.8 + 18.1 + 17.9 + 18.7 + 17.6}{12}$$

$$= \frac{213.6}{12} = 17.8$$

We see that the mean time of Sturdycells is higher than that of Eternreadies and thus conclude that Sturdycell is "better." (It should be noted that statisticians might question whether these differences are what they call "significant." The answer to that question belongs to a later math course.)

Do Exercise 17.

---

17. **Growth of Wheat.** Rudy experiments to see which of two kinds of wheat is better. (In this situation, the shorter wheat is considered "better.") He grows both kinds under similar conditions and measures stalk heights, in inches, as follows. Which kind is better?

WHEAT A STALK HEIGHTS (in inches)			
16.2	42.3	19.5	25.7
25.6	18.0	15.6	41.7
22.6	26.4	18.4	12.6
41.5	13.7	42.0	21.6

WHEAT B STALK HEIGHTS (in inches)			
19.7	18.4	19.7	17.2
19.7	14.6	32.0	25.7
14.0	21.6	42.5	32.6
22.6	10.9	26.7	22.8

Answer on page A-20

6.5

EXERCISE SET

For Extra Help

Digital Video
Tutor CD 5
Videotape 6

InterAct
Math

Math Tutor
Center

MathXL

MyMathLab

a , b , c   For each set of numbers, find the average, the median, and any modes that exist.

1. 17, 19, 29, 18, 14, 29

2. 72, 83, 85, 88, 92

3. 5, 37, 20, 20, 35, 5, 25

4. 13, 32, 25, 27, 13

5. 4.3, 7.4, 1.2, 5.7, 7.4

6. 13.4, 13.4, 12.6, 42.9

7. 234, 228, 234, 229, 234, 278

8. $29.95, $28.79, $30.95, $29.95

9. *Basketball.*   Lisa Leslie of the Los Angeles Sparks once scored 23, 21, 19, 23, and 20 points in consecutive games. What was the mean for the five games? the median? the mode?

10. *PBA Scores.*   Chris Barnes rolled scores of 224, 224, 254, and 187 in a recent tournament of the Professional Bowlers Association. What was his mean? his median? his mode?
Source: Professional Bowlers Association

11. *Gas Mileage.*   The Saturn SW gets 342 miles of highway driving on 9 gallons of gasoline. What is the average number of miles expected per gallon—that is, what is its gas mileage?
Source: *ACEE Green Book: The Environmental Guide to Cars & Trucks, Model Year 2001*

12. *Gas Mileage.*   The Toyota Camry gets 322 miles of city driving on 14 gallons of gasoline. What is the average number of miles expected per gallon—that is, what is its gas mileage?
Source: *ACEE Green Book: The Environmental Guide to Cars & Trucks, Model Year 2001*

Grade Point Average.   The tables in Exercises 13 and 14 show the grades of a student for one semester. In each case, find the grade point average. Assume that the grade point values are 4.0 for an A, 3.0 for a B, and so on. Round to the nearest tenth.

13.

COURSE	GRADE	NUMBER OF CREDIT HOURS IN COURSE
Chemistry	B	4
Prealgebra	A	5
French I	D	3
Pastels	C	4

14.

COURSE	GRADE	NUMBER OF CREDIT HOURS IN COURSE
Botany	A	5
U.S. History	C	4
Drawing I	F	3
Basic Math	B	5

15. *Salmon Prices.* The following prices per pound of Atlantic salmon were found at five fish markets:

$6.99, $8.49, $8.99, $6.99, $9.49.

What was the average price per pound? the median price? the mode?

16. *Cheddar Cheese Prices.* The following prices per pound of sharp cheddar cheese were found at five supermarkets:

$5.99, $6.79, $5.99, $6.99, $6.79.

What was the average price per pound? the median price? the mode?

17. *Drinking and Driving.* Alcohol-related traffic deaths remain a national problem in the United States. Use the table below to determine the mean number of alcohol-related traffic deaths annually for the years 1990–2001.

YEAR	ALCOHOL-RELATED TRAFFIC DEATHS
1990	22,587
1991	20,159
1992	18,290
1993	17,908
1994	17,308
1995	17,732
1996	17,673
1997	16,711
1998	16,673
1999	16,572
2000	17,380
2001	17,448

Source: National Highway Traffic Safety Administration

18. *Commuting Time.* Americans spend more and more time commuting to work. Use the table below to compute the mean commute time for the cities listed.

CITY	COMMUTING TIME (in minutes each way)
New York	30.6
Los Angeles	26.4
Phoenix	23.0
Dallas	24.1
Indianapolis	21.9
Orlando	22.9

Source: U.S. Census Bureau

19. *Grading.* To receive a B in math, Rich must average at least 80 on five tests. Scores on his first four tests were 80, 74, 81, and 75. What is the lowest score that Rich can get on the last test and still receive a B?

20. *Grading.* To receive an A in math, Sybil must average at least 90 on five tests. Scores on her first four tests were 90, 91, 81, and 92. What is the lowest score that Sybil can get on the last test and still receive an A?

21. *Length of Pregnancy.* Marta was pregnant 270 days, 259 days, and 272 days for her first three pregnancies. After her fourth pregnancy, Marta's average pregnancy was exactly the worldwide average of 266 days. How long was her fourth pregnancy?

Source: David Crystal (ed.), *The Cambridge Factfinder.* Cambridge CB2 1RP: Cambridge University Press, 2000, p. 90.

22. *Male Height.* Jason's brothers are 174 cm, 180 cm, 179 cm, and 172 cm tall. The average male is 176.5 cm tall. How tall is Jason if he and his brothers have an average height of 176.5 cm?

d Solve.

23. *Light-Bulb Testing.* An experiment is performed to compare the lives of two types of light bulbs. Several bulbs of each type were tested and the results are listed in the following table. On the basis of this test, which bulb is better?

BULB A: HOTLIGHT TIMES (in hours)			BULB B: BRIGHTBULB TIMES (in hours)		
983	964	1214	979	1083	1344
1417	1211	1521	984	1445	975
1084	1075	892	1492	1325	1283
1423	949	1322	1325	1352	1432

24. *Cola Testing.* An experiment is conducted to determine which of two colas tastes better. Students drank each cola and gave a rating from 1 to 10. The results are given in the following table. On the basis of this test, which cola tastes better?

VERVCOLA				FROSTEE-COLA			
6	8	10	7	10	9	9	6
7	9	9	8	8	8	10	7
5	10	9	10	8	7	4	3
9	4	7	6	7	8	10	9

25. **D**W People fishing in parts of California are forbidden from keeping any salmon that are less than 22 in. long. Kelly's catch of salmon averages 25 in. in length. How is it possible that the law was broken?

26. **D**W How is it possible for a sports team to average the most games won per season over a five-year span without ever leading the league in games won?

Multiply.

27. $14 \cdot 14$ [1.5a]

28. $\dfrac{2}{3} \cdot \dfrac{2}{3}$ [3.4b]

29. 1.4×1.4 [5.3a]

30. 1.414×1.414 [5.3a]

31. 12.86×17.5 [5.3a]

32. 222×0.5678 [5.3a]

33. $\dfrac{4}{5} \cdot \dfrac{3}{28}$ [3.6a]

34. $\dfrac{28}{45} \cdot \dfrac{3}{2}$ [3.6a]

Solve. [5.8a]

35. A disc jockey charges a $40 setup fee and $50 an hour. How long can the disc jockey work for $165?

36. To rent a floor sander costs $15 an hour plus a $10 supply fee. For how long can the machine be rented if $100 has been budgeted for the sander?

37. D_W Some instructors "curve" grades so that each of the traditional cut-off scores of 90, 80, 70, and 60 are adjusted up or down. If your instructor offered to curve grades on a test, would you want the instructor to center the curve around the mean or median test score? Why?

38. D_W The following is a list of the number of children in each family in a certain Glen View neighborhood: 0, 2, 3, 0, 5, 2, 2, 0, 0, 2, 0, 0. Explain why the mode might be the most indicative statistic for the number of children in a family.

Bowling Averages. Bowling averages are always computed by rounding down to the nearest integer. For example, suppose a bowler gets a total of 599 for 3 games. To find the average, we divide 599 by 3 and drop the amount to the right of the decimal point:

$$\frac{599}{3} \approx 199.67. \qquad \text{The bowler's average is 199.}$$

39. 🔢 If Frances bowls 4176 in 23 games, what is her average?

40. 🔢 If Eric bowls 4621 in 27 games, what is his average?

41. *Hank Aaron.* Hank Aaron averaged $34\frac{7}{22}$ home runs per year over a 22-yr career. After 21 yr, Aaron had averaged $35\frac{10}{21}$ home runs per year. How many home runs did Aaron hit in his final year?

42. Because of a poor grade on the fifth and final test, Chris's mean test grade fell from 90.5 to 84.0. What did Chris score on the fifth test? Assume that all tests are equally important.

43. *Price Negotiations.* Amy offers $3200 for a used Ford Taurus advertised at $4000. The first offer from Jim, the car's owner, is to "split the difference" and sell the car for $(3200 + 4000) \div 2$, or $3600. Amy's second offer is to split the difference between Jim's offer and her first offer. Jim's second offer is to split the difference between Amy's second offer and his first offer. If this pattern continues and Amy accepts Jim's third (and final) offer, how much will she pay for the car?

44. The ordered set of data 18, 21, 24, a, 36, 37, b has a median of 30 and a mean of 32. Find a and b.

45. *Gas Mileage.* The Honda Insight, a gas/electric hybrid car, averages 61 mpg in city driving and has a 10.5 gallon gas tank. How much city driving can be done on $\frac{3}{4}$ of a tank of gas?
Source. Based on information from EPA and Honda Motors.

46. *Gas Mileage.* The Toyota Prius, a gas/electric hybrid car, averages 52 mpg in city driving and has an 11.9 gallon gas tank. How much city driving can be done on $\frac{4}{5}$ of a tank of gas?
Source: Based on information from EPA and Toyota Corp.

47. D_W 🔢 After bowling 15 games, Liz had an average of 207. In her 16th game, Liz bowled a 244 and raised her average to 210. Andrew also had a 207 average after 15 games, but needed to bowl a 255 in his 16th game in order to raise his average to 210. How is this possible?

6.6 PREDICTIONS AND PROBABILITY

Objectives

a Make predictions from a set of data using interpolation or extrapolation.

b Calculate the probability of an event occurring.

a Making Predictions

Sometimes we use data to make predictions or estimates of missing data points. One process for doing so is called **interpolation.** Interpolation enables us to estimate missing "in-between values" on the basis of known information.

■ **EXAMPLE 1** *Monthly Mortgage Payments.* When money is borrowed and then repaid in monthly installments, the payment amount increases as the number of payments decreases. The table below lists the size of a monthly payment when $110,000 is borrowed (at 9% interest) for various lengths of time. Use interpolation to estimate the monthly payment on a 35-yr loan.

YEAR	MONTHLY PAYMENT
5	$2283.42
10	1393.43
15	1115.69
20	989.70
25	923.12
30	885.08
35	?
40	848.50

To use interpolation, we first plot the points and look for a trend. It seems reasonable to draw a line between the points corresponding to 30 and 40. We can "zoom-in" to better visualize the situation. To estimate the second coordinate that is paired with 35, we trace a vertical line up from 35 to the graph and then left to the vertical axis. Thus we estimate the value to be 867. We can also estimate this value by averaging $885.08 and $848.50:

$$\frac{\$885.08 + \$848.50}{2} = \$866.79.$$

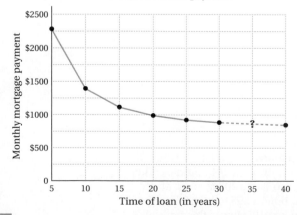

$110,000 Loan Repayment

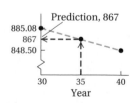

When we estimate in this manner to find an in-between value, we are *interpolating*. Real-world information about the data might tell us that an estimate found in this way is unreliable. For example, data from the stock market might be too erratic for interpolation.

Do Exercise 1.

We often analyze data with the intention of going "beyond" the data. One process for doing so is called **extrapolation.**

EXAMPLE 2 *Movies Released.* The data in the following table and graphs show the number of movie releases over a period of years. Use extrapolation to estimate the number of movies released in 2002.

YEAR	MOVIES RELEASED
1996	471
1997	510
1998	509
1999	461
2000	478
2001	482

Source: Motion Picture Association of America

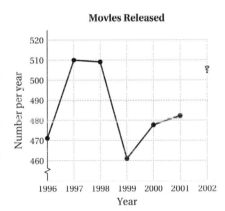

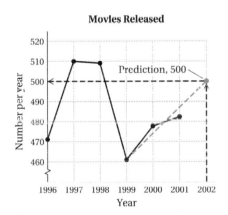

First, we analyze the data and note that they tend to follow a straight line past 1999. Keeping this trend in mind, we draw a "representative" line through the data and beyond. To estimate a value for 2002, we draw a vertical line up from 2002 until it hits the representative line. We go to the left and read off a value—about 500. When we estimate in this way to find a "go-beyond value," we are *extrapolating*. Answers found with this method can vary greatly depending on the points chosen to determine the "representative" line.

Do Exercise 2.

In calculus and statistics, other methods of interpolation and extrapolation are developed. The two basic concepts remain unchanged, but more complicated methods of determining what line "best fits" the given data are used. Most of these methods involve use of a graphing calculator or computer software.

1. **World Bicycle Production.** Use interpolation to estimate world bicycle production in 1999 from the information in the following table.

YEAR	WORLD BICYCLE PRODUCTION (in millions)
1995	106
1996	98
1997	92
1998	76
1999	?
2000	101

Source: Worldwatch Institute, *Vital Signs 2002*

2. **Study Time and Test Scores.** A professor gathered the following data comparing study time and test scores. Use extrapolation to estimate the test score received when studying for 23 hr.

STUDY TIME (in hours)	TEST GRADE (in percent)
19	83
20	85
21	88
22	91
23	?

Answers on page A-21

3. A presentation of *The Lion King* is attended by 250 people: 40 children, 60 seniors, and 150 (nonsenior) adults. After everyone has been seated, one audience member is selected at random. Find the probability of each of the following.

  a) A child is selected.
  b) A senior is selected.
  c) A (nonsenior) adult is selected.

b   Probability

The predictions made in Examples 1 and 2 have a good chance of being reasonably accurate. A branch of mathematics known as *probability* is used to attach a numerical value to the likelihood that a specific event will occur.

Suppose we were to flip a coin. Because the coin is just as likely to land heads as it is to land tails, we say that the *probability* of it landing heads is $\frac{1}{2}$. Similarly, if we roll a die (plural: dice), we are as likely to roll a ⚃ as we are to roll a ⚀, ⚁, ⚂, ⚃, or ⚄. Because of this, we say that the probability of rolling a ⚄ is $\frac{1}{6}$.

EXAMPLE 3   A die is about to be rolled. Find the probability that a number greater than 4 will be rolled.

Since rolling a ⚀, ⚁, ⚂, ⚃, ⚄, or ⚅ are all equally likely to occur, and since two of these possibilities involve numbers greater than 4, we have

$$\begin{array}{l} \text{The probability of rolling} \\ \text{a number greater than 4} \end{array} = \dfrac{2}{6} \begin{array}{l} \leftarrow \text{Number of ways to roll a 5 or 6} \\ \leftarrow \text{Number of (equally likely) possible} \\ \text{outcomes} \end{array}$$

$$= \frac{1}{3}.$$

The reasoning shown in Example 3 is used in a variety of applications.

EXAMPLE 4   A cloth bag contains 20 equally sized marbles: 5 are red, 7 are blue, and 8 are yellow. A marble is randomly selected. Find the probability that **(a)** a red marble is selected; **(b)** a blue marble is selected; **(c)** a yellow marble is selected.

a) Since all 20 marbles are equally likely to be selected, we have

$$\begin{array}{l} \text{The probability of} \\ \text{selecting a red marble} \end{array} = \dfrac{\text{Number of ways to select a red marble}}{\text{Number of ways to select any marble}}$$

$$= \frac{5}{20} = \frac{1}{4}, \text{ or } 0.25 \ .$$

b)
$$\begin{array}{l} \text{The probability of} \\ \text{selecting a blue marble} \end{array} = \dfrac{\text{Number of ways to select a blue marble}}{\text{Number of ways to select any marble}}$$

$$= \frac{7}{20}, \text{ or } 0.35 \ .$$

c)
$$\begin{array}{l} \text{The probability} \\ \text{of selecting a} \\ \text{yellow marble} \end{array} = \dfrac{\text{Number of ways to select a yellow marble}}{\text{Number of ways to select any marble}}$$

$$= \frac{8}{20} = \frac{2}{5}, \text{ or } 0.4 \ .$$

Do Exercise 3.

Answers on page A-21

Many probability problems involve a standard deck of 52 playing cards. Such a deck is made up as shown below.

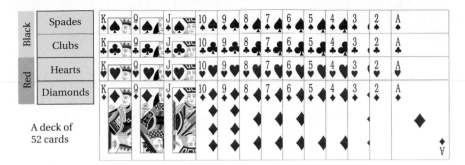

A deck of 52 cards

EXAMPLE 5 A card is randomly selected from a well-shuffled (mixed) deck of cards. Find the probability that **(a)** the card is a jack; **(b)** the card is a club.

a) The probability of selecting a jack $= \dfrac{\text{Number of ways to select a jack}}{\text{Number of ways to select any card}}$

$= \dfrac{4}{52} = \dfrac{1}{13}.$

b) The probability of selecting a club $= \dfrac{\text{Number of ways to select a club}}{\text{Number of ways to select any card}}$

$= \dfrac{13}{52} = \dfrac{1}{4}.$

Do Exercise 4.

In Examples 3–5, several "events" were discussed: rolling a number greater than 4, selecting a marble of a certain color, and selecting a certain type of playing card. The likelihood of each event occurring was determined by considering the total number of possible outcomes, using the principle formally stated below.

THE PRIMARY PRINCIPLE OF PROBABILITY

If an event E can occur m ways out of n equally likely possible outcomes, then

$$\text{The probability of } E \text{ occurring} = \frac{m}{n}.$$

4. A card is randomly selected from a well-shuffled deck of cards. Find the probability of each of the following.

a) The card is a diamond.

b) The card is a king or queen.

Answers on page A-21

Digital Video
Tutor CD 5
Videotape 6

InterAct
Math

Math Tutor
Center

MathXL

MyMathLab

a Use interpolation or extrapolation to find the missing data values.

1. *Study Time and Grades.*   A math instructor asked her students to keep track of how much time each spent studying the chapter on decimal notation. They collected the information together with test scores from that chapter's test. The data are given in the following table. Estimate the missing value.

STUDY TIME (in hours)	TEST GRADE
9	75
11	93
13	80
15	85
16	85
17	80
19	?
21	86
23	91

2. *Maximum Heart Rate.*   A person's maximum heart rate depends on his or her gender, age, and resting heart rate. The following table relates resting heart rate and maximum heart rate for a 30-yr-old woman. Estimate the missing value.

RESTING HEART RATE (in beats per minute)	MAXIMUM HEART RATE (in beats per minute)
58	173
65	178
70	?
78	185
85	188

Source: American Heart Association

Estimate the missing value in each of the following tables.

3. *Motion Picture Expense.*

YEAR	AVERAGE EXPENSE PER PICTURE (in millions)
1997	$53.4
1998	52.7
1999	51.5
2000	54.8
2001	47.7
2002	?

Source: Motion Picture Association of America

4. *Ozone Layer.*

YEAR	OZONE LEVEL (in Dobson Units)
1998	294
1999	293
2000	292
2001	290.5
2002	290
2003	?

Source: johnstonsarchive.net

5. *U.S. Book-Buying Growth.*

YEAR	BOOK SALES (in billions)
1992	$21
1993	23
1994	24
1995	25
1996	26
1997	?

Source: Book Industry Trends 1995

6. *Credit-Card Spending.*

YEAR	CREDIT-CARD SPENDING FROM THANKSGIVING TO CHRISTMAS (in billions)
1991	$ 59.8
1992	66.8
1993	79.1
1994	96.9
1995	116.3
1996	131.4
1997	?

Source: RAM Research Group, National Credit Counseling Services

7. *Recycling.*

YEAR	THOUSANDS OF TONS OF WASTE DIVERTED FROM VERMONT'S LANDFILLS
1995	42.3
1996	49.7
1997	52.2
1998	?
1999	55.6
2000	56.4

Source: Chittenden County, VT, Solid Waste District

8. *Telecommunications.*

YEAR	REVENUE (in billions of dollars)
1995	190
1996	?
1997	231
1998	246
1999	269

Source: Based on information from U.S. Federal Communications Commission, *Trends in Telephone Service*, December 2000

b   Find each of the following probabilities.

Rolling a die.   In Exercises 9–12, assume that a die is about to be rolled.

9. Find the probability that a ⚃ is rolled.

10. Find the probability that a ⚄ is rolled.

11. Find the probability that an odd number is rolled.

12. Find the probability that a number greater than 2 is rolled.

Playing Cards.   In Exercises 13–18, assume that one card is randomly selected from a well-shuffled deck (see p. 463).

13. Find the probability that the card is the jack of spades.

14. Find the probability that the card is a picture card (jack, queen, or king).

15. Find the probability that an 8 or a 6 is selected.

16. Find the probability that a black five is selected.

17. Find the probability that a red picture card (jack, queen, or king) is selected.

18. Find the probability that a 10 is selected.

Candy Colors.   Made by the Tootsie Industries of Chicago, Illinois, Mason Dots® is a gumdrop candy. A box was opened by the authors and found to contain the following number of gumdrops:

Strawberry	7
Lemon	8
Orange	9
Cherry	4
Lime	5
Grape	6

In Exercises 19–22, assume that one of the Dots is randomly chosen from the box.

19. Find the probability that a cherry Dot is selected.

20. Find the probability that an orange Dot is selected.

21. Find the probability that the Dot is *not* lime.

22. Find the probability that the Dot is *not* lemon.

23. $\mathbf{D_W}$ Would a company considering expansion be more interested in interpolation or extrapolation? Why?

24. $\mathbf{D_W}$ Would a bookkeeper who is lacking records from a firm's third year of operation be more interested in interpolation or extrapolation? Why?

SKILL MAINTENANCE

Perform the indicated operation and, if possible, simplify.   [4.2b], [4.3a]

25. $\dfrac{3}{7} + \dfrac{5}{14}$

26. $\dfrac{9}{16} + \dfrac{3}{10}$

27. $\dfrac{5}{8t} - \dfrac{1}{12t}$

28. $\dfrac{7}{15x} - \dfrac{1}{10x}$

Solve.   [5.7b]

29. $-3x + 8 = 2x - 7$

30. $3(x - 4) = 7x - 2$

31. $-7 + 3x - 5 = 8x - 1$

Convert to decimal notation.   [5.5a]

32. $\dfrac{4}{9}$

33. $\dfrac{17}{15}$

34. $-\dfrac{5}{8}$

SYNTHESIS

35. $\mathbf{D_W}$ The answer given for Exercise 7 does not match the real-world figure, which was actually 65.8. What might account for such a discrepancy?

36. $\mathbf{D_W}$ Bluebird Building, Inc., had 23 employees in 1997, but only 18 employees in 1998, and 11 employees in 2000. Can extrapolation be used to predict the number of employees at Bluebird in 2010? Why or why not?

37. A coin is flipped twice. What is the probability that two heads will occur?

38. A coin is flipped twice. What is the probability that one head and one tail will occur?

39. A die is rolled twice. What is the probability that a ⚁ is rolled twice?

40. A day is chosen randomly during a leap year. What is the probability that the day is in July?

41. $\mathbf{D_W}$ Is it possible for the probability of an event occurring to exceed 1? Why or why not?

The review that follows is meant to prepare you for a chapter exam. It consists of two parts. The first part is a checklist of some of the Study Tips referred to in this and preceding chapters. The second part is the Review Exercises. These provide practice exercises for the exam, together with references to section objectives so you can go back and review. Before beginning, stop and look back over the skills you have obtained. What skills in mathematics do you have now that you did not have before studying this chapter?

STUDY TIPS CHECKLIST

The foundation of all your study skills is TIME!	☐ Are you continuing to focus on a lesson even if it contains some review material?
	☐ Are you using the math you've learned as part of your everyday life?
	☐ As new topics are introduced, are you careful to make sure you thoroughly understand the material?
	☐ If you miss a class do you make certain that you find out all that you missed?

REVIEW EXERCISES

FedEx Mailing Costs. Federal Express has three types of delivery service for packages of various weights within a certain distance, as shown in the following table. Use this table for Exercises 1–5. [6.1a]

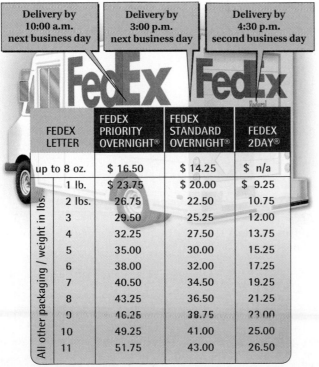

All other packaging / weight in lbs.	FEDEX LETTER	FEDEX PRIORITY OVERNIGHT®	FEDEX STANDARD OVERNIGHT®	FEDEX 2DAY®
up to 8 oz.		$ 16.50	$ 14.25	$ n/a
1 lb.		$ 23.75	$ 20.00	$ 9.25
2 lbs.		26.75	22.50	10.75
3		29.50	25.25	12.00
4		32.25	27.50	13.75
5		35.00	30.00	15.25
6		38.00	32.00	17.25
7		40.50	34.50	19.25
8		43.25	36.50	21.25
9		46.25	38.75	23.00
10		49.25	41.00	25.00
11		51.75	43.00	26.50

Delivery by 10:00 a.m. next business day

Delivery by 3:00 p.m. next business day

Delivery by 4:30 p.m. second business day

Source: Federal Express Corporation

1. Find the cost of a 3-lb FedEx Priority Overnight delivery.

2. Find the cost of a 10 lb FedEx Standard Overnight delivery.

3. How much would you save by sending the package listed in Exercise 1 by FedEx 2Day delivery?

4. How much would you save by sending the package in Exercise 2 by FedEx 2Day delivery?

5. Is there any difference in price between sending a 5-oz package FedEx Priority Overnight and sending a 7.5-oz package the same way?

This pictograph shows the number of officers in the largest U.S. police forces. Use the pictograph for Exercises 6–9.

America's Largest Police Forces

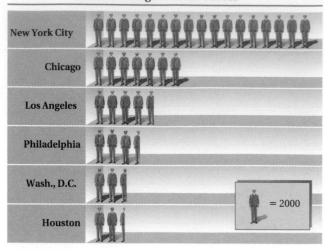

= 2000

Source: International Association of Chiefs of Police

6. About how many officers are in the Chicago police force?   [6.1b]

7. Which city has about 9000 officers on its force?   [6.1b]

8. Of the cities listed, which has the smallest police force? [6.1b]

9. Estimate the average size of these six police forces. [6.1b], [6.5a]

The following bar graph shows the number of U.S. households that owned different types of pets in a recent year. Use the graph for Exercises 10–15.   [6.2a]

American Pet Ownership
(Millions of U.S. households)

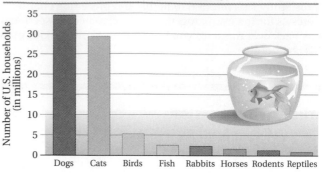

Source: American Veterinary Medical Association

10. About how many U.S. households have pet fish?

11. What type of pet is owned by about 5 million U.S. households?

12. Of the pets listed, which type is owned by the smallest number of U.S. households?

13. About how many more dog owners are there than cat owners?

14. True or false? There are more cat owners than bird, fish, rabbit, horse, rodent, and reptile owners combined.

15. True or false? There are more dog owners than all other pet owners combined.

The following line graph shows the number of accidents per 100 drivers, by age. Use the graph for Exercises 16–21. [6.2c]

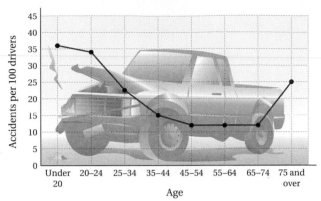

Source: Based on information in *The U.S. Statistical Abstract,* 2002

16. Which age group has the most accidents per 100 drivers?

17. What is the fewest number of accidents per 100 drivers in any age group?

18. How many more accidents per 100 drivers do people over 75 yr of age have than those in the age range of 65–74?

19. Between what ages does the number of accidents per 100 drivers stay basically the same?

20. About how many fewer accidents per 100 drivers do people 25–34 yr of age have than those 20–24 yr of age?

21. Which age group has accidents about three times as often as people 55–64 yr of age?

First-Class Postage. The following table shows the cost of first-class postage in various years. Use the table for Exercises 22 and 23.

YEAR	FIRST-CLASS POSTAGE
1989	25¢
1991	29¢
1995	32¢
1999	33¢
2001	34¢
2002	37¢

Source: U.S. Postal Service

22. Make a vertical bar graph of the data. [6.2b]

23. Make a line graph of the data. [6.2d]

Determine the coordinates for each point. [6.3a]

24. A

25. B

26. C

27. D

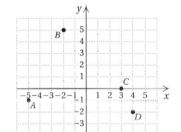

Plot each point on the graph below. [6.3a]

28. (2, 5)   **29.** (0, −3)   **30.** (−4, −2)

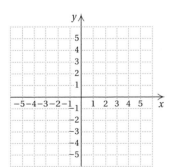

In which quadrant is each point located? [6.3b]

31. $(3, -8)$ **32.** $(-20, -14)$ **33.** $\left(4\dfrac{9}{10}, 1\dfrac{3}{10}\right)$

34. Complete these solutions of $2x + 4y = 10$:
$(1, \square)$; $(\square, -2)$. [6.4a]

Graph on a plane. [6.4b, c]

35. $y = 2x - 5$

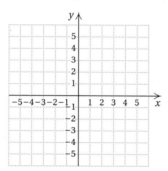

36. $y = -\dfrac{3}{4}x$

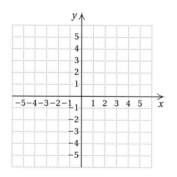

37. $x + y = 4$

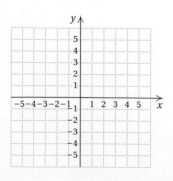

38. $x = -5$

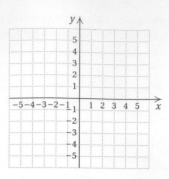

39. $y = 6$

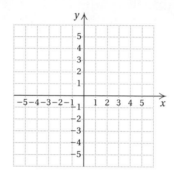

In Exercises 40–44, find **(a)** the mean, **(b)** the median, and **(c)** any modes that exist. [6.5a, b, c]

40. 26, 51, 34, 26, 43   **41.** 11, 14, 17, 17, 21, 7, 11

42. 500, 25, 470, 190, 470, 280

43. 700, 700, 1900, 2700, 3000

44. $30,000, $75,000, $20,000, $25,000

45. To get an A in math, Sasha must average at least 90 on four tests. Scores on her first three tests were 94, 78, and 92. What is the lowest score that she can receive on the last test and still get an A? [6.5a]

46. Use interpolation and the graph in Exercises 16–21 to estimate the number of accidents per 100 drivers that are 30 to 40 yr old. [6.6a]

A deck of 52 playing cards is thoroughly shuffled and a card is randomly selected. [6.6b]

47. Find the probability that the five of clubs was selected.

48. Find the probability that a red card was selected.

49. **D_W** Is it possible for the mean of a set of numbers to be greater than all but one of the numbers in the set? Why or why not? [6.5a]

50. **D_W** Is it possible for the median of a set of four numbers to be one of the numbers in the set? Why or why not? [6.5b]

SKILL MAINTENANCE

51. Divide: $-405 \div 3$. [2.5a]

52. A cutting board measures $\frac{2}{3}$ m by $\frac{1}{2}$ m. What is its area? [3.4c]

53. Simplify: $-\dfrac{32}{4}$. [3.5b]

54. Solve: $3.1 + 4x = -2.7$. [5.7a]

SYNTHESIS

55. ▦ Find three solutions and then graph $34x + 47y = 100$. [6.4a, b]

56. A typing pool consists of four senior typists who earn \$12.35 per hour and nine other typists who earn \$11.15 per hour. Find the mean hourly wage. [6.5a]

For Exercises 57 and 58 refer to the graph in Exercises 10–15.

57. If the average dog-owning household has 1.2 dogs, how many pet dogs are there in the United States? [6.2a]

58. If the average fish-owning household has 14.3 fish, how many pet fish are there in the United States? [6.2a]

59. (See the table in Exercises 1–5). An author has a 3.9-lb manuscript to send by FedEx Standard Overnight delivery to her publisher. She calls and the package is picked up. Later that day she completes work on another part of her manuscript that weighs 4.8 lb. She calls and sends it by FedEx Standard Overnight delivery to the same address. How much could she have saved if she had waited and sent both packages as one? [6.1a]

Graph on a plane. [6.4b]

60. $1\dfrac{2}{3}x + \dfrac{3}{4}y = 2$

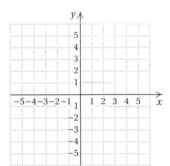

61. $\dfrac{3}{4}x - 2\dfrac{1}{2}y = 3$

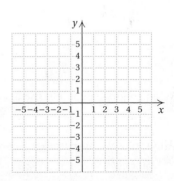

This table lists the number of calories burned during various walking activities. Use it for Questions 1 and 2.

WALKING ACTIVITY	CALORIES BURNED IN 30 MIN		
	110 lb	132 lb	154 lb
Walking			
Fitness (5 mph)	183	213	246
Mildly energetic (3.5 mph)	111	132	159
Strolling (2 mph)	69	84	99
Hiking			
3 mph with 20-lb load	210	249	285
3 mph with 10-lb load	195	228	264
3 mph with no load	183	213	246

1. Which activity provides the greatest benefit in burned calories for a person who weighs 132 lb?

2. What is the least strenuous activity for someone weighing 154 lb who wants to burn at least 250 calories every 30 min?

Water Consumption. The following pictograph shows water consumption, per person, in different regions of the world in a recent year. Use the pictograph for Questions 3–6.

= 100,000 gallons

Sources: World Resources Institute; U.S. Energy Information Administration

3. Which region consumes the least water?

4. Which region consumes the most water?

5. About how many gallons are consumed per person in North America?

6. About how many gallons are consumed per person in Europe?

7. *Animal Speeds.* The following table lists maximum speeds of movement for various animals, in miles per hour. Make a vertical bar graph of the data.

ANIMAL	SPEED (in miles per hour)
Antelope	61
Peregrine falcon	225
Cheetah	70
Fastest human	28
Greyhound	42
Golden eagle	150
Grant's gazelle	47

Source: Barbara Ann Kipfer, *The Order of Things.*
New York: Random House, 1998.

Refer to the table and the graph in Question 7 for Questions 8 and 9.

8. By how much does the fastest speed exceed the slowest speed?

9. Does a human have a chance of outrunning a greyhound? Explain.

Maple Syrup Prices The line graph below shows the price of a gallon of Vermont maple syrup.

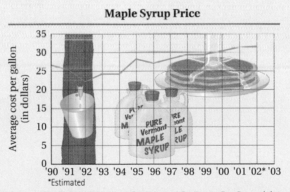

Maple Syrup Price

*Estimated

Sources: New England Agricultural Statistics and *Burlington Free Press*, 4/4/02

10. In which year was the average price the lowest?

11. Between which years did the price rise the most?

12. For which year was the price about $26?

13. Use extrapolation to estimate the price of a gallon of Vermont maple syrup in 2003.

In which quadrant is each point located?

14. $\left(-\frac{1}{2}, 7\right)$

15. $(-5, -6)$

Determine the coordinates of each point.

16. A

17. B

18. C

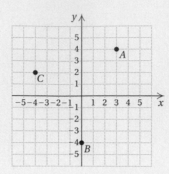

19. Complete the following solution of the equation $y - 3x = -10$: $(\square, 2)$.

Graph.

20. $y = 2x - 2$

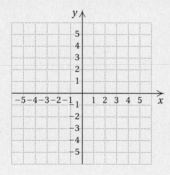

21. $y = -\dfrac{3}{2}x$

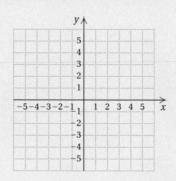

22. $x = -2$

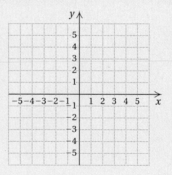

Find the mean.

23. 45, 49, 52, 54

24. 1, 2, 3, 4, 5

25. 3, 17, 17, 18, 18, 20

Find the median and any modes that exist.

26. 45, 47, 54, 54

27. 1, 2, 3, 4, 5

28. 20, 17, 17, 18, 3, 18

29. Stephanie drove 754 km in 13 hr. What was the average number of kilometers per hour?

30. To get a C in chemistry, Ernie must score an average of 70 on four tests. Scores on his first three tests were 68, 71, and 65. What is the lowest score that Ernie can receive on the last test and still get a C?

31. A month of the year is randomly selected for a company's party. What is the probability that a month whose name begins with J is chosen?

SKILL MAINTENANCE

32. Divide: $\dfrac{-700}{35}$.

33. Simplify: $\dfrac{75}{45}$.

34. A recipe for nachos calls for $\frac{3}{4}$ lb of shredded cheese. How much cheese should be used to make $\frac{1}{3}$ of a recipe?

35. Solve: $-9.8 = 5x - 1.7$.

SYNTHESIS

Graph.

36. $\dfrac{1}{4}x + 3\dfrac{1}{2}y = 1$

37. $\dfrac{5}{6}x - 2\dfrac{1}{3}y = 1$

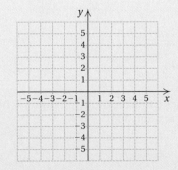

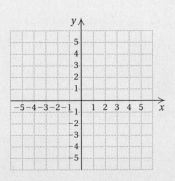

38. Find the area of a rectangle whose vertices are $(-3, 1)$, $(5, 1)$, $(5, 8)$, and $(-3, 8)$.

CHAPTERS
1–6 Cumulative Review

1. Write expanded notation for 3671.

2. Jonathan pedals 23 mi on each of 5 days. How many miles are bicycled in all?

3. Write standard notation for the number in this sentence: Experts predict the global population to surpass 8 billion by the year 2030.

4. Find the perimeter and the area of the rectangle.

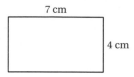

7 cm

4 cm

5. Kati poured 129 g of carbon and then 87 g of sodium chloride into a beaker. How many grams of chemicals were poured into the beaker altogether?

6. Write exponential notation: $7 \cdot 7 \cdot 7 \cdot 7$.

7. Tell which integers correspond to this situation: Monique won 8 cases and Jacques lost 7 cases.

Use either $<$ or $>$ for $\square$ to form a true statement.

8. $1 \square -7$

9. $\dfrac{4}{9} \square \dfrac{3}{7}$

10. $-4.8 \square -4.09$

11. Find $-x$ when $x = -9$.

12. Find $-(-x)$ when $x = 17$.

13. Evaluate $2x - y$ for $x = 3$ and $y = 8$.

14. Combine like terms: $6x + 4y - 8x - 3y$.

15. List all factors of 36.

16. Determine whether 732 is divisible by 6.

17. Write two different expressions for $\dfrac{-7}{x}$ with negative signs in different places.

18. Multiply: $5(2a - 3b + 1)$.

19. What fraction of the figure is shaded?

20. Find another name for the given number but with the denominator indicated.

$$\dfrac{2}{7} = \dfrac{?}{35}$$

Perform the indicated operation and, if possible, simplify. Assume that all variables are nonzero.

21. $536 - 398$

22. $17 \cdot 28$

23. $63 \div (-7)$

24. $-18 + (-21)$

25. $\dfrac{3}{7} + \dfrac{2}{7}$

26. $\dfrac{3}{7} \div \dfrac{9}{5}$

27. $\dfrac{5}{6} - \dfrac{1}{9}$

28. $\dfrac{-2}{15} + \dfrac{3}{10}$

29. $\dfrac{8}{11} \cdot \dfrac{11}{8}$

30. $3\dfrac{1}{4} + 5\dfrac{7}{8}$

31. $7\dfrac{2}{3}x - 5\dfrac{1}{4}x$

32. $4\dfrac{1}{5} \cdot 3\dfrac{1}{7}$

33. $39.72 + 43.56$

34. $1334.183 \div 21.4$

35. $17.4(-2.43)$

36. $\dfrac{8t}{8t}$

37. $\dfrac{4x}{1}$

38. $\dfrac{0}{7x}$

Solve.

39. $x + \dfrac{2}{3} = -\dfrac{1}{5}$

40. $\dfrac{3}{8}x + 2 = 11$

41. $3(x - 5) = 7x + 2$

42. In which quadrant is the point $(-4, 9)$ located?

43. Graph: $y = \dfrac{1}{2}x - 4$.

44. Find the mean:

    19, 39, 34, 52.

45. Find the median:

    7, 9, 12, 35.

46. Find the mode:

    43, 56, 56, 43, 49, 49, 49.

47. Marilyn bicycled 59 km in 3 hr. What was the average number of kilometers per hour?

SYNTHESIS

48. Simplify:

$$\left(\dfrac{3}{4}\right)^2 - \dfrac{1}{8} \cdot \left(3 - 1\dfrac{1}{2}\right)^2.$$

49. Add and write the answer as a mixed numeral:

$$-5\dfrac{42}{100} + \dfrac{355}{100} + \dfrac{89}{10} + \dfrac{17}{1000}.$$

50. A square with sides parallel to the axes has the point $(2, 3)$ at its center. Find the coordinates of the square's vertices if each side is 8 units long.

Ratio and Proportion

Gateway to Chapter 7

In Chapter 3, we introduced fraction notation as a ratio. Here we use ratios and proportions to solve real-world problems. We also examine the concepts of rate, unit pricing, and similarity between geometric shapes.

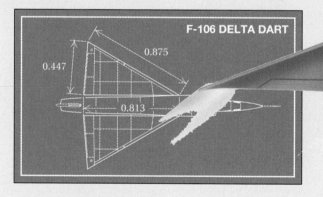

Real–World Application

A blueprint is a drawing in which the actual measurements in the diagram correspond in a precise manner to the real-life dimensions of the object. In the blueprint shown, each wing of the F-106 Delta Dart jet has a triangular shape. The width of a wing that is 0.447 ft on the blueprint is actually 19.2 ft in real life. Use the data provided to determine the length of each wing's longest side.

This problem appears as Example 3 in Section 7.5.

CHAPTER

7

19.2 ft

a

1. Write fraction notation for the ratio 31 to 54.   [7.1a]

2. In this rectangle, find the ratio of width to length and simplify.   [7.1b]

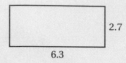

2.7

6.3

3. Kate's Honda Civic can travel 332 mi on 8 gal of gasoline. What is the rate in miles per gallon? [7.2a]

4. **Folgers Coffee®.**   For each package listed below, find the unit price rounded to the nearest hundredth. Then determine which package has the lower unit price.   [7.2b]

PACKAGE	PRICE	UNIT PRICE
11.5 oz	$2.32	
34.5 oz	$5.67	

5. Which has the lower unit price?   [7.2b]

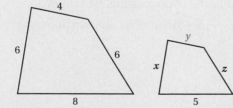

MINERAL WATER

Sparkle: 93¢ for 12 oz

Cleary's: $1.07 for 16 oz

6. Determine whether the pairs 3, 5 and 21, 35 are proportional.   [7.3a]

Solve.   [7.3b]

7. $\dfrac{6}{5} = \dfrac{27}{x}$

8. $\dfrac{y}{0.25} = \dfrac{0.3}{0.1}$

9. The clock on Sharon's stove loses 5 min every 10 hr. At this rate, how many minutes will it lose in 24 hr? [7.4a]

10. On a California state map, 4 in. represents 225 mi. If two cities are 7 in. apart on the map, how far apart are they in reality?   [7.4a]

11. The figures below represent two similar polygons. Find the missing lengths.   [7.5b]

4

6   6

8

y

x   z

5

12. How high is a steeple that casts a 97.5-ft shadow at the same time that an 8-ft road sign casts a 13-ft shadow?   [7.5a]

7.1

INTRODUCTION TO RATIOS

a | Ratio

> **RATIO**
>
> A **ratio** is the quotient of two quantities.

For every 26 lb of waste produced in the United States, about 7 lb are recycled. The *ratio* of the amount of waste recycled to the amount of waste produced is shown by the fraction notation

$$\frac{7}{26}, \quad \text{or by the notation} \quad 7:26.$$

We can read such notation as "the ratio of 7 to 26," naming the numerator first and the denominator second. Note that a ratio is a comparison of the size of one quantity to another.

> **RATIO NOTATION**
>
> The ratio of a to b is written $\frac{a}{b}$ or $a:b$.

For most of our work, we will use fraction notation for ratios. On p. 482 we will show how this notation can sometimes be simplified.

EXAMPLE 1 Write fraction notation for the ratio of 7 to 8.

The ratio is $\frac{7}{8}$.

EXAMPLE 2 Write fraction notation for the ratio of 31.4 to 100. Do not simplify.

The ratio is $\frac{31.4}{100}$.

Do Exercises 1–3.

EXAMPLE 3 *Drive-Through Fast Food.* For every 3 people using a fast-food restaurant's drive-through window, 2 others order indoors. What is the ratio of drive-through orders to indoor orders?

The ratio is $\frac{3}{2}$.

EXAMPLE 4 *Car Expenses.* A family earning $42,800 per year allocates about $6420 for car expenses. What is the ratio of car expenses to yearly income? Do not simplify.

The ratio is $\frac{6420}{42,800}$.

1. Write fraction notation for the ratio of 5 to 11.

2. Write fraction notation for the ratio of 57.3 to 86.1. Do not simplify.

3. Write fraction notation for the ratio of $6\frac{3}{4}$ to $7\frac{2}{5}$. Do not simplify.

Answers on page A-23

Study Tips

PLAN YOUR FUTURE

As you register for next semester's courses, be careful to consider your work and family commitments. Speak to faculty and other students to estimate how demanding each course is before signing up. If in doubt, it is usually better to take one less course than one too many.

527

4. Household Economics. A family earning $34,500 per year will spend about $8620 for food. What is the ratio of food expenses to yearly income? Do not simplify.

5. Rainfall. The greatest amount of rainfall ever recorded for a 12-month period was 739 in. in Kukui, Maui, Hawaii, from December 1981 to December 1982. Find the ratio of rainfall to time in months.
Source: *The Handy Science Answer Book*

6. In the parallelogram below, what is the ratio of the height to the length of the base?

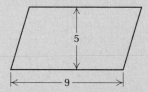

7. In the triangle below, what is the ratio of the length of the shortest side to the length of the longest side? Do not simplify.

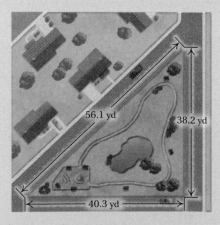

EXAMPLE 5 Refer to the triangle in the figure.

Rear view of CD case

5 ft   3 ft   4 ft

Front view of CD case

a) What is the ratio of the length of the longest side to the length of the shortest side?

$$\frac{\text{Length of longest side}}{\text{Length of shortest side}} = \frac{5\,\text{ft}}{3\,\text{ft}} = \frac{5}{3}$$

b) What is the ratio of the length of the shortest side to the length of the longest side?

$$\frac{\text{Length of shortest side}}{\text{Length of longest side}} = \frac{3\,\text{ft}}{5\,\text{ft}} = \frac{3}{5}$$

Do Exercises 4–7.

EXAMPLE 6 *Packaging.* For every dollar spent on food, about 13 cents goes to pay for the packaging. What is the ratio of the cost of the packaging to the cost of the package's contents?

If 13 cents of each dollar pays for packaging, then $100 - 13 = 87$ cents of each dollar pays for the package's contents. Thus the ratio of the cost of the packaging to the cost of the contents is

$$\frac{13}{87}.$$

Do Exercise 8 on the following page.

b **Simplifying Notation for Ratios**

Sometimes a ratio can be simplified. This provides one method of finding other pairs of numbers with the same ratio.

EXAMPLE 7 *TV Dimensions.* Most television screens have the same ratio of width to height. Emilio's television has a screen that is 20 in. wide and 15 in. high. What is the ratio of width to height?

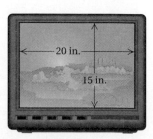

20 in.   15 in.

We write the ratio in fraction notation and then simplify:

$$\frac{20}{15} = \frac{5 \cdot 4}{5 \cdot 3} = \frac{5}{5} \cdot \frac{4}{3} = \frac{4}{3}.$$

Thus we can say that the ratio of width to height is 4 to 3.

Simplified form does not contain decimals. If the ratio contains decimals, we can first multiply the numerator and denominator by a power of 10 and then attempt to simplify.

EXAMPLE 8 Write the ratio of 2.4 to 9.2. Then simplify and find two other numbers in the same ratio.

We first write the ratio. Next, we multiply by $\frac{10}{10}$, or 1, to clear the decimals from the numerator and the denominator. Then we simplify:

$$\frac{2.4}{9.2} = \frac{2.4}{9.2} \cdot \frac{10}{10} = \frac{24}{92} = \frac{4 \cdot 6}{4 \cdot 23} = \frac{4}{4} \cdot \frac{6}{23} = \frac{6}{23}.$$

The ratio 2.4 : 9.2 is equivalent to the ratio 6 : 23.

Do Exercises 9–12.

EXAMPLE 9 Write the ratio of $4\frac{2}{3}$ to $2\frac{5}{6}$ as a fraction in simplified form.

We first write the ratio. Then we rewrite each mixed numeral in fraction notation. Finally, we perform the division.

$$\frac{4\frac{2}{3}}{2\frac{5}{6}} = \frac{\frac{14}{3}}{\frac{17}{6}}$$

$$= \frac{14}{3} \div \frac{17}{6}$$

$$= \frac{14}{3} \cdot \frac{6}{17} \qquad \text{Multiplying by the reciprocal of } \frac{17}{6}$$

$$= \frac{14 \cdot 3 \cdot 2}{3 \cdot 17} \qquad \text{Removing a factor equal to 1: } \frac{3}{3} = 1$$

$$= \frac{28}{17}$$

Do Exercise 13.

CALCULATOR CORNER

If you are permitted use of a calculator to solve exercises like Example 9, be careful to enter the mixed numerals using the $\boxed{a^{b}/_{c}}$ key. The final ratio—if it's greater than 1—will also appear as a mixed numeral. This can be converted to fraction notation either by hand or by using the $\boxed{d/c}$ key.

Exercises

1. Use a calculator to find the ratio of $5\frac{1}{7}$ to $2\frac{3}{4}$.

8. **Commuting by Car.** According to an Eno Transportation Foundation study, 73 of every 100 American workers drive to work alone. Find the ratio of drivers with no passengers to those who do not drive to work alone.

9. In Example 7, what is the ratio of the height to the width?

Write the ratio of the two given numbers. Then simplify each to find two other numbers in the same ratio.

10. 18 to 27

11. 3.6 to 12

12. 1.2 to 1.5

13. Write the ratio of $3\frac{1}{4}$ to $5\frac{1}{2}$ and simplify.

Answers on page A-23

EXERCISE SET

For Extra Help

Digital Video
Tutor CD 5
Videotape 7 | InterAct
Math | Math Tutor
Center | MathXL | MyMathLab

a Write fraction notation for each ratio. You need not simplify.

1. 4 to 5

2. 3 to 2

3. 178 to 572

4. 329 to 967

5. 0.4 to 12

6. 2.3 to 22

7. 3.8 to 7.4

8. 0.6 to 0.7

9. 56.78 to 98.35

10. 456.2 to 333.1

11. $8\frac{3}{4}$ to $9\frac{5}{6}$

12. $10\frac{1}{2}$ to $43\frac{1}{4}$

13. *Music.* One person in four plays a musical instrument. In a typical group of people, what is the ratio of those who play an instrument to the total number of people? What is the ratio of those who do not play an instrument to those who do?

14. *Taxes.* Of the 365 days in a year, it takes 107 days of work for the average person to pay his or her taxes. What is the ratio of days worked for taxes to total number of days in a year?

15. *Field Hockey.* A diagram of the playing area for field hockey is shown below. **(a)** What is the ratio of width to length? **(b)** What is the ratio of length to width?
Source: *Sports: The Complete Visual Reference*

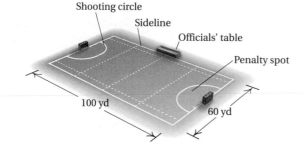

Shooting circle
Sideline
Officials' table
Penalty spot
100 yd
60 yd

16. *The Leaning Tower of Pisa.* At the time of this writing, the Leaning Tower of Pisa is still standing. It is 184.5 ft tall but leans about 17 ft out from its base. **(a)** What is the ratio of the distance it leans to its height? **(b)** What is the ratio of its height to the distance it leans?
Source: *The Handy Science Answer Book*

184.5 ft
17 ft

17. *Beverage Consumption.* The average American drinks 182.5 gal of liquid each year. Of this, 21.1 gal is milk. Find the ratio of milk consumed to total liquids consumed.

18. *Fat Grams.* In one serving $\left(\frac{1}{2}\text{ cup}\right)$ of fried scallops, there are 12 g of fat. In one serving $\left(\frac{1}{2}\text{ cup}\right)$ of fried oysters, there are 14 g of fat. What is the ratio of fat in a serving of scallops to fat in a serving of oysters?
Source: *Better Homes and Gardens: A New Cook Book*

19. *Silicon in the Earth's Crust.* In every 100 tons of the earth's crust, there are about 28 tons of silicon. What is the ratio of silicon to the weight of crust? of the weight of crust to the weight of silicon?
Source: *The Handy Science Answer Book*

20. *Smokers.* In 2000, of every 100 people 18 years or older, 23.3 smoked cigarettes. Find the ratio of smokers to every 100 people.
Source: U.S. Centers for Disease Control

21. *Heart Disease.* In the state of Minnesota, of every 1000 people, 93.2 will die of heart disease. Find the ratio of those who die of heart disease to those who do not die of heart disease.
Source: "Reforming the Health Care System; State Profiles 1999," AARP

22. *Cancer Deaths.* In the state of Texas, of every 1000 people, 122.8 will die of cancer. Find the ratio of those who die of cancer to those who don't.
Source: "Reforming the Health Care System; State Profiles 1999," AARP

23. In this rectangle, find the ratios of length to width and of width to length.

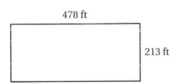

478 ft

213 ft

24. In this right triangle, find the ratios of shortest length to longest length and of longest length to shortest length.

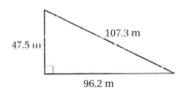

107.3 m

47.5 m

96.2 m

b Write each ratio as a fraction in simplified form.

25. 4 to 6

26. 6 to 10

27. 18 to 24

28. 28 to 36

29. 4.8 to 10

30. 5.6 to 10

31. 2.8 to 3.6

32. 4.8 to 6.4

33. 20 to 30

34. 40 to 60

35. 56 to 100

36. 42 to 100

37. 128 to 256

38. 232 to 116

39. 0.48 to 0.64

40. 0.32 to 0.96

41. The ratio of females to all people worldwide is 51 to 100. Write the ratio of females to males as a simplified fraction.

42. The ratio of Americans ages 18–24 living with their parents to all Americans aged 18–24 is 54 to 100. Write the ratio of those living with parents to those living apart from parents as a simplified fraction.

43. In this right triangle, find the ratio of shortest length to longest length and simplify.

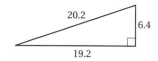

44. In this rectangle, find the ratio of width to length and simplify.

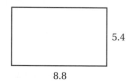

45. *New York Commuters.* Of every 10 people who commute to work in New York City, 4 spend more than 90 min a day commuting. Write, in simplified form, the ratio of people whose commute to New York exceeds 90 min a day to those whose commute is 90 min or less.
Source: *The Amicus Journal*

46. *Corvette Accidents.* Of every 10 fatal accidents involving a Corvette, 8 do not involve another vehicle. Write, in simplified form, the ratio of fatal accidents involving just a Corvette to those involving a Corvette and at least one other vehicle.
Source: *Harper's Magazine*

Write each ratio in simplified form.

47. $3\frac{1}{5}$ to $4\frac{1}{10}$

48. $2\frac{1}{4}$ to $5\frac{1}{2}$

49. $7\frac{1}{8}$ to $2\frac{3}{4}$

50. $6\frac{3}{10}$ to $1\frac{4}{5}$

51. $8\frac{2}{9}$ to $7\frac{1}{6}$

52. $6\frac{3}{8}$ to $5\frac{1}{12}$

53. **D**_{**W**} Van Zandt College has a student-to-faculty ratio of 12 to 1 while Townes College has a faculty-to-student ratio of 2 to 26. On the basis of this information, which school would you rather attend? Why?

54. **D**_{**W**} The width-to-height ratio of HDTV screens exceeds the width-to-height ratio of conventional TV's. Do HDTV screens always have more area than conventional screens? Why or why not?

Use $<$ or $>$ for $\square$ to write a true sentence.   [4.2c]

55. $-\dfrac{5}{6} \square -\dfrac{3}{4}$

56. $\dfrac{12}{8} \square \dfrac{7}{4}$

57. $\dfrac{5}{9} \square \dfrac{6}{11}$

58. $-\dfrac{3}{4} \square -\dfrac{2}{3}$

Divide, using decimal notation for the answer.   [5.4a]

59. $200 \div 4$

60. $95 \div 10$

61. $232 \div 16$

62. $342 \div 2.25$

Solve.   [4.6c]

63. Rocky is $187\frac{1}{10}$ cm tall and his daughter is $180\frac{3}{4}$ cm tall. How much taller is Rocky?

64. Aunt Louise is $168\frac{1}{4}$ cm tall and her son is $150\frac{7}{10}$ cm tall. How much taller is Aunt Louise?

65. **D**$_W$ Can every ratio be written as the ratio of some number to 1? Why or why not?

66. **D**$_W$ What can be concluded about the width of a rectangle if the ratio of length to perimeter is 1 to 3? Make some sketches and explain your reasoning.

67. ▦ In 2002, the total payroll of major league baseball teams was \$2,024,677,522. The New York Yankees payroll was the highest at \$125,928,583. Find the ratio, as a ratio to 1, of the Yankees payroll to the overall payroll.
Source: *USA Today* Baseball Salaries Database

68. ▦ See Exercise 67. In 2001, the total payroll of major league baseball teams was \$1,962,841,814. Find the ratio, as a ratio to 1, of the payroll in 2002 to the payroll in 2001.
Source: *USA Today* Baseball Salaries Database

69. ▦ See Exercises 63 and 64. Find the ratio of the parents' total height to their children's total height and simplify.

Exercises 70 and 71 refer to a common fertilizer known as "5-10-15." This mixture contains 5 parts of potassium for every 10 parts of phosphorus and 15 parts of nitrogen (this is often denoted $5:10:15$).

70. Find the ratio of potassium to nitrogen and of nitrogen to phosphorus.

71. Simplify the ratio $5:10:15$.

a **Rates**

A 2003 Toyota Echo can go 287 miles on 7 gallons of gasoline. Let's consider the ratio of miles to gallons:

Source: Heritage Toyota Inc.

$$\frac{287 \text{ mi}}{7 \text{ gal}} = \frac{287}{7} \frac{\text{miles}}{\text{gallons}} = \frac{41}{1} \frac{\text{miles}}{\text{gallon}} \qquad \text{Simplifying: } \frac{287}{7} = \frac{41}{1}$$

$$= 41 \text{ miles per gallon} = 41 \text{ mpg.} \qquad \text{Miles per gallon is abbreviated mpg.}$$

"per" means division, or "for each."

The ratio

$$\frac{287 \text{ mi}}{7 \text{ gal}}, \quad \text{or} \quad \frac{41}{1} \frac{\text{mi}}{\text{gal}}, \quad \text{or } 41 \text{ mpg}$$

is called a **rate.**

> ### RATE
>
> When a ratio is used to compare two different kinds of measure, we call it a **rate.**

Alyssa's Ford Focus goes 231.2 mi on 7.9 gal of gasoline. Is the mpg (gas mileage) of her car better or worse than that of the Echo above? To find out, it helps to convert to decimal notation and perhaps round. Then we have

$$\frac{231.2 \text{ miles}}{7.9 \text{ gallons}} = \frac{231.2}{7.9} \text{ mpg} \approx 29.266 \text{ mpg.}$$

Since $29.266 < 41$, Alyssa's car gets worse gas mileage than the Echo does.

> ### CONNECTING THE CONCEPTS
>
> It is impossible to overemphasize the importance of using proper units when describing real-world phenomena. Earlier we stressed the importance of labeling units like cm, ft, or hr. Now that we are studying rates, we will consistently be working with *two* units at a time. Again proper labeling is crucial. For example, a train traveling 90 mi/hr is considered fast, but a train moving 90 mi/day would probably be regarded as slow.
>
> Paying attention to units can also be helpful in solving certain rate problems. For example, if we expect an answer to be a rate in dollars per ounce, we may need to look for a way to introduce a calculation that causes an amount of money to be divided by a number of ounces. In this manner, the rate, dollars/ounce, will be formed.

Study Tips

EXAMPLE 1 *Landscaping.* It takes 60 oz of grass seed to grow 3000 sq ft of lawn. What is the rate in ounces per square foot?

$$\frac{60 \text{ oz}}{3000 \text{ sq ft}} = \frac{1}{50}\frac{\text{oz}}{\text{sq ft}}, \quad \text{or} \quad 0.02\frac{\text{oz}}{\text{sq ft}}$$

EXAMPLE 2 *Wage Rate.* A student nurse working in a health center earned $3690 for working 3 months one summer. What was the rate of pay per month?

The rate of pay is the ratio of money earned per length of time worked, or

$$\frac{\$3690}{3 \text{ mo}} = 1230\frac{\text{dollars}}{\text{month}}, \quad \text{or} \quad \$1230 \text{ per month.}$$

Do Exercises 1 and 2.

EXAMPLE 3 *At-Bats to Home-Run Rate.* At one point during the 2002 baseball season, slugger Barry Bonds had hit 40 home runs in 340 at-bats (times at bat). Find his at-bats per home-run rate.

$$\text{His rate was } \frac{340 \text{ at-bats}}{40 \text{ home runs}} = 8.5\frac{\text{at-bats}}{\text{home runs}}.$$

Suppose that a car is driven 200 km in 4 hr. The ratio

$$\frac{200 \text{ km}}{4 \text{ hr}}, \quad \text{or} \quad 50\frac{\text{km}}{\text{hr}}, \quad 50 \text{ kilometers per hour}, \quad \text{or } 50 \text{ km/h}$$

is the rate of travel in kilometers per hour, which is the division of the number of kilometers by the number of hours. A ratio of distance traveled to time is also called **speed.**

EXAMPLE 4 *Motorcycling.* Pierre rides his Harley 145 mi in 2.5 hr. What is the rate in miles per hour?

$$\text{The rate is } \frac{145 \text{ mi}}{2.5 \text{ hr}}, \quad \text{or} \quad 58 \text{ mph.} \qquad \text{Miles per hour is abbreviated mph.}$$

Do Exercises 3–8.

1. A leaky faucet can lose 14 gal of water in a week. What is the rate in gallons per day?

2. Helping Hands Daycare distributes 39 cookies among 13 toddlers. What is the rate in cookies per toddler?

What is the rate, or speed, in miles per hour?

3. 45 mi, 9 hr

4. 120 mi, 10 hr

5. 3 mi, 10 hr

What is the rate, or speed, in feet per second?

6. 2200 ft, 2 sec

7. 232 ft, 16 sec

8. A well-hit golf ball can travel 500 ft in 2 sec. What is the rate, or speed, of the golf ball in feet per second?

Answers on page A-23

9. Kate bought a 14-oz package of bran flakes for $2.89. What is the unit price in cents per ounce? Round to the nearest hundredth of a cent.

 **Unit Pricing**

In order to get the best purchase possible, many consumers pay great attention to an item's *unit price*.

> **UNIT PRICE**
>
> A **unit price** or **unit rate** is the ratio of price to the number of units.

By carrying out the division indicated by the ratio, we can find the price per unit.

EXAMPLE 5 A cook buys 10 lb of potatoes for $3.69. What is the rate or unit price in cents per pound?

Because we are asked for the rate in cents per pound, the monetary amount must be in the numerator. We also need to convert dollars to cents before dividing.

$$\frac{\$3.69}{10 \text{ lb}} = \frac{369 \text{ cents}}{10 \text{ lb}}$$

$$= 36.9 \text{ cents per pound, or } 36.9 \text{ ¢/lb.}$$

EXAMPLE 6 Ruby bought a 20-lb bag of Nutro™ dog food for $25. What is the unit price in dollars per pound?

The unit price is the price in dollars for each pound.

$$\text{Unit price} = \frac{\text{Price}}{\text{Number of units}}$$

$$= \frac{\$25}{20 \text{ lb}}$$

$$= \frac{25}{20} \cdot \frac{\text{dollars}}{\text{lb}}$$

$$= 1.25 \text{ dollars per pound, or } \$1.25/\text{lb}$$

Do Exercise 9.

 CALCULATOR CORNER

If, in Example 1, we wished to determine the rate of lawn coverage in sq ft/oz, we could simply find the reciprocal of 0.02 oz/sq ft by pressing 0 . 0 2 1/x .

Exercises

1. Use the solution of Example 3 to find Bonds' rate of home runs per at-bat.

2. Use the solution of Example 6 to determine the cost of Nutro in pounds per dollar.

Answer on page A-23

Unit prices often vary with the size of the item being sold.

EXAMPLE 7 *Unit Price of Heinz Ketchup.* Many factors can contribute to determining unit pricing in food, such as variations in store pricing and special discounts. Heinz produces ketchup in containers of various sizes. The table below lists several examples of pricing for these packages from a Meijer store. Compute the unit prices and then decide which is the best purchase based on the unit price per ounce.

Source: Meijer Stores

BOTTLE SIZE	PRICE	UNIT PRICE
14 oz	$1.19	8.5 ¢/oz
24 oz	1.39	5.792 ¢/oz
36 oz	1.99	5.528 ¢/oz
46 oz	2.67	5.804 ¢/oz
101-oz twin pack (two 50½-oz bottles)	4.99	4.941 ¢/oz < Lowest unit price

We compute the unit price for the 24-oz bottle and leave the remaining unit prices to the student to check. The unit price for the 24 oz, $1.39 bottle is given by

$$\frac{\$1.39}{24\ oz} = \frac{139\ cents}{24\ oz} = \frac{139}{24}\frac{cents}{oz} \approx 5.792 \text{ cents per ounce} = 5.792 \text{ ¢/oz.}$$

Based on unit price alone, the 101-oz twin pack is the best buy.

Sometimes, as you will see in Margin Exercise 10, a larger size may not have the lower unit price. It is also worth noting that "bigger" is not always "better." (For example, you may not have room for larger packages or the food may spoil before it is used.)

Do Exercise 10.

10. Meijer Brand Olives.
Complete the following table of unit prices for Meijer Brand olives. Which jar has the better unit price?
Source: Meijer Stores

JAR SIZE	PRICE	UNIT PRICE
7 oz	$1.69	
10 oz	$2.59	
$5\frac{3}{4}$ oz	$1.39	

Answers on page A-23

7.2

EXERCISE SET

For Extra Help

Digital Video
Tutor CD 5
Videotape 7

InterAct
Math

Math Tutor
Center

MathXL

MyMathLab

a

1. *Human Heartbeat.* The heart of a human, at rest, will beat an average of 4200 beats in 60 min. What is the heart rate in beats per minute?
Source: *The Handy Science Answer Book*

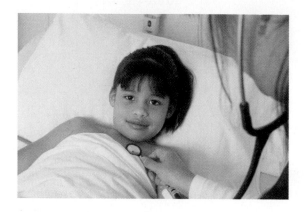

2. *Elephant Heartbeat.* The heart of an elephant, at rest, will beat an average of 1500 beats in 60 min. What is the heart rate in beats per minute?
Source: *The Handy Science Answer Book*

3. *Gastronomic Feats.* In 2001, Takeru Kobayashi set a world record by eating 50 hot dogs in 12 min. Find Kobayashi's rate of consumption in hot dogs per minute.
Source: CNN.com

4. *Gastronomic Feats.* In 2002, Crazy Legs Conti set a world record by eating 168 oysters in 10 min. Find Conti's rate of consumption in oysters per minute.
Source: seattletimes.com

5. *Phone Rates.* A Bigzoo.com long-distance telephone call between two cities costs 39¢ for 10 min. What is the unit price, or rate, in cents per minute?

6. *Culinary Arts.* An 8-lb boneless ham contains 36 servings of meat. What is the ratio in servings per pound?

7. A thoroughly watered lawn requires 623 gal of water for every 1000 ft². What is the watering rate in gallons per square foot?

8. A limousine is driven 200 km on 40 L of gasoline. What is the rate in kilometers per liter?

9. The Walsh's 2003 Windstar minivan traveled 228 mi on 12 gal of gasoline. What was the fuel-consumption rate in miles per gallon?

10. The Tulis' 2003 Camry traveled 243 mi on 9 gal of gasoline. What was the fuel-consumption rate in miles per gallon?

11. *Points Per Game.* During a recent season, Shaquille O'Neal of the Los Angeles Lakers scored 826 points in 32 games. What was his scoring rate in points per game?
Source: National Basketball Association

12. *Points Per Game.* During a recent season, Allen Iverson of the Philadelphia 76ers scored 884 points in 33 games. What was his scoring rate in points per game?
Source: National Basketball Association

13. *Batting Average.* In a recent season, Gary Sheffield of the Los Angeles Dodgers got 163 hits in 501 at-bats. What was his rate of hits per at-bat? (Hits per at-bat is commonly called *batting average*.)
Source: Major League Baseball

14. *Population Density.* Monaco is a tiny country on the Mediterranean coast of France. It has an area of 1.21 square miles and a population of 32,149 people. What is the rate of number of people per square mile? The rate per square mile is called the *population density.* Monaco has the highest population density of any country in the world.
Sources: *The New York Times Almanac; The Handy Geography Answer Book*

In Exercises 15–18, find the rate, or speed, as a ratio of distance to time. Round to the nearest hundredth where appropriate.

15. 120 km, 3 hr

16. 18 mi, 9 hr

17. 217 mi, 29 sec

18. 443 m, 48 sec

19. *Human Physiology.* Impulses in nerve fibers travel 310 km in 2.5 hr. What is the rate, or speed, in kilometers per hour?

20. *Biology.* A black racer snake can travel 4.6 km in 2 hr. What is its rate, or speed, in kilometers per hour?

21. *Acoustics.* Sound travels 66,000 ft in 1 min. What is its rate, or speed, in feet per second?

22. *Optics.* Light travels 11,160,000 mi in 1 min. What is its rate, or speed, in miles per second?

23. Bonnie travels 320 mi in 5 hr. What is her rate in miles per hour? in hours per mile?

24. Andy travels 180 mi in 3 hr. What is his rate in miles per hour? in hours per mile?

b Find each unit price in Exercises 25–34. Then determine which package has the lower unit price.

25. *Scope® Mouthwash.*

SIZE	PRICE	UNIT PRICE
33 fl oz	$3.97	
50 fl oz	$5.78	

26. *Deodorant Stick.*

SIZE	PRICE	UNIT PRICE
2.25 oz	$2.19	
2.5 oz	$2.89	

27. *Crest® Toothpaste.*

SIZE	PRICE	UNIT PRICE
6.2 oz	$2.97	
8.0 oz	$3.47	

28. *Colgate® Toothpaste.*

SIZE	PRICE	UNIT PRICE
6.0 oz	$2.97	
7.8 oz	$3.47	

29. *Meijer® Coffee.*

SIZE	PRICE	UNIT PRICE
11.5 oz	$2.09	
34.5 oz	$5.27	

30. *Maxwell House® Coffee.*

SIZE	PRICE	UNIT PRICE
13 oz	$2.28	
26 oz	$4.88	

31. *Paper Towels.*

SIZE	PRICE	UNIT PRICE
53.7 sq ft	$0.85	
59.5 sq ft	$1.97	
61.8 sq ft	$0.95	
80.6 sq ft	$1.95	
90 sq ft	$1.39	
94 sq ft	$1.79	

32. *Downy® Fabric Softener.*

SIZE	PRICE	UNIT PRICE
20 oz	$2.69	
40 oz	$3.87	
64 oz	$3.57	
90 oz	$8.69	
120 oz	$10.99	

33. *Tide® Liquid Laundry Detergent.*

SIZE	PRICE	UNIT PRICE
50 fl oz	$3.97	
100 fl oz	$4.99	
200 fl oz	$12.24	
300 fl oz	$17.97	

34. *All® Liquid Laundry Detergent.*

SIZE	PRICE	UNIT PRICE
100 fl oz	$3.97	
200 fl oz	$9.49	
300 fl oz	$13.99	

35. ^{D}**W** The unit price of an item generally drops when larger packages of that item are purchased. Why do you think manufacturers do this?

36. ^{D}**W** Describe a situation in which the number of gallons per mile would be a useful number to know.

SKILL MAINTENANCE

Replace the ☐ with < or > to form a true statement.   [4.2c]

37. $\dfrac{3}{11}$ ☐ $\dfrac{5}{13}$

38. $\dfrac{9}{7}$ ☐ $\dfrac{7}{5}$

39. $\dfrac{4}{9}$ ☐ $\dfrac{3}{7}$

40. $\dfrac{3}{19}$ ☐ $\dfrac{2}{17}$

41. $-\dfrac{3}{10}$ ☐ $-\dfrac{2}{7}$

42. $-\dfrac{9}{8}$ ☐ $-\dfrac{15}{13}$

43. There are 20.6 million people in this country who play the piano and 18.9 million who play the guitar. How many more play the piano than the guitar?   [5.8a]

44. A serving of fish steak (cross section) is generally $\frac{1}{2}$ lb. How many servings can be prepared from a cleaned $12\frac{3}{4}$-lb salmon?   [4.7d]

45. D_W Suppose that the same type of juice is available in two sizes and that the larger bottle has the lower unit price. If the larger bottle costs $3.79 and contains twice as much juice, what can you conclude about the price of the smaller bottle? Why?

46. D_W Manufacturers of laundry detergent often charge a higher unit price for their largest packages. Why do you think they do so?

47. A common practice among certain manufacturers is to shrink the size and price of a product so that the consumer thinks the price of a product has been lowered when, in reality, a higher unit price is being charged.

a) Some aluminum juice cans are now concave (curved in) on the bottom. Suppose the volume of the can in the figure has been reduced from a fluid capacity of 6 oz to 5.5 oz, and the price of each can has been reduced from 65¢ to 60¢. Find the unit price of each container in cents per ounce.

b) Suppose that at one time the cost of a certain kind of paper towel was $0.89 for a roll containing 78 ft² of absorbent surface. Later the surface area was changed to 65 ft², and the price was decreased to $0.79. Find the unit price of each product in cents per square foot.

48. In 1994, Coca-Cola introduced a 20-oz soda bottle. At first it was sold for 64¢ a bottle, the same price as their 16-oz bottle. After about a month, the price of a 20-oz bottle rose to 80¢. How did the unit price change for a consumer who made the switch from the 16-oz to the 20-oz bottle?

49. Suppose that a pasta manufacturer shrinks the size of a box from 1 lb to 14 oz, but keeps the price at 85 cents a box. By how much does the unit price change?

50. Use the formula for the area of a circle, $A = \pi r^2$, to determine which is a better deal: a 14-in. pizza for $10.50 or a 16-in. pizza for $11.95. Use 3.14 for π.

51. Suppose that, 25 mi from where you're standing, a bolt of lightning splits a tree. How long will it take for you to hear the accompanying crack of thunder? How long will it take for you to see the flash of light? (*Hint*: Use the information in Exercises 21 and 22.)

52. A six-pack of 12-oz cans of Santa Cruz Ginger Ale was recently on sale for $2.99. Find the unit price in ounces per dollar.

53. A case of 12-oz cans of Santa Cruz Ginger Ale (4 six-packs) is on sale for $11. Find the unit price in ounces per dollar.

Objectives

a Determine whether two pairs of numbers are proportional.

b Solve proportions.

a Proportion

When two pairs of numbers (such as 3, 2 and 6, 4) have the same ratio, we say that they are **proportional.** The equation

$$\frac{3}{2} = \frac{6}{4}$$

states that the pairs 3, 2 and 6, 4 are proportional. Such an equation is called a **proportion.** We sometimes read $\frac{3}{2} = \frac{6}{4}$ as "3 is to 2 as 6 is to 4." Because proportions arise frequently and in many fields of study, being able to solve them when one of the four numbers is unknown, is an *extremely* useful skill. Several important applications of proportions are considered in Section 7.4.

Checking to see whether two pairs of numbers are proportional is the same as checking to see whether two fractions are equal. To develop a quick way of doing this, consider a/b and c/d and assume that neither b nor d is 0.

Note that if

$$\frac{a}{b} = \frac{c}{d}$$

is true, then (using the multiplication principle)

$$bd \cdot \frac{a}{b} = bd \cdot \frac{c}{d} \qquad \text{Multiplying both sides by } bd$$

is also true. Simplifying, we have

$$da = bc.$$

If neither b nor d is 0, the above equations are all equivalent. Thus, any time that $da = bc$ (with $d \neq 0$ and $b \neq 0$), it follows that

$$\frac{a}{b} = \frac{c}{d}.$$

This is the basis for the following.

A TEST FOR EQUALITY

We multiply these two numbers: $3 \cdot 4$.

We multiply these two numbers: $2 \cdot 6$.

$$\frac{3}{2} \overset{?}{=} \frac{6}{4}$$

Since $3 \cdot 4 = 2 \cdot 6$, we know that

$$\frac{3}{2} = \frac{6}{4}.$$

We call $3 \cdot 4$ and $2 \cdot 6$ *cross products.*

EXAMPLE 1 Determine whether 1, 2 and 3, 6 are proportional.

We can use cross products to check an equivalent equation:

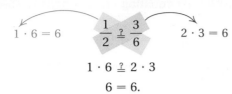

$$1 \cdot 6 = 6 \qquad \frac{1}{2} \overset{?}{=} \frac{3}{6} \qquad 2 \cdot 3 = 6$$

$$1 \cdot 6 \overset{?}{=} 2 \cdot 3$$

$$6 = 6.$$

Since this last equation is true, we know that the first equation is also true and the numbers 1, 2 and 3, 6 are proportional.

EXAMPLE 2 Determine whether 2, 5 and 4, 7 are proportional.

We can check an equivalent equation using cross products:

$$2 \cdot 7 = 14 \qquad \frac{2}{5} \overset{?}{=} \frac{4}{7} \qquad 5 \cdot 4 = 20$$

$$2 \cdot 7 \overset{?}{=} 5 \cdot 4$$

$$14 \neq 20.$$

Since $14 \neq 20$, we know that $\frac{2}{5} \neq \frac{4}{7}$, so 2, 5 and 4, 7 are not proportional.

Do Exercises 1–3.

EXAMPLE 3 Determine whether $1\frac{1}{4}, \frac{1}{2}$ and $1, \frac{2}{5}$ are proportional.

We can use cross products:

$$1\frac{1}{4} \cdot \frac{2}{5} = \frac{5}{4} \cdot \frac{2}{5} \qquad \frac{1\frac{1}{4}}{\frac{1}{2}} \overset{?}{=} \frac{1}{\frac{2}{5}} \qquad \frac{1}{2} \cdot 1 = \frac{1}{2}$$

$$\frac{5}{4} \cdot \frac{2}{5} \overset{?}{=} \frac{1}{2}$$

$$\frac{10}{20} = \frac{1}{2}. \qquad \text{We can also note that } \frac{5}{4} \cdot \frac{2}{5} = \frac{2}{4}.$$

Since $\frac{10}{20} = \frac{1}{2}$, we know that

$$\frac{1\frac{1}{4}}{\frac{1}{2}} = \frac{1}{\frac{2}{5}}.$$

The numbers $1\frac{1}{4}, \frac{1}{2}$ and $1, \frac{2}{5}$ are proportional.

Do Exercises 4 and 5.

b Solving Proportions

Often one of the four numbers in a proportion is unknown. Cross products can be used to find the missing number and "solve" the proportion.

Determine whether the two pairs of numbers are proportional.

1. 3, 4 and 6, 8

2. 1, 4 and 10, 39

3. 1, 2 and 20, 39

Determine whether the two pairs of numbers are proportional.

4. $4\frac{2}{3}, 5\frac{1}{2}$ and $14, 16\frac{1}{2}$

5. 7.4, 6.8 and 4.2, 3.6

Answers on page A-23

6. Solve: $\dfrac{x}{63} = \dfrac{2}{9}$.

7. Solve: $\dfrac{x}{9} = \dfrac{5}{4}$.

8. Solve: $\dfrac{2.1}{0.5} = \dfrac{n}{2.5}$.

9. Solve: $\dfrac{2}{3} = \dfrac{6}{x}$.

10. Solve: $\dfrac{\frac{2}{5}}{\frac{9}{10}} = \dfrac{4\frac{4}{5}}{t}$.

■ **EXAMPLE 4** Solve: $\dfrac{x}{8} = \dfrac{3}{5}$.

We form an equivalent equation by equating cross products. Then we solve for x.

$$5 \cdot x = 8 \cdot 3 \qquad \text{Equating cross products}$$

$$\frac{5x}{5} = \frac{24}{5} \qquad \text{Dividing both sides by 5}$$

$$x = \frac{24}{5} \qquad \text{Simplifying}$$

$$= 4.8 \qquad \text{Dividing}$$

To check that 4.8 is the solution, we replace x with 4.8 and use cross products:

$$4.8 \cdot 5 = 24 \qquad \frac{4.8}{8} \overset{?}{=} \frac{3}{5} \qquad 8 \cdot 3 = 24. \qquad \text{The cross products are the same.}$$

Since the cross products are the same, it follows that $\frac{4.8}{8} = \frac{3}{5}$. Thus 4.8, 8 and 3, 5 are proportional, and 4.8 is the solution of the equation.

SOLVING PROPORTIONS

To solve $\dfrac{a}{b} = \dfrac{c}{d}$ for a specific variable, equate cross products and then divide on both sides to get that variable alone. (Assume $b, d \neq 0$.)

Do Exercise 6.

■ **EXAMPLE 5** Solve: $\dfrac{x}{7} = \dfrac{5}{3}$. Write a mixed numeral for the answer.

We have

$$\frac{x}{7} = \frac{5}{3}$$

$$3 \cdot x = 7 \cdot 5 \qquad \text{Equating cross products}$$

$$\frac{3x}{3} = \frac{35}{3} \qquad \text{Dividing both sides by 3}$$

$$x = \frac{35}{3}, \text{ or } 11\frac{2}{3}.$$

CHECK: $\dfrac{\frac{35}{3}}{7} \overset{?}{=} \dfrac{5}{3}$

$$\frac{35}{3} \cdot 3 = 35 \text{ and } 7 \cdot 5 = 35.$$

The cross products are the same, so we have a check. The solution is $11\frac{2}{3}$.

Do Exercise 7.

EXAMPLE 6 Solve: $\frac{7.7}{15.4} = \frac{y}{2.2}$. Write decimal notation for the answer.

We have

$$\frac{7.7}{15.4} = \frac{y}{2.2}$$

$(7.7)(2.2) = 15.4y$ Equating cross products; if you prefer, write $15.4y = (7.7)(2.2)$.

$$\frac{(7.7)(2.2)}{15.4} = \frac{15.4y}{15.4}$$ Dividing both sides by 15.4

$$\frac{16.94}{15.4} = y$$ Simplifying

$1.1 = y.$ Dividing:
$$
15.4 \overline{)\begin{array}{r} 1.1 \\ 1\,6.9_\wedge 4 \\ \underline{1\,5\,4\,0} \\ 1\,5\,4 \\ \underline{1\,5\,4} \\ 0 \end{array}}
$$

We leave the check for the student. The solution is 1.1.

Do Exercise 8 on the previous page.

EXAMPLE 7 Solve: $\frac{3}{x} = \frac{6}{4}$.

We have

$$\frac{3}{x} = \frac{6}{4}$$

$3 \cdot 4 = x \cdot 6$ Equating cross products; we could also write $6 \cdot x = 3 \cdot 4$.

$$\frac{12}{6} = \frac{6x}{6}$$ Dividing both sides by 6

$2 = x.$ Simplifying

The solution is 2.

Do Exercise 9 on the previous page.

EXAMPLE 8 Solve: $\frac{\frac{17}{8}}{\frac{3}{4}} = \frac{1\frac{1}{2}}{n}$.

We have

$$\frac{\frac{17}{8}}{\frac{3}{4}} = \frac{\frac{3}{2}}{n}$$ Rewriting $1\frac{1}{2}$ as $\frac{3}{2}$

$$\frac{17}{8} \cdot n = \frac{3}{4} \cdot \frac{3}{2}$$ Equating cross products

$$n = \frac{8 \cdot 3 \cdot 3}{17 \cdot 4 \cdot 2}$$ Multiplying both sides by $\frac{8}{17}$

$$n = \frac{3 \cdot 3}{17} = \frac{9}{17}.$$ Removing a factor equal to 1: $\frac{8}{4 \cdot 2} = 1$

The solution is $\frac{9}{17}$.

Do Exercise 10 on the previous page.

CALCULATOR CORNER

Note in Examples 4–8 that when we solve a proportion, we equate cross products and then we divide on both sides to isolate the variable on one side of the equation. We can use a calculator to do the calculations in this situation. In Example 6, for instance, after equating cross products and dividing by 15.4 on both sides, we have

$$y = \frac{7.7 \times 2.2}{15.4}.$$

To compute y on a calculator, we can press $\boxed{7}\,\boxed{.}\,\boxed{7}\,\boxed{\times}$ $\boxed{2}\,\boxed{.}\,\boxed{2}\,\boxed{\div}\,\boxed{1}\,\boxed{5}\,\boxed{.}\,\boxed{4}$ $\boxed{=}$. The result is 1.1, so $y = 1.1$.

Exercises

1. Use a calculator to solve each of the proportions in Examples 5–7.

2. Use a calculator to solve each of the proportions in Margin Exercises 6–10.

Solve each proportion.

3. $\frac{15.75}{20} = \frac{a}{35}$

4. $\frac{32}{x} = \frac{25}{20}$

5. $\frac{t}{57} = \frac{17}{64}$

6. $\frac{71.2}{a} = \frac{42.5}{23.9}$

7. $\frac{29.6}{3.15} = \frac{x}{4.23}$

8. $\frac{a}{3.01} = \frac{1.7}{0.043}$

545

For Extra Help

Digital Video
Tutor CD 5
Videotape 7

InterAct
Math

Math Tutor
Center

MathXL

MyMathLab

a Determine whether the two pairs of numbers are proportional.

1. 5, 6 and 7, 9

2. 7, 5 and 6, 4

3. 1, 2 and 10, 20

4. 7, 3 and 21, 9

5. 4.5, 3.0 and 4.8, 3.2

6. 4.5, 3.8 and 6.7, 5.2

7. $5\frac{1}{3}$, $8\frac{1}{4}$ and $2\frac{1}{5}$, $9\frac{1}{2}$

8. $2\frac{1}{3}$, $3\frac{1}{2}$ and 14, 21

b Solve.

9. $\frac{8}{6} = \frac{x}{9}$

10. $\frac{x}{45} = \frac{20}{25}$

11. $\frac{x}{18} = \frac{10}{4}$

12. $\frac{8}{10} = \frac{n}{5}$

13. $\frac{t}{12} = \frac{5}{6}$

14. $\frac{12}{4} = \frac{x}{3}$

15. $\frac{6}{15} = \frac{8}{n}$

16. $\frac{10}{6} = \frac{5}{x}$

17. $\frac{n}{21} = \frac{10}{30}$

18. $\frac{2}{24} = \frac{x}{36}$

19. $\frac{24}{x} = \frac{16}{12}$

20. $\frac{7}{11} = \frac{2}{x}$

21. $\frac{6}{11} = \frac{12}{x}$

22. $\frac{8}{9} = \frac{32}{n}$

23. $\frac{20}{7} = \frac{60}{x}$

24. $\frac{5}{x} = \frac{4}{10}$

25. $\frac{7}{x} = \frac{9}{12}$

26. $\frac{x}{20} = \frac{16}{15}$

27. $\frac{x}{13} = \frac{2}{9}$

28. $\frac{1.2}{4} = \frac{x}{9}$

29. $\frac{0.15}{0.40} = \frac{t}{0.16}$

30. $\frac{x}{11} = \frac{7.1}{2}$

31. $\frac{80}{20} = \frac{20}{n}$

32. $\frac{35}{125} = \frac{7}{m}$

33. $\dfrac{28}{x} = \dfrac{7}{\frac{1}{4}}$

34. $\dfrac{x}{6} = \dfrac{1}{6}$

35. $\dfrac{\frac{1}{4}}{\frac{1}{2}} = \dfrac{\frac{1}{2}}{x}$

36. $\dfrac{1}{7} = \dfrac{x}{4\frac{1}{2}}$

37. $\dfrac{x}{\frac{4}{5}} = \dfrac{0}{\frac{9}{11}}$

38. $\dfrac{\frac{2}{7}}{\frac{3}{4}} = \dfrac{\frac{5}{6}}{y}$

39. $\dfrac{2\frac{1}{2}}{3\frac{1}{3}} = \dfrac{x}{4\frac{1}{4}}$

40. $\dfrac{5\frac{1}{5}}{6\frac{1}{6}} = \dfrac{y}{3\frac{1}{2}}$

41. $\dfrac{1.28}{3.76} = \dfrac{4.28}{y}$

42. $\dfrac{10.4}{12.4} = \dfrac{6.76}{t}$

43. $\dfrac{10\frac{3}{8}}{12\frac{2}{3}} = \dfrac{5\frac{3}{4}}{y}$

44. $\dfrac{12\frac{7}{8}}{20\frac{3}{4}} = \dfrac{5\frac{2}{3}}{y}$

45. $\mathbf{D_W}$ Instead of equating cross products, Melba solves $\frac{x}{7} = \frac{5}{3}$ (see Example 5) by multiplying on both sides by the least common denominator, 21. Is her approach a good one? Why or why not?

46. $\mathbf{D_W}$ An instructor predicts that a student's test grade will be proportional to the amount of time the student spends studying. What is meant by this? Write an example of a proportion that involves the grades of two students and their study times.

SKILL MAINTENANCE

Divide. Write decimal notation for the answer.   [5.4a]

47. $260 \div (-5)$

48. $395 \div (-20)$

49. $4648 \div 16$

50. $3427 \div 2.25$

Multiply.   [5.3a]

51. $\begin{array}{r} 4\,5.6\,7 \\ \times \quad\ 2.4 \\ \hline \end{array}$

52. $\begin{array}{r} 6\,7\,8.1\,9 \\ \times \quad\ 1\,0\,0 \\ \hline \end{array}$

53. $(-3.21)(-4.75)$

54. $(79.2)(-2.05)$

SYNTHESIS

55. $\mathbf{D_W}$ If a true proportion is formed using exactly three different nonzero numbers, what can you conclude about the number that is used twice? Why?

56. $\mathbf{D_W}$ Joaquin argues that $\frac{0}{0}$ is equal to $\frac{3}{4}$ because $0 \cdot 3 = 4 \cdot 0$. Is he correct? Why or why not?

Solve.

57. ▦ $\dfrac{1728}{5643} = \dfrac{836.4}{x}$

58. ▦ $\dfrac{328.56}{627.48} = \dfrac{y}{127.66}$

59. $\dfrac{x}{4} = \dfrac{x-1}{6}$

60. $\dfrac{x+3}{5} = \dfrac{x}{7}$

61. Use a sequence of steps—each of which can be justified—to show that for $a, b, c, d, \neq 0$,

$$\dfrac{a}{b} = \dfrac{c}{d} \quad \text{is equivalent to} \quad \dfrac{d}{b} = \dfrac{c}{a}.$$

Objective

a   Solve applied problems involving proportions.

1. Brian drives his delivery van 8000 mi in 5 months. At this rate, how far will he travel in a year?

a   Problem Solving

Proportions have applications in business, the natural and social sciences, medicine, home economics, and many other areas of daily life.

EXAMPLE 1 *Calories Burned.* Marv's stairmaster tells him that if he exercises for 24 min, he will burn 356 calories. How many calories will he burn if he exercises for 30 min?

Let n = the number of calories that Marv will burn in 30 min. Then we translate the given information to a proportion in which each side is the ratio of the number of calories burned to the number of minutes spent exercising.

$$\text{Calories burned in 30 min} \longrightarrow \frac{n}{30} = \frac{356}{24} \longleftarrow \text{Calories burned in 24 min}$$
$$\text{Time} \longrightarrow \qquad\qquad \longleftarrow \text{Time}$$

Each side of the equation represents the same ratio. It may help to verbalize the proportion as "The unknown number of calories is to 30 min, as 356 calories is to 24 min." We solve as follows:

A calculator can shorten these steps

$$24 \cdot n = 30 \cdot 356 \qquad \text{Equating cross products}$$

$$\frac{24n}{24} = \frac{30 \cdot 356}{24} \qquad \text{Dividing both sides by 24}$$

$$n = \frac{6 \cdot 5 \cdot 4 \cdot 89}{6 \cdot 4} \qquad \text{Factoring}$$

$$= 5 \cdot 89 \qquad \text{Removing a factor equal to 1: } \frac{6 \cdot 4}{6 \cdot 4} = 1$$

$$= 445.$$

As a partial check, note that 30 is greater than 24 and, as expected, 445 is greater than 356. Marv will burn 445 calories in 30 min.

Do Exercise 1.

Answer on page A-23

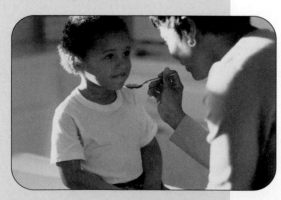

Proportion problems can be solved in more than one way. For Example 1, any one of the following equations could have been used:

$$\frac{356}{24} = \frac{n}{30}, \qquad \frac{30}{n} = \frac{24}{356}, \qquad \frac{30}{24} = \frac{n}{356}, \qquad \frac{356}{n} = \frac{24}{30}.$$

EXAMPLE 2 *Nursing.* To control a fever, a doctor suggests that a child weighing 28 kg be given 420 mg of Tylenol™. Under similar circumstances, how much Tylenol™ could be recommended for a child weighing 35 kg?

We let t = the number of milligrams of Tylenol™ recommended for a 35 kg child. Then we form and solve a proportion:

$$\text{Tylenol suggested} \longrightarrow \frac{420}{28} = \frac{t}{35} \longleftarrow \text{Tylenol suggested}$$
$$\text{Child's weight} \longrightarrow \qquad\qquad \longleftarrow \text{Child's weight}$$

$$420 \cdot 35 = 28 \cdot t \qquad \text{Equating cross products}$$

$$\frac{420 \cdot 35}{28} = \frac{28t}{28} \qquad \text{Dividing both sides by 28}$$

$$\frac{\cancel{4} \cdot 105 \cdot 5 \cdot \cancel{7}}{\cancel{4} \cdot \cancel{7}} = t \qquad \text{Removing a factor equal to 1: } \frac{4 \cdot 7}{4 \cdot 7} = 1$$

$$525 = t.$$

Thus, 525 mg could be recommended for a 35-kg child.

Do Exercise 2.

EXAMPLE 3 *Ticket Purchases.* Stacy bought 8 tickets to an international food festival for $52. How many tickets can she purchase with $90?

We let $n =$ the number of tickets that can be purchased with $90. Then we translate to a proportion and solve:

$$\text{Cost} \longrightarrow \frac{52}{8} = \frac{90}{n} \longleftarrow \text{Cost}$$
$$\text{Tickets} \longrightarrow \qquad \qquad \longleftarrow \text{Tickets}$$

$$52n = 8 \cdot 90 \qquad \text{Equating cross products}$$

$$n = \frac{8 \cdot 90}{52} \qquad \text{Dividing both sides by 52}$$

$$\approx 13.8 . \qquad \text{Simplifying and rounding}$$

Because it is impossible to buy a fractional part of a ticket, we must round the answer *down* to 13. As a check, we use a different approach: We find the cost per ticket and then divide $90 by that price. Since $52 \div 8 = 6.50$ and $90 \div 6.50 \approx 13.8$, we have a check. Stacy can purchase 13 tickets with $90.

Do Exercise 3.

EXAMPLE 4 *Waist-to-Hip Ratio.* For improved health, it is recommended that a woman's waist-to-hip ratio be at most 0.85 (for men, see Margin Exercise 4.) Marta's hip measurement is 40 in. To meet the recommendation, what should Marta's waist measurement be?
Source: David Schmidt, "Lifting Weight Myths," *Nutrition Action Newsletter* 20, no. 4, October 1993.

Hip measurement is the largest measurement around the widest part of the buttocks.

Waist measurement is the smallest measurement below the ribs but above the navel.

Note that $0.85 = \frac{85}{100}$. We let $w =$ Marta's waist measurement, translate to a proportion, and solve:

$$\text{Waist measurement} \longrightarrow \frac{w}{40} = \frac{85}{100} \longleftarrow \text{Recommended}$$
$$\text{Hip measurement} \longrightarrow \qquad \qquad \text{waist-to-hip ratio}$$

$$100w = 40 \cdot 85 \qquad \text{Equating cross products}$$

$$w = \frac{40 \cdot 85}{100} \qquad \text{Dividing both sides by 100}$$

$$= 34.$$

Marta's recommended waist measurement is 34 in. (or less).

Do Exercise 4.

2. **House Painting.** Campus Painting, Inc., can paint 1700 ft² of clapboard with 4 gal of paint. How much paint would be needed for a building with 6800 ft² of clapboard?

3. **Purchasing Shirts.** If 2 shirts can be bought for $47, how many shirts can be bought with $200?

4. **Waist-to-Hip Ratio.** It is recommended that a man's waist-to-hip ratio be 0.95 (or lower). Uri's hip measurement is 45 in. To meet the recommendation, what should Uri's waist measurement be?

Answers on page A-23

Answer on page A-23

5. Estimating a Deer Population. To determine the number of deer in a forest, a conservationist catches 612 deer, tags them, and releases them. Later, 244 deer are caught, and it is found that 72 of them are tagged. Estimate how many deer are in the forest.

Study Tips

AVOIDING TEMPTATION

Be kind to yourself when studying—in a supportive way. For example, sit in a comfortable chair in a well-lit location, but stay away from a coffee shop where friends may stop by. Once you begin studying, let the answering machine answer the phone, shut off any cell phones, and do not check e-mail during your study session.

EXAMPLE 5 *Estimating a Wildlife Population.* To determine the number of fish in a pond, a conservationist catches 225 fish, tags them, and releases them back into the pond. Later, 108 fish are caught, and 15 of them are found to be tagged. Estimate how many fish are in the pond.

For more complicated problems like this, our five-step problem-solving approach is helpful.

1. **Familiarize.** Our strategy is to form two different ratios which can be used to represent the ratio of tagged fish to all fish in the pond. One way to write such a ratio is simply *Number of tagged fish/Number of fish in pond*. A second way to represent this ratio assumes that the tagged fish become uniformly distributed throughout the pond. We then form the ratio *Number of tagged fish caught/Total number of fish caught*.

2. **Translate.** We translate to a proportion as follows:

$$\text{Fish tagged originally} \rightarrow \frac{225}{F} = \frac{15}{108}. \leftarrow \text{Tagged fish caught later}$$
$$\text{Fish in lake} \rightarrow \phantom{\frac{225}{F}} \phantom{\frac{15}{108}} \leftarrow \text{Fish caught later}$$

3. **Solve.** Next, we solve the proportion:

$$225 \cdot 108 = F \cdot 15 \qquad \text{Equating cross products}$$

$$\frac{225 \cdot 108}{15} = \frac{F \cdot 15}{15} \qquad \text{Dividing both sides by 15}$$

$$\frac{225 \cdot 108}{15} = F$$

$$1620 = F. \qquad \text{Multiplying and dividing}$$

4. **Check.** We substitute into the proportion and check cross products:

$$\frac{225}{1620} = \frac{15}{108};$$

$$225 \cdot 108 = 24,300; \qquad 1620 \cdot 15 = 24,300.$$

The cross products are the same.

5. **State.** We estimate that there are 1620 fish in the lake.

Do Exercise 5.

a Solve.

1. *Waterproofing.* Florence can waterproof 450 ft² of decking with 2 gal of sealant. How many gallons should Florence buy for a 1200-ft² deck?

2. *Painting.* Helen can spray 950 ft² with 2 gal of paint. How many 1-gal cans does she need in order to spray a building with 30,000 ft² of exterior walls?

3. *Complete™ Cereal.* The nutritional chart on the side of a box of Kellogg's Complete™ Cereal states that there are 90 calories in a $\frac{3}{4}$-cup serving. How many calories are there in 5 cups of the cereal?

4. *Coco Wheats® Cereal.* The nutritional chart on the side of a box of Little Crow Foods' Coco Wheats® Cereal states that there are 200 calories in $\frac{1}{3}$ cup of precooked mix. How many calories are there in 4 cups of the mix?

Source: Kellogg's

Source: Little Crow Foods

5. *Overweight Americans.* A study recently confirmed that of every 100 Americans, 60 are considered overweight. There were 281 million Americans in 2001. How many would have been considered overweight?
Source: U.S. Centers for Disease Control

6. *Cancer Death Rate in Illinois.* It is predicted that for every 1000 people in the state of Illinois, 130.9 will die of cancer. The population of Chicago is about 2,721,547. How many of these people will die of cancer?
Source: New York Times Almanac 2001

7. *Study Time and Test Grades.* An English instructor believes that students' test grades are directly proportional to the amount of time spent studying. Lisa studies 9 hr for a particular test and gets a score of 75. At this rate, for how many hours would she need to study to get a score of 92?

8. *Study Time and Test Grades.* A mathematics instructor insists that students' test grades are directly proportional to the amount of time spent studying. Brent studies 15 hr for a final exam and gets a score of 85. At this rate, what score would he have received if he had studied 16 hr?

9. *Turkey Servings.* An 8-lb turkey breast contains 36 servings of meat. How many pounds of turkey breast would be needed for 54 servings?

10. *Bicycling.* Roy bicycled 234 mi in 14 days. At this rate, how far would Roy travel in 42 days?

11. *Snow to Water.* Under typical conditions, $1\frac{1}{2}$ ft of snow will melt to 2 in. of water. To how many inches of water will $5\frac{1}{2}$ ft of snow melt?

12. *Grading.* A professor must grade 32 essays in a literature class. She can grade 5 essays in 40 min. At this rate, how long will it take her to grade all 32 essays?

13. *Map Scaling.* On a map, $\frac{1}{4}$ in. represents 50 mi. If two cities are $3\frac{1}{4}$ in. apart on the map, how far apart are they in reality?

14. *Map Scaling.* On a road atlas map, 1 in. represents 16.6 mi. If two cities are 3.5 in. apart on the map, how far apart are they in reality?

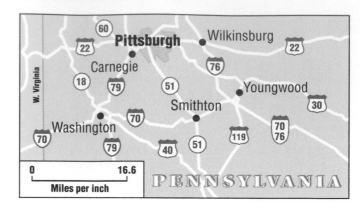

15. Halo grass seed is sold in 1-lb bags. Each bag covers 800 ft^2 of lawn. How many bags must be purchased in order to cover a 4300-ft^2 lawn?

16. At the Bertocinis' church, two pews can seat 14 people. How many pews will be needed for a wedding party of 44 people?

17. *Coffee Production.* Coffee beans from 14 trees are required to produce the 17 lb of coffee that the average person in the United States drinks each year. How many trees are required to produce 375 lb of coffee?

18. *Class Size.* Pane College advertises that its student-to-faculty ratio is 14 to 1. If 56 students register for Introductory Spanish, how many sections of the course would you expect to see offered?

19. *Sugaring.* When 76 gal of maple sap are boiled down, the result is 2 gal of maple syrup. How much sap is needed to produce 9 gal of syrup?

20. *Quality Control.* A quality-control inspector examined 100 lightbulbs and found 7 of them to be defective. At this rate, how many defective bulbs will there be in a lot of 2500?

21. *Lefties.* In a class of 40 students, on average, 6 will be left-handed. If a class includes 9 "lefties," how many students would you estimate are in the class?

22. *Metallurgy.* In a certain metal alloy, the ratio of zinc to copper is 3 to 13. If there are 520 lb of copper, how many pounds of zinc are there?

23. *Fuel Economy.* Harold's Toyota Echo can travel 380 mi on 8 gal of gas. How much gas will be needed to drive 95 mi?

24. *Fuel Economy.* Jolene's 1992 Tercel can travel 190 mi on 5 gal of gas. How much gas will be needed to drive 285 mi?

25. *Estimating a Deer Population.* To determine the number of deer in a wildlife preserve, a forest ranger catches 159 deer, tags them, and releases them. Later, 84 deer are caught, and it is found that 28 of them are tagged. Estimate how many deer are in the wildlife preserve.

26. *Estimating a Trout Population.* To determine the number of trout in a lake, a conservationist catches 112 trout, tags them, and releases them back into the lake. Later, 82 trout are caught, and it is found that 32 of them are tagged. Estimate how many trout there are in the lake.

27. *Estimating a Bear Population.* To determine the number of bears in a state forest, a park ranger catches 20 bears, tags them, and releases them. Later, 16 bears are caught, 5 of which have tags. Estimate how many bears are in the forest.

28. *Estimating a Raccoon Population.* To determine the size of an island's raccoon population, a naturalist catches, tags, and releases 25 raccoons. Later, 20 raccoons are caught, of which 5 have tags. Estimate the size of the raccoon population.

29. **D**$_W$ Can unit prices be used to solve proportions that involve money? Why or why not?

30. **D**$_W$ Polly solved Example 3 by forming the proportion

$$\frac{90}{52} = \frac{n}{8},$$

whereas Rudy wrote

$$\frac{52}{n} = \frac{90}{8}.$$

Are both approaches valid? Why or why not?

SKILL MAINTENANCE

Find the prime factorization of each number. [3.2c]

31. 808   **32.** 28   **33.** 866   **34.** 93   **35.** 2020

36. Multiply: $-19.3(4.1)$. [5.3a]

37. Divide: $-13.11 \div 5.7$. [5.4a]

38. Divide: $169.36 \div (-23.2)$. [5.4a]

39. Add: $-19.7 + 12.5$. [5.2c]

40. Subtract: $-3.7 - (-1.9)$. [5.2c]

41. **D**_W Examine Exercises 27 and 28. Which of the estimates do you think is more reliable? Why?

42. **D**_W Rob's waist and hips measure 35 in. and 33 in., respectively (see Margin Exercise 4). Suppose that Rob can either gain or lose 1 in. from one of his measurements. Where should the inch come from or go to? Why?

43. ▦ *Exchanging Money.* On 25 January, 2003, 1 U.S. dollar was worth about 1.69 Australian dollars.
Source: xe.com

a) How much would 250 U.S. dollars be worth in Australian dollars?
b) Derek was traveling in Australia and bought a sweatshirt that cost 50 Australian dollars. How much would it cost in U.S. dollars?

44. ▦ *Exchanging Money.* On 25 January, 2003, 1 U.S. dollar was worth about 0.612 British pound.
Source: xe.com

a) How much would 250 U.S. dollars be worth in British pounds?
b) Brittany was traveling in England and bought a bicycle that cost 320 British pounds. How much would it cost in U.S. dollars?

45. ▦ Carney College is expanding from 850 to 1050 students. To avoid any rise in the student-to-faculty ratio, the faculty of 69 professors must also increase. How many new faculty positions should be created?

46. ▦ In recognition of her outstanding work, Sheri's salary has been increased from $26,000 to $29,380. Tim is earning $23,000 and is requesting a proportional raise. How much more should he ask for?

47. *Baseball Statistics.* Cy Young, one of the greatest baseball pitchers of all time, gave up an average of 2.63 earned runs every 9 innings. Young pitched 7356 innings, the most in the history of baseball. How many earned runs did he give up?

48. ▦ *Real-Estate Values.* According to Coldwell Banker Real Estate Corporation, a home selling for $189,000 in Austin, Texas, would sell for $665,795 in San Francisco. How much would a $450,000 home in San Francisco sell for in Austin? Round to the nearest $1000.
Source: Coldwell Banker Real Estate Corporation

49. ▦ The ratio 1:3:2 is used to estimate the relative costs of a CD player, receiver, and speakers when shopping for a stereo. That is, the receiver should cost three times the amount spent on the CD player and the speakers should cost twice as much as the amount spent on the CD player. If you had $800 to spend, how would you allocate the money, using this ratio?

7.5

GEOMETRIC APPLICATIONS

a Proportions and Similar Triangles

Look at the pair of triangles below. Note that they appear to have the same shape, but their sizes are different. These are examples of **similar triangles.** By using a magnifying glass, you could imagine enlarging the smaller triangle to get the larger. This process works because the corresponding sides of each triangle have the same ratio. That is, the following proportion is true.

$$\frac{a}{d} = \frac{b}{e} = \frac{c}{f}$$

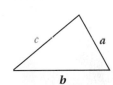
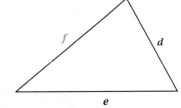

SIMILAR TRIANGLES

Similar triangles have the same shape. The lengths of their corresponding sides have the same ratio—that is, they are proportional.

■ **EXAMPLE 1** The triangles below are similar triangles. Find the unknown length x.

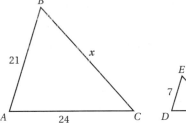

The ratio of x to 9 is the same as the ratio of 24 to 8 or 21 to 7. We get the proportions

$$\frac{x}{9} = \frac{24}{8} \quad \text{and} \quad \frac{x}{9} = \frac{21}{7}. \qquad \text{Other proportions could also be used.}$$

We can solve either one of these proportions. We use the first:

$$\frac{x}{9} = 3 \qquad \text{Simplifying}$$

$$x = 3 \cdot 9 \qquad \text{Multiplying both sides by 9}$$

$$= 27. \qquad \text{Simplifying}$$

As a check, note that each of the sides in the larger triangle is three times the length of the corresponding side in the smaller triangle. The missing length x is 27.

Do Exercise 1.

Objectives

a Find lengths of sides of similar triangles using proportions.

b Use proportions to find lengths in pairs of figures that differ only in size.

---

1. This pair of triangles is similar. Find the unknown length x.

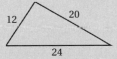

Answer on page A-23

Study Tips

MAKING SKETCHES

One need not be an artist to make highly useful mathematical sketches. That said, it is important to make sure that your sketches are drawn accurately enough to represent the relative sizes within each shape. For example, if one side of a triangle is clearly the longest, make sure your drawing reflects this.

2. Rodin's most famous sculpture, *The Thinker*, was originally 28 in. high. If the man's head on that version was 6 in. long, how long would the head be in the more famous 79 in. rendition? Round to the nearest tenth of an inch.

Source: www.cantorfoundation.org

Similar triangles and proportions are often used to compute lengths that would ordinarily be difficult to measure. For example, we could find the height of a flagpole without climbing it or the distance across a river without crossing it.

■ **EXAMPLE 2** *Sculpture.* The works of the great sculptor Auguste Rodin were so popular that he arranged to have enlarged or reduced copies produced of many pieces. Using a Collas machine, Rodin's assistants were able to create a proportionately larger or smaller duplicate of the original sculpture.

Source: www.cantorfoundation.org

Suppose a Collas machine is used to enlarge a statue that is 35 cm tall into one that is 50 cm tall. If the original statue includes a forearm that is 4 cm long, how long will the forearm be in the enlargement?

We let l = the length of the enlarged forearm, in centimeters. Then we translate to a proportion and solve:

$$\begin{array}{c}\text{Length of} \\ \text{enlarged forearm} \rightarrow \\ \text{Height of} \rightarrow \\ \text{enlarged statue}\end{array} \quad \frac{l}{50} = \frac{4}{35} \quad \begin{array}{c}\leftarrow \text{Length of} \\ \text{original forearm} \\ \leftarrow \text{Height of} \\ \text{original statue}\end{array}$$

$$35 \cdot l = 4 \cdot 50 \qquad \text{Equating cross products}$$

$$l = \frac{4 \cdot 50}{35} \qquad \text{Dividing both sides by 35}$$

$$l \approx 5.7. \qquad \begin{array}{l}\text{Simplifying and rounding to} \\ \text{the nearest tenth}\end{array}$$

As a partial check, note that, as expected, the length of the enlarged forearm is longer than the length of the original forearm. The enlarged forearm will be about 5.7 cm long.

Do Exercise 2.

Answer on page A-23

EXAMPLE 3 *F-106 Blueprint.* A blueprint for an F-106 Delta Dart jet is a scale drawing. A wing that is actually 19.2 ft wide is 0.447 ft wide on the blueprint. Find the length of side *a* of the wing.

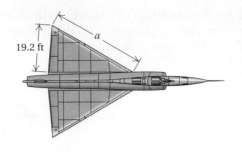

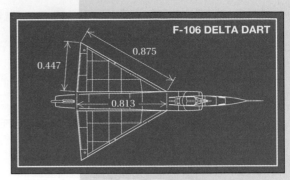

We let *a* = the length of the wing. Then we form a proportion and solve:

$$\text{Length on the blueprint} \rightarrow \frac{0.447}{19.2} = \frac{0.875}{a} \leftarrow \text{Length on the blueprint}$$
$$\text{Length of the wing} \rightarrow \qquad\qquad\qquad \leftarrow \text{Length of the wing}$$

$$0.447 \cdot a = 19.2 \cdot 0.875 \qquad \text{Equating cross products}$$

$$a = \frac{19.2 \cdot 0.875}{0.447} \qquad \text{Dividing both sides by 0.447}$$

$$\approx 37.6 \text{ ft.}$$

The length of side *a* of the wing is about 37.6 ft.

Do Exercise 3.

b Proportions and Geometric Shapes

When one geometric figure is a magnification of another, the figures are similar. Thus, the corresponding lengths are proportional.

EXAMPLE 4 The sides in the negative and the photograph shown are proportional. Find the width of the photograph.

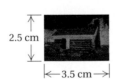

We let *x* = the width of the photograph. Then we translate to a proportion and solve:

$$\text{Photo width} \rightarrow \frac{x}{2.5} = \frac{10.5}{3.5} \leftarrow \text{Photo length}$$
$$\text{Negative width} \rightarrow \qquad\qquad\qquad \leftarrow \text{Negative length}$$

$$\frac{x}{2.5} = 3 \qquad \text{Simplifying}$$

$$x = 3(2.5) \qquad \text{Multiplying both sides by 2.5}$$

$$= 7.5. \qquad \text{Simplifying}$$

Thus the width of the photograph is 7.5 cm.

Do Exercise 4.

3. F-106 Blueprint. Refer to Example 3. Find the length of the wing's side that is attached to the plane's main body.

4. The sides in the photographs below are proportional. Find the width of the larger photograph.

Answers on page A-23

5. Refer to the figures in Example 5. If a model skylight is 3 cm wide, how wide will the actual skylight be?

EXAMPLE 5 A scale model of an addition to an athletic facility is 12 cm wide at the base and rises to a height of 15 cm. If the actual base is to be 116 ft, what will be the actual height of the addition?

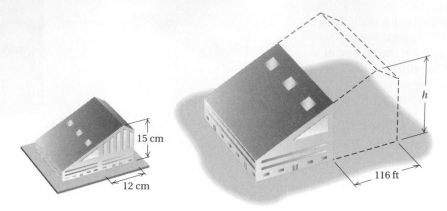

15 cm

12 cm

116 ft

h

We let h = the height, in feet, of the addition. Then we translate to a proportion and solve:

Width in model → $\dfrac{12}{116} = \dfrac{15}{h}$ ← Height in model
Actual width →   ← Actual height

$$12h = 116 \cdot 15 \qquad \text{Equating cross products}$$

$$h = \frac{116 \cdot 15}{12} \qquad \text{Dividing both sides by 12}$$

$$= \frac{4 \cdot 29 \cdot 3 \cdot 5}{4 \cdot 3} \qquad \text{Removing a factor equal to 1: } \frac{4 \cdot 3}{4 \cdot 3} = 1$$

$$= 145. \qquad \text{Multiplying}$$

As a partial check, note that $h > 116$, as expected. The height of the addition will be 145 ft.

Do Exercise 5.

Answer on page A-23

a   The triangles in each exercise are similar. Find the unknown lengths.

1.

2.

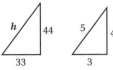

3.

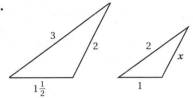

4.

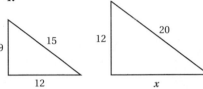

5.

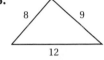

6.

7.

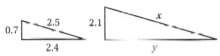

8.

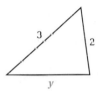

9. How tall is a flagpole that casts a 56-ft shadow at the same time that a 6-ft man casts a 5-ft shadow?

10. How tall is a billboard that casts a 45-ft shadow at the same time that a 5.5-ft woman casts a 10-ft shadow?

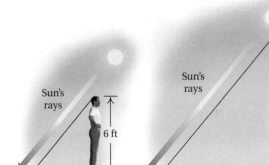

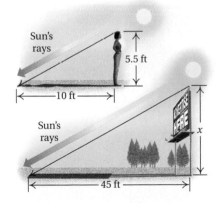

11. How tall is a flagpole that casts a 42-ft shadow at the same time that a $5\frac{1}{2}$-ft woman casts a 7-ft shadow?

12. When a tree 8 m tall casts a shadow 5 m long, how long is the shadow cast by a man who is 2 m tall?

13. How tall is a tree that casts a 32-ft shadow at the same time that an 8-ft light pole casts a 9-ft shadow?

14. How tall is a tree that casts a 27-ft shadow at the same time that a 4-ft fence post casts a 3-ft shadow?

15. Find the length L of the lake.

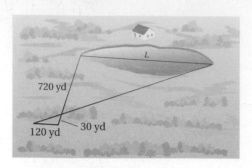

720 yd

L

120 yd   30 yd

16. Find the height h of the wall.

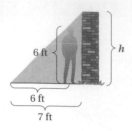

6 ft

h

6 ft

7 ft

17. To measure the height of a cliff, a string is drawn tight from level ground to the top of the cliff. A 3-ft stick is placed under the string, touching it at point P, a distance of 5 ft from point G where the string touches the ground. The string is then detached and found to be 120 ft long. How high is the cliff?

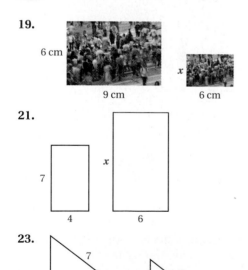

120 ft

h

5 ft

P

G

3 ft

18. Find the distance across the river. Assume that the ratio of d to 25 ft is the same as the ratio of 40 ft to 10 ft.

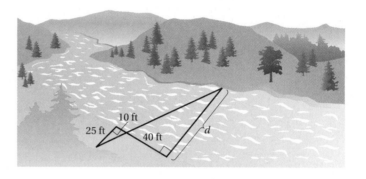

10 ft

25 ft   40 ft

d

b The sides in each pair of figures are proportional. Find the unknown lengths.

19.

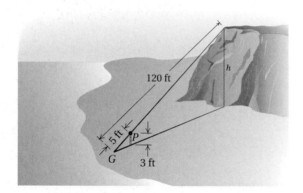

6 cm

x

9 cm   6 cm

20.

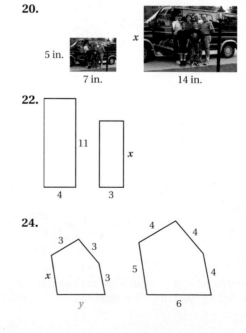

x

5 in.

7 in.   14 in.

21.

7

x

4   6

22.

11

x

4   3

23.

7

8

4

4

y

x

z

3

24.

3   3

x

3

y

4   4

5

4

6

25.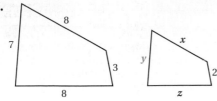

26.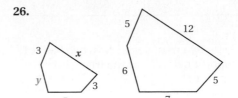

27.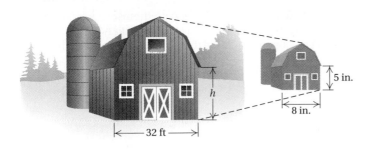

28.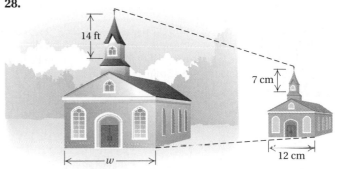

29. A scale model of an addition to an athletic facility is 15 cm wide at the base and rises to a height of 19 cm. If the actual base is to be 120 ft, what will be the height of the addition?

30. Refer to the figures in Exercise 29. If a model skylight is 3 cm wide, how wide will the actual skylight be?

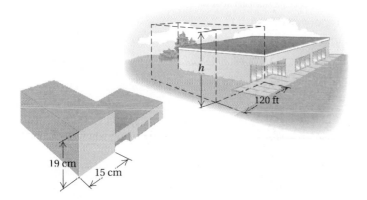

31. **D**_W Design a problem for a classmate to solve (see Exercises 9–18) so that the solution is "The height of the sail is 12 ft."

32. **D**_W Design a problem for a classmate to solve (see Exercises 27–30) so that the solution is "The new building's windows will be 8 ft tall."

33. Kathy has $34.97 to spend for a book costing $49.95, a CD costing $14.88, and a sweatshirt costing $29.95. How much more money does she need to make these purchases? [5.8a]

34. Divide: $80.892 \div 8.4$. [5.4a]

Multiply. [5.3a]

35. -8.4×80.892

36. 0.01×274.568

37. 100×274.568

38. $-0.002(-274.568)$

39. 0.01×459

40. 0.01×723

41. **Dw** Is it possible for two triangles to have two pairs of sides that are proportional without the triangles being similar? Why or why not?

42. **Dw** Suppose that all the sides in one triangle are half the size of the corresponding sides in a similar triangle. Does it follow that the area of the smaller triangle is half the area of the larger triangle? Why or why not?

Hockey Goals. An official hockey goal is 6 ft wide. To make scoring more difficult, goalies often locate themselves far in front of the goal to "cut down the angle." In Exercises 43 and 44, suppose that a slapshot from point *A* is attempted and that the goalie is 2.7 ft wide. Determine how far from the goal the goalie should be located if point *A* is the given distance from the goal. (*Hint*: First find how far the goalie should be from point *A*.)

43. 🖩 25 ft

44. 🖩 35 ft

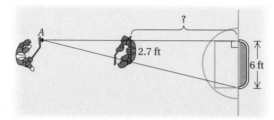

🖩 The triangles in each exercise are similar triangles. Find the lengths not given.

45.

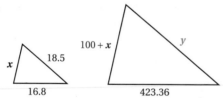

46.

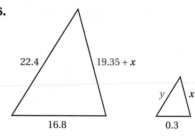

47. 🖩 A miniature basketball hoop is built for the model referred to in Example 5. An actual hoop is 10 ft high. How high should the model hoop be? Round to the nearest thousandth of a centimeter.

48. 🖩 A miniature baseball diamond is drawn to accompany the model used in Example 5. If the actual baseball diamond is a 90-ft by 90-ft square, what will the area of the model diamond be?

49. **Dw** Design for a classmate a problem involving similar triangles for which

$$\frac{18}{128.95} = \frac{x}{789.89}.$$

The review that follows is meant to prepare you for a chapter exam. It consists of two parts. The first part is a checklist of some of the Study Tips referred to in this and preceding chapters. The second part is the Review Exercises. These provide practice exercises for the exam, together with references to section objectives so you can go back and review. Before beginning, stop and look back over the skills you have obtained. What skills in mathematics do you have now that you did not have before studying this chapter?

STUDY TIPS CHECKLIST

The foundation of all your study skills is TIME!

☐ Have you given careful consideration to your course selections and workload for next semester?

☐ Have you tried using audio cassettes as a study aid?

☐ If something seems incorrect in your notes, have you consulted with your instructor?

☐ Are you minimizing the likelihood of distraction during your study sessions?

☐ Are you making sure that your drawings are accurate enough to represent the problem being solved?

REVIEW EXERCISES

1. Write fraction notation for the ratio 21 to 73.   [7.1a]

2. In this rectangle, find the ratio of length to width and simplify.   [7.1b]

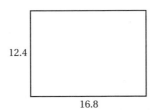

3. It takes approximately 10 min to download 24 MB of catalog photos using an online DSL service, and about 96 min using a dial-up connection with a 56K modem (running at 32 kilobytes per second). Write simplified fraction notation for the ratio of dial-up time required to DSL time required.   [7.1a, b]
Source: Verizon, Inc.

4. Scott ran the 26.2-mi Portland Marathon in 4 hr. What was his rate in miles per hour? in hours per mile?   [7.2a]

5. Dev kayaked the $\frac{1}{2}$-mi distance to Summerlake Park in 9.6 min. What was his rate in minutes per mile?   [7.2a]

6. A 16-oz brick of Tillamook sharp cheddar is on sale for $3.44. Find the unit price in dollars per ounce.   [7.2b]

7. Which has the lower unit cost?   [7.2b]

ORANGE JUICE (not from concentrate)
128-oz plastic container for $4.49
64-oz carton, 2 for $5

8. Determine whether the pairs 17, 3 and 119, 21 are proportional.   [7.3a]

Solve. [7.3b]

9. $\dfrac{15}{6} = \dfrac{x}{2}$

10. $\dfrac{9}{8} = \dfrac{6}{x}$

11. $\dfrac{\frac{5}{7}}{x} = \dfrac{15}{9}$

12. $\dfrac{3.6}{48} = \dfrac{1.5}{x}$

Solve. [7.4a]

13. If 2 six-packs of cream soda cost $3.50, how much will 5 six-packs cost?

14. A clothing inspector found that out of 75 pairs of shoes, 12 pairs were flawed. At this rate, how many flawed pairs would you expect to find in a batch of 500 pairs of the shoes?

15. An acting teacher reserves 9 copies of *The Complete Works of William Shakespeare* for her class. If the ratio of books to students is 3 to 5, how many students are in the class?

16. Madeline drove her car 165 mi in 3 hr. At this rate, how far would she travel in 5 hr? What is her speed?

17. A city measure in Oregon proposed that homeowners be taxed 39 cents per every $1000 of property value to help maintain parks and to fund recreation programs. How much would the owner of a $135,000 home pay?

18. A television-viewer rating of 20.5 indicates that 219,145 households are tuned to a show. How many households are tuned to a show with a rating of 15.1?
Source: KGW-TV

Each pair of triangles in Exercises 19 and 20 is similar. Find the unknown length. [7.5a]

19.

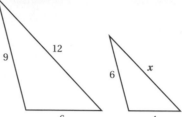

20.

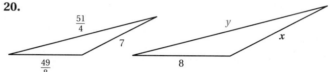

21. How tall is a man who casts a 180-cm shadow at the same time that a woman 174-cm tall casts a 160-cm shadow? [7.5a]

22. The lengths in the figures are proportional. Find the unknown lengths. [7.5b]

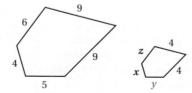

23. Raija has $1937.09 in her checking account. If she writes a check for $209.37 and another for $19.85, how much will she have left in her account?   [5.8a]

24. In which quadrant is each point located?   [6.3b]

$(2, 15)$, $(-12, -7)$, $(-8, 1)$, and $(7, -3)$

25. Multiply: $-21.7(-28.3)$.   [5.3a]

26. Divide. Write decimal notation for the answer.   [5.4a]

$$3\,4.2\,\overline{)\,6\,1\,2.1\,8}$$

27. **D**_W Write a proportion problem for a classmate to solve. Design the problem so that the solution is "Claire drove 418 mi with 22 gal of gasoline."   [7.4a]

28. **D**_W If you were a college president, which would you prefer: a low or high faculty-to-student ratio? Why? What about the student-to-faculty ratio?   [7.1a]

State Areas.   The following table shows the areas of selected states. Use the information for Exercises 29–32.

STATE	LAND AREA (square miles)	WATER AREA (square miles)
Alaska	570,374	86,051
Texas	261,914	6687
California	155,973	7734
Montana	145,556	1490
New Mexico	121,365	234
Arizona	113,642	364
Nevada	109,806	761
Colorado	103,730	371
Oregon	96,003	2383
Wyoming	97,105	714
Maine	30,865	4523
Massachusetts	7838	2717
Vermont	9249	366
New Hampshire	8969	382
Connecticut	4845	698
Rhode Island	1045	500

Source: www.netstate.com

29. What is the ratio of land area to water area in Alaska? of Alaska's water area to the state's total area?   [7.1a]

30. What is the ratio of the largest land area to the smallest land area? of the largest water area to the smallest water area?   [7.1a]

31. The population of California was 33,871,648 in 2000. If water area were excluded from the calculation, what would be the population density for California?   [7.2a]
Source: U.S. Census Bureau

32. The population of Vermont was 608,827 in 2000. If water area were excluded from the calculation, what would be the population density?   [7.2a]
Source: U.S. Census Bureau

33. Sari is making beaded bracelets from purple beads and lavender beads. If the ratio of purple to lavender beads is 3 to 5 and each bracelet contains 40 beads, how many bracelets can Sari make from 60 purple beads? How many lavender beads will she need?   [7.4a]

34. A medical insurance claims service analyst can type 8500 keystrokes per hour. At this rate, how many minutes would 34,000 keystrokes require?   [7.4a]
Source: www.or.regence.com

35. Shine-and-Glo Painters uses 2 gal of finishing paint for every 3 gal of primer. Each gallon of finishing paint covers 450 ft². If a surface of 4950 ft² needs both primer and finishing paint, how many gallons should be purchased altogether?   [7.4a]

Write fraction notation for each ratio. Do not simplify.

1. 21 to 17

2. 0.37 to 89

3. Simplify the ratio of length to width in this rectangle.

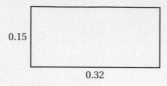

0.15

0.32

4. A diver descends 10 ft in 16 sec. What is the rate of descent in feet per second?

5. In 1 hr 20 min, a bicycle racer biked 48 km. What was the racer's rate, or speed, in minutes per kilometer?

6. An 18-oz jar of blackberry jam is on sale for $4.50. Find the unit price in dollars per ounce.

7. Determine whether the pairs 10, 8 and 38, 26 are proportional.

Solve.

8. $\dfrac{x}{18} = \dfrac{7}{2}$

9. $\dfrac{4.8}{3} = \dfrac{92}{x}$

10. An ocean liner traveled 432 km in 12 hr. At this rate, how far would the boat travel in 42 hr?

11. Angie's alarm clock loses 0.6 min in 10 hr. At this rate, how much will it lose in 24 hr?

12. On a map, 3 in. represents 225 mi. If two cities are 7 in. apart on the map, how far are they apart in reality?

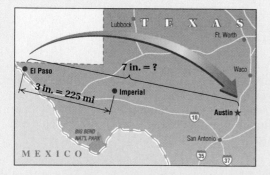

13. A birdhouse built on a pole that is 3 m high casts a shadow 5 m long. At the same time, the shadow of a monument is 110 m long. How high is the monument?

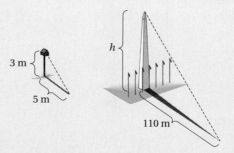

The lengths in each pair of figures are proportional. Find the missing lengths.

14.

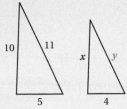

15.

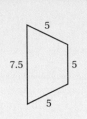 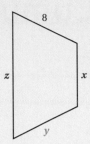

16. According to a 2001 study, annual federal and state government smoking-caused Medicaid payments totaled $23.5 billion, of which the federal share was $13.4 billion. How much was the state share?
Source: www.tobaccofreekids.org

17. In which quadrant is each point located?
$$(6, -12), (-10, -8), (-15, 2), \text{ and } (37, 18)$$

18. Multiply: $287.3(-24.1)$.

19. Divide: $\dfrac{38.48}{-2.6}$.

Solve.

20. $\dfrac{x + 3}{4} - \dfrac{5x + 2}{8}$

21. $\dfrac{4 - 6x}{5} = \dfrac{x + 3}{2}$

22. Lara needs 3 balls of burgundy yarn and $2\frac{1}{2}$ balls of black yarn to knit a sweater. She buys 10 balls of the black yarn. How much burgundy yarn does she need and how many sweaters can she knit?

23. The Johnson triplets and the Solomini twins went out to dinner and decided to split the bill of $79.85 proportionately. How much will the Johnsons pay?

24. Find the width of the river in the following diagram.

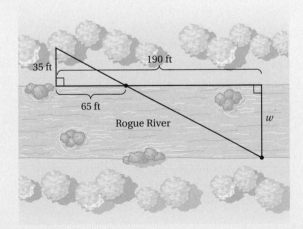

25. A soccer goalie wishing to block an opponent's shot moves toward the shooter to reduce the shooter's view of the goal. If the goalie can only defend a region 10 ft wide, how far in front of the goal should the goalie be? (See the following figure.)

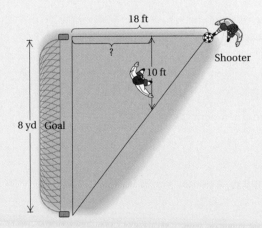

Add and simplify.

1.
$$
\begin{array}{r}
1\,3\,7.1\,8\,6 \\
2\,3.0\,1\,9 \\
+\ 4\,8\,3.2\,9\,7 \\
\hline
\end{array}
$$

2.
$$
\begin{array}{r}
3\dfrac{4}{5} \\
+\ 8\dfrac{7}{10} \\
\hline
\end{array}
$$

3. $\dfrac{6}{35} + \dfrac{5}{28}$

Perform the indicated operation and, if possible, simplify.

4.
$$
\begin{array}{r}
1\,9\,3\,5.0\,5 \\
-\ \ \ \ \ \ 6\,6.8\,3\,4 \\
\hline
\end{array}
$$

5. $-32 - (-15)$

6. $\dfrac{4}{15} - \dfrac{3}{20}$

7.
$$
\begin{array}{r}
3\,7.6\,4 \\
\times\ \ \ \ \ 5.9 \\
\hline
\end{array}
$$

8. $-43(15)$

9. $7\dfrac{4}{5} \cdot 3\dfrac{1}{2}$

10. $2.3\,\overline{)\,9\,8.9}$

11. $-306 \div 6$

12. $\dfrac{7}{11} \div \dfrac{14}{33}$

13. Write expanded notation for 30,074.

14. Write a word name for 120.07 .

Which number is larger?

15. 0.7,　0.698

16. $-0.799,\ -0.8$

17. Find the prime factorization of 144.

18. Find the LCM of 42 and 78.

19. What fractional part is shaded?

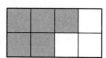

20. Simplify: $\dfrac{108}{128}$.

Calculate.

21. $\dfrac{3}{5} \times 9.53$

22. $7.2 \div 0.4(-1.5) + (1.2)^2$

23. Find the mean: 23, 49, 52, 71.

24. Determine whether the pairs 6, 8 and 14, 196 are proportional.

25. Graph on a plane: $y = -2x + 1$.

26. Evaluate $\dfrac{t - 7}{w}$ for $t = -3$ and $w = -2$.

Solve.

27. $\dfrac{14}{25} = \dfrac{x}{54}$

28. $-423 = 16 \cdot t$

29. $9x - 7 = -43$

30. $2(x - 3) + 9 = 5x - 6$

31. $34.56 + n = 67.9$

32. $\dfrac{2}{3}x = \dfrac{16}{27}$

Solve.

33. A truck can reach its destination 143 miles away in 2.6 hr. How far could it travel in 3.8 hr?

34. Thomas can type 384 words in 8 min. At this rate, how long will it take him to type a 1250-word letter? What is his typing speed in words per minute (wpm)?

35. Dee ran 13.6 mi, 11.2 mi, 14.7 mi, and 10.3 mi one week in preparation for a marathon. How many miles total did she run that week?

36. In 2001, there were an estimated 900 million cell phone users and 600 million PC (personal computer) users in the world.
Source: www.mctimes.net

a) Find the ratio of cell phone users to PC users.
b) Find the ratio of PC users to cell phone users.

37. A diamond-shaped tablecloth consists of two identical triangles, as shown. What is the area of the tablecloth?

38. The *Cassini/Huygens* spacecraft is expected to orbit Saturn more than 70 times during a 4-year study of the planet. Assuming a steady rate, about how many orbits will the spacecraft make per year?
Source: www.solarsystem.nasa.gov

39. A 46-oz juice can contains $5\frac{3}{4}$ cups of juice. A recipe calls for $3\frac{1}{2}$ cups of juice. How many cups are left?

(SYNTHESIS)

40. A car travels 88 ft in 1 sec. What is the rate in miles per hour?

41. A 12-oz bag of shredded mozzarella cheese is on sale for $2.07. Blocks of mozzarella cheese are on sale for $2.79 per pound. Which is the better buy?

42. Hans attends a university where the academic year consists of two 16-week semesters. He budgets $1200 for incidental expenses for the academic year. After 3 weeks, Hans has spent $150 for incidental expenses. Assuming he continues to spend at the same rate, will his budget for incidental expenses be adequate? If not, when will the money be exhausted and how much more will be needed to complete the year?

43. A basic sound system consists of a CD player, a receiver, and two speakers. A standard rule of thumb on the relative investment in these components is $1:3:2$. That is, the receiver should cost three times as much as the CD player and the speakers should cost twice as much as the CD player. Eileen has already spent $250 on speakers. If she is to follow this rule of thumb, how much will she spend on her sound system?

44. Connor typically spends his paycheck according to the ratio $1:3:2$, which indicates the ratio of Leisure & Incidental Expenses to Food & Other Necessary Expenses to Debt Payments. If Connor gets paid $4800 a month, how is his paycheck allocated? How much does Connor allot per year to debts? To Leisure & Incidental Expenses?

Percent Notation

Gateway to Chapter 8

This chapter introduces percent notation. We will see that $\frac{3}{8}$ (fraction notation), 0.375 (decimal notation), and 37.5% (percent notation) are all names for the same number. Percent notation has widespread applications in everyday life, in such diverse areas as business, sports, science, and medicine. We consider, as well, applications involving sales tax, commission, discount, and interest rates.

Real-World Application

George W. Bush was inaugurated as the 43rd president of the United States in 2001. Because Grover Cleveland was both the 22nd and the 24th president, there have been only 42 different presidents. Of these 42 presidents, 8 died while in office: William Henry Harrison, Zachary Taylor, Abraham Lincoln, James A. Garfield, William McKinley, Warren G. Harding, Franklin D. Roosevelt, and John F. Kennedy. What percent died while in office?

This problem appears as Example 1 in Section 8.4.

CHAPTER

8

1. Insurance costs account for 13.3% of the annual cost of owning and operating an automobile. Find decimal notation for 13.3%.   [8.1b]
   Source: Runzheimer International

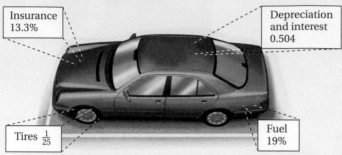

Insurance 13.3%

Depreciation and interest 0.504

Tires $\frac{1}{25}$

Fuel 19%

2. Depreciation and interest charges on a car loan account for 0.504 of the annual cost of owning and operating an automobile. Find percent notation for 0.504.   [8.1b]
   Source: Runzheimer International

3. Tire costs account for $\frac{1}{25}$ of the annual cost of owning and operating an automobile. Find percent notation for $\frac{1}{25}$.   [8.1c]
   Source: Runzheimer International

4. Fuel costs account for 19% of the annual cost of owning and operating an automobile. Find fraction notation for 19%.   [8.1c]
   Source: Runzheimer International

5. Translate to a percent equation. Then solve.
   What is 60% of 75?   [8.3a, b]

6. Translate to a proportion. Then solve.
   What percent of 50 is 35?   [8.2a, b]

Solve.

7. **Weight of Muscles.**   The weight of muscles in a human body is 40% of total body weight. A person weighs 225 lb. What do the muscles weigh?   [8.4a]

8. **Ticket Price Increase.**   In 2001, the Indianapolis Colts raised the price of a ticket from $125 to $149 for a seat between the 30-yd lines on the lower level. What was the percent of increase?   [8.4b]
   Source: The Indianapolis Colts

9. **Massachusetts Sales Tax.**   The sales tax rate in Massachusetts is 5%. How much tax is charged on a television costing $286? What is the total price? [8.5a]

10. At Flo's Antique Barn, the commission rate is 28%. What is the commission from the sale of $18,400 worth of antiques?   [8.5b]

11. The marked price of a personal computer is $745. The computer is on sale at Lowland Appliances for 25% off. What is the discount and what is the sale price?   [8.5c]

12. What is the simple interest on $1200 principal at the interest rate of 8.3% for 1 year?   [8.6a]

13. What is the simple interest on $500 at 8% for $\frac{1}{2}$ year? [8.6a]

14. Find the amount in an account if $6000 is invested at 9% for 2 years with interest compounded annually.   [8.6b]

15. ▣ The Beechers invest $7500 in an investment account paying 6%, compounded semiannually. How much is in the account after 5 years?   [8.6b]

16. After completing her medical training, Libby begins paying off a $37,500 loan. At 7.24% interest, she will make 180 monthly payments of $342.11. How much of Libby's first payment is interest and how much is applied to reduce the principal?   [8.7a]

8.1

PERCENT NOTATION

a Understanding Percent Notation

Of the total surface area of the earth, 70% is covered by water. What does this mean? It means that of every 100 square miles of the earth's surface area, 70 square miles are covered by water. Thus, 70% is a ratio of 70 to 100, or $\frac{70}{100}$.

Source: *The Handy Geography Answer Book*

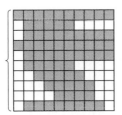

70 of 100 squares are shaded.

70% or $\frac{70}{100}$ or 0.70 of the large square is shaded.

Percent notation is used extensively in our everyday lives. Here are some examples:

63% of the aluminum used in the United States is recycled.

46% of the people at major-league baseball games are women.

33% of all U.S. citizens say the day they dread the most is the day they go to the dentist.

20% of the time that people declare as sick leave is actually used for personal needs.

60% of the vehicles involved in rollover fatalities are sport utility vehicles.

0.08% blood alcohol level is a standard used by most states as the legal limit for drunk driving.

Percent notation is often represented in pie charts to show how the parts of a quantity are related. For example, the chart below relates the amounts of different kinds of juices that are sold.

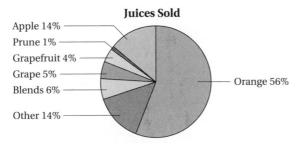

Juices Sold

Apple 14%
Prune 1%
Grapefruit 4%
Grape 5%
Blends 6%
Other 14%
Orange 56%

Source: Beverage Marketing Corporation

To draw a pie chart like the one above, think of a pie cut into 100 equally sized pieces. Then shade in a wedge equal in size to 20 of these pieces to represent 20%. Shade in a wedge equal in size to 35 of the 100 pieces to represent 35%, and so on.

Do Exercise 1.

1. The circle below is divided into 100 sections. Use the following information on the length of time couples are engaged before marrying.

More than 2 years: 35%
1–2 years: 21%
Greater than 0, but less than 1 year: 24%
Never engaged: 20%

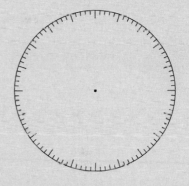

Express each percent in three different forms, as in Examples 1 and 2.

2. 70%

3. 23.4%

4. 100%

Answers on page A-24

573

From 1998 to 2008, the number of jobs for professional chefs will increase by 13.4%.
Source: *Handbook of U.S. Labor Statistics*

It is thought that the Roman emperor Augustus began percent notation by taxing goods sold at a rate of $\frac{1}{100}$. In time, the symbol "%" evolved by changing the parts of the symbol "100" to "0/0" and then to "%." Today it is widely understood that $n\%$ means "n per hundred."

NOTATION FOR $n\%$

Percent notation, $n\%$, can be expressed using:

ratio $\longrightarrow n\% =$ the ratio of n to $100 = \dfrac{n}{100}$,

fraction notation $\longrightarrow n\% = n \times \dfrac{1}{100}$, or

decimal notation $\longrightarrow n\% = n \times 0.01$.

EXAMPLE 1 Express 35% in three different forms.

Using ratio:	$35\% = \dfrac{35}{100}$	A ratio of 35 to 100
Using fraction notation:	$35\% = 35 \times \dfrac{1}{100}$	Replacing % with $\times \dfrac{1}{100}$
Using decimal notation:	$35\% = 35 \times 0.01$	Replacing % with $\times 0.01$

EXAMPLE 2 Express 67.8% in three different forms.

Using ratio:	$67.8\% = \dfrac{67.8}{100}$	A ratio of 67.8 to 100
Using fraction notation:	$67.8\% = 67.8 \times \dfrac{1}{100}$	Replacing % with $\times \dfrac{1}{100}$
Using decimal notation:	$67.8\% = 67.8 \times 0.01$	Replacing % with $\times 0.01$

Do Exercises 2–4 on the preceding page.

b Converting Between Percent Notation and Decimal Notation

To write decimal notation for a number like 78%, we can replace "%" with "$\times 0.01$" and multiply:

$$78\% = 78 \times 0.01 \qquad \text{Replacing \% with} \times 0.01$$
$$= 0.78. \qquad \text{Multiplying}$$

Similarly,

$$4.9\% = 4.9 \times 0.01 \qquad \text{Replacing \% with} \times 0.01$$
$$= 0.049, \qquad \text{Multiplying}$$

$$265\% = 265 \times 0.01 \qquad \text{Replacing \% with} \times 0.01$$
$$= 2.65, \qquad \text{Multiplying}$$

and

$$100\% = 100 \times 0.01 \qquad \text{Replacing \% with} \times 0.01$$
$$= 1. \qquad \text{Multiplying}$$

To convert from percent notation to decimal notation,	36.5%
a) replace the percent symbol % with × 0.01, and	36.5 × 0.01
b) multiply by 0.01, which means move the decimal point two places to the left.	0.36.5 Move 2 places to the left. 36.5% = 0.365

Write each percent as an equivalent decimal.

5. 34%

■ **EXAMPLE 3** Write an equivalent decimal for 92.43%.

a) Replace the percent symbol with × 0.01.   92.43 × 0.01

b) Multiply to move the decimal point two places to the left.   0.92.43

Thus, 92.43% = 0.9243 .

6. 78.9%

Sometimes it may be necessary to write zeros as placeholders.

■ **EXAMPLE 4** In 2002, the population of the United States was 4.6% of the world population. Write decimal notation for 4.6%.
Source: U.S. Census Bureau

a) Replace the percent symbol with × 0.01.   4.6 × 0.01

b) Multiply to move the decimal point two places to the left.

                This zero serves as a placeholder.

         0.04.6

Thus, 4.6% = 0.046 .

7. 2.1%

Find decimal notation for the percent notation in each sentence.

8. According to a Bayer Corporation survey, 24% of U.S. college students believe they are "the next Bill Gates."
Source: *Harper's Magazine*, 11/02, p. 13

Do Exercises 5–9.

With practice, you will be able to make this conversion mentally.

■ **EXAMPLE 5** Write 74% as an equivalent decimal.

    74% = 0.74   Dropping the percent symbol and moving the decimal point two places to the left

9. A blood alcohol level of 0.08% is a standard used by most states as the legal limit for drunk driving.

Do Exercises 10 and 11.

The procedure used in Examples 3 and 4 can be reversed to write a decimal, like 0.38, as an equivalent percent. To see why, note that

    0.38 = 0.38 × 100% = (0.38 × 100)% = 38%.

Write each percent as an equivalent decimal.

10. 29%

To convert from decimal notation to percent notation, multiply by 100%. That is,	0.675 = 0.675 × 100%
a) move the decimal point two places to the right, and	0.67.5 Move 2 places to the right.
b) write a % symbol.	67.5% 0.675 = 67.5%

11. 143%

Answers on page A-24

Write each decimal as an equivalent percent.

12. 0.24

13. 3.47

14. 1

15. Muscles make up 0.4 of an adult male's body. Find percent notation for 0.4 .

16. The average television set is on 0.25 of the time. Find percent notation for 0.25 .

Write each decimal as an equivalent percent.

17. 0.62

18. 0.094

◾ EXAMPLE 6 Babies are born before their "due" date 0.3 of the time. Write percent notation for 0.3 .

a) Multiply by 100 to move the decimal point two places to the right. Recall that 0.3 = 0.30 since $\frac{3}{10} = \frac{30}{100}$.

This zero serves as a placeholder.

0.30.

b) Write a % symbol.   30%

Thus, 0.3 = 30%.

◾ EXAMPLE 7 Property values in Dorchester were multiplied by 1.23 when reassessment was performed. Find percent notation for 1.23.

a) Multiply by 100 to move the decimal point two places to the right.   1.23.

b) Write a % symbol.   123%

Thus, 1.23 = 123%.

Do Exercises 12–16.

With practice, these conversions can be made mentally.

◾ EXAMPLE 8 Rewrite 0.93 as an equivalent percent.

0.93 = 93%   Moving the decimal point two places to the right and writing a % symbol

Do Exercises 17 and 18.

⬛ C   Converting Between Fraction Notation and Percent Notation

To convert from fraction notation to percent notation,

$\frac{3}{5}$ Fraction notation

a) find decimal notation by division, and

$$5 \overline{)\ 3.0} \\ \underline{3\ 0} \\ 0$$

$$0.6$$

b) convert the decimal notation to percent notation.

0.6 = 0.60 = 60%   Percent notation

$\frac{3}{5} = 60\%$

EXAMPLE 9 Write an equivalent percent for $\frac{3}{8}$.

a) Find decimal notation by division.

$$
\begin{array}{r}
0.3\ 7\ 5 \\
8\ \overline{)\ 3.0\ 0\ 0} \\
\underline{2\ 4} \\
6\ 0 \\
\underline{5\ 6} \\
4\ 0 \\
\underline{4\ 0} \\
0
\end{array}
\qquad \frac{3}{8} = 0.375
$$

b) Convert the decimal notation to percent notation. To do so, multiply by 100 to move the decimal point two places to the right, and write a % symbol.

$$0.37.5$$

$$\frac{3}{8} = 0.375 = 37.5\%, \text{ or } 37\frac{1}{2}\%$$

Don't forget the % symbol.

Do Exercises 19 and 20.

EXAMPLE 10 Of all meals, $\frac{1}{3}$ are eaten outside the home. Write percent notation for $\frac{1}{3}$.

a) Find decimal notation by division.

$$
\begin{array}{r}
0.3\ 3\ 3 \\
3\ \overline{)\ 1.0\ 0\ 0} \\
\underline{9} \\
1\ 0 \\
\underline{9} \\
1\ 0 \\
\underline{9} \\
1
\end{array}
$$

Remember that to find percent notation, we will need to move the decimal point two places to the right.

We get a repeating decimal: $0.33\overline{3}$.

b) Convert the answer to percent notation.

$$0.33.\overline{3}$$

$$\frac{1}{3} = 33.\overline{3}\%, \text{ or } 33\frac{1}{3}\%$$ This result is useful to remember.

Do Exercises 21 and 22.

Write each fraction as an equivalent percent.

19. $\frac{1}{4}$

20. $\frac{7}{8}$

21. The human body is $\frac{2}{3}$ water Write percent notation for $\frac{2}{3}$.

22. Write an equivalent percent for $\frac{15}{8}$.

Answers on page A-24

Study Tips

REVIEW MATERIAL ON YOUR OWN

Never hesitate to review earlier material in which you feel a lack of confidence. For example, if you feel unsure about how to multiply with fraction notation, be sure to review that material before studying any new material that involves multiplication of fractions. Doing (and checking) some practice problems from that section is also a good way to sharpen any skills that may not have been used for a while.

Write each fraction as an equivalent percent.

23. $\dfrac{57}{100}$

24. $\dfrac{19}{25}$

Answers on page A-24

In some cases, division is not the fastest way to convert to percent notation. The following are some optional ways in which conversion might be done.

EXAMPLE 11 Write $\dfrac{69}{100}$ as an equivalent percent.

We use the definition of percent as a ratio.

$$\frac{69}{100} = 69\%$$

EXAMPLE 12 Write $\dfrac{17}{20}$ as an equivalent percent.

We multiply $\dfrac{17}{20}$ by 1, writing 1 as 100%:

$$\frac{17}{20} \times 100\% = \frac{17 \times 100}{20}\%$$
$$= (17 \times 5)\% \qquad 100 \div 20 = 5$$
$$= 85\%.$$

This shortcut works best when the given denominator is a factor of 100.

Do Exercises 23 and 24.

The method used in Example 11 is reversed when we convert from percent notation to fraction notation.

To convert from percent notation to fraction notation,	30%	Percent notation
a) use the definition of percent as a ratio, and	$\dfrac{30}{100}$	
b) simplify, if possible.	$\dfrac{3}{10}$	Fraction notation

EXAMPLE 13 Write an equivalent fraction for 75% and simplify.

$$75\% = \frac{75}{100} \qquad \text{Using the definition of percent}$$
$$= \frac{3 \cdot 25}{4 \cdot 25}$$
$$= \frac{3}{4} \cdot \frac{25}{25} \qquad \text{Simplifying by removing a factor equal to 1: } \frac{25}{25} = 1.$$
$$= \frac{3}{4}$$

EXAMPLE 14 Write an equivalent fraction for 112.5% and simplify.

$$112.5\% = \frac{112.5}{100}$$ Using the definition of percent

$$= \frac{112.5}{100} \times \frac{10}{10}$$ Multiplying by 1 to eliminate the decimal point in the numerator

$$= \frac{1125}{1000}$$

$$= \frac{5}{5} \cdot \frac{225}{200}$$

$$= \frac{225}{200}$$

$$= \frac{25}{25} \cdot \frac{9}{8}$$ Simplifying

$$= \frac{9}{8}$$

Sometimes, rather than divide by 100, it is easier to multiply by $\frac{1}{100}$.

EXAMPLE 15 Write an equivalent fraction for $16\frac{2}{3}\%$ and simplify.

$$16\frac{2}{3}\% = \frac{50}{3}\%$$ Converting from the mixed numeral to fraction notation

$$= \frac{50}{3} \times \frac{1}{100}$$ Using the definition of percent

$$= \frac{50 \cdot 1}{3 \cdot 50 \cdot 2}$$

$$= \frac{1}{6} \cdot \frac{50}{50}$$ Simplifying

$$= \frac{1}{6}$$

Do Exercises 25–27.

After mastering the material in this section, consider memorizing the fraction, decimal, and percent equivalents that are listed on the inside front cover. This will allow you to save time by solving problems like Example 13 mentally.

Do Exercise 28.

Write each fraction as an equivalent percent. Simplify, if possible.

25. 180%

26. 3.25%

27. $66\frac{2}{3}\%$

28. Complete this table.

Fraction Notation	$\frac{1}{5}$		
Decimal Notation		$0.83\overline{3}$	
Percent Notation			$37\frac{1}{2}\%$

For Extra Help

a Use the given information to complete a circle graph. Note that each circle is divided into 100 sections.

1. *How Teens Spend Their Money*

Clothing	34%
Entertainment	22%
Food	22%
Other	22%

Source: Rand Youth Poll, eMarketer

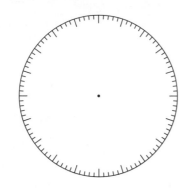

2. *Reasons for Drinking Coffee*

To get going in the morning:	32%
Like the taste:	33%
Not sure:	2%
To relax:	4%
As a pick-me-up:	10%
It's a habit:	19%

Source: LMK Associates survey for Au Bon Pain Co., Inc.

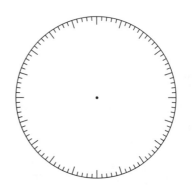

Write each percent in three different forms as in Examples 1 and 2 on p. 528.

3. 90%   **4.** 43.8%   **5.** 12.5%   **6.** 120%

b Write each percent as an equivalent decimal.

7. 67%   **8.** 17%   **9.** 45.6%   **10.** 76.3%

11. 59.01%   **12.** 30.02%   **13.** 10%   **14.** 80%

15. 1%   **16.** 100%   **17.** 200%   **18.** 300%

19. 0.1%   **20.** 0.4%   **21.** 0.09%   **22.** 0.12%

23. 0.18%   **24.** 5.5%   **25.** 23.19%   **26.** 87.99%

27. 109.4%   **28.** 105.7%   **29.** 319.8%   **30.** 417.1%

31. According to a recent survey, 29% of those asked to name their favorite ice cream chose vanilla.
Source: International Ice Cream Association

32. According to a recent survey, 95.1% of those asked to name what sports they participate in listed swimming.
Source: Sporting Goods Manufacturers

33. Individuals who pay quarterly taxes and experience a large increase in yearly income are required to pay at least 110% of the previous year's taxes.

34. Airlines frequently sell 120% of the seats on certain flights.

Write each decimal as an equivalent percent.

35. 0.47　　　　**36.** 0.87　　　　**37.** 0.03　　　　**38.** 0.01　　　　**39.** 8.7

40. 4　　　　**41.** 0.334　　　　**42.** 0.889　　　　**43.** 0.75　　　　**44.** 0.99

45. 0.9　　　　**46.** 0.5　　　　**47.** 0.006　　　　**48.** 0.008　　　　**49.** 0.017

50. 0.024　　　　**51.** 0.2718　　　　**52.** 0.8911　　　　**53.** 1.374　　　　**54.** 2.403

Write percent notation for the decimal notation in each sentence.

55. According to a recent survey, 0.526 of those asked to name what sports they participate in listed bowling.
Source: Sporting Goods Manufacturers

56. About 0.69 of all newspapers are recycled.
Sources: American Forest and Paper Association; Newspaper Association of America

57. In 2000, the cost of college to a middle-income family was 0.17 of their income.
Source: College Board

58. About 0.026 of all college football players go on to play professional football.

59. During the 2001–2002 NBA season, Vince Carter of the Toronto Raptors made 0.428 of his field goals.
Source: National Basketball Association

60. It is known that 0.458 of us sleep between 7 and 8 hours.

C   Write each fraction as an equivalent percent.

61. $\dfrac{41}{100}$

62. $\dfrac{36}{100}$

63. $\dfrac{5}{100}$

64. $\dfrac{1}{100}$

65. $\dfrac{2}{10}$

66. $\dfrac{7}{10}$

67. $\dfrac{7}{25}$

68. $\dfrac{1}{20}$

69. $\dfrac{3}{20}$

70. $\dfrac{3}{4}$

71. $\dfrac{5}{8}$

72. $\dfrac{13}{50}$

73. $\dfrac{4}{5}$

74. $\dfrac{2}{5}$

75. $\dfrac{2}{3}$

76. $\dfrac{1}{3}$

77. $\dfrac{29}{50}$

78. $\dfrac{13}{25}$

Write an equivalent percent for the fraction in each sentence.

79. Bread is $\frac{9}{25}$ water.

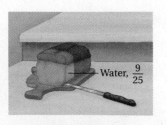

Water, $\dfrac{9}{25}$

80. Milk is $\frac{7}{8}$ water.

Water, $\dfrac{7}{8}$

For each percent, write an equivalent fraction. When possible, simplify and use the information in the table that appears on the inside front cover.

81. 85%

82. 55%

83. 62.5%

84. 12.5%

85. $33\frac{1}{3}\%$

86. $83\frac{1}{3}\%$

87. $16.\overline{6}\%$

88. $66.\overline{6}\%$

89. 7.25%

90. 4.85%

91. 0.8%

92. 0.2%

Use this bar graph to write fraction notation for the percentage of all people who "greatly enjoy" each type of food.

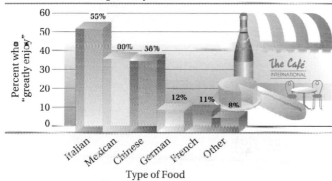

Popularity of Ethnic Foods

93. Italian

94. Mexican

95. Chinese

96. German

97. French

98. Other

99. *Energy Consumption.* The United States uses 26.4% of the world's energy. Write fraction notation for 26.4%.
Source: U.S. Energy Information Administration, *International Energy Annual*

100. *Voting-Age Population.* Only 40.5% of U.S. citizens between the ages of 18 and 20 are registered to vote. Write fraction notation for 40.5%
Source: U.S. Census Bureau, 2001

101. *Election Turnouts.* In the 2002 congressional elections, approximately 39% of the voting-age population voted. Write fraction notation for 39%.
Source: Center for Voting and Democracy

102. *Recordings Purchased.* Of the money spent on all sound recordings, 84.5% comes from people less than 45 yr old. Write fraction notation for 84.5%.
Source: Recording Industry Association of America, Inc., *1997 Consumer Profile*

Complete the table.

103.

FRACTION NOTATION	DECIMAL NOTATION	PERCENT NOTATION
$\frac{1}{8}$		$12\frac{1}{2}\%$, or 12.5%
$\frac{1}{6}$		
		20%
	0.25	
		$33\frac{1}{3}\%$, or $33.\overline{3}\%$
		$37\frac{1}{2}\%$, or 37.5%
		40%
	0.5	

104.

FRACTION NOTATION	DECIMAL NOTATION	PERCENT NOTATION
$\frac{3}{5}$		
	0.625	
$\frac{2}{3}$		
	0.75	75%
$\frac{4}{5}$		
$\frac{5}{6}$		$83\frac{1}{3}\%$, or $83.\overline{3}\%$
$\frac{7}{8}$		$87\frac{1}{2}\%$, or 87.5%
		100%

105.

FRACTION NOTATION	DECIMAL NOTATION	PERCENT NOTATION
	0.5	
$\frac{1}{3}$		
		25%
		$16\frac{2}{3}\%$, or $16.\overline{6}\%$
	0.125	
$\frac{3}{4}$		
	0.8$\overline{3}$	
$\frac{3}{8}$		

106.

FRACTION NOTATION	DECIMAL NOTATION	PERCENT NOTATION
		40%
		$62\frac{1}{2}\%$, or 62.5%
	0.875	
$\frac{1}{1}$		
	0.6	
	0.$\overline{6}$	
$\frac{1}{5}$		
	0.8	

107. **Dw** *Winning Percentage.* During the 2002 regular baseball season, the New York Yankees won 103 of 161 games. Find the ratio of number of wins to total number of games played in the regular season and convert it to decimal notation. Such a rate is often called a "winning percentage." Explain why.

108. **Dw** Athletes sometimes speak of "giving 110%" effort. Does this make sense? Explain.

SKILL MAINTENANCE

Convert to a mixed numeral. [4.5b]

109. $\dfrac{100}{3}$

110. $-\dfrac{75}{2}$

Solve. [7.3b]

111. $\dfrac{17}{51} = \dfrac{x}{18}$

112. $\dfrac{8}{40} = \dfrac{15}{x}$

113. $\dfrac{24}{37} = \dfrac{15}{x}$

114. $\dfrac{17}{18} = \dfrac{x}{27}$

SYNTHESIS

115. **Dw** Tammy remembers that $\frac{1}{4} = 25\%$. Explain how she can use this to (a) write $\frac{1}{8}$ in percent notation and (b) write $\frac{5}{8}$ in percent notation.

116. **Dw** Is it always best to convert from fraction notation to percent notation by first finding decimal notation? Why or why not?

Write each number as an equivalent percent.

117. ▦ $\dfrac{41}{369}$

118. ▦ $\dfrac{54}{999}$

119. $2.5\overline{74631}$

120. $3.2\overline{93847}$

Write each percent as an equivalent decimal.

121. $\dfrac{14}{9}\%$

122. $\dfrac{19}{12}\%$

123. $\dfrac{729}{7}\%$

124. $\dfrac{637}{6}\%$

Objectives

a Translate percent problems to proportions.

b Solve basic percent problems.

8.2 SOLVING PERCENT PROBLEMS USING PROPORTIONS*

a Translating to Proportions

A percent is a ratio of some number to 100. For example, 75% is the ratio $\frac{75}{100}$. The numbers 3 and 4 have the same ratio as 75 and 100. Thus,

$$75\% = \frac{75}{100} = \frac{3}{4}.$$

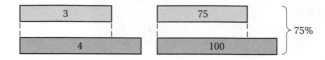

To solve a percent problem using a proportion, we translate as follows:

$$\text{Number} \longrightarrow \frac{N}{100} \xrightarrow{} = \frac{a}{b} \xleftarrow{} \text{Amount}$$
$$100 \qquad\qquad \xleftarrow{} \text{Base}$$

You might find it helpful to read this as "part is to whole as part is to whole."

For example,

60% of 25 is 15

translates to

$$\frac{60}{100} = \frac{15}{25}. \xleftarrow{} \text{Amount} \quad (\text{or part})$$
$$\phantom{\frac{60}{100} = }\xleftarrow{} \text{Base} \quad (\text{or whole})$$

A clue in translating is that the base, b, corresponds to 100 and usually follows the wording "percent of." Also, $N\%$ always translates to $N/100$ and the amount a is usually written next to the words "*is, are, was,* or *were.*" Another aid is to make a *comparison drawing*. To do this, start with the percent side and list 0% at the top and 100% near the bottom. Then estimate where the specified percent—in this case, 60%—is located. The corresponding quantities are then filled in. The base—in this case, 25—always corresponds to 100% and the amount—in this case, 15—corresponds to the specified percent.

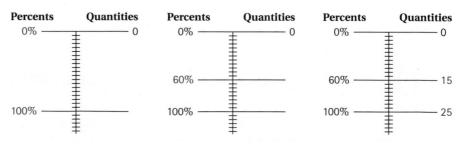

The proportion can then be read easily from the drawing.

In the examples that follow, we use comparison drawings as an aid for visualization. It is not necessary to always make a drawing to solve problems of this sort.

*Note: Sections 8.2 and 8.3 present two methods for solving percent problems. You may prefer one method over the other, or your instructor may specify the method to be used. Section 8.2 is used as a check in Section 8.4, but otherwise it is not used in future sections of this book.

Study Tips

WHICH APPROACH IS BEST?

Some instructors have special approaches or methods that do not appear in your text. If you find that one approach is your favorite, check with your instructor regarding the importance of learning the other approaches as well.

■ **EXAMPLE 1** Translate to a proportion.

23% of 5 is what?

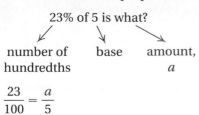

number of   base   amount,
hundredths   *a*

$$\frac{23}{100} = \frac{a}{5}$$

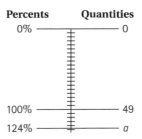

■ **EXAMPLE 2** Translate to a proportion.

What is 124% of 49?

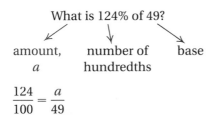

amount,   number of   base
a   hundredths

$$\frac{124}{100} = \frac{a}{49}$$

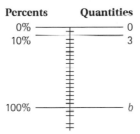

Do Exercises 1–3.

■ **EXAMPLE 3** Translate to a proportion.

3 is 10% of what?

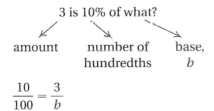

amount   number of   base,
hundredths   *b*

$$\frac{10}{100} = \frac{3}{b}$$

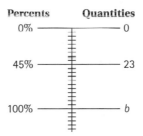

■ **EXAMPLE 4** Translate to a proportion.

45% of what is 23?

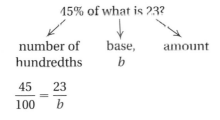

number of   base,   amount
hundredths   *b*

$$\frac{45}{100} = \frac{23}{b}$$

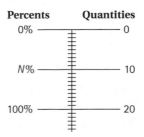

Do Exercises 4 and 5.

■ **EXAMPLE 5** Translate to a proportion.

10 is what percent of 20?

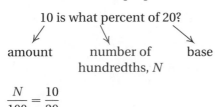

amount   number of   base
hundredths, *N*

$$\frac{N}{100} = \frac{10}{20}$$

Translate to a proportion. Do not solve.

1. 12% of 50 is what?

2. What is 40% of 60?

3. 130% of 72 is what?

Translate to a proportion. Do not solve.

4. 45 is 20% of what?

5. 120% of what is 60?

Answers on page A-25

Translate to a proportion. Do not solve.

6. 16 is what percent of 40?

7. What percent of 84 is 10.5?

8. Solve:

20% of what is $45?

Solve.

9. 64% of 55 is what?

10. What is 12% of 50?

Answers on page A-25

EXAMPLE 6 Translate to a proportion.

What percent of 50 is 7?

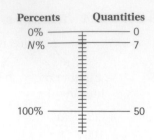

number of   base   amount
hundredths, N

$$\frac{N}{100} = \frac{7}{50}$$

Do Exercises 6 and 7.

b Solving Percent Problems

After a percent problem has been translated to a proportion, we solve as in Section 7.3.

EXAMPLE 7   5% of what is $20?

number of   base,   amount
hundredths b

Translate: $\dfrac{5}{100} = \dfrac{20}{b}$.

Solve: $5 \cdot b = 100 \cdot 20$ Equating cross products

$\dfrac{5b}{5} = \dfrac{2000}{5}$ Dividing both sides by 5

$b = 400$.   Simplifying

Thus, 5% of $400 is $20. The answer is $400.

Do Exercise 8.

EXAMPLE 8   120% of 42 is what?

number of   base   amount,
hundredths a

Translate: $\dfrac{120}{100} = \dfrac{a}{42}$.

Solve: $120 \cdot 42 = 100 \cdot a$ Equating cross products

$\dfrac{5040}{100} = \dfrac{100a}{100}$ Dividing both sides by 100

$50.4 = a$.   Simplifying

Thus, 120% of 42 is 50.4 . The answer is 50.4 .

Do Exercises 9 and 10.

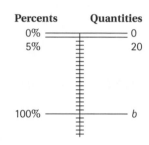

EXAMPLE 9   3 is 16% of what?

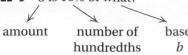

amount   number of   base,
          hundredths b

Translate: $\dfrac{3}{b} = \dfrac{16}{100}$.

Solve: $3 \cdot 100 = b \cdot 16$ Equating cross products

      $\dfrac{300}{16} = \dfrac{16b}{16}$ Dividing both sides by 16

      $18.75 = b.$ Simplifying

Thus, 3 is 16% of 18.75 . The answer is 18.75 .

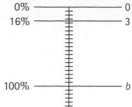

Percents	Quantities
0%	0
16%	3
100%	b

Do Exercise 11.

EXAMPLE 10 $10 is what percent of $20?

amount   number of   base
         hundredths, N

Translate: $\dfrac{10}{20} = \dfrac{N}{100}$.

Solve: $10 \cdot 100 = 20 \cdot N$ Equating cross products

      $\dfrac{1000}{20} = \dfrac{20N}{20}$ Dividing both sides by 20

      $50 = N.$ Simplifying

Thus, $10 is 50% of $20. The answer is 50%.

Percents	Quantities
0%	0
N%	$10
100%	$20

> Always "look before you leap." Many students can solve this problem mentally: $10 is half, or 50%, of $20.

Do Exercise 12.

EXAMPLE 11   What percent of 50 is 16?

number of   base   amount
hundredths, N

Translate: $\dfrac{N}{100} = \dfrac{16}{50}$.

Solve: $50 \cdot N = 100 \cdot 16$ Equating cross products

      $\dfrac{50 \cdot N}{50} = \dfrac{100 \cdot 16}{50}$ Dividing both sides by 50

      $N = \dfrac{2 \cdot 50 \cdot 16}{50}$ Removing a factor equal to 1: $\dfrac{50}{50} = 1$

      $N = 32.$ Multiplying

Percents	Quantities
0%	0
N%	16
100%	50

Thus, 32% of 50 is 16. The answer is 32%. A quick alternative approach is to note that, since $50 \cdot 2 = 100$, we have $\frac{16}{50} = \frac{16 \cdot 2}{50 \cdot 2} = \frac{32}{100}$, or 32%.

Do Exercise 13.

11. Solve:

    60 is 120% of what?

12. Solve:

    $12 is what percent of $40?

13. Solve:

    What percent of 84 is 10.5?

Answers on page A-25

8.2 EXERCISE SET

Digital Video Tutor CD 5 Videotape 8 · InterAct Math · Math Tutor Center · MathXL · MyMathLab

a   Translate to a proportion. Do not solve.

1. What is 29% of 84?

2. 53% of 74 is what?

3. 4.3 is what percent of 5.9?

4. What percent of 6.8 is 5.3?

5. 8 is 25% of what?

6. 133% of what is 40?

7. 9% of what is 37?

8. What is 132% of 75?

9. 80% of 730 is what?

10. 17 is 23% of what?

b   Solve.

11. What is 7% of 2000?

12. What is 6% of 1000?

13. 4.8% of 60 is what?

14. 63.1% of 80 is what?

15. $24 is what percent of $96?

16. $14 is what percent of $70?

17. 102 is what percent of 100?

18. 103 is what percent of 100?

19. What percent of $480 is $120?

20. What percent of $80 is $60?

21. What percent of 80 is 75?

22. What percent of 66 is 22?

23. $18 is 25% of what?

24. $75 is 20% of what?

25. 30% of what is 54?

26. 80% of what is 96?

27. 65.12 is 74% of what?

28. 63.7 is 65% of what?

29. 70% of what is 14?

30. 80% of what is 10?

31. What is $62\frac{1}{2}\%$ of 40?

32. What is $43\frac{1}{4}\%$ of 2600?

33. What is 9.4% of $8300?

34. What is 8.7% of $76,000?

35. 9.48 is 120% of what?

36. 8.45 is 130% of what?

37. ^{D}**W** In your own words, list steps that a classmate could use to solve any percent problem in this section.

38. ^{D}**W** In solving Example 10, a student simplifies $\frac{10}{20}$ before solving. Is this a good idea? Why or why not?

SKILL MAINTENANCE

Graph. [6.4b]

39. $y = -\frac{1}{2}x$

40. $y = 3x$

41. $y = 2x - 4$

42. $y = \frac{1}{2}x - 3$

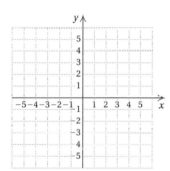
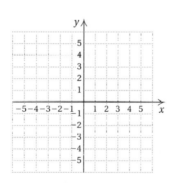
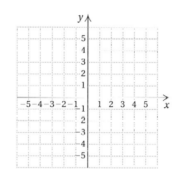
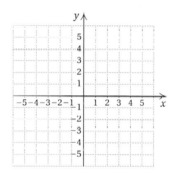

Solve.

43. A recipe for pancakes calls for $\frac{1}{2}$ qt of buttermilk, $\frac{1}{3}$ qt of skim milk, and $\frac{1}{16}$ qt of oil. How many quarts of liquid ingredients does the recipe call for? [4.2d]

44. Guilford Gardeners purchased $\frac{3}{4}$ ton (T) of top soil. If the soil is to be shared equally among 6 gardeners, how much will each gardener receive? [3.8b]

45. $0.05x = 40$ [5.7a]

46. $3 = 0.16t$ [5.7a]

47. $1.3n = 10.4$ [5.7a]

48. $1.2x = 8.4$ [5.7a]

SYNTHESIS

49. ^{D}**W** Does it make sense to talk about a negative percentage? Why or why not?

50. ^{D}**W** Can "comparison drawings," like those used in this section, be used to solve *any* proportion? Why or why not?

Solve.

51. ▦ What is 8.85% of $12,640?
Estimate _____
Calculate _____

52. ▦ 78.8% of what is 9809.024?
Estimate _____
Calculate _____

53. 30% of 80 is what percent of 120?

54. 40% of what is the same as 30% of 200?

55. ▦ What percent of 90 is the same as 26% of 135?

56. ▦ What percent of 80 is the same as 76% of 150?

SOLVING PERCENT PROBLEMS USING EQUATIONS

Objectives

a Translate percent problems to equations.

b Solve basic percent problems.

Translate to an equation. Do not solve.

1. 12% of 73 is what?

2. What is 40% of 60?

Translate to an equation. Do not solve.

3. 45 is 20% of what?

4. 120% of what is 79?

Translate to an equation. Do not solve.

5. 16 is what percent of 40?

6. What percent of 84 is 10.5?

Answers on page A-26

a Translating to Equations

A second method for solving percent problems is to translate a problem's wording directly to an equation. For example, "23% of 5 is what?" translates as follows.

$$\begin{array}{ccccc} 23\% & \text{of} & 5 & \text{is} & \text{what?} \\ \downarrow & \downarrow & \downarrow & \downarrow & \downarrow \\ 0.23 & \cdot & 5 & = & a \end{array}$$

Note how the key words are translated.

KEY WORDS IN PERCENT TRANSLATIONS

"Of" translates to "·", or "×". **"Is"** translates to "=".

"What" translates to a variable. **%** translates to "× $\frac{1}{100}$" or "× 0.01".

EXAMPLE 1 Translate: What is 17% of 69?

$$\begin{array}{ccccc} \text{What} & \text{is} & 17\% & \text{of} & 69? \\ \downarrow & \downarrow & \downarrow & \downarrow & \downarrow \\ a & = & 0.17 & \cdot & 69 \end{array}$$ Any letter can be used as the variable.

Do Exercises 1 and 2.

EXAMPLE 2 Translate: 3 is 10% of what?

$$\begin{array}{ccccc} 3 & \text{is} & 10\% & \text{of} & \text{what?} \\ \downarrow & \downarrow & \downarrow & \downarrow & \downarrow \\ 3 & = & 0.10 & \cdot & b \end{array}$$

EXAMPLE 3 Translate: 65 percent of what is 23?

$$\begin{array}{ccccc} 65\% & \text{of} & \text{what} & \text{is} & 23? \\ \downarrow & \downarrow & \downarrow & \downarrow & \downarrow \\ 0.65 & \cdot & b & = & 23 \end{array}$$

Do Exercises 3 and 4.

EXAMPLE 4 Translate: 10 is what percent of 47?

$$\begin{array}{ccccc} 10 & \text{is} & \underline{\text{what percent}} & \text{of} & 47? \\ \downarrow & \downarrow & \downarrow & \downarrow & \downarrow \\ 10 & = & p & \cdot & 47 \end{array}$$

EXAMPLE 5 Translate: What percent of 62 is 13?

$$\begin{array}{ccccc} \underline{\text{What percent}} & \text{of} & 62 & \text{is} & 13? \\ \downarrow & \downarrow & \downarrow & \downarrow & \downarrow \\ p & \cdot & 62 & = & 13 \end{array}$$

Do Exercises 5 and 6.

b   Solving Percent Problems

In solving percent problems, we use the *Translate* and *Solve* steps in the problem-solving strategy used throughout this text.

Percent problems are actually of three different types. Although the method we present does not *require* that you be able to identify which type we are studying, it is helpful to know them.

We know that

15 is 25% of 60,   or

$15 = 0.25 \cdot 60.$

We can think of this as:

THE "AMOUNT" EQUATION

Amount = Percent number · Base.

Each of the three types of percent problems depends on which of the three pieces of information is missing.

1. **Finding the *amount* (the result of taking the percent)**

Example:	What	is	25%	of	60?
	↓	↓	↓	↓	↓
Translation:	a	=	0.25	·	60

2. **Finding the *base* (the number you are taking the percent of)**

Example:	15	is	25%	of	what number?
	↓	↓	↓	↓	↓
Translation:	15	=	0.25	·	b

3. **Finding the *percent number* (the percent itself)**

Example:	15	is	what percent	of	60?
	↓	↓	↓	↓	↓
Translation:	15	=	p	·	60

FINDING THE AMOUNT

EXAMPLE 6   What is 11% of 49?

Translate: $a = 0.11 \cdot 49$.

Solve: The variable is by itself. To solve the equation, we just convert 11% to decimal notation and multiply.

$$a = 0.11(49)$$

$$
\begin{array}{r}
4\ 9 \\
\times\ 0.1\ 1 \\
\hline
4\ 9 \\
4\ 9\ 0 \\
\hline
5.3\ 9
\end{array}
$$

$$a = 5.39$$

> A way of checking answers is by estimating as follows:
>
> $$0.11 \times 49 \approx 0.10(50) = 5.$$
>
> Since 5 is close to 5.39, our answer is reasonable.

Thus, 5.39 is 11% of 49. The answer is 5.39.

Do Exercise 7.

Answer on page A-26

Study Tips

MEMORIZING

Occasionally, memorizing can be very helpful in mathematics. Don't underestimate its power as you study the table of decimal, fraction, and percent notation on the inside front cover. Eventually, you will simply remember these equivalences because they are so useful.

8. Solve:

64% of $55 is what?

Solve.

9. 20% of what is 45?

10. $60 is 120% of what?

11. Solve:

16 is what percent of 40?

12. Solve:

What percent of $84 is $10.50?

Answers on page A-26

EXAMPLE 7 120% of $42 is what?

Translate: $1.20 \cdot 42 = a$.

Solve: The variable is by itself. To solve the equation, we rewrite 1.20 as 1.2 and carry out the calculation.

$$1.2(42) = a$$

$$\begin{array}{r} 4\ 2 \\ \times\ 1.2 \\ \hline 8\ 4 \\ 4\ 2\ 0 \\ \hline \end{array}$$

$$50.4 = a \qquad 5\ 0.4 \qquad \text{50.4 dollars is \$50.40}$$

Thus, 120% of $42 is $50.40. The answer is $50.40.

Do Exercise 8.

FINDING THE BASE

EXAMPLE 8 5% of what is 20?

Translate: $0.05 \cdot b = 20$.

Solve: This time the variable is *not* by itself. To solve the equation, we divide both sides by 0.05:

$$\frac{0.05 \cdot b}{0.05} = \frac{20}{0.05} \qquad \text{Dividing both sides by 0.05}$$

$$b = \frac{20}{0.05}$$

$$= 400.$$

$$\begin{array}{r} 4\ 0\ 0. \\ 0.0\ 5\ )\overline{2\ 0.0\ 0_\wedge} \\ \underline{2\ 0\ 0\ 0} \\ 0 \end{array}$$

Thus, 5% of 400 is 20. The answer is 400.

EXAMPLE 9 $3 is 16% of what?

Translate:

$$\begin{array}{ccccc} \$3 & \text{is} & 16\% & \text{of} & \text{what?} \\ \downarrow & \downarrow & \downarrow & \downarrow & \downarrow \\ 3 & = & 0.16 & \cdot & b. \end{array}$$

Solve: Again, the variable is not by itself. To solve the equation, we divide both sides by 0.16:

$$\frac{3}{0.16} = \frac{0.16 \cdot b}{0.16} \qquad \text{Dividing both sides by 0.16}$$

$$\frac{3}{0.16} = b$$

$$18.75 = b.$$

$$\begin{array}{r} 1\ 8.7\ 5 \\ 0.1\ 6\ )\overline{3.0\ 0_\wedge 0\ 0} \\ \underline{1\ 6} \\ 1\ 4\ 0 \\ \underline{1\ 2\ 8} \\ 1\ 2\ 0 \\ \underline{1\ 1\ 2} \\ 8\ 0 \\ \underline{8\ 0} \\ 0 \end{array}$$

Thus, $3 is 16% of $18.75. The answer is $18.75.

Do Exercises 9 and 10.

FINDING THE PERCENT

In solving these problems, it is essential that you remember to convert to percent notation after you have solved the equation.

EXAMPLE 10 17 is what percent of 20?

Translate:
$$\underset{\downarrow}{17} \quad \underset{\downarrow}{is} \quad \underbrace{what\ percent}_{\downarrow} \quad \underset{\downarrow}{of} \quad \underset{\downarrow}{20?}$$
$$17 \quad = \quad p \quad \cdot \quad 20.$$

Solve: To solve the equation, we divide both sides by 20 and convert the result to percent notation:

$$17 = p \cdot 20$$

$$\frac{17}{20} = \frac{p \cdot 20}{20} \qquad \text{Dividing both sides by 20:} \qquad 20\overline{\smash{)}17.00}$$

$$0.85 = p$$

$$p = 85\%.$$

```
       .8 5
20 ) 1 7.0 0
     1 6 0
       1 0 0
       1 0 0
           0
```

Thus, 17 is 85% of 20. The answer is 85%.

Do Exercise 11 on the previous page.

EXAMPLE 11 What percent of $50 is $16?

Translate:
$$\underbrace{What\ percent}_{\downarrow} \quad \underset{\downarrow}{of} \quad \underset{\downarrow}{\$50} \quad \underset{\downarrow}{is} \quad \underset{\downarrow}{\$16?}$$
$$p \quad \cdot \quad 50 \quad = \quad 16.$$

Solve: To solve the equation, we divide both sides by 50 and convert the answer to percent notation:

$$\frac{p \cdot 50}{50} = \frac{16}{50} \qquad \text{Dividing both sides by 50}$$

$$p = \frac{16}{50}$$

$$= \frac{16}{50} \cdot \frac{2}{2} \qquad \text{Multiplying by } \frac{2}{2}, \text{ or 1, to get a denominator of 100}$$

$$= \frac{32}{100} \qquad \text{Had we preferred, we could have divided 16 by 50 to find decimal notation.}$$

$$= 32\%. \qquad \text{Converting to percent notation}$$

Thus, 32% of $50 is $16. The answer is 32%.

Do Exercise 12 on the previous page.

> **CAUTION!**
>
> When a question asks "what percent?", be sure to give the answer in percent notation.

CALCULATOR CORNER

Many calculators have a $\boxed{\%}$ key that can be used in computations. For example, to find 11% of 49, we press $\boxed{1}\boxed{1}\boxed{2nd}\boxed{\%}\boxed{\times}\boxed{4}\boxed{9}$ $\boxed{=}$ or $\boxed{4}\boxed{9}\boxed{\times}\boxed{1}\boxed{1}$ $\boxed{SHIFT}\boxed{\%}$. The display reads $\boxed{\qquad 5.39}$, so 11% of 49 is 5.39.

In Example 8, we divide 20 by 5%. To use the $\boxed{\%}$ key in this computation, we press $\boxed{2}\boxed{0}\boxed{\div}\boxed{5}\boxed{2nd}\boxed{\%}\boxed{=}$, or $\boxed{2}\boxed{0}\boxed{\div}\boxed{5}\boxed{SHIFT}\boxed{\%}$. The result is 400.

We can also use the $\boxed{\%}$ key to find the percent number in a problem. In Example 10, for instance, we answer the question "17 is what percent of 20?" On a calculator, we press $\boxed{1}\boxed{7}$ $\boxed{\div}\boxed{2}\boxed{0}\boxed{2nd}\boxed{\%}\boxed{=}$, or $\boxed{1}\boxed{7}\boxed{\div}\boxed{2}\boxed{0}\boxed{SHIFT}\boxed{\%}$. The result is 85, so 17 is 85% of 20.

Exercises: Use a calculator to find each of the following.

1. What is 5% of 24?

2. What is 12.6% of $40?

3. What is 19% of 256?

4. 140% of $16 is what?

5. 0.04% of 28 is what?

6. 33% of $90 is what?

7. Use the percent key to perform the computations in Margin Exercises 9 and 10.

8. Use the percent key to perform the computations in Margin Exercises 11 and 12.

8.3

EXERCISE SET

For Extra Help

 Digital Video Tutor CD 5 Videotape 8

 InterAct Math

 Math Tutor Center

 MathXL

 MyMathLab

a Translate to an equation using *a* for any unknown amounts, *b* for any unknown bases, and *p* for any unknown percent numbers. Do not solve.

1. What is 32% of 78?

2. 98% of 57 is what?

3. 89 is what percent of 99?

4. What percent of 25 is 8?

5. 13 is 25% of what?

6. 21.4% of what is 20?

b Solve.

7. What is 85% of 276?

8. What is 74% of 53?

9. 150% of 40 is what?

10. 100% of 13 is what?

11. What is 6% of $300?

12. What is 4% of $45?

13. 3.8% of 50 is what?

14. $33\frac{1}{3}$% of 480 is what? $\left(Hint:\ 33\frac{1}{3}\% = \frac{1}{3}.\right)$

15. $39 is what percent of $50?

16. $16 is what percent of $90?

17. 50 is what percent of 25?

18. 60 is what percent of 20?

19. What percent of $340 is $170?

20. What percent of $50 is $40?

21. What percent of 80 is 100?

22. What percent of 60 is 15?

23. 20 is 50% of what?

24. 57 is 20% of what?

25. 40% of what is $32?

26. 100% of what is $74?

27. 56.32 is 64% of what?

28. 71.04 is 96% of what?

29. 70% of what is 14?

30. 70% of what is 35?

31. What is $62\frac{1}{2}$% of 10?

32. What is $35\frac{1}{4}$% of 1200?

33. What is 8.3% of $10,200?

34. What is 9.2% of $5600?

35. $66\frac{2}{3}$% of what is 27.4?
$\left(Hint:\ 66\frac{2}{3}\% = \frac{2}{3}.\right)$

36. $33\frac{1}{3}$% of what is 17.2?

37. **D**_W Write a percent problem that could be translated to the equation
$$25 = 0.04 \cdot b.$$

38. **D**_W Write a percent problem that could be translated to the equation
$$30 = p \cdot 80.$$

SKILL MAINTENANCE

Write fraction notation. [5.1b]

39. 0.623

40. 1.9

41. 2.37

Write decimal notation. [5.1b]

42. $\dfrac{9}{1000}$

43. $\dfrac{39}{100}$

44. $\dfrac{57}{10}$

45. Each mocha served at Razer's Coffee House requires $\frac{2}{3}$ oz of chocolate. How many mochas can be made with one 12-oz can of chocolate? [3.8b]

46. Each of Sadie's digital photos uses $\frac{3}{5}$ megabytes of computer memory. How many photos can be stored in a file with 12 megabytes available? [3.8b]

SYNTHESIS

47. **D**_W Suppose we know that 40% of 92 is 36.8. What is a quick way to find 4% of 92? 400% of 92? Explain.

48. **D**_W To calculate a 15% tip on a $24 bill, a customer adds $2.40 and half of $2.40, or $1.20, to get $3.60. Is this procedure valid? Why or why not?

Solve.

49. ▦ What is 7.75% of $10,880?
Estimate _____
Calculate _____

50. ▦ 50,951.775 is what percent of 78,995?
Estimate _____
Calculate _____

51. *Recyclables.* It is estimated that 40% to 50% of all trash is recyclable. If a community produces 270 tons of trash, how much of their trash is recyclable?

52. *Batting.* An all-star baseball player gets a hit in 30% to 35% of all at-bats. If an all-star had 520 to 580 at-bats, how many hits would he have had?

8.4 APPLICATIONS OF PERCENT

Objectives

a Solve applied problems involving percent.

b Solve applied problems involving percent of increase or decrease.

a Applied Problems Involving Percent

CONNECTING THE CONCEPTS

Perhaps no topic in mathematics offers more applications to the real world than the study of percents. Most students have some idea of what percents are before they begin a course in Prealgebra, but for many it is only a rough idea based loosely on intuition. Although intuition is valuable, you should rely upon it now mainly as a check. As is usually the case with real-world problems, finding exact solutions requires that you possess a solid understanding of the underlying mathematics. With that understanding in place, you should feel confident that you can solve a wide array of real-world problems. As with earlier applications, look for similarities between problems that may appear to be quite different. You will find that whether it's money collecting interest or a population that is growing, the same type of math is used.

EXAMPLE 1 *Presidential Deaths in Office.* George W. Bush was inaugurated as the 43rd President of the United States in 2001. Because Grover Cleveland was both the 22nd and the 24th president, there have been only 42 different presidents. Of the 42 presidents, 8 died while in office: William Henry Harrison, Zachary Taylor, Abraham Lincoln, James A. Garfield, William McKinley, Warren G. Harding, Franklin D. Roosevelt, and John F. Kennedy. What percent died while in office?

Harrison   Taylor   Garfield   McKinley

Harding   Roosevelt   Kennedy

1. Familiarize. The question asks for the percent of presidents who died in office. We note that 42 is approximately 40 and 8 is $\frac{1}{5}$, or 20%, of 40, so our answer should be close to 20%. We let $p =$ the percent who died in office.

2. Translate.   We can rephrase the question and translate as follows.*

8   is   what percent   of   42?
↓   ↓   ↓   ↓   ↓
8   = p ·   42

3. Solve.   We solve as we did in Section 8.3:

$$8 = p \cdot 42$$

$$\frac{8}{42} = \frac{p \cdot 42}{42} \qquad \text{Dividing both sides by 42}$$

$$\frac{8}{42} = p$$

$$0.190 \approx p \qquad \text{Finding decimal notation and rounding to the nearest thousandth}$$

$$19.0\% \approx p \qquad \text{Remember to find percent notation.}$$

Note here that the solution, p, includes the % symbol.

4. Check.   To check, we note that the answer 19.0% is close to 20%, as estimated in the *Familiarize* step.

5. State.   About 19.0% of the U.S. presidents died while in office.

Do Exercise 1.

◼ **EXAMPLE 2**   *Water Consumed in Beverages.*   The average adult ingests 2500 milliliters (mL) of water each day, which is about 2.5 qt. About 60% of this comes from beverages. How many milliliters of water does the average adult ingest as beverages in one day?
Source: Elaine N. Meriab, *Essentials of Anatomy & Physiology*, 6th ed. San Francisco: Benjamin/Cummings Science Publishing, 2000

1. Familiarize.   We can make a drawing of a pie chart to help familiarize ourselves with the problem. We let b = the total number of milliliters of water consumed through beverages.

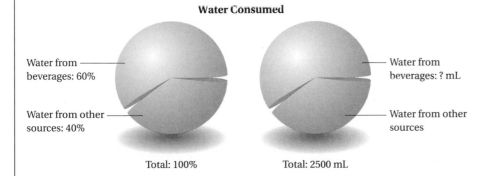

Water Consumed

Water from beverages: 60%
Water from other sources: 40%
Total: 100%

Water from beverages: ? mL
Water from other sources
Total: 2500 mL

2. Translate.   The question can be rephrased and translated as follows:*

Percent equation:

What number   is   60%   of   2500?
     ↓   ↓   ↓   ↓   ↓
     b =   0.60   ·   2500

3. Solve.   To solve, we need only multiply:

$$b = 0.60 \cdot 2500 = 1500.$$

---

*We can also use the proportion method of Section 8.2 to solve.

1. Presidential Assassinations in Office.   Of the 42 U.S. presidents, 4 were assassinated in office. These were Garfield, McKinley, Lincoln, and Kennedy. What percent were assassinated in office?

2. Water Consumed in Food.   The average adult ingests 2500 mL of water each day. About 30% of this comes from foods. How many milliliters of water does the average adult consume in food in one day?
Source: Elaine N. Meriab, *Essentials of Anatomy & Physiology*, 6th ed. San Francisco: Benjamin/Cummings Science Publishing, 2000

Answers on page A-26

3. Energy Consumption. By using only cold water in the washing machine, a household with a monthly fuel bill of $78.00 can reduce their bill to $74.88. What is the percent of decrease?

Answer on page A-26

CALCULATOR CORNER

On many calculators, there is a fast way to increase or decrease a number by any given percentage. In Example 4, the result of taking 6% of $27,000 and adding it to $27,000 can often be found by pressing

[2][7][0][0][0][+]
[6][SHIFT][%][=].

The displayed result would be

[28620].

If the salary had been *reduced* by 6%, the computation would be

[2][7][0][0][0][−]
[6][SHIFT][%][=].

The result would then be

[25380].

Check your manual for other procedures for determining percents.

Exercises:

1. Use a calculator with a [%] key to confirm your answer to Margin Exercise 4.

2. The selling price of Lisa's $87,000 condominium was reduced 8%. Find the new price.

---

4. Check. To check, we can repeat the calculations. We can also note that 60% of 2500 is the same as three-fifths of 2500, and $\frac{3}{5} \cdot 2500$ is 1500.

5. State. The amount of water consumed in beverages by the average adult in one day is 1500 mL.

Do Exercise 2 on the previous page.

[b] Percent of Increase or Decrease

What does it mean to say that the price of oil has decreased 8%? If the price was $7.00 per barrel and it went down to $6.44 per barrel, then the decrease is $0.56, which is 8% of the original price. We can see this in the following figure.

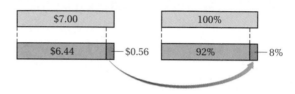

EXAMPLE 3 *Energy Consumption.* With proper furnace maintenance, a family that pays a monthly fuel bill of $78.00 can reduce their bill to $70.20. What is the percent of decrease?

1. **Familiarize.** We find the amount of decrease and then make a drawing.

$$
\begin{array}{rl}
7\,8.0\,0 & \text{Original bill} \\
-\ 7\,0.2\,0 & \text{New bill} \\
\hline
7.8\,0 & \text{Decrease}
\end{array}
$$

We let p = the percent of decrease.

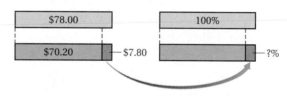

2. **Translate.** We rephrase and translate as follows.*

$$
\begin{array}{ccccc}
7.80 & \text{is} & \underline{\text{what percent}} & \text{of} & 78.00? \\
\downarrow & \downarrow & \downarrow & \downarrow & \downarrow \\
7.80 & = & p & \cdot & 78.00
\end{array}
$$

3. **Solve.** To solve the equation, we divide both sides by 78:

$$\frac{7.80}{78.00} = \frac{p \cdot 78.00}{78.00} \qquad \text{Dividing both sides by 78}$$

$$0.1 = p \qquad \text{You may have noticed earlier that 7.8 is 10\% of 78.}$$

$$10\% = p. \qquad \text{Changing from decimal to percent notation}$$

4. **Check.** To check, we note that, with a 10% decrease, the reduced bill should be 90% of the original bill. Since 90% of $78 = 0.9(78) = 70.20$, our answer checks.

5. **State.** The percent of decrease of the fuel bill is 10%.

Do Exercise 3.

---

*We can also use the proportion method of Section 8.2 to solve.

EXAMPLE 4 *Wages.* A new sixth-grade teacher earns a starting salary of $27,000 for one year and receives a 6% raise the following year. What is the new salary?

1. **Familiarize.** We note that the amount of the raise can be found and then added to the starting salary. A drawing can help us visualize this. We let x = the new salary.

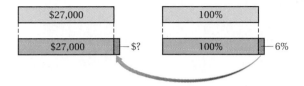

2. **Translate.** We rephrase the question and translate as follows.

What is the starting salary plus 6% of the starting salary?
x = 27,000 + 0.06 · 27,000

3. **Solve.** To solve, we simplify:

$x = 27,000 + 0.06(27,000)$

$= 27,000 + 1620$ The value of the raise is $1620.

$= 28,620.$

4. **Check.** To check, we note that the new salary is 100% of the starting salary plus 6% of the starting salary. Thus the new salary is 106% of the starting salary. Since $1.06(27,000) = 28,620$, our answer checks.

5. **State.** The new salary is $28,620.

Do Exercise 4.

Percents provide a way to measure increases or decreases relative to the original amount. For example, the average salary of an NBA basketball player increased from $4.2 million in 2000 to $4.55 million in 2002. To find the *percent of increase* in salary, we first subtract to find out how much more the salary was in 2002: $4.55 million − $4.2 million = $0.35 million. Then we determine what percent of the original amount the increase was:
Sources: *USA Today*; ESPN.com

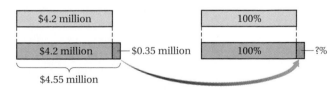

$0.35 = p \cdot 4.2$

$\dfrac{0.35}{4.2} = p$ Dividing both sides by 4.2

$0.08\overline{3} = p$

From 2000 to 2002 the average NBA salary grew $8\frac{1}{3}\%$.

Answer on page A-26

4. Wages. A daycare worker earns $20,500 one year and receives a 6% raise the next year. What is the new salary?

5. Doctor Visits. The average length of a visit paid for by Health Maintenance Organizations increased from 15.4 min in 1989 to 17.9 min in 1998. What was the percent of increase in the length of an average visit?
Source: *The New England Journal of Medicine*

■ **EXAMPLE 5**   *Doctor Visits.*   The average length of a doctor's visit paid for by a patient or insurance company increased from 16.4 min in 1989 to 18.5 min in 1998. What was the percent of increase in the time of an average visit?
Source: *The New England Journal of Medicine*

1. **Familiarize.**   We note that the increase in time was 18.5 − 16.4, or 2.1 min. A drawing can help us visualize the situation. We let $p = $ the percent of increase.

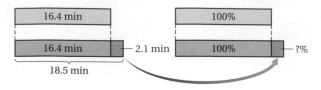

2. **Translate.**   We rephrase the question and translate:

$$\underbrace{2.1 \text{ min}}_{2.1} \quad \underset{=}{\text{is}} \quad \underbrace{\text{what percent}}_{p} \quad \underset{\cdot}{\text{of}} \quad \underbrace{16.4?}_{16.4}$$

3. **Solve.**   To solve the equation, we divide both sides by 16.4:*

$$2.1 = p \cdot 16.4$$

$$\frac{2.1}{16.4} = \frac{p \cdot 16.4}{16.4} \qquad \text{Dividing both sides by 16.4}$$

$$\frac{2.1}{16.4} = p$$

$$0.128 \approx p \qquad \text{Rounding to the nearest thousandth}$$

$$12.8\% \approx p. \qquad \text{Converting to percent notation}$$

4. **Check.**   To check, we take 12.8% of 16.4:

$$0.128 \cdot 16.4 = 2.0992.$$

Since we rounded the percent, this approximation is close enough to 2.1 to be a good check.

5. **State.**   The percent of increase in the average length of a visit to a doctor was 12.8%.

Do Exercise 5.

---

*We can also use the proportion method of Section 8.2 and solve:

$$\frac{N}{100} = \frac{2.1}{16.4}.$$

Answer on page A-26

CALCULATOR CORNER

Calculators can be very useful when analyzing stock performance. Two important statistics, the price-earnings ratio and the yield, are discussed below.

The Price–Earnings Ratio   If the total earnings of a company one year were $5,000,000 and 100,000 shares of stock were issued, the earnings per share was $50. At one time, the price per share of Coca-Cola was $58.125 and the earnings per share was $0.76. The **price-earnings ratio,** P/E, is the price of the stock divided by the earnings per share. For the Coca-Cola stock, the price–earnings ratio, P/E, is given by

$$\frac{P}{E} = \frac{58.125}{0.76} \approx 76.48.$$ Dividing, using a calculator, and rounding to the nearest hundredth

Stock Yields   At one time, the price per share of Coca-Cola stock was $58.125 and the company was paying a yearly dividend of $0.68 per share. It is helpful to those interested in stocks to know what percent the dividend is of the price of the stock. The percent is called the **yield.** For the Coca-Cola stock, the yield is given by

$$\text{Yield} = \frac{\text{Dividend}}{\text{Price per share}} = \frac{0.68}{58.125} \approx 0.0117$$ Dividing and rounding to the nearest ten-thousandth

$$= 1.17\%$$ Converting to percent notation

Exercises: Compute the price–earnings ratio and the yield for each stock listed below.

	STOCK	PRICE PER SHARE	EARNINGS	DIVIDEND	P/E	YIELD
1.	Pepsi (PEP)	$42.75	$1.40	$0.56		
2.	Pearson (PSO)	$25.00	$0.78	$0.30		
3.	Quaker Oats (OAT)	$92.375	$2.68	$1.10		
4.	Texas Insts (TEX)	$42.875	$1.62	$0.43		
5.	Ford Motor Co (F)	$27.5625	$2.30	$1.19		
6.	Wendy's Intl (WEN)	$25.75	$1.47	$0.23		

8.4

EXERCISE SET

For Extra Help

Digital Video
Tutor CD 5
Videotape 8

InterAct
Math

Math Tutor
Center

MathXL

MyMathLab

a   Solve.

1. *Panda Survival.*   Breeding the much-loved panda bear in captivity has been quite difficult for zookeepers.

   a) From 1964 to 1997, of 133 panda cubs born in captivity, only 90 lived to be one month old. What percent lived to be one month old?

   b) In 1999, Mark Edwards of the San Diego Zoo developed a nutritional formula on which 18 of 20 newborns lived to be one month old. What percent lived to be one month old?

2. *Politics.*   In the 2000 election, George W. Bush received 50.5 million of the 105.4 million votes cast. What percent of the votes did he receive?
   Source: *Congressional Quarterly*

3. *Pass Completions.*   At one point in 2003, Tennessee Titan quarterback Steve McNair had completed 58.78% of his passes throughout his career. He had attempted 2780 passes. How many did he complete?
   Source: National Football League

4. *Pass Completions.*   At one point during the 2002 NFL season, Kerry Collins, quarterback of the New York Giants, had completed 64.0% of his passes. He had attempted 203 passes. How many did he complete?
   Source: National Football League

5. *Overweight and Obese.*   Of the 281 million people in the United States, 60% are considered overweight and 25% are considered obese. How many are overweight? How many are obese?
   Source: U.S. Centers for Disease Control

6. *Smoking and Diabetes.*   Of the 281 million people in the United States, 25% are smokers and 6.5% have diabetes. How many are smokers? How many have diabetes?
   Source: U.S. Centers for Disease Control

7. A lab technician has 680 mL of a solution of water and acid; 3% is acid. How many milliliters are acid? water?

8. A lab technician has 540 mL of a solution of alcohol and water; 8% is alcohol. How many milliliters are alcohol? water?

9. *Field Goals.* At one point in the 2002–2003 NBA season, Tracy McGrady of the Orlando Magic had made 46.7% of his field goal attempts. He made 298 field goals. How many did he attempt?
Source: National Basketball Association

10. *Field Goals.* At one point in the 2002–2003 NBA season, Allen Iverson of the Philadelphia 76ers had made 38.8% of his field goal attempts. He made 306 field goals. How many did he attempt?
Source: National Basketball Association

11. *Test Results.* On a test of 80 items, Antonio got 76 correct. What percent were correct? incorrect?

12. *Test Results.* On a test of 40 items, Cole got 33 correct. What percent were correct? incorrect?

13. *Test Results.* On a test of 40 items, Christina got 91% correct. (There was partial credit on one item.) How many items did she get incorrect?

14. *Test Results.* On a test of 80 items, Pedro got 93% correct. (There was partial credit on one item.) How many items did he get incorrect?

15. *Test Results.* On a test, Maj Ling got 86%, or 81.7, of the items correct. (There was partial credit on some items.) How many items were on the test?

16. *Test Results.* On a test, Juan got 85%, or 119, of the items correct. How many items were on the test?

17. *TV Usage.* Of the 8760 hr in a year, most television sets are on for 2190 hr. What percent is this?

18. *Colds from Kissing.* In a medical study, it was determined that if 800 people kiss someone who has a cold, only 56 will actually catch a cold. What percent is this?
Source: U.S. Centers for Disease Control

19. *Maximum Heart Rate.* Treadmill tests are often administered to diagnose heart ailments. A guideline in such a test is to try to get you to reach your *maximum heart rate*, in beats per minute. The maximum heart rate is found by subtracting your age from 220 and then multiplying by 85%. What is the maximum heart rate of someone whose age is 25? 36? 48? 55? 76? Round to the nearest one.

20. It costs an oil company $40,000 a day to operate two refineries. Refinery A accounts for 37.5% of the cost, and refinery B for the rest of the cost.

   a) What percent of the cost does it take to run refinery B?

   b) What is the cost of operating refinery A? refinery B?

b Solve.

21. *Savings Increase.* The amount in a savings account increased from $200 to $216. What was the percent of increase?

22. *Population Increase.* The population of a small mountain town increased from 840 to 882. What was the percent of increase?

23. During a sale, a dress decreased in price from $90 to $72. What was the percent of decrease?

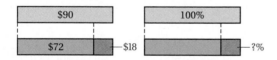

24. A person on a diet goes from a weight of 125 lb to a weight of 110 lb. What is the percent of decrease?

25. *Population Increase.* The population of the state of New York increased from 18,989,332 in 2000 to 19,011,378 in 2001. What is the percent of increase?
Source: U.S. Bureau of the Census

26. *Population Increase.* The population of the state of Oregon increased from 3,429,293 in 2000 to 3,472,867 in 2001. What is the percent of increase?
Source: U.S. Bureau of the Census

27. Ike earns $28,600 one year and receives a 5% raise in salary. What is his new salary?

28. Rhonda earns $30,500 one year and receives an 8% raise in salary. What is her new salary?

29. *Cooling Costs.* By increasing the thermostat from 72° to 78°, a family can reduce its cooling bill by 50%. If the cooling bill was $106.00, what would the new bill be?

30. *World Population.* World population is increasing by 1.6% each year. In 2002, it was 6.2 billion. Estimate the population in 2003.
Sources: Population Reference Bureau; U.S. Bureau of the Census

31. *Two-by-Four.* A cross-section of a standard or nominal "two-by-four" board actually measures $1\frac{1}{2}$ in. by $3\frac{1}{2}$ in. The rough board is 2 in. by 4 in., but is planed and dried to the finished size. What percent of the wood is removed in planing and drying?

32. *Portable DVD Player.* Several years ago, a Sharp Portable DVD video player had a retail price of $1,499.95. Amazon.com offered it on its Web site at a sale price of $899.88. What was the percent of decrease?
Sources: Sharp Electronics Corporation; Amazon.com

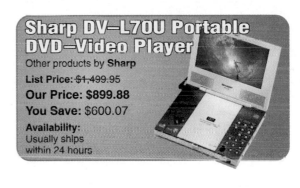

33. *DVD Price.* The set of DVDs *Ken Burns: Jazz* has a retail price of $199.98. Barnes & Noble offers it on its Web site at a sale price of $149.98. What is the percent of decrease?
Source: Barnes & Noble

34. *Tipping.* Diners frequently add a 15% tip when paying for a meal at a restaurant. What is the total amount paid if the cost of the meal, without tip, is $18? $34? $49?

35. *Population Decrease.* Between 1990 and 2000, the population of Washington, D.C., decreased from 606,900 to 572,059.

a) What is the percent of decrease?
b) If this percent of decrease repeated itself in the following decade, what would the population be in 2010?

Source: U.S. Bureau of the Census

36. *U.S. Population.* Between 2010 and 2015, the U.S. population is expected to grow from 298,710,000 to 311,069,000.

a) What is the percent of increase?
b) If this percent of increase repeated itself, what would the population be in 2020?

Source: U.S. Bureau of the Census

Life Insurance Rates for Smokers and Nonsmokers. The following table provides data showing how yearly rates (premiums) for a $500,000 term life insurance policy are increased for smokers. Complete the missing numbers in the table.

TYPICAL INSURANCE PREMIUMS (DOLLARS)

	AGE	RATE FOR NONSMOKER	RATE FOR SMOKER	PERCENT INCREASE FOR SMOKER
	35	$ 345	$ 630	83%
37.	40	$ 430	$ 735	
38.	45	$ 565		84%
39.	50	$ 780		100%
40.	55	$ 985		117%
41.	60	$1645	$2955	
42.	65	$2943	$5445	

Source: Pacific Life PL Protector Term Life Portfolio, OYT Rates

Population Increase. The following table provides data showing how the populations of various states increased from 1990 to 2000. Complete the missing numbers in the table.

	STATE	POPULATION IN 1990	POPULATION IN 2000	CHANGE	PERCENT CHANGE
43.	Vermont	562,758	608,827		
44.	Virginia	6,187,358	7,078,515		
45.	Washington	4,866,692	5,894,121		
46.	West Virginia	1,793,477		14,867	
47.	Wisconsin		5,363,675	471,906	
48.	Wyoming	453,588		40,194	

Source: U.S. Bureau of the Census

49. *Car Depreciation.* A car generally depreciates 25% of its original value in the first year. A car is worth $27,300 after the first year. What was its original cost?

50. *Car Depreciation.* Given normal use, an American-made car will depreciate 25% of its original cost the first year and 14% of its remaining value in the second year. What is the value of a car at the end of the second year if its original cost was $36,400? $28,400? $26,800?

51. *Strike Zone.* In baseball, the *strike zone* is normally a 17-in. by 30-in. rectangle. Some batters give the pitcher an advantage by swinging at pitches thrown out of the strike zone. By what percent is the area of the strike zone increased if a 2-in. border is added to the outside?
Source: Major League Baseball

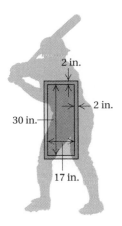

52. Tony is planting grass on a 24-ft by 36-ft area in his back yard. He installs a 6-ft by 8-ft garden. By what percent has he reduced the area he has to mow?

53. *Fetal Acoustic Stimulation.* Each year there are about 4 million births in the United States. Of these, about 120,000 births occur in breech position (with the buttocks or feet appearing first). A technique called *fetal acoustic stimulation (FAS)* uses sound directed through a mother's abdomen to stimulate movement of the fetus to a safer position. In a study of this procedure, FAS enabled doctors to turn the baby in 34 of 38 cases.
Source: Johnson and Elliott, "Fetal Acoustic Stimulation, an Adjunct to External Cephalic Versions: A Blinded, Randomized Crossover Study," *American Journal of Obstetrics & Gynecology* **173**, no. 5 (1995): 1369–1372

a) What percent of U.S. births are breech?
b) What percent (rounded to the nearest tenth) of cases showed success with FAS?
c) About how many breech babies yearly might be turned if FAS could be implemented in all breech births in the United States?
d) Breech position is one reason for performing Caesarean section (or C-section) birth surgery. Researchers expect that FAS alone can eliminate the need for about 2000 C-sections yearly in the United States. Given this information, how many C-sections per year are due to breech position alone?

54. *Drunk Driving Fatalities.* The data in the table show the number of deaths due to drunk drivers from 1990 to 2000.

a) What is the percent of increase in the number of alcohol-related deaths from 1999 to 2000?
b) What is the percent of decrease in the number of alcohol-related deaths from 1990 to 2000?

ALCOHOL-RELATED TRAFFIC DEATHS INCREASING OR DECREASING?

YEAR	DEATHS	YEAR	DEATHS
1990	22,084	1996	17,218
1991	19,887	1997	16,189
1992	17,859	1998	16,020
1993	17,473	1999	15,976
1994	16,589	2000	16,653
1995	17,274		

Source: National Highway Traffic Safety Administration

55. D_W What makes better sense (see Exercises 49 and 50): buying a new car, or buying a one-year-old car for 25% less? Why?

56. D_W See Exercise 29. Does it follow that raising the thermostat from 78° to 84° would reduce the cooling bill to 0?

Convert to decimal notation. [5.1a], [5.5a]

57. $\dfrac{25}{11}$

58. $\dfrac{11}{25}$

59. $\dfrac{27}{8}$

60. $\dfrac{43}{9}$

61. $\dfrac{23}{25}$

62. $\dfrac{20}{24}$

63. $\dfrac{14}{32}$

64. $\dfrac{2317}{1000}$

65. $\dfrac{34,809}{10,000}$

66. $\dfrac{27}{40}$

67. D_W Exercise 17 reads: "Of the 8760 hr in a year, most television sets are on for 2190 hr. What percent is this?" Will the answer to this change for a leap year? Why or why not?

68. D_W Which is better for a wage earner, and why: a 10% raise followed by a 5% raise a year later, or a 5% raise followed by a 10% raise a year later?

69. *Adult Height.* It has been determined that at the age of 10, a girl has reached 84.4% of her final adult height. Cynthia is 4 ft, 8 in. at the age of 10. What will be her final adult height?

70. *Adult Height.* It has been determined that at the age of 15, a boy has reached 96.1% of his final adult height. Claude is 6 ft, 4 in. at the age of 15. What will be his final adult height?

71. If p is 120% of q, then q is what percent of p?

72. A coupon allows a couple to have dinner and then have $10 subtracted from the bill. Before subtracting $10, however, the restaurant adds a tip of 15%. If the couple is presented with an adjusted bill for $44.05, how much would the dinner (without tip) have cost without the coupon?

The article below appeared in the *New York Times* on January 14, 2003. Use the information in the article to answer Exercises 73 and 74.

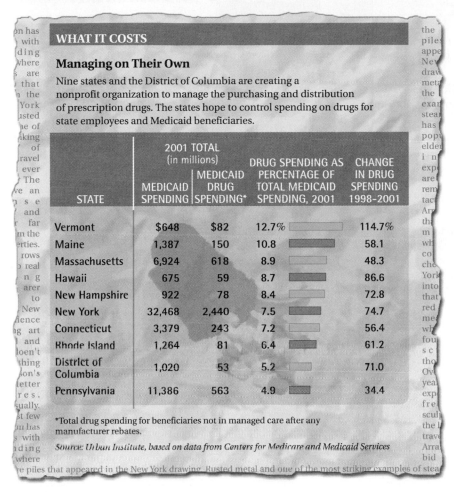

WHAT IT COSTS

Managing on Their Own

Nine states and the District of Columbia are creating a nonprofit organization to manage the purchasing and distribution of prescription drugs. The states hope to control spending on drugs for state employees and Medicaid beneficiaries.

STATE	2001 TOTAL (in millions)		DRUG SPENDING AS PERCENTAGE OF TOTAL MEDICAID SPENDING, 2001	CHANGE IN DRUG SPENDING 1998-2001
	MEDICAID SPENDING	MEDICAID DRUG SPENDING*		
Vermont	$648	$82	12.7%	114.7%
Maine	1,387	150	10.8	58.1
Massachusetts	6,924	618	8.9	48.3
Hawaii	675	59	8.7	86.6
New Hampshire	922	78	8.4	72.8
New York	32,468	2,440	7.5	74.7
Connecticut	3,379	243	7.2	56.4
Rhode Island	1,264	81	6.4	61.2
District of Columbia	1,020	53	5.2	71.0
Pennsylvania	11,386	563	4.9	34.4

*Total drug spending for beneficiaries not in managed care after any manufacturer rebates.

Source: Urban Institute, based on data from Centers for Medicare and Medicaid Services

re piles that appeared in the New York drawing. Rusted metal and one of the most striking examples of stea

Source: *The New York Times*, January 14, 2003

73. How much more did New York spend than Hawaii on Medicaid drugs in 1998?

74. How much more did Pennsylvania spend than Massachusetts on Medicaid drugs in 1998?

75. A worker receives raises of 3%, 6%, and then 9%. By what percent has the original salary increased?

76. **DW** The former baseball player and manager Yogi Berra once said that "Ninety percent of the game is half mental." If this is true, what percent of the game is mental? Explain your reasoning.

77. **DW** A workers' union is offered either a 5% "across-the-board" raise in which all salaries would increase 5%, or a flat $1650 raise for each worker. If the total payroll for the 123 workers is $4,213,365, which offer should the union select? Why?

1. California Sales Tax. The sales tax rate in parts of California is 8%. How much tax is charged on the purchase of a refrigerator that sells for $668.95? What is the total price?

2. Mississippi Sales Tax. For her book group, Maggie buys 5 copies of Dean Koontz's novel *From the Corner of His Eye* for $26.95 each. The sales tax rate in Mississippi is 7%. How much sales tax will be charged? What is the total price?

a Sales Tax

Sales tax computations represent a special type of percent of increase problem. For example, in Maryland the sales tax rate is 5%. This means that the tax is 5% of the purchase price. Suppose the purchase price on a coat is $124.95. The sales tax is then 5% of $124.95, or $0.05 \cdot 124.95$, or 6.2475, or about $6.25.

BILL:

Purchase price	=	$124.95
Sales tax (5% of $124.95)	=	+ 6.25
Total price		$131.20

The total that you pay is the price plus the sales tax:

$124.95 + $6.25, or $131.20.

SALES TAX

Sales tax = Sales tax rate · Purchase price

Total price = Purchase price + Sales tax

EXAMPLE 1 *Florida Sales Tax.* The sales tax rate in Florida is 6%. How much tax is charged on the purchase of 3 copies of the DVD *Red Dragon* at $19.98 each? What is the total price?

a) We first find the cost of the DVDs. It is

$3 \cdot \$19.98 = \$59.94$.

b) The sales tax on items costing $59.94 is

$$\underbrace{\text{Sales tax rate}}_{} \cdot \underbrace{\text{Purchase price}}_{}$$
$$6\% \quad \cdot \quad \$59.94, \quad \text{or} \quad 0.06 \cdot 59.94$$

or 3.5964 . Thus the tax is $3.60.

c) The total price is given by the purchase price plus the sales tax:

$59.94 + $3.60, or $63.54.

To check, note that the total price is the purchase price plus 6% of the purchase price. Thus the total price is 106% of the purchase price. Since $1.06 \cdot 59.94 \approx 63.54$, we have a check. The sales tax is $3.60 and the total price is $63.54.

Do Exercises 1 and 2.

EXAMPLE 2 The sales tax is $83.96 on the purchase of building materials, which cost $2099. What is the sales tax rate?

GERI's Building Supplies

Total Merchandise: $2099.00
Sales Tax: $83.96

Total: $2182.96

Rephrase: Sales tax is what percent of purchase price?

Translate: $83.96 $=$ r $\cdot$ $2099

To solve the equation, we divide both sides by 2099:

$$\frac{83.96}{2099} = \frac{r \cdot 2099}{2099}$$

$$\frac{83.96}{2099} = r$$

$$0.04 = r$$

$$4\% = r.$$

The sales tax rate is 4%.

Do Exercise 3.

EXAMPLE 3 The sales tax on an inkjet photo printer is $17.19 and the sales tax rate is 5%. Find the purchase price (the price before taxes are added).

Rephrase: Sales tax is 5% of what?

Translate: 17.19 $=$ 5% $\cdot$ b, or 17.19 $= 0.05 \cdot b$.

To solve, we divide both sides by 0.05:

$$\frac{17.19}{0.05} = \frac{0.05 \cdot b}{0.05}$$

$$\frac{17.19}{0.05} = b$$

$$343.80 = b.$$

The purchase price is $343.80.

Do Exercise 4.

3. The sales tax is $50.94 on the purchase of a washer and dryer that cost $849. What is the sales tax?

4. The sales tax on a cable-ready television is $25.20 and the sales tax rate is 6%. Find the purchase price (the price before taxes are added).

Cable Ready
TV $?
$25.20 tax
at 6%

New
Low Price

$?
$17.19
TAX
@5%

Answers on page A-26

b Commission

When you work for a **salary,** you receive the same amount of money each week or month. When you work for a **commission,** you are paid a percentage of the total sales you complete.

COMMISSION

Commission = Commission rate · Sales

EXAMPLE 4 *Stereo Equipment Sales.* A salesperson's commission rate is 7%. What is the commission from the sale of $25,560 worth of stereophonic equipment?

Commission	=	Commission rate	·	Sales
C	=	7%	·	25,560
C	=	0.07	·	25,560
C	=	1789.20		

The commission is $1789.20.

Do Exercise 5.

EXAMPLE 5 *Farm Machinery Sales.* Dawn earns a commission of $31,000 from selling $620,000 worth of farm machinery. What is the commission rate?

Commission	=	Commission rate	·	Sales
31,000	=	r	·	620,000

Answer on page A-26

Study Tips

STUDYING TOGETHER BY PHONE

Working with a classmate over the telephone can be a very effective way to receive or give help. The fact that you cannot point to figures on paper forces you to verbalize the mathematics and the act of speaking mathematics will improve your understanding of the material. In some cases it may be more effective to study with a classmate over the phone than in person.

To solve this equation, we divide both sides by 620,000:

$$\frac{31,000}{620,000} = \frac{r \cdot 620,000}{620,000}$$

$$\frac{1}{20} \cdot \frac{31,000}{31,000} = r \qquad \text{Removing a factor equal to 1: } \frac{31,000}{31,000} = 1$$

$$0.05 = r$$

$$5\% = r.$$

The commission rate is 5%.

Do Exercise 6.

EXAMPLE 6 *Motorcycle Sales.* Joyce's commission rate is 8%. She receives a commission of $425 on the sale of a motorcycle. How much did the motorcycle cost?

$$\begin{array}{ccccc}
Commission & = & Commission\ rate & \cdot & Sales \\
425 & = & 8\% & \cdot & S, \qquad \text{or } 425 = 0.08 \cdot S
\end{array}$$

To solve this equation, we divide both sides by 0.08:

$$\frac{425}{0.08} = \frac{0.08 \cdot S}{0.08}$$

$$\frac{42,500}{8} = S \qquad \text{Multiplying } \frac{425}{0.08} \text{ by } \frac{100}{100}, \text{ or } 1$$

$$5312.50 = S. \qquad \text{Dividing 42,500 by 8}$$

The motorcycle cost $5312.50.

Do Exercise 7.

C Discount

Suppose that the regular price of a rug is $60, and the rug is on sale at 25% off. Since 25% of $60 is $15, the sale price is $60 − $15, or $45. We call $60 the **original,** or **marked price,** 25% the **rate of discount,** $15 the **discount,** and $45 the **sale price.** Note that discount problems are a type of percent of decrease problem.

> ### DISCOUNT AND SALE PRICE
>
> **Discount** = Rate of discount · Original price
> **Sale price** = Original price − Discount

6. Liz earns a commission of $3000 selling $24,000 worth of Phish concert tickets. What is the commission rate?

7. Ben's commission rate is 16%. He receives a commission of $268 from sales of clothing. How many dollars worth of clothing were sold?

Answers on page A-26

8. As part of their 16th anniversary celebration, Benninger's has a $350 suit on sale at 16% off. What is the discount? the sale price?

9. A pair of hiking boots is reduced from $95 to $76. Find the rate of discount.

Answers on page A-26

EXAMPLE 7 A rug marked $240 is on sale at $33\frac{1}{3}\%$ off. What is the discount? the sale price?

a) *Discount* = *Rate of discount* · *Original price*

$$D = 33\frac{1}{3}\% \cdot 240$$

$$D = \frac{1}{3} \cdot 240 \qquad \text{Note that } 33\frac{1}{3}\% = \frac{1}{3}$$

$$D = \frac{240}{3} = 80$$

b) *Sale price* = *Original price* − *Discount*

$$S = 240 - 80$$

$$S = 160$$

> To check, note that the sale price is $\frac{2}{3}$ of the marked price: $\frac{2}{3} \cdot 240 = 160$.

The discount is $80 and the sale price is $160.

Do Exercise 8.

EXAMPLE 8 *Antiques.* An antique table is marked down from $620 to $527. What is the rate of discount?

We first find the discount by subtracting the sale price from the original price:

$$620 - 527 = 93.$$

The discount is $93.

Next, we use the equation for discount:

Discount = *Rate of discount* · *Original price*

$$93 = r \cdot 620.$$

To solve, we divide both sides by 620:

$$\frac{93}{620} = \frac{r \cdot 620}{620}$$

$$\frac{93}{620} = r$$

$$0.15 = r$$

$$15\% = r.$$

> To check, note that a 15% discount rate means that 85% of the original price is paid: $0.85 \times 620 = 527$.

The discount rate is 15%.

Do Exercise 9.

Solve.

1. *Iowa Sales Tax.* The sales tax rate in Iowa is 5%. How much sales tax would be charged on an I-JAM MP-3 player that costs $219?

2. *Pennsylvania Sales Tax.* The sales tax rate in Pennsylvania is 6%. How much sales tax would be charged on an I-JAM MP-3 player that costs $219?

3. *Washington, D.C., Sales Tax.* The sales tax rate in Washington, D.C., is 5.75%. How much sales tax would be charged on a copy of J. K. Rowling's novel, *Harry Potter and the Order of the Phoenix,* which sells for $17.97?

4. *Fort Worth, Texas, Sales Tax.* The sales tax rate in Fort Worth, Texas, is 8.25%. How much sales tax would be charged on a copy of John Grisham's novel *A Painted House,* which sells for $27.95?
Sources: Borders Bookstore; Andrea Sutcliffe, *Numbers*

5. *Rhode Island Sales Tax.* The sales tax rate in Rhode Island is 7%. How much tax is charged on a purchase of 5 telephones at $53 apiece? What is the total price?

6. *Kentucky Sales Tax.* The sales tax rate in Kentucky is 6%. How much tax is charged on a purchase of 5 team sweatshirts at $37.99 apiece? What is the total price?

7. The sales tax is $24 on the purchase of a new transmission that sells for $480. What is the sales tax rate?

8. The sales tax is $15 on the purchase of a diamond ring that sells for $500. What is the sales tax rate?

9. The sales tax is $3.58 on the purchase of a camera that sells for $89.50. What is the sales tax rate?

10. The sales tax is $9.12 on the purchase of a patio set that sells for $456. What is the sales tax rate?

11. The transfer tax on a used car is $150 and the transfer tax rate is 5%. Find the purchase price (the price before taxes are added).

12. The sales tax on the purchase of a new boat is $112 and the sales tax rate is 2%. Find the purchase price.

13. The sales tax on a dining room set is $28 and the sales tax rate is 3.5%. Find the purchase price.

14. The sales tax on a portable CD player is $4.40 and the sales tax rate is 5.5%. Find the purchase price.

15. The sales tax rate in Austin is 2% for the city and county and 6.25% for the state. Find the total amount paid for 2 shower units at $332.50 apiece.

16. The sales tax rate in Omaha is 1.5% for the city and 5.5% for the state. Find the total amount paid for 3 air conditioners at $260 apiece.

17. The sales tax is $1464.75 on the purchase of a Dodge Caravan costing $23,625. What is the sales tax rate?

18. The sales tax is $1299.20 on the purchase of a Ford Mustang costing $22,400. What is the sales tax rate?

b   Solve.

19. Katrina's commission rate is 6%. What is her commission from the sale of $45,000 worth of furnaces?

20. Jose's commission rate is 32%. What is his commission from the sale of $12,500 worth of sailboards?

21. Vince earns $120 selling $2400 worth of television sets in a consignment shop. What is his commission rate?

22. Donna earns $408 selling $3400 worth of shoes. What is her commission rate?

23. The Fierson Gallery of Fine Art has a commission rate of 40%. They receive a commission of $392. How many dollars worth of artwork were sold?

24. A real-estate agent's commission rate is 7%. She receives a commission of $11,200 on the sale of a home. How much did the home sell for?

25. A real-estate commission is 6%. What is the commission on the sale of a $98,000 home?

26. A real-estate commission is 8%. What is the commission on the sale of a piece of land for $68,000?

27. Bonnie earns $280.80 selling $2340 worth of tee shirts. What is the commission rate?

28. Chuck earns $1147.50 selling $7650 worth of ski passes. What is the commission rate?

29. Miguel's commission is increased according to how much he sells. He receives a commission of 5% for the first $2000 and 8% on any amount over $2000. What is the total commission on sales of $6000?

30. Lucinda earns a salary of $500 a month, plus a 2% commission on sales. One month, she sold $990 worth of posters. What were her wages that month?

C Find what is missing.

	MARKED PRICE	RATE OF DISCOUNT	DISCOUNT	SALE PRICE
31.	$300	10%		
32.	$2000	40%		
33.	$17	15%		
34.	$20	25%		
35.		10%	$12.50	
36.		15%	$65.70	
37.	$600		$240	
38.	$12,800		$1920	

39. Find the discount and the rate of discount for the ring in this ad.

40. Find the discount and the rate of discount for the calculator in this ad.

1/2 CARAT T.W. DIAMOND, 14K GOLD LADY'S BRIDAL SET
WAS $1275.00
$888

Calc-U-Sure C96
Graphing Calculator
- 8 line × 16 character display
- Pull-down menus
- Uses 3 "AAA" batteries
- Sliding plastic cover
- Model C96
- Mfr. List $115.00

69⁹⁸

41. Find the original price and the rate of discount for the camcorder in this ad.

CANON
DIGITAL CAMCORDER

Reduced $83

• Large Video Head Cylinder For Jitter Free, Crisp Pictures
• 12:1 Variable Speed Power Zoom
• Lens Cover Opens Automatically When Camera Is Turned On

$377

Source: Canon U.S.A., Inc.

42. Find the marked price and the rate of discount for the cedar chest in this ad.

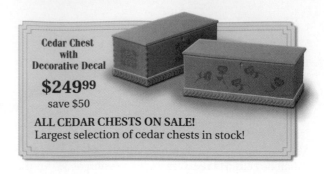

Cedar Chest with Decorative Decal

$249⁹⁹
save $50

ALL CEDAR CHESTS ON SALE!
Largest selection of cedar chests in stock!

43. **D**_W Is the following ad mathematically correct? Why or why not?

FAMOUS MAKER WATCHES

$13.95   Regularly $19.95

30% OFF

Choose from men's and ladies' casual or dress designs

Limited time offer

44. **D**_W Is a 40% discount the same as taking 20% off of a price that reflects a previous 20% discount? Why or why not?

SKILL MAINTENANCE

Solve.   [7.3b]

45. $\dfrac{x}{12} = \dfrac{24}{16}$

46. $\dfrac{7}{2} = \dfrac{11}{x}$

Graph.   [6.4b]

47. $y = \dfrac{4}{3}x$

48. $y = -\dfrac{4}{3}x + 1$

Write decimal notation.   [5.1b]

49. $\dfrac{5}{9}$

50. $\dfrac{23}{11}$

Simplify.   [5.4b]

51. $80\left(1 + \dfrac{0.06}{2}\right)^2$

52. $70\left(1 + \dfrac{0.08}{2}\right)^2$

53. $\mathbf{D_W}$ Carl's Car Care mistakenly charged Dawn 5% tax for a cleaning job that was all labor. To correct the mistake, they subtracted 5% from what Dawn paid. Was this correct? Why or why not?

54. $\mathbf{D_W}$ An item that is no longer on sale at "25% off" receives a price tag that is $33\frac{1}{3}\%$ more than the sale price. Has the item price been restored to its original price? Why or why not?

Cigarette Tax. Before taxes are added, the price of a pack of cigarettes is approximately $2.70. Use this information for Exercises 55 and 56.
Source: Campaign for Tobacco-Free Kids® 2003

55. State cigarette tax adds anywhere from 3¢ (in Kentucky) to $1.50 (in New Jersey) to the price of a pack. Approximate the range of state cigarette taxes as a percentage of the per-pack price.
Source: Campaign for Tobacco-Free Kids® 2003

56. State sales tax and federal cigarette tax combine to add another 39¢ (AL, CO, DE, MT, NH, OR) to 69¢ (RI, WA) to the price of a pack. Approximate the range of state sales and federal cigarette taxes (combined) as a percentage of the per-pack price.
Source: Campaign for Tobacco-Free Kids® 2003

57. 🔢 *Magazine Subscriptions.* In a recent subscription drive, *People* offered a subscription of 52 weekly issues for a price of $1.89 per issue. They advertised that this was a savings of 29.7% off the newsstand price. What was the newsstand price?

58. 🔢 Gordon receives a 10% commission on the first $5000 in sales and 15% on all sales beyond $5000. If Gordon receives a commission of $2405, how much did he sell? Use a calculator and trial and error if you wish.

59. Tee shirts are being sold at the mall for $5 each, or 3 for $10. If you buy three tee shirts, what is the rate of discount?

60. 🔢 A real-estate commission rate is 7.5%. A house sells for $98,500. How much does the seller get for the house after paying the commission?

61. $\mathbf{D_W}$ Herb collects baseball memorabilia. He bought two autographed plaques, but became short of funds and had to sell them quickly for $200 each. On one, he made a 20% profit and on the other, he lost 20%. Did he make or lose money on the sale? Explain.

SIMPLE AND COMPOUND INTEREST

Objectives

a Solve applied problems involving simple interest.

b Solve applied problems involving compound interest.

1. What is the simple interest on $4300 invested at an interest rate of 7% for 1 year?

2. What is the simple interest on a principal of $4300 invested at an interest rate of 7% for $\frac{3}{4}$ year?

Answers on page A-26

Study Tips

A CALCULATOR IN HAND IS BETTER THAN TWO IN A DESK

When reading material that involves lengthy calculations, it can be a big help to keep a calculator nearby. Checking the author's multiplication or division can help increase your confidence and, with that, your comprehension.

---

a **Simple Interest**

Suppose you put $1000 into an investment for 1 year. The $1000 is called the **principal.** If the yearly **interest rate** is 8%, in addition to the principal, you get back 8% of the principal, which is

8% of $1000, or 0.08 · $1000, or $80.00.

The $80.00 is called the **interest,** or more precisely, the **simple interest.** It is, in effect, the price paid for the use of the money over time.

> ### SIMPLE INTEREST FORMULA
>
> The **simple interest** I on principal P, invested for t years at interest rate r, is given by
> $$I = P \cdot r \cdot t.$$

EXAMPLE 1 What is the simple interest on $2500 invested at an interest rate of 6% for 1 year?

We use the formula $I = P \cdot r \cdot t$:

$$I = P \cdot r \cdot t = \$2500 \cdot 6\% \cdot 1$$
$$= \$2500 \cdot 0.06$$
$$= \$150.$$

The simple interest for 1 year is $150.

Do Exercise 1.

EXAMPLE 2 What is the simple interest on a principal of $2500 invested at an interest rate of 6% for $\frac{1}{4}$ year?

We use the formula $I = P \cdot r \cdot t$:

$$I = P \cdot r \cdot t = \$2500 \cdot 6\% \cdot \frac{1}{4}$$
$$= \frac{\$2500 \cdot 0.06}{4}$$
$$= \frac{\$150}{4} \qquad \text{Multiplying}$$
$$= \$37.50.$$

> We could instead have found $\frac{1}{4}$ of 6% and then multiplied by 2500.

$$
\begin{array}{r}
3\,7.5 \\
4\,)\,\overline{1\,5\,0.0} \\
\underline{1\,2\,0} \\
3\,0 \\
\underline{2\,8} \\
2\,0 \\
\underline{2\,0} \\
0
\end{array}
$$

The simple interest for $\frac{1}{4}$ year is $37.50.

Do Exercise 2.

When time is given in days, we generally divide it by 365 to express the time as a fractional part of a year.

EXAMPLE 3 To pay for a shipment of tee shirts, New Wave Designs borrows $8000 at $9\frac{3}{4}$% for 60 days. Find (a) the amount of simple interest that is due and (b) the total amount that must be paid after 60 days.

a) We express 60 days as a fractional part of a year:

$$I = P \cdot r \cdot t = \$8000 \cdot 9\frac{3}{4}\% \cdot \frac{60}{365}$$

$$= \$8000 \cdot 0.0975 \cdot \frac{12}{73} \qquad \begin{array}{l}\text{Writing decimal notation for} \\ 9\frac{3}{4} \text{ and removing a factor} \\ \text{equal to 1: } \frac{60}{365} = \frac{12}{73} \cdot \frac{5}{5}\end{array}$$

$$\approx \$128.22.$$

The interest due for 60 days is $128.22.

b) The total amount to be paid after 60 days is the principal plus the interest:

$$\$8000 + \$128.22 = \$8128.22.$$

The total amount due is $8128.22.

Do Exercise 3.

3. The Glass Nook borrows $4800 at $9\frac{1}{2}$% for 30 days. Find (a) the amount of simple interest due and (b) the total amount that must be paid after 30 days.

b   Compound Interest

When interest is paid on *interest,* we call it **compound interest.** This is the type of interest usually paid on investments or loans. Suppose you have $5000 in a savings account at 6%. In 1 year, the account will contain the original $5000 plus 6% of $5000. Thus, the total in the account after 1 year will be

106% of $5000,   or   1.06 · $5000,   or $5300.

Now suppose that the total of $5300 remains in the account for another year. At the end of this second year, the account will contain the $5300 plus 6% of $5300. The total in the account would then be

106% of $5300,   or   1.06 · $5300,   or   **$5618.**

Note that in the second year, interest is earned on the first year's interest. When this happens, we say that interest is **compounded annually.**

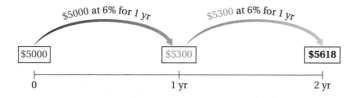

4. Find the amount in an account if $2000 is invested at 11%, compounded annually, for 2 years.

EXAMPLE 4 Find the amount in an account if $2000 is invested at 8%, compounded annually, for 2 years.

a) After 1 year, the account will contain 108% of $2000:

$$1.08 \cdot \$2000 = \$2160.$$

b) At the end of the second year, the account will contain 108% of $2160:

$$1.08 \cdot \$2160 = \$2332.80.$$

The amount in the account after 2 years is $2332.80.

Do Exercise 4.

Suppose that the interest in Example 4 were **compounded semi-annually**—that is, every half year. Interest would then be calculated twice a year at a rate of 8% ÷ 2, or 4% each time. The approach used in Example 4 can then be adapted, as follows.

After the first $\frac{1}{2}$ year, the account will contain 104% of $2000:

$$1.04 \cdot \$2000 = \$2080.$$

After a second $\frac{1}{2}$ year (1 full year), the account will contain 104% of $2080:

$$1.04 \cdot \$2080 = \$2163.20.$$

After a third $\frac{1}{2}$ year $\left(1\frac{1}{2} \text{ full years}\right)$, the account will contain 104% of $2163.20:

$$1.04 \cdot \$2163.20 = \$2249.728$$
$$\approx \$2249.73. \qquad \text{Rounding to the nearest cent}$$

Finally, after a fourth $\frac{1}{2}$ year (2 full years), the account will contain 104% of $2249.73:

$$1.04 \cdot \$2249.73 = \$2339.7192$$
$$\approx \$2339.72. \qquad \text{Rounding to the nearest cent}$$

Let's summarize our results and look at them another way:

End of 1st $\frac{1}{2}$ year $\;\rightarrow\; 1.04 \cdot 2000 = 2000 \cdot (1.04)^1$;
End of 2nd $\frac{1}{2}$ year $\;\rightarrow\; 1.04 \cdot (1.04 \cdot 2000) = 2000 \cdot (1.04)^2$;
End of 3rd $\frac{1}{2}$ year $\;\rightarrow\; 1.04 \cdot (1.04 \cdot 1.04 \cdot 2000) = 2000 \cdot (1.04)^3$;
End of 4th $\frac{1}{2}$ year $\;\rightarrow\; 1.04 \cdot (1.04 \cdot 1.04 \cdot 1.04 \cdot 2000) = 2000 \cdot (1.04)^4$.

Note that each multiplication was by 1.04 and that

$$\$2000 \cdot 1.04^4 \approx \$2339.72. \qquad \text{Using a calculator and rounding to the nearest cent}$$

We have illustrated the following result.

COMPOUND INTEREST FORMULA

If a principal P has been invested at interest rate r, compounded n times a year, in t years it will grow to an amount A given by

$$A = P \cdot \left(1 + \frac{r}{n}\right)^{n \cdot t}.$$

Here $n \cdot t$ is the total number of compounding periods, r is written in decimal notation, and $\dfrac{r}{n}$ is the interest rate for each period.

Answer on page A-26

EXAMPLE 5 The Ibsens invest $7000 in an account paying 8%, compounded quarterly. Find the amount in the account after $2\frac{1}{2}$ years.

The compounding is quarterly, so n is 4. We substitute $7000 for P, replace r with 0.08, substitute $2\frac{1}{2}$ for t, and solve for A:

$$A = P \cdot \left(1 + \frac{r}{n}\right)^{n \cdot t}$$

$$= 7000 \cdot \left(1 + \frac{0.08}{4}\right)^{4 \cdot (5/2)} \qquad \text{Substituting and writing } 2\frac{1}{2} \text{ as } \frac{5}{2}$$

$$= 7000 \cdot (1 + 0.02)^{10} \qquad 4 \cdot \frac{5}{2} = \frac{20}{2} = 10$$

$$= 7000 \cdot (1.02)^{10}$$

$$\approx 8532.96. \qquad \text{Using a calculator (see below)}$$

The amount in the account after $2\frac{1}{2}$ years is $8532.96.

Do Exercise 5.

EXAMPLE 6 Rosa and Sven are borrowing $5000 for 30 days at 14% interest, compounded daily. Find the amount due after 30 days.

We substitute $5000 for P and 0.14 for r. There are 365 days per year, so $n = 365$. Since 30 days $= \frac{30}{365}$ yr, we replace t with $\frac{30}{365}$:

$$A = P \cdot \left(1 + \frac{r}{n}\right)^{n \cdot t} = 5000 \cdot \left(1 + \frac{0.14}{365}\right)^{365 \cdot \frac{30}{365}}$$

$$= 5000\left(1 + \frac{0.14}{365}\right)^{30} \qquad \begin{array}{l}\text{Try to go directly to}\\\text{this step.}\end{array}$$

$$\approx \$5057.86. \qquad \begin{array}{l}\text{Rounding to the nearest cent and}\\\text{using a calculator (see below)}\end{array}$$

Do Exercise 6.

5. A couple invests $7000 in an account paying 10% compounded semiannually. Find the amount in the account after $1\frac{1}{2}$ years.

6. Phillipe and Chantrelle borrow $9000 for 20 days at 13% interest, compounded daily. Find the amount due after 20 days.

Answers on page A-26

CALCULATOR CORNER

A calculator is useful in computing compound interest. Not only does it do computations quickly but it also eliminates the need to round until the computation is completed. This minimizes "round-off errors" that occur when rounding is done at each stage of the computation. We must keep order of operations in mind when computing compound interest.

To find the amount due on a $20,000 loan made for 25 days at 11% interest, compounded daily, we would compute $20,000\left(1 + \frac{0.11}{365}\right)^{25}$. To do this on a calculator, we press $\boxed{2}\boxed{0}\boxed{0}\boxed{0}\boxed{0} \boxed{\times} \boxed{(}\boxed{(}\boxed{1}\boxed{+}\boxed{.}\boxed{1}\boxed{1}\boxed{\div}\boxed{3}\boxed{6}\boxed{5}\boxed{)}\boxed{y^x}$

(or $\boxed{x^y}$ or $\boxed{\wedge}$) $\boxed{2}\boxed{5}\boxed{=}$. Without parentheses, we would first find $1 + \frac{0.11}{365}$, raise this result to the 25th power, and then multiply by 20,000. To do this, we press $\boxed{1}\boxed{+}\boxed{.}\boxed{1}\boxed{1}\boxed{\div}\boxed{3}\boxed{6}\boxed{5}\boxed{=}\boxed{y^x}$ (or $\boxed{x^y}$ or $\boxed{\wedge}$) $\boxed{2}\boxed{5}\boxed{=}\boxed{\times}$ $\boxed{2}\boxed{0}\boxed{0}\boxed{0}\boxed{0}$. In either case, the result is 20,151.23, rounded to the nearest cent.

Some calculators have business keys that allow such computations to be done more quickly.

Exercises:

1. Find the amount due on a $16,000 loan made for 62 days at 13% interest, compounded daily.

2. An investment of $12,500 is made for 90 days at 8.5% interest, compounded daily. How much is the investment worth after 90 days?

a   Find the simple interest.

	PRINCIPAL	RATE OF INTEREST	TIME	SIMPLE INTEREST
1.	$200	8%	1 year	
2.	$450	6%	1 year	
3.	$2,000	8.4%	$\frac{1}{2}$ year	
4.	$200	7.7%	$\frac{1}{2}$ year	
5.	$4,300	10.56%	$\frac{1}{4}$ year	
6.	$8,000	9.42%	$\frac{1}{6}$ year	
7.	$20,000	$7\frac{5}{8}\%$	1 year	
8.	$100,000	$8\frac{7}{8}\%$	1 year	
9.	$50,000	$5\frac{3}{8}\%$	$\frac{1}{4}$ year	
10.	$80,000	$6\frac{3}{4}\%$	$\frac{1}{12}$ year	

Solve. Assume that simple interest is being calculated in each case.

11. CopiPix, Inc., borrows $10,000 at 9% for $\frac{1}{4}$ year. Find (a) the amount of interest due and (b) the total amount that must be paid after $\frac{1}{4}$ year.

12. Sal's Laundry borrows $8000 at 10% for $\frac{1}{2}$ year. Find (a) the amount of interest due and (b) the total amount that must be paid after $\frac{1}{2}$ year.

13. Squeaky's Car Wash invests $5000 at 8% interest for six months. Find (a) the amount of interest earned and (b) the value of the investment after six months.

14. Barton Coin and Stamps invests $3000 at 10% interest for three months. Find (a) the amount of interest earned and (b) the value of the investment after three months.

15. Animal Instinct, a pet shop, borrows $6500 at 8% for 90 days. Find (a) the amount of interest due and (b) the total amount that must be paid after 90 days.

16. Andante's Cafe borrows $4500 at 9% for 60 days. Find (a) the amount of interest due and (b) the total amount that must be paid after 60 days.

17. Jean's Garage borrows $5600 at 10% for 30 days. Find (a) the amount of interest due and (b) the total amount that must be paid after 30 days.

18. Shear Delights, a hair salon, borrows $3600 at 8% for 30 days. Find (a) the amount of interest due and (b) the total amount that must be paid after 30 days.

b Interest is compounded annually. Find the amount in the account after the given length of time. Round to the nearest cent.

	PRINCIPAL	RATE OF INTEREST	TIME	AMOUNT IN THE ACCOUNT
19.	$400	10%	2 years	
20.	$450	8%	2 years	
21.	$2,000	8.8%	4 years	
22.	$4,000	7.7%	4 years	
23.	$4,300	10.56%	6 years	
24.	$8,000	9.42%	6 years	
25.	$20,000	$7\frac{5}{8}\%$	25 years	
26.	$100,000	$8\frac{7}{8}\%$	30 years	

Interest is compounded semiannually. Find the amount in the account after the given length of time. Round to the nearest cent.

	PRINCIPAL	RATE OF INTEREST	TIME	AMOUNT IN THE ACCOUNT
27.	$4,000	7%	1 year	
28.	$1,000	5%	1 year	
29. ▦	$20,000	8.8%	4 years	
30. ▦	$40,000	7.7%	4 years	
31. ▦	$5,000	10.56%	6 years	
32. ▦	$8,000	9.42%	8 years	
33. ▦	$20,000	$7\frac{5}{8}\%$	25 years	
34. ▦	$100,000	$8\frac{7}{8}\%$	30 years	

Solve.

35. ▦ The Tampinis invest $4000 in an account paying 6%, compounded monthly. How much is in the account after 5 months?

36. ▦ Brenda and Brian invest $2500 in an account paying 9%, compounded monthly. How much is in the account after 6 months?

37. ▦ Ricky and Lucy invest $1200 in an account paying 10%, compounded quarterly. How much is in the account after 1 year?

38. ▦ The O'Hares invest $6000 in an account paying 8%, compounded quarterly. How much is in the account after 18 months?

39. ▦ The Wexler-Pratts borrow $9000 at 8% interest, compounded daily, for 25 days. Find the amount due after 25 days.

40. ▦ Monica and Mindy borrow $10,000 for 20 days at 12% interest, compounded daily. Find the amount due after 20 days.

41. ▦ Emilio loans his niece's business $20,000 for 50 days at 6% interest, compounded daily. How much is Emilio owed after 50 days?

42. ▦ Elsa loans her nephew's business $25,000 for 40 days at 5% interest, compounded daily. How much is Elsa owed after 40 days?

43. **D**w Which is a better investment and why: $1000 invested at $14\frac{3}{4}\%$ simple interest for 1 year, or $1000 invested at 14% compounded monthly for 1 year?

44. **D**w A firm must choose between borrowing $5000 at 10% (compounded daily) for 30 days or borrowing $10,000 at 8% (compounded daily) for 60 days. Give arguments in favor of and against each option.

Solve. [7.3b]

45. $\dfrac{9}{10} = \dfrac{x}{5}$

46. $\dfrac{7}{x} = \dfrac{4}{5}$

47. $\dfrac{3}{4} = \dfrac{6}{x}$

48. $\dfrac{7}{8} = \dfrac{x}{100}$

Convert to a mixed numeral. [4.5b]

49. $-\dfrac{64}{17}$

50. $\dfrac{38}{11}$

Convert from a mixed numeral to fraction notation. [4.5a]

51. $1\dfrac{1}{17}$

52. $20\dfrac{9}{10}$

Find the perimeter of each polygon. [2.7b]

53.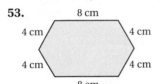

54.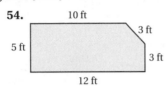

55.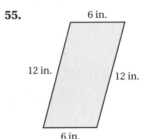

56.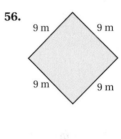

57. **D_W** Without performing the multiplications, determine which gives the most interest: $\$1000 \times 8\% \times \frac{1}{12}$, or $\$1000 \times 8\% \times \frac{30}{365}$? How did you decide?

58. **D_W** Erik is in the 25% tax bracket. Would he be better off investing in an account earning 4.5% interest, compounded daily, that would be taxed, or a tax-free account earning 3.5% compounded daily? Explain.

59. ▦ Interest is compounded semiannually. Find the value of the investment if $24,800 is invested at 6.4% for 5 years and then at 9% for 2 additional years.

60. ▦ Interest is compounded quarterly. Find the value of the investment after 4 years if $125,000 is invested at 9.2% for $2\frac{1}{2}$ years and then at 8% for an additional $1\frac{1}{2}$ years.

Effective Yield.   The *effective yield* is the yearly rate of simple interest that corresponds to an interest rate that is compounded two or more times a year. For example, if P is invested at 12%, compounded quarterly, we would multiply P by $(1 + 0.12/4)^4$, or 1.03^4. Since $1.03^4 \approx 1.126$ or 112.6%, the 12% compounded quarterly corresponds to an effective yield of approximately 12.6%. In Exercises 61 and 62, find the effective yield for the indicated account.

61. ▦ The account pays 9% compounded monthly.

62. ▦ The account pays 10% compounded daily.

63. ▦ Rather than spend $20,000 on a new car that will lose 30% of its value in 1 year, the Coniglios invest the money at 9%, compounded daily. By not buying the car (which would have *de*creased their net worth), and investing instead (which *in*creased their net worth), how much have the Coniglios saved after 1 year?

Objective

a Solve applied problems involving interest rates on credit cards and loans.

a Credit Cards and Loans

Look at the following graphs. They offer good reason for a study of the real-world applications of percent, interest, loans, and credit cards.

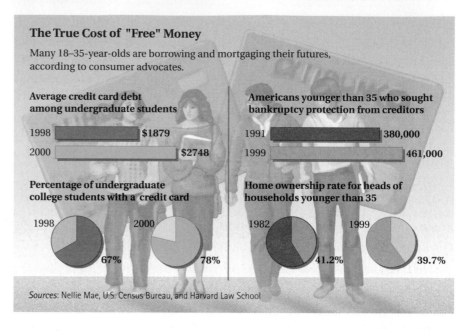

The True Cost of "Free" Money

Many 18–35-year-olds are borrowing and mortgaging their futures, according to consumer advocates.

Average credit card debt among undergraduate students

1998 — $1879
2000 — $2748

Americans younger than 35 who sought bankruptcy protection from creditors

1991 — 380,000
1999 — 461,000

Percentage of undergraduate college students with a credit card

1998 — 67%   2000 — 78%

Home ownership rate for heads of households younger than 35

1982 — 41.2%   1999 — 39.7%

Sources: Nellie Mae, U.S. Census Bureau, and Harvard Law School

Comparing interest rates is essential if one is to become financially responsible. A small change in an interest rate can make a *large* difference in the cost of a loan. When you make a payment on a loan, do you know how much of that payment is interest and how much is applied to reducing the principal?

We begin with an example involving credit cards. A balance carried on a credit card is a type of loan. Last year in the United States, 100,000 young adults declared bankruptcy because of excessive credit card debt. The money you obtain through the use of a credit card is not "free" money. There is a price (interest) to be paid for the privilege.

EXAMPLE 1 *Credit Cards.* After the holidays, Sarah has a balance of $3216.28 on a credit card with an annual percentage rate (APR) of 19.7%. She decides to not make any additional purchases with this card until she has paid off the balance.

a) Many credit cards require a minimum monthly payment of 2% of the balance. What is Sarah's minimum payment on a balance of $3216.28? Round the answer to the nearest dollar.

b) For the minimum payment found in part (a), find the amount of interest and the amount applied to reduce the principal.

c) If Sarah had the same balance on a card with an APR of 12.5%, how much of her first payment would be interest? How much would be applied to reduce the principal?

d) Compare the amounts for 12.5% from part (c) with the amounts for 19.7% from part (b).

We solve as follows.

a) We multiply the balance of $3216.28 by 2%:

$$0.02 \cdot \$3216.28 = \$64.3256.$$ Sarah's minimum payment, rounded to the nearest dollar, is $64.

b) The amount of interest on $3216.28 at 19.7% for one month* is given by

$$I = P \cdot r \cdot t = \$3216.28 \cdot 0.197 \cdot \frac{1}{12} \approx \$52.80.$$

We subtract to find the amount applied to reduce the principal in the first payment:

$$\begin{aligned} \text{Amount applied to} \atop \text{reduce the principal} &= \text{Minimum payment} - {\text{Interest for} \atop \text{the month}} \\ &= \$64 - \$52.80 \\ &= \$11.20. \end{aligned}$$

Thus the principal of $3216.28 is decreased by only $11.20 with the first payment. (Sarah still owes $3205.08.)

c) The amount of interest on $3216.28 at 12.5% for one month is

$$I = P \cdot r \cdot t = \$3216.28 \cdot 0.125 \cdot \frac{1}{12} \approx \$33.50.$$

We subtract to find the amount applied to reduce the principal in the first payment:

$$\begin{aligned} \text{Amount applied to} \atop \text{reduce the principal} &= \text{Minimum payment} - {\text{Interest for} \atop \text{the month}} \\ &= \$64 - \$33.50 \\ &= \$30.50. \end{aligned}$$

Thus the principal of $3216.28 is decreased by $30.50 with the first payment. (Sarah still owes $3185.78.)

d) Let's organize the information for both rates in the following table.

BALANCE BEFORE FIRST PAYMENT	FIRST MONTH'S PAYMENT	% APR	AMOUNT OF INTEREST	AMOUNT APPLIED TO PRINCIPAL	BALANCE AFTER FIRST PAYMENT
$3216.28	$64	19.7%	$52.80	$11.20	$3205.08
3216.28	64	12.5	33.50	30.50	3185.78

At 19.7%, the interest is $52.80 and the principal is decreased by $11.20. At 12.5%, the interest is $33.50 and the principal is decreased by $30.50. Taken together, we see that at 19.7% the interest is $30.50 − $11.20, or $19.30 greater than the interest at 12.5%.

Do Exercise 1.

---

*Actually, the interest on a credit card is computed daily with a rate called a daily percentage rate (DPR). The DPR for Example 1 would be 19.7%/365 ≈ 0.054%. When no payments or additional purchases are made during the month, the difference in total interest for the month is minimal and we will not deal with it here.

1. **Credit Cards.** After the holidays, Jamal has a balance of $4867.59 on a credit card with an annual percentage rate (APR) of 21.3%. He decides to not make any additional purchases with this card until he has paid off the balance.

a) Many credit cards require a minimum monthly payment of 2% of the balance. What is Jamal's minimum payment on a balance of $4867.59? Round the answer to the nearest dollar.

b) Find the amount of interest and the amount applied to reduce the principal in the minimum payment found in part (a).

c) If Jamal had the same balance on a card with an APR of 13.6%, how much of his first payment would be interest and how much would be applied to reduce the principal?

d) How much less interest is in the first payment at 13.6% than in the first payment at 21.3%?

Answers on page A-26

Even though the mathematics used to create the chart below is beyond the scope of this text, it is interesting to compare the time required to pay off the balance of Example 1 at $64 per payment with the time it takes to pay it off at $128 per payment. Financial consultants frequently tell clients that if they want to take control of their debt, they should at least double the minimum payment each month.

RATE	PAYMENT PER MONTH	NUMBER OF PAYMENTS TO PAY OFF DEBT	TOTAL PAID BACK	TOTAL INTEREST PAID
19.7%	$64	107, or 8 yr 11 mo	$6848	$3631.72
19.7	128	33, or 2 yr 9 mo	4224	1007.72
12.5	64	72, or 6 yr	4608	1391.72
12.5	128	29, or 2 yr 5 mo	3712	495.72

As with most loans, if you pay an extra amount toward the principal with each payment, the length of the loan can be greatly reduced. Note that at the rate of 19.7%, it will take Sarah almost 9 yr to pay off her debt if she pays only $64 per month and does not make additional purchases. If she transfers her balance to a card with a 12.5% rate and pays $128 per month, she could pay off her debt in approximately $2\frac{1}{2}$ yr. Any time you continue to make purchases and pay only the minimum payment, your debt will never be eliminated.

The Federal Stafford Loan program provides educational loans to students at interest rates (usually from 6.5% to 8.5%) that are much lower than those on credit cards. Payments on a loan do not begin until 6 months after graduation. At that time, the student has 10 years, or 120 monthly payments, to pay off the loan.

EXAMPLE 2 *Federal Stafford Loans.* After graduation, the balance on Taylor's Stafford loan is $28,650. If the rate on his loan is 7%, he will make 120 payments of approximately $333 each to pay off the loan.

a) Find the amount of interest and the amount of principal in the first payment.

b) If the interest rate were 8.25%, he would make 120 monthly payments of approximately $351 each. How much more of the first payment is interest when the loan is 8.25% rather than 7%?

c) How much less total interest would Taylor pay on the 7% loan than on the 8.25% loan?

We solve as follows.

a) We use the formula $I = P \cdot r \cdot t$, substituting $28,650 for P, 0.07 for r, and 1/12 for t:

$$I = \$28{,}650 \cdot 0.07 \cdot \frac{1}{12}$$

$$\approx \$167.13.$$

The amount of interest in the first payment is $167.13. The payment is $333. We subtract to determine the amount applied to the principal:

$$\$333 - \$167.13 = \$165.87.$$

With the first payment, the principal will be reduced by $165.87.

b) The interest at 8.25% would be

$$I = \$28{,}650 \cdot 0.0825 \cdot \frac{1}{12}$$

$$\approx \$196.97.$$

The interest at 8.25% minus the interest at 7% is

$$\$196.97 - \$167.13 = \$29.84.$$

The higher interest rate results in an additional $29.84 in interest in the first payment.

c) For the 7% loan, there will be 120 payments of $333 each:

$$120 \cdot \$333 = \$39{,}960.$$

The total paid minus the total borrowed is the total interest paid:

$$\$39{,}960 - \$28{,}650 = \$11{,}310.$$

For the 8.25% loan, there will be 120 payments of $351 each:

$$120 \cdot \$351 = \$42{,}120.$$

The total amount of interest at this rate is

$$\$42{,}120 - \$28{,}650 = \$13{,}470.$$

The 7% loan would cost Taylor

$$\$13{,}470 - \$11{,}310 = \$2160$$

less in interest than the 8.25% loan.

Do Exercise 2.

EXAMPLE 3   *Home Loans.*   The Sawyers recently purchased their first home. They borrowed $123,000 at $8\frac{7}{8}$% for 30 years (360 payments). Their monthly payment (excluding insurance and taxes) is $978.64.

a) How much of the first payment is interest and how much is applied to reduce the principal?

b) If the Sawyers pay the entire 360 payments, how much interest will be paid on the loan?

We solve as follows.

a) To find the amount of interest paid in the first payment, we use the formula $I = P \cdot r \cdot t$:

$$I = P \cdot r \cdot t = \$123{,}000 \cdot 0.08875 \cdot \frac{1}{12} \approx \$909.69.$$

The portion of their first payment applied to the principal is

$$\$978.64 - \$909.69, \text{ or } \$68.95.$$

b) Over the 30-year period, the total paid will be

$$360 \cdot \$978.64, \text{ or } \$352{,}310.40.$$

The total amount of interest paid over the lifetime of the loan is

$$\$352{,}310.40 - \$123{,}000, \text{ or } \$229{,}310.40.$$

Do Exercises 3 and 4 on the following page.

2. Federal Stafford Loans. After graduation, the balance on Maggie's Stafford loan is $32,680. To pay off the loan at 7.25%, she will make 120 payments of approximately $384 each.

a) Find the amount of interest and the amount of principal in the first payment.

b) If the interest rate were 8.5%, she would make 120 payments of approximately $405 each. How much more of the first payment is interest when the loan is 8.5% rather than 7.25%?

c) Compare the total amount of interest on the 7.25% loan with the amount of interest on the 8.5% loan. How much more would Maggie pay in interest on the 8.5% loan than on the 7.25% loan?

Answers on page A-26

Refer to Example 3 for Margin Exercises 3 and 4.

3. **Home Loans.** Since the principal has been reduced by the first payment, at the time of the second payment of the Sawyers' 30-year loan, the new principal is the decreased principal

$$\$123,000 - \$68.95,$$

or

$$\$122,931.05.$$

Use $122,931.05 as the principal, and determine how much of the second payment is interest and how much is applied to reduce the principal. (In effect, repeat Example 3(a) using the new principal.)

4. **Home Loans.** The Sawyers decide to change the period of their home loan from 30 years to 15 years. Their monthly payment increases to $1238.42.

a) How much of the first payment is interest and how much is applied to reduce the principal?

b) If the Sawyers pay the entire 180 payments, how much interest will be paid on this loan?

c) How much less total interest is paid on the 15-yr loan than on the 30-yr loan?

Answers on page A-26

AMORTIZATION TABLES

If we make 360 calculations as in Example 3(a) and continue with a decreased principal as in Margin Exercise 3, we can create an *amortization table*, part of which is shown below. Such tables can also be found in reference books, at banks, and on the Internet. The beginning, middle, and last part of the loan described are shown. Look over the table and note how small a portion of the payment reduces the principal at the beginning of the loan and how that portion increases throughout the lifetime of the loan. Do you see again why a loan is not "free?"

MORTGAGE AMORTIZATION PROGRAM

MORTGAGE AMOUNT: $123,000
INTEREST RATE: 8.875%
NUMBER OF YEARS: 30
MONTHLY PAYMENTS ARE: $978.64

PAYMENT	PRINCIPAL	INTEREST	BALANCE	
1	$ 68.95	$909.69	$122,931.05	← Example 3
2	69.46	909.18	122,861.59	← Margin
3	69.98	908.66	122,791.61	Exercise 3
4	70.49	908.15	122,721.12	
5	71.02	907.62	122,650.10	
6	71.54	907.10	122,578.56	
7	72.07	906.57	122,506.49	
8	72.60	906.04	122,433.89	
9	73.14	905.50	122,360.75	
10	73.68	904.96	122,287.07	
11	74.23	904.41	122,212.84	
12	74.77	903.87	122,138.07	

⤷ Interest for 12 periods = $10,881.75

175	248.53	730.11	98,470.83
176	250.37	728.27	98,220.46
177	252.22	726.42	97,968.24
178	254.08	724.56	97,714.16
179	255.96	722.68	97,458.20
180	257.86	720.78	97,200.34
181	259.76	718.88	96,940.58
182	261.68	716.96	96,678.90
183	263.62	715.02	96,415.28
184	265.57	713.07	96,149.71
185	267.53	711.11	95,882.18
186	269.51	709.13	95,612.67

⤷ Interest for 12 periods = $8636.99

349	895.78	82.86	10,307.76
350	902.41	76.23	9,405.35
351	909.08	69.56	8,496.27
352	915.80	62.84	7,580.47
353	922.58	56.06	6,657.89
354	929.40	49.24	5,728.49
355	936.27	42.37	4,792.22
356	943.20	35.44	3,849.02
357	950.17	28.47	2,898.85
358	957.20	21.44	1,941.65
359	964.28	14.36	977.37
360	971.41	7.23	5.96

⤷ Interest for 12 periods = $546.10

Total Interest for 360 Periods = $229,310.40

EXAMPLE 4 *Refinancing a Home Loan.* Refer to Example 3. Ten months after the Sawyers buy their home financed at a rate of $8\frac{7}{8}\%$, the rates drop to $6\frac{1}{2}\%$. After much consideration, they decide to refinance even though the new loan will cost them $1200 in refinance charges. They have reduced the principal a small amount in the 10 payments they have made, but they decide to again borrow $123,000 for 30 years at the new rate. Their new monthly payment is $777.44.

a) How much of the first payment is interest and how much is applied to the principal?

b) What is the difference between the amount of the first payment applied to the principal at $6\frac{1}{2}\%$ and the amount of the first payment applied to the principal at $8\frac{7}{8}\%$? (Use part (a) and Example 3).

c) With the lower house payment, how long will it take the Sawyers to recoup the refinance charge of $1200?

d) If the Sawyers pay the entire 360 payments, how much interest will be paid on this loan? How much less is the total interest at $6\frac{1}{2}\%$ than at $8\frac{7}{8}\%$?

We solve as follows.

a) To find the interest paid in the first payment, we use the formula $I = P \cdot r \cdot t$:

$$I = P \cdot r \cdot t = \$123,000 \cdot 0.065 \cdot \frac{1}{12} = \$666.25.$$

The amount applied to the principal is

$$\$777.44 - \$666.25, \text{ or } \$111.19.$$

b) We subtract the amount of principal paid, as calculated in Example 3(a), from the amount of principal paid in part (a) above:

Amount of first payment applied to principal at $6\frac{1}{2}\%$		Amount of first payment applied to principal at $8\frac{7}{8}\%$		
$\downarrow$		$\downarrow$		
$111.19	−	$68.95	=	$42.24.

At $6\frac{1}{2}\%$, the amount applied to the principal is $42.24 more than at $8\frac{7}{8}\%$.

c) The monthly payment at $6\frac{1}{2}\%$ is $978.64 − $777.44, or $201.20 less than the payment at $8\frac{7}{8}\%$. The total savings each month is approximately $200. We can divide the cost of the refinancing by this monthly savings to determine the number of months it will take to recoup the $1200 refinancing charge: $1200 ÷ $200 = 6. It will take the Sawyers approximately 6 months to recoup their refinance charge.

d) Over the 30-year period, the total paid on the $6\frac{1}{2}\%$ mortgage is

$$360 \cdot \$777.44, \text{ or } \$279,878.40.$$

The total amount of interest paid over the lifetime of the loan is

$$\$279,878.40 - \$123,000, \text{ or } \$156,878.40.$$

To find how much less interest is paid at $6\frac{1}{2}\%$, we subtract:

$$\$229,310.40 \text{ (see Example 3)} - \$156,878.40 = \$72,432.$$

The $6\frac{1}{2}\%$ loan saves the Sawyers approximately $70,000 in interest charges over the 30 years.

Do Exercise 5.

5. Refinancing a Home Loan.
Consider Example 4 for a 15-yr loan. The new monthly payment is $1071.46.
a) How much of the first payment is interest and how much is applied to reduce the principal?

b) If the Sawyers pay the entire 180 payments, how much interest will be paid on this loan?

c) How much less interest is paid in the course of paying off the 15-yr loan at $6\frac{1}{2}\%$ than in the course of paying off the 15-yr loan at $8\frac{7}{8}\%$ in Margin Exercise 4?

Answers on page A-26

Study Tips

ASK REAL-WORLD QUESTIONS

You have studied and learned a good deal of mathematics. When, in your daily life, a merchant or business presents you with facts and figures, don't hesitate to ask for explanations if something is unclear. Your understanding of mathematics will continue to grow as your areas of inquiry extend beyond the classroom.

a Solve.

1. *Credit Cards.* At the end of his first year of college, Antonio has a balance of $4876.54 on a credit card with an annual percentage rate (APR) of 21.3%. He decides to not make any additional purchases with his card until he has paid off the balance.

   a) Many credit cards require a minimum monthly payment of 2% of the balance. What is Antonio's minimum payment on a balance of $4876.54? Round the answer to the nearest dollar.

   b) Find the amount of interest and the amount applied to reduce the principal in the minimum payment found in part (a).

   c) If Antonio had transferred his balance to a card with an APR of 12.6%, how much of his first payment would be interest and how much would be applied to reduce the principal?

   d) How much less interest is in the first payment at 12.6% than in the first payment at 21.3%?

2. *Credit Cards.* At the end of her junior year of college, Becky had a balance of $5328.88 on a credit card with an annual percentage rate (APR) of 18.7%. She decides to not make any additional purchases with this card until she has paid off the balance.

   a) Many credit cards require a minimum monthly payment of 2% of the balance. What is Becky's minimum payment on a balance of $5328.88? Round the answer to the nearest dollar.

   b) Find the amount of interest and the amount applied to reduce the principal in the minimum payment found in part (a).

   c) If Becky had transferred her balance to a card with an APR of 13.2%, how much of her first payment would be interest and how much would be applied to reduce the principal?

   d) How much less interest is in the first payment at 13.2% than in the first payment at 18.7%?

3. *Federal Stafford Loans.* After graduation, the balance on Grace's Stafford loan is $44,560. To pay off the loan at 6.5%, she will make 120 payments of approximately $505.97 each.

   a) Find the amount of interest and the amount applied to reduce the principal in the first payment.

   b) If the interest rate were 8.5%, she would make 120 monthly payments of approximately $552.48 each. How much more of the first payment is interest if the loan is 8.5% rather than 6.5%?

   c) Compare the total amount of interest on a loan at 6.5% with the amount on the loan at 8.5%. How much more would Grace pay on the 8.5% loan than on the 6.5% loan?

4. *Federal Stafford Loans.* After graduation, the balance on Ricky's Stafford loan is $38,970. To pay off the loan at 8.2%, he will make 120 payments of approximately $476.94 each.

   a) Find the amount of interest and the amount applied to reduce the principal in the first payment.

   b) If the interest rate were 7.4%, he would make 120 monthly payments of approximately $460.55 each. How much less of the first payment is interest if the loan is 7.4% rather than 8.2%?

   c) Compare the total amount of interest on the loan at 8.2% with the amount on the loan at 7.4%. How much more would Ricky pay on the 8.2% loan than on the 7.4% loan?

5. *Home Loan.* The Martinez family recently purchased a home. They borrowed $150,000 at 6.98% for 30 years (360 payments). Their monthly payment (excluding insurance and taxes) is $995.94.

   a) How much of the first payment is interest and how much is applied to reduce the principal?

   b) If this family pays the entire 360 payments, how much interest will be paid on the loan?

   c) Determine the new principal after the first payment. Use that new principal to determine how much of the second payment is interest and how much is applied to reduce the principal.

6. *Home Loan.* The Kaufmans recently purchased a home. They borrowed $180,000 at 8.36% for 30 years (360 payments). Their monthly payment (excluding insurance and taxes) is $1366.22.

   a) How much of the first payment is interest and how much is applied to reduce the principal?

   b) If the Kaufmans pay the entire 360 payments, how much interest will be paid on the loan?

   c) Determine the new principal after the first payment. Use that new principal to determine how much of the second payment is interest and how much is applied to reduce the principal.

7. *Refinancing a Home Loan.*   Refer to Exercise 5.
Suppose the Martinez family decides to change the
period of their home loan to 15 years. Their monthly
payment would then increase to $1346.57.

  a) How much of the first payment is interest and how
much is applied to reduce the principal?

  b) If the Martinez family pays the entire 180 payments,
how much interest will be paid on the loan?

  c) How much less total interest is paid on the 15-yr loan
than on the 30-yr loan?

8. *Refinancing a Home Loan.*   Refer to Exercise 6.
Suppose the Kaufmans decide to change the period of
their home loan to 15 years. Their monthly payment
would then increase to $1757.79.

  a) How much of the first payment is interest and how
much is applied to reduce the principal?

  b) If the Kaufmans pay the entire 180 payments, how
much interest will be paid on the loan?

  c) How much less total interest is paid on the 15-yr loan
than on the 30-yr loan?

Complete the following table, assuming monthly payments as given.

	INTEREST RATE	HOME MORTGAGE	TIME OF LOAN	MONTHLY PAYMENT	PRINCIPAL AFTER FIRST PAYMENT	PRINCIPAL AFTER SECOND PAYMENT
9.	6.98%	$100,000	360 mos	$663.96		
10.	6.98%	$100,000	180 mos	$897.71		
11.	8.04%	$100,000	180 mos	$957.96		
12.	8.04%	$100,000	360 mos	$736.55		
13.	7.24%	$150,000	360 mos	$1022.25		
14.	7.24%	$75,000	180 mos	$684.22		
15.	7.24%	$200,000	180 mos	$1824.60		
16.	7.24%	$180,000	360 mos	$1226.70		

17. *New-Car Loan.*   After working at her first job for
2 years, Janice buys a new Saturn for $16,385. She
makes a down payment of $1385 and finances $15,000
for 4 years at a new-car loan rate of 8.99%. Her monthly
payment is $373.20.

  a) How much of her first payment is interest and how
much is applied to reduce the principal?

  b) Find the principal balance at the beginning of the
second month and determine how much less interest
she will pay in the second payment than in the first.

  c) What is the total interest cost of the loan if she pays
all of the 48 payments?

18. *Manufacturer's Car Loan Offer.*   For a trip to
Colorado, Michael and Rebecca buy a new Jeep
Cherokee Classic for $22,085. For financing, they accept
the promotion from the manufacturer that offers a
36-month loan at 1.9% with 20% down. Their monthly
payment is $505.29.

  a) What is the down payment? the amount borrowed?

  b) How much of the first payment is interest and how
much is applied to reduce the principal?

  c) What is the total interest cost of the loan if they pay
all of the 36 payments?

19. *Used-Car Loan.* Twin brothers, Jerry and Terry, each take a job at the college cafeteria in order to have the money to make payments on the purchase of a used 1999 Ford Taurus for $7900. They make a down payment of 10% and finance the remainder at 12.49% for 3 years. (Used-car loan rates are generally higher than new-car loan rates.) Their monthly payment is $237.82.

a) What is the down payment? the amount borrowed?
b) How much of the first payment is interest and how much is applied to reduce the principal?
c) If they pay all 36 payments, how much interest will they pay for the loan?

20. *Used-Car Loan.* For her work Tawana buys a 1996 Chevrolet S-10 truck for $5350. She makes a down payment of $550 and finances the remainder for 2 years at 11.3%. The monthly payment is $224.39.

a) How much is financed?
b) How much of the first payment is interest and how much is applied to reduce the principal?
c) If she pays all 24 payments, how much interest will she pay for the loan?

21. D_W Look over the examples and exercises in this section. What happens to the monthly payment on a loan if the time of payment changes from 30 years to 15 years, assuming the interest rate stays the same? Discuss the pros and cons of both time periods.

22. D_W Examine the information in the graphs at the beginning of this section. Discuss how a knowledge of this section might have been of help to some of these students.

Find the area of each figure.

23. [3.6b]

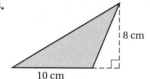

8 cm
10 cm

24. [3.6b]

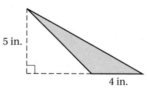

5 in.
4 in.

25. [1.5c]

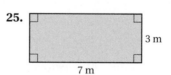

3 m
7 m

26. [1.5c]

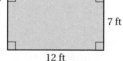

7 ft
12 ft

27. [1.5c]

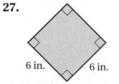

6 in.   6 in.

28. [1.5c]

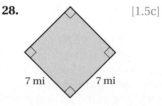

7 mi   7 mi

29. D_W After receiving her monthly credit card bill, Beverly usually waits about 10 days before mailing her check. Assuming she pays off her entire balance each month, why is this a smart thing for her to do?

30. D_W Suppose a friend owes you $100 and offers to repay you by giving you either $10 a month for 12 months, or $60 every 6 months for 12 months. Which would you select and why?

The review that follows is meant to prepare you for a chapter exam. It consists of two parts. The first part is a checklist of some of the Study Tips referred to in this and preceding chapters, as well as a list of important properties and formulas. The second part is the Review Exercises. These provide practice exercises for the exam, together with references to section objectives so you can go back and review. Before beginning, stop and look back over the skills you have obtained. What skills in mathematics do you have now that you did not have before studying this chapter?

STUDY TIPS CHECKLIST

The foundation of all your study skills is TIME!

☐ Are you, on your own, reviewing earlier material in which you lack confidence?

☐ Have you made an effort to memorize especially useful pieces of information?

☐ Have you tried using a second (alternative) approach to check a solution?

☐ Are you studying with a classmate over the telephone?

☐ Are you using a calculator to check lengthy calculations?

IMPORTANT PROPERTIES AND FORMULAS

Commission = Commission rate · Sales

Sale price = Original price − Discount

Compound interest: $A = P \cdot \left(1 + \dfrac{r}{n}\right)^{n \cdot t}$

Discount = Rate of discount · Original price

Simple interest: $I = P \cdot r \cdot t$

REVIEW EXERCISES

Write each decimal as an equivalent percent. [8.1b]

1. 0.871

2. 0.6

Write each fraction as an equivalent percent. [8.1c]

3. $\dfrac{3}{8}$

4. $\dfrac{1}{3}$

Write each percent as an equivalent decimal. [8.1b]

5. 73.5%

6. $6\dfrac{1}{2}\%$

Write an equivalent fraction for each percent. Simplify, if possible. [8.1c]

7. 24%

8. 6.3%

Translate to a proportion. Then solve. [8.2a, b]

9. 28 percent of what is 20.72?

10. 36 is what percent of 30?

11. What is 10.5% of 84?

Translate to an equation. Then solve. [8.3a, b]

12. 30.6 is what percent of 90?

13. 63 is 84 percent of what?

14. What is $38\dfrac{1}{2}\%$ of 146?

639

Solve. [8.4a, b]

15. Food expenses account for 26% of the average family's budget. A family makes $2300 one month. How much do they spend for food?

16. The price of a graphing calculator was reduced from $110 to $93.50. Find the percent of decrease in price.

17. Gerrin County has a population that is increasing 3% each year. This year the population is 80,000. What will it be next year?

18. *Prescriptions.* Of the 281 million people in the United States, 123.64 million take at least one kind of prescription drug per day. What percent take at least one kind of prescription drug per day?
Source: American Society of Health-System Pharmacies

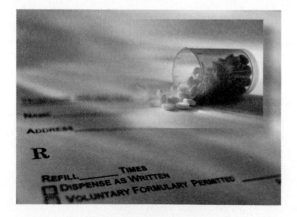

19. In 1990, the U.S. population was approximately 248.7 million. By 2000, the population grew 13.1%. By how many people did the population increase during the 1990s?

Solve. [8.5a, b, c]

20. A city charges a meals tax of $4\frac{1}{2}\%$. What is the meals tax charged on a dinner party costing $320?

21. In Massachusetts, a sales tax of $378 is collected on the purchase of a used car for $7560. What is the sales tax rate?

22. Kim earns $753.50 selling $6850 worth of televisions. What is the commission rate?

23. A dishwasher priced at $450 is placed on sale at 12% off. What are the discount and the sale price?

24. An iPod priced at $375 is discounted at the rate of 14%. What are the discount and the sale price?

25. Percy sells insurance and receives a 7% commission. If he sells $21,000 worth of life insurance, what is the commission?

Solve. [8.6a, b]

26. What is the simple interest on $1800 at 6% for $\frac{1}{3}$ year?

27. The Dress Rack borrows $24,000 at 10% simple interest for 60 days. Find (a) the amount of interest due and (b) the total amount that must be paid after 60 days.

28. What is the simple interest on $2200 principal at the interest rate of 5.5% for 1 year?

29. The Kleins invest $7500 in an investment account paying 12%, compounded monthly. How much is in the account after 3 months?

30. Find the rate of discount. [8.5c]

31. Frida is faced with a $50,000 student loan, at 7.24% interest. To repay the loan she will make 180 monthly payments of $456.15. How much of Frida's first payment is interest and how much is applied to reduce the principal? [8.7a]

SKILL MAINTENANCE

Find the area of each figure.

32. [1.5c]

8 cm

13 cm

33. [1.5c]
7 in.

7 in.

34. [3.6b]
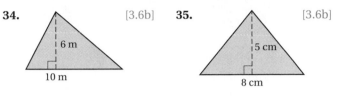
6 m

10 m

35. [3.6b]
5 cm

8 cm

Convert to decimal notation. [5.5a]

36. $\dfrac{12,672}{5280}$

37. $\dfrac{7329}{100}$

Convert to a mixed numeral. [4.5b]

38. $\dfrac{11}{3}$

39. $\dfrac{63}{12}$

40. Subtract: $(-5x^4 - 10x^3 + 6) - (x^4 - x^2 + 8)$ [2.9 c]

SYNTHESIS

41. $\mathbf{D_W}$ Ollie buys a microwave oven during a 10%-off sale. The sale price that Ollie paid was $162. To find the original price, Ollie calculates 10% of $162 and adds that to $162. Is this correct? Why or why not? [8.5c]

42. $\mathbf{D_W}$ Which is a better deal for a consumer and why: a discount of 40% or a discount of 20% followed by another of 22%? [8.5c]

43. 🖩 *Land Area of the United States.* When Hawaii and Alaska became states, the total land area of the United States increased from 2,963,681 mi^2 to 3,540,939 mi^2. What was the percent of increase? [8.4b]

43. *Girl Scout Cookies.* Nationwide, Girl Scout troops typically receive 12% to 17% of the price of each box of cookies sold. If boxes sell for $2.25 to $3.75, how much does a troop make on each box sold? [8.4a]
Source: Girl Scouts of the USA

45. Rhonda's Dress Shop reduces the price of a dress by 40% during a sale. By what percent must the store increase the sale price, after the sale, to get back to the original price? [8.5c]

46. How many successive 10% discounts are necessary to lower the price of an item to below 50% of its original price? [8.5c]

1. Write 26% as an equivalent decimal.

2. Write 0.674 as an equivalent percent.

3. Write $\frac{11}{8}$ as an equivalent percent.

4. Write 65% as an equivalent fraction. Simplify, if possible.

5. Translate to an equation. Then solve.

   What is 40% of 55?

6. Translate to a proportion. Then solve.

   What percent of 80 is 65?

Solve.

7. *Water Output.* The average person expels 200 mL of water per day by sweating. This is 8% of the total output of water from the body. How much is the total output of water?

   Source: Elaine N. Marieb, *Essentials of Human Anatomy and Physiology,* 6th ed. Boston: Addison Wesley Longman, Inc., 2000

8. *Population Growth.* The population of Wyoming increased from 454,000 in 1990 to 494,000 in 2000. Find the percent of increase in population.

9. *New Mexico Tax Rate.* The sales tax rate in New Mexico is 5%. How much tax is charged on a purchase of rugs costing $324? What is the total price?

10. *Sales Commissions.* Gwen's commission rate is 15%. What is her commission from the sale of $4200 worth of merchandise?

11. The regular price of a 5-disc CD player is $200 and the item is on sale at 20% off. What are the discount and the sale price?

12. What is the simple interest on a principal of $950 at the interest rate of 4.6% for 1 year?

13. The Burnham Parents-Teachers Association invests $5200 at 6% simple interest. How much is in the account after $\frac{1}{2}$ year?

14. Find the amount owed if $3000 is borrowed at 5%, compounded annually, for 2 years.

15. The Suarez family invests $10,000 at 9%, compounded monthly. How much is in the account after 3 months?

16. Find the discount and the discount rate of the bed in this ad.

WHITE IRON DAYBED
WITH BRASS ACCENTS

100 TO SELL
FANTASTIC VALUE!

MARKET VALUE
$249.95
CHOICE OF FINISH!

$**118** Springs Included!

17. *Job Opportunities.* The table below lists job opportunities, in thousands, in 1998 and projected increases to 2008. Find the missing numbers.

OCCUPATION	NUMBER OF JOBS IN 1998 (in thousands)	NUMBER OF JOBS IN 2008 (in thousands)	CHANGE	PERCENT OF INCREASE
Restaurant waitstaff	2019	2322	303	15.0%
Dental assistant	229		97	
Nurse psychiatric aide	1461	1794		
Child-care worker		1141	236	
Hairdresser/hairstylist/cosmetologist		670		10.2%

Source: Handbook of U.S. Labor Statistics

18. The Larsons purchased a condominium with a $100,000 mortgage. At 7.24%, the mortgage will be paid with 180 monthly payments of $912.30. How much of the Larsons' first payment is interest and how much will be applied to reduce the principal?

SKILL MAINTENANCE

19. Find the area.

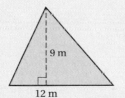

9 m
12 m

20. Solve: $\dfrac{5}{8} = \dfrac{10}{x}$.

21. Convert to decimal notation: $\dfrac{17}{12}$.

22. Convert to a mixed numeral: $\dfrac{19,008}{5280}$.

SYNTHESIS

23. By selling a home without using a realtor, Juan and Marie can avoid paying a 7.5% commission. They receive an offer of $109,000 from a potential buyer. In order to give a comparable offer, for what price would a realtor need to sell the house? Round to the nearest hundred.

24. Karen's commission rate is 16%. She invests her commission from the sale of $15,000 worth of merchandise at the interest rate of 12%, compounded quarterly. How much is Karen's investment worth after 6 months?

25. A housing development is constructed on a dead-end road along a river and ends in a cul-de-sac, as shown in the figure. The property owners agree to share the cost of maintaining the road in the following manner. The first fifth of the road in front of lot 1 is to be shared equally among all five lot owners. The cost of the second fifth in front of lot 2 is to be shared equally among the owners of lots 2–5, and so on. Assume that all five sections of the road cost the same to maintain.

a) What fractional part of the cost is paid by each owner?

b) What percent of the cost is paid by each owner?

c) If lots 3, 4, and 5 were all owned by the same person, what percent of the cost of maintenance would this person pay?

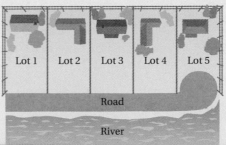

Lot 1   Lot 2   Lot 3   Lot 4   Lot 5

Road

River

1. Write fraction notation for 0.091 .

2. Write decimal notation for $\frac{13}{6}$.

3. Write an equivalent decimal for 3%.

4. Write $\frac{9}{8}$ as an equivalent percent.

5. Write fraction notation for the ratio 0.6 to 8.

6. Write the rate in kilometers per hour.

      350 km,   15 hr

Use <, >, or = for □ to write a true sentence.

7. $\frac{5}{7}$ □ $\frac{6}{8}$

8. -3.78 □ -37.8

Estimate the sum or difference by rounding to the nearest hundred.

9. $263{,}961 + 32{,}090 + 127.89$

10. $73{,}510 - 23{,}450$

11. Calculate: $46 - [4(6 + 4 \div 2) + 2 \times 3 - 5]$.

12. Combine like terms: $5x - 9 - 7x - 5$.

Perform the indicated operation and, if possible, simplify.

13. $\frac{6}{5} + 1\frac{5}{6}$

14. $-46.9 + 32.7$

15. $\begin{array}{r} 4\ 8\ 7{,}0\ 9\ 4 \\ 6{,}9\ 3\ 6 \\ +\quad 2\ 1{,}1\ 2\ 0 \\ \hline \end{array}$

16. $35 - 34.98$

17. $3\frac{1}{3} - 2\frac{2}{3}$

18. $-\frac{8}{9} - \frac{6}{7}$

19. $\frac{7}{9} \cdot \frac{3}{14}$

20. $(-32)(-4)(-3)$

21. $\begin{array}{r} 4\ 6.0\ 1\ 2 \\ \times\quad\ 0.0\ 3 \\ \hline \end{array}$

22. $6\frac{3}{5} \div 4\frac{2}{5}$

23. $431.2 \div (-35.2)$

24. $15\overline{)\ 1\ 8\ 5\ 0}$

Solve.

25. $18 \cdot x = 1710$

26. $y + 142.87 = 151$

27. $\frac{3}{7}x - 5 = 16$

28. $\frac{3}{4} + x = \frac{5}{6}$

29. $3(x - 7) + 2 = 12x - 3$

30. $\frac{16}{n} = \frac{21}{11}$

31. In what quadrant does the point $(-3, -1)$ lie?

32. Graph on a plane: $y = -\frac{3}{5}x$.

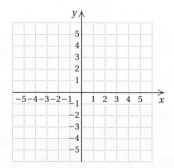

33. Find the mean: 19, 29, 34, 39, 45.

34. Find the median: 7, 7, 12, 15, 21.

35. Find the perimeter of a 15-in. by 15-in. chessboard.

36. Find the area of a 40-yd by 90-yd soccer field.

Solve.

37. A 12-oz box of cereal costs $3.60. Find the unit price in cents per ounce.

38. A bus travels 456 km in 6 hr. At this rate, how far would the bus travel in 8 hr?

39. In a recent year, Americans recycled 37 million lb of paper. It is projected that this will increase to 53 million lb in 2005. Find the percent of increase.

40. *Favorite Ice Creams.*   According to a recent survey, 8.9% of those interviewed chose chocolate as their favorite ice cream flavor and 4.2% chose butter pecan. Of the 2500 students in a college's entering class, how many would choose chocolate as their favorite ice cream? butter pecan?
Source: International Ice Cream Association

41. How many pieces of ribbon $1\frac{4}{5}$ yd long can be cut from a length of ribbon 9 yd long?

42. Bobbie walked $\frac{7}{10}$ km to school and then walked $\frac{8}{10}$ km to the library. How far did she walk?

(**SYNTHESIS**)

On a trip through the mountains, a Dodge Neon traveled 240 mi on $7\frac{1}{2}$ gal of gasoline. Going across the plains, the same car averaged 36 miles per gallon.

43. What was the percent of increase or decrease in miles per gallon when the car left the mountains for the plains?

44. How many miles per gallon did the Dodge average over the entire trip if it used 5 gal of gas to cross the plains?

The bar graph below shows how the winning times in the Olympic marathon and the qualifying times for 18–34-year-old men in the Boston Marathon have changed over time.

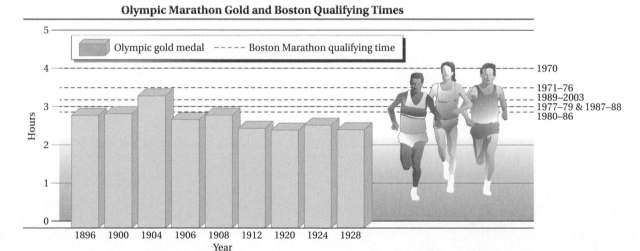

Olympic Marathon Gold and Boston Qualifying Times

Sources: Boston Athletic Association; *Guinness Book of Olympics*

45. During which of the years listed would the winner of the Olympic marathon have qualified for the 1985 Boston Marathon?

46. What was the first year in which the Boston Marathon's qualifying time was lower than a time that had been good enough to win an Olympic gold medal?

47. A $200 coat is marked up 20%. After 30 days, it is marked down 30% and sold. What was the final selling price of the coat?

Sets and Algebra

Gateway to Chapter 9
A.D. 1700 to A.D. 1850

This era produced tremendous innovation in both the development of computing machines and the development of the mathematics behind the modern-day computer. In 1820, Charles-Xavier Thomas invented a mechanical calculator that became the first commercially available calculator. In 1847, George Boole published *Mathematical Analysis of Logic.* This became the foundation for what we now call Boolean algebra.

CHAPTER

9

1. Use Set notation to list the months of the year.

2. List all possible subsets of the set {1, 2}

3. Given that
   A = {1, 2, 3, 4, 5} and B = {3, 4, 5, 6, 7}
   Find
   a. A ∩ B
   b. A ∪ B

4. Let U = {a, b, c, d, e, f, g, h, i, j} and A = {a, c, e, i}. Find A′

5. Given that A = {1, 2, 3, 4}, Find |A|.

6. Let A = {1, 2, 3, 4, 5} and B = {2, 4, 6, 8, 10}. Draw a Venn diagram to illustrate A ∩ B.

7. Is the phrase "9 is less than 4" a proposition?

8. Find a negation of "2 is less than 6."

9.1

THE LANGUAGE OF SETS

a Sets and Set Notation

> **DEFINITION:**
>
> A **set** is a collection of distinct objects. Those objects can be people, books, numbers, letters, or anything else that is described. An object must be clearly defined as part of a set, or not part of a set. An **element** is an object contained in a particular set.

We use braces, "{" and "}", to designate the contents of a set. We usually name a set with a capital letter, so that we can refer to it without listing all of its elements. Each of the following is a set.

$$A = \{a, b, c, d\}$$
$$C = \{\text{Segur, Wiechec, Cook, Nunn}\}$$
$$D = \{0, 1\}$$
$$N = \{1, 2, 3, \ldots\}$$

Note that the fourth set ends with three dots (called an ellipsis). Ellipses indicate that the remaining elements of the set can be found by continuing the same pattern. This can be used only when the pattern is clear.

$$S = \{\text{Madison, Thomas, Mare}, \ldots\}$$

and

$$T = \{6, 24, 13, 7, \ldots\}$$

do not indicate patterns that can be continued.

EXAMPLE 1 Use set notation to list the elements for each of the following.

(a) the U.S. presidents who served in the eighteenth century

(b) the natural numbers that are divisible by 3

Solutions

(a) {George Washington, John Adams}

(b) {3, 6, 9, 12, ... }

b Subsets and Special Sets

> **DEFINITION:**
>
> A **subset** is a set of elements that are all in a specified set.

For example, the set
$A = \{2, 4, 6, 8\}$ is a subset of the set
$N = \{1, 2, 3, \ldots\}$.

Bits of History

A.D. 1800–1900 Much of set theory is attributed to the brilliant, but tragic mathematical genius, Georg Cantor. In 1897, he published the first formal paper on set theory, introducing such concepts as set and subset as well as establishing rules for operating on sets. Cantor, with some aid of his contemporaries, was also the first to prove there were different orders or magnitude of infinity. In an attempt to free all of mathematics using sets, Cantor found himself in various stages of mental instability throughout his life.

1. Use set notation to list the elements for each of the following.
   (a) the U.S. presidents whose fathers were U.S. presidents
   (b) negative integers that are divisible by 5

Answers on page A-28

2. Which of the following are subsets of the set $S = \{0, 1, 2, 3, 4, 5, 6, 7, 8, 9, A, B, C, D, E, F\}$?
(a) $A = \{6, 9, A, 10\}$
(b) $B = \{F, A, C, E\}$
(c) $C = \{0, F\}$

EXAMPLE 2 Which of the following are subsets of the set $S = \{a, b, c, d, e, f, g, h\}$?

(a) $A = \{b, c, d\}$ is a subset, as all three elements are in S.

(b) $B = \{f, a, c, e\}$ is a subset (note that the order of elements in a set is unimportant).

(c) $C = \{a, c, t, e\}$ is not a subset because the element t is not in set S.

Following are two important definitions that are part of the language of sets.

> **DEFINITION:**
>
> The **universal set** (sometimes referred to as the **universe**) is the collection of all elements under consideration. The universal set is usually designated with the symbol U.

> **DEFINITION:**
>
> A set that contains no elements is called the **empty set.** The empty set is designated with either a pair of empty brackets, { } or the symbol $\varnothing$.

3. Use set notation to designate each of the following.
(a) the universal set of English letters
(b) the set of all twentieth century women U.S. presidents

EXAMPLE 3 Use set notation to designate each of the following.

(a) the universal set of Greek letters

(b) the set of all even prime numbers greater than 2

Solutions

(a) $U = \{\alpha, \beta, \gamma, \ldots, \omega\}$, (the ellipsis indicates all of the letters between γ and ω).

(b) $\varnothing$

It is sometimes important to know how many elements are in a set.

C Cardinality

> **DEFINITION:**
>
> The **cardinality** of a set is the number of elements in the set. Cardinality is designated by placing the set name between two vertical lines. $|A|$ is the number of elements in set **A.**

Note the similarity between cardinality and absolute value. In mathematics, we say that both cardinality and absolute value represent magnitude.

What about sets with an infinite number of elements? In subsequent courses you may encounter two infinite sets with different cardinalities, but in this text, we do not distinguish between sizes of infinity and just say that such sets have a cardinality that is infinite.

4. Given the following sets, find the cardinality for each.
(a) $A = \{a, b, c, d, e, f\}$
(b) $B = \{$the letters in the word *Mississippi*$\}$
(c) $C = \{3, 4, 5, 6, \ldots, 44\}$
(d) $D = \{\ \}$

Answers on page A-28

EXAMPLE 4 Given the following sets, find the cardinality for each.

(a) $A = \{2, 4, 6, 8, 10\}$ (b) $B = \{$the letters of the English alphabet$\}$

(c) $C = \{2, 4, 6, 8, \ldots, 48\}$ (d) $D = \{1, 2, 3, 4, \ldots\}$ (e) $E = \varnothing$

Solutions

(a) $|A| = 5$ (b) $|B| = 26$ (c) $|C| = 24$ (d) $|D|$ is infinite   (e) $E = 0$

For Extra Help

EXERCISE SET

 a

1. Use set notation to list the elements for each of the following.
   (a) the U.S. states whose names start with the letter A

   (b) the days of the week

   (c) the natural numbers that are divisible by 10

   (d) the prime numbers that are less than 14

2. Use set notation to list the elements for each of the following.
   (a) the months of the year whose names start with the letter J

   (b) the natural numbers that are divisible by 7

   (c) the first five digits of the number π

   (d) the negative integers that are divisible by 6

3. Use set notation to represent each of the following.
   (a) the universal set of vowels in the English alphabet (excluding y)

   (b) the set of all U.S. states in Europe

   (c) the universal set of octal digits

   (d) the set of all prime numbers less than 2

4. Use set notation to represent each of the following.
   (a) the universal set of English letters on the fourth row of a standard keyboard (the row starting with the Shift key)

   (b) the set of oceans that border the U.S. state of Missouri

   (c) the set of all U.S. states that are islands

   (d) the universal set of hexadecimal digits

5. Which of the following are subsets of the set F, where $F = \{$Taurus, Ranger, Explorer, Escort, Windstar, Contour, Mustang$\}$?
    (a) {Explorer, Escort, Mustang}

    (b) {Escort, Ranger, Expedition, Windstar}

    (c) {Mustang, Taurus, Explorer, Ranger}

    (d) {Explorer, Blazer, Escort}

6. Which of the following are subsets of the set C, where $C = \{$black, blue, cyan, green, magenta, red, white, yellow$\}$?
    (a) {red, green, blue}

    (b) {black, white, gray, blue}

    (c) {white}

    (d) {cyan, magenta, black, yellow}

    (e) {red, orange, yellow}

7. Which of the following are subsets of the set N, where $N = \{1, 2, 3, \ldots\}$?
    (a) {0, 1}

    (b) {1, 3, 5, 7, 9}

    (c) {2, 4, 6, . . . }

8. Which of the following are subsets of the set Z, where
    $Z = \{\ldots, -2, -1, 0, 1, 2, \ldots\}$?
    (a) {6, 28}

    (b) $\{0, 1, 2, \ldots, E, F\}$

    (c) $\{-5, -6, -7, \ldots\}$

    (d) N (from Exercise 5)

    (e) {1, 1.1, 1.11, . . .}

9. Given the following sets, find the cardinality of each.
   (a) $A = \{3, 5, 7, 9\}$

   (b) $B = \{$the letters in the word *Oregon*$\}$

   (c) $C = \{10, 20, 30, 40, \ldots 100\}$

   (d) $D = \{1, 3, 5, \ldots\}$

   (e) $E = \{\emptyset\}$

   (f) $F = \{$the set of U.S. capitols$\}$

10. Given the following sets, find the cardinality of each.
   (a) $A = \{$digits on a standard clock$\}$

   (b) $B = \{$the letters in the word *coffee*$\}$

   (c) $C = \emptyset$

   (d) $D = \{$all real numbers$\}$

   (e) $E = \{$months that have 28 days$\}$

9.2 SET OPERATORS

Bits of History

A.D. 1800–1900 A bank clerk named William S. Burroughs invented an adding and listing machine in the late nineteenth century. This was the first mechanical calculating device with keys and a printer that was both reliable and affordable for commerce. The Burroughs machine continued its popularity until World War I, when it was replaced by more sophisticated devices.

a   Union and Intersection

In arithmetic, we can add two numbers and get a third number. For example, we say

$$4 + 3 = 7.$$

In the expression $4 + 3$, we call the plus sign an **operator.** In particular, it is a binary operator, because it calls for two numbers to be added.

There are also different operators that can be used with sets. The first we will look at is called the union.

DEFINITION:

If A and B are sets, their **union**, which we write as $A \cup B$, is the set consisting of all elements that are in A or B or in both A and B.

1. Let $A = \{1, 3, 5, 7, 9\}$, and let $B = \{2, 3, 5, 7, 11\}$. Find $A \cup B$.

■ **EXAMPLE 1**   Let $A = \{e, g, b, d, f\}$, and let $B = \{f, a, c, e\}$. Find $A \cup B$.

Since $A \cup B$ consists of all the elements from either set A or set B, then

$$A \cup B = \{a, b, c, d, e, f, g\}.$$

In arithmetic, multiplication is also a binary operator. There is also a second operator for sets.

DEFINITION:

If A and B are sets, their **intersection**, written as $A \cap B$, is the set consisting of all elements that are common to **both** A and B.

2. Let $A = \{1, 3, 5, 7, 9\}$, and let $B = \{2, 3, 5, 7, 11\}$. Find $A \cap B$.

■ **EXAMPLE 2**   Let $A = \{e, g, b, d, f\}$, and let $B = \{f, a, c, e\}$. Find $A \cap B$.

Since $A \cap B$ consists of all the elements that belong in common to both A and B, then

$$A \cap B = \{e, f\}.$$

DEFINITION:

If two sets have nothing in common, they are said to be **disjoint**. The next example illustrates such a case.

Answers on page A-28

EXAMPLE 3 Find $A \cap B$ if $A = \{$Stan, Kyle, Kenny, Cartmen$\}$ and $B = \{$Simon, Alvin, Theodore$\}$.

In this case, the sets are disjoint, so they do not share any common elements. Therefore, the intersection is empty, and we write

$$A \cap B = \varnothing \quad \text{or} \quad A \cap B = \{\,\}.$$

In arithmetic, a negative sign is used to make a positive number negative (or a negative number positive). Negation is called a **unary operator** because it requires only one number. There is also a unary operator for sets.

b The Complement of a Set

DEFINITION:

Sometimes we are interested in finding the items that are not in a set. If A is a set, then we define the **complement** of A, which we write as A' to be the set of elements that are in the universal set that are not in A.

EXAMPLE 4 Let $U = \{0, 1, 2, 3, 4, 5, 6, 7, 8, 9\}$ and $A = \{0, 2, 4, 6, 8\}$. Find A'.

Because our universal set is the set of digits for base ten and A is the set of even digits,

$$A' = \{1, 3, 5, 7, 9\}, \text{ which is also the set of odd digits.}$$

In Section 9.1, we looked at the cardinality of a set. The following equation relates to the cardinality of the union of two sets, which we will call the **cardinality principle for two sets:**

$$|A \cup B| = |A| + |B| - |A \cap B|.$$

EXAMPLE 5 Given that $|A \cap B| = 132$, $|B| = 55$, and $|A \cap B| = 33$, find $|A|$.

From the previous equation, we know that

$$132 = |A| + 55 - 32.$$

Solving the equation for $|A|$, we find

$$|A| = 132 - 23 = 109.$$

There are 109 elements in set A.

In the next example, the same equation is used to solve an application.

EXAMPLE 6 Let $A = \{$VSU students who like math$\}$ and $B = \{$VSU students who like computer science$\}$.

Assume that there are 50 VSU students who like computer science, 30 who like math, and 65 students who like at least one of them. How many students like both?

3. Let $A = \{ \text{チ, ス, ム, ヨ} \}$, and let $B = \{\pi, \phi, \psi, \alpha\}$. Find $A \cap B$.

4. Let $U = \{0, 1, 2, 3, 4, 5, 6, 7, 8, 9, A, B, C, D, E, F\}$ and $A = \{0, 2, 4, 6, 8, A, C, E\}$. Find A'.

5. Given that $|A \cup B| = 72$, $|A| = 44$, and $|B| = 55$, find $|A \cap B|$.

6. In a random sample of MS patients, it was found that 25 had allergies to milk products, 32 had allergies to peanuts, and 15 had allergies to both. How many had allergies to at least one of the two?

Answers on page A-28

Solution

From the sentence above, we have $|A| = 30$, $|B| = 50$, and $|A \cup B| = 65$. We wish to find $|A \cap B|$.

We know that

$$|A \cup B| = |A| + |B| - |A \cap B|, \text{ so}$$
$$65 = 30 + 50 - |A \cap B|. \text{ Solving for } |A \cap B|,$$
$$|A \cap B| = 80 - 65 = 15.$$

There are 15 VSU students who like both math and computer science.

The final example uses the **cardinality principle for three sets**:

$$|A \cup B \cup C| = |A| + |B| + |C| - |A \cap B| - |A \cap C| - |B \cap C| + |A \cap B \cap C|$$

EXAMPLE 7 $A = \{\text{students taking a foreign language class}\}$, with $|A| = 125$, $B = \{\text{students who own the DVD } Star\ Trek\ VI\}$, with $|B| = 40$, and $C = \{\text{students who have their own apartment}\}$, with $|C| = 140$.

Also let $|A \cap B| = 2$, $|A \cap C| = 88$, $|B \cap C| = 16$, and $|A \cup B \cup C| = 200$.

(a)   Describe an element of the set $A \cap B \cap C$.

(b)   Find $|A \cap B \cap C|$.

Solutions

(a) $A \cap B \cap C$ represents the set of students taking a foreign language who have their own apartment and own the DVD *Star Trek VI*.

(b)   Because $|A \cup B \cup C| = |A| + |B| + |C| - |A \cap B| - |A \cap C| - |B \cap C| + |A \cap B \cap C|$,

we have $200 = 125 + 40 + 140 - 2 - 88 - 16 + |A \cap B \cap C|$

$200 = 305 - 106 + |A \cap B \cap C|$

$200 = 199 + |A \cap B \cap C|$

$|A \cap B \cap C| = 1.$

There is only one foreign-language student who has an apartment and owns the DVD *Star Trek VI*.

7.
$A = \{\text{CDs that cost more than \$15}\}$, with $|A| = 20$,
$B = \{\text{CDs that are played on radio station WILD in their entirety}\}$, with $|B| = 6$, and
$C = \{\text{CDs that contain at least one single from a hit movie}\}$, with $|C| = 40$.

Also let $|A \cap B| = 4$, $|A \cap C| = 10$, $|B \cap C| = 3$, and $|A \cap B \cap C| = 2$.

(a)   Describe an element of the set $A \cup B \cup C$.

(b)   Find $|A \cup B \cup C|$.

Answers on page A-28

9.2
EXERCISE SET

1. Let $U = \{0, 1, 2, 3, 4, 5, 6, 7, 8, 9\}$, $A = \{2, 4, 5, 7, 8, 9\}$, and $B = \{1, 2, 5, 6, 8\}$.

Find the following:

(a) $A \cup B$

(b) $A \cap B$

(c) A'

(d) B'

(e) $|A \cup B|$

(f) $|A \cap B|$

(g) $|A|$

(h) $|A'|$

(i) $|U|$

2. Let $U = \{0, 1, 2, 3, 4, 5, 6, 7, 8, 9\}$, $A = \{1, 3, 5, 7, 9\}$, $B = \{0, 2, 4, 6, 8\}$, and $C = \{3, 6, 9\}$.

Find the following:

(a) $A \cup C$

(b) $A \cap C$

(c) $A \cup B$

(d) U'

(e) $|A \cup B|$

(f) $|A \cap B|$

(g) $|C|$

(h) $|C'|$

(i) $|U'|$

3. Let $U = \{0, 1, 2, 3, 4, 5, 6, 7, 8, 9\}$, $A = \{0, 2, 5, 7, 8\}$, and $B = \{1, 2, 6, 7\}$.

Find the following:

(a) A'

(b) B'

(c) $A' \cap B'$

(d) $A \cup B$

(e) $(A \cup B)'$

(f) What is the relationship of the answers to parts c and e?

4. Let $U = \{0, 1, 2, 3, 4, 5, 6, 7, 8, 9, 10, 11\}$, $P = \{2, 3, 5, 7, 11\}$, $O = \{1, 3, 5, 7, 9, 11\}$, and $A = \{2, 5, 8, 11\}$.

Find the following:

(a) $P \cup A$

(b) $O \cap A$

(c) O'

(d) A'

(e) $O' \cup A'$

(f) $(O \cap A)'$

(g) What is the relationship of the answers to parts e and f?

5. Let $U = \{$films listed below$\}$,

$D = \{$*Taxi Driver, Cape Fear, Raging Bull, Casino, Goodfellas*$\}$,

$P = \{$*Raging Bull, Casino, Goodfellas, Home Alone, Lethal Weapon 2*$\}$, and

$G = \{$*Braveheart, Road Warrior, Lethal Weapon 2, Hamlet*$\}$.

Find the following:

(a) $D \cap P$

(b) $P \cup G$

(c) $D \cap G$

(d) D'

(e) P'

(f) $P \cap G$

6. Let $U = \{$Disney films listed below$\}$

$A = \{$*Aladdin, Fantasia, The Lion King, The Little Mermaid, Snow White*$\}$,

$N = \{$*Flubber, Herbie, The Parent Trap, Escape to Witch Mountain, Mary Poppins*$\}$, and

$Y = \{$*Aladdin, Flubber, The Lion King, The Little Mermaid, The Parent Trap*$\}$.

Find the following:

(a) $A \cap Y$

(b) $N \cap A$

(c) $A \cap N$

(d) Y'

(e) $A \cup N \cup Y$

(f) $N' \cap A$

7. Given $|A \cap B| = 8$, $|A \cup B| = 37$ and $|A| = 30$, find $|B|$.

8. Given $|A \cup B| = 44$, $|A| = 13$, and , $|B| = 39$, find $|A \cap B|$.

9. Let $A = \{$Community College students in Math 92$\}$ and

$B = \{$Community College students in CS 160$\}$.

Assume there are 31 Community College students in Math 92, 45 in CS 160, and 62 in at least one of the two courses. How many Community College students are in both courses?

10. Let $N = \{$students who use Netscape$\}$ and

$E = \{$students who use Internet Explorer$\}$.

Assume there are 15 students who use Netscape, 38 who use Internet Explorer, and 7 who use both. How many students use at least one of the two Web browsers?

11. Let $P = \{$computers with a Pentium 4 processor$\}$, with $|P| = 125$,

$R = \{$computers with 256 MB of RAM$\}$, with $|R| = 45$, and

$D = \{$computers with a DVD-ROM drive$\}$, with $|D| = 35$.

Also, let $|P \cap R| = 40$, $|R \cap D| = 27$, $|P \cap D| = 32$, and

$|P \cap R \cap D| = 25$. Answer the following:

(a) Describe an element of the set $|P \cup R \cup D|$.

(b) Find $|P \cup R \cup D|$.

12. Let $W = \{\text{computers with Winamp}\}$, with $|W| = 143$,
$R = \{\text{computers with RealPlayer}\}$, with $|R| = 70$, and
$C = \{\text{computers with a CD writer}\}$, with $|C| = 33$.

Also, let $|W \cap C| = 20$, $|R \cap C| = 7$, and $|W \cap R| = 28$, and let 193 machines have at least one of the three.

How many computers have Winamp, RealPlayer, and a CD writer?

Bits of History

In 1881, the English mathematician John Venn published the book, *Symbolic Logic,* which made lasting contributions to the fields of logic and probability. Venn provided a visual model of representing the union and intersection of sets by producing three circles inside a box that generated eight nonoverlapping regions. Each region could be filled or unfilled, thus creating 256 different combinations or outcomes.

1. Shade $A \cap B$ on a Venn diagram.

In Section 9.2, we looked at the set operators **union**, **intersection**, and **complementation**. In this section, we use a common set theory tool, a **Venn diagram**, to illustrate these operators.

> **DEFINITION:**
>
> A **Venn diagram** consist of a rectangle that represents the universal set, together with inner circles, each representing a specific subset of the universal set.

The first systematic use of these diagrams was made by the German philosopher and mathematician Gottfried W. von Leibniz. The diagrams used today are sometimes called Euler diagrams, after the Swiss mathematician Leonhard Euler who devised them. The English logician John Venn greatly improved and popularized the use of these diagrams.

EXAMPLE 1 Shade $A \cup B$ on a Venn diagram.

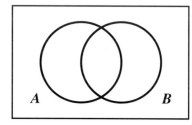

Solution

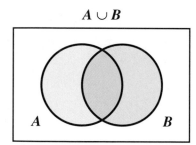

A Venn diagram can be an excellent tool for solving some logic problems. The first step requires that elements be properly placed within the diagram. The next example illustrates.

Answers on page A-28

EXAMPLE 2 Let $A = \{e, g, b, d, f\}$, and let $B = \{f, a, c, e\}$. Use a Venn diagram to illustrate the sets.

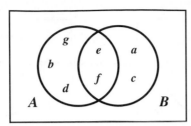

In most applications of Venn diagrams, there are important elements of the universal set that are not in one of the specified subsets.

EXAMPLE 3 Let $A = \{e, g, b, d, f\}$, $B = \{f, a, c, e\}$, and $U = \{a, b, c, d, e, f, g, h, i, j\}$. Use a Venn diagram to illustrate the sets.

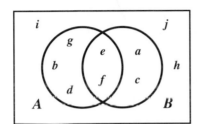

EXAMPLE 4 Let $A = \{e, g, b, d, f\}$, $B = \{f, a, c, e\}$, and $U = \{a, b, c, d, e, f, g, h, i, j\}$. Use a Venn diagram to illustrate A'.

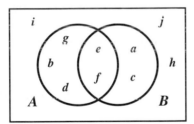

Solution

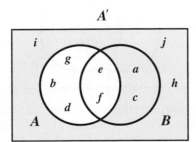

In the next example, Venn diagrams are used to illustrate an important mathematical idea credited to Augustus De Morgan, an early nineteenth-century British mathematician.

2. Let $A = \{1, 3, 5, 7, 9\}$, and let $B = \{2, 3, 5, 7, 11\}$. Use a Venn diagram to illustrate the sets.

3. Let $A = \{1, 3, 5, 7, 9\}$, $B = \{2, 3, 5, 7, 11\}$, and $U = \{1, 2, 3, 4, 5, 6, 7, 8, 9, 10, 11, 12\}$. Use a Venn diagram to illustrate the sets.

4. Let $A = \{1, 3, 5, 7, 9\}$, $B = \{2, 3, 5, 7, 11\}$, and $U = \{1, 2, 3, 4, 5, 6, 7, 8, 9, 10, 11, 12\}$. Use a Venn diagram to illustrate A'.

Answers on page A-28–A-29

5. Use a Venn diagram to show that $(A \cap B)' = A' \cup B'$. (This is the second form of De Morgan's law.)

EXAMPLE 5 Use Venn diagrams to show that $(A \cup B)' = A' \cap B'$ (This is one form of De Morgan's law.)

$A \cup B$

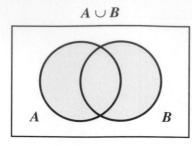

$(A \cup B)'$

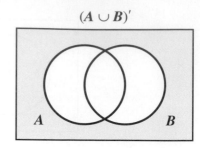

A'

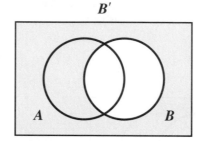

B'

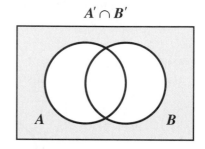

$A' \cap B'$

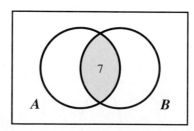

Note that while the diagrams at the end are obtained in different ways, they are the same, which means that the expressions $(A \cup B)'$ and $A' \cap B'$ are equivalent.

Venn diagrams can also be used to indicate cardinality, as in the following example.

6. Draw the Venn diagram for which the following cardinalities apply:

$|A| = 200$, $|B| = 150$, and $|A \cup B| = 325$.

EXAMPLE 6 Draw the Venn diagram for which the following cardinalities apply:

$$|A| = 10, |B| = 20, \text{ and } |A \cap B| = 7$$

Solution

To draw such a diagram, we must start with the intersection. Note that we write the cardinality, 7, inside the intersection.

Now, we must make certain that the total inside the circle for set A is 10. That means that there are $10 - 7 = 3$ elements of A that are not in the intersec-

Answers on page A-29

tion of A and B. Likewise, there are $20 - 7 = 13$ elements of B that are not in the intersection of A and B. Here is the Venn diagram.

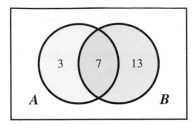

Example 6 should remind you of the cardinality principle for two sets from Section 9.2,

$$|A \cup B| = |A| + |B| - |A \cap B|$$ (Again, we subtract the intersection once because it is counted twice, once in $|A|$ and once in $|B|$).

EXAMPLE 7   Draw the Venn diagram for which the following cardinalities apply:

$|A| = 20, |B| = 19, |C| = 24, |A \cap B| = 6, |A \cap C| = 10,$
$|B \cap C| = 7,$ and $|A \cup B \cup C| = 46.$

Solution

To draw such a diagram, we first determine the number of elements in the intersection and then work outward. This is similar to the previous example, but now we are dealing with the intersection of three sets. We can use an algorithm to help solve this problem.

First, we identify the eight pieces of information needed to solve this problem.

These are the eight parts of the cardinality principle for three sets in Section 9.2. We then substitute the known quantities into the equation:

$$
\begin{array}{rcl}
|A \cup B \cup C| & = & |A| + |B| + |C| - |A \cap B| - |A \cap C| - |B \cap C| + |A \cap B \cap C| \\
46 & = & 20 + 19 + 24 - 6 - 10 - 7 + |A \cap B \cap C|
\end{array}
$$

This is just like solving a linear equation in a beginning algebra class; our unknown quantity, or "x," is $|A \cap B \cap C|$.

Combining like terms on the right, we obtain

$$40 = 40 + |A \cap B \cap C|.$$

Subtracting 40 from both sides of the equation, we find

$$6 = |A \cap B \cap C|.$$

Now that we know the cardinality of the intersection of all three sets, we place that value on the Venn diagram and work outward, determining the cardinality of the intersecting regions just outside the center.

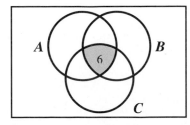

7. Draw the Venn diagram for which the following cardinalities apply:

$|A| = 29, |B| = 30, |C| = 45,$
$|A \cap B| - 24, |A \cap C| = 16,$
$|B \cap C| = 20,$ and $|A \cup B \cup C| = 60.$

Answers on page A-29

Note that $A \cap B$ is made up of two parts, $A \cap B \cap C$ and $A \cap B \cap C'$. We know that $|A \cap B| = |A \cap B \cap C| + |A \cap B \cap C'|$.

$$6 = 6 + |A \cap B \cap C'|.$$

So, $|A \cap B \cap C'| = 0$, which means we put a 0 in that region on the Venn diagram.

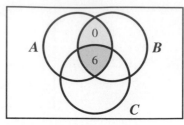

Continuing the process for the other two regions, we obtain

$$|A \cap C| = |A \cap B \cap C| + |A \cap B' \cap C| = 10 = 6 + 4$$

$$|B \cap C| = |A \cap B \cap C| + |A' \cap B \cap C| = 7 = 6 + 1.$$

To find the cardinality of the final three regions, we use a similar process. To determine the cardinality of the region inside A, we find the cardinality of the four parts that make up region A.

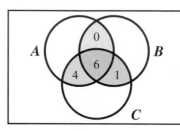

$$|A| = |A \cap B \cap C| + |A \cap B \cap C'| + |A \cap B' \cap C| + |A \cap B' \cap C'|$$

$$20 = 6 + 0 + 4 + |A \cap B' \cap C'|$$

so, $|A \cap B' \cap C'| = 10$,

$$|B| = |A \cap B \cap C| + |A \cap B \cap C'| + |A' \cap B \cap C| + |A' \cap B \cap C'|$$
$$19 = \qquad 6 \qquad + \qquad 0 \qquad + \qquad 1 \qquad + \qquad 12 \qquad,$$

and

$$|C| = |A \cap B \cap C| + |A' \cap B \cap C| + |A \cap B' \cap C| + |A' \cap B' \cap C|$$
$$24 = \qquad 6 \qquad + \qquad 1 \qquad + \qquad 4 \qquad + \qquad 13 \qquad.$$

Finally, we fill in the last of the Venn diagram.

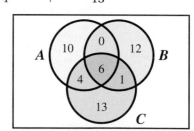

1. Shade the specified regions on the following Venn diagrams:

$A \cup B$

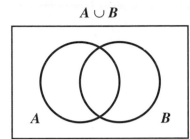

B'

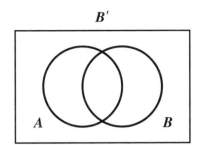

2. Shade the specified regions on the following Venn diagrams:

A'

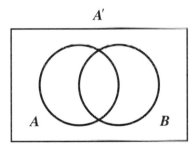

U

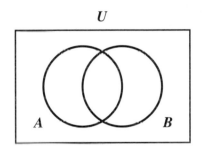

3. Label the following sets on the Venn diagram below.
   Let $A = \{0, 3, 6, 9\}$
   $B = \{0, 2, 4, 6, 8\}$
   $U = \{0, 1, 2, 3, 4, 5, 6, 7, 8, 9\}$

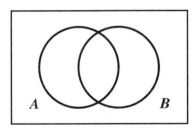

4. Label the following sets on the Venn diagram below.

Let $A = \{0, 2, 4, 7\}$

$B = \{1, 2, 4, 8, 9\}$

$U = \{0, 1, 2, 3, 4, 5, 6, 7, 8, 9\}$

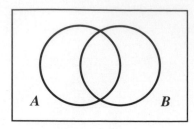

5. Draw a Venn diagram to illustrate the set A'.

Let $A = \{0, 1, 6, 7\}$

$B = \{1, 2, 4, 7, 8, 9\}$

$U = \{0, 1, 2, 3, 4, 5, 6, 7, 8, 9\}$

6. Draw a Venn diagram to illustrate the set B'.

Let $A = \{0, 1, 6, 7\}$

$B = \{1, 2, 4, 7, 8, 9\}$

$U = \{0, 1, 2, 3, 4, 5, 6, 7, 8, 9\}$.

7. Label the following sets on the Venn diagram below.

Let $A' = \{1, 2, 3, 4\}$

$B' = \{1, 2, 4, 8, 9\}$

$U = \{0, 1, 2, 3, 4, 5, 6, 7, 8, 9\}$

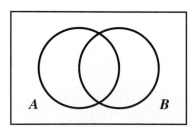

8. Shade the specified regions on the following Venn diagrams.

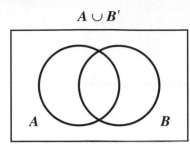

$A \cup B'$

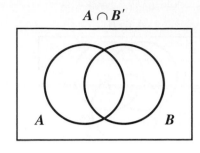

$A \cap B'$

9. Draw a Venn diagram that indicates $|A \cap B| = 13$, $|A| = 52$, and $|B| = 25$. What is $|A \cup B|$?

10. Draw a Venn diagram that indicates $|A \cup B| = 40$, $|A| = 11$, and $|B| = 35$. What is $|A \cap B|$?

11. Let $A = \{$Community College students in Math 92$\}$ and
$B = \{$Community College students in CS 160$\}$.

Assume there are 37 Community College students in Math 92, 43 in CS 160, and 65 in at least one of the two courses. How many Community College students are in both courses? Illustrate your solution on the following Venn diagram.

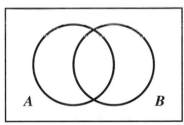

12. Let $N = \{$students who use Netscape$\}$ and
$E = \{$students who use Internet Explorer$\}$.

Assume there are 14 students who use Netscape, 39 who use Internet Explorer, and 9 who use both. How many students use at least one of the two Web browsers? Illustrate your solution on the following Venn diagram.

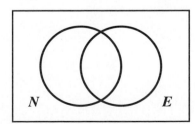

13. Shade the specified regions on the following Venn diagrams:

$A \cup C$

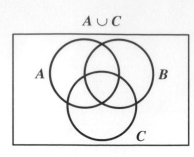

$(A \cap B)'$

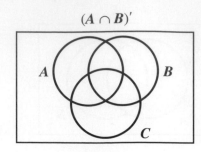

14. Shade the specified regions on the following Venn diagrams:

C'

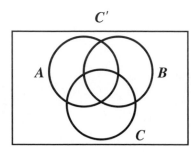

$A' \cap (B \cup C)$

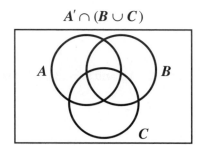

15. Draw the Venn diagram for which the following cardinalities apply:

$|A \cap B| = 8$, $|A| = 41$, and $|B| = 42$, $|A \cap C| = 24$, $|B \cap C| = 11$, $|C| = 42$, and $|A \cup B \cup C| = 85$. What is $|A \cap B \cap C|$?

16. Draw the Venn diagram for which the following cardinalities apply: $|A = B| = 36$, $|A| = 216$, and $|B| = 41$, $|A \cap C| = 123$, $|B \cap C| = 23$, $|C| = 126$, and $|A \cap B \cap C| = 21$. What is $|A \cup B \cup C|$?

17. Let $P = \{$computers with a Pentium 4 processor$\}$, with $|P| = 125$,
  $R = \{$computers with 512 MB of RAM$\}$, with $|R| = 45$, and
  $D = \{$computers with a DVD writer drive$\}$, with $|D| = 35$.

Also, let $|P \cap R| = 40$, $|R \cap D| = 27$, $|P \cap D| = 32$, and $|P \cap R \cap D| = 25$.

(a) Draw the Venn diagram for which the given cardinalities apply.

(b) How many computers had only a DVD writer drive?

(c) How many computers had only a Pentium 4 processor?

18. Let $W = \{$computers with Winamp$\}$, with $|W| = 143$,
  $R = \{$computers with RealPlayer$\}$, with $|R| = 70$, and
  $C = \{$computers with a CD writer$\}$, with $|C| = 33$.
Also, let $|W \cap C| = 20$, $|R \cap C| = 7$, and $|W \cap R| = 28$, and let 193 machines have at least one of the three.

(a) Draw the Venn diagram for which the given cardinalities apply.

(b) How many computers have only Winamp?

(c) How many computers have only a CD writer?

(d) How many computers have only RealPlayer?

9.4 PROPOSITIONS AND TRUTH TABLES

a | Propositions

The mathematics behind decision-making is called **logic**. All of our work in this chapter is based on mathematical logic.

In arithmetic, we create expressions using numbers and operators. Examples of such expressions include

$$27 + 38 \quad \text{and} \quad 457 - (2 \times 3)^3.$$

In algebra, we use variables to represent numbers. Those same expressions can be written as algebraic expressions

$$x + y \quad \text{and} \quad a - (bc)^3$$

where $x = 27$, $y = 38$, $a = 457$, $b = 2$, and $c = 3$.

In logic, instead of numbers, we work with propositions.

A **proposition** is a declarative statement that is either true or false. Here are a few examples of propositions.

> It rained in West Virginia yesterday.
> Tex ate barbecued tofu for dinner last night.
> $12_{16} + 9_{16} = 21_{16}.$ Do you recognize this as a false statement?

1. Determine whether each of the following is a proposition.
  (a) $8 - 2 = 5$
  (b) Is this difficult for you?
  (c) The final will be 12 pages long.
  (d) The surface is slippery when wet.
  (e) Turn left at the next light.

EXAMPLE 1 Determine whether each of the following is a proposition.

(a) Is it raining?

No, this is a question and not a declarative statement.

(b) $4 + 2 = 6$

Yes, this is a proposition that is always true.

(c) The temperature in Dallas is over 90°F.

Yes, this is a proposition that is sometimes true and sometimes false.

(d) Turn in your homework on Friday.

No, this statement cannot be labeled as true or false.

(e) I did all of the homework last night.

Yes, this statement is either true or false.

As in algebra, we could assign a variable name to each statement. We put braces around each statement to make it clear where the statement begins and ends.

> $p = \{$It rained in West Virginia yesterday.$\}$
> $q = \{$Tex ate barbecued tofu for dinner last night.$\}$
> $r = \{12_{16} + 9_{16} = 21_{16}\}$

2. Given $p = \{$Trinh is going to law school.$\}$
  $q = \{$Maria got an A on her math test.$\}$
  $r = \{12_{16} + 9_{16} = 1B_{16}\}$
  $s = \{x - 5 \leq -2\},$

write each of the following propositions in words or symbols. There may be more than one correct answer.

  (a) $\sim p$ **(b)** $\sim q$ **(c)** $\sim r$ **(d)** $\sim s$

Also, as in algebra, each proposition has a negative. We write the negative of p as $\sim p$, which we read as "not p" or "the **negation** of p."

EXAMPLE 2 Given $p = \{$It rained in West Virginia yesterday.$\}$
  $q = \{$Tex ate barbecued tofu for dinner last night.$\}$
  $r = \{12_{16} + 9_{16} = 21_{16}\}$
  $s = \{3x + 2 \geq 7\}$

write each of the following propositions in words or symbols.

Answers on page A-30

Solutions

(a) ~*p*   We could write, "It did not rain in West Virginia last night."

(b) ~*q*   "Tex did not eat barbecued tofu for dinner last night."

(c) ~*r* $12_{16} + 9_{16} \neq 21_{16}$

(d) ~*s* $3x + 2 \geq 7$

b   Truth Tables

The relationship of the truth value of a statement and its negation can be shown in a **truth table**.

p	$\sim p$
True	False
False	True

Each row of a truth table is independent. The first row indicates that when p is true, its negation is false. The second row indicates that when p is false, its negation is true. We could abbreviate truth value with the letters T and F, as below.

p	$\sim p$
T	F
F	T

Because a computer computes the value of a statement, true is given a value of 1 and false is given a value of 0. When we are working with computer logic, our truth tables will consist of 1s and 0s rather than Ts and Fs. The table for negation becomes:

p	$\sim p$
1	0
0	1

EXAMPLE 3   Complete the following truth table.

p	q	$\sim p$	$\sim q$
1	1		
1	0		
0	1		
0	0		

3. Complete the following truth table.

r	s	$\sim s$	$\sim r$
1	1		
1	0		
0	1		
0	0		

Answers on page A-31

Before proceeding, note that, with two statements, there are four possible combinations, 11, 10, 01, and 00.

To complete the table, we examine each row, assigning the opposite value for the negation of a statement.

p	q	$\sim p$	$\sim q$
1	1	0	0
1	0	0	1
0	1	1	0
0	0	1	1

1. Which of the following are propositions?

   (a) Is the sky blue?

   (b) $4 + 5 = 9$

   (c) $x = 3$

   (d) Do your homework.

   (e) 7 is less than 3.

   (f) Eat your vegetables.

   (g) $24(-36) < 0$

   (h) Is this a proposition?

2. For each of the following propositions, find a proposition that is equivalent.

   (a) $x + 7 = -3$

   (b) 4 is less than 7.

   (c) It is Tuesday.

   (d) $4 > -6$

   (e) $25 < -26$

3. For each of the following propositions, find a negation.

   (a) $x - 7 = 2$

   (b) 5 is more than 3.

   (c) It is 97°F outside.

   (d) $12 > -4$

   (e) Math is fun.

   (f) $9 < 2$

4. For each of the following statements, find a negation.

(a) $x + 7 \neq 10$

(b) It is not raining today.

(c) He never takes out the trash.

(d) $12 \not\leq 13$

(e) $4 \not> -6$

(f) Mark did not fail his test.

5. The following is a truth table containing truth values for two propositions, p and q. Complete the table.

p	q	$\sim p$	$\sim q$	$\sim(\sim p)$	$\sim(\sim q)$	$\sim(\sim(\sim p))$	$\sim(\sim(\sim q))$
1	1						
1	0						
0	1						
0	0						

6. The following is a truth table containing truth values for two propositions, p and $\sim q$. Complete the table.

p	$\sim q$	$\sim p$	$\sim(\sim q)$	$\sim(\sim p)$	$\sim(\sim(\sim q))$	$\sim(\sim(\sim p))$	$\sim(\sim(\sim(\sim q)))$
1	0						
1	1						
0	0						
0	1						

7. Find a negation of the following propositions.

(a) Pat never has none of the answers.

(b) John ain't got no friends.

8. In logic, if two negations occur successively, what happens? In English, what happens? What property is similar in mathematics?

a Logical Operators

Propositions are like numbers and variables in that we can operate on them. The operations we use are not addition and multiplication. Instead they are what we call **logical operators**. These include AND, OR, and NOT.

If p is a true statement and q is a false statement, then the statement p AND q is false, so it has a value of 0. In fact, the statement p AND q is true only when both p and q are true. We summarize all of the possibilities for a logical operator in a truth table. The following is the truth table for the proposition p AND q.

p	q	p AND q
1	1	1
1	0	0
0	1	0
0	0	0

Just as we use the symbol "·" to represent the operator "times," we can use the symbol "∧" to represent the operator "AND."

p	q	$p \wedge q$
1	1	1
1	0	0
0	1	0
0	0	0

Examine the following truth table for the proposition p OR q.

p	q	p OR q
1	1	1
1	0	1
0	1	1
0	0	0

Notice that p OR q is true when at least one of the two statements is true. The symbol "∨" represents "OR."

p	q	$p \vee q$
1	1	1
1	0	1
0	1	1
0	0	0

Bits of History

Not formally educated in advanced mathematics, George Boole studied the works of some of the great mathematicians on his own. Perhaps this independent research led to his new approach of bridging logic and mathematics, which he published in 1854. By creating analogs between logic and mathematical symbols, a branch of mathematics later known as Boolean algebra resulted that would eventually form the basis of computer logic.

1. Use the tables to find the value of each statement Algent.
   (a) $1 \wedge 0$

   (b) $1 \vee 1$

   (c) $0 \wedge 0$

   (d) ~ 0

EXAMPLE 1 Use the tables to find the value of each statement.
(a) $1 \wedge 1$
(b) $1 \vee 1$
(c) $0 \wedge 1$
(d) ~ 1

Solution

(a) $1 \wedge 1 = 1$
(b) $1 \vee 0 = 1$
(c) $0 \wedge 1 = 0$
(d) $\sim 1 = 0$

Now go back and compare the three tables to multiplication, addition, and negation. How do they compare?

In the next example, we look at the compound proposition $\sim(p \wedge q)$. To do this, we find the truth table for p AND q, and change every result.

2. Find the truth table for the statement $\sim(p \vee q)$.

EXAMPLE 2 Find the truth table for the statement $\sim(p \wedge q)$.

p	q	$p \wedge q$	$\sim(p \wedge q)$
1	1	1	0
1	0	0	1
0	1	0	1
0	0	0	1

b Functions

One of the most important mathematical concepts that is relevant to the computer field is that of the function.

> **DEFINITION:**
>
> A **function** is a rule that guarantees that a given input always results in the same output.

Think about what difficulty you would have if you put the same expression into your calculator twice and got two different answers. If you contend that this has happened, then either you or your calculator did not function properly!

Example 2 could be written as:

Find the truth table for the function $f(p, q) = \sim(p \wedge q)$.

p	q	$p \wedge q$	$f(p, q)$
1	1	1	0
1	0	0	1
0	1	0	1
0	0	0	1

Answers on page A-31

The statement $f(p, q) = \sim(p \wedge q)$ simply says that the value of $\sim(p \wedge q)$ is a function of the values of p and q. The next example illustrates this concept.

EXAMPLE 3   Given the function $f(p, q) = \sim(p \wedge q)$, find $f(1, 0)$.

$f(1, 0)$ is asking for the value in the final column of the table above when $p = 1$ and $q = 0$.

In the second row, p has a value of 1 and q has a value of 0. The function value (from the last column) is 1. We can say

$$f(1, 0) = 1.$$

DEFINITION:

De Morgan's laws comprise two important rules in logic.

Version 1   **not (p and q)** is equivalent to the statement **not p or not q**.

In symbols, we write $\sim(p \wedge q) \Leftrightarrow \sim p \vee \sim q$.

Version 2   **not (p or q)** is equivalent to the statement **not p and not q**.

In symbols, we write $\sim(p \vee q) \Leftrightarrow \sim p \wedge \sim q$.

EXAMPLE 4   Show that $\sim(p \wedge q)$ is equivalent to $\sim p \vee \sim q$.
We can let $f(p, q) = \sim p \vee \sim q$ and $g(p, q) = \sim(p \wedge q)$.

p	q	$\sim p$	$\sim q$	$f(p, q)$	$p \wedge q$	$g(p, q)$
1	1	0	0	0	1	0
1	0	0	1	1	0	1
0	1	1	0	1	0	1
0	0	1	1	1	0	1

Note that the columns labeled $f(p, q)$ and $g(p, q)$ are identical. The two statements are equivalent.

With the ever-increasing amount of information being added to the Internet, understanding the logic behind search engines will help you find results more quickly. It is important to know what types of input particular search engines accept. Some require quotations around the terms being searched, and others may require the logical operator to be in ALL CAPS. For our exercises, we put the logical operators in ALL CAPS but omit the quotation marks.

EXAMPLE 5   Suppose we are doing a search on the musical artist Don Henley. Because Don Henley was also in a group called the Eagles, we may want to broaden our search to include the Eagles. We would accomplish this by doing an "OR" search. The "OR" command allows any of the specified search terms to be present on the Web pages listed in results. The "OR" search can also be described as a "Match Any" search.

The command typed into the search engine could be: Don Henley OR the Eagles. Logically represented, this equates to $p \vee q$.

3. Given the function $f(p, q) = \sim(p \wedge q)$, find $f(0, 0)$.

4. Show that $\sim(p \vee q)$ is equivalent to $\sim p \wedge \sim q$. The truth table from this practice problem should demonstrate the other law of De Morgan

5. What command could you type into a search engine if you wanted information about
   (a) the baseball player Babe Ruth or one of his famous teams, the 1927 Yankees?
   (b) the state of Missouri?

Answers on page A-31

6. What command could you type into a search engine if you wanted information about
   (a) the mathematics associated with M. C. Escher's artwork?
   (b) car seat safety for children?

7. What command could you type into a search engine if you wanted information about
   (a) the comedians, the Marx Brothers?
   (b) a python (a type of snake)?
   (c) pollution in rivers but not in oceans?

EXAMPLE 6 Suppose you are doing a more specific search about the relationship between mathematics and art. These two topics are very broad, so doing an OR search would give you more information than you need. The "AND" command requires that all search terms be present on the Web pages listed in results. It can also be described as a "Match All" search.

The command typed into the search engine could be: mathematics AND art.

Logically represented, this equates to $p \wedge q$.

EXAMPLE 7 Suppose you want some information on disc golf, a sport in which one throws a Frisbee or disc into a basket. Because the word "golf" is probably more recognizable, an AND search may still yield too much unwanted information about golf. In this case, a combination search using both the AND and NOT operators would probably work better.
The command typed into the search engine could be: disc golf AND NOT golf.

The search engine would look for Web pages that contain the words "disc" and "golf" but exclude pages that just contain "golf."

Logically represented, this equates to $p \wedge (\sim q)$.

Most search engines now use the negative sign instead of the word "NOT." To get Frisbee and not golf, you could type, "Frisbee–golf"

Answers on page A-31–A-32

CHAPTER 9: Sets and Algebra

1. Consider the two propositions:

   p: Austin can have coffee with cream.
   q: Austin can have coffee with sugar.

   (a) Write the proposition $p \wedge q$ in sentence form.

   (b) Write the proposition $p \vee q$ in sentence form.

2. Consider the two propositions:

   p: Jane went to the movies.
   q: Jane went to the beach.

   (a) Write the proposition $p \wedge q$ in sentence form.

   (b) Write the proposition $p \vee q$ in sentence form.

3. Compare the propositions in Exercises 1b and 2b. How are they the same? How are they different?

4. Complete the following truth table.

p	q	$\sim p$	$q \vee \sim p$
1	1		
1	0		
0	1		
0	0		

5. Using Exercise 1, write the proposition $q \vee \sim p$ in sentence form.

6. Using Exercise 2, write the proposition $\sim q \vee p$ in sentence form.

7. Complete the following truth table.

p	q	$\sim q$	$\sim q \vee p$
1	1		
1	0		
0	1		
0	0		

8. Complete the following truth table.

p	q	$\sim p$	$\sim p \vee p$
1	1		
1	0		
0	1		
0	0		

9. Complete the following truth table.

p	q	$\sim q$	$\sim q \wedge q$
1	1		
1	0		
0	1		
0	0		

10. Look at the last column of your truth tables in Exercises 8 and 9. What can you say about the proposition $\sim p \vee p$? What can you say about the proposition $\sim q \wedge q$?

11. Complete the following truth table for $f(A, B) = \sim A \wedge B$.

A	B	$\sim A$	$f(A, B)$
1	1		
1	0		
0	1		
0	0		

12. Complete the following truth table for $g(A, B) = A \vee {\sim}B$.

A	B	~B	g(A, B)
1	1		
1	0		
0	1		
0	0		

13. Use Exercise 11 to find the following.

   (a) $f(1, 1)$ **(b)** $f(1, 0)$ **(c)** $f(0, 0)$

14. Use Exercise 12 to find the following.

   (a) $g(1, 1)$ **(b)** $g(1, 0)$ **(c)** $g(0, 0)$

15. Compare the last column of your truth tables in Exercises 11 and 12. What can you say about the two columns? What rule does this demonstrate?

16. Consider the proposition: "He is not going to the store, or he is not going to the bank." Use De Morgan's law to write an equivalent proposition.

17. Consider the proposition: "Abby is not playing softball and is playing soccer." Use De Morgan's law to write an equivalent proposition.

18. Choose a sport and a famous person associated with that particular sport, and then describe how you would do an Internet search using logical operators.

19. Choose a film and a famous actor or actress in that particular film, and then describe how you would do an Internet search using logical operators.

20. What command could you type into a search engine if you wanted information about the state of Minnesota?

21. What command could you type into a search engine if you wanted information about Portland, Maine?

22. Find three specific propositions (or strings) that would match a logical search of the following form: $\sim p \wedge (q \vee r)$.

Summary and Review

The review that follows is meant to prepare you for a chapter exam. It consists of two parts. The first part is a checklist of some of the Study Tips referred to in this text. The second part is the Review Exercises. These provide practice exercises for the exam, together with references to section objectives so you can go back and review. Before beginning, stop and look back over the skills you have obtained. What powers in mathematics do you have now that you did not have before studying this chapter?

STUDY TIPS CHECKLIST

The foundation of all your study skills is TIME!	☐	Have you found ways (in class, on-line, or by phone) to get your questions answered?
	☐	Are you making a conscious effort to keep your work legible and well organized?
	☐	Are you familiar with the operation of your calculator—if one is permitted?
	☐	Do you use a highlighter to help you study important concepts?
	☐	Are you alert to opportunities to put your math to work in your everyday life?

REVIEW EXERCISES

Use set notation to list the elements for each of the following.   [9.1]

1. The countries that are located on the continent of North America.

2. The first names of the *Brady Bunch* kids.

3. The seven colors in the visible spectrum.

4. The prime numbers between 8 and 16.

5. The letters in the word *Windows*.

6. The natural numbers that are divisible by 5.

7. Which of the following are subsets of the set O, where $O =$ {Portland, Eugene, Salem, Corvallis, Bend, Klamath Falls, Medford}   [9.1]

(a) {Eugene, Medford, Salem}

(b) {Corvallis, Vancouver, Eugene, Portland}

(c) {Bend, Portland, Oregon}

(d) {Salem, Portland, Eugene, Bend}

(e) $\varnothing$

8. Which of the following are subsets of E, where $E =$ {2, 4, 6, 8, ...}   [9.1]

(a) {32, 16, 24}

(b) {6, 9, 12, 15, 18}

(c) {0, 2, 4}

(d) {2000, 4000, 8000, ...}

(e) {2, 4, 6, 8, ...}

Use set notation to represent each of the following: [9.1]

9. The set of all U.S. states that border California.

10. The universal set of hexadecimal digits.

11. The set of the seven castaways on the television show, *Gilligan's Island*.

12. The universal set of Zodiac signs.

13. The set of odd integers between 2 and 100.

Given the following set, find the cardinality of each.   [9.1]

14. $P =$ {pine nuts, basil, olive oil, parmesan cheese}

15. $S =$ {current members of the U.S. Senate}

16. $F =$ {Gandalf, Frodo, Sam, Aragorn, Merry, Pippin, Legolas, Gimli, Boromir}

17. $O =$ {all odd integers}

18. $B =$ {all natural numbers less than 100 that are divisible by 15}

19. Let $U = \{0, 1, 2, 3, 4, 5, 6, 7, 8, 9, A, B, C, D, E, F\}$
   $A = \{0, 2, 4, 6, 8, A, C, E\}$
   $B = \{2, 3, 5, 7, B, D\}$
   $C = \{0, 3, 6, 9, C, F\}$ [9.1]

Find the following:

(a) $A \cup B$

(b) $A \cap B$

(c) $A \cap C$

(d) B'

(e) $A' \cap C'$

(f) $|A'|$

(g) $|A \cup C|$

(h) $|U|$

20. Let $U = \{$films listed below$\}$,   [9.2]
   $P = \{$Emma, Shakespeare in Love, Bounce, The Talented Mr. Ripley, Seven, Possession, Sliding Doors$\}$,
   $A = \{$Shakespeare in Love, Good Will Hunting, Dogma, Bounce, Pearl Harbor, Phantoms, Armageddon, Changing Lanes, Chasing Amy, Boiler Room$\}$, and
   $D = \{$The Talented Mr. Ripley, Good Will Hunting, The Bourne Identity, School Ties, Dogma, All the Pretty Horses, Courage Under Fire, Chasing Amy, Mystic Pizza$\}$.

Find the following:

(a) $P \cap A$ **(d)** A' **(g)** $|A \cap D \cap P|$

(b) $P \cup A$ **(e)** $A \cap D \cap P$ **(h)** $|U|$

(c) $A \cap D$ **(f)** $|D'|$ **(i)** $|P \cap A|$

21. Let $A = \{$students who use Frontpage$\}$ [9.2]
   $B = \{$students who use Dreamweaver$\}$

Assume there are 29 students who use Frontpage, 21 students who use Dreamweaver, and 7 students who use both. How many students use at least one of the two Web page design programs?

22. Let $W = \{$computers running Windows XP$\}$
   $R = \{$computers with 1 GB of RAM$\}$
   $D = \{$computers with a DVD+RW drive$\}$

A computer technician needs to get the computer lab ready for the new term. She starts by doing an inventory and finds that

• There are 39 computers in the lab.
• Nineteen are running Windows XP
• Sixteen have a DVD+RW drive, and 20 of them have 1 GB of RAM
• Seven of the machines running Windows XP have a DVD+RW drive
• Six of the machines running Windows XP have 1 GB of RAM
• Eight of the machines that have a DVD+RW drive also have 1 GB of RAM

How many of the computers running Windows XP have both 1 GB of RAM and a DVD+RW drive?

23. Shade the specified regions on the following Venn diagrams.   [9.3]

$B \cap A$

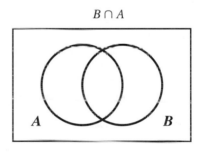

A'

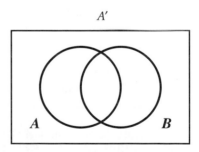

24. Label the following sets on the Venn diagram below. [9.3]

Let $U = \{0, 1, 2, 3, 4, 5, 6, 7, 8, 9, A, B, C, D, E, F\}$
  $O = \{1, 3, 5, 7, 9, B, D, F\}$
  $P = \{2, 3, 5, 7, B, D\}$

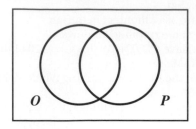

25. Draw a Venn diagram to illustrate the set B'. [9.3]

Let $U = \{0, 1, 2, 3, 4, 5, 6, 7, 8, 9\}$
  $A = \{2, 4, 6, 8, 0\}$,
  $B = \{8, 2, 5, 1\}$

26. Shade the specified regions on the following Venn diagrams. [9.3]

$A' \cup B$

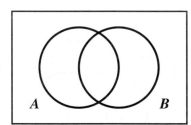

$A' \cap B'$

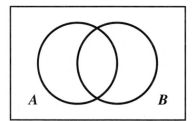

27. Draw a Venn diagram that indicates $|A \cap B| = 12$, $|A| = 30$, and $|B| = 19$. What is $|A \cup B|$? [9.3]

28. Draw a Venn diagram that indicates $|A \cup B| = 95$, $|A| = 23$, and $|B| = 80$. What is $|A \cap B|$?

29. Let $A = \{$students taking computer math$\}$
  $B = \{$students taking PC repair$\}$

Assume there are 22 students taking computer math, 17 taking PC repair, and 31 taking at least one of the two courses. How many students are taking both courses? Illustrate your solution on the following Venn diagram.

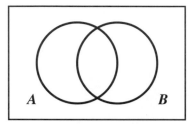

30. Shade the specified regions on the following Venn diagrams. [9.3]

$(A \cap C)'$

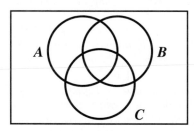

$(A \cup B') \cap C$

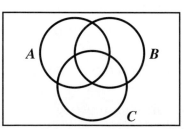

31. Draw a Venn diagram that indicates $|A \cup B \cup C| = 63$, $|A| = 58$, $|B| = 12$, $|C| = 38$, $|A \cap B| = 11$, $|A \cap C| = 33$, and $|B \cap C| = 6$.
What is $|A \cap B \cap C|$? [9.3]

32. Let N = {computers with Nero}, with $|N| = 21$,
T = {computers with two CD-ROM drives}, with $|T| = 30$, and
W = {computers with WinMX}, with $|W| = 21$ [9.3]

Also, let $|N \cap T| = 16$, $|N \cap W| = 9$, $|T \cap W| = 20$, and $|N \cap T \cap W| = 8$

(a) Draw a Venn diagram for which the given cardinalities apply.

(b) Describe an element in the set $N \cap T \cap W$.

(c) How many computers have only WinMX?

(d) How many computers have Nero and two CD-ROM drives, but not WinMX?

33. Which of the following are propositions? [9.4]
(a) $4 \times 16 > 50$

(b) Walk this way.

(c) $5 - 8 > -1$

(d) Does Kate know how to play the board game *Go*?

(e) $5 + 8 = 12$

(f) The pug is snoring.

(g) $x = 2$ or $x = -1$

(h) Is the computer working properly?

34. For each of the following propositions, find a negation.
(a) $x + 9 = 16$

(b) The Bulldogs won the swim meet.

(c) $6 + 2 \not< 5$

(d) Sam didn't tell the truth.

(e) $x = 0$ or $x = 1$

(f) The coffee has neither cream nor sugar added.

(g) There is no way out.

35. Complete the following truth table. [9.4]

p	q	$\sim p$	$\sim(\sim p)$	$\sim(\sim(\sim p))$	$\sim q$
1	1				
1	0				
0	1				
0	0				

36. Consider following the two propositions: [9.5]

p: Chris can study for his math test.

q: Chris can watch football.

(a) Write the proposition $p \vee q$ in sentence form.

(b) Write the proposition $p \wedge q$ in sentence form.

(c) Write the proposition p in sentence form.

(d) Write the proposition $p \wedge {\sim} q$ in sentence form.

37. Complete the following truth tables.   [9.5]

(a)

p	q	${\sim}p$	${\sim}p \vee q$
1	1		
1	0		
0	1		
0	0		

(b)

p	q	${\sim}q$	${\sim}q \vee q$
1	1		
1	0		
0	1		
0	0		

(c)

p	q	${\sim}p$	$p \wedge {\sim}p$
1	1		
1	0		
0	1		
0	0		

38. Complete the following truth table for $f(A, B) = A \wedge {\sim} B.$ [9.5]

A	B	${\sim}B$	$f(A, B)$
1	1		
1	0		
0	1		
0	0		

39. Use Exercise 38 to find the values of the following.   [9.5]

(a) $f(0, 1)$ **(b)** $f(0, 0)$ **(c)** $f(1, 1)$

40. Consider the proposition and use De Morgan's law to write its negation. "Allison is not working in Chicago and is moving to St. Louis."   [9.5]

41. What command could you type into a search engine if you wanted information about the NFL team, the Miami Dolphins? What command could you type into a search engine if you wanted information about swimming with dolphins in the city of Miami?   [9.5]

42. What command could you type into a search engine if you wanted information about the town of California in the state of Missouri?   [9.5]

Chapter Test

1. Use set notation to represent each of the following.
    (a) The set of five oceans on the earth.

    (b) The set of prime numbers between 20 and 40.

    (c) The universal set of octal digits.

    (d) The set of letters in the word *spanakopita*.

    (e) The universal set of all natural numbers that are divisible by 11.

2. Which of the following are subsets of the set S, where $S = \{1, 2, 4, 8, 16, 32, 64, 128, 256, ...\}$
    (a) $\{1, 16, 4, 64\}$ (b) $\{2, 4, 6, 8\}$ (c) $\{8, 64, 512, ...\}$

    (d) $\{2^0, 2^1, 2^2, ...\}$ (e) $\{1^2, 2^2, 3^2, ...\}$

3. Let $U = \{0, 1, 2, 3, 4, 5, 6, 7, 8, 9, a, b\}$,
    $A = \{0, 3, 6, 9\}$,
    $B = \{2, 3, 5, 7, b\}$,
    $C = \{1, 3, 5, 7, 9, b\}$
    Find the following:
    (a) $A \cup B$ (b) $C \cap B$

    (c) C' (d) $B' \cup C$ (e) $A \cap C'$

    (f) $|C'|$ (g) $|B' \cup C|$ (h) $|U|$

4. Shade the specified regions on the following Venn diagrams.

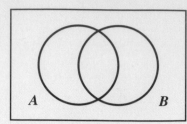

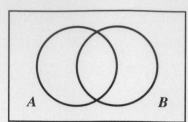

5. Let U = {Bengals, Bills, Broncos, Browns, Chargers, Chiefs, Colts, Dolphins, Jaguars, Jets, Patriots, Raiders, Ravens, Steelers, Texans, Titans}
A = {Dolphins, Ravens, Colts, Bengals, Browns, Jaguars, Broncos}
B = {Browns, Bills, Broncos, Bengals}
E = {Dolphins, Patriots, Jets, Bills}
Find the following:

(a) $E \cap A$

(b) $A \cup B$

(c) $E \cup B$

(d) A'

(e) $|E'|$

(f) $|A' \cap B|$

6. Label the following regions on the Venn diagram below:
Let U = {0, 1, 2, 3, 4, 5, 6, 7, 8, 9, A, B}
O = {1, 3, 5, 7, 9}
P = {2, 3, 5, 7, B}

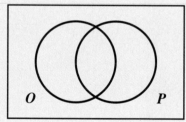

7. Let A = {students taking a Web-design class}
B = {students taking a networking class}

Assume there are 30 students taking a Web-design class, 22 students taking a networking class, and 39 students taking at least one of the two classes. How many students are taking both a Web-design class and a networking class? Draw a Venn diagram to illustrate your solution.

8. Draw a Venn diagram for which the following cardinalities apply:
$|A \cap B \cap C| = 26, |A| = 39, |B| = 45, |C| = 76, |A \cap B| = 27, |A \cap C| = 35,$ and $|B \cap C| = 26.$

What is $|A \cup B \cup C|$?

9. For each of the following propositions, find a negation.
   (a) $x + 4 = 12$

   (b) Yellow and blue make green.

   (c) Stefan was late for class.

   (d) $-3y < 15$

10. Let $F =$ {computers with a flat screen monitor}, with $|F| = 31$
    $H =$ {computers with a 100 GB hard drive}, with $|H| = 24$
    $D =$ {computers with a DVD+RW drive}, with $|D| = 40$
    Also, let $|F \cap H| = 15, |F \cap D| = 16, |D \cap H| = 20,$ and $|F \cup H \cup D| = 58.$

    (a) Draw a Venn diagram for which the given cardinalities apply.

    (b) Describe an element in the set $F \cup H \cup D$.

    (c) How many computers have a flat screen monitor, a 100 GB hard drive, and a DVD+RW drive?

    (d) How many computers have only a DVD+RW drive?

    (e) How many computers have a 100 GB hard drive and a DVD+RW drive, but do not have a flat screen monitor?

11. Complete the following truth table for $f(A, B) = \sim A \vee B$, then use the truth table to evaluate the following:

(a) $f(0, 1)$ (b) $f(0, 0)$ (c) $f(1, 1)$

A	B	$\sim A$	$f(A, B)$
1	1		
1	0		
0	1		
0	0		

12. What command could you type into a search engine if you wanted information about the music group REM?

REM is also germane to the field of medicine. What command would you type into a search engine if you want information on this type of REM?

13. Which of the following are propositions?
   (a) White is not a primary color.

   (b) September comes before December.

   (c) Is your birthday in September?

   (d) $x + x = 3$

   (e) Get your feet off the coffee table.

14. Complete the following truth tables.

(a)

p	q	$\sim p$	$\sim p \wedge p$
1	1		
1	0		
0	1		
0	0		

(b)

p	q	$\sim p$	$\sim q$	$\sim p \vee \sim q$
1	1			
1	0			
0	1			
0	0			

(c)

p	q	$\sim q$	$q \vee \sim q$
1	1		
1	0		
0	1		
0	0		

1. $-2^3 + 5(-1 - 4) =$

2. $\dfrac{2}{3} \times \dfrac{7}{9} =$

3. $4\dfrac{1}{3} + 6\dfrac{5}{8} =$

4. Multiply:
$$\begin{array}{r} 3.54 \\ \times 0.76 \\ \hline \end{array}$$

5. Divide: $0.7\overline{)0.00042}$

6. Solve for x: $x + 2 = 7$

7. Find the mean of the given list:
2, 3, 5, -1, 8, 12

8. What number must be inserted into the box to yield a correct proportion?
$$\dfrac{\square}{12} = \dfrac{4}{16}$$

9. Calculate 52% of 25

10. Given that A = {a, b, c, d, e, f} and B = {d, e, i, h}

Find

a. $A \cap B$
b. $A \cup B$

Binary Numbers

Gateway to Chapter 10
A.D. 1 to A.D. 1500

This era was characterized by a battle of the abacists (those who did arithmetic mechanically) and the algorists (those who did algebra). The algorists were able to persevere because of the development of the printing press. Both the symbols and the algorithms were standardized as a result of publishing books.

CHAPTER

10

1. Convert the decimal number 34 into binary.

2. Convert the binary number 110010011_2 into decimal.

3. Add:
$$1011_2$$
$$+1101_2$$

4. Find the product:
$$1111_2$$
$$\times 101_2$$

5. Subtract:
$$1001_2$$
$$-0010_2$$

6. Divide:
$$10_2\overline{)110110_2}$$

7. Translate the decimal number -7 into two's complement notation. Use a 4-bit representation.

8. The number 0111_{2^*} is in 4-bit, two's complement notation. Translate it into its decimal equivalent.

9. Translate the decimal number -25 into two's complement, 8-bit notation.

10. The number 10110001_{2^*} is in 8-bit, two's complement notation. Translate it into its decimal equivalent.

11. Find the decimal equivalent of the binary number 0.0011_2.

12. Find the decimal equivalent of the binary number
$$\frac{11011_2}{1110111_2}$$

13. Find the binary equivalent of the decimal number 0.125.

14. How many bytes are in 2 MB?

15. How many bits are in 3 GB?

10.1 THE BINARY SYSTEM

Information Storage

When we use a computer, we expect it to store and retrieve information in a variety of forms. Here are a few examples of the kinds of data one expects to find in a computer:

- A word-processing program that can be used to create, correct, and save text files.
- Text files that have been created on the computer.
- A spreadsheet program that can store and manipulate numeric-based data.
- Numeric files that have been created using a spreadsheet.
- Paintbrush, computer-aided design (CAD) programs, or other programs designed to create graphics.
- Graphics files created by these programs.
- Directions that allow the computer to locate stored files.
- Instructions for creating and digitizing sound.
- Games that involve graphics, numbers, words, and sounds.
- Sets of commands (programs) that will add to the utility of the computer.

To work with such data, the computer needs to use a **code** to represent the information being processed. We use codes every day of our lives. The set of all English words is a code used to communicate ideas. The set of twenty-six letters of the English alphabet is a code used to represent the pronunciation of those words. The set of musical notes is a code used to represent musical pitches. The set of ten digits (0 through 9) is a code used to represent quantities.

It is this last code, the set of digits, which comes closest to the computer code. The difference is that a computer knows only two basic code values (0 and 1), which we simplify as **on/off** or **positive/negative**. The on/off model is the original computer model. Early computers used electronic circuitry that connected vacuum tubes. The more modern silicon chips are a miniature version of this idea. Disk storage is an example of the positive/negative model. Floppy disks are covered with a thin layer of ferromagnetic material in which each cell can be polarized as positive or negative. A sequence of cells creates a code that is interpreted by the computer. Because the prefix *bi-* means two, we call the computer code a ***binary* code**.

Binary Code

In base ten, each place has a value that is ten times greater than the place to its right:

$$11,111 = 1 \times 10^4 + 1 \times 10^3 + 1 \times 10^2 + 1 \times 10^1 + 1 \times 10^0$$
$$= 10,000 + 1000 + 100 + 10 + 1.$$

In base two, each place has a value that is twice as great as the place to its right. As in base ten, we begin at a place value of 1. The next place to the left

In addition to the decimal (base ten) system, other number systems have been developed throughout history. The Babylonians employed a base sixty system (sexigesimal), while the ancient Maya of Central America used a modified base twenty system (vigesimal). The Maya are also one of the first civilizations to have a symbol for zero, a remarkable accomplishment.

has a value twice that, or 2. Again moving left we get a place value twice 2, which is 4. Moving left, subsequent place values are 8, 16, 32, 64, 128, 256, 512,... . Note that every place is a power of two.

The following model may help you start to think in base two. In Canada there are coins that represent 25¢ 50¢, $1.00, and $2.00. In the table below, those coins are labeled Q, H, D, and T.

T	D	H	Q	TOTAL QUARTERS
0	0	0	0	0
0	0	0	1	1
0	0	1	0	2
0	0	1	1	3
0	1	0	0	4
0	1	0	1	5
0	1	1	0	6
0	1	1	1	7
1	0	0	0	8
1	0	0	1	9
1	0	1	0	10
1	0	1	1	11
1	1	0	0	12
1	1	0	1	13
1	1	1	0	14
1	1	1	1	15

Note that with one of each of the four coins, we can create the equivalent of any number of quarters from 1 to 15. This is essentially the same concept used in the base two system.

$2	$1	50¢	25¢

When we write a number in base two, we write a subscript 2 at the end of the number. If a number is written without a subscript, we assume that it is a decimal number, which is base ten.

$$11111_2 = 1 \times 2^4 + 1 \times 2^3 + 1 \times 2^2 + 1 \times 2^1 + 1 \times 2^0$$
$$= 16 + 8 + 4 + 2 + 1$$
$$= 31$$

Notice the pattern when you count in binary.

$0000_2 = 0$	$1000_2 = 8$
$0001_2 = 1$	$1001_2 = 9$
$0010_2 = 2$	$1010_2 = 10$
$0011_2 = 3$	$1011_2 = 11$
$0100_2 = 4$	$1100_2 = 12$
$0101_2 = 5$	$1101_2 = 13$
$0110_2 = 6$	$1110_2 = 14$
$0111_2 = 7$	$1111_2 = 15$

It is the same pattern we created with our coin table. This pattern will be useful later. You should practice writing these sixteen numbers in order until the pattern is obvious to you.

Now, we will examine place values for an eight-digit binary number. Refer to the following table for the next few examples.

BIT LOCATION	Eighth	Seventh	Sixth	Fifth	Fourth	Third	Second	First
POWER	2^7	2^6	2^5	2^4	2^3	2^2	2^1	2^0
VALUE	128	64	32	16	8	4	2	1

EXAMPLE 1   Find the place value for the 1 in each binary representation.

(a) 00000100_2 Because the 1 is in the third place from the right, the place value is 4. (1, 2, 4,...)

(b) 00010000_2 The place value is 16.

(c) 01000000_2 The place value is 64.

By summing the place values of a binary number, we can find its decimal equivalent. Let's first try it with some four-digit binary numbers.

EXAMPLE 2   Find the decimal equivalent for each binary representation.

BINARY	DECIMAL
0111_2	$0 + 4 + 2 + 1 = 7$
1010_2	$8 + 0 + 2 + 0 = 10$
1101_2	$8 + 4 + 0 + 1 = 13$

1. Find the place value for the 1 in each binary representation.
   (a) 00000010_2
   (b) 00100000_2
   (c) 10000000_2

2. Find the decimal equivalent for each binary representation.
   (a) 0011_2
   (b) 1100_2
   (c) 1111_2

Answers on page A-34

In the next example, we look at the decimal equivalent for some eight-digit binary numbers.

3. Find the decimal equivalent for each binary representation.
   (a) 01000011_2
   (b) 01111000_2
   (c) 11111111_2

EXAMPLE 3   Find the decimal equivalent for each binary representation.

BINARY	DECIMAL
01010111_2	$0 + 64 + 0 + 16 + 0 + 4 + 2 + 1 = 87$
10111000_2	$128 + 0 + 32 + 16 + 8 + 0 + 0 + 0 = 184$
11001101_2	$128 + 64 + 0 + 0 + 8 + 4 + 0 + 1 = 205$

How do we go about rewriting a decimal number as its binary equivalent? As we noted earlier, each place in a binary representation is a power of two. We find the binary equivalent for a decimal number by subtracting the largest power of two that is less than the decimal number, noting a 1 in that binary place, then continuing the process with the result until we are left with zero. Let's look at an example.

4. Rewrite the decimal number 199 as a binary number.

EXAMPLE 4   Rewrite the decimal number 231 as a binary number.

The largest power of two that is less than 231 is 128. 128 is represented in base two by a 1 in the eighth place to the left (128, 64, 32, 16, 8, 4, 2, 1).

$231 - 128 = 103$

128	64	32	16	8	4	2	1
1							

The largest power of two less than 103 is 64, which is represented in base two by a 1 in the seventh place to the left.

$103 - 64 = 39$

128	64	32	16	8	4	2	1
1	1						

The largest power of two less than 39 is 32, which is represented in base two by a 1 in the sixth place to the left.

$39 - 32 = 7$

128	64	32	16	8	4	2	1
1	1	1					

Note that $7 = 4 + 2 + 1$. We also need 1s in the third, second, and first places.

128	64	32	16	8	4	2	1
1	1	1	0	0	1	1	1

Thus,

DECIMAL	BINARY
231	11100111_2

Note there are zeros in the fifth and fourth places. When we were subtracting, the decimal value was reduced from 39 to 7, so we skipped both 16 and 8 because they were both greater than 7.

Answers on page A-34

When we use the term *digit,* we usually think of decimal digits. When we wish to refer to a binary digit, the common contraction **bit** is used. In a computer, bits are usually arranged in groups of eight. A collection of eight consecutive bits is so common that it is often referred to as a **byte.** It is because of the common grouping that most of the binary representations we have seen in this section were in byte form. For larger numbers two or more bytes are combined. Later on, we will look at some of these arrangements.

Find the decimal equivalent for each of the following binary numbers.

1. 0101_2

2. 0011_2

3. 1101_2

4. 1010_2

5. 01101101_2

6. 11000110_2

7. 10101010_2

8. 11111110_2

9. 111100001111_2

10. 110011001100_2

11. 100000000001_2

12. 110000000011_2

Find the binary equivalent for each of the following decimal numbers.

13. 7

14. 2

15. 12

16. 10

17. 15

18. 49

19. 57

20. 64

21. 107

22. 112

23. 1024

24. 2003

Translate the following binary phone numbers into their decimal equivalents. Each digit is separated by a hyphen.

25. $1000_2 - 0110_2 - 0111_2 - 0101_2 - 0011_2 - 0000_2 - 1001_2$

26. $0101_2 - 0101_2 - 0101_2 - 0010_2 - 0111_2 - 0100_2 - 0011_2$

27. $0001_2 - 1000_2 - 0000_2 - 0000_2 - 1000_2 - 0111_2 - 0110_2 - 0101_2 - 0011_2 - 0101_2 - 0011_2$

28. $0001_2 - 1000_2 - 0000_2 - 0000_2 - 0010_2 - 0110_2 - 0101_2 - 0101_2 - 0011_2 - 0010_2 - 1000_2$

Translate the following binary combination into its decimal equivalent.

29. $1001_2 - 1010_2 - 0100_2$

30. Explain the difference between your answer in Exercise 29 and the decimal equivalent of the binary number: 100110100100_2.

Binary numbers can also be represented as groups of blocks. Instead of taking values of 1 and 0, the blocks can be filled or unfilled. For example, the binary number 1101 (equivalent to the decimal number 13) could be expressed as the following group of blocks:

2^3	2^2	2^1	2^0
8	4	2	1
1	1	0	1

Write the binary number represented by the following sets of blocks, then translate each binary number into its decimal equivalent.

31.

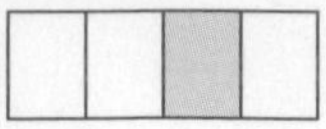

32.

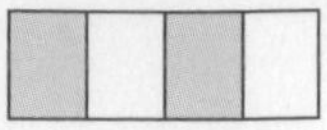

33.

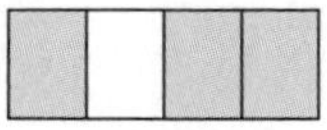

34.

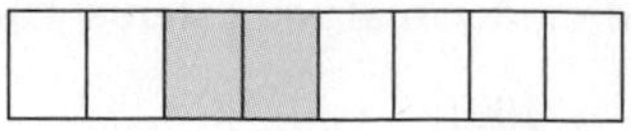

35.

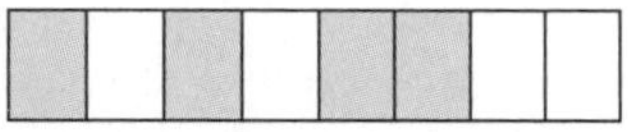

36.

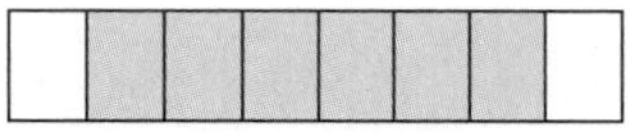

10.2 BASE TWO ARITHMETIC: ADDITION AND MULTIPLICATION

Adding in Base Two

The principles of adding binary numbers are exactly the same as the principles of adding decimal numbers. We work right to left and carry when we do not have a digit large enough to express the sum. First, as a reminder, look at this decimal sum.

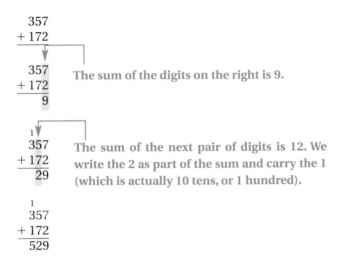

$$
\begin{array}{r}
357 \\
+\,172 \\
\hline
\end{array}
$$

$$
\begin{array}{r}
357 \\
+\,172 \\
\hline
9
\end{array}
$$
The sum of the digits on the right is 9.

$$
\begin{array}{r}
{}^{1} \\
357 \\
+\,172 \\
\hline
29
\end{array}
$$
The sum of the next pair of digits is 12. We write the 2 as part of the sum and carry the 1 (which is actually 10 tens, or 1 hundred).

$$
\begin{array}{r}
{}^{1} \\
357 \\
+\,172 \\
\hline
529
\end{array}
$$

In our first example, we use the same process to add two binary numbers. Note that, when we add two binary numbers, we get the following sums.

$0_2 + 0_2 = 0_2$ In decimal notation, this is $0 + 0 = 0$.

$0_2 + 1_2 = 1_2$ This is the same as in decimal notation.

$1_2 + 0_2 = 1_2$ Again, it's the same as the decimal form.

$1_2 + 1_2 = 10_2$ In decimal notation, we say $1 + 1 = 2$. The 10_2 indicates 1 in the twos' place and 0 in the ones' place.

■ **EXAMPLE 1**   Add the two binary numbers.

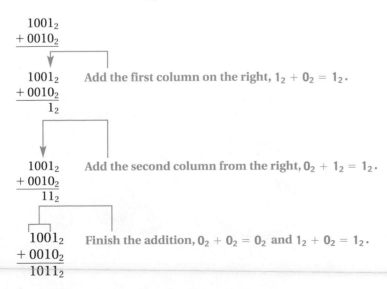

$$
\begin{array}{r}
1001_2 \\
+\,0010_2 \\
\hline
\end{array}
$$

$$
\begin{array}{r}
1001_2 \\
+\,0010_2 \\
\hline
1_2
\end{array}
$$
Add the first column on the right, $1_2 + 0_2 = 1_2$.

$$
\begin{array}{r}
1001_2 \\
+\,0010_2 \\
\hline
11_2
\end{array}
$$
Add the second column from the right, $0_2 + 1_2 = 1_2$.

$$
\begin{array}{r}
1001_2 \\
+\,0010_2 \\
\hline
1011_2
\end{array}
$$
Finish the addition, $0_2 + 0_2 = 0_2$ and $1_2 + 0_2 = 1_2$.

Bits of History

A.D. 300–400 The birth of the modern decimal system can be traced back to India. While many cultures used some sort of base ten system, the Brâhmî system of nine digits was modified to include a small circle or dot, which represented zero. The beginning of our modern numerical notation and modern arithmetic can be attributed to both Indian and Arabic scholars, but it would still be almost a thousand years before Western Europe would employ the Hindu-Arabic numerals.

1. Add the two binary numbers. Verify your result by adding the decimal equivalents.

$$
\begin{array}{r}
1010_2 \\
+\,0101_2 \\
\hline
\end{array}
$$

Answer on page A-34

We can verify our result by converting all three numbers to their decimal equivalent:

$$1001_2 = 9, \qquad 0010_2 = 2, \qquad 1011_2 = 11.$$

Because $9 + 2 = 11$, we have verified the result.

In decimal addition, what happens when we add 2 two-digit numbers such as 67 and 84? Because we carry in the tens' place, we end up with a three-digit answer, 151. Addition of binary numbers is similar.

2. Add the two binary numbers. Verify your result by adding the decimal equivalents.

$$1110_2$$
$$+1101_2$$

EXAMPLE 2   Add the binary numbers 1101_2 and 1011_2.

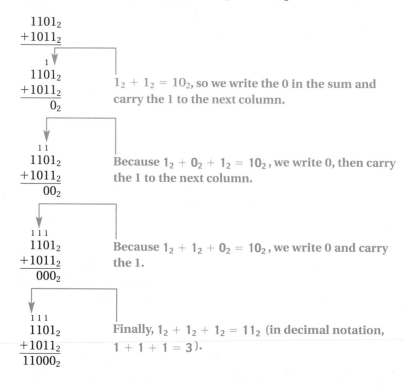

$$1101_2$$
$$+1011_2$$

$$\overset{1}{\underset{}{}}$$
$$1101_2$$
$$+1011_2$$
$$\overline{0_2}$$

$1_2 + 1_2 = 10_2$, so we write the 0 in the sum and carry the 1 to the next column.

$$\overset{1\,1}{\underset{}{}}$$
$$1101_2$$
$$+1011_2$$
$$\overline{00_2}$$

Because $1_2 + 0_2 + 1_2 = 10_2$, we write 0, then carry the 1 to the next column.

$$\overset{1\,1\,1}{\underset{}{}}$$
$$1101_2$$
$$+1011_2$$
$$\overline{000_2}$$

Because $1_2 + 1_2 + 0_2 = 10_2$, we write 0 and carry the 1.

$$\overset{1\,1\,1}{\underset{}{}}$$
$$1101_2$$
$$+1011_2$$
$$\overline{11000_2}$$

Finally, $1_2 + 1_2 + 1_2 = 11_2$ (in decimal notation, $1 + 1 + 1 = 3$).

Now, let's convert all three numbers to the decimal equivalent to check our result:

$$1101_2 = 13, \qquad 1011_2 = 11, \qquad 11000_2 = 24.$$

Indeed, $13 + 11 = 24$. We have verified our result.

If you recall the Canadian coins discussed in Section 10.1, you may be able to better relate to the idea of carrying in binary addition. Let 0101_C represent (from right to left) one quarter, no halves, one dollar and no two-dollar coins.

Answer on page A-34

By the same model, 0011_C would represent one quarter and one half.

What happens when we add these two together ($001c + 0101c$)?

  **+**

The 2 quarters become a half.

The 2 halves become a dollar.

The 2 one-dollar coins become a two-dollar coin.

We have demonstrated that $0101_C + 0011_C = 1000_C$.

3. Add the 2 bytes. Verify your result by adding the decimal equivalents.

$$10101001_2$$
$$+ \ 01001101_2$$

EXAMPLE 3 Add the two bytes. Verify your result by adding the decimal equivalents.

$$\overset{1111}{}$$
$$10110110_2$$
$$+ \ 00111101_2$$
$$\overline{11110011_2}$$

Now let's convert each byte to its decimal equivalent to check our results.

$$10110110_2 = 128 + \ \ 0 + 32 + 16 + 0 + 4 + 2 + 0 = 182$$
$$00111101_2 = 0 \ \ \ + \ \ 0 + 32 + 16 + 8 + 4 + 0 + 1 = 61$$
$$11110011_2 = 128 + 64 + 32 + 16 + 0 + 0 + 2 + 1 = 243$$

Because $182 + 61 = 243$, we have verified the results.

Once you are confident in your ability to add two binary numbers, there will be no need to convert to base ten to verify your result. In fact, you may want to convert decimals to binary numbers to verify the result of adding two decimals!

Multiplying in Base Two

When you work in base ten, the easiest multiplications involve multiplying by a power of ten. Look at the following products.

$$53 \times 10 = 530$$
$$53 \times 100 = 5300$$
$$53 \times 1000 = 53000$$
$$53 \times 10000 = 530000$$

The same principle works in the binary system, except that you are multiplying by powers of two.

$$11_2 \times 10_2 = 110_2$$
$$11_2 \times 100_2 = 1100_2$$
$$11_2 \times 1000_2 = 11000_2$$

This principle is used in the next example.

4. Find the product.

$$1011_2 \times 1000_2$$

EXAMPLE 4 Find the product.

$$1011_2 \times 100_2 = 101100_2$$

In Example 5, we will learn to multiply any two binary numbers. First, let's look at a decimal multiplication model.

Because $1123 \times 122 = 1123 \times 102 + 1123 \times 22 = 1230 + 246$, we can multiply in the following way:

$$123$$
$$\underline{\times \ \ 12} \qquad \text{First, we multiply by the 2.}$$
$$246$$

$$123$$
$$\underline{\times \ \ 12}$$
$$246$$
$$0 \qquad \text{We write a 0 to indicate that we are multiplying by tens.}$$

Answers on page A-34

$$\begin{array}{r} 123 \\ \times\ 12 \\ \hline 246 \\ 1230 \\ \hline 1476 \end{array}$$ **We multiply by 1 and then add.**

EXAMPLE 5   Find the product.

$$1011_2 \times 111_2$$

Recall that $111_2 = 100_2 + 10_2 + 1_2$.

When you multiply binary numbers, you use a process that is sometimes called "shift and add."

$$\begin{array}{r} 1011_2 \\ \times\ \ 111_2 \\ \hline 1011_2 \end{array}$$ **Multiply by the 1.**

$$\begin{array}{r} 1011_2 \\ \times\ \ 111_2 \\ \hline 1011 \\ 10110 \end{array}$$

Multiply by the 10_2.
Write the result (10110) under the 1011.

$$\begin{array}{r} 1011_2 \\ \times\ \ 111_2 \\ \hline 1011 \\ 10110 \\ 101100 \\ \hline 1001101_2 \end{array}$$

Multiply by the 100_2 and then add.

5. Find the product.

$$\begin{array}{r} 1101_2 \\ \times\ \ 101_2 \end{array}$$

Answers on page A-34

Add the following binary numbers. Rewrite each problem in decimal notation to check your work.

1. $\begin{array}{r} 0100_2 \\ + 0010_2 \\ \hline \end{array}$

2. $\begin{array}{r} 0101_2 \\ + 0010_2 \\ \hline \end{array}$

3. $\begin{array}{r} 0101_2 \\ + 0110_2 \\ \hline \end{array}$

4. $\begin{array}{r} 1010_2 \\ + 0011_2 \\ \hline \end{array}$

5. $\begin{array}{r} 1101_2 \\ + 0111_2 \\ \hline \end{array}$

6. $\begin{array}{r} 1011_2 \\ + 0111_2 \\ \hline \end{array}$

7. $\begin{array}{r} 1010_2 \\ 1101_2 \\ + 1011_2 \\ \hline \end{array}$

8. $\begin{array}{r} 1011_2 \\ 1101_2 \\ + 1111_2 \\ \hline \end{array}$

9. $\begin{array}{r} 10010010_2 \\ + 10101010_2 \\ \hline \end{array}$

10. $\begin{array}{r} 10001110_2 \\ + 10101010_2 \\ \hline \end{array}$

11. $\begin{array}{r} 10110111_2 \\ + 01100100_2 \\ \hline \end{array}$

12. $\begin{array}{r} 00011010_2 \\ + 11010111_2 \\ \hline \end{array}$

Add the following binary numbers in block form. Shade each answer in the empty set of blocks below.

13.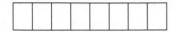

14.

15.

Multiply each pair of binary numbers. Rewrite each problem in decimal notation to check your work.

16. $\begin{array}{r} 100_2 \\ \times\ \ 10_2 \end{array}$

17. $\begin{array}{r} 1101_2 \\ \times\ \ \ 10_2 \end{array}$

18. $\begin{array}{r} 101_2 \\ \times\ 110_2 \end{array}$

19. $\begin{array}{r} 1110_2 \\ \times\ \ \ 11_2 \end{array}$

20. $\begin{array}{r} 1101_2 \\ \times\ \ 111_2 \end{array}$

21. $\begin{array}{r} 1011_2 \\ \times\ \ 111_2 \end{array}$

22. Is the sum of 2 bits always a bit? Justify your answer.

23. Is the product of 2 bits always a bit? Justify your answer.

10.3 BASE TWO ARITHMETIC: SUBTRACTION AND DIVISION

Subtracting in Base Two

As was the case with addition, the principles of subtracting binary numbers are exactly the same as the principles of subtracting decimal numbers. First, as a reminder, look at this decimal difference.

$$
\begin{array}{r}
247 \\
-\,162 \\
\hline
\end{array}
$$

$$
\begin{array}{r}
247 \\
-\,162 \\
\hline
5
\end{array}
$$
The difference of the digits on the right is 5.

$$
\begin{array}{r}
{\scriptstyle 1\,1} \\
2\!\!47 \\
-\,162 \\
\hline
85
\end{array}
$$
We cannot subtract 6 from 4. We borrow from the hundreds' column, and the 4 tens is now 14 tens.

$$
\begin{array}{r}
{\scriptstyle 1} \\
2\!\!47 \\
-\,162 \\
\hline
85
\end{array}
$$
Finally, in the hundreds' column, $1 - 1 = 0$.

In our first two examples, we use the same process to subtract two binary numbers. Note that when we subtract two binary numbers, we have the following possibilities:

$0_2 - 0_2 = 0_2$ In decimal notation, this is $0 - 0 = 0$.

$1_2 - 1_2 = 0_2$ It is the same as in decimal notation.

$1_2 - 0_2 = 1_2$ Again, it is the same as the decimal form.

$0_2 - 1_2 = ?$ We must borrow from the column to the left to perform this operation.

EXAMPLE 1 Subtract the binary numbers.

$$\begin{array}{r} 1011_2 \\ -\ 0010_2 \end{array}$$

$$\begin{array}{r} 1011_2 \\ -\ 0010_2 \\ \hline 1_2 \end{array}$$ Subtract the first column on the right, $1_2 - 0_2 = 1_2$.

$$\begin{array}{r} 1011_2 \\ -\ 0010_2 \\ \hline 01_2 \end{array}$$ Subtract the second column from the right, $1_2 - 1_2 = 0_2$.

$$\begin{array}{r} 1011_2 \\ -\ 0010_2 \\ \hline 1001_2 \end{array}$$ Finish the subtraction, $0_2 - 0_2 = 0_2$ and $1_2 - 0_2 = 1_2$.

We can verify our result by converting all three numbers to their decimal equivalent:

$$1011_2 = 11, \qquad 0010_2 = 2, \qquad 1001_2 = 9.$$

Because $11 - 2 = 9$, so we have verified the result.

In our second example, we look at a situation in which we must borrow from a column on the left to complete the subtraction.

EXAMPLE 2 Subtract the binary number 1101_2 from 10011_2.

$$\begin{array}{r} 10011_2 \\ -\ 01101_2 \\ \hline 10_2 \end{array}$$ The two columns on the right give us straightforward results.

$$\begin{array}{r} \overset{0\ 1}{\cancel{1}0011_2} \\ -\ 01101_2 \\ \hline 110_2 \end{array}$$ We cannot find $0_2 - 1_2$, so we borrow, remembering that $10_2 - 1_2 = 1_2$.

As in base ten arithmetic, we can check our results through addition. Note that $110_2 + 01101_2 = 10011_2$ (in base ten, $6 + 13 = 19$).

Once again we refer to the coins discussed in Section 10.1. This time we demonstrate the idea of borrowing. Let 1001_c represent (from right to left) 1 quarter, no halves, no dollars, and 1 two-dollar coin.

1. Subtract the binary numbers. Verify your result by subtracting the decimal equivalents.

$$\begin{array}{r} 1111_2 \\ -\ 0101_2 \end{array}$$

2. Subtract the binary number 10111_2 from 11011_2. Verify your results by converting the problem into decimal subtraction.

From this collection, we wish to subtract 1 dollar, which is represented as 100_C.

To accomplish this subtraction, we break the two-dollar coin into 2 one-dollar coins and use one of them to make the payment. Essentially, we borrow from the fourth place to the left. We have a dollar and the quarter remaining.

We have demonstrated that $1001_C - 0100_C = 101_C$.

Dividing in Base Two

In the same way that multiplication can be viewed as repeated addition, it is reasonable that we view division as repeated subtraction. For example, when dividing 20 by 5, you find that there are four groups of 5 in the number 20.

$$20 - 5 = 15$$
$$15 - 5 = 10$$
$$10 - 5 = 5$$
$$5 - 5 = 0$$

This is similar to one process by which a computer accomplishes division.

When you actually started doing division, you learned an algorithm we refer to as *long division*. We will examine that algorithm as it applies to binary division, but before we move to that example, you should review a base ten division problem.

We suggest that you recreate the steps used to divide 5,016 by 11 using long division.

$$\begin{array}{r} 456 \\ 11\overline{)5016} \end{array}$$

3. Divide 10010_2 by 10_2, and then verify your answer using binary multiplication.

◼ **EXAMPLE 3**   Divide 10010_2 by 11_2.

$11_2\overline{)10010_2}$ 11_2 does not go into 10_2, but 11_2 *does* go into 100_2 one time.

$$\begin{array}{r} 1 \\ 11_2\overline{)10010_2} \\ \underline{-11} \\ 1 \end{array}$$ Multiply 1_2 times 11_2 to get 11_2, and then subtract 11_2 from 100_2 to get 1_2.

$$\begin{array}{r} 1 \\ 11_2\overline{)10010_2} \\ \underline{-11} \\ 11 \end{array}$$ Bring down the 1.

Answers on page A-34

$$\begin{array}{r} 11 \\ 11_2 \overline{)10010_2} \\ \underline{-11} \\ 11 \\ \underline{-11} \\ 00 \end{array}$$

11_2 goes into 11_2 one time. Bring down the 0.

$$\begin{array}{r} 110 \\ 11_2 \overline{)10010_2} \\ \underline{-11} \\ 11 \\ \underline{-11} \\ 00 \\ \underline{-00} \\ 0 \end{array}$$

11_2 goes into 0_2 zero times. There is no remainder.

We can check our answer using binary multiplication.

$$\begin{array}{r} 110_2 \\ \times\ \ 11_2 \\ \hline 110_2 \\ 1100_2 \\ \hline 10010_2 \end{array}$$

Perform the following binary subtractions. Rewrite each problem in decimal notation to check your work.

1. $\begin{array}{r} 0110_2 \\ -\ 0010_2 \\ \hline \end{array}$

2. $\begin{array}{r} 0111_2 \\ -\ 0010_2 \\ \hline \end{array}$

3. $\begin{array}{r} 1111_2 \\ -\ 0110_2 \\ \hline \end{array}$

4. $\begin{array}{r} 0100_2 \\ -\ 0010_2 \\ \hline \end{array}$

5. $\begin{array}{r} 0101_2 \\ -\ 0010_2 \\ \hline \end{array}$

6. $\begin{array}{r} 1001_2 \\ -\ 0110_2 \\ \hline \end{array}$

7. $\begin{array}{r} 10011010_2 \\ -\ 00011111_2 \\ \hline \end{array}$

8. $\begin{array}{r} 10101101_2 \\ -\ 01000111_2 \\ \hline \end{array}$

9. Use repeated subtraction to find the number of times 10_2 goes into 1010_2.

10. Use repeated subtraction to find the number of times 11_2 goes into 1001_2.

11. Use long division to find the number of times 10_2 goes into 1010_2.

12. Use long division to find the number of times 11_2 goes into 1001_2.

Simplify each of the following by using long division. Convert the values to decimal notation to verify your answer.

13. $11000110_2 \div 110_2$

14. $11011101_2 \div 1101_2$

Simplify each of the following by using long division. Once you have found the quotient, use it to rewrite the problem as a multiplication problem. (*Hint:* There will be a remainder. Practice with base ten first so that you remember what to do with the remainder.)

15. $11000110_2 \div 111_2$

16. $11000101_2 \div 1101_2$

10.4 TWO'S COMPLEMENT NOTATION

To this point, we have seen only non-negative integers represented in binary notation, yet we know that the computer must be able to represent many other kinds of numbers, including decimals, fractions, and negative numbers. We will now examine the way in which bits can be used to represent negative integers.

> In a computer, signed numbers are represented using something called **two's complement notation.** This form is used to ensure that addition and multiplication work efficiently. The method used in Examples 1 and 2 to add two binary numbers must work for any two integers, positive or negative.

To write an integer in two's complement notation, we must first identify whether the given number is positive, negative, or zero. If the number is a positive integer or zero, its binary representation begins with a 0. No matter how many bits we have available for non-negative integer representation, the bit farthest to the left is zero. This bit is called the **sign bit**, because it tells us the sign of the number. If we have 4 bits available, the non-negative numbers will have the following binary representation.

BINARY	DECIMAL
0111_2	7
0110_2	6
0101_2	5
0100_2	4
0011_2	3
0010_2	2
0001_2	1
0000_2	0

Earlier in this chapter, we used 4 bits to represent the decimal numbers 0–15. In two's complement notation, 4 bits allows us to represent only the non-negative decimal numbers 0–7, because the sign bit (now set to zero) is in the fourth position. You may have guessed that the binary representation for a negative number will begin with a 1, and you are correct. Given a negative integer, its representation can be found by using the following algorithm.

Finding the Two's Complement Representation for a Negative Integer

To find the two's complement representation for negative integer x,

Step 1. Find the binary representation for $|x|$.

Step 2. Find the complement of that binary number (change the 1s to 0s and the 0s to 1s).

Step 3. Add 1 to the result of step 2.

The result is the two's complement representation for x.

EXAMPLE 1 **(a)** Find the two's complement notation for –1, using 4 bits.

1. Find the binary representation for $|-1|$.

$$|-1| = 1$$
$$1 = 0001_2$$

2. Find the complement of that binary number (change the 1s to 0s and the 0s to 1s).

The complement of 0001_2 is 1110_2.

3. Add 1 to the result of step 2.

Adding 1, we get 1111_2, so

$$-1 = 1111_{2*}.$$

We will use the subscript 2* to indicate a binary number that uses two's complement representation. Note that $1111_2 = 15$, whereas $1111_{2*} = -1$ (two very different numbers).

(b) Find the two's complement notation for 24, using 4 bits.

1. Find the binary representation for $|24|$.

$$4 = 0100_2$$

2. Find the complement of that binary number (change the 1s to 0s and the 0s to 1s).

The complement of 0100_2 is 1011_2.

3. Add 1 to the result of step 2.

Adding 1, we get

$$\begin{array}{r} {\scriptstyle 1\,1} \\ 1011_2 \\ +\quad 1_2 \\ \hline 1100_2 \end{array}$$

so $4 = 1100_{2*}$.

Again, notice that $1100_2 = 12$, whereas $1100_{2*} = -4$.

1. Find the two's complement notation for −6 and −5, using 4 bits.

It is sometimes useful to find the decimal equivalent for a given two's complement representation. The following algorithm will help you do this.

Finding a Negative Integer for a Two's Complement Representation

To find a negative integer when you are given its two's complement representation,

Step 1. Find the complement of the given binary number (change the 1s to 0s and the 0s to 1s).

Step 2. Add 1 to the result of step 1.

Step 3. Convert the result of step 2 into an integer.

Step 4. The negative of the integer from step 3 is the decimal equivalent of the two's complement representation.

EXAMPLE 2 Convert the two's complement number 1110_{2*} into its decimal equivalent.

Step 1. Find the complement of 1110_2, which is 0001_2.

Step 2. Add 1, so $0001_2 + 1_2 = 0010_2$.

Step 3. $0010_2 = 2$

Step 4. $1110_{2*} = -2$

2. Convert the two's complement number $1001_2{}^*$ into its decimal equivalent.

Answers on page A-34

Two's Complement Addition

You may be asking yourself why we should learn the two's complement notation when it seems so complicated. The answer lies in the elegance and efficiency with which the computer can now add two signed numbers. To add in two's complement notation, we simply use the same rule that we used when we added two binary numbers in Section 10.2. The next example illustrates this process.

3. Using two's complement notation, add the following numbers.

$$0001_2.$$
$$+ 1100_2.$$

EXAMPLE 3 Using two's complement notation, add the following numbers.

(a)

$0010_2.$	2 in decimal notation.
$+ 0100_2.$	4 in decimal notation.
$0110_2.$	6 in decimal notation.

(b)

$1100_2.$	-4 in decimal notation.
$+ 0010_2.$	2 in decimal notation.
$1110_2.$	As we saw in the first example, this is -2 in decimal notation.

Any binary addition that involves the sum of a negative and a positive can be done using two's complement representation.

4. Using two's complement notation, add the following numbers.

$$1110_2.$$
$$+ 0111_2.$$

EXAMPLE 4 Using two's complement notation, add the following numbers.

$1100_2.$	-4 in decimal notation.
$+ 0110_2.$	6 in decimal notation.
$1120010_2.$	If you ignore the 1 in the fifth bit, $0010_2.$ is positive 2 in decimal notation.

Any time we are adding a positive number and a negative number using two's complement notation, we can ignore a 1 in the bit to the left of the sign bit.

When you are adding two positive or two negative numbers using four bits, a 1 in the fifth bit may create a problem. The next example illustrates such a case.

EXAMPLE 5 Using two's complement notation, add the following numbers.

$1010_2.$	-6 in decimal notation.
$+ 1101_2.$	-3 in decimal notation.
$1120111_2.$	If you ignore the 1 in the fifth bit, the result in decimal notation is 7, clearly not the sum of -3 and -6.

Here, we have what is called an **overflow error.** Such an error occurs whenever the information is too large for the storage that is allotted. Note that the answer (-9) is correct if we use 5 bits, but we are restricted to 4 bits in this example. The size of the numbers we can add (and of the answers we can reasonably interpret) is determined by the number of bits we have to work with. In the 4-bit notation used in the previous example, we are limited to $2^4 = 16$ different numbers. That is to say, we can represent only sixteen different numbers, $-8, -7, -6, -5, -4, -3, -2, -1, 0, 1, 2, 3, 4, 5, 6, 7$.

Answers on page A-34

If we had 8 bits, we could represent $2^8 = 256$ different numbers (-128 to 127). With 32 bits, we can represent $2^{32} = 4,294,967,296$ different numbers. No matter how many bits we use, there are numbers that are too large or too small to be represented in our system. When we try to represent such numbers, or we end up with answers that are too large, we encounter an overflow error. Some overflow errors are caught by the computer, some disable the computer, and (perhaps the most dangerous) some just return an incorrect answer. In subsequent courses, you will learn more about overflow errors.

10.4 EXERCISE SET

Translate each of the following decimal numbers into two's complement notation. Use a 4-bit representation.

1. 2   **2.** 6   **3.** -6 **4.** -1

Each of the following numbers is in 4-bit, two's complement notation. Translate each into its decimal equivalent.

5. 0101_2.   **6.** 1101_2.   **7.** 1011_2.   **8.** 0100_2.

Translate each of the following decimal numbers into two's complement notation. Use an 8-bit representation.

9. 6   **10.** -13 **11.** -62

12. 95   **13.** -108 **14.** -121

Each of the following numbers is in 8-bit, two's complement notation. Translate each into its decimal equivalent.

15. 00011101_2.   **16.** 11111011_2.   **17.** 10111010_2.

18. 01100010_2.   **19.** 11111111_2.   **20.** 10000010_2.

Add the following binary numbers in 4-bit, two's complement notation. Identify any overflow errors.

21. 0101_2.
     $+\ 0010_2$.

22. 1010_2.
     $+\ 1111_2$.

23. 1010_2.
     $+\ 0110_2$.

24. 0110_2.
     $+\ 0100_2$.

25. 1001_2.
     $+1011_2$.

26. 1011_2.
     $+\ 0111_2$.

Add the following binary numbers in 8-bit, two's complement notation. Rewrite each problem in decimal notation to check your work.

27. 10001110_{2^*}
  $+\ 10101010_{2^*}$

28. 10110111_{2^*}
  $+\ 01100100_{2^*}$

29. 00011010_{2^*}
  $+\ 11010111_{2^*}$

30. How many different numbers can be represented in 4-bit, two's complement notation? What is the minimum value? What is the maximum value?

31. How many different numbers can be represented in 8-bit, two's complement notation? What is the minimum value? What is the maximum value?

32. Many computers use 32-bit, two's complement notation. How many different numbers can be represented in 32-bit, two's complement notation? What is the minimum value? What is the maximum value?

Bits of History

Although fractions were used during ancient times, their notation was cumbersome. It was not until the late fifteenth century that advances in notation for decimal fractions would become apparent. The Swiss mathematician and watchmaker Jost Bürgi made a significant improvement on previous notation by placing a ring sign above the digit in the unit's position. For example, our modern $73\frac{25}{100}$ would have been written $73\overset{\circ}{\ }25$. The Italian Magini is credited with replacing the ring with a dot we now call a decimal point between the units and the tenths position, thus giving us our modern convention of 73.25.

Before we introduce binary fractions, let's review some concepts you have encountered while learning about decimal fractions.

The following diagram shows the value of each place of the decimal number 452,976.

DIGIT	4	5	2	9	7	6
PLACE VALUE	10^5	10^4	10^3	10^2	10^1	10^0

What happens to place value as we move to the right of a decimal point?

First, let's look at the names associated with the place values for the decimal fraction 0.3574, which can also be written as $\frac{3574}{10,000}$.

NUMBER	.3	5	7	4
DIGIT	3	5	7	4
PLACE VALUE NAME	tenths	hundredths	thousandths	ten thousandths
PLACE VALUE	$\frac{1}{10}$	$\frac{1}{100}$	$\frac{1}{1000}$	$\frac{1}{10,000}$

Now, look at the same decimal fraction if we label the place values as powers of ten.

NUMBER	.3	5	7	4
DIGIT	3	5	7	4
PLACE VALUE NAME	tenths	hundredths	thousandths	ten thousandths
PLACE VALUE	10^{-1}	10^{-2}	10^{-3}	10^{-4}

Note that the pattern established to the left of the decimal continues to the right. The same pattern holds true when we write binary fractions. There are a couple of obvious differences when the fraction is binary. Although the pattern of the powers is the same, the base is two instead of ten. Also, we cannot call the period a decimal point, so we call it a **binary point**.

Look at the place values for the binary fraction 111.1111_2.

DIGIT	1	1	1	.	1	1	1	1
PLACE VALUE NAME	fours	twos	ones	BINARY POINT	halfs	fourths	eighths	sixteenths
PLACE VALUE	2^2	2^1	2^0		2^{-1}	2^{-2}	2^{-3}	2^{-4}
DECIMAL EQUIVALENT	4	2	1		$\frac{1}{2}$	$\frac{1}{4}$	$\frac{1}{8}$	$\frac{1}{16}$

Do you see the pattern? Each place value is one-half the place value to the left. We will use this decimal equivalence to rewrite binary fractions as the decimal equivalent.

EXAMPLE 1 Find the place value for the 1 in the binary fraction 0.001_2.

The place value is $2^{-3} = \dfrac{1}{8}$.

EXAMPLE 2 Rewrite the binary fraction 110.0101_2 as its decimal equivalent.

Summing the place values, we find

$$110.0101_2 = 4 + 2 + 0 + 0 + \frac{1}{4} + \frac{1}{16} = 6\frac{5}{16} = 6.3125.$$

(We work from the binary point to the left, and then from the binary point to the right.)

Using the same technique that allows us to write 0.3574 as $\dfrac{3574}{10,000}$ rather than as $\dfrac{3}{10} + \dfrac{5}{100} + \dfrac{7}{1000} + \dfrac{4}{10,000}$, we can more quickly compute a binary fraction's decimal equivalent. The important thing to note from the decimal fraction is this:

To write a decimal as a decimal fraction, we use the number after the decimal point as the numerator, and we write the denominator as a 1 followed by a zero for each place after the decimal point.

EXAMPLE 3 Write each binary as a binary fraction.

(a) $0.011_2 = \dfrac{11_2}{1000_2}$

Note that we use the same process that we use to write 0.3574 as $\dfrac{3574}{10,000}$.

(b) $0.00000001_2 = \dfrac{1_2}{100000000_2}$

(c) $0.01001011_2 = \dfrac{1001011_2}{100000000_2}$

In the next example, we translate binary fractions into decimal fractions.

EXAMPLE 4 Using the fractions from Example 3, write each binary fraction as a decimal fraction.

(a) $\dfrac{11_2}{1000_2} = \dfrac{3}{8}$ or we could say that $0.011_2 = 0 + 0 + \dfrac{1}{4} + \dfrac{1}{8} = \dfrac{3}{8}$

(b) $\dfrac{1_2}{100000000_2} = \dfrac{1}{256}$ or $0.00000001_2 = \dfrac{1}{256}$

(c) $\dfrac{1001011_2}{100000000_2} = \dfrac{75}{256}$ or $0.01001011_2 = \dfrac{75}{256}$

Note that any time we have 8 zeros after the binary point, the decimal equivalent fraction has a denominator of 256. Because there are 8 bits in a byte, this is a commonly occurring denominator.

Answers on page A-35

1. Find the place value for the 1 in the binary fraction 0.0001_2.

2. Rewrite the binary fraction 11.101_2 as its decimal equivalent.

3. Write each binary as a binary fraction.

   (a) 0.0101_2
   (b) 0.00000011_2
   (c) 0.11111111_2

4. Write each binary fraction as a decimal fraction.

   (a) 0.0101_2
   (b) 0.00000011_2
   (c) 0.11111111_2

To rewrite a decimal as a binary fraction, we first check to see if we can express the decimal with a denominator that is a power of two. As stated earlier, we usually use 8 bits to represent the fraction, which results in a denominator of 256.

5. Find the binary equivalent for each decimal fraction.

(a) $\dfrac{93}{256}$ (b) $\dfrac{11}{256}$

EXAMPLE 5   Find the binary equivalent for each decimal fraction.

(a) $\dfrac{79}{256} = \dfrac{1001111_2}{100000000_2}$ or 0.01001111_2

(b) $\dfrac{5}{256} = \dfrac{101_2}{100000000_2}$ or 0.00000101_2

Sometimes we need to rewrite a decimal fraction so that the denominator is 256. To accomplish that, we multiply the decimal by $\dfrac{256}{256}$, which equals 1. Example 6 illustrates this technique.

6. Rewrite each decimal as a fraction with denominator 256, and then convert that fraction to its binary equivalent.

(a) 0.01953125
(b) 0.3125

EXAMPLE 6   Rewrite each decimal as a fraction with denominator 256, and then convert that fraction to its binary equivalent.

(a) 0.01171875

$0.01171875 \times \dfrac{256}{256} = \dfrac{3}{256} = \dfrac{11_2}{100000000_2}$ or 0.00000011_2

(b) 0.1875

$0.1875 \times \dfrac{256}{256} = \dfrac{48}{256} = \dfrac{110000_2}{100000000_2}$ or 0.00110000_2

Can every decimal fraction be rewritten as a binary fraction? Any rational number can be written as a binary fraction. But if the denominator of the fraction is not a power of two, the fraction can be approximated only as a terminating binary.

7. Find the 8-bit binary fraction that most closely approximates each of the following.

(a) 0.2   (b) $\dfrac{1}{3}$

EXAMPLE 7   Find the 8-bit binary fraction that most closely approximates each of the following.

(a) 0.1

$0.1 \times \dfrac{256}{256} = \dfrac{25.6}{256} \approx \dfrac{26}{256} = 0.00011010_2$

(Note that $\dfrac{26}{256}$ actually equals 0.1015625. As we said, we are approximating 0.1.)

(b) $\dfrac{2}{3}$

$\dfrac{2}{3} \approx 0.66666667$

$0.66666667 \times \dfrac{256}{256} \approx \dfrac{170.6}{256} \approx \dfrac{171}{256}$

$\dfrac{171}{256} = 0.10101011_2$

(Again, note that $\dfrac{171}{256} = 0.10101011_2 = 0.66796875$, which is not exactly $\dfrac{2}{3}$.)

Answers on page A-35

EXAMPLE 8 Find the absolute and relative errors for each of the following approximations.

(a) 0.0010_2 for the decimal value 0.1

(Recall that the **absolute error** is the absolute value of the difference.)

Because $0.0010_2 = 0 + 0 + \frac{1}{8} + 0 = 0.125$, the absolute error

$= |0.125 - 0.1| = 0.025$.

(Recall that the **relative error** is the ratio of the absolute error to the actual value, usually expressed as a percentage.)

The relative error $= \dfrac{|0.125 - 0.1|}{0.1} = \dfrac{0.025}{0.1} = 0.25 = 25\%$.

(b) 0.1011_2 for $\dfrac{2}{3}$

Because $0.1011_2 = 0 + \frac{1}{2} + 0 + \frac{1}{8} + \frac{1}{16} = \frac{11}{16} = 0.6875$, the absolute

error $= \left|.6875 - \dfrac{2}{3}\right| = \left|\dfrac{11}{16} - \dfrac{2}{3}\right| = \left|\dfrac{33}{48} - \dfrac{32}{48}\right| = \dfrac{1}{48}$

and the

relative error $= \dfrac{\frac{1}{48}}{\frac{2}{3}} = \dfrac{1}{48} \times \dfrac{3}{2} = \dfrac{3}{96} = \dfrac{1}{32} = 0.03125 = 3.125\%$.

The concepts of this chapter have many applications in both mathematics and computer science. The binary representation that you have seen is the foundation for (although not identical to) floating-point notation. You will encounter further discussion of floating-point notation in your computer science course.

8. Find the absolute and relative errors for each of the approximations you found in Practice Problems 7a and 7b.

Answers on page A-35

Find the decimal equivalent for each of the following binary numbers.

1. 0.1000_2

2. 0.0010_2

3. 0.0110_2

4. 0.1011_2

5. 0.01101100_2

6. 0.11000110_2

7. 1011.1010_2

8. 1101.1110_2

9. 1111.01100100_2

10. $\dfrac{110_2}{1000_2}$

11. $\dfrac{1010_2}{10000_2}$

12. $\dfrac{1001010_2}{10000000_2}$

13. $\dfrac{11111110_2}{100000000_2}$

14. $\dfrac{111010_2}{10000000_2}$

15. $\dfrac{10101010_2}{100000000_2}$

Find the binary equivalent for each of the following decimal numbers.

16. 0.25

17. 0.03125

18. 0.6875

19. 0.9375

20. 0.1640625

21. 0.33203125

22. 8.75

23. 12.625

24. 14.25390625

Use long division to convert each decimal fraction into a binary expansion.

25. $\dfrac{1}{8}$

26. $\dfrac{3}{4}$

27. $\dfrac{2}{3}$

28. $\dfrac{3}{5}$

29. Compare your answers in Exercises 25–28. Which fractions terminate in base ten? Which fractions terminate in base two? How can you tell?

30. Suppose we want to approximate the decimal fraction $\dfrac{1}{3}$ using a binary representation. Find the absolute and relative errors of each approximation. Which of the following is closest to the actual value?

(a) 0.0100_2

(b) 0.0101_2

(c) 0.01010100_2

31. Suppose we want to approximate the decimal fraction $\frac{1}{5}$ using a binary representation. Find the absolute and relative errors of each approximation. Which of the following is closest to the actual value?

(a) 0.0011_2

(b) 0.00110011_2

(c) 0.00110010_2

32. What is the best approximation of the decimal fraction $\frac{2}{3}$, using a denominator of 8, of 16, and of 256?

33. What is the best approximation of the decimal fraction $\frac{1}{6}$ using a denominator of 8, of 16, and of 256?

Each block of three represents a single binary number. Translate each binary number into its decimal equivalent.

34.

35.

36.

37.

38.

10.6 COMPUTER MEMORY AND QUANTITATIVE PREFIXES

Earlier in this chapter, we defined a byte as a basic computer memory unit, consisting of 8 bits. We are now prepared to delve further into the topic of computer memory. Much of our work in this section depends on the material covered in Section 1.6, Dimensional Analysis.

What is meant by the phrase "4K of memory"? The K is generally accepted to mean approximately 1000 bytes (8 bits unless otherwise specified), although, in fact, 1 K is actually 2^{10} (1024) bytes.

EXAMPLE 1 How many bytes and how many bits are in 64 K of memory?

$$64K = 64 \times 2^{10} \text{ bytes} = 2^6 \times 2^{10} \text{ bytes} = 2^{16} \text{ bytes} = 65,536 \text{ bytes}$$
$$2^{16} \text{ bytes} = 2^{16} \times 8 \text{ bits} = 2^{16} \times 2^3 \text{ bits} = 2^{19} \text{ bits} = 524,288 \text{ bits}$$

Note that, using dimensional analysis, we could also write

$$64 \text{ K} = 2^{16} \text{ bytes} \times \frac{2^3 \text{ bits}}{1 \text{ byte}} = 2^{19} \text{ bits}.$$

Note further that our use of unit analysis has helped us keep track of the appropriate units in the answer.

When we speak of 64 K of memory, K is an abbreviation for kilobyte. *Kilo* is the metric prefix that means 1000. A kilometer is 1000 meters, and a kilogram is 1000 grams. As we said earlier, when referring to memory, the 1000 is only an approximation. The actual value is 2^{10}, which equals 1024.

All of the prefixes used to describe computer memory come from the list of standard metric prefixes. The following table summarizes the units commonly used for computer memory.

PREFIX	METRIC MEANING	MEMORY USAGE	ACTUAL NUMBER OF BYTES	INTEGER EQUIVALENT
KILO-	1,000	Kilobyte (K)	2^{10}	1,024
MEGA-	1,000,000	Megabyte (MB)	2^{20}	1,048,576
GIGA-	1,000,000,000	Gigabyte (GB)	2^{30}	1,073,741,824
TERA-	1,000,000,000,000	Terabyte (TB)	2^{40}	1,099,511,627,776

EXAMPLE 2 How many bytes are there in 128 GB?

This is an example of a conversion problem. To make the conversion, we will use unit ratios. Here the unit ratio is $\dfrac{2^{30} \text{ bytes}}{1 \text{ GB}}$ from the preceding table.

$$128 \text{ GB} = 2^7 \text{ GB} = 2^7 \text{ GB} \times \frac{2^{30} \text{ bytes}}{1 \text{ GB}} = 2^{37} \text{ bytes}$$

Bits of History

In 1202, Leonardo Fibonacci formally introduced the Western World to the Hindu-Arabic number system as well as posing many problems in both arithmetic and algebra.

1. How many bytes and how many bits are in 128 K of memory?

2. How many bytes are there in 512 TB?

Answers on page A 35

A typical computer monitor display might have 1024 columns and 768 rows of **pixels** (this word derives from *picture elements*). In a monochrome (black and white) monitor, each pixel can be represented by a single bit. If the pixel is on (white), the bit has a value of 1. If the pixel is off (black), it has a value of 0. Different configurations of white pixels next to black ones can produce various shades of gray on a monochrome monitor.

3. How many bytes are required to store a monochrome display that uses 2048 columns and 1536 rows of pixels?

EXAMPLE 3 How many bytes are required to store a monochrome display that uses 1024 columns and 768 rows of pixels? (Note that we could say we have 1024 columns with 768 pixels per column.)

The important conversion factors are $\dfrac{1 \text{ bit}}{1 \text{ pixel}}$ and $\dfrac{1 \text{ byte}}{8 \text{ bits}}$.

We have the expression

$$1024 \text{ columns} \times \frac{768 \text{ pixels}}{1 \text{ column}} \times \frac{1 \text{ bit}}{1 \text{ pixel}} \times \frac{1 \text{ byte}}{8 \text{ bits}}.$$

Simplifying the units, we have

$$\frac{1024 \times 768}{8} \text{ bytes} = 98{,}304 \text{ bytes}.$$

In the previous example, we assumed that we were using a monochrome monitor. In most cases, the monitor has a palette of colors from which to choose. Such a selection requires more than 1 bit per pixel, as we see in the next example.

4. Assume that 2 bytes are used to store the color for each pixel on a display screen. How many megabytes are required to store a display that uses 2048 columns and 1536 rows of pixels?

EXAMPLE 4 Assume that 2 bytes are used to store the color for each pixel on a display screen. How many kilobytes are required to store a display that uses 1024 columns and 768 rows of pixels?

The conversion factors are $\dfrac{2 \text{ bytes}}{1 \text{ pixel}}$ and $\dfrac{1 \text{ kilobyte}}{1024 \text{ bytes}}$.

We have the expression

$$1024 \text{ columns} \times \frac{768 \text{ pixels}}{1 \text{ column}} \times \frac{2 \text{ bytes}}{1 \text{ pixel}} \times \frac{1 \text{ kilobyte}}{1024 \text{ bytes}}.$$

Simplifying the units, we have

$$\frac{1024 \times 768 \times 2}{1024} \text{ kilobytes} = 1536 \text{ kilobytes}.$$

In Example 5, we examine the computer memory required for computer animation.

Answers on page A-35

EXAMPLE 5 Computer animation requires an ever-increasing amount of computer memory. One form of animation uses a series of pictures that is stored in memory. Assume that a picture is represented on a monitor screen by a rectangular array containing 1024 columns and 768 rows of pixels. How many bytes of memory are required to store an animation that consists of 32 pictures, if each pixel requires 1 byte of storage? After you find the number of bytes, convert the answer to megabytes.

First, let's find the number of pixels required for each picture. There are 1024 columns and 768 rows of pixels, so

$$1024 \times 768 = 786{,}432 \, \frac{\text{pixels}}{\text{picture}}.$$

Alternatively, we could factor the 1024 and the 768 and get

$$1024 \times 768 = 2^{10} \times (3 \cdot 2^8) = 3 \times 2^{18} \, \frac{\text{pixels}}{\text{picture}}.$$

We want to find the number of pixels per animation.

$$32 \, \frac{\text{pictures}}{\text{animation}} = 2^5 \, \frac{\text{pictures}}{\text{animation}}$$

$$2^5 \, \frac{\text{pictures}}{\text{animation}} \times 3 \times 2^{18} \, \frac{\text{pixels}}{\text{picture}} = 3 \times 2^{23} \, \frac{\text{pixels}}{\text{animation}}$$

The problem indicates that each pixel takes 1 byte of memory, so the memory needed is 3×2^{23} bytes.

Converting that to MB, we have

$$3 \times 2^{23} \, \text{bytes} \times \frac{1 \, \text{MB}}{2^{20} \, \text{bytes}} = 3 \times 2^3 \, \text{MB} = 24 \, \text{MB}.$$

We use MB for abbreviating megabyte. Mb is commonly used for megabits.

To communicate very large and very small numbers, scientists throughout the world developed and agreed upon a set of prefixes that could be used with any unit of measure. Although these prefixes were not developed with the computer in mind, no other product or process comes close to the computer in terms of their usefulness. As computers become faster and memory larger, there is already a prefix designed to describe the change.

This set of prefixes is generally referred to as the SI, the International System of Units. The SI communicates the magnitude of the units by the use of appropriate prefixes. For example, the electrical unit of a watt is not a big unit, even in terms of ordinary household use, so it is generally used in terms of 1000 watts at a time. The prefix for 1000 is *kilo-*, so we use kilowatts (kW) as our unit of measurement. For makers of electricity, or bigger users such as industry, it is common to use megawatts (MW) or even gigawatts (GW).

5. Assume that a picture is represented on a monitor screen by a rectangular array containing 2048 columns and 1536 rows of pixels. Assuming that each pixel takes 1 byte of memory, how many bytes of memory are required to store an animation that consists of 512 pictures? After finding the number of bytes, convert the answer to megabytes.

Answers on page A 35

The following table includes the full range of prefixes, their symbols or abbreviations, and their multiplying factors. These prefixes can be used to describe very large and very small numbers. We refer to this table later in this text.

PREFIX	SYMBOL	FACTOR	
Yotta-	Y	1 000 000 000 000 000 000 000 000	$= 10^{24}$
Zetta-	Z	1 000 000 000 000 000 000 000	$= 10^{21}$
Exa-	E	1 000 000 000 000 000 000	$= 10^{18}$
Peta-	P	1 000 000 000 000 000	$= 10^{15}$
Tera-	T	1 000 000 000 000	$= 10^{12}$
Giga-	G	1 000 000 000 (a thousand millions = a billion)	$= 10^{9}$
Mega-	M	1 000 000 (a million)	$= 10^{6}$
Kilo-	k	1 000 (a thousand)	$= 10^{3}$
Hecto-	h	100	$= 10^{2}$
Deca-	da	10	$= 10^{1}$
		1	$= 10^{0}$
Deci-	d	0.1	$= 10^{-1}$
Centi-	c	0.01	$= 10^{-2}$
Milli-	m	0.001 (a thousandth)	$= 10^{-3}$
Micro-	μ	0.000 001 (a millionth)	$= 10^{-6}$
Nano-	n	0.000 000 001 (a thousand millionth)	$= 10^{-9}$
Pico-	p	0.000 000 000 001	$= 10^{-12}$
Femto-	f	0.000 000 000 000 001	$= 10^{-15}$
Atto-	a	0.000 000 000 000 000 001	$= 10^{-18}$
Zepto-	z	0.000 000 000 000 000 000 001	$= 10^{-21}$
Yocto-	y	0.000 000 000 000 000 000 000 001	$= 10^{-24}$

6. What is the multiplying factor associated with each of the following metric prefixes?

   (a) deca   (b) pico

EXAMPLE 6   What is the multiplying factor associated with each of the following metric prefixes?

(a) nano   (b) yotta

(a) From the table above, we see that **nano** means "a thousand millionth" and has a corresponding multiplying factor of 10^{-9}.

(b) From the table, we see that **yotta** is "a trillion trillions" and has a multiplying factor of 10^{24}.

It is important to note that because these metric prefixes are multiples or submultiples of 10, they are not used precisely in the context of computers, which relies upon base two. For example, 1 kilometer = 1000 meters, whereas 1 kilobyte = 1024 bytes.

7. Compute the absolute and relative errors when 1,000,000 bytes are used to approximate 1 MB.

EXAMPLE 7   Compute the absolute and relative errors when 1000 bytes are used to approximate 1 KB.

The actual value of 1 KB is 1024 bytes, and the approximation is 1000 bytes. Hence the absolute error is given by $a.e. = |1000 - 1024| = |-24| = 24$ bytes.

The relative error is given by $r.e. = \dfrac{|1000 - 1024|}{1024} = \dfrac{|-24|}{1024}$

$= \dfrac{24}{1024} = \dfrac{3}{128} \approx 2.34\%.$

Answers on page A-35

10.6

EXERCISE SET

For Extra Help

InterAct
Math

Math Tutor
Center

MathXL

MyMathLab

Exactly how many *bytes* are in each of the following?

1. 1 K

2. 1 MB

3. 5 MB

4. 10 TB

5. 64 K

6. 60 MB

Exactly how many *bits* are in each of the following?

7. 1 K

8. 1 GB

9. 20 MB

10. 40 GB

11. 640 K

12. 5 TB

Give the multiplying factor associated with each of the following metric prefixes.

13. kilo-

14. deci-

15. centi-

16. giga-

17. micro-

18. tera-

19. An 8-page document consumes 72.5 K of disk space. How many documents of this size can fit onto a 1.44-MB floppy disk?

20. A computer modem is connected at 2.4 $\frac{Kb}{sec}$. What is the modem's transfer rate in $\frac{Mb}{hr}$?

21. A computer modem is connected at 9 $\frac{Mb}{hr}$. What is the modem's transfer rate in $\frac{Kb}{sec}$?

22. How many bytes are required to store a monochrome display (assume 1 bit is needed for each pixel) that uses 640 columns and 480 rows of pixels?

23. The Game Boy Advance uses a 15-bit color scheme for its display. Assuming each pixel requires 15 bits, how many bits are needed if the display is 240 columns and 160 rows?

24. Many color monitors use 24-bit true color for their displays. Assuming each pixel needs 3 bytes for storage, find the number of bytes required for a color display of 640 columns and 480 rows.

25. Some color monitors use 32-bit true color for their displays. Assuming each pixel requires 4 bytes for storage, find the number of bytes required for a color display of 1024 columns and 768 rows.

26. Assume that a picture is represented on a monitor screen, which requires 1 byte per pixel (gray scale) by a rectangular array containing 1024 columns and 768 rows of pixels. How many bytes of memory are required to store an animation that consists of 64 pictures? After finding the number of bytes, convert the answer to megabytes.

27. Assume the animation described in Exercise 26 is done in 24-bit true color, which requires 3 bytes per pixel. How many megabytes are required to store the same animation in color?

28. A computer-animated GIF of a dog that is 127 by 77 pixels is designed in 16-bit color (two bytes per pixel). If the animation consists of 10 pictures, how many bytes are required to store the image? After finding the number of bytes, convert the answer to kilobytes.

29. A computer-animated short film that is 640 by 480 pixels is designed in 16-bit color (two bytes per pixel). The film is produced at a rate of 10 frames (pictures) per second and it is two minutes in length. How many megabytes are required to store this film?

30. Compute the absolute and relative error when 1,000,000,000 bytes are used to approximate 1 GB.

31. Compute the absolute and relative error when 1,000,000,000,000 bytes are used to approximate 1 TB.

32. Compute the absolute and relative error when 100 KB is used to approximate 1 Mb (megabit).

The review that follows is meant to prepare you for a chapter exam. It consists of two parts. The first part is a checklist of some of the Study Tips referred to in this and preceding chapters. The second part is the Review Exercises. These provide practice exercises for the exam, together with references to section objectives so you can go back and review. Before beginning, stop and look back over the skills you have obtained. What skills in mathematics do you have now that you did not have before studying this chapter?

STUDY TIPS CHECKLIST

The foundation of all your study skills is TIME!	☐ Are you continuing to focus on a lesson even if it contains some review material?
	☐ Are you using the math you've learned as part of your everyday life?
	☐ As new topics are introduced, are you careful to make sure you thoroughly understand the material?
	☐ If you miss a class do you make certain that you find out all that you missed?

REVIEW EXERCISES

For help with exercises, refer to the section number given in the brackets.

Find the decimal equivalent for each of the following binary numbers.   [10.1]

1. 0100_2 **2.** 1111_2 **3.** 10110001_2

4. 11100100_2 **5.** 101100111111_2

Find the binary equivalent for each of the following decimal numbers.   [10.1]

6. 9   **7.** 14   **8.** 29

9. 172   **10.** 509

Translate the following binary phone numbers into their decimal equivalents. Each digit is separated by a hyphen. [10.1]

11. $0101_2 - 0000_2 - 0011_2 - 0110_2 - 0101_2 - 0111_2 - 0110_2$ $- 1001_2 - 0101_2 - 1000_2$

12. $0111_2 - 1000_2 - 0001_2 - 1001_2 - 0100_2 - 0100_2 - 0011_2$ $- 0111_2 - 0000_2 - 0000_2$

Write the binary number represented by the following sets of blocks, then translate each binary number into its decimal equivalent.   [10.1]

13.

14.

15.

Add the following binary numbers. Rewrite each problem in decimal notation to check your work. [10.2]

16. $\begin{array}{r} 0110_2 \\ + \ 0001_2 \\ \hline \end{array}$

17. $\begin{array}{r} 1011_2 \\ + \ 0110_2 \\ \hline \end{array}$

18. $\begin{array}{r} 1101_2 \\ 0110_2 \\ + \ 1001_2 \\ \hline \end{array}$

19. $\begin{array}{r} 1011_2 \\ 1001_2 \\ + \ 1001_2 \\ \hline \end{array}$

20. $\begin{array}{r} 10111110_2 \\ + \ 10101010_2 \\ \hline \end{array}$

Multiply each pair of binary numbers. Rewrite each problem in decimal notation to check your work. [10.2]

21. $\begin{array}{r} 101_2 \\ \times \ \ 10_2 \\ \hline \end{array}$

22. $\begin{array}{r} 1101_2 \\ \times \ \ \ 11_2 \\ \hline \end{array}$

23. $\begin{array}{r} 1010 \\ \times \ \ 101_2 \\ \hline \end{array}$

Perform the following binary subtractions. Rewrite each problem in decimal notation to check your work. [10.3]

24. $\begin{array}{r} 1011_2 \\ - \ 0011_2 \\ \hline \end{array}$

25. $\begin{array}{r} 1101_2 \\ - \ 0110_2 \\ \hline \end{array}$

26. $\begin{array}{r} 10010110_2 \\ - \ 00001010_2 \\ \hline \end{array}$

27. $\begin{array}{r} 10000000_2 \\ - \ 01111110_2 \\ \hline \end{array}$

28. Use repeated subtraction to find the number of times 11_2 goes into 1111_2. [10.3]

29. Use long division to find the number of times 11_2 goes into 1111_2.

Simplify each of the following by using long division. Convert the values to decimal to verify your answer. Some answers may have a remainder. [10.3]

30. $10110_2 \div 10_2$ 31. $11001_2 \div 101_2$

32. $10100011_2 \div 100_2$ 33. $1011010110_2 \div 101_2$

Translate each of the following decimal numbers into two's complement notation. Use an 8-bit representation. [10.4]

34. 3   35. -3 36. 29

37. -75 38. 102   39. -115

Each of the following numbers are in 8-bit, two's complement notation. Translate each into its decimal equivalent. [10.4]

40. 00000010_{2^*} 41. 11111101_{2^*} 42. 10010001_{2^*}

43. 01011111_{2^*} 44. 10110101_{2^*} 45. 11011101_{2^*}

Add the following binary numbers in 4-bit, two's complement notation. Rewrite each problem in decimal notation to check your work. Identify any overflow errors. [10.4]

46. $\begin{array}{r} 1101_{2^*} \\ + \ 1011_{2^*} \\ \hline \end{array}$

47. $\begin{array}{r} 0011_{2^*} \\ + \ 1111_{2^*} \\ \hline \end{array}$

48. $\begin{array}{r} 0110_{2^*} \\ + \ 0111_{2^*} \\ \hline \end{array}$

Find the decimal equivalent for each of the following binary numbers. [10.5]

49. 0.0101_2 **50.** 0.1101_2

51. 0.11010110_2 **52.** 1110.1011_2

53. $\dfrac{111_2}{1000_2}$ **54.** $\dfrac{100100_2}{10000000_2}$

55. $\dfrac{1010101_2}{10000000_2}$ **56.** $\dfrac{1110111_2}{10000000_2}$

Find the binary equivalent for each of the following decimal numbers. [10.5]

57. 0.125 **58.** 0.34375

59. 13.296875 **60.** 9.2734375

Use long division to convert each decimal fraction into a binary expansion. [10.5]

61. $\dfrac{1}{16}$ **62.** $\dfrac{7}{8}$ **63.** $\dfrac{4}{5}$

64. What is the best approximation of the decimal fraction $\dfrac{3}{5}$ using a denominator of 8, of 16, and of 256?

Exactly how many *bytes* are in each of the following? [10.6]

65. 1 GB   **66.** 12 MB   **67.** 640 K

Exactly how many *bits* are in each of the following? [10.6]

68. 1 MB   **69.** 120 GB   **70.** 1 TB

71. A 12-page document consumes 200 K of disk space. How many documents of this size can fit onto a 1.44 MB floppy disk? [10.6]

72. According to Samsung, the Syncmaster 151S monitor uses 24-bit True Color for its display. Assuming each pixel needs 3 bytes for storage, find the number of bytes required for the Syncmaster's display of 1024 columns and 768 rows.

1. Find the decimal equivalent for each of the following binary numbers.
   (a) 1101_2 (b) 10111111_2 (c) 10100001_2

2. Find the binary equivalent for each of the following decimal numbers.
   (a) 2   (b) 27   (c) 113

3. Add the following binary numbers. Rewrite each problem in decimal notation to check your work.

   (a) $\begin{array}{r} 1101_2 \\ +\,0110_2 \end{array}$ (b) $\begin{array}{r} 10011101_2 \\ +\,01110110_2 \end{array}$

4. Multiply each pair of binary numbers. Rewrite each problem in decimal notation to check your work.

   (a) $\begin{array}{r} 111_2 \\ \times\ 10_2 \end{array}$ (b) $\begin{array}{r} 1011_2 \\ \times\ 11_2 \end{array}$ (c) $\begin{array}{r} 11010_2 \\ \times\ 101_2 \end{array}$

5. Perform the following binary subtractions. Rewrite each problem in decimal notation to check your work.

   (a) $\begin{array}{r} 1011_2 \\ -\ 0011_2 \\ \hline \end{array}$

   (b) $\begin{array}{r} 1101_2 \\ -\ 0110_2 \\ \hline \end{array}$

6. Simplify each of the following by using long division. Convert the values to decimal to verify your answer. Some answers may have a remainder.

   (a) $11010_2 \div 10_2$

   (b) $10101101_2 \div 11_2$

   (c) $1101101_2 \div 10_2$

7. Translate each of the following decimal numbers into two's complement notation. Use an 8-bit representation.

   (a) 98

   (b) −13

   (c) −116

8. Each of the following numbers are in 8-bit, two's complement notation. Translate each into its decimal equivalent.

   (a) 00001110_2.

   (b) 11111101_2.

   (c) 100010001_2.

9. Add the following binary numbers in 4-bit, two's complement notation. Rewrite each problem in decimal notation to check your work. Identify any overflow errors.

   (a) $\begin{array}{r} 1011_2. \\ +\ 0111_2. \\ \hline \end{array}$

   (b) $\begin{array}{r} 1001_2. \\ +\ 1010_2. \\ \hline \end{array}$

   (c) $\begin{array}{r} 1111_2. \\ +\ 1100_2. \\ \hline \end{array}$

10. Find the decimal equivalent for each of the following binary numbers.

(a) 0.11001_2

(b) 110.1001_2

(c) $\dfrac{10001_2}{10000000_2}$

(d) $\dfrac{1101101_2}{10000000_2}$

11. Find the binary equivalent for each of the following decimal numbers.

(a) 0.0625

(b) 5.34375

(c) 11.34375

12. Use long division to convert each decimal fraction into a binary expansion.

(a) $\dfrac{1}{32}$

(b) $\dfrac{3}{64}$

(c) $\dfrac{4}{9}$

13. Exactly how many *bytes* are in each of the following?

    (a) 1 MB   (b) 5 K

14. Exactly how many *bits* are in each of the following?

    (a) 40 GB   (b) 200 K

15. A 25-slide PowerPoint presentation consumes 8550 K of disk space. How many 1.44 MB floppy disks are required to store the presentation?

1–10 Cumulative Review

1. $-3(4-7)^2 =$

2. Evaluate the expression $x^2 + 3x$ at $x = -2$

3. Factor 1096 into its prime factors.

4. $3\frac{1}{7} \times 2\frac{1}{5} =$

5. On a single roll of die, what is the probability of rolling a number less than 5?

6. Sketch a graph of the line $y = 3x - 4$.

7. Given that A = {a, e, i, o, u}, find |A|.

8. Given that A = {1, 2, 3, 4} and B = {4, 5, 6, 7, 8} sketch a Venn diagram that illustrates A ∩ B.

9. Express the decimal number 83 as a binary number.

10. $100111_2 + 1110_2 =$

Octal and Hexadecimal Numbers

Gateway to Chapter 11
A.D. 1500 to A.D. 1700

There were three significant mechanical computing machines invented in this era. The first, in 1525, was a mechanical pedometer that estimated distances by counting footsteps. The second was Blaise Pascal's computing clock. It had the theoretical ability to do multiplication and division but needed the user to do interim calculations to make it work. Finally, Gottfried Leibniz constructed a machine in 1694 that did multiplication and division by repeated addition and subtraction.

CHAPTER

11

1. Find the decimal equivalent of the octal number 22_8.

2. Find the octal equivalent of the decimal number 54.

3. Find the octal equivalent of the binary number 10110111_2.

4. Find the binary equivalent of the octal number 33_8.

5. Find the decimal equivalent of hexadecimal number $5B7_{16}$.

6. Find the hexadecimal equivalent of the decimal number 110.

7. Find the hexadecimal equivalent of the binary number 10110001_2.

8. Find the binary equivalent of the hexadecimal number 38_{16}.

9. B_{16}
   $+9_{16}$

10. $1B7_{16}$
    $+92A_{16}$

11. $6F_{16}$
    $\times 25_{16}$

12. Find the decimal ASCII code for the character H.

13. Find the ASCII bit pattern for the character j.

14. Find the hexadecimal ASCII code for the character 9.

11.1 THE OCTAL SYSTEM

The base ten system is a natural choice for human beings because most people have ten fingers. The base two system is a nice model for computers because machine information is stored in a manner that accepts one of two states. Are these the only number systems that exist?

The characters of Matt Groening's *The Simpsons* all have eight digits (fingers), so how do they count to our decimal equivalent of ten? Lisa would start just as we would, 1, 2, 3, 4, 5, 6, 7, and 8, then she would need to use two digits on a hand she already used. In other words, she uses an entire group of hands and then needs two more digits to finish counting.

Reprinted with permission.

In this section, we introduce a third number base, base eight. This is called the **octal number system.** The place value pattern is the same as the two bases above.

Bits of History

A.D.1600–1700 One of the most important achievements in mathematics occurred in the early seventeenth century when John Napier developed logarithms. Logarithms, allowed for multiplication and division by adding and subtracting exponents. In addition to the practical applications of logarithms in mathematics and astronomy at the time, logarithms and exponents were key ingredients in the emergence of modern computers.

OCTAL NUMBER	10000_8	1000_8	100_8	10_8	1_8
BASE TEN VALUE	4096	512	64	8	1
POWER OF EIGHT	8^4	8^3	8^2	8^1	8^0

In base ten, we use ten different symbols, 0, 1, 2, 3, 4, 5, 6, 7, 8, and 9. In base two, we use only two symbols, 0 and 1. In base eight, we use eight symbols, 0, 1, 2, 3, 4, 5, 6, and 7. Notice the counting pattern in base eight.

Note: As before, when there is no subscript, we are dealing with base ten.

00_8	01_8	02_8	03_8	04_8	05_8	06_8	07_8	10_8	11_8	12_8	13_8	14_8	15_8	16_8	17_8	20_8
0	1	2	3	4	5	6	7	8	9	10	11	12	13	14	15	16

In our first example, we determine the value of given octal digits.

EXAMPLE 1 Find the decimal equivalent value for the given octal digit. Note that the given place is counted from right to left.

(a) 1352_8 *The first digit*:
The first digit has a value of $2 \times 8^0 = 2 \times 1 = 2$.

(b) 1352_8 *The second digit*:
The second digit has a value of $5 \times 8^1 = 5 \times 8 = 40$.

(c) 1352_8 *The third digit*:
The third digit has a value of $3 \times 8^2 = 3 \times 64 = 192$.

As is the case with binary numbers, we can find an octal number's decimal equivalent by converting and summing its place values. In our next example, we convert from octal to decimal numbers.

1. Find the decimal equivalent value for the given octal digit.

(a) 0276_8 The first digit:

_____

(b) 0276_8 The second digit:

_____

(c) 0276_8 The third digit:

_____

Answers on page A 36

2. Find the decimal equivalent for each octal representation.

(a) 0276_8 (b) 2133_8

EXAMPLE 2   Find the decimal equivalent for the octal representation 1352_8.

OCTAL DIGIT LOCATION	fourth	third	second	first
POWER	8^3	8^2	8^1	8^0
VALUE	512	64	8	1

$$1352_8 = 1 \times 512 + 3 \times 64 + 5 \times 8 + 2 \times 1$$
$$= 512 + 192 + 40 + 2$$
$$= 746$$

How do we go about rewriting a decimal number as its octal equivalent? One possibility is a process that is nearly identical to the one we use for converting decimal numbers to their binary equivalent.

3. Rewrite the decimal number 199 as an octal number.

EXAMPLE 3   Rewrite the decimal number 231 as an octal number.

The largest power of eight that is less than 231 is 64 (the next power of eight, 8^3, equals 512). Unlike base two, we must find the *number* of 64s in 231 (between 0 and 7), so we divide. Dividing 231 by 64, we find that 64 goes in three times with a remainder of 39.

So far, we have $231 = 3$___ ___ $_8$ ◄——— **That is, 3 in the 64s' place and unknown amounts in the 8s' and 1s' places.**

Next, we look at the number of 8s in 39. There are 4 eights with a remainder of 7. From this information, we can find the octal equivalent of 231.

$231 = 347_8$ ◄——————— **There are 3 sixty-fours, 4 eights, and 7 ones.**

We have two more conversions to master in this section, binary to octal and octal to binary. In our next example, we convert a binary number to its octal equivalent.

4. Rewrite the binary number 11101101110_2 as an octal number.

EXAMPLE 4   Rewrite the binary number 1010011011_2 as its octal equivalent.

We could convert the binary number to its decimal equivalent, and then convert that decimal number to its octal equivalent, but there is no need to do that much work! All we need to do is break the binary number into groups of 3 bits, starting on the right. We call these groups of 3 bits **tribbles.**

$1010011011_2 = 001\,010\,011\,011_2$ **We add the 2 zeros on the left so that we have groups of three.**

Just convert each tribble to its octal equivalent, and you have made the conversion!

1010011011_2	=	001	010	011	011_2
	=	1	2	3	3_8

$1010011011_2 = 1233_8$

To convert octal numbers to their binary equivalent, we reverse the process.

Answers on page A-36

EXAMPLE 5 Convert the octal number 3715_8 to its binary equivalent.

Convert each digit to its tribble. The series of tribbles becomes the binary equivalent.

$$\begin{array}{cccc} 3 & 7 & 1 & 5_8 \\ 011 & 111 & 001 & 101_2 \end{array} = 011111001101_2$$

5. Rewrite the octal number 5624_8 as a binary number.

Our goal in this section was to help you understand the octal number system and to convert between the different bases we have discussed. When converting from base ten into other bases, there is a nice algorithm that uses division rather than repeated subtraction. We illustrate this in Example 6.

EXAMPLE 6 Rewrite the decimal number 231 as an octal number.

We start by taking 231 and dividing it by 8. We could set up the problem using our traditional long division, but the algorithm requires information about the remainders, so we use a modified division.

6. Use the division algorithm above to rewrite the decimal number 199 as an octal number.

$$8\lfloor 231$$
$$\quad 28 \text{ R}7 \longleftarrow$$

First, 8 goes into 231 twenty-eight times, with a remainder of 7.

Next, we divide the 28 by 8 and again keep track of the remainder.

$$8\lfloor 231$$
$$8\lfloor 28 \text{ R}7 \longleftarrow$$
$$\quad 3 \text{ R}4$$

Then, 8 goes into 28 three times, with a remainder of 4.

Now, starting with the 3 and working upward, we write the digits 347.

So, $231 = 347_8$.

Answers on page A-36

Find the decimal equivalent for each of the following octal numbers.

1. 7_8

2. 2_8

3. 11_8

4. 25_8

5. 40_8

6. 76_8

7. 61_8

8. 124_8

9. 256_8

10. 423_8

11. 1066_8

12. 1776_8

Find the octal equivalent for each of the following decimal numbers.

13. 5

14. 2

15. 10

16. 25

17. 32

18. 46

19. 65

20. 79

21. 128

22. 501

23. 1925

24. 2004

Find the octal equivalent for each of the following binary numbers.

25. 00101010_2

26. 00111011_2

27. 01001000_2

28. 11101111_2

29. 10101010_2

30. 11111110_2

31. 111100101010_2

32. 101010101111_2

33. 111010110101_2

Find the binary equivalent for each of the following octal numbers.

34. 26_8

35. 31_8

36. 75_8

37. 126_8

38. 255_8

39. 307_8

40. 624_8

41. 1057_8

42. 3120_8

43. What is true of the octal equivalent of any odd number?

44. What is true of the octal equivalent of any even number?

45. Suppose you want to work in base nine. What digits would you use?

46. Suppose you want to work in base twelve. What digits would you use? How would you write the decimal number 11 in base twelve?

In Chapter 10, we presented the binary numbering system, which is the system used within every computer. While computers work well in base two, you may have noticed that it is somewhat difficult for humans to sort through long strings of 1s and 0s, and that it is somewhat easier to look at the octal representation of that number. Most computer applications use one of two systems to make it easier for users to read and represent these strings. The octal system is one of those systems. However, the octal system can still be cumbersome when it is used to represent large base ten numbers. It is also the case that octal numbers, which represent three-bit segments, do not easily translate the byte, which has 8 bits. The other system that computer applications use, the hexadecimal system, can easily represent a byte and has become more standard in recent years.

Binary numbers have a base of two. Octal numbers have a base of eight. Decimal numbers have a base of ten. Hexadecimal numbers have a base of sixteen. We compare the four systems in the following table.

DECIMAL	BINARY	OCTAL	HEXADECIMAL
0	0000_2	0_8	0_{16}
1	0001_2	1_8	1_{16}
2	0010_2	2_8	2_{16}
3	0011_2	3_8	3_{16}
4	0100_2	4_8	4_{16}
5	0101_2	5_8	5_{16}
6	0110_2	6_8	6_{16}
7	0111_2	7_8	7_{16}
8	1000_2	10_8	8_{16}
9	1001_2	11_8	9_{16}
10	1010_2	12_8	A_{16}
11	1011_2	13_8	B_{16}
12	1100_2	14_8	C_{16}
13	1101_2	15_8	D_{16}
14	1110_2	16_8	E_{16}
15	1111_2	17_8	F_{16}
16	10000_2	20_8	10_{16}

The first thing you probably notice is the letters used in the base sixteen representations. When this system was designed, it was obvious that some new symbol needed to be used for the digits 10 to 15. In base two, we need only two different symbols (0 and 1) in each place. In base ten, we need ten different symbols for each place. In base sixteen, we need sixteen different symbols. The symbols A, B, C, D, E, and F were chosen for their familiarity.

Converting from Binary to Hexadecimal Notation

It may sound intimidating, but this process is similar to the binary to octal conversion discussed earlier. All that is needed is the preceding table. The next example illustrates the conversion process.

EXAMPLE 1   Convert each binary number to its hexadecimal equivalent.

(a) 0101_2 From the table on page 754, we see that $0101_2 = 5_{16}$.

(b) 1101_2 Again, from the table on page 754, we have $1101_2 = D_{16}$.

(c) 10100111_2 To convert a string of bits to hexadecimal notation, we group the bits in sets of four (sometimes called a nibble) starting at the right. We then convert each nibble by using the table on page 754.

$$10100111_2 = 1010\ 0111_2 = A7_{16}$$

(d) $11001011_2 = 1100\ 1011_2 = CB_{16}$

(e) $1101011010101101010_2 = 0001\ 1010\ 1101\ 0110\ 1010_2 = 1AD6A_{16}$

Note that in (e) we add extra zeros to the left to complete the nibble, just as we added them when we worked with the tribbles in the previous section.

Converting from Hexadecimal to Binary Notation

To convert from hexadecimal to binary notation, we again use the table on page 754.

EXAMPLE 2   Convert the hexadecimal number $A4C_{16}$ to its binary equivalent.

Using the table on page 754, we see that $A_{16} = 1010_2$, $4_{10} = 0100_2$, and $C_{16} = 1100_2$.

Putting these together, we see that $A4C_{16} = 101001001100_2$.

Hexadecimal Place Values

We have seen the pattern of place values for decimal and binary numbers. The pattern for hexadecimal numbers uses the same exponential pattern.

HEXADECIMAL NUMBER	1000_{16}	100_{16}	10_{16}	1_{16}
BASE TEN VALUE	16^3	16^2	16^1	16^0
DECIMAL EQUIVALENT	4096	256	16	1

1. Convert each binary to its hexadecimal equivalent.

   (a) 0111_2

   (b) 1110_2

   (c) 10110000_2

   (d) 1011011_2

   (e) 110100000_2

2. Convert the hexadecimal number $0C29_{16}$ to its binary equivalent.

Answers on page A 36

Converting from Hexadecimal to Decimal Notation

The preceding table is used in the next example.

EXAMPLE 3   Convert each hexadecimal number to its decimal equivalent.

3. Convert each hexadecimal number to its decimal equivalent.

(a) $B21_{16}$ (b) $9F2C_{16}$

(a) $3A4_{16}$ We have $3 \times 16^2 + A\ 1$which is $102 \times 16^1 + 4 \times 16^0$.

$= 3 \times 256 + 10 \times 16 + 4 \times 1$

$= 768 + 160 + 4$

$= 932$ in decimal

(b) $B52C_{16} = 11 \times 16^3 + 5 \times 16^2 + 2 \times 16^1 + 12 = 46{,}380$

Converting from Decimal to Hexadecimal Notation

We discussed the conversion of decimals to binary numbers in Chapter 2. When we need to convert from decimal to hexadecimal notation, we use a similar process.

4. Convert the decimal number 5999 to its hexadecimal equivalent.

EXAMPLE 4   Convert the decimal number 3728 to its hexadecimal equivalent.

3728 is less than 4096, so the value of the fourth digit is 0. Moving to the next place (value 256), we find the number of 256s in 3728.

$3728 \div 256 = 14$, with a remainder of 144.

The 14 is E in hexadecimal, so now we have $0E_____{16}$ as our hexadecimal equivalent.

The remainder of 144 is now divided by the 16 of the next place value to the right.

$144 \div 16 = 9$, with no remainder.

We have $3728 = 0E90_{16}$.

Again, we can use the division algorithm discussed in Section 11.1 to convert a base ten number into its hexadecimal equivalent.

5. Use the division algorithm to convert the decimal number 2607 to its hexadecimal equivalent.

EXAMPLE 5   Use the division algorithm to convert the decimal number 3728 to its hexadecimal equivalent.

$16\lfloor\underline{3728}$

233 R0   First, 16 goes into 3728 two hundred thirty-three times, with a remainder of 0.

Next, we divide the 233 by 16 and again keep track of the remainder.

$16\lfloor\underline{3728}$

$16\lfloor\underline{233}$ R0   Then, 16 goes into 233 fourteen times, with a remainder of 9.

$\boxed{14}$ R9   We must be careful when we write down the digits of our answer. If we write 1490, this is incorrect. Why? Because in base sixteen the 14 represents a single digit. We need to convert 14 to its hexadecimal equivalent, which is E.

So, $3728 = E90_{16}$.

Answers on page A-36

For Extra Help

Find the decimal equivalent for each of the following hexadecimal numbers.

1. 5_{16}

2. E_{16}

3. 13_{16}

4. 16_{16}

5. $A1_{16}$

6. $C4_{16}$

7. 70_{16}

8. ACE_{16}

9. $D12_{16}$

10. $AD8_{16}$

11. $ABBA_{16}$

12. $F150_{16}$

Find the hexadecimal equivalent for each of the following decimal numbers.

13. 1

14. 8

15. 12

16. 31

17. 47

18. 65

19. 72

20. 108

21. 121

22. 340

23. 1783

24. 5294

Find the hexadecimal equivalent for each of the following binary numbers.

25. 01001000_2

26. 00111011_2

27. 00101010_2

28. 10101010_2

29. 11101111_2

30. 11111110_2

31. 111010110101_2

32. 101010101111_2

33. 111100101010_2

757

Find the binary equivalent for each of the following hexadecimal numbers.

34. 25_{16}

35. 37_{16}

36. $4A_{16}$

37. FF_{16}

38. $B07_{16}$

39. $C29_{16}$

40. $E41_{16}$

41. $369C_{16}$

42. $A2D2_{16}$

Convert each binary fraction into both its octal and hexadecimal equivalents by grouping into tribbles and nibbles working away from the binary point.

43. 0.1010_2

44. 0.1110_2

45. 0.01010100_2

46. 0.01101101_2

47. 0.110101101001_2

48. 0.100111101011_2

11.3 BASE SIXTEEN ARITHMETIC

We have seen that, in hexadecimal notation, the sixteen digits are

0, 1, 2, 3, 4, 5, 6, 7, 8, 9, A, B, C, D, E, F

Keeping this order in mind can help us add hexadecimal numbers. What is $4 + 5$ in decimal notation? You probably answer "9" almost immediately. When you first learned to add, you probably started at 4, then counted 5 more on your fingers. It would be easiest to teach you to add this way in base sixteen, if only you had sixteen fingers! Instead, you will have to use the list of digits (figuratively, "fingers") above.

EXAMPLE 1 Add each pair of hexadecimal numbers.

(a) $4_{16} + 5_{16}$ — If we start at 4 and move five places, we get 9. In base sixteen, as in base ten, $4_{16} + 5_{16} = 9_{16}$.

(b) $8_{16} + 3_{16}$ — Starting at 8, we move three digits. We end at B (this would be 11 in base ten). $8_{16} + 3_{16} = B_{16}$.

(c) $C_{16} + 2_{16}$ — By the same method, $C_{16} + 2_{16} = E_{16}$.

What do we do when our sum takes us "off the chart"? As we did in decimal notation, we add one in the place to the left each time we get to the end of the digit list. Recall from the last section that the place to the left of the 1s' place was the 16s' place. Every time we get to the end of the digits list, we have accumulated another 16, so we add 1 to that place. This is sometimes easier to see if we draw a base sixteen clock face.

Hexadecimal Clock

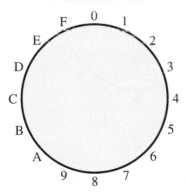

Every time we get back to 0, we add 1 in the 16s' column. We will refer to this clock in the following example.

Bits of History

A.D.1600–1700 Blaise Pascal is often referred to as the inventor of the first digital calculator. His machine called the Pascaline was a five-digit calculator about the size of a shoebox that used a nine's complement (similar to the modern computer's two's complement) for subtraction. Although often noted as a mathematician, Pascal is immortalized in computer science by the computer language PASCAL.

1. Add each pair of hexadecimal numbers.

    (a) $7_{16} + 3_{16}$
    (b) $7_{16} + 7_{16}$
    (c) $C_{16} + 3_{16}$

Answers on page A-36

2. Use the base sixteen clock face to add each pair of hexadecimal numbers.

(a) $F_{16} + 3_{16}$

(b) $D_{16} + D_{16}$

EXAMPLE 2 Find the sum for each pair of hexadecimal numbers.

(a) $9_{16} + 9_{16}$

Using the following figure, we start at the 9, count off nine digits. Note that, after getting to the 0 on the clock face, you must continue two more digits to finish. The resulting sum is $9_{16} + 9_{16} = 12_{16}$. You could think of this as "$9_{16} + 9_{16}$ is one 16 and one 2."

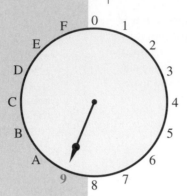

Start at 9.

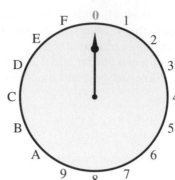

As you get back to 0, this is one trip around the clock.

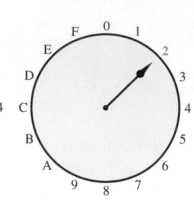

After passing 0, you finish at 2.

(b) $D_{16} + F_{16}$

Using the following figure, start at the D, count F (15) digits. Again, we pass the 0 as we are counting. The result is $D_{16} + F_{16} = 1C_{16}$.

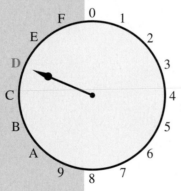

Start at D.

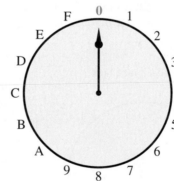

As you get back to 0, this is one trip around the clock.

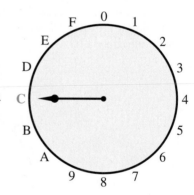

After passing 0, you finish at C.

Now that you can add single digits, the transition to multiple-digit addition requires only that you are prepared to carry.

3. Add the following pair of hexadecimal numbers.

$$47AA9_{16}$$
$$+ 583AE_{16}$$

EXAMPLE 3 Add the following pair of hexadecimal numbers.

$$23DE3_{16}$$
$$+ 38152_{16}$$

$$23DE3_{16}$$
$$+ 38152_{16}$$
$$\overline{5_{16}}$$

$3_{16} + 2_{16} = 5_{16}.$

Answers on page A-36

$$\overset{1}{2}3DE3_{16}$$
$$+\ 3815\fbox{2}_{16}$$
$$\underline{\fbox{35}_{16}}$$

      $E_{16} + 5_{16} = 13_{16}.$

$$23\overset{1}{D}E3_{16}$$
$$+\ 38\ 152_{16}$$
$$\underline{F35_{16}}$$

      $1_{16} + D_{16} + 1_{16} = F_{16}.$

$$\overset{1}{2}3DE3_{16}$$
$$+\ 38\ 152_{16}$$
$$\underline{5B\,F35_{16}}$$

      $3_{16} + 8_{16} = B_{16}$ and finally $2_{16} + 3_{16} = 5_{16}.$

Let's look at a couple of hexadecimal subtraction problems.

EXAMPLE 4   Subtract each pair of hexadecimal numbers.

(a) $3E5_{16}$ **From the right, we see that** $5_{16} - 4_{16} = 1_{16},$
     $\underline{-\ 1B4_{16}}$ $E_{16} - B_{16} = 3_{16},$ **and** $3_{16} - 1_{16} = 2_{16}.$
      231_{16}

(b) $56A2_{16}$ $2_{16}\quad 0_{16} = 2_{16}$
     $\underline{-\ 45E0_{16}}$
         2_{16}

      $\overset{5}{5}\overset{1}{6}A2_{16}$
     $\underline{-45E0_{16}}$
        $C2_{16}$

E_{16} is larger than A_{16}, so we borrow one group of 16 from the 6. The 6 becomes a 5 and the A becomes 1A. We can also use the base sixteen clock face for subtraction. If we start at A and count backward E places, we pass the 0 as we go in a counterclockwise direction, which indicates borrowing. Subtracting E from 1A can be rephrased as, "What do we add to E_{16} to get $1A_{16}$?" Counting forward, we find the answer is C_{16}.

      $\overset{5}{5}\overset{1}{6}A2_{16}$ $5_{16} - 5_{16} = 0_{16}$ and $5_{16} - 4_{16} = 1_{16}$
     $\underline{-\ 45E0_{16}}$
       $10C2_{16}$

When you first learned to multiply decimals, you memorized the following one-digit multiplication table.

4. Subtract each pair of hexadecimal numbers.

(a) $\begin{array}{r} B28_{16} \\ -\ 837_{16} \end{array}$ (b) $\begin{array}{r} 3A8B_{16} \\ -\ 1FF9_{16} \end{array}$

Answers on page A-36

Decimal Multiplication Table

×	0	1	2	3	4	5	6	7	8	9
0	0	0	0	0	0	0	0	0	0	0
1	0	1	2	3	4	5	6	7.	8	9
2	0	2	4	6	8	10	12	14	16	18
3	0	3	6	9	12	15	18	21	24	27
4	0	4	8	12	16	20	24	28	32	36
5	0	5	10	15	20	25	30	35	40	45
6	0	6	12	18	24	30	36	42	48	54
7	0	7	14	21	28	35	42	49	56	63
8	0	8	16	24	32	40	48	56	64	72
9	0	9	18	27	36	45	54	63	72	81

To easily multiply hexadecimal numbers, you should memorize the following one-digit multiplication table. This text will not assume that you have done so, but you will occasionally be reminded of this table.

Hexadecimal Multiplication Table

×	0	1	2	3	4	5	6	7	8	9	A	B	C	D	E	F
0	0	0	0	0	0	0	0	0	0	0	0	0	0	0	0	0
1	0	1	2	3	4	5	6	7	8	9	A	B	C	D	E	F
2	0	2	4	6	8	A	C	E	10	12	14	16	18	1A	1C	1E
3	0	3	6	9	C	F	12	15	18	1B	1E	21	24	27	2A	2D
4	0	4	8	C	10	14	18	1C	20	24	28	2C	30	34	38	3C
5	0	5	A	F	14	19	1E	23	28	2D	32	37	3C	41	46	4B
6	0	6	C	12	18	1E	24	2A	30	36	3C	42	48	4E	54	5A
7	0	7	E	15	1C	23	2A	31	38	3F	46	4D	54	5B	62	69
8	0	8	10	18	20	28	30	38	40	48	50	58	60	68	70	78
9	0	9	12	1B	24	2D	36	3F	48	51	5A	64	6C	75	7E	87
A	0	A	14	1E	28	32	3C	46	50	5A	64	6E	78	82	8C	96
B	0	B	16	21	2C	37	42	4D	58	64	6E	79	84	8F	9A	A5
C	0	C	18	24	30	3C	48	54	60	6C	78	84	90	9C	A8	B4
D	0	D	1A	27	34	41	4E	5B	68	75	82	8F	9C	A9	B6	C3
E	0	E	1C	2A	38	46	54	62	70	7E	8C	9A	A8	B6	C4	D2
F	0	F	1E	2D	3C	4B	5A	69	78	87	96	A5	B4	C3	D2	E1

5. Use the hexadecimal multiplication table to find the product $5_{16} \times D_{16}$.

EXAMPLE 5   Use the table above to find the product $A_{16} \times B_{16}$.

The shading indicates that the intersection of column A and row B gives the result 6E. We can say that

$$A_{16} \times B_{16} = 6E_{16}.$$

Multiplying hexadecimal numbers with more than one digit follows an algorithm that parallels that of multiplying decimal numbers with more than one digit.

Answer on page A-36

EXAMPLE 6 Find the product.

$$3A_{16} \times B_{16}$$

We will set up the problem in the vertical multiplication format.

$$\begin{array}{r} 3A_{16} \\ \times\, B_{16} \end{array}$$

From the table (and Example 5) we know that $A_{16} \times B_{16} = 6E_{16}$.

$$\begin{array}{r} 6 \\ 3A_{16} \\ \times\ \ B_{16} \\ \hline E \end{array}$$ ← We write the E in the 1s' column and put the 6 over the next (16s') column to the left.

Again, using the table, we find that $B_{16} \times 3_{16} = 21_{16}$.

We need to add the 6 that we carried. $21_{16} + 6_{16} = 27_{16}$.

$$\begin{array}{r} 3A_{16} \\ \times\ \ B_{16} \\ \hline 27E_{16} \end{array}$$

We see that
$$3A_{10} \times B_{16} = 27E_{16}$$

If we convert these numbers into decimal equivalents, we would have
$$58 \times 11 = 638$$

In our final example, we demonstrate the multiplication of hexadecimal numbers with several digits.

EXAMPLE 7 Find the product of the two hexadecimal numbers.

(a)
$$\begin{array}{r} 15_{16} \\ \times\ 13_{16} \end{array}$$

Using the multiplication table, we first multiply by the 3.

$$\begin{array}{r} 15_{16} \\ \times\ 13_{16} \\ \hline 3F \end{array}$$

As in decimal multiplication, place a 0 in the 1s' column before multiplying by the 1 in the 16s' column.

$$\begin{array}{r} 15_{16} \\ \times\ 13_{16} \\ \hline 3F \\ 0 \end{array}$$

Now, multiply by the 1.

$$\begin{array}{r} 15_{16} \\ \times\ 13_{16} \\ \hline 3F \\ 150 \end{array}$$

6. Find the product.
$$4C_{16} \times 9_{16}$$

7. Find the product of the two hexadecimal numbers.

(a)
$$\begin{array}{r} 1F_{16} \\ \times 21_{16} \end{array}$$

(b)
$$\begin{array}{r} 3BB7_{16} \\ \times\ \ \ \ \ 12_{16} \end{array}$$

Answers on page A 36

Add to get the result.

$$15_{16}$$
$$\underline{\times \, 13_{16}}$$
$$3F$$
$$\underline{150}$$
$$18F_{16}$$

$$15_{16} \times 13_{16} = 18F_{16}$$

(b)
$$2AD3_{16}$$
$$\underline{\times \quad \; 12_{16}}$$

First, multiply by the 2.

$$2AD3_{16}$$
$$\underline{\times \quad \; 12_{16}}$$
$$55A6$$

$$2AD3_{16}$$
$$\underline{\times \quad \; 12_{16}}$$
$$55A6$$
$$\underline{2AD30} \longleftarrow$$ Use a 0 as a placeholder under the 6, and then multiply by 1.

$$2AD3_{16}$$
$$\underline{\times \quad \; 12_{16}}$$
$$55A6$$
$$\underline{2AD30} \longleftarrow$$ Add the two results.
$$302D6_{16}$$

$$2AD3_{16} \times 12_{16} = 302D6_{16}$$

Using a calculator, confirm the result.

InterAct Math   Math Tutor Center   MathXL   MyMathLab

Use the hexadecimal clock shown at the right to add the following hexadecimal numbers.

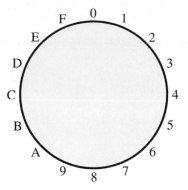

1. 4_{16}
     $+ 5_{16}$

2. 2_{16}
     $+ 9_{16}$

3. A_{16}
     $+ 7_{16}$

4. $B2_{16}$
     $+ 1F_{16}$

5. $E9_{16}$
     $+ 18_{16}$

6. $C4_{16}$
     $+ A4_{16}$

7. $9E2_{16}$
     $+ 3D0_{16}$

8. $17F_{16}$
     $+ C15_{16}$

9. $AD2_{16}$
     $| FCC_{16}$

10. 2435_{16}
      $+ 9E7B_{16}$

11. 2039_{16}
      $+ 8747_{16}$

12. $ABBA_{16}$
      $+ ACE_{16}$

Use the hexadecimal clock at the right to subtract the
following hexadecimal numbers.

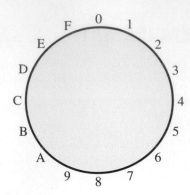

13. 9_{16}
$- 3_{16}$

14. A_{16}
$- 9_{16}$

15. 12_{16}
$- 7_{16}$

16. 23_{16}
$- 4_{16}$

17. $E1_{16}$
$- 1E_{16}$

18. $C4_{16}$
$- 7F_{16}$

19. 912_{16}
$- 3D0_{16}$

20. $FF0_{16}$
$- B14_{16}$

21. $62C_{16}$
$- 1DC_{16}$

22. $FACE_{16}$
$- EC2D_{16}$

23. 1601_{16}
$- 1342_{16}$

24. $420A_{16}$
$- 1FF3_{16}$

Use the following table to help you multiply the following hexadecimal numbers.

×	0	1	2	3	4	5	6	7	8	9	A	B	C	D	E	F
0	0	0	0	0	0	0	0	0	0	0	0	0	0	0	0	0
1	0	1	2	3	4	5	6	7	8	9	A	B	C	D	E	F
2	0	2	4	6	8	A	C	E	10	12	14	16	18	1A	1C	1E
3	0	3	6	9	C	F	12	15	18	1B	1E	21	24	27	2A	2D
4	0	4	8	C	10	14	18	1C	20	24	28	2C	30	34	38	3C
5	0	5	A	F	14	19	1E	23	28	2D	32	37	3C	41	46	4B
6	0	6	C	12	18	1E	24	2A	30	36	3C	42	48	4E	54	5A
7	0	7	E	15	1C	23	2A	31	38	3F	46	4D	54	5B	62	69
8	0	8	10	18	20	28	30	38	40	48	50	58	60	68	70	78
9	0	9	12	1B	24	2D	36	3F	48	51	5A	64	6C	75	7E	87
A	0	A	14	1E	28	32	3C	46	50	5A	64	6E	78	82	8C	96
B	0	B	16	21	2C	37	42	4D	58	64	6E	79	84	8F	9A	A5
C	0	C	18	24	30	3C	48	54	60	6C	78	84	90	9C	A8	B4
D	0	D	1A	27	34	41	4E	5B	68	75	82	8F	9C	A9	B6	C3
E	0	E	1C	2A	38	46	54	62	70	7E	8C	9A	A8	B6	C4	D2
F	0	F	1E	2D	3C	4B	5A	69	78	87	96	A5	B4	C3	D2	E1

25. 8_{16}
$\times\, 3_{16}$

26. A_{16}
$\times\, 4_{16}$

27. $5E_{16}$
$\times\;\; 2_{16}$

28. BED_{16}
$\times\;\; 12_{16}$

29. $59F_{16}$
$\times\;\; 13_{16}$

30. $D8C_{16}$
$\times\;\; 41_{16}$

Add the following octal numbers.

31. 4_8
$+\, 2_8$

32. 6_8
$+\, 3_8$

33. 12_8
$+\;\; 6_8$

34. 32_8
$+\, 17_8$

35. 50_8
$+\, 47_8$

36. 54_8
$+\, 36_8$

The ancient Maya of Central America used a number system partially based on twenty. A base twenty system is called a *vigesimal system* and requires twenty different symbols to represent numbers. The Maya often used elaborate symbols (many were human faces), but in modern notation the digits used are 0, 1, 2, 3, 4, 5, 6, 7, 8, 9, A, B, C, D, E, F, G, H, I, and J.

Find the decimal equivalent for each of the following vigesimal (base twenty) numbers.

37. 5_{20}

38. H_{20}

39. 10_{20}

40. 20_{20}

41. AI_{20}

42. $G0B_{20}$

Find the vigesimal (base twenty) equivalent for each of the following decimal numbers.

43. 17

44. 50

45. 192

46. 512

47. 971

48. 2004

Add the following vigesimal (base twenty) numbers.

49. $\begin{array}{r} 14_{20} \\ + \ 5_{20} \end{array}$

50. $\begin{array}{r} 21_{20} \\ + \ 9_{20} \end{array}$

51. $\begin{array}{r} GI_{20} \\ + \ E_{20} \end{array}$

52. $\begin{array}{r} 3J_{20} \\ + 4F_{20} \end{array}$

53. $\begin{array}{r} HE_{20} \\ + HA_{20} \end{array}$

54. $\begin{array}{r} J J_{20} \\ + H0_{20} \end{array}$

55. Why do you think the ancient Maya used a system based on twenty?

56. What other number bases make sense to you? Why?

11.4 ELEMENTS OF CODING

A computer stores all information using only 1s and 0s. This includes all of the words that are typed into a word processor. To make the storage of information as consistent as possible, the computer industry has agreed on several standard codes. One of the first such major codes was the **American Standard Code for Information Interchange**, abbreviated as **ASCII** (or, redundantly, the ASCII code).

ASCII assigns a unique integer between 0 and 127 (decimal) for each symbol that can be entered into the computer, including numbers, letters, keyboard symbols, punctuation, and some control characters. The following table shows which integer (and its hexadecimal equivalent) is assigned to which character.

DECIMAL RANGE	HEXADECIMAL RANGE	CHARACTERS
0–31	0_{16}–$1F_{16}$	control characters
32	20_{16}	SPACE
33–47	21_{16}–$2F_{16}$	nonnumeric symbols on the top row of the keyboard
48–57	30_{16}–39_{16}	0, 1, 2, ..., 9
58 63	$3A_{16}$–$3F_{16}$	:, ;, <, =, >, ?
64	40_{16}	@
65–90	41_{16}–$5A_{16}$	A, B, C, ..., Z
91–96	$5B_{16}$ 60_{16}	[, \,], ^, _, `
97–122	61_{16}–$7A_{16}$	a, b, c, ..., z
123–127	$7B_{16}$–$7F_{16}$	{, |, }, ~, DEL

There are many patterns that emerge from examining this table. Look at the hexadecimal and bit patterns for A and a.

CHARACTER	HEX	BIT PATTERN
A	41_{16}	$0100\ 0001_2$
a	61_{16}	$0110\ 0001_2$

Note: We often split ASCII bytes into nibbles for conversion purposes.

Can you see why these were chosen as the starting points for upper- and lowercase letters? You may see the justification more clearly when you are asked to find the bit pattern for a given letter!

EXAMPLE 1 Find the ASCII bit pattern associated with each of the following: T, E, s, t, 2.

"T" is the twentieth letter of the alphabet, so its decimal ASCII is $64 + 20 = 84$.

The ASCII bit pattern for "T" is $0101\ 0100_2$ (5 sixteens and 4 ones is 84).

"E" is the fifth letter, so the decimal ASCII is $64 + 5 = 69$.

Bits of History

A.D.1600–1700 Gottfried Leibniz was a man of extraordinary talents and diverse interests. He is often listed with Newton as the cofather of calculus, and much like his contemporary, Leibniz dabbled in other areas of science and mathematics. He was possibly the first person to publish a paper about binary numbers. Along with a skilled craftsman, he built a calculating device called the stepped reckoner, which was more sophisticated than the Pascaline. It is speculated that Leibniz had contemplated designing a binary calculator, but no such device has ever been found.

1. Find the ASCII bit pattern associated with each of the following:

   (a) S   (b) G   (c) b
   (d) g   (e) 5

Answers on page A-37

The ASCII bit pattern for "E" is $0100\ 0101_2$ (4 sixteens and 5 ones).

"s" is the nineteenth lowercase letter. Its decimal ASCII is $96 + 19 = 115$.

The ASCII bit pattern for "s" is $0111\ 0011_2$ (7 sixteens and 3 ones).

The ASCII bit pattern for "t" is right after the s, so it is $0111\ 0100_2$.

"2" is one more than 1 (which has decimal ASCII of 49), so its decimal ASCII is 50.

The ASCII bit pattern for "2" is $0011\ 0010_2$ (3 sixteens and 2 ones).

In the next example, you are asked to interpret a bit pattern.

2. What symbol is generated by each of the following bit patterns?

(a) $0110\ 1110_2$

(b) $0011\ 1001_2$

EXAMPLE 2 What symbol is generated by each of the following bit patterns?

(a) $0110\ 0011_2$ This is the third character after 96. It is the letter "c."

(b) $0011\ 0111_2$ This is the seventh character after 48. It is the character "7."

Two extremely important elements of coding are **error detection** (finding that there is an error in transmission) and **error correction** (finding and fixing the error). Because bytes are sent through electronic channels, it is common to have a bit accidentally turned on or turned off in the transmission process. The simplest method of error detection is the use of a **parity bit**. A parity bit (which we will assume to be the left-most bit) allows the computer that is receiving information to determine whether data was corrupted during transmission. There are many kinds of parity, but here we study two kinds, **even-parity** and **odd-parity**. The following example uses odd-parity.

3. Assuming odd-parity, determine whether each of the following bytes was most likely correctly transmitted.

(a) $1010\ 1001_2$

(b) $1111\ 0100_2$

(c) $0001\ 1010_2$

EXAMPLE 3 Assuming odd-parity, determine whether each of the following bytes was most likely correctly transmitted.

(a) $0111\ 1001_2$ Because there is an odd number of 1s (in this case, 5) this byte has odd-parity and was most likely correctly transmitted.

(b) $1101\ 0100_2$ This byte has an even number of 1s; it was not correctly transmitted.

(c) $0111\ 1111_2$ This byte has odd-parity and was most likely correctly transmitted.

We mentioned that parity allows the computer to determine whether a byte is reasonably correct, but not whether it is absolutely correct. The difficulty comes when an even number of errors occurs in the transmission. An example follows.

Assume that we want to send the ASCII character "c" to another computer. The ASCII bit pattern is

$\_110\ 0011_2$.

(The eighth bit is reserved as the **parity bit.**)

To encode our character using odd-parity, we set the parity bit to one and then transmit.

$1110\ 0011_2$.

Answers on page A-37

Now, assume that the second and third bits are altered in the transmission, so that what is received is

$$1110\ 0101_2.$$

The computer receiving the message checks the parity and okays the byte because there is an odd number of 1s. The computer then translates the byte as the character "e." Is this reasonably correct? According to the parity, yes. We know there was a mistake only because we knew which character we were transmitting.

EXAMPLE 4   Assuming odd-parity, translate each of the following bytes.

(a) $1101\ 0101_2$

Because there is an odd number of 1s (in this case, 5) this byte has odd-parity. Eliminating the parity bit, we find the ASCII for the character "U."

(b) $1011\ 0100_2$

This byte has an even number of 1s; it was not correctly transmitted.

(c) $0011\ 0111_2$

This byte has odd-parity. It represents the character "7."

Although ASCII is still the most commonly used code, its limitations have encouraged the development and implementation of more extensive codes. What are the limitations of ASCII? Obviously, its 7-bit restriction (with the eighth bit acting as a parity bit) means that only 128 different characters can be represented. By freeing up the eighth bit, an additional 128 characters were added. Many of these characters appear in Latin-based alphabets and include "ñ" (Spanish), "ç" (French), and "ö" (German). This modified ASCII is commonly known as **Extended ASCII**, which consists of 256 different characters.

Given the increased input (including Cyrillic, Arabic, and Chinese characters) used on computers, still more flexibility is needed.

A code currently in use in many environments is Unicode. Unicode uses a 16-bit representation, so it can recognize up to 65,536 different characters. It also incorporates ASCII and Extended ASCII by setting the last 8 bits to 0 and keeping the original code. Here are the bit patterns for the letter "S" in all three codes.

ASCII	EXTENDED ASCII	UNICODE
01010011	01010011	00000000 01010011

A code being developed by ISO has 32-bit representation. This code will be large enough to encode languages that are no longer spoken, such as ancient Egyptian. By encoding the hieroglyphs into a modern script, Egyptologists will be able to communicate more efficiently and produce documents much more easily. How many different characters can this 32-bit code recognize?

4. Assuming odd-parity, translate each of the following bytes.

   (a) $1101\ 1001_2$

   (b) $1011\ 1001_2$

   (c) $1011\ 0010_2$

Answers on page A 37

Find the decimal ASCII code for each of the following characters.

1. X

2. F

3. G

4. q

5. 9

6. ?

Find the ASCII bit pattern associated with each character.

7. Y

8. 5

9. B

10. b

11. 0

12. z

Find the hexadecimal ASCII code for each of the following characters.

13. O

14. t

15. K

16. 7

17. q

18. R

Translate the following ASCII bit patterns into names of science fiction characters.

19. 01010010_2 00110010_2 01000100_2 00110010_2

20. 01010011_2 01100101_2 01110110_2 01100101_2 01101110_2

21. 01001110_2 01100101_2 01101111_2

22. 01011001_2 01101111_2 01100100_2 01100001_2

23. 01010011_2 01110000_2 01101111_2 01100011_2 01101011_2

24. 01010001_2 01110101_2 01101001_2 01100111_2 01101111_2 01101110_2

25. How many different characters could be encoded in a 12-bit code?

26. How many different characters could be encoded in a 24-bit code?

Determine whether each of the following bit patterns has an error (assuming odd-parity).

27. 01110010_2 **28.** 11001101_2 **29.** 01111010_2

30. 10010100_2 **31.** 00100101_2 **32.** 11101110_2

33. Assuming even-parity, translate the following ASCII bytes.

(a) 1100 0101   **(b)** 0111 0001   **(c)** 0111 1010

34. Does a parity bit allow you to find an error if you know that the error has been encoded? Explain your answer.

35. The following block is coded in even-parity. The shaded bits in each column and row are the parity bits. Assuming the parity bits are correct and only one error is detected, circle the bit that most likely causes the error. Justify your answer.

	A	B	C	PARITY
1	1	1	1	1
2	1	0	1	0
3	0	1	1	1
PARITY	0	1	1	0

36. The following ASCII block is coded in even-parity. The shaded eighth bit is the parity bit, and the bottom row is the even block parity byte. Decode the message.

0	1	0	1	0	1	0	1
1	0	1	1	0	0	1	0
1	0	1	0	0	0	0	0
1	1	0	1	0	0	1	0
1	1	0	0	1	1	1	1
1	1	0	0	0	0	1	1
0	1	0	0	1	0	1	1
0	1	0	1	0	0	1	1
1	0	0	0	0	0	0	1

37. Assume an error-detecting code repeats every bit sent three times. For example, if 101 is the original message, then 111 000 111 should be sent. How would you correct an errant message? How certain would you be about your correction?

11 Summary and Review

The review that follows is meant to prepare you for a chapter exam. It consists of two parts. The first part is a checklist of the Study Tips referred to so far in this text. The second part is the Review Exercises. These provide practice exercises for the exam, together with references to section objectives so you can go back and review. Before beginning, stop and look back over the skills you have obtained. What skills in mathematics do you have now that you did not have before studying this chapter?

STUDY TIPS CHECKLIST

The foundation of all your study skills is TIME!		Have you started your own glossary of terms in your notebook?
	☐	Are you spreading your study time over several days rather than cramming it all into one day?
	☐	Are you inspecting papers that your instructor returns so that you can learn from your mistakes?
	☐	Are you writing helpful notes to yourself in your text?
	☐	Have you tried using a second book as a reference text?
	☐	Have you located a suitable study partner?
	☐	Have you identified those exercises that gave you difficulty and are worth revisiting?

REVIEW EXERCISES

Find the decimal equivalent for each of the following octal numbers.   [11.1]

1. 6_8

2. 17_8

3. 65_8

4. 130_8

5. 241_8

6. 1503_8

Find the octal equivalent for each of the following decimal numbers.   [11.1]

7. 3

8. 16

9. 49

10. 102

11. 357

12. 1492

Find the octal equivalent for each of the following binary numbers.   [11.1]

13. 00001110_2

14. 00111101_2

15. 11000100_2

16. 110010011111_2

Find the binary equivalent for each of the following octal numbers.   [11.1]

17. 15_8

18. 74_8

19. 236_8

20. 1043_8

Find the decimal equivalent for each of the following hexadecimal numbers.   [11.1]

21. 6_{16} **22.** C_{16} **23.** $B2_{16}$

24. ADD_{16} **25.** BEE_{16} **26.** $F179_{16}$

Find the hexadecimal equivalent for each of the following decimal numbers.   [11.2]

27. 3   **28.** 15   **29.** 43

30. 97   **31.** 608   **32.** 1812

Find the hexadecimal equivalent for each of the following binary numbers.   [11.2]

33. 00001001_2 **34.** 00110011_2 **35.** 10011001_2

36. 10000001_2 **37.** 01011111011_2 **38.** 1010011010111_2

Find the binary equivalent for each of the following hexadecimal numbers.   [11.2]

39. 41_{16} **40.** $F8_{16}$ **41.** $23E_{16}$

42. CAB_{16} **43.** $52B9_{16}$ **44.** $F07D_{16}$

Convert each binary fraction into both its octal and hexadecimal equivalent by grouping into tribbles and nibbles working away from the binary point.   [11.2]

45. 0.1100_2 **46.** 0.0110_2 **47.** 0.10100011_2

Add the following hexadecimal numbers.   [11.3]

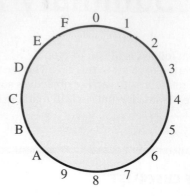

48. 3_{16}
     $+ 5_{16}$

49. 15_{16}
     $+\ \ 9_{16}$

50. $F7_{16}$
     $+ 2A_{16}$

51. $4C9_{16}$
     $+ 2B6_{16}$

52. $BEDE_{16}$
     $+ D1B2_{16}$

53. $DEC0_{16}$
     $+\ \ FAC_{16}$

Subtract the following hexadecimal numbers.   [11.3]

54. 7_{16}
     $- 2_{16}$

55. $7B_{16}$
     $- 44_{16}$

56. $F92_{16}$
     $- CC_{16}$

57. $E0B_{16}$
     $- 34D_{16}$

58. $D81E_{16}$
     $-\ \ E7F_{16}$

Use the table on page 762 to help you multiply the following hexadecimal numbers.   [11.3]

59. D_{16}
     $\times 5_{16}$

60. 18_{16}
     $\times C2_{16}$

61. ACE_{16}
     $\times\ \ 12_{16}$

Find the decimal ASCII code for each of the following characters.   [11.4]

62. 6   **63.** i   **64.** P

Find the ASCII bit pattern associated with each character. [11.4]

65. e   **66.** 7   **67.** Q

Find the character associated with each ASCII bit pattern. [11.4]

68. 01011001_2 **69.** 00110100_2 **70.** 01101101_2

Find the hexadecimal ASCII code for each of the following characters.   [11.4]

71. I   **72.** 9   **73.** r

Translate the following ASCII bit patterns into the names of musical artists or groups.   [11.4]

74. 01010011_2 01110100_2 01101001_2 01101110_2
   01100111_2

75. 01000010_2 01101100_2 01101001_2 01101110_2
   01101011_2 00110001_2 00111000_2 00110010_2

76. 01000101_2 01101110_2 01101001_2 01100111_2
   01101101_2 01100001_2

77. 01010000_2 00101110_2 01000100_2 01101001_2
   01100100_2 01100100_2 01111001_2

Assuming even-parity, determine whether each of the following bit patterns has an error.   [11.4]

78. 00010011_2 **79.** 10100101_2 **80.** 10111111_2

1. Find the decimal equivalent for each of the following octal numbers.

    (a) 13_8 **(b)** 46_8 **(c)** 257_8

2. Find the octal equivalent for each of the following decimal numbers.

    (a) 29   **(b)** 78   **(c)** 165

3. Find the octal equivalent for each of the following binary numbers.

    (a) 00001011_2 **(b)** 00011101_2 **(c)** 10111110_2

4. Find the decimal equivalent for each of the following hexadecimal numbers.

    (a) $3D_{16}$ **(b)** $B4_{16}$ **(c)** $A1A_{16}$

5. Assuming even-parity, determine whether each of the following bit patterns contains an error.

    (a) 10000000_2 **(b)** 01001001_2 **(c)** 11111111_2

6. Find the hexadecimal equivalent for each of the following decimal numbers.

    (a) 62   **(b)** 105   **(c)** 237

7. Find the hexadecimal equivalent for each of the following binary numbers.

   (a) 10110011_2 **(b)** 00101000_2

   (c) 0.1100_2 **(d)** 10000011.0011_2

8. Find the binary equivalent for each of the following hexadecimal numbers.

   (a) $A4_{16}$ **(b)** $B0E_{16}$ **(c)** $FC2_{16}$

9. Find the decimal ASCII code for each of the following characters.

   (a) T   **(b)** 4

10. Perform the operations on the following hexadecimal numbers.

   (a) $\quad 42_{16}$ **(b)** $\quad 6E_{16}$
          $+\,53_{16}$ $+\,9D_{16}$

   (c) $\quad 1C_{16}$ **(d)** $\quad A3_{16}$
          $-\ \ 7_{16}$ $-\,5F_{16}$

   (e) $\quad A2_{16}$ **(f)** $\quad D0_{16}$
          $\times\ \ 5_{16}$ $\times\,76_{16}$

11. Find the ASCII bit pattern associated with each character.

    (a) 8   **(b)** d

12. Translate the following ASCII bit patterns into the names of U.S. cities.

    (a) 01010000_2 01101000_2 01101111_2 01100101_2 01101110_2 01101001_2 01111000_2

    (b) 01010011_2 01100101_2 01100001_2 01110100_2 01110100_2 01101100_2 01100101_2

    (c) 01000100_2 01100101_2 01110100_2 01110010_2 01101111_2 01101001_2 01110100_2

1. 32946
   298
   +6118

2. Solve the equation $2x - 1 = 9$.

3. $(6x^3 - 9x^2 + 3x) + (x^3 + x^2 + 12) =$

4. $\dfrac{\dfrac{1}{5}}{\dfrac{2}{7}} =$

5. $6\dfrac{1}{8} + 3.25 =$
   (Express your answer as both a decimal and a mixed number.)

6. Find the median for the given list of numbers:
   2.63, 1.98, -4.27, 5.13, 0.24

7. What is 0.5% of 0.002?

8. Find a negation of the statement "2 is less than 9."

9. Multiply:
   1101
   ×0111

10. Express the decimal number 43 as a hexadecimal number.

Geometry and Measurement

Gateway to Chapter 12

This chapter examines the American and metric systems used to measure length, area, volume, weight, mass, and temperature. We will also study parallelograms, trapezoids, circles, spheres, cylinders, and rectangular solids, as well as properties of angles and triangles, and the Pythagorean theorem.

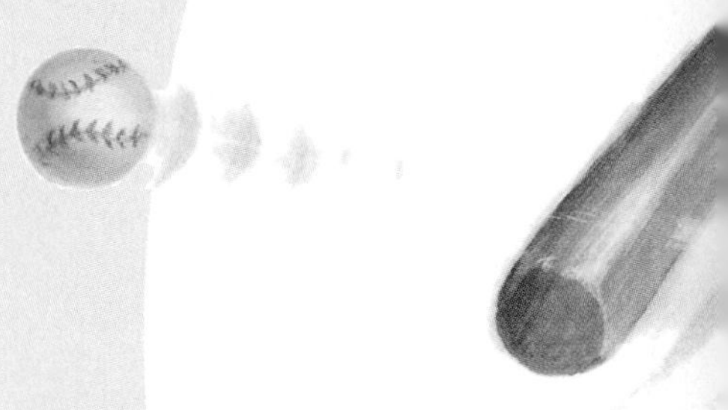

Real-World Application

Between the 2000 and 2001 seasons, Major League Baseball redefined the shape of the strike zone. Over the years before 2001, the strike zone evolved to something resembling the region *AQRST* in the diagram. In 2001, the strike zone was changed to rectangle *ABCD* in the illustration. By what percent has the area of the strike zone been increased by the change?

Sources: The Cincinnati Enquirer; Major League Baseball; Gannett News Service; The Sporting News Official Baseball Rules Book

This problem appears as Exercise 86 in Section 12.3.

C H A P T E R

12

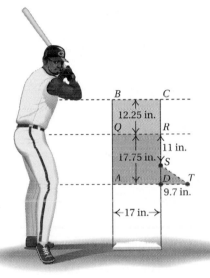

Complete.

1. 8 ft = _____ in.   [12.1a]

2. 9 in. = _____ ft   [12.1a]

3. 7.32 km = _____ m   [12.1b]

4. 7.5 mm = _____ cm   [12.1b]

5. 3 ft² = _____ in²   [12.2a]

6. 108 ft² = _____ yd²   [12.2a]

7. 4.2 cm² = _____ mm²   [12.2b]

8. 7 gal = _____ oz   [12.4b]

9. 5 T = _____ lb   [12.7a]

10. 48 oz = _____ lb   [12.7a]

11. 913 g = _____ kg   [12.7b]

12. 0.4 kg = _____ mg   [12.7b]

Find each area. Use 3.14 for π.

13.   [12.3a]

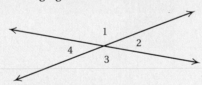

14.

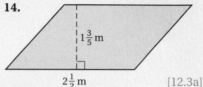

[12.3a]

15.   [12.3b]

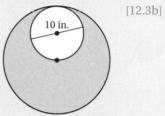

16. Find the length of a diameter of a circle with a radius of 9.4 m.   [12.3b]

17. Find the circumference of a 70-cm–diameter bicycle wheel. Use $\frac{22}{7}$ for π.   [12.3b]

18. Find the area of a 20-cm–wide circular mat. Use 3.14 for π.   [12.3b]

19. A nurse administers a 35-mL allergy shot. How many liters are injected?   [12.4b]

Use the following figure for Problems 20–22.   [12.5c]

20. List two pairs of vertical angles.

21. List two pairs of supplementary angles.

22. Complete: $m\angle 1 =$ _____.

23. Find the measure of the complement of a 37° angle.   [12.5c]

In a right triangle, find the length of the side not given. Assume that c represents the length of the hypotenuse and a and b are the lengths of the legs. Find an exact answer and an approximation to three decimal places.   [12.6c]

24. $a = 12, b = 16$

25. $a = 2, c = 7$

Find each volume. Use $\frac{22}{7}$ for π.   [12.4a]

26.

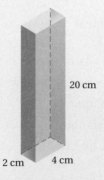

27.

28.

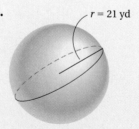

29. A medic orders 1800 mL of 0.5% saline solution to be administered intravenously over a 24-hr period. How many liters were ordered?   [12.8a]

12.1

SYSTEMS OF LINEAR MEASUREMENT

Objectives

a Convert from one American unit of length to another.

b Convert from one metric unit of length to another.

c Convert between American and metric units of length.

Length, or distance, is one kind of measure. To find lengths, we start with some **unit segment** and assign to it a measure of 1. Suppose $\overline{AB}$ below is a unit segment.

Let's measure segment $\overline{CD}$ below, using $\overline{AB}$ as our unit segment.

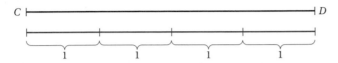

Since 4 unit segments fit end to end along $\overline{CD}$, the measure of $\overline{CD}$ is 4 units.

Sometimes we have to use parts of units. For example, the measure of the segment $\overline{MN}$ below is $1\frac{1}{2}$.

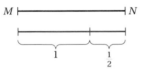

Do Exercises 1–4.

a   American Measures

American units of length are related as follows.

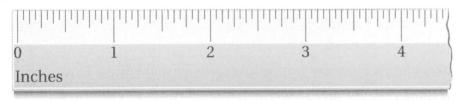

(Actual size, in inches)

AMERICAN UNITS OF LENGTH

12 inches (in.) = 1 foot (ft)	3 feet = 1 yard (yd)
36 inches = 1 yard	5280 feet = 1 mile (mi)

The symbolism 13 in. = 13″ and 27 ft = 27′ is also used for inches and feet. American units have also been called "English," or "British–American," because at one time they were used in both North America and Britain. Today, both Canada and England have officially converted to the metric system. However, if you travel in England, you will still see units such as "miles" on road signs.

Use the unit below to measure the length of each segment or object.

1. ├──────────────────────┤

2.
├────────────────────────────────┤

3.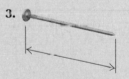

4.

Answers on page A-38

Complete.

5. 8 yd = _____ in.

6. 14.5 yd = _____ ft

7. 3.8 mi = _____ in.

Complete.

8. 72 in. = _____ ft

9. 24 ft = _____ yd

Complete.

10. 18 yd = _____ ft

11. 35 ft = _____ yd

Answers on page A-38

■ **EXAMPLE 1**   Complete: 5 yd = _____ in.

$$5 \text{ yd} = 5 \cdot 1 \text{ yd}$$
$$= 5 \cdot 36 \text{ in.} \qquad \text{Substituting 36 in. for 1 yd}$$
$$= 180 \text{ in.} \qquad \text{Multiplying}$$

■ **EXAMPLE 2**   Complete: 2 mi = _____ in.

$$2 \text{ mi} = 2 \cdot 1 \text{ mi}$$
$$= 2 \cdot 5280 \text{ ft} \qquad \text{Substituting 5280 ft for 1 mi}$$
$$= 10{,}560 \cdot 1 \text{ ft} \qquad \text{Multiplying}$$
$$= 10{,}560 \cdot 12 \text{ in.} \qquad \text{Substituting 12 in. for 1 ft}$$
$$= 126{,}720 \text{ in.} \qquad \text{The student should check the multiplication.}$$

Do Exercises 5–7.

In Examples 1 and 2, we converted from larger units to smaller ones and used substitution. Sometimes—especially when converting from smaller to larger units—it helps to multiply by 1. For example, 12 in. = 1 ft, so we might choose to write 1 as

$$\frac{12 \text{ in.}}{1 \text{ ft}} \quad \text{or} \quad \frac{1 \text{ ft}}{12 \text{ in.}}.$$

■ **EXAMPLE 3**   Complete: 48 in. = _____ ft.

To convert from "in." to "ft," we multiply by 1 using a symbol for 1 with "in." on the bottom and "ft" on the top. This process introduces feet and at the same time eliminates inches.

$$48 \text{ in.} = \frac{48 \text{ in.}}{1} \cdot \frac{1 \text{ ft}}{12 \text{ in.}} \qquad \text{Multiplying by 1 using } \frac{1 \text{ ft}}{12 \text{ in.}} \text{ to eliminate in.}$$
$$= \frac{48 \text{ in.}}{12 \text{ in.}} \cdot 1 \text{ ft} \qquad \text{Pay careful attention to the units.}$$
$$= \frac{48}{12} \cdot \frac{\text{in.}}{\text{in.}} \cdot 1 \text{ ft} \qquad \text{The } \frac{\text{in.}}{\text{in.}} \text{ acts like 1, so we can omit it.}$$
$$= 4 \cdot 1 \text{ ft} = 4 \text{ ft.} \qquad \text{Dividing}$$

The conversion can also be regarded as "canceling" units:

$$48 \text{ in.} = \frac{48 \text{ i\!n.}}{1} \cdot \frac{1 \text{ ft}}{12 \text{ i\!n.}} = \frac{48}{12} \cdot 1 \text{ ft} = 4 \text{ ft.}$$

Do Exercises 8 and 9.

In Examples 4 and 5, we will use only the "canceling" method.

■ **EXAMPLE 4**   Complete: 75 yd = _____ ft.

Since we are converting from "yd" to "ft," we choose a symbol for 1 with "ft" on the top and "yd" on the bottom:

$$75 \text{ yd} = 75 \text{ y\!d} \cdot \frac{3 \text{ ft}}{1 \text{ y\!d}} \qquad \text{If it helps, write 75 yd as } \frac{75 \text{ yd}}{1}.$$
$$= 75 \cdot 3 \text{ ft} = 225 \text{ ft.} \qquad \text{Multiplying}$$

Do Exercises 10 and 11.

EXAMPLE 5 Complete: 23,760 ft = _____ mi.

We choose a symbol for 1 with "mi" on the top and "ft" on the bottom:

$$23{,}760 \text{ ft} = 23{,}760 \text{ ft} \cdot \frac{1 \text{ mi}}{5280 \text{ ft}} \qquad 5280 \text{ ft} = 1 \text{ mi, so } \frac{1 \text{ mi}}{5280 \text{ ft}} = 1.$$

$$= \frac{23{,}760}{5280} \cdot 1 \text{ mi}$$

$$= 4.5 \cdot 1 \text{ mi} \qquad \text{Dividing by 5280}$$

$$= 4.5 \text{ mi.}$$

Note that when we convert from smaller units to larger units, we divide. When converting from larger units to smaller units, we multiply.

Do Exercises 12 and 13.

b   The Metric System

The **metric system** is used by most of the world, and the United States is now making greater use of it as well. Because it is based on powers of 10, the metric system allows for easy conversion between smaller and larger units. The metric system does not use inches, feet, pounds, and so on, but the units for time and electricity are the same as those you use now.

The basic unit of length is the **meter.** It is just over a yard. In fact, 1 meter ≈ 1.1 yd.

(Comparative sizes are shown.)

1 Meter

1 Yard

The other units of length are multiples of the length of a meter:

10 times a meter, 100 times a meter, 1000 times a meter,

or fractions of a meter:

$\frac{1}{10}$ of a meter, $\frac{1}{100}$ of a meter, $\frac{1}{1000}$ of a meter.

METRIC UNITS OF LENGTH

1 *kilo*meter (km) = 1000 meters (m)
1 *hecto*meter (hm) = 100 meters (m)
1 *deka*meter (dam) = 10 meters (m)
1 meter (m)
1 *deci*meter (dm) = $\frac{1}{10}$ meter (m)

1 *centi*meter (cm) = $\frac{1}{100}$ meter (m)

1 *milli*meter (mm) = $\frac{1}{1000}$ meter (m)

The units hm, dam, and dm are not used often.

Small

1 mm = 0.001 m   1 cm = 0.01 m   1 dm = 0.1 m   1 m

Large

1 dam = 10 m   1 hm = 100 m   1 km = 1000 m

Complete.

12. 26,400 ft = _____ mi

13. 6 mi = _____ ft

Answers on page A-38

Study Tips

Use the centimeter ruler provided to measure each object.

14.

15.

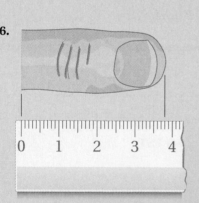

16.

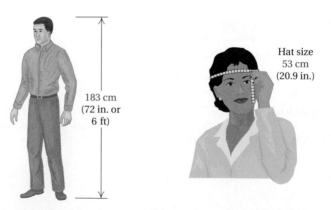

It is important to remember these names and abbreviations—especially *kilo-* for 1000, *deci-* for $\frac{1}{10}$, *centi-* for $\frac{1}{100}$, and *milli-* for $\frac{1}{1000}$. These prefixes are also used when measuring volume and mass (weight).

To familiarize yourself with metric units, consider the following.

1 kilometer (1000 meters)	is a bit more than $\frac{1}{2}$ mile ($\approx$0.6 mi).
1 meter	is just over a yard ($\approx$1.1 yd).
1 centimeter (0.01 meter)	is a little more than the width of a jumbo paperclip ($\approx$0.4 inch).
1 millimeter	is about the diameter of a paperclip wire.

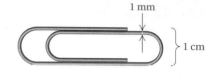

1 inch is about 2.54 centimeters.

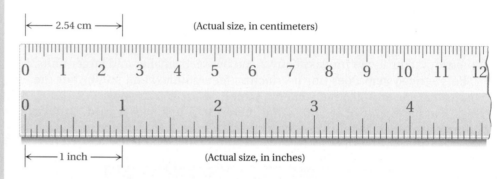

Millimeters (mm) are used for small distances, especially in industry.

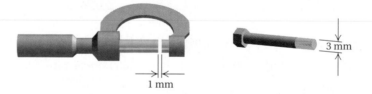

Centimeters (cm) are used for body dimensions, clothing sizes, and household measurements.

Do Exercises 14–16.

Answers on page A-38

Meters (m) are used for expressing dimensions of larger objects—say, the length of a building—and for shorter distances, such as the length of a rug.

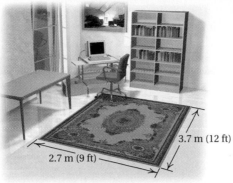

25 m (82 ft)

3.7 m (12 ft)

2.7 m (9 ft)

Kilometers (km) are used for longer distances, mostly in cases where miles are now being used.

1 mile is about 1.6 km.

1 km

1 mi

ALBUQUERQUE
80 mi

ALBUQUERQUE
128 km

Do Exercises 17–22.

Metric conversions from larger units to smaller ones are often most easily made using substitution, much as we did in Examples 1 and 2.

EXAMPLE 6 Complete: 4 km = _____ m.

$$4 \text{ km} = 4 \cdot 1 \text{ km}$$
$$= 4 \cdot 1000 \text{ m} \quad \text{Substituting 1000 m for 1 km}$$
$$= 4000 \text{ m} \quad \text{Multiplying by 1000}$$

Do Exercises 23 and 24.

Complete with mm, cm, m, or km.

17. A stick of gum is 7 _____ long and 2 _____ thick.

18. Minneapolis is 3213 _____ from San Francisco.

19. A dime is 1 _____ thick.

20. The record for running the 100 _____ dash is 9.78 sec.
Source: www.recordholders.org

21. The book is 3 _____ thick.

22. The desk is 2 _____ long.

Complete.

23. 37 km = _____ m

24. 5 hm = _____ m

Answers on page A-38

Complete.

25. 1.78 m = _____ cm

26. 9.04 m = _____ mm

Complete.

27. 7814 m = _____ km

28. 7814 m = _____ dam

Complete.

29. 87.2 mm = _____ cm

30. 89 km = _____ cm

Answers on page A-38

Since

$$\frac{1}{10} \text{ m} = 1 \text{ dm}, \qquad \frac{1}{100} \text{ m} = 1 \text{ cm}, \quad \text{and} \quad \frac{1}{1000} \text{ m} = 1 \text{ mm},$$

it follows that

METRIC CONVERSIONS

$$1 \text{ m} = 10 \text{ dm}, \qquad 1 \text{ m} = 100 \text{ cm}, \quad \text{and} \quad 1 \text{ m} = 1000 \text{ mm}.$$

Remembering these equations will help you to write forms of 1 when canceling to make conversions. The procedure is the same as that used in Examples 4 and 5.

EXAMPLE 7 Complete: 93.4 m = _____ cm.

To convert from "m" to "cm," we multiply by 1 using a symbol for 1 with "m" on the bottom and "cm" on the top. This process introduces centimeters and at the same time eliminates meters.

$$93.4 \text{ m} = 93.4 \text{ m} \cdot \frac{100 \text{ cm}}{1 \text{ m}} \qquad \text{Multiplying by 1 using } \frac{100 \text{ cm}}{1 \text{ m}}$$

$$= 93.4 \text{ m} \cdot \frac{100 \text{ cm}}{1 \text{ m}} = 93.4 \cdot 100 \text{ cm} = 9340 \text{ cm}$$

EXAMPLE 8 Complete: 0.248 m = _____ mm.

We are converting from "m" to "mm," so we choose a symbol for 1 with "mm" on the top and "m" on the bottom:

$$0.248 \text{ m} = 0.248 \text{ m} \cdot \frac{1000 \text{ mm}}{1 \text{ m}} = 0.248 \cdot 1000 \text{ mm} = 248 \text{ mm}.$$

Do Exercises 25 and 26.

EXAMPLE 9 Complete: 2347 m = _____ km.

We multiply by 1 using $\frac{1 \text{ km}}{1000 \text{ m}}$:

$$2347 \text{ m} = 2347 \text{ m} \cdot \frac{1 \text{ km}}{1000 \text{ m}} = \frac{2347}{1000} \cdot 1 \text{ km} = 2.347 \text{ km}.$$

Do Exercises 27 and 28.

It is helpful to remember that 1000 mm = 100 cm and, more simply, 10 mm = 1 cm.

EXAMPLE 10 Complete: 8.42 mm = _____ cm.

We can multiply by 1 using either $\frac{1 \text{ cm}}{10 \text{ mm}}$ or $\frac{100 \text{ cm}}{1000 \text{ mm}}$. Both expressions for 1 will eliminate mm and leave cm:

$$8.42 \text{ mm} = 8.42 \text{ mm} \cdot \frac{1 \text{ cm}}{10 \text{ mm}} = \frac{8.42}{10} \cdot 1 \text{ cm} = 0.842 \text{ cm}.$$

Do Exercises 29 and 30.

MENTAL CONVERSION

Note in Examples 6–10 that changing from one unit to another in the metric system involves moving a decimal point. This occurs because the metric system is based on 10. To find a faster way to convert, consider these equivalent ways of expressing the width of a standard sheet of paper.

> ### EQUIVALENT WAYS OF EXPRESSING DIMENSIONS
>
> Width of a standard sheet of paper = 216 mm = 21.6 cm = 2.16 dm = 0.216 m = 0.0216 dam = 0.00216 hm = 0.000216 km

Each unit in the box above is ten times as large as the next smaller unit. Thus, converting to the next larger unit means moving the decimal point one place to the left.

EXAMPLE 11   Complete: 35.7 mm = _____ cm.

Think: Centimeters is the next larger unit after millimeters. Thus, we move the decimal point one place to the left.

35.7   3.5.7   35.7 mm = 3.57 cm   Converting to a larger unit shifts the decimal point to the left.

Converting to the next *smaller* unit means moving the decimal point one place to the right.

EXAMPLE 12   Complete: 3 m = _____ cm.

Think: A centimeter is two units smaller than a meter (cm, dm, m), so we move the decimal point two places to the right. To do so, we write two additional zeros.

3   3.00.   3 m = 300 cm   Converting to a smaller unit shifts the decimal point to the right.

EXAMPLE 13   Complete: 4.37 km = _____ cm.

Think: A kilometer is 1000 times as large as a meter and a meter is 100 times as large as a centimeter. Thus, we move the decimal point 3 + 2, or 5, places to the right. This requires writing three additional zeros.

4.37   4.37000.   4.37 km = 437,000 cm

> The most commonly used metric units of length are km, m, cm, and mm. We have purposely used these more often than the others in the exercises and examples.

Do Exercises 31–34.

Complete. Try to do this mentally using the table on page 605.

31. 6780 m = _____ km

32. 9.74 cm = _____ mm

33. 1 mm = _____ cm

34. 845.1 mm = _____ dm

Answers on page A-38

Complete. Answers may vary
slightly, depending on the
conversion used.

35. 100 yd = _____ m
   (The length of a football field)

36. 500 mi = _____ km
   (The Indianapolis 500-mile
   race)

37. 2383 km = _____ mi
   (The distance from St. Louis to
   Phoenix)

C Converting Between American and Metric Units

We can make conversions between American and metric units by using
the following table. Again, we either make a substitution or multiply by 1
appropriately.

METRIC	AMERICAN
1 m	39.37 in.
1 m	3.3 ft
0.303 m	1 ft
2.54 cm	1 in.
1 km	0.621 mi
1.609 km	1 mi

EXAMPLE 14 Complete: 26.2 mi = _____ km (the length of the Olympic
marathon).

$$26.2 \text{ mi} = 26.2 \cdot 1 \text{ mi}$$
$$\approx 26.2 \cdot 1.609 \text{ km} \qquad \text{Converting from mi to km}$$
$$\approx 42.1558 \text{ km}$$

EXAMPLE 15 Complete: 100 m = _____ yd (the length of a dash in track).

$$100 \text{ m} = 100 \cdot 1 \text{ m} \approx 100 \cdot 3.3 \text{ ft} \approx 330 \text{ ft} \qquad \text{Converting to feet}$$
$$\approx 330 \text{ ft} \cdot \frac{1 \text{ yd}}{3 \text{ ft}} \approx \frac{330}{3} \text{ yd} \approx 110 \text{ yd} \qquad \text{Converting feet to yards}$$

EXAMPLE 16 Complete: 170 cm = _____ in. (a common ski length).

$$170 \text{ cm} = 170 \text{ cm} \cdot \frac{1 \text{ in.}}{2.54 \text{ cm}} \qquad \text{Converting to inches from cm}$$
$$\approx 66.93 \text{ in.}$$

Do Exercises 35–37.

a Complete.

1. 1 yd = _____ ft

2. 1 ft = _____ in.

3. 1 in. = _____ ft

4. 1 mi = _____ ft

5. 1 mi = _____ yd

6. 1 ft = _____ yd

7. 3 yd = _____ ft

8. 4 yd = _____ in.

9. 84 in. = _____ ft

10. 18 in. = _____ ft

11. 48 ft = _____ yd

12. 29 ft = _____ yd

13. 5 mi = _____ yd

14. 5 mi = _____ ft

15. 48 in. = _____ ft

16. 19 ft = _____ yd

17. 11,616 ft = _____ mi

18. 5.2 yd = _____ ft

19. 15,840 ft = _____ mi

20. 10 mi = _____ ft

21. $7\frac{1}{2}$ ft = _____ yd

22. 360 in. = _____ yd

23. 36 in. = _____ ft

24. 7.2 ft = _____ in.

25. 1760 yd = _____ mi

26. 330 ft = _____ yd

27. 3520 yd = _____ mi

28. 100 yd = _____ ft

29. 25 mi = _____ ft

30. 240 in. = _____ ft

31. 2 mi = _____ in.

32. 63,360 in. = _____ mi

Complete. Do as much as possible mentally.

33. a) 1 km = _____ m

b) 1 m = _____ km

34. a) 1 hm = _____ m

b) 1 m = _____ hm

35. a) 1 dam = _____ m

b) 1 m = _____ dam

36. a) 1 dm = _____ m

b) 1 m = _____ dm

37. a) 1 cm = _____ m

b) 1 m = _____ cm

38. a) 1 mm = _____ m

b) 1 m = _____ mm

39. 8.3 km = _____ m

40. 27 km = _____ m

41. 98 cm = _____ m

42. 53 cm = _____ m

43. 8921 m = _____ km

44. 8664 m = _____ km

45. 32.17 m = _____ km

46. 4.733 m = _____ km

47. 289 m = _____ cm

48. 869 m = _____ cm

49. 477 cm = _____ m

50. 6.27 mm = _____ m

51. 6.88 m = _____ cm

52. 6.88 m = _____ dm

53. 1 mm = _____ cm

54. 1 cm = _____ km

55. 1 km = _____ cm

56. 2 km = _____ cm

57. 14.2 cm = _____ mm

58. 25.3 cm = _____ mm

59. 8.2 mm = _____ cm

60. 9.7 mm = _____ cm

61. 4500 mm = _____ cm

62. 8,000,000 m = _____ km

63. 0.024 mm = _____ m

64. 60,000 mm = _____ dam

65. 6.88 m = _____ dam

66. 7.44 m = _____ hm

67. 2.3 dam = _____ dm

68. 9 km = _____ hm

C Complete. Answers may vary slightly, depending on the conversion used.

69. 10 km = _____ mi
(A common running distance)

70. 5 mi = _____ km
(A common running distance)

71. 14 in. = _____ cm
(A common paper length)

72. 400 m = _____ yd
(A common race distance)

73. 65 mph = _____ km/h
(A common speed limit in the
United States)

74. 100 km/h = _____ mph
(A common speed limit in
Canada)

75. 330 ft = _____ m
(The length of most baseball
foul lines)

76. 165 cm − _____ in.
(A common height for a woman)

77. 180 cm = _____ in.
(A common snowboard length)

78. 450 ft = _____ m
(The length of a long home run
in baseball)

79. 36 yd = _____ m
(A common length for a roll
of tape)

80. 70 in. = _____ cm
(A common height for a man)

81. D_W Would you expect the world record for the 100-m
dash to be greater or less than the record for the
100-yd dash? Why?

82. D_W A student incorrectly writes the following
conversion:

$$23 \text{ in.} = 23 \cdot (12 \text{ ft}) = 276 \text{ ft.}$$

What mistake has been made?

Solve.

83. $-7x - 9x = 24$ [5.7b]

84. $-2a + 9 = 5a + 23$ [5.7b]

85. If 3 calculators cost $43.50, how much would 7 calculators cost?   [7.4a]

86. A principal of $500 is invested at a rate of 8.9% for 1 year. Find the simple interest.   [8.6a]

Convert to percent notation.

87. 0.47   [8.1b]

88. $\dfrac{7}{20}$ [8.1c]

89. A living room is 12 ft by 16 ft. Find the perimeter and area of the room.   [1.2c], [1.5c]

90. A bedroom measures 10 ft by 12 ft. Find the perimeter and area of the room.   [1.2c], [1.5c]

91. **D**_{**W**} Why do you think 8-km road races are more common than 8-mi road races?

92. **D**_{**W**} The Olympic marathon is 26.2 mi. Do you think that this was originally a metric length? Why or why not?

In Exercises 93–96, each sentence is incorrect. Insert or alter a decimal point to make the sentence correct.

93. When my right arm is extended, the distance from my left shoulder to the end of my right hand is 10 m.

94. The height of the Empire State Building is 38.1 m.

95. A stack of ten quarters is 140 cm high.

96. The width of an adult's hand is 112 cm.

97. *Noah's Ark.*   In biblical measures, it is thought that 1 cubit ≈ 18 in. The dimensions of Noah's ark are given as follows: "The length of the ark shall be three hundred cubits, the breadth of it fifty cubits, and the height of it thirty cubits." What were the dimensions of Noah's ark in inches? in feet?
Source: *Holy Bible, King James Version*, Gen. 6:15

98. *Goliath's Height.*   In biblical measures, a span was considered to be half of a cubit (1 cubit = 18 in.; see Exercise 97). The giant Goliath's height was "six cubits and a span." What was the height of Goliath in inches? in feet?
Source: *Holy Bible, King James Version*, 1 Sam. 17:4

Complete. Answers may vary, depending on the conversion used.

99. ▦ 2 mi = _____ cm

100. ▦ 10 km = _____ in.

101. ▦ Audio cassettes are generally played at a rate of $1\frac{7}{8}$ in. per second. How many meters of tape are used for a 60-min cassette? (*Note:* A 60-min cassette has 30 min of playing time on each side.)

102. ▦ The current world record for the 100-m dash is 9.78 sec. How fast is this in miles per hour? Round to the nearest tenth of a mile per hour.

103. ▦ *National Debt.*   Recently the national debt was $5.103 trillion. To get an idea of this amount, picture that if that many $1 bills were stacked on top of each other, they would reach 1.382 times the distance to the moon. The distance to the moon is 238,866 mi. How thick, in inches, is a $1 bill?

Use < or > to complete the following. Perform only approximate, mental calculations.

104. 59 in. ☐ 59 cm

105. 35 yd ☐ 35 m

106. 7 km ☐ 6 mi

107. 9 mi ☐ 18 km

108. 24 ft ☐ 6 m

109. 30 in. ☐ 90 cm

12.2

CONVERTING UNITS OF AREA

Objectives

a Convert from one American unit of area to another.

b Convert from one metric unit of area to another.

a American Units

It is often necessary to convert units of area. First we will convert from one American unit of area to another.

EXAMPLE 1 Complete: $1 \text{ yd}^2 =$ _____ ft^2.

We recall that 1 yd = 3 ft and make a sketch. Note that $1 \text{ yd}^2 = 9 \text{ ft}^2$. The same result can be found as follows:

$$1 \text{ yd}^2 = 1 \cdot (3 \text{ ft})^2 \quad \text{Substituting 3 ft for 1 yd}$$
$$= 3 \text{ ft} \cdot 3 \text{ ft}$$
$$= 9 \text{ ft}^2. \qquad \text{Note that ft} \cdot \text{ft} = \text{ft}^2.$$

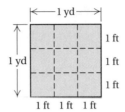

EXAMPLE 2 Complete: $2 \text{ ft}^2 =$ _____ in^2.

$$2 \text{ ft}^2 = 2 \cdot (12 \text{ in.})^2 \qquad \text{Substituting 12 in. for 1 ft}$$
$$= 2 \cdot 12 \text{ in.} \cdot 12 \text{ in.} = 288 \text{ in}^2 \qquad \text{Note that in.} \cdot \text{in.} = \text{in}^2.$$

Do Exercises 1–3.

American units of area are related as follows.

> **AMERICAN UNITS OF AREA**
>
> 1 square yard (yd^2) = 9 square feet (ft^2)
> 1 square foot (ft^2) = 144 square inches (in^2)
> 1 square mile (mi^2) = 640 acres
> 1 acre = 43,560 ft^2

EXAMPLE 3 Complete: $36 \text{ ft}^2 =$ _____ yd^2.

To convert from "ft^2" to "yd^2" we write 1 with yd^2 on top and ft^2 on the bottom.

$$36 \text{ ft}^2 = 36 \text{ ft}^2 \cdot \frac{1 \text{ yd}^2}{9 \text{ ft}^2} \qquad \text{Multiplying by 1 using } \frac{1 \text{ yd}^2}{9 \text{ ft}^2}$$

$$= \frac{36}{9} \cdot \text{yd}^2 = 4 \text{ yd}^2$$

As in Section 12.1, when converting from larger to smaller units, it is usually easiest to use substitution.

EXAMPLE 4 Complete: $7 \text{ mi}^2 =$ _____ acres.

$$7 \text{ mi}^2 = 7 \cdot 640 \text{ acres} \qquad \text{Substituting 640 acres for 1 mi}^2$$
$$= 4480 \text{ acres}$$

Had we used canceling, we could have multiplied 7 mi^2 by $\dfrac{640 \text{ acres}}{1 \text{ mi}^2}$ to find the same answer.

Do Exercises 4 and 5.

Complete.

1. $1 \text{ ft}^2 =$ _____ in^2

2. $10 \text{ ft}^2 =$ _____ in^2

3. $7 \text{ yd}^2 =$ _____ ft^2

Complete.

4. $360 \text{ in}^2 =$ _____ ft^2

5. $5 \text{ mi}^2 =$ _____ acres

Answers on page A-38

Complete.

6. $1 \text{ m}^2 = $ _____ mm^2

7. $1 \text{ cm}^2 = $ _____ mm^2

Complete.

8. $2.88 \text{ m}^2 = $ _____ cm^2

9. $4.3 \text{ mm}^2 = $ _____ cm^2

10. $678,000 \text{ m}^2 = $ _____ km^2

Answers on page A-38

Study Tips

MENTAL CONVERSIONS

Don't feel obliged to do work in your head. Often—when a mistake is made—the root of the mistake lies in trying to do too much in your head. It is safe to say: "When in doubt, write it out."

b **Metric Units**

We next convert from one metric unit of area to another.

EXAMPLE 5 Complete: $1 \text{ km}^2 = $ _____ m^2.

$$1 \text{ km}^2 = 1 \cdot (1000 \text{ m})^2 \qquad \text{Substituting 1000 m for 1 km}$$
$$= 1000 \text{ m} \cdot 1000 \text{ m}$$
$$= 1,000,000 \text{ m}^2 \qquad \text{Note that m} \cdot \text{m} = \text{m}^2.$$

EXAMPLE 6 Complete: $1 \text{ m}^2 = $ _____ cm^2.

$$1 \text{ m}^2 = 1 \cdot (100 \text{ cm})^2 \qquad \text{Substituting 100 cm for 1 m}$$
$$= 100 \text{ cm} \cdot 100 \text{ cm}$$
$$= 10,000 \text{ cm}^2 \qquad \text{Note that cm} \cdot \text{cm} = \text{cm}^2.$$

Do Exercises 6 and 7.

MENTAL CONVERSION

Note in Example 5 that whereas it takes 1000 m to make 1 km, it takes 1,000,000 m^2 to make 1 km^2. Similarly, in Example 6, we saw that although it takes 100 cm to make 1 m, it takes 10,000 cm^2 to make 1 m^2. In general, an area conversion requires moving the decimal point twice as many places as the corresponding length conversion. For example, below we list four equivalent ways of expressing the area of a standard sheet of paper.

$$\text{Area of a standard sheet of paper} = 60,264. \text{ mm}^2$$
$$= 602.64 \text{ cm}^2$$
$$= 0.060264 \text{ m}^2$$
$$\approx 0.00000006 \text{ km}^2$$

EXAMPLE 7 Complete: $3.48 \text{ km}^2 = $ _____ m^2.

Think: A kilometer is 1000 times as big as a meter, so 1 km^2 is 1,000,000 times as big as 1 m^2. We shift the decimal point *six* places to the right.

$$3.48 \qquad 3.480000. \qquad 3.48 \text{ km}^2 = 3,480,000 \text{ m}^2$$

EXAMPLE 8 Complete: $586.78 \text{ cm}^2 = $ _____ m^2.

Think: To convert from cm to m, we shift the decimal point two places to the left. To convert from cm^2 to m^2, we shift the decimal point *four* places to the left.

$$586.78 \qquad 0.0586.78 \qquad 586.78 \text{ cm}^2 = 0.058678 \text{ m}^2$$

Do Exercises 8–10.

12.2

EXERCISE SET

For Extra Help

Digital Video
Tutor CD 6
Videotape 9

InterAct
Math

Math Tutor
Center

MathXL

MyMathLab

a Complete.

1. $5 \text{ yd}^2 = \underline{\qquad} \text{ ft}^2$

2. $4 \text{ ft}^2 = \underline{\qquad} \text{ in}^2$

3. $7 \text{ ft}^2 = \underline{\qquad} \text{ in}^2$

4. $2 \text{ acres} = \underline{\qquad} \text{ ft}^2$

5. $432 \text{ in}^2 = \underline{\qquad} \text{ ft}^2$

6. $54 \text{ ft}^2 = \underline{\qquad} \text{ yd}^2$

7. $22 \text{ yd}^2 = \underline{\qquad} \text{ ft}^2$

8. $40 \text{ ft}^2 = \underline{\qquad} \text{ in}^2$

9. $15 \text{ ft}^2 = \underline{\qquad} \text{ in}^2$

10. $144 \text{ ft}^2 = \underline{\qquad} \text{ yd}^2$

11. $20 \text{ mi}^2 = \underline{\qquad} \text{ acres}$

12. $576 \text{ in}^2 = \underline{\qquad} \text{ ft}^2$

13. $69 \text{ ft}^2 = \underline{\qquad} \text{ yd}^2$

14. $1 \text{ mi}^2 = \underline{\qquad} \text{ yd}^2$

15. $720 \text{ in}^2 = \underline{\qquad} \text{ ft}^2$

16. $27 \text{ ft}^2 = \underline{\qquad} \text{ yd}^2$

17. $1 \text{ in}^2 = \underline{\qquad} \text{ ft}^2$

18. $72 \text{ in}^2 = \underline{\qquad} \text{ ft}^2$

19. $1 \text{ acre} = \underline{\qquad} \text{ mi}^2$

20. $4 \text{ acres} = \underline{\qquad} \text{ ft}^2$

b Complete.

21. $19 \text{ km}^2 = \underline{\qquad} \text{ m}^2$

22. $39 \text{ km}^2 = \underline{\qquad} \text{ m}^2$

23. $6.31 \text{ m}^2 = \underline{\qquad} \text{ cm}^2$

24. $2.7 \text{ m}^2 = \underline{\qquad} \text{ mm}^2$

25. $6.5432 \text{ mm}^2 = \underline{\qquad} \text{ cm}^2$

26. $8.38 \text{ cm}^2 = \underline{\qquad} \text{ mm}^2$

27. $349 \text{ cm}^2 = \underline{\qquad} \text{ m}^2$

28. $125 \text{ mm}^2 = \underline{\qquad} \text{ m}^2$

29. $250,000 \text{ mm}^2 = \underline{\qquad} \text{ cm}^2$

30. $5900 \text{ mm}^2 = \underline{\qquad} \text{ cm}^2$

31. $472,800 \text{ m}^2 = \underline{\qquad} \text{ km}^2$

32. $1.37 \text{ cm}^2 = \underline{\qquad} \text{ mm}^2$

Find the area of the shaded region of each figure. Give the answer in square feet. (Figures are not drawn to scale.)

33.

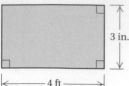

3 in.

4 ft

34.

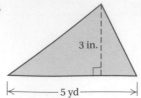

3 in.

5 yd

35.

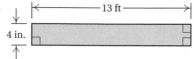

13 ft

4 in.

36.

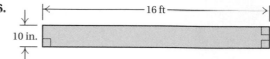

16 ft

10 in.

Find the area of the shaded region of each figure.

37.

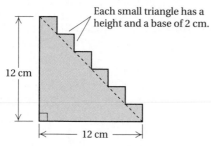

Each small triangle has a height and a base of 2 cm.

12 cm

12 cm

38.

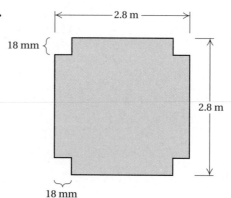

2.8 m

18 mm

2.8 m

18 mm

39. **D**_W What advantage do metric units offer over American units when we are converting area measurements?

40. **D**_W Why might a scientist choose to give area measurements in mm² rather than cm²?

Find the simple interest.   [8.6a]

	Principal	Rate of interest	Time
41.	$700	5%	$\frac{1}{2}$ year
42.	$500	4%	$\frac{3}{4}$ year
43.	$450	6%	$\frac{1}{4}$ year
44.	$1200	8.9%	30 days
45.	$1800	12%	60 days
46.	$2500	14%	90 days

SYNTHESIS

47. D_W Which is larger and why: one square meter or nine square feet?

48. D_W What unit of measurement from this section would you use for measuring the area of a postage stamp? Why?

49. A 30-ft by 60-ft ballroom is to be turned into a nightclub by placing an 18-ft by 42-ft dance floor in the middle and carpeting the rest of the room. The new dance floor is laid in tiles that are 8-in. by 8-in. squares. How many such tiles are needed? What percent of the area is the dance floor?

Complete the following. Answers may vary slightly, depending on the conversion used.

50. $1 \text{ m}^2 = $ _____ ft^2

51. $1 \text{ in}^2 = $ _____ cm^2

52. $2 \text{ yd}^2 = $ _____ m^2

53. $1 \text{ acre} = $ _____ m^2

54. The president's family has about 20,175 ft^2 of living area in the White House. Estimate the living area in square meters.

55. A handwoven scarf is 2 m long and 10 in. wide. Find its area in square centimeters.

56. In order to remodel an office, a carpenter needs to purchase carpeting, at $8.45 a square yard, and molding for the base of the walls, at $0.87 a foot. If the room is 9 ft by 12 ft, with a 3-ft–wide doorway, what will the materials cost?

57. Janie's Rubik's Cube has 54 cm^2 of area. Each side of Norm's cube is twice as wide as Janie's. Find the area of Norm's cube.

12.3 MORE WITH PERIMETER AND AREA

Objectives

a Find the area of a parallelogram or trapezoid.

b Find the circumference, area, radius, or diameter of a circle, given the length of a radius or diameter.

We have already studied how to find the perimeter of polygons and the area of squares, rectangles, and triangles. In this section, we learn how to find the area of *parallelograms*, *trapezoids*, and *circles*. We also learn how to calculate the perimeter, or *circumference*, of a circle.

a Parallelograms and Trapezoids

A **parallelogram** is a four-sided figure with two pairs of parallel sides, as shown below.

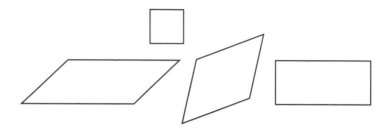

To find the area of a parallelogram, consider the one below.

If we cut off a piece and move it to the other end, we get a rectangle.

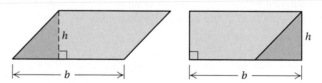

We can find the area by multiplying the length of a **base** b, by h, the **height.**

AREA OF A PARALLELOGRAM

The **area of a parallelogram** is the product of the length of a base b and the height h:

$$A = b \cdot h.$$

EXAMPLE 1 Find the area of this parallelogram.

$A = b \cdot h$
$\quad = 7 \text{ km} \cdot 5 \text{ km}$
$\quad = 35 \text{ km}^2$

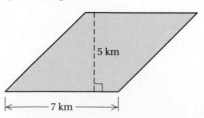

Study Tips

SLOW DOWN FOR SKETCHES

When writing notes, we often use abbreviations and sometimes list only the first letter of a word if we are rushing. If a sketch of a geometric shape is called for, try to make sure the sketch is drawn carefully enough to be realistic.

EXAMPLE 2 Find the area of this parallelogram.

$$A = b \cdot h$$
$$= (1.2 \text{ m}) \cdot (6 \text{ m})$$
$$= 7.2 \text{ m}^2$$

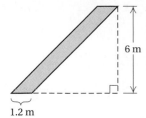

Do Exercises 1 and 2.

TRAPEZOIDS

A **trapezoid** is a polygon with four sides, two of which are parallel to each other.* The parallel sides are called the **bases.**

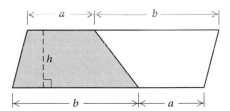

To find the area of a trapezoid, think of cutting out another just like it.

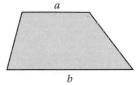

Then place the second one like this.

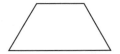

The resulting figure is a parallelogram with an area of

$$h \cdot (a + b). \qquad \text{The base of the parallelogram has length } a + b.$$

The trapezoid we started with has half the area of the parallelogram, or

$$\frac{1}{2} \cdot h \cdot (a + b).$$

AREA OF A TRAPEZOID

The **area of a trapezoid** is half the product of the height and the sum of the lengths of the parallel sides, or the product of the height and the average length of the bases:

$$A = \frac{1}{2} \cdot h \cdot (a + b) = h \cdot \frac{a + b}{2}.$$

Find the area.

1.

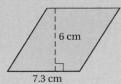

2.

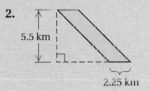

Answers on page A-38

12.3   More with Perimeter and Area

---

*Some definitions of trapezoid specify *exactly* two parallel sides. We refrain from doing so. Thus we consider a parallelogram a special type of trapezoid.

Find the area.

3.

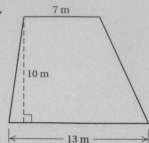

7 m
10 m
13 m

4.

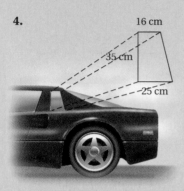

16 cm
35 cm
25 cm

5. Find the length of a radius.

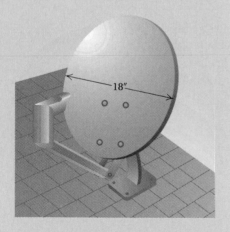

18″

6. Find the length of a diameter.

$2\frac{1}{2}$ ft

Answers on page A-38

EXAMPLE 3 Find the area of this trapezoid.

$$A = \frac{1}{2} \cdot h \cdot (a + b)$$

$$= \frac{1}{2} \cdot 7 \text{ cm} \cdot (12 + 18) \text{ cm}$$

$$= \frac{7 \cdot 30}{2} \cdot \text{cm}^2 = \frac{7 \cdot 15 \cdot \cancel{2}}{1 \cdot \cancel{2}} \text{ cm}^2$$

$$= 105 \text{ cm}^2 \qquad \text{Removing a factor equal to } 1 \left(\frac{2}{2} = 1\right) \text{ and multiplying}$$

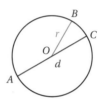

12 cm
7 cm
18 cm

Do Exercises 3 and 4.

b Circles

RADIUS AND DIAMETER

At right is a circle with center O. Segment $\overline{AC}$ is a *diameter*. A **diameter** is a segment that passes through the center of the circle and has endpoints on the circle. Segment $\overline{OB}$ is called a *radius*. A **radius** is a segment with one endpoint on the center and the other endpoint on the circle. The words *radius* and *diameter* are also used to represent the lengths of a circle's radius and diameter, respectively.

B
r
C
O
d
A

DIAMETER AND RADIUS

Suppose that d is the diameter of a circle and r is the radius. Then

$$d = 2 \cdot r \quad \text{and} \quad r = \frac{d}{2}.$$

EXAMPLE 4 Find the length of a radius of this circle.

$$r = \frac{d}{2}$$

$$= \frac{12 \text{ m}}{2}$$

$$= 6 \text{ m}$$

12 m

The radius is 6 m.

EXAMPLE 5 Find the length of a diameter of this circle.

$$d = 2 \cdot r$$

$$= 2 \cdot \frac{1}{4} \text{ ft}$$

$$= \frac{1}{2} \text{ ft}$$

$\frac{1}{4}$ ft

The diameter is $\frac{1}{2}$ ft.

Do Exercises 5 and 6.

CIRCUMFERENCE

The perimeter of a circle is called its **circumference.** Take a 12-oz soda can and measure its circumference C and diameter d. Next, consider the ratio C/d:

$C \approx 7.8$ in.

$\leftarrow d \approx 2.5$ in. $\rightarrow$

$$\frac{C}{d} = \frac{7.8 \text{ in.}}{2.5 \text{ in.}} \approx 3.1.$$

If we did this with cans and circles of several sizes, the result would always be a number close to 3.1. For any circle, if we divide the circumference C by the diameter d, we get the same number. We call this number π (pi). The number π is a nonterminating, nonrepeating decimal. It is impossible to precisely express π as a decimal or a fraction.

CIRCUMFERENCE AND DIAMETER

The circumference C of a circle of diameter d is given by

$$C = \pi \cdot d.$$

The number π is about 3.14, or about $\frac{22}{7}$.

EXAMPLE 6 Find the circumference of this circle. Use 3.14 for π.

$C = \pi \cdot d$

$\approx 3.14 \cdot 6$ cm

≈ 18.84 cm

6 cm

The circumference is about 18.84 cm.

Do Exercise 7.

Since $d = 2 \cdot r$, where r is the length of a radius, it follows that

$$C = \pi \cdot d = \pi \cdot (2 \cdot r).$$

CIRCUMFERENCE AND RADIUS

The circumference C of a circle of radius r is given by

$$C = 2 \cdot \pi \cdot r.$$

7. Find the circumference of this circle. Use 3.14 for π.

20 m

Answer on page A 38

8. Find the circumference of this circle. Use 3.14 for π.

2.5 m

9. Find the circumference of this bicycle wheel. Use $\frac{22}{7}$ for π.

35 cm

10. Find the perimeter of this figure. Use 3.14 for π.

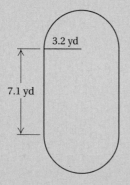
3.2 yd
7.1 yd

Answers on page A-38

EXAMPLE 7   Find the circumference of this circle. Use $\frac{22}{7}$ for π.

$$C = 2 \cdot \pi \cdot r$$

$$\approx 2 \cdot \frac{22}{7} \cdot 70 \text{ in.}$$

$$\approx 2 \cdot 22 \cdot \frac{70}{7} \text{ in.}$$

$$\approx 44 \cdot 10 \text{ in.}$$

$$\approx 440 \text{ in.}$$

The circumference is about 440 in.

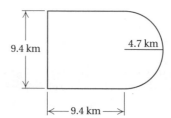
70 in.

EXAMPLE 8   Find the perimeter of this figure. Use 3.14 for π.

We let $P =$ the perimeter. Since there is half a circle replacing the fourth side of a square, we add half the circumference to the lengths of the three line segments.

$$P = 3 \cdot 9.4 \text{ km} + \frac{1}{2} \cdot 2 \cdot \pi \cdot 4.7 \text{ km}$$

$$\approx 28.2 \text{ km} + 3.14 \cdot 4.7 \text{ km}$$

$$\approx 28.2 \text{ km} + 14.758 \text{ km}$$

$$\approx 42.958 \text{ km}$$

9.4 km   4.7 km
9.4 km

The perimeter is about 42.958 km. Note that the radius, 4.7 km, *could* have been found by halving the width (9.4 km).

Do Exercises 8–10.

AREA

To find the area of a circle with radius r, we cut half a circular region into small slices and arrange them as shown below. Note that half of the circumference is half of $2\pi r$, or simply πr.

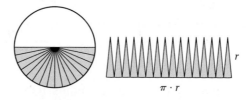
$\pi \cdot r$

Next we slice the remaining half of the circular region and arrange the pieces in between the others as shown below.

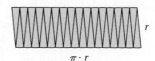
$\pi \cdot r$

The thinner the slices, the closer this comes to being a rectangle. Its length is πr and its width is r, so its area is

$$(\pi \cdot r) \cdot r.$$

This is the area of a circle.

AREA OF A CIRCLE

The **area of a circle** with radius of length r is given by

$$A = \pi \cdot r \cdot r, \quad \text{or} \quad A = \pi \cdot r^2.$$

EXAMPLE 9 Find the area of this circle. Use $\frac{22}{7}$ for π.

$$A = \pi \cdot r^2 = \pi \cdot r \cdot r$$

$$\approx \frac{22}{7} \cdot 14 \text{ cm} \cdot 14 \text{ cm}$$

$$\approx \frac{22}{\cancel{7}} \cdot \frac{\cancel{7} \cdot 2}{1} \text{ cm} \cdot 14 \text{ cm}$$

$$\approx 616 \text{ cm}^2 \quad \textit{Note: } r^2 \neq 2r.$$

The area is about 616 cm².

14 cm

Do Exercise 11.

EXAMPLE 10 Find the area of this circle. Use 3.14 for π. Round to the nearest hundredth.

$$A = \pi \cdot r \cdot r$$

$$\approx 3.14 \cdot 2.1 \text{ m} \cdot 2.1 \text{ m}$$

$$\approx 3.14 \cdot 4.41 \text{ m}^2$$

$$\approx 13.8474 \text{ m}^2 \approx 13.85 \text{ m}^2$$

The area is about 13.85 m².

2.1 m

Do Exercise 12.

CALCULATOR CORNER

On certain calculators, there is a pi key, $\boxed{\pi}$. You can use a $\boxed{\pi}$ key for most computations instead of stopping to round the value of π. Rounding, if necessary, is done at the end.

Exercises:

1. If you have a $\boxed{\pi}$ key on your calculator, to how many decimal places does this key give the value of π?

2. Find the circumference and the area of a circle with a radius of 225.68 in.

3. Find the area of a circle with a diameter of $46\frac{12}{13}$ in.

4. Find the area of a large irrigated farming circle with a diameter of 400 ft.

11. Find the area of this circle. Use $\frac{22}{7}$ for π.

5 km

12. Find the area of this circle. Use 3.14 for π.

10.4 cm

Answers on page A-38

13. Which is larger and by how much: a 10-ft–square flower bed or a 12-ft–diameter flower bed?

EXAMPLE 11 *Art Design.* As an assignment in an art design course at Austin Community College, students design artwork to decorate a CD "jewelbox." Part of the artwork inside the case covers a 12-cm square, over which a CD with a 12-cm diameter rests. How much of the artwork behind the CD will be visible?

1. **Familiarize.** From examining a drawing, we see that the corners of the design will be visible when the CD is in place. We let A = the area of the design visible behind the CD.

2. **Translate.** The problem can be rephrased as follows:

$$\underbrace{\text{Area of case}}_{s \cdot s} \quad \underbrace{\text{minus}}_{-} \quad \underbrace{\text{Area of CD}}_{\pi \cdot r \cdot r} \quad \underbrace{\text{is}}_{=} \quad \underbrace{\text{Visible area.}}_{A}$$

3. **Solve.** Note that the radius of the CD is half the diameter, or 6 cm.

$$12\text{ cm} \cdot 12\text{ cm} - 3.14 \cdot 6\text{ cm} \cdot 6\text{ cm} \approx A \qquad \begin{array}{l}\text{Substituting 6 cm for } r,\\ \text{12 cm for } s, \text{ and 3.14 for } \pi\end{array}$$

$$144\text{ cm}^2 - 113.04\text{ cm}^2 \approx A$$

$$31.0\text{ cm}^2 \approx A \qquad \begin{array}{l}\text{Rounding to the}\\ \text{nearest tenth}\end{array}$$

4. **Check.** We can check by repeating our calculations. Note also that the area of the case does exceed the area of the CD, as expected.

5. **State.** When the CD is in place, about 31 cm² of artwork will be visible.

Do Exercise 13.

AREA AND CIRCUMFERENCE FORMULAS

Area of a parallelogram: $A = b \cdot h$

Area of a trapezoid: $A = \dfrac{1}{2} \cdot h \cdot (a + b)$

or $A = h \cdot \dfrac{a + b}{2}$

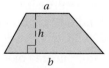

Circumference of a circle: $C = \pi \cdot d$
or $C = 2 \cdot \pi \cdot r$

Area of a circle: $A = \pi \cdot r^2$

Note: $d = 2r$ and $\pi \approx 3.14 \approx \frac{22}{7}$.

Answer on page A-38

a Find the area of each parallelogram or trapezoid.

1.
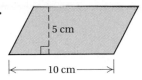
5 cm
10 cm

2.

4 cm
4 cm

3.

6 ft
8 ft
20 ft

4.
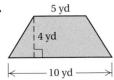
5 yd
4 yd
10 yd

5.
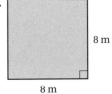
8 m
8 m

6.
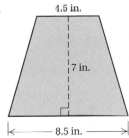
4.5 in.
7 in.
8.5 in.

7.
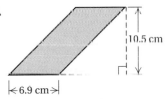
10.5 cm
6.9 cm

8.
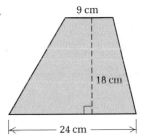
9 cm
18 cm
24 cm

9.
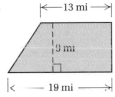
13 mi
9 mi
19 mi

10.
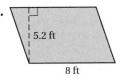
5.2 ft
8 ft

11.
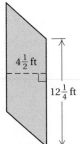
$4\frac{1}{2}$ ft
$12\frac{1}{4}$ ft

12.
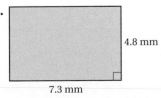
4.8 mm
7.3 mm

13.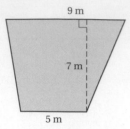

9 m

7 m

5 m

14.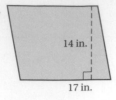

14 in.

17 in.

15.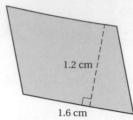

1.2 cm

1.6 cm

16.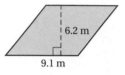

6.2 m

9.1 m

17.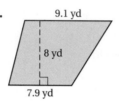

9.1 yd

8 yd

7.9 yd

18.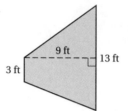

9 ft

13 ft

3 ft

---

b Find the length of a diameter of each circle.

19.

7 cm

20.

8 m

21.

$\frac{7}{8}$ in.

22.

$8\frac{2}{3}$ mi

Find the length of a radius of each circle.

23.
20 ft

24.
10 in.

25.
1.4 cm

26.
60.9 km

Find the circumference of each circle in Exercises 19–22. Use $\frac{22}{7}$ for π.

27. Exercise 19   **28.** Exercise 20   **29.** Exercise 21   **30.** Exercise 22

Find the circumference of each circle in Exercises 23–26. Use 3.14 for π.

31. Exercise 23   **32.** Exercise 24   **33.** Exercise 25   **34.** Exercise 26

Find the area of each circle in Exercises 19–22. Use $\frac{22}{7}$ for π.

35. Exercise 19   **36.** Exercise 20   **37.** Exercise 21   **38.** Exercise 22

Find the area of each circle in Exercises 23–26. Use 3.14 for π.

39. Exercise 23   **40.** Exercise 24   **41.** Exercise 25   **42.** Exercise 26

Little Caesars® is a national chain of pizzerias that offers both square and round pizzas. The various sizes are shown in the table below. Use the table to answer Exercises 43–50. Use 3.14 for π.

SIZE	ROUND (diameter)	SQUARE (width)
Small	10 in.	8.5 in.
Medium	12 in.	10 in.
Large	14 in.	12 in.
Extra-Large	16 in.	NA

43. Which shape of small pie has more area? How much more area does it have?

44. Which shape of medium pie has more area? How much more area does it have?

45. Which shape of large pie has more area? How much more area does it have?

46. Which has more area: a medium round pizza or a large square pizza?

47. Which has more area: two small round pizzas, or one large square pizza? How much more?

48. Which has more area: two small square pizzas, or one large round pizza? How much more?

49. Which has more area: two medium square pizzas, or one extra-large round pizza? How much more?

50. Which has more area: three small square pizzas or one extra-large round pizza? How much more?

CHAPTER 12: Geometry and Measurement

Solve. Use 3.14 for π.

51. *Trampoline.* The standard backyard trampoline has a diameter of 14 ft. What is its area?
Source: International Trampoline Industry Association, Inc.

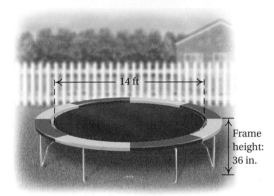

14 ft

Frame height: 36 in.

52. *Soda-Can Top.* The top of a soda can has a 6-cm diameter. What is its radius? its circumference? its area?

6 cm

53. A college radio station is allowed by the FCC to broadcast over an area with a radius of 7 mi. How much area is this?

54. The diameter of a dime is 1.8 cm. What is the circumference? area?

55. *Botany.* To protect an elm tree, 47.1 in. of gypsy moth tape is wrapped once around the trunk. What is the diameter of the tree?

56. *Farming.* The circumference of a silo is 62.8 ft. What is the diameter of the silo?

57. *Track and Field.* Track meets are held on a track similar to the one shown below. Find the shortest distance around the track.

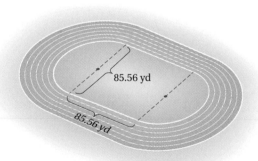

85.56 yd

85.56 yd

58. *Masonry.* The Harris Regency Hotel plans to install a 1-yd–wide walk around a circular pool. The diameter of the pool is 8 yd. What will the area of the walk be?

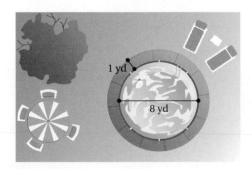

1 yd

8 yd

Find the perimeter of each figure. Use 3.14 for π.

59.

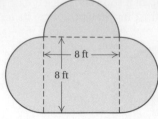

60.

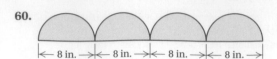

61.

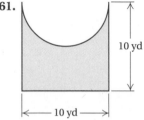

62.

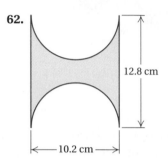

Find the area of the shaded region in each figure. Use 3.14 for π.

63.

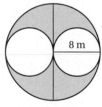

64.

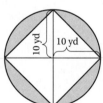

65.

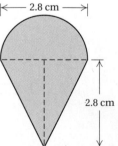

66.

67. ^{D}W Devise a problem for a classmate to solve that involves the area of a circular object. Design the problem so that it is most easily solved using the approximation 3.14 for π.

68. ^{D}W Devise a problem for a classmate to solve that involves the circumference of a circular object. Design the problem so that it is most easily solved using the approximation $\frac{22}{7}$ for π.

SKILL MAINTENANCE

Convert to fraction notation. [8.1c]

69. 9.25%

70. $87\frac{1}{2}\%$

Convert to percent notation. [8.1c]

71. $\frac{11}{8}$

72. $\frac{2}{3}$

73. $\frac{5}{4}$

74. $\frac{8}{5}$

SYNTHESIS

75. ^{D}W The radius of one circle is twice the size of another circle's radius. Is the area of the first circle twice the area of the other circle? Why or why not?

76. ^{D}W The radius of one circle is twice the size of another circle's radius. Is the circumference of the first circle twice the circumference of the other circle? Why or why not?

77. 🖩 Calculate the surface area of an unopened steel can that has a height of 3.5 in. and a diameter of 2.5 in. (*Hint*: Make a sketch and "unroll" the sides of the can.) Use 3.14 for π.

78. 🖩 The sides of a cake box are trapezoidal, as shown in the figure. Determine the surface area of the box.

79. 🖩 $\pi \approx \frac{3927}{1250}$ is another approximation for π. Find decimal notation using a calculator. Round to the nearest thousandth.

80. 🖩 *Landscaping.* Seed is needed for the field surrounded by the track in Exercise 57. If seed comes in 3-lb boxes, and each pound covers 120 ft^2, how many boxes must be purchased?

81. ^{D}W 🖩 See Exercises 43–50. Little Caesars® recently charged $10.99 for a large pizza. Which shaped pie is a better value? Why?

82. ^{D}W 🖩 *Pricing.* See Exercises 43–50. Little Caesars® recently charged $6.99 for a 10-in. square pizza or a 12-in. diameter pizza. Which is a better value? Why?

83. *Sports Marketing.* Tennis balls are generally packed vertically, three in a can, one on top of another. Without using a calculator, determine the larger measurement: the can's circumference or the can's height.

84. ▦ The distance from Kansas City to Indianapolis is 500 mi. A car was driven this distance using tires with a radius of 14 in. How many revolutions of each tire occurred on the trip? Use $\frac{22}{7}$ for π.

85. **D**_W ▦ *Urban Planning.* Years ago, when a 12-in.–diameter tree was cut down in New York City, new trees with a combined diameter of 12 in. had to be planted. Now, instead of being able to use four 3-in.–diameter trees as replacement, a total of *sixteen* 3-in.–diameter trees must be planted. Consider area and explain why the new replacement calculation is more correct mathematically.
Source: *The New York Times 7/24/88, p. 6; article by David W. Dunlap*

86. *Baseball's Strike Zones.* Between the 2000 and 2001 seasons, Major League Baseball redefined the shape of the strike zone. Over the years before 2001, the strike zone evolved to something resembling the region *AQRST* in the diagram. In 2001, the strike zone was changed to rectangle *ABCD* in the illustration. By what percent has the area of the strike zone been increased by the change?
Sources: *The Cincinnati Enquirer*; Major League Baseball; Gannett News Service; *The Sporting News Official Baseball Rules Book*

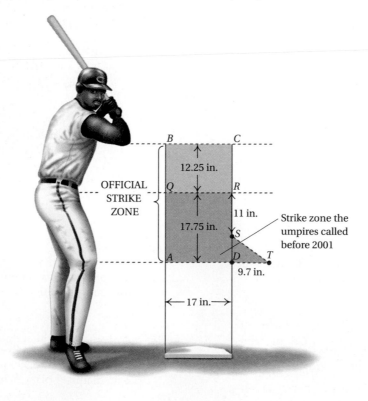

12.4 VOLUME AND CAPACITY

a Volume

The **volume** of an object is the number of unit cubes needed to fill it.

Unit
cube

Volume = 18 unit cubes

Two common units are shown below (actual size).

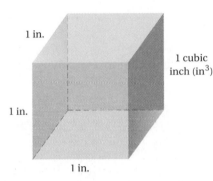

1 in.

1 cubic
inch (in³)

1 in.

1 in.

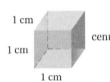

1 cm

1 cm

1 cubic
centimeter (cm³)

1 cm

The volume of a **rectangular solid** can be found by taking the product of the length, width, and height.

EXAMPLE 1 Find the volume.

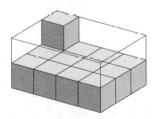
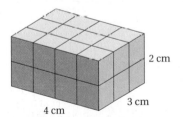

2 cm

4 cm

3 cm

The figure is made up of 2 layers of 12 cubes each, so its volume is 24 cubic centimeters (cm³).

Do Exercise 1.

VOLUME OF A RECTANGULAR SOLID

The **volume of a rectangular solid** is found by multiplying length by width by height:

$$V = \underbrace{l \cdot w}_{\substack{\uparrow \\ \text{Area} \\ \text{of} \\ \text{base}}} \cdot \underbrace{h.}_{\substack{\uparrow \\ \text{Height}}}$$

h

w   l

Objectives

a Find the volume of a rectangular solid, a cylinder, and a sphere.

b Convert from one unit of capacity to another.

c Solve applied problems involving volume and capacity.

1. Find the volume.

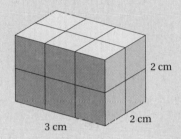

2 cm

3 cm

2 cm

Answer on page A-38

Study Tips

TRY TO SPOT TRENDS

In this section you will learn that for certain solids the volume is the product of the solid's base area and its height. In future work with solids that are not studied in this text, you may want to try extending the base · height approach to these new objects

817

2. Popcorn. In a recent year, people in the United States bought enough unpopped popcorn to provide every person in the country with a bag of popped corn measuring 2 ft by 2 ft by 5 ft. Find the volume of such a bag.

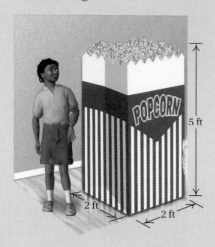

3. Firewood. A cord of wood measures 4 ft by 4 ft by 8 ft. What is the volume of a cord of wood?

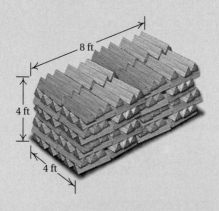

CONNECTING THE CONCEPTS

Throughout this text we have emphasized the importance of using the proper units when describing real-world quantities. As you can see on the preceding page, there is a significant difference between 1 cubic inch and 1 cubic centimeter. Furthermore, there is a fundamental difference between 1 cm^2 and 1 cm^3. To determine the correct unit for an answer, examine the steps leading up to the answer. If two or more measurements are being added, as in a perimeter problem, a one-dimensional unit of length is used (3 ft + 2 ft + 7 ft = 12 ft). If two measurements of length are multiplied, a two-dimensional unit of area is used (8 ft × 7 ft = 56 ft^2). And finally, if three measurements of length are multiplied, a three-dimensional unit of volume is formed (3 m · 2 m · 4 m = 24 m^3). Dimensional analysis can be a great way of figuring out what units are needed for an answer or as a way of determining what figures (and how many figures) are used in a calculation.

EXAMPLE 2 *Carry-on Luggage.* The largest piece of luggage that you can carry on an airplane measures 23 in. by 10 in. by 13 in. Find the volume of this solid.

$$V = l \cdot w \cdot h$$
$$= 23 \text{ in.} \cdot 10 \text{ in.} \cdot 13 \text{ in.}$$
$$= 230 \cdot 13 \text{ in}^3$$
$$= 2990 \text{ in}^3$$

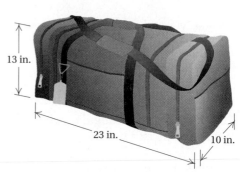

Do Exercises 2 and 3.

We can think of the volume of a rectangular solid as the product of the area of the base times the height:

$$V = l \cdot w \cdot h$$
$$= (l \cdot w) \cdot h$$
$$= (\text{Area of the base}) \cdot h$$
$$= B \cdot h,$$

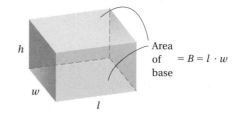

where B represents the area of the base.

Like rectangular solids, **circular cylinders** have bases of equal area that lie in parallel planes. The bases of circular cylinders are circular regions.

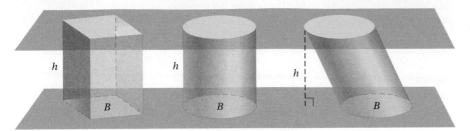

The volume of a circular cylinder is found in a manner similar to finding the volume of a rectangular solid—it is the product of the base area and the height. Height, as always, is measured perpendicular to the base.

VOLUME OF A CIRCULAR CYLINDER

The **volume of a circular cylinder** is the product of the base area B and the height h:

$$V = B \cdot h, \quad \text{or} \quad V = \pi \cdot r^2 \cdot h.$$

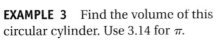

EXAMPLE 3   Find the volume of this circular cylinder. Use 3.14 for π.

$$V = Bh = \pi \cdot r^2 \cdot h$$
$$\approx 3.14 \cdot 4 \text{ cm} \cdot 4 \text{ cm} \cdot 12 \text{ cm}$$
$$= 602.88 \text{ cm}^3$$

12 cm

4 cm

Do Exercises 4 and 5.

A **sphere** is the three-dimensional counterpart of a circle. It is the set of all points in space that are a given distance (the radius) from a given point (the center). The volume of a sphere depends on its radius.

We find the volume of a sphere as follows.

VOLUME OF A SPHERE

The **volume of a sphere** of radius r is given by

$$V = \frac{4}{3} \cdot \pi \cdot r^3.$$

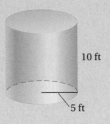

4. Find the volume of the cylinder. Use 3.14 for π.

10 ft

5 ft

5. Find the volume of the cylinder. Use $\frac{22}{7}$ for π.

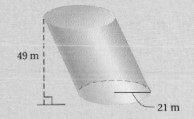

49 m

21 m

Answers on page A-38

6. Find the volume of the sphere. Use 3.14 for π.

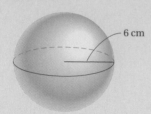

6 cm

7. The radius of a standard-sized golf ball is about $\frac{4}{5}$ in. Find its volume. Use $\frac{22}{7}$ for π.
Source: D. Ellenbogen

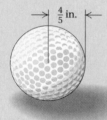

$\frac{4}{5}$ in.

Complete.

8. 80 qt = _____ gal

Answers on page A-38

EXAMPLE 4 *Bowling Ball.* The radius of a standard-sized bowling ball is 4.2915 in. Find the volume of a standard-sized bowling ball. Round to the nearest hundredth of a cubic inch. Use 3.14 for π.
Source: M. Bittinger

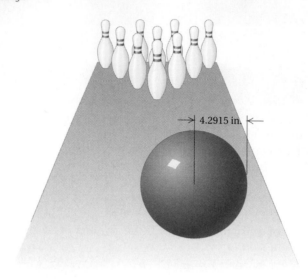

4.2915 in.

$$V = \tfrac{4}{3} \cdot \pi \cdot r^3 \approx \tfrac{4}{3} \cdot 3.14 \cdot (4.2915 \text{ in.})^3$$
$$\approx \frac{4 \cdot 3.14 \cdot 79.0364 \text{ in}^3}{3} \approx 330.90 \text{ in}^3 \qquad \text{Using a calculator}$$

Do Exercises 6 and 7.

b | Capacity

Since many substances come in containers that have irregular shape, to answer a question like "How much soda is in the bottle?" we need measures of **capacity.** American units of capacity are ounces, cups, pints, quarts, and gallons. These units are related as follows.

AMERICAN UNITS OF CAPACITY	
1 gallon (gal) = 4 quarts (qt)	1 pt = 2 cups = 16 ounces (oz)
1 qt = 2 pints (pt)	1 cup = 8 oz

EXAMPLE 5 Complete: 24 qt = _____ gal.

In this case, we multiply by 1 using 1 gal in the numerator, since we are converting *to* gallons, and 4 qt in the denominator, since we are converting *from* quarts.

$$24 \text{ qt} = 24 \text{ qt} \cdot \frac{1 \text{ gal}}{4 \text{ qt}} = \frac{24}{4} \cdot 1 \text{ gal} = 6 \text{ gal}$$

To check that our answer is reasonable, note that since we are converting from smaller to larger units, our answer is a smaller number than the one with which we started.

Do Exercise 8.

EXAMPLE 6 Complete: 9 gal = _____ oz.

First, we multiply by 1 using 4 qt on the top and 1 gal on the bottom:

$$9 \text{ gal} = 9 \text{ gal} \cdot \frac{4 \text{ qt}}{1 \text{ gal}}$$ This converts from gallons to quarts.

$$= 9 \cdot 4 \text{ qt}$$

$$= 36 \text{ qt}.$$

Next, we convert 36 qt to ounces by multiplying by 32 oz/1 qt:

$$9 \text{ gal} = 36 \text{ qt}$$

$$= 36 \text{ qt} \cdot \frac{32 \text{ oz}}{1 \text{ qt}}$$ This converts from quarts to ounces.

$$= 36 \cdot 32 \text{ oz}$$

$$= 1152 \text{ oz}.$$

This conversion could have been done in one step had we known that 1 gal = 128 oz. We then would have multiplied 9 gal by 128 oz/1 gal.

Do Exercise 9.

The basic unit of capacity for the metric system is the **liter**. A liter is just a bit more than a quart (1 liter = 1.06 quarts). It is defined as follows.

1 liter   1 quart

METRIC UNITS OF CAPACITY

1 liter (L) = 1000 cubic centimeters (1000 cm³)
The script letter ℓ is also used for "liter."

Metric prefixes are used with liters. The most common is **milli-**. The milliliter (mL) is, then, $\frac{1}{1000}$ liter. Thus,

1 L = 1000 mL = 1000 cm³;
0.001 L = 1 mL = 1 cm³.

Complete.

9. 4 gal = _____ pt

Answer on page A-38

Complete with mL or L.

10. To prevent infection, a patient received an injection of 2 _____ of penicillin.

11. There are 250 _____ in a coffee cup.

12. The gas tank holds 80 _____.

13. Bring home 8 _____ of milk.

Complete.

14. 0.97 L = _____ mL

15. 8990 mL = _____ L

16. At the same station, the price of 87-octane gasoline is 46.9 cents a liter. Estimate the price of 1 gallon in dollars.

A common unit for drug dosage is the milliliter (mL) or the cubic centimeter (cm³). The notation "cc" is also used for cubic centimeter, especially in medicine. A milliliter and a cubic centimeter are the same size. Each is about the size of a sugar cube.

1 cm³   5 mL   3 cm³

$$1 \text{ mL} = 1 \text{ cm}^3 = 1 \text{ cc}$$

Volumes for which quarts and gallons are used are expressed in liters. Large volumes may be expressed using cubic meters (m³).

Do Exercises 10–13.

EXAMPLE 7 Complete: 4.5 L = _____ mL.

$$4.5 \text{ L} = 4.5 \text{ \cancel{L}} \cdot \frac{1000 \text{ mL}}{1 \text{ \cancel{L}}}$$
$$= 4.5 \cdot 1000 \text{ mL}$$
$$= 4500 \text{ mL}$$

EXAMPLE 8 Complete: 280 mL = _____ L.

$$280 \text{ mL} = 280 \text{ \cancel{mL}} \cdot \frac{1 \text{ L}}{1000 \text{ \cancel{mL}}}$$
$$= \frac{280}{1000} \text{ L}$$
$$= 0.28 \text{ L}$$

Do Exercises 14 and 15.

C Solving Problems

EXAMPLE 9 At a self-service gasoline station, 89-octane gasoline sells for 48.8¢ a liter. Estimate the price of 1 gal in dollars.

Since 1 liter is about 1 quart and there are 4 quarts in a gallon, the price of a gallon is about 4 times the price of a liter:

$$4 \cdot 48.8¢ = 195.2¢ = \$1.952$$

Thus 89-octane gasoline sells for about \$1.95 a gallon.

Do Exercise 16.

Answers on page A-38

EXAMPLE 10 *Propane Gas Tank.* A propane gas tank is shaped like a circular cylinder with half of a sphere at each end. Find the volume of the tank if the cylindrical section is 5 ft long with a 4-ft diameter. Use 3.14 for π.

1. Familiarize. We first make a drawing.

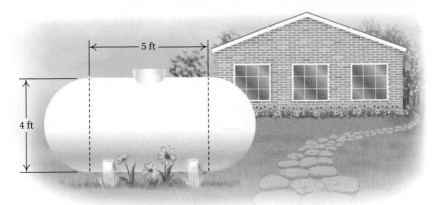

2. Translate. This is a two-step problem. We first find the volume of the cylindrical portion. Then we find the volume of the two ends and add. Note that the radius is 2 ft and that together the two ends make a sphere. We let V = the total volume.

Total volume is Volume of the cylinder plus Volume of the two ends

$$\pi \cdot r^2 \cdot h \qquad \frac{4}{3} \cdot \pi \cdot r^3$$

$$V = 3.14 \cdot (2\text{ ft})^2 \cdot 5\text{ ft} \quad + \quad \frac{4}{3} \cdot 3.14 \cdot (2\text{ ft})^3$$

3. Solve. The volume of the cylinder is approximately

$$3.14 \cdot (2\text{ ft})^2 \cdot 5\text{ ft} \approx 3.14 \cdot 2\text{ ft} \cdot 2\text{ ft} \cdot 5\text{ ft}$$
$$\approx 62.8\text{ ft}^3.$$

The volume of the two ends is approximately

$$\frac{4}{3} \cdot 3.14 \cdot (2\text{ ft})^3 \approx 1.33 \cdot 3.14 \cdot 2\text{ ft} \cdot 2\text{ ft} \cdot 2\text{ ft}$$
$$\approx 33.4\text{ ft}^3.$$

The total volume is approximately

$$62.8\text{ ft}^3 + 33.4\text{ ft}^3 = 96.2\text{ ft}^3.$$

4. Check. The check is left to the student.

5. State. The volume of the tank is about 96.2 ft³.

Do Exercise 17.

17. Medicine Capsule. A cold capsule is 8 mm long and 4 mm in diameter. Find the volume of the capsule. Use 3.14 for π. (*Hint*: First find the length of the cylindrical section.)

CALCULATOR CORNER

Most calculators have a $\boxed{\pi}$ key that can be used to enter the value of π in a computation. It might be necessary to press a $\boxed{\text{2nd}}$ or $\boxed{\text{SHIFT}}$ key before pressing the $\boxed{\pi}$ key on some calculators. Since 3.14 is a rounded value for π, results obtained using the $\boxed{\pi}$ key will vary from those obtained when 3.14 is used in a computation.

To find the volume of the circular cylinder in Example 3, we press $\boxed{\text{2nd}}$ $\boxed{\pi}$ $\boxed{\times}$ $\boxed{4}$ $\boxed{\times}$ $\boxed{4}$ $\boxed{\times}$ $\boxed{1}$ $\boxed{2}$ $\boxed{=}$ or $\boxed{\text{SHIFT}}$ $\boxed{\pi}$ $\boxed{\times}$ $\boxed{4}$ $\boxed{\times}$ $\boxed{4}$ $\boxed{\times}$ $\boxed{1}$ $\boxed{2}$ $\boxed{=}$. The result is approximately 603.19. Note that this is slightly different from the result found using 3.14 for π.

Exercises:

1. Use a calculator with a $\boxed{\pi}$ key to perform the computations in Examples 4 and 10.

2. Use a calculator with a $\boxed{\pi}$ key to perform the computations in Margin Exercises 4–7.

12.4
EXERCISE SET

For Extra Help

Digital Video
Tutor CD 6
Videotape 9

InterAct
Math

Math Tutor
Center

MathXL

MyMathLab

a   Find each volume. Use 3.14 for π in Exercises 9–12.

1.

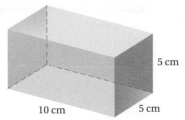

5 cm

10 cm   5 cm

2.

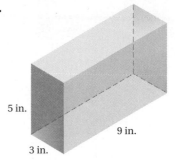

4 ft

4 ft

4 ft

3.

5 in.

9 in.

3 in.

4.

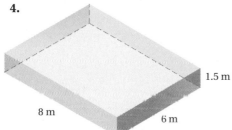

1.5 m

8 m

6 m

5.

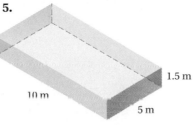

1.5 m

10 m

5 m

6.

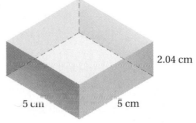

2.04 cm

5 cm   5 cm

7.

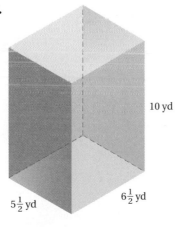

10 yd

$5\frac{1}{2}$ yd $6\frac{1}{2}$ yd

8.

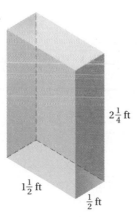

$2\frac{1}{4}$ ft

$1\frac{1}{2}$ ft $\frac{1}{2}$ ft

9.

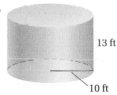

13 ft

10 ft

10.

4 in.

8 in.

11.

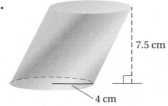

7.5 cm

4 cm

12.

15.1 m

3 m

Find each volume. Use $\frac{22}{7}$ for π in Exercises 13, 14, 19, and 20. Use 3.14 for π in Exercises 15–18.

13.
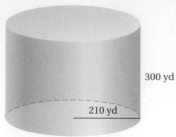
300 yd

210 yd

14.
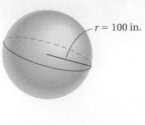
28 km

4 km

15.
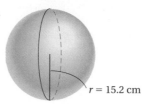
r = 100 in.

16.
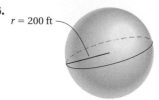
r = 200 ft

17.
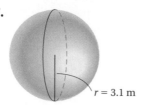
r = 3.1 m

18.
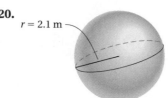
r = 15.2 cm

19.
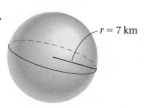
r = 7 km

20.
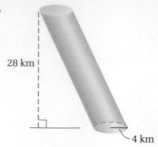
r = 2.1 m

b Complete.

21. 1 L = _____ mL = _____ cm³

22. _____ L = 1 mL = _____ cm³

23. 59 L = _____ mL

24. 714 L = _____ mL

25. 49 mL = _____ L

26. 43 mL = _____ L

27. 27.3 L = _____ cm³

28. 49.2 L = _____ cm³

29. 5 gal = _____ pt

30. 48 oz = _____ pt

31. 10 qt = _____ oz

32. 2 gal = _____ cups

33. 24 oz = _____ cups

34. 20 cups = _____ pt

35. 10 gal = _____ qt

36. 5 gal = _____ cups

37. 3 gal = _____ cups

38. 72 oz = _____ cups

39. 15 pt = _____ gal

40. 9 qt = _____ gal

41. *Volume of a Trash Can.*   The diameter of the base of a cylindrical trash can is 0.7 yd. The height is 1.1 yd. Find the volume. Use 3.14 for π.

42. *Ladder Rung.*   A rung of a ladder is 2 in. in diameter and 16 in. long. Find the volume. Use 3.14 for π.

43. *Barn Silo.*   A barn silo, excluding the top, is a circular cylinder. The silo is 6 m in diameter and the height is 13 m. Find the volume of the silo. Use 3.14 for π.

44. *Clouds.*   Find the volume of a spherical cloud with a 1000-m diameter. Use 3.14 for π.

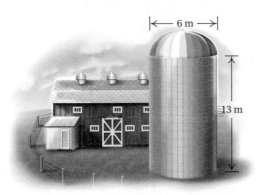

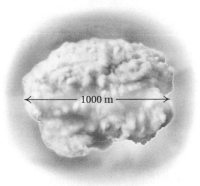

45. *Tennis Ball.*   The diameter of a tennis ball is 6.5 cm. Find the volume. Use 3.14 for π.
Source: D. Ellenbogen

46. *Oak Log.*   An oak log has a diameter of 12 cm and a length (height) of 42 cm. Find the volume. Use 3.14 for π.

47. *Volume of Earth.*   The radius of the earth is about 3980 mi. Find the volume of the earth. Use 3.14 for π. Round to the nearest ten thousand cubic miles.
Source: *The Cambridge Factfinder,* 4th ed.

48. *Astronomy.*   The radius of Pluto's moon is about 600 km. Find the volume of this satellite. Use $\frac{22}{7}$ for π.
Source: *The Cambridge Factfinder,* 4th ed.

49. *Oceanographic Research.*   The original "yellow submarine," the *Alvin,* is a deep-sea research vessel that has completed thousands of dives, including those in which the remains of the *Titanic* were discovered. The "pressure sphere," occupied by three humans, measures two meters in diameter. Find the volume of the pressure sphere. Use 3.14 for π.
Source: Woods Hole Oceanographic Institution

50. *Weather Forecasting.*   Every day, the National Weather Service launches spherical weather balloons from 100 locations in the United States. Each balloon can rise over 100,000 ft and measures anywhere from 15 in. to 20 ft in diameter. Find the volume of a 6-ft–diameter weather balloon. Use 3.14 for π.
Source: Kaysam Worldwide, Inc.

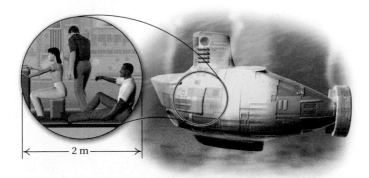

51. *Tennis-Ball Packaging.* Tennis balls are generally packaged in circular cylinders that hold 3 balls each. The diameter of a tennis ball is 6.5 cm. Find the volume of an empty can of tennis balls. Use 3.14 for π.

52. ▦ *Golf-Ball Packaging.* The box shown is just big enough to hold 3 golf balls. If the radius of a golf ball is 2.1 cm, how much air surrounds the three balls? Use 3.14 for π.

53. *Conservation.* Many people leave the water running while brushing their teeth. Suppose that one person wastes 32 oz of water in such a manner each day. How much water, in gallons, would that person waste in a week? in 30 days? in a year? If each of 261 million Americans wastes water this way, estimate how much water is wasted in a year.

54. *Water Storage.* A water storage tank is a circular cylinder with a radius of 5 m and a height of 14 m. What is the tank's volume? Use $\frac{22}{7}$ for π.

55. ▦ *Truck Rental.* The storage compartment of the U-Haul Mini Mover® is 9.83' by 5.67' by 5.83', with an "attic" measuring 1.5' by 5.67' by 2.5'. Find the total volume of the compartment.

56. *Metallurgy.* If all the gold in the world could be gathered together, it would form a cube 18 yd on a side. Find the volume of the world's gold.

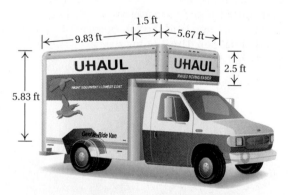

57. **D**w How could you use the volume formulas given in this section to help estimate the volume of an egg?

58. **D**w What advantages do metric units of capacity have over American units?

59. Find the simple interest on $600 at 8% for $\frac{1}{2}$ yr.   [8.6a]

60. Find the simple interest on $5000 at 7% for $\frac{1}{2}$ yr.   [8.6a]

61. If 9 pens cost $8.01, how much would 12 pens cost?   [7.4a]

62. Solve: $9(x - 1) = 3x + 5$.   [5.7b]

63. Solve: $-5y + 3 = -12y - 4$.   [5.7b]

64. A barge travels 320 km in 15 days. At this rate, how far will it travel in 21 days?   [7.4a]

65. Evaluate $\frac{9}{5}C + 32$ for $C = 15$.   [4.7c]

66. Evaluate $\frac{5}{9}(F - 32)$ for $F = 50$.   [4.7c]

67. D_W Which occupies more volume: two spheres, each with radius r, or one sphere with radius $2r$? Explain why.

68. D_W Nate reasons that since 1 yard is 3 times the length of a foot, 1 cubic yard is 3 times the volume of a cubic foot. Is his reasoning valid? Why or why not?

69. *Remarkable Feat.* In 1982, Larry Walters captured the world's imagination by riding a lawn chair attached to 42 helium-filled weather balloons to an altitude of 16,000 ft, before using a BB gun to pop a few balloons and safely descend. Walters used balloons measuring approximately seven feet in diameter. Find the total volume of the balloons used. Use $\frac{22}{7}$ for π.
Source: MarkBarry.com

70. The volume of a ball is 36π cm^3. Find the dimensions of a rectangular box that is just large enough to hold the ball.

71. Audio-cassette cases are typically 7 cm by 10.75 cm by 1.5 cm and contain 90 min of music. Compact-disc cases are typically 12.4 cm by 14.1 cm by 1 cm and contain 50 min of music. Which container holds the most music per cubic centimeter?

72. A 2-cm–wide stream of water passes through a 30-m–long garden hose. At the instant that the water is turned off, how many liters of water are in the hose? Use 3.141593 for π.

73. The volume of a basketball is 2304π cm³. Find the volume of a cube-shaped box that is just large enough to hold the ball.

74. *Moving Trucks.* The U-Haul Easy Loading Mover® has cargo space measuring 14' 1" by 7' 7" by 7' 2" with an attic of 2' 5" by 7' 7" by 2' 7". How much more volume than the Mini Mover (see Exercise 55) does it have?

75. The width of a dollar bill is 2.3125 in., the length is 6.0625 in., and the thickness is 0.0041 in. Find the volume occupied by one million one-dollar bills.

76. *Circumference of Earth.* The circumference of the earth at the equator is about 24,901.55 mi. Due to the irregular shape of the earth, the circumference of a circle of longitude wrapped around the earth between the north and south poles is about 24,859.82 mi. Describe and carry out a procedure for estimating the volume of the earth.
Source: *The Handy Geography Answer Book*

12.5

ANGLES AND TRIANGLES

a Measuring Angles

We see a real-world application of *angles* of various types in the spokes of these bicycles and the different back postures of the riders.

Style of Biking Determines Cycling Posture

Road	Mountain	Comfort
About 180° flat	About 45°	About 90°

Riders prefer a more aerodynamic flat-back position.

Riders prefer a semi-upright position to help lift the front wheel over obstacles.

Riders prefer an upright position that lessens stress on the lower back and neck.

Source: USA TODAY

An **angle** is a set of points consisting of two **rays,** or half-lines, with a common endpoint. The endpoint is called the **vertex.**

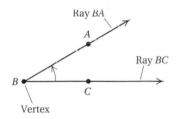

The rays are called the *sides*. The angle above can be named

 angle *ABC*, angle *CBA*, angle *B*, ∠*ABC*, ∠*CBA*, or ∠*B*.

Note that the name of the vertex is either in the middle or, if no confusion results, listed by itself.

Do Exercises 1 and 2.

Name the angle in six different ways.

1.

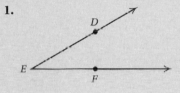

2.

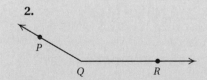

Answers on page A-38

3. Use a protractor to measure this angle.

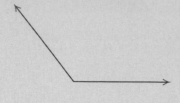

Answer on page A-39

Study Tips

LEARNING VOCABULARY

Occasionally you may encounter a lesson with which you are already familiar. When this occurs, make a special effort to remember the terminology that is used. By learning the proper names for the concepts, you will solidify your understanding of those concepts.

Measuring angles is similar to measuring segments. To measure angles, we start with some predetermined angle and assign to it a measure of 1. We call it a *unit angle*. Suppose that $\angle U$ is a unit angle. Let's measure $\angle DEF$. If we made 3 copies of $\angle U$, they would "fill up" $\angle DEF$. Thus the measure of $\angle DEF$ would be 3 units.

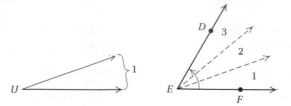

The unit most commonly used for angle measure is the degree. Below is such a unit. Its measure is 1 degree, or 1°.

A 1° angle:

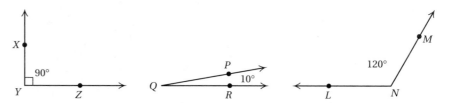

To indicate the *measure* of $\angle XYZ$, we write $m \angle XYZ = 90°$. Here are some other angles with their degree measures.

A device called a **protractor** is used to measure angles. Protractors have two scales. To measure an angle like $\angle Q$ below, we place the protractor's ▲ at the vertex and line up one of the angle's sides at 0°. Then we check where the angle's other side crosses the scale. In the figure below, 0° is on the inside scale, so we check where the angle's other side crosses the inside scale. We see that $m \angle Q = 145°$. Remember to read $m \angle Q$ as "the measure of angle Q."

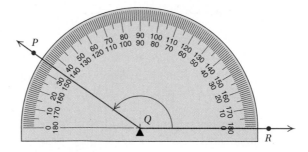

Do Exercise 3.

Let's find the measure of $\angle ABC$. This time we will use the 0° on the outside scale. We see that $m \angle ABC = 68°$.

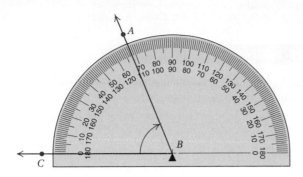

Do Exercise 4.

■ **EXAMPLE 1** *Water Supplies.* Predictions indicate that by the year 2050, water supplies will be scarce in 18% of the world, stressed in 24% of the world, and sufficient in just 58% of the world. Draw a circle graph to represent these figures.

Source: Simon, Paul, *Tapped Out*, New York, 1998, Welcome Rain Publishers

Every circle graph contains a total of 360°. Thus,

24% of the circle is a 0.24(360°), or 86.4° angle;

18% of the circle is a 0.18(360°), or 64.8° angle; and

58% of the circle is a 0.58(360°), or 208.8° angle.

To draw an 86.4° angle, we first draw a horizontal segment and use a protractor to mark off an 86.4° angle. From that mark, we draw a segment to complete the angle. From that segment, we repeat the procedure to draw a 64.8° angle.

To confirm that the remainder of the circle is indeed 208.8°, we measure 180°, make a mark, and from there measure another 28.8°.

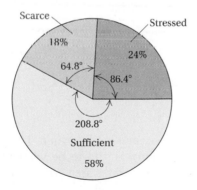

Do Exercise 5.

Answers on page A-39

833

---

4. Use a protractor to measure this angle.

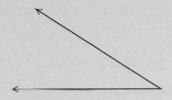

5. **Lengths of Engagement of Married Couples.** The data below list the percent of married couples who were engaged for a certain time period before marriage. Use this information to draw a circle graph.

Source: Bruskin Goldring Research

Less than 1 yr:	24%
1–2 yr:	21%
More than 2 yr:	35%
Never engaged:	20%

Classify each angle as right, straight, acute, or obtuse. Use a protractor if necessary.

6.

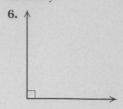

7.

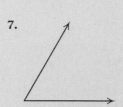

8.

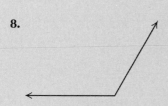

9.

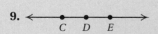

Answers on page A-39

b Classifying Angles

The following are ways in which we classify angles.

> ### TYPES OF ANGLES
>
> **Right angle:** An angle that measures 90°.
>
> **Straight angle:** An angle that measures 180°.
>
> **Acute angle:** An angle that measures more than 0° but less than 90°.
>
> **Obtuse angle:** An angle that measures more than 90° but less than 180°.

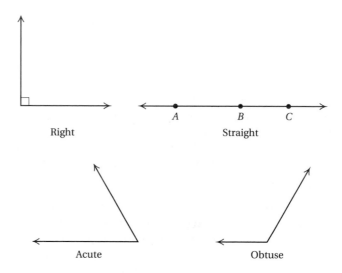

Do Exercises 6–9.

c Vertical, Complementary, and Supplementary Angles

Certain pairs of angles share special properties.

VERTICAL ANGLES

When two lines intersect, four angles are formed. The pairs of angles that do not share any side in common are said to be **vertical** (or *opposite*) angles. Thus, in the drawing below, $\angle 1$ and $\angle 3$ are vertical angles, as are $\angle 4$ and $\angle 2$. Note that $m\angle 1 = m\angle 3$ and $m\angle 4 = m\angle 2$.

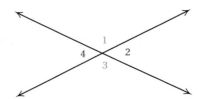

VERTICAL ANGLES

Two angles are **vertical** if they are formed by two intersecting lines and have no side in common. Vertical angles have the same measure.

EXAMPLE 2 Identify each pair of vertical angles.

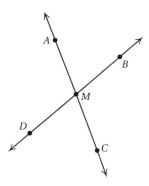

$\angle AMB$ and $\angle CMD$ are vertical angles.

$\angle BMC$ and $\angle DMA$ are vertical angles.

Do Exercises 10 and 11.

COMPLEMENTARY ANGLES

When the sum of the measures of two angles is 90°, the angles are said to be **complementary.** For example, in the figure below, $\angle 1$ and $\angle 2$ are complementary.

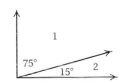

$$m\angle 1 + m\angle 2 = 90°$$
$$75° \;+\; 15° \;\; = 90°$$

COMPLEMENTARY ANGLES

Two angles are **complementary** if the sum of their measures is 90°. Each angle is called a **complement** of the other.

If two angles are complementary, each is an acute angle. When complementary angles are adjacent to each other, they form a right angle.

---

10. Identify each pair of vertical angles.

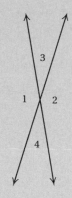

11. Complete:

$$m\angle ANC = \text{_____}.$$
$$m\angle ANB = \text{_____}.$$

Answers on page A-39

12. Identify each pair of complementary angles.

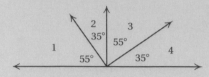

Find the measure of a complement of each angle.

13.

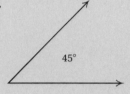
45°

14.

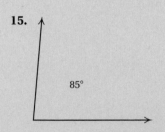
18°

15.

85°

EXAMPLE 3   Identify each pair of complementary angles.

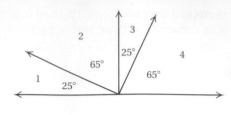

∠1   and   ∠2 $25° + 65° = 90°$ ∠2   and   ∠3

∠1   and   ∠4   ∠3   and   ∠4

EXAMPLE 4   Find the measure of a complement of a 39° angle.

(90–39)°
39°

$$90° - 39° = 51°$$

The measure of a complement is 51°.

Do Exercises 12–15.

SUPPLEMENTARY ANGLES

Next, consider ∠1 and ∠2 as shown below. Because the sum of their measures is 180°, ∠1 and ∠2 are said to be **supplementary.** Note that when supplementary angles are adjacent, they form a straight angle.

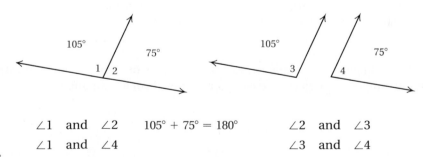

$$m\angle 1 + m\angle 2 = 180°$$
$$30° + 150° = 180°$$

> ### SUPPLEMENTARY ANGLES
>
> Two angles are **supplementary** if the sum of their measures is 180°. Each angle is called a **supplement** of the other.

EXAMPLE 5   Identify each pair of supplementary angles.

∠1   and   ∠2 $105° + 75° = 180°$ ∠2   and   ∠3

∠1   and   ∠4   ∠3   and   ∠4

EXAMPLE 6 Find the measure of a supplement of an angle of 112°.

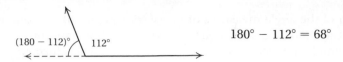

$180° - 112° = 68°$

The measure of a supplement is 68°.

Do Exercises 16–19.

d Triangles

A **triangle** is a polygon made up of three segments, or sides. Consider these triangles. The triangle with vertices A, B, and C can be named △ABC.

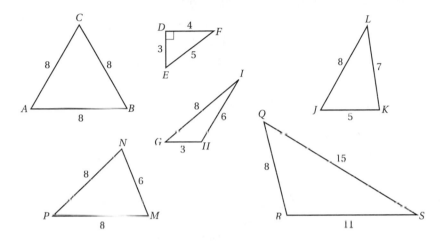

We can classify triangles according to sides and according to angles.

Do Exercises 20–23.

16. Identify each pair of supplementary angles.

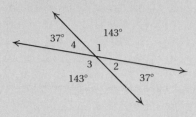

Find the measure of a supplement of an angle with the given measure.

17. 38°

18. 157°

19. 90°

20. Which triangles on this page are:
  a) equilateral?
  b) isosceles?
  c) scalene?

21. Are all equilateral triangles isosceles?

22. Are all isosceles triangles equilateral?

23. Which triangles on this page are:
  a) right triangles?
  b) obtuse triangles?
  c) acute triangles?

Answers on page A-39

24. Find $m(\angle P) + m(\angle Q) + m(\angle R)$.

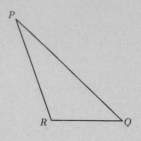

25. Find the missing angle measure.

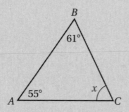

e ## Sum of the Angle Measures of a Triangle

The sum of the angle measures of every triangle is 180°. To see this, note that we can think of cutting apart a triangle as shown on the left below. If we reassemble the pieces, we see that a straight angle is formed.

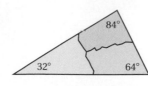
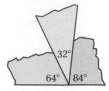

$$64° + 32° + 84° = 180°$$

SUM OF THE ANGLE MEASURES OF A TRIANGLE

In any triangle *ABC*, the sum of the measures of the angles is 180°:
$$m(\angle A) + m(\angle B) + m(\angle C) = 180°.$$

Do Exercise 24.

If we know the measures of two angles of a triangle, we can calculate the measure of the remaining angle.

EXAMPLE 7 Find the missing angle measure.

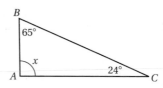

$$m(\angle A) + m(\angle B) + m(\angle C) = 180°$$
$$x + 65° + 24° = 180°$$
$$x + 89° = 180°$$
$$x = 180° - 89° \qquad \text{Subtracting 89° from both sides}$$
$$x = 91°$$

The measure of $\angle A$ is 91°.

Do Exercise 25.

a Name each angle in six different ways.

1.

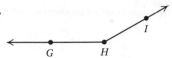

G H I

2.

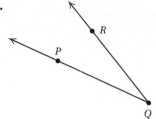

R P Q

Use a protractor to measure each angle.

3.

4.

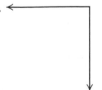

5.

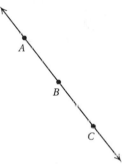

A B C

6.

7.

8.

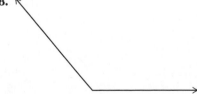

Use the given information and a protractor to draw a circle graph.

9. *Pregnancy Weight Gain.* The table below lists the amounts of weight gain during pregnancy.

WEIGHT GAIN (in pounds)	PERCENT
Less than 20	22%
21–30	32%
31–40	27%
41 or more	19%

Source: National Vital Statistics Report

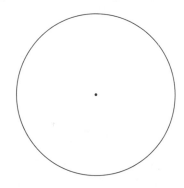

10. *e-mail.* The table below lists the numbers of e-mails people get per day at work.

NUMBER OF E-MAILS PER DAY	PERCENT
Less than 1	28%
1–5	20%
6–10	12%
11–20	9%
21 or more	31%

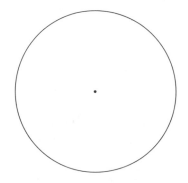

Source: John J. Heldrich Center for Workforce Development

11. *Kids in Foster Care.* There are approximately one-half million children in foster care in the United States. Most of these children are under the age of 10. The table below lists the percentages by ages of children in foster care.

AGE GROUP	PERCENT
Under 1	3%
1–5	25%
6–10	27%
11–15	27%
16+	18%

Source: The Administration for Children and Families

12. *Causes of Spinal Cord Injuries.* The table below lists the causes of spinal cord injury.

CAUSES	PERCENT
Motor vehicle accidents	44%
Acts of violence	24%
Falls	22%
Sports	8%
Other	2%

Source: National Spinal Cord Injury Association

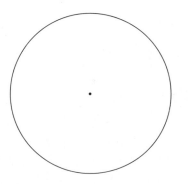

13.–20. Classify each of the angles in Exercises 1–8 as right, straight, acute, or obtuse.

21.–24. Classify each of the angles in Margin Exercises 1–4 as right, straight, acute, or obtuse.

c Identify two pairs of vertical angles for each figure.

25.

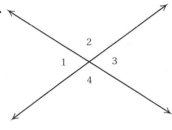

26.

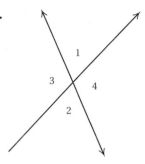

27.

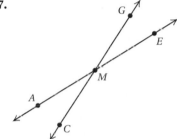

28.

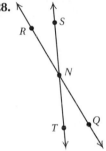

Complete.

29. Refer to Exercise 25.

$$m \angle 2 = \underline{\hspace{2cm}}$$
$$m \angle 3 = \underline{\hspace{2cm}}$$

30. Refer to Exercise 26.

$$m \angle 1 = \underline{\hspace{2cm}}$$
$$m \angle 2 = \underline{\hspace{2cm}}$$

31. Refer to Exercise 27.

$$m \angle AMC = \underline{\hspace{2cm}}$$
$$m \angle AMG = \underline{\hspace{2cm}}$$

32. Refer to Exercise 28.

$$m \angle RNS = \underline{\hspace{2cm}}$$
$$m \angle TNR = \underline{\hspace{2cm}}$$

Find the measure of a complement of an angle with the given measure.

33. $11°$ **34.** $83°$ **35.** $67°$ **36.** $5°$

37. $58°$ **38.** $32°$ **39.** $29°$ **40.** $54°$

Find the measure of a supplement of an angle with the given measure.

41. $3°$ **42.** $54°$ **43.** $139°$ **44.** $13°$

45. $75°$ **46.** $128°$ **47.** $104°$ **48.** $49°$

Classify each triangle as equilateral, isosceles, or scalene. Then classify it as right, obtuse, or acute.

49.

50.
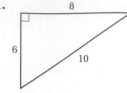

51.
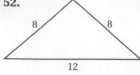

52.
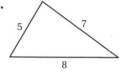

53.

54.
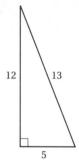

55.
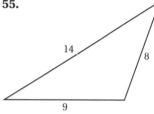

56.
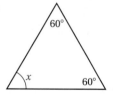

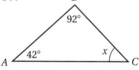 Find each missing angle measure.

57.
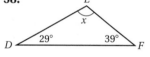

58.

59.

60.

61. **D**w Can both an angle and its supplement be obtuse? Why or why not?

62. **D**w Explain a procedure that could be used to determine the measure of an angle's supplement from the measure of the angle's complement.

Find the simple interest.   [8.6a]

	PRINCIPAL	RATE OF INTEREST	TIME	SIMPLE INTEREST
63.	$2000	8%	1 year	
64.	$750	6%	$\frac{1}{2}$ year	
65.	$4000	7.4%	$\frac{1}{2}$ year	
66.	$200,000	6.7%	$\frac{1}{12}$ year	

Interest is compounded semiannually. Find the amount in the account after the given length of time. Round to the nearest cent.   [8.6b]

	PRINCIPAL	RATE OF INTEREST	TIME	AMOUNT IN THE ACCOUNT
67.	$25,000	6%	5 years	
68.	$150,000	$6\frac{7}{8}$%	15 years	
69.	$150,000	7.4%	20 years	
70.	$160,000	7.4%	20 years	

Simplify.   [1.9c]

71. $2^2 + 3^2 + 4^2$

72. $5^2 - 4^2 + 1^2$

SYNTHESIS

73. **D$_W$** Explain how you might use triangles to find the sum of the angle measures of this figure.

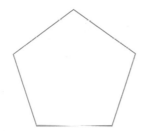

74. **D$_W$** Do parallelograms always contain two acute and two obtuse angles? Why or why not?

75. ▦ In the figure, $m \angle 1 = 79.8°$ and $m \angle 3 = 33.07°$. Find $m \angle 2$, $m \angle 4$, $m \angle 5$, and $m \angle 6$.

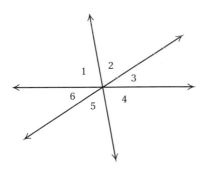

76. ▦ In the figure, $m \angle 2 = 42.17°$ and $m \angle 6 = 81.9°$. Find $m \angle 1$, $m \angle 3$, $m \angle 4$, and $m \angle 5$.

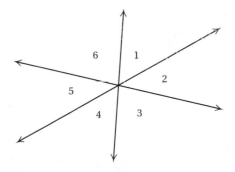

77. Find $m \angle ACB$, $m \angle CAB$, $m \angle EBC$, $m \angle EBA$, $m \angle AEB$, and $m \angle ADB$ in the rectangle shown below.

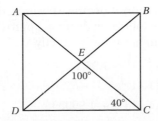

Objectives

a Simplify square roots of squares, such as $\sqrt{25}$.

b Approximate square roots.

c Given the lengths of any two sides of a right triangle, find the length of the third side.

d Solve applied problems involving right triangles.

Find each square.

1. 9^2

2. $(-10)^2$

3. 11^2

4. 12^2

It would be helpful to memorize the squares of numbers from 1 to 25.

---

5. 13^2

6. 14^2

7. 15^2

8. 16^2

Find all square roots. Use the results of Exercises 1–8 above, if necessary.

9. 100

10. 81

11. 49

12. 196

Simplify. Use the results of Exercises 1–8 above, if necessary.

13. $\sqrt{49}$

14. $\sqrt{16}$

15. $\sqrt{121}$

16. $\sqrt{100}$

17. $\sqrt{81}$

18. $\sqrt{64}$

19. $\sqrt{225}$

20. $\sqrt{169}$

21. $\sqrt{1}$

22. $\sqrt{0}$

Answers on page A-39

a Square Roots

> ### SQUARE ROOT
>
> If a number is a product of a factor times itself, then that factor is a **square root** of the number. (If $c^2 = a$, then c is a square root of a.)

For example, 36 has two square roots, 6 and -6. To see this, note that $6 \cdot 6 = 36$ and $(-6) \cdot (-6) = 36$.

EXAMPLE 1 Find the square roots of 25.

The square roots of 25 are 5 and -5, because $5^2 = 25$ and $(-5)^2 = 25$.

> **CAUTION!**
>
> To find the *square* of a number, multiply the number by itself. To find a *square root* of a number, find a number that, when squared, gives the original number.

Do Exercises 1–12.

Since every positive number has two square roots, the symbol $\sqrt{}$ (called a *radical* sign) is used to denote the positive square root of the number underneath. Thus, $\sqrt{9}$ means 3, not -3. When we refer to *the* square root of some number n, we mean the positive square root, $\sqrt{n}$.

EXAMPLES Simplify.

2. $\sqrt{36} = 6$ The square root of 36 is 6 because $6^2 = 36$ and 6 is positive.

3. $\sqrt{25} = 5$ Note that $5^2 = 25$.

4. $\sqrt{144} = 12$ Note that $12^2 = 144$.

5. $\sqrt{256} = 16$ Note that $16^2 = 256$.

Do Exercises 13–22.

b Approximating Square Roots

Many square roots can't be written as whole numbers or fractions. For example, $\sqrt{2}$, $\sqrt{3}$, $\sqrt{39}$, and $\sqrt{70}$ cannot be precisely represented in decimal notation. To see this, consider the following decimal approximations for $\sqrt{2}$. Each gives a closer approximation, but none is exactly $\sqrt{2}$:

$$\sqrt{2} \approx 1.4 \quad \text{because} \quad (1.4)^2 = 1.96;$$
$$\sqrt{2} \approx 1.41 \quad \text{because} \quad (1.41)^2 = 1.9881;$$
$$\sqrt{2} \approx 1.414 \quad \text{because} \quad (1.414)^2 = 1.999396;$$
$$\sqrt{2} \approx 1.4142 \quad \text{because} \quad (1.4142)^2 = 1.99996164.$$

Decimal approximations like these are commonly found by using a calculator.

EXAMPLE 6 Approximate $\sqrt{3}$, $\sqrt{27}$, and $\sqrt{180}$ to the nearest thousandth. Use a calculator.

We use a calculator to find each square root. Since more than three decimal places are given, we round back to three places.

$$\sqrt{3} \approx 1.732,$$
$$\sqrt{27} \approx 5.196,$$
$$\sqrt{180} \approx 13.416$$

As a check, note that because $1 \cdot 1 = 1$ and $2 \cdot 2 = 4$, we expect $\sqrt{3}$ to be between 1 and 2. Similarly, we expect $\sqrt{27}$ to be between 5 and 6 and $\sqrt{180}$ to be between 13 and 14.

If you continue in algebra, you will probably learn techniques for rewriting $\sqrt{27}$ as $3\sqrt{3}$ and $\sqrt{180}$ as $6\sqrt{5}$. Such techniques are beyond the scope of this text.

Do Exercises 23–25.

CALCULATOR CORNER

Most calculators have a square root key, $\boxed{\sqrt{}}$. On some calculators, square roots are found by pressing the $\boxed{x^2}$ key after first pressing a key labeled $\boxed{\text{2nd}}$ or $\boxed{\text{SHIFT}}$. (On these calculators, finding square roots is a secondary function.)

To find an approximation for $\sqrt{30}$ on a scientific calculator, we press

$\boxed{3}\ \boxed{0}\ \boxed{\sqrt{}}$.

On a graphing calculator, we press $\boxed{\text{2nd}}\ \boxed{\sqrt{}}\ \boxed{3}\ \boxed{0}\ \boxed{\text{ENTER}}$. In either case, the value 5.477225575 appears (results may vary slightly).

It is always best to finish all calculations before rounding off. For example, to round $9 \cdot \sqrt{5}$ to the nearest tenth, we do *not* first determine that $\sqrt{5} \approx 2.2$. Rather, we press

$\boxed{9}\ \boxed{\times}\ \boxed{5}\ \boxed{\sqrt{}}\ \boxed{=}$ or $\boxed{9}\ \boxed{\times}\ \boxed{\text{2nd}}\ \boxed{\sqrt{}}\ \boxed{5}\ \boxed{\text{ENTER}}$.

The result, 20.1246118, is then rounded to 20.1.

Exercises: Round to the nearest tenth.

1. $\sqrt{43}$ 2. $\sqrt{94}$
3. $7 \cdot \sqrt{8}$ 4. $5 \cdot \sqrt{12}$
5. $\sqrt{35} + 19$ 6. $17 + \sqrt{57}$
7. $13 \cdot \sqrt{68} + 14$ 8. $24 \cdot \sqrt{31} - 18$
9. $5 \cdot \sqrt{30} - 3 \cdot \sqrt{14}$ 10. $7 \cdot \sqrt{90} + 3 \cdot \sqrt{40}$

Approximate to the nearest thousandth. Use a calculator.

23. $\sqrt{5}$

24. $\sqrt{78}$

25. $\sqrt{168}$

Answers on page A-39

12.6 Square Roots and the Pythagorean Theorem

C | The Pythagorean Theorem

Recall that a right triangle is a triangle with a 90° angle, as shown here.

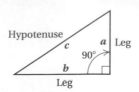

In a right triangle, the longest side is called the **hypotenuse.** It is also the side opposite the right angle. The other two sides are called **legs.** We generally use the letters a and b for the lengths of the legs (in either order) and c for the length of the hypotenuse. They are related as follows.

THE PYTHAGOREAN THEOREM

In any right triangle, if a and b are the lengths of the legs and c is the length of the hypotenuse, then
$$a^2 + b^2 = c^2, \quad \text{or}$$
$$(\text{Leg})^2 + (\text{Other leg})^2 = (\text{Hypotenuse})^2.$$

The equation $a^2 + b^2 = c^2$ is called the **Pythagorean equation.***

It is important to remember this theorem because it is extremely useful. By using the Pythagorean theorem, we can find the length of any side in a right triangle if the lengths of the other sides are known.

The Pythagorean theorem is named for the Greek mathematician Pythagoras (569?–500? B.C.). We can think of this relationship as adding areas.

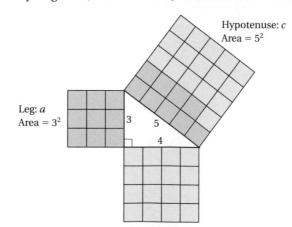

$$a^2 + b^2 = c^2$$
$$3^2 + 4^2 = 5^2$$
$$9 + 16 = 25$$

If we know the lengths of any two sides of a right triangle, we can use the Pythagorean equation to determine the length of the third side.

---

*The *converse* of the Pythagorean theorem is also true. That is, if $a^2 + b^2 = c^2$, then the triangle is a right triangle.

EXAMPLE 7 Find the length of the hypotenuse of this right triangle.

We substitute in the Pythagorean equation:

$a^2 + b^2 = c^2$

$6^2 + 8^2 = c^2$ Substituting

$36 + 64 = c^2$

$100 = c^2.$

The solution of this equation is the square root of 100, which is 10:

$c = \sqrt{100} = 10.$

Do Exercise 26.

EXAMPLE 8 Find the length b for the right triangle shown. Give an exact answer and an approximation to three decimal places.

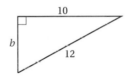

We first substitute in the Pythagorean equation.

$a^2 + b^2 = c^2$

$10^2 + b^2 = 12^2$ Substituting

$100 + b^2 = 144.$

Next, we solve for b^2 and then b, as follows:

$100 + b^2 - 100 = 144 - 100$ Subtracting 100 from both sides

$b^2 = 144 - 100$

$b^2 = 44$ We have now solved for b^2.

Exact answer: $b = \sqrt{44}$ Solving for b

Approximation: $b \approx 6.633.$ Using a calculator

Do Exercises 27–29.

26. Find the length of the hypotenuse of this right triangle.

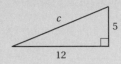

Find the length of the leg of the right triangle. Give an exact answer and an approximation to three decimal places.

27.

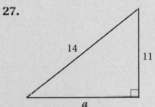

28.

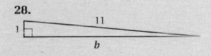

29.

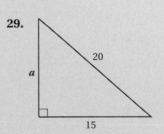

Answer on page A-39

30. How long is a guy wire reaching from the top of an 18-ft pole to a point on the ground 10 ft from the pole? Give an exact answer and an approximation to the nearest tenth of a foot.

18 ft $c = ?$

10 ft

---

d   Applications

▪ **EXAMPLE 9**   *Height of Ladder.*   A 12-ft ladder leans against a building. The bottom of the ladder is 7 ft from the building. How high is the top of the ladder? Give an exact answer and an approximation to the nearest tenth of a foot.

1. **Familiarize.**   We first make a drawing. In it we see a right triangle. We let h = the unknown height.

12 ft h

7 ft

2. **Translate.**   We substitute 7 for a, h for b, and 12 for c in the Pythagorean equation:

$$a^2 + b^2 = c^2 \qquad \text{Pythagorean equation}$$
$$7^2 + h^2 = 12^2.$$

3. **Solve.**   We solve for h^2 and then h:

$$49 + h^2 = 144 \qquad \text{Replacing } 7^2 \text{ with 49 and } 12^2 \text{ with 144}$$
$$49 + h^2 - 49 = 144 - 49 \qquad \text{Subtracting 49 from both sides}$$
$$h^2 = 144 - 49$$
$$h^2 = 95$$

     Exact answer: $h = \sqrt{95}$ Solving for h

     Approximation: $h \approx 9.7$ ft.

4. **Check.** $7^2 + \left(\sqrt{95}\right)^2 = 49 + 95 = 144 = 12^2.$

5. **State.**   The top of the ladder is $\sqrt{95}$, or about 9.7 ft from the ground.

Do Exercise 30.

Answer on page A-39

12.6 EXERCISE SET

For Extra Help

Digital Video
Tutor CD 6
Videotape 9

InterAct
Math

Math Tutor
Center

MathXL

MyMathLab

a   Find both square roots for each number listed.

1. 16

2. 9

3. 121

4. 49

5. 169

6. 144

7. 2500

8. 3600

Simplify.

9. $\sqrt{64}$

10. $\sqrt{4}$

11. $\sqrt{81}$

12. $\sqrt{49}$

13. $\sqrt{225}$

14. $\sqrt{121}$

15. $\sqrt{625}$

16. $\sqrt{900}$

17. $\sqrt{400}$

18. $\sqrt{169}$

19. $\sqrt{10,000}$

20. $\sqrt{1,000,000}$

b   Approximate each number to the nearest thousandth. Use a calculator.

21. $\sqrt{48}$

22. $\sqrt{17}$

23. $\sqrt{8}$

24. $\sqrt{7}$

25. $\sqrt{3}$

26. $\sqrt{6}$

27. $\sqrt{12}$

28. $\sqrt{18}$

29. $\sqrt{19}$

30. $\sqrt{75}$

31. $\sqrt{110}$

32. $\sqrt{10}$

c   Find the length of the third side of each right triangle. Give an exact answer and, when appropriate, an approximation to the nearest thousandth.

33.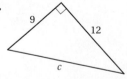

34.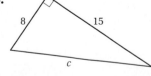

35.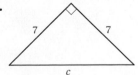

36.

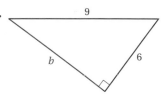

37.

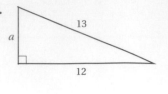

38.

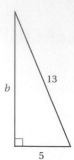

39.

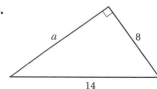

40.

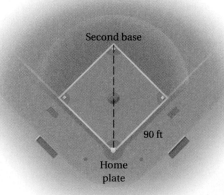

For each right triangle, find the length of the side not given. Assume that c represents the length of the hypotenuse. Give an exact answer and, when appropriate, an approximation to the nearest thousandth.

41. $a = 10, b = 24$

42. $a = 5, b = 12$

43. $a = 9, c = 15$

44. $a = 18, c = 30$

45. $a = 4, b = 5$

46. $a = 5, b = 6$

47. $a = 1, c = 32$

48. $b = 1, c = 20$

d In Exercises 49–56, give an exact answer and an approximation to the nearest tenth.

49. How long is a string of lights reaching from the top of a 12-ft pole to a point 8 ft from the base of the pole?

50. How long must a wire be in order to reach from the top of a 13-m telephone pole to a point on the ground 9 m from the base of the pole?

51. *Softball Diamond.* A slow-pitch softball diamond is actually a square 65 ft on a side. How far is it from home plate to second base?

52. *Baseball Diamond.* A baseball diamond is actually a square 90 ft on a side. How far is it from home plate to second base?

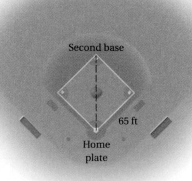

53. How tall is this tree?

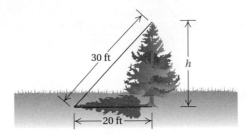

54. How far is the base of the fence post from point *A*?

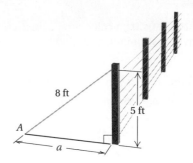

55. An airplane is flying at an altitude of 4100 ft. The slanted distance directly to the airport is 15,100 ft. How far is the airplane horizontally from the airport?

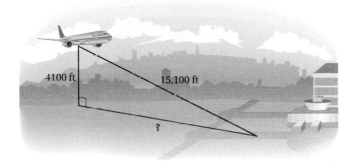

56. A surveyor had poles located at points *P*, *Q*, and *R* around a lake. The distances that the surveyor was able to measure are marked on the drawing. What is the distance from *P* to *R* across the lake?

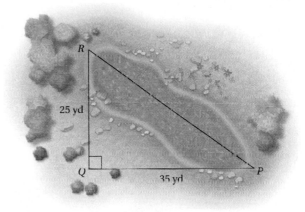

57. **D**ʷ Write a problem similar to Exercises 49–56 for a classmate to solve. Design the problem so that its solution involves the length $\sqrt{58}$ m.

58. **D**ʷ Does every number have two square roots? Why or why not?

SKILL MAINTENANCE

Solve.

59. Food expenses account for 26% of the average family's budget. A family makes $1800 one month. How much do they spend for food?   [8.4a]

60. Blakely County has a population that is increasing by 4% each year. This year the population is 180,000. What will it be next year?   [8.4b]

61. Dexter College has a student body of 1850 students. Of these, 17.5% are seniors. How many students are seniors?   [8.4a]

62. The price of a cellular phone was reduced from $70 to $61.60. Find the percent of decrease in price.   [8.4b]

Simplify.   [1.9b]

63. 2^3

64. 5^3

65. 4^3

66. 3^3

67. **D**_W Without using a calculator, explain how you could convince someone that $\sqrt{902}$ is not a whole number.

68. **D**_W Without using a protractor, how is it possible to determine if a triangle is a *right* triangle?

69. 🖩 Find the area of the trapezoid shown. Round to the nearest hundredth.

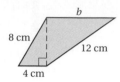

70. Which of the triangles below has the larger area? If the areas are the same, state so.

71. 🖩 One of the largest TVs ever made, the Toshiba TW65X81, has a screen that measures $31\frac{3}{4}$ in. by $56\frac{1}{2}$ in. Determine the diagonal measurement of the screen. Round your answer to the nearest tenth of an inch.
Source: keohi.com

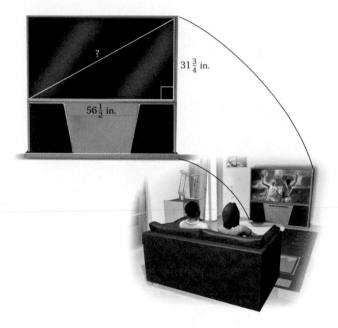

72. A Philips 42-in. plasma television has a rectangular screen that measures 42 in. diagonally. The ratio of width to height is 16 to 9. Find the width and the height of the screen.

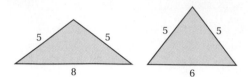

73. A conventional 19-in. television set has a rectangular screen that measures 19 in. diagonally. The ratio of width to height in a conventional television set is 4 to 3. Find the width and the height of the screen.

74. 🖩 A cube is circumscribed by a sphere with a 1-m diameter. How much more volume is in the sphere?

12.7

WEIGHT, MASS, AND TEMPERATURE

Objectives

a Convert from one American unit of weight to another.

b Convert from one metric unit of mass to another.

c Convert temperatures from Celsius to Fahrenheit and from Fahrenheit to Celsius.

a Weight: The American System

The American units of weight are as follows.

> **AMERICAN UNITS OF WEIGHT**
>
> 1 lb = 16 ounces (oz)
>
> 1 ton (T) = 2000 pounds (lb)

The term "ounce" used here for weight is different from the "ounce" we used for capacity in Section 12.4. Often, however, one fluid ounce weighs approximately one ounce.

EXAMPLE 1 A well-known hamburger is called a "quarter-pounder." Find its name in ounces: a "_____ ouncer."

$$\frac{1}{4}\text{ lb} = \frac{1}{4} \cdot 1\text{ lb}$$

$$= \frac{1}{4} \cdot 16\text{ oz} \qquad \text{Substituting 16 oz for 1 lb}$$

$$= 4\text{ oz}$$

A "quarter-pounder" can also be called a "four-ouncer."

EXAMPLE 2 Complete: 15,360 lb = _____ T.

$$15{,}360\text{ lb} = 15{,}360\text{ lb} \cdot \frac{1\text{ T}}{2000\text{ lb}} \qquad \text{Multiplying by 1}$$

$$\left. \begin{array}{l} = \dfrac{15{,}360}{2000}\text{ T} \\[2mm] = 7.68\text{ T} \end{array} \right\} \quad \text{Dividing by 2000}$$

Do Exercises 1–3.

b Mass: The Metric System

There is a difference between **mass** and **weight,** but the terms are often used interchangeably. People sometimes use the word "weight" instead of "mass." Weight is related to the force of the earth's gravity. The farther you are from the center of the earth, the less you weigh. Your mass, on the other hand, stays the same no matter where you are.

The basic unit of mass is the **gram** (g), which is the mass of 1 cubic centimeter (1 cm^3 or 1 mL) of water. Since a cubic centimeter is small, a gram is a small unit of mass.

Complete.

1. 5 lb = _____ oz

2. 8640 lb = _____ T

3. 1 T = _____ oz

Answers on page A-39

Complete with mg, g, kg, or t.

4. A laptop computer has a mass of 2 _____ .

5. Evan has a body mass of 76 _____ .

6. For her sprained ankle, Roz took 400 _____ of ibuprofen.

7. A pen has a mass of 12 _____ .

8. A pickup truck has a mass of 1.5 _____ .

Answers on page A-39

Study Tips

BEGINNING TO STUDY FOR THE FINAL EXAM

It is never too soon to begin to study for the final examination. Take a few minutes each week to review the highlighted information, such as formulas, properties, and procedures. Make special use of the Summary and Reviews, Chapter Tests, and Cumulative Reviews, as well as the supplements such as Interact Math Tutorial and MathXL. The Cumulative Reviews and Final Examination for Chapters 1–12 can be used for practice.

1 g = 1 gram = the mass of 1 cm^3 (1 mL) of water

The metric prefixes for mass are the same as those used for length and capacity.

METRIC UNITS OF MASS

1 metric ton (t) = 1000 kilograms (kg)

1 *kilo*gram (kg) = 1000 grams (g)

1 *hecto*gram (hg) = 100 grams (g)

1 *deka*gram (dag) = 10 grams (g)

1 gram (g)

1 *deci*gram (dg) = $\dfrac{1}{10}$ gram (g)

1 *centi*gram (cg) = $\dfrac{1}{100}$ gram (g)

1 *milli*gram (mg) = $\dfrac{1}{1000}$ gram (g)

> Hectograms, dekagrams, decigrams, and centigrams are only rarely used.

THINKING METRIC

The mass of 1 raisin or 1 paperclip is approximately 1 gram (g). Since 1 metric ton is 1000 kg and 1 kg is about 2.2 lb, it follows that 1 metric ton (t) is about 2200 lb, or about 10% more than 1 American ton (T). The metric ton is used for very large masses, such as vehicles; the kilogram is used for masses of people or larger food packages; the gram is used for smaller food packages or objects like a coin or a ring; the milligram is used for even smaller masses like a dosage of medicine.

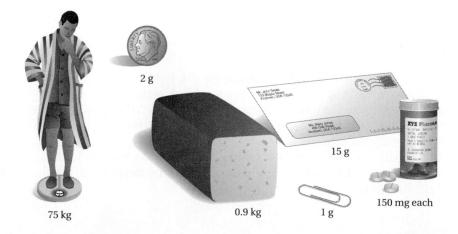

Do Exercises 4–8.

CHANGING UNITS MENTALLY

As before, changing from one metric unit to another amounts to only the movement of a decimal point. Consider these equivalent masses.

MASS OF A STANDARD SHEET OF PAPER

4260 mg = 426 cg = 4.26 g = 0.00426 kg

EXAMPLE 3 Complete: 8 kg = _____ g.

Think: A kilogram is 1000 times the mass of a gram. Thus we move the decimal point three places to the right.

8.0   8.000.   8 kg = 8000 g

EXAMPLE 4 Complete: 4235 g = _____ kg.

Think: There are 1000 grams in 1 kilogram. Thus we move the decimal point three places to the left.

4235.0   4.235.0   4235 g = 4.235 kg

EXAMPLE 5 Complete: 6.98 cg = _____ mg.

Think: One centigram has the mass of 10 milligrams. Thus we move the decimal point one place to the right.

6.98   6.9.8   6.98 cg = 69.8 mg

The most commonly used metric units of mass are kg, g, and mg. We have intentionally used those more often than the others in the exercises.

Do Exercises 9–12.

Complete.

9. 6.2 kg = _____ g

10. 93.1 g = _____ kg

11. 7.7 cg = _____ mg

12. 2344 mg = _____ cg

Answers on page A-39

Use a straightedge and the scales shown to the right to convert the following temperatures to either Celsius or Fahrenheit. Answers may be approximate.

13. 25°F (Cold day)

14. 30°C (Warm beach day)

15. −10°F (Extremely cold day)

16. 10°C (A cold mountain stream)

C Temperature

ESTIMATED CONVERSIONS

Below are two temperature scales: **Fahrenheit,** which is most often used in the United States, and **Celsius,** which is used internationally and in science.

By laying a straightedge horizontally between the scales, we can approximate conversions between Celsius and Fahrenheit.

EXAMPLES Use a straightedge to approximate each of the following conversions. Use the scales above.

6. 110°F (Hot bath) ≈ 43°C

7. 50°C (Warm food) = 122°F   This is exact.

8. 160°F (Temperature of a sauna) ≈ 72°C

9. 0°C (Freezing point of water) = 32°F   This is exact and worth remembering.

Do Exercises 13–16.

Answers on page A-39

EXACT CONVERSIONS

A formula allows us to make exact conversions from Celsius to Fahrenheit.

> ### CELSIUS TO FAHRENHEIT
>
> $$F = \frac{9}{5} \cdot C + 32, \quad \text{or} \quad F = 1.8 \cdot C + 32$$
>
> $\left(\text{Multiply the Celsius temperature by } \frac{9}{5}, \text{ or } 1.8, \text{ and add } 32.\right)$

EXAMPLES   Convert to Fahrenheit.

10. 0°C $F = \frac{9}{5} \cdot 0 + 32 = 0 + 32 = 32°$ Substituting 0 for C

Thus, 0°C = 32°F.   This is the freezing point of water.

11. 37°C $F = 1.8 \cdot 37 + 32 = 66.6 + 32 = 98.6°$ Substituting 37 for C

Thus, 37°C = 98.6°F.   This is normal body temperature.

A second formula gives exact conversions from Fahrenheit to Celsius.

> ### FAHRENHEIT TO CELSIUS
>
> $$C = \frac{5}{9} \cdot (F - 32)$$
>
> $\left(\text{Subtract 32 from the Fahrenheit temperature and multiply by } \frac{5}{9}.\right)$

EXAMPLES   Convert to Celsius.

12. 212°F $C = \frac{5}{9} \cdot (F - 32)$

$\quad\quad\quad = \frac{5}{9} \cdot (212 - 32) = \frac{5}{9} \cdot 180 = 100°$

Thus, 212°F = 100°C.   This is the boiling point of water.

13. 77°F $C = \frac{5}{9} \cdot (F - 32)$

$\quad\quad\quad = \frac{5}{9} \cdot (77 - 32) = \frac{5}{9} \cdot 45 = 25°$

Thus, 77°F = 25°C.

Do Exercises 17–20.

Convert to Fahrenheit or Celsius.

17. 80°C

18. 35°C

19. 95°F

20. 113°F

12.7 **EXERCISE SET**

For Extra Help

Digital Video Tutor CD 6 Videotape 9 | InterAct Math | Math Tutor Center | MathXL | MyMathLab

a Complete.

1. 1 lb = _____ oz

2. 1 T = _____ lb

3. 8000 lb = _____ T

4. 7 T = _____ lb

5. 3 lb = _____ oz

6. 10 lb = _____ oz

7. 4.5 T = _____ lb

8. 2.5 T = _____ lb

9. 4800 lb = _____ T

10. 7500 lb = _____ T

11. 72 oz = _____ lb

12. 960 oz = _____ lb

b Complete.

13. 4 kg = _____ g

14. 9 kg = _____ g

15. 1 g = _____ kg

16. 1 dg = _____ g

17. 1 cg = _____ g

18. 1 mg = _____ g

19. 1 g = _____ mg

20. 1 g = _____ cg

21. 1 g = _____ dg

22. 57 kg = _____ g

23. 934 kg = _____ g

24. 678 g = _____ kg

25. 6345 g = _____ kg

26. 42.75 kg = _____ g

27. 897 mg = _____ kg

28. 45 cg = _____ g

29. 7.32 kg = _____ g

30. 0.439 cg = _____ mg

31. 9350 g = _____ kg

32. 5640 g = _____ kg

33. 69 mg = _____ cg

34. 76.1 mg = _____ cg

35. 8 kg = _____ cg

36. 0.02 kg = _____ mg

37. 1 t = _____ kg

38. 2 t = _____ kg

39. 3.4 cg = _____ dag

40. 9.34 g = _____ mg

C   Convert to Celsius. Round the answer to the nearest ten degrees. Use the scales on p. 857.

41. 178°F

42. 195°F

43. 140°F

44. 107°F

45. 68°F

46. 45°F

47. 10°F

48. 120°F

Convert to Fahrenheit. Round the answer to the nearest ten degrees. Use the scales on p. 857.

49. 86°C

50. 93°C

51. 58°C

52. 33°C

53. −10°C

54. −5°C

55. 5°C

56. 15°C

Convert to Fahrenheit. Use the formula $F = \frac{9}{5} \cdot C + 32$.

57. 30°C   **58.** 85°C   **59.** 40°C   **60.** 90°C

61. 3000°C (melting point of iron)   **62.** 1000°C (melting point of gold)

Convert to Celsius. Use the formula $C = \frac{5}{9} \cdot (F - 32)$.

63. 77°F   **64.** 59°F   **65.** 131°F   **66.** 140°F

67. 98.6°F (normal body temperature)   **68.** 104°F (high-fevered body temperature)

69. **D$_W$** Describe a situation in which one object weighs 70 kg, another object weighs 3 g, and a third object weighs 125 mg.

70. **D$_W$** Give at least two reasons why someone might prefer the use of grams to the use of ounces.

SKILL MAINTENANCE

Convert to percent notation.   [8.1b]

71. 0.0043   **72.** 2.31

73. If 2 cans of tomato paste cost $1.49, how many cans of tomato paste can you buy for $7.45?   [7.4a]

74. *Sound Levels.*   Make a horizontal bar graph to show the loudness of various sounds, as listed below. A decibel is a measure of the loudness of sounds.   [6.2b]

SOUND	LOUDNESS (in decibels)
Whisper	15
Tick of watch	30
Speaking aloud	60
Noisy factory	90
Moving car	80
Car horn	98
Subway	104

75. Solve: $9(x - 3) = 4x - 5$.   [5.7b]

76. Solve: $34.1 - 17.4x = 2.1x - 14.65$.   [5.7b]

CHAPTER 12: Geometry and Measurement

77. D_W Near the Canadian border, a radio forecast calls for an overnight low of 60°. Was the temperature given in Celsius or Fahrenheit? Explain how you can tell.

78. D_W Which represents a bigger change in temperature: a drop of 5°F or a drop of 5°C? Why?

Complete. Use 453.6 = 1 lb. Round to four decimal places.

79. ▦ 1 lb = _____ kg

80. ▦ 1 g = _____ lb

81. Use the formula $F = \frac{9}{5} \cdot C + 32$ to find the temperature that is the same for both the Fahrenheit and Celsius scales.

82. *Large Diamonds.*   A **carat** (also spelled **karat**) is a unit of weight for precious stones; 1 carat = 200 mg. The Golden Jubilee Diamond weighs 545.67 carats and is the largest cut diamond in the world. The Hope Diamond, located at the Smithsonian Institution Museum of Natural History, weighs 45.52 carats.
Source: *National Geographic,* February 2001

   a) How many grams does the Golden Jubilee Diamond weigh?

   b) How many grams does the Hope Diamond weigh?

   c) ▦ Given that 1 lb = 453.6 g, how many ounces does each diamond weigh?

83. *Nutrition.*   A jar of flaxseed oil capsules contains 250 capsules, each of which contains 1000 mg of flaxseed oil. Given that 1 lb = 454 g, find the weight, in ounces, of flaxseed oil in a new, unopened jar.

861

84. *Chemistry.* Another temperature scale often used is the **Kelvin** scale. Conversions from Celsius to Kelvin can be carried out using the formula

$$K = C + 273.$$

A chemistry textbook describes an experiment in which a reaction takes place at a temperature of 400° Kelvin. A student wishes to perform the experiment, but has only a Fahrenheit thermometer. At what Fahrenheit temperature will the reaction take place?

85. 🖩 A large egg is about $5\frac{1}{2}$ cm tall with a diameter of 4 cm. Estimate the mass of such an egg by averaging the volumes of two spheres. (*Hint:* 1 cc of water has a mass of 1 g.)

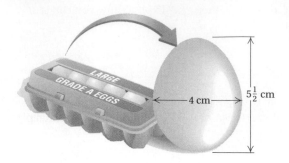

86. *Medicine.* Quinidine is a medicine that comes mixed with water. There are 80 mg of Quinidine in every milliliter of liquid. A standard dosage requires 200 mg of Quinidine. How much of the liquid mixture would be required in order to achieve this dosage?
Source: National Library of Medicine

87. 🖩 *Track and Field.* A woman's shot put weighs 8.8 lb and has a 4.5-in. diameter. Find its mass per cubic centimeter.
Source: National Collegiate Athletic Association

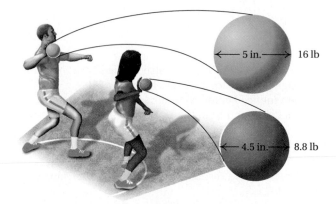

88. 🖩 *Track and Field.* A man's shot put weighs 16 lb and has a 5-in. diameter. Find its mass per cubic centimeter.

89. 🖩 A shrink-wrapped brick of pudding boxes weighs $15\frac{17}{20}$ lb. If each box of pudding weighs $1\frac{3}{4}$ oz, how many boxes are in the brick and how much does the plastic shrink wrap weigh?

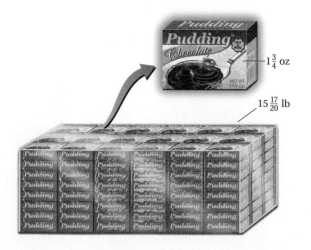

12.8

MEDICAL APPLICATIONS

a   Measurements and Medicine

Measurements play a critical role in health care. Doctors, nurses, aides, technicians, and others all need to use the proper units and perform the proper calculations to assure the best possible care of patients.

   Because of the ease with which conversions can be made and its extensive use in science—among other reasons—the metric system is the primary system of measurement in medicine.

EXAMPLE 1   *Medical Dosage.*   A physician orders 3.5 L of 5% dextrose in water (abbrev. D5W) to be administered over a 24-hr period. How many milliliters were ordered?

   We convert 3.5 L to milliliters:

$$3.5\text{ L} = 3.5 \cdot 1\text{ L}$$
$$= 3.5 \cdot 1000\text{ mL}\qquad \text{Substituting}$$
$$= 3500\text{ mL.}$$

The physician had ordered 3500 mL of D5W.

Do Exercise 1.

   Liquids at a pharmacy are often labeled in liters or milliliters. Thus if a physician's prescription is given in ounces, it must be converted. For conversion, a pharmacist knows that 1 oz ≈ 29.57 mL.*

EXAMPLE 2   *Prescription Size.*   A prescription calls for 3 oz of theophylline, a drug commonly used for children with asthma. For how many milliliters is the prescription?

   We convert as follows:

$$3\text{ oz} = 3 \cdot 1\text{ oz}$$
$$\approx 3 \cdot 29.57\text{ mL}\qquad \text{Substituting}$$
$$= 88.71\text{ mL.}$$

The prescription calls for 88.71 mL of theophylline.

Do Exercise 2.

Objectives

a   Make conversions and solve applied problems concerning medical dosages.

1. **Medical Dosage.**   A physician orders 2400 mL of 0.9% saline solution to be administered intravenously over a 24-hr period. How many liters were ordered?

2. **Prescription Size.**   A prescription calls for 2 oz of theophylline.
   a) For how many milliliters is the prescription?
   b) For how many liters is the prescription?

Answers on page A-40

3. Pill Splitting. If Tania's physician originally prescribed 14 tablets that were each 25 mg, how many milligrams were in the original prescription? How many 12.5-mg doses could be obtained from the original prescription?

4. Complete:
$3 \text{ mg} = \underline{\hspace{1cm}} \text{ mcg}.$

EXAMPLE 3 *Pill Splitting.* Chlorthalidone is a commonly prescribed drug used to treat hypertension. Tania's physician directs her to reduce her dosage from 25 mg to 12.5 mg. Tania's original prescription contained 30 tablets, each 25 mg.

a) How many milligrams of chlorthalidone, in total, were in the original prescription?
b) How many 12.5-mg doses can Tania obtain from the original prescription?

a) The original prescription contained 30 tablets, each containing 25 mg of chlorthalidone. To find the total amount in the prescription, we multiply:

$$30 \text{ tablets} \cdot 25 \text{ mg/tablet} = 750 \text{ mg}.$$

The original prescription contained 750 mg of chlorthalidone.

b) Since 12.5 mg is half of 25 mg ($25 \div 2 = 12.5$), Tania's original 30 doses can each be split in half, yielding $30 \cdot 2$, or 60, doses at 12.5 mg per dose.

Do Exercise 3.

Another metric unit that is used in medicine is the microgram (mcg). It is defined as follows.

MICROGRAM

$$1 \text{ microgram} = 1 \text{ mcg} = \frac{1}{1,000,000} \text{ g} = 0.000001 \text{ g}$$

$$1,000,000 \text{ mcg} = 1 \text{ g}$$

One microgram is one-millionth of a gram, so one million micrograms is one gram. A microgram is also one-thousandth of a milligram, so one thousand micrograms is one milligram.

EXAMPLE 4 Complete: $1 \text{ mg} = \underline{\hspace{1cm}} \text{ mcg}.$

We convert to grams and then to micrograms:

$$\begin{aligned} 1 \text{ mg} &= 0.001 \text{ g} \\ &= 0.001 \cdot 1 \text{ g} \\ &= 0.001 \cdot 1,000,000 \text{ mcg} \qquad \text{Substituting 1,000,000 mcg for 1 g} \\ &= 1000 \text{ mcg.} \end{aligned}$$

Do Exercise 4.

EXAMPLE 5 *Medical Dosage.* Nitroglycerin sublingual tablets come in 0.4-mg tablets. How many micrograms are in each tablet?
Source: Steven R. Smith, M.D.

We are to complete: 0.4 mg = _____ mcg. Thus,

$$0.4 \text{ mg} = 0.4 \cdot 1 \text{ mg}$$
$$= 0.4 \cdot 1000 \text{ mcg} \quad \text{Substituting 1000 mcg for 1 mg}$$
$$= 400 \text{ mcg.}$$

We can also do this problem in a manner similar to Example 4.

Do Exercise 5.

5. Medical Dosage. A physician prescribes 500 mcg of alprazolam, an antianxiety medication. How many milligrams is this dosage?
Source: Steven R. Smith, M.D.

Answer on page A-40

Study Tips

THE FOURTEEN BEST JOBS: HOW MATH STACKS UP

We list the Top 14 here and note whether math is an important aspect or requirement of the job. Note that math is significant in 11 of the 14 jobs and has at least some use in all the jobs!

	JOB	MATH EMPHASIS	MID-LEVEL SALARY
1.	Financial planner	Yes	$107,000
2.	Web site manager	Yes	68,000
3.	Computer systems analyst	Yes	54,000
4.	Actuary	Yes	71,000
5.	Computer programmer (tie)	Yes	57,000
6.	Software engineer	Yes	53,000
7.	Meteorologist	Some	57,000
8.	Biologist	Some	53,000
9.	Astronomer	Yes	74,000
10.	Paralegal assistant	Some	37,000
11.	Statistician	Yes	55,000
12.	Hospital administrator	Yes	64,000
13.	Dietician	Yes	39,000
14.	Mathematician	Yes	45,000

Source: Les Krantz. *Jobs Related Almanac.* New York: St. Martin's Press, 2000

12.8

EXERCISE SET

For Extra Help

Digital Video
Tutor CD 6
Videotape 9

InterAct
Math

Math Tutor
Center

MathXL

MyMathLab

a *Medical Dosage.* Solve each of the following. (None of these medications should be taken without consulting your own physician.)

1. Dr. Dover ordered 0.5 L of normal saline solution. How many milliliters were ordered?

2. Ingrid receives 84 mL per hour of normal saline solution. How many liters did Ingrid receive in a 24-hr period?

3. An emergency-room physician orders 3 L of Ringer's lactate to be administered over 4 hr for a patient suffering from shock and severe low blood pressure. How many milliliters is this?

4. An allergist recommends that a 9-year-old be given 25 mg of diphenhydramine HCL to combat sneezing due to allergies. If, in the course of 48 hours, 5 doses are administered, how many grams is this?

5. To battle hypertension and prostate enlargement, Rick is directed to take 4 mg of doxazosin each day for 30 days. How many grams is this?

6. To battle high cholesterol, Kit is directed to take 40 mg of atorvastatin for 60 days. How many grams is this?

7. Cephalexin is an antibiotic that frequently is prescribed in a 500-mg tablet form. A physician prescribes 2 grams of cephalexin per day for a patient with a skin abscess. How many 500-mg tablets would have to be taken in order to achieve this daily dosage?

8. Quinidine gluconate is a liquid mixture, part medicine and part water, which is administered intravenously. There are 80 mg of quinidine gluconate in each cubic centimeter (cc) of the liquid mixture. A physician orders 900 mg of quinidine gluconate to be administered daily to a patient with malaria. How much of the solution would have to be administered in order to achieve the recommended daily dosage?

9. Albuterol is a medication used for the treatment of asthma. It comes in an inhaler that contains 17 mg albuterol mixed with a liquid. One actuation (inhalation) from the mouthpiece delivers a 90-mcg dose of albuterol.

   a) A physician orders 2 inhalations 4 times per day. How many micrograms of albuterol does the patient inhale per day?

   b) How many actuations/inhalations are contained in one inhaler?

   c) Danielle is going away for 4 months of college and wants to take enough albuterol to last for that time. Her physician has prescribed 2 inhalations 4 times per day. Estimate how many inhalers Danielle will need to take with her for the 4-month period.

10. Amoxicillin is a common antibiotic prescribed for children. It is a liquid suspension composed of part amoxicillin and part water. In one formulation of amoxicillin suspension, there are 250 mg of amoxicillin in 5 cc of the liquid suspension. A physician prescribes 400 mg per day for a 2-year-old child with an ear infection. How much of the amoxicillin liquid suspension would the child's parent need to administer in order to achieve the recommended daily dosage of amoxicillin?

11. Dr. Norris tells a patient to purchase 0.5 L of hydrogen peroxide. Commercially, hydrogen peroxide is found on the shelf in bottles that hold 4 oz, 8 oz, and 16 oz. Which bottle comes closest to filling the prescription?

12. Dr. Gomez wants a patient to receive 3 L of a normal glucose solution in a 24-hr period. How many milliliters per hour should the patient receive?

13. Remeron® is a commonly prescribed antianxiety drug. Joanne has a 14-tablet supply of 30-mg tablets and her physician now directs her to reduce her dosage to 15 mg.

   a) How many grams were originally prescribed?

   b) How many 15-mg doses can Joanne obtain from the original prescription?

14. Serzone® is a commonly prescribed antidepressant. Chad has a 90-tablet supply of 200-mg tablets, when his physician directs him to cut his dosage size to 100 mg.

   a) How many grams are in Chad's current supply?

   b) How many 100-mg doses can Chad obtain from his supply?

15. Amoxicillin is an antibiotic obtainable in a liquid suspension form, part medication and part water, and is frequently used to treat infections in infants. One formulation of the drug contains 125 mg of amoxicillin per 5 mL of liquid. A pediatrician orders 150 mg per day for a 4-month-old child with an ear infection. How much of the amoxicillin suspension would the parent need to administer to the infant in order to achieve the recommended daily dose?

16. Diphenhydramine HCL is an antihistamine available in liquid form, part medication and part water. One formulation contains 25 mg of medication in 5 mL of liquid. A physician orders 40-mg doses for a high school student. How many milliliters should be in each dose?

Complete.

17. 1 mg = _____ mcg

18. 1 mcg = _____ mg

19. 325 mcg = _____ mg

20. 0.45 mg = _____ mcg

21. A physician prescribes 0.25 mg of alprazolam, an antianxiety medication. How many micrograms are in this dose?

22. A physician prescribes 0.4 mg of alprazolam, an antianxiety medication. How many micrograms are in this dose?

23. Digoxin is a medication used to treat heart problems. A physician orders 0.125 mg of digoxin to be taken once daily. How many micrograms of digoxin are there in the daily dosage?

24. Digoxin is a medication used to treat heart problems. A physician orders 0.25 mg of digoxin to be taken once a day. How many micrograms of digoxin are there in the daily dosage?

25. Triazolam is a medication used for the short-term treatment of insomnia. A physician advises her patient to take one of the 0.125-mg tablets each night for 7 nights. How many milligrams of triazolam will the patient have ingested over that 7-day period? How many micrograms?

26. Clonidine is a medication used to treat high blood pressure. The usual starting dose of clonidine is one 0.1-mg tablet twice a day. If a patient is started on this dose by his physician, how many total milligrams of clonidine will the patient have taken before he returns to see his physician 14 days later? How many micrograms?

CHAPTER 12: Geometry and Measurement

27. $\mathbf{D_W}$ A nursing student is reprimanded for moving a decimal point one place to the right instead of one place to the left. Why was this considered such a serious mistake?

28. $\mathbf{D_W}$ Why might a patient want to purchase 200-mg tablets and split them in half rather than simply purchase 100-mg tablets?

SKILL MAINTENANCE

Subtract. [1.3d]

29.
$$\begin{array}{r} 5\ 7\ 8\ 9 \\ -\ 2\ 4\ 3\ 1 \end{array}$$

30.
$$\begin{array}{r} 8\ 4\ 2\ 9 \\ -\ 1\ 0\ 1\ 5 \end{array}$$

31.
$$\begin{array}{r} 4\ 0\ 9\ 7 \\ -\ 3\ 2\ 4\ 3 \end{array}$$

32.
$$\begin{array}{r} 8\ 3\ 9\ 0 \\ -\ 2\ 0\ 5\ 6 \end{array}$$

Simplify. [2.7a]

33. $7x + 9 - 2x - 1$

34. $8x + 12 - 2x - 7$

35. $8t - 5 - t - 4$

36. $9r - 6 - r - 4$

SYNTHESIS

37. $\mathbf{D_W}$ Describe a situation in which someone would need to convert from kilograms to micrograms.

38. $\mathbf{D_W}$ Alan's dose is being reduced, yet the size of the tablets in the prescription is being increased. Why do you think this might be?

39. A patient is directed to take 200 mg of Serzone® 3 times a day for one week, then 200 mg twice a day for a week, and then 100 mg three times a day for a week.

a) How many grams of medication are used altogether?
b) What is the average dosage size?

40. A patient is directed to take 200 mg of Wellbutrin® twice a day for a week, then 200 mg in the evening and 100 mg in the morning for a week, and then 100 mg twice a day for a week.

a) How many grams of medication are used altogether?
b) What is the average dosage size?

41. Naproxen sodium, sometimes sold under the brand name Aleve, is a painkiller that lasts approximately 12 hours. A typical dose is one 220-mg tablet. Ibuprofen is a similar painkiller that lasts about 6 hours and has a typical dosage of two 200-mg tablets. What would be a better purchase: a bottle containing 44 g of naproxen sodium costing $11, or a bottle containing 72 g of ibuprofen costing $11.24? Why?

42. $\mathbf{D_W}$ Why might someone ignore the answer to Exercise 41 when shopping for naproxen sodium or ibuprofen?

The review that follows is meant to prepare you for a chapter exam. It consists of two parts. The first part is a checklist of some of the Study Tips referred to in this chapter, as well as a list of important properties and formulas. The second part is the Review Exercises. These provide practice exercises for the exam, together with references to section objectives so you can go back and review. Before beginning, stop and look back over the skills you have obtained. What skills in mathematics do you have now that you did not have before studying this chapter?

STUDY TIPS CHECKLIST

The foundation of all your study skills is TIME!	☐ Are you using abbreviations when you take notes?
	☐ Are your sketches drawn carefully enough to be realistic?
	☐ When familiar material is covered, are you maintaining your focus and mastering the terminology in use?
	☐ Have you been able to leave any bitter memories from previous courses in the past?
	☐ Are you keeping an eye open for new patterns that may prove useful in the future?
	☐ Have you begun studying for the final exam?

IMPORTANT PROPERTIES AND FORMULAS

Area of a Parallelogram:	$A = b \cdot h$
Area of a Trapezoid:	$A = \dfrac{1}{2} \cdot h \cdot (a + b)$
Radius and Diameter of a Circle:	$d = 2 \cdot r$, or $r = \dfrac{d}{2}$
Circumference of a Circle:	$C = \pi \cdot d$, or $C = 2 \cdot \pi \cdot r$
Area of a Circle:	$A = \pi \cdot r \cdot r$, or $A = \pi \cdot r^2$
Volume of a Rectangular Solid:	$V = l \cdot w \cdot h$
Volume of a Circular Cylinder:	$V = \pi \cdot r^2 \cdot h$
Volume of a Sphere:	$V = \frac{4}{3} \cdot \pi \cdot r^3$
Pythagorean Equation:	$a^2 + b^2 = c^2$
Temperature Conversion:	$F = \frac{9}{5} \cdot C + 32$; $C = \frac{5}{9} \cdot (F - 32)$

See tables inside chapter for units of length, weight, mass, and capacity.

REVIEW EXERCISES

Complete.

1. 10 ft = _____ yd
   [12.1a]

2. $\frac{5}{6}$ yd = _____ in.
   [12.1a]

3. 1.7 mm = _____ cm
   [12.1b]

4. 6 m = _____ km
   [12.1b]

5. 4 km = _____ cm
   [12.1b]

6. 14 in. = _____ ft
   [12.1a]

7. 5 lb = _____ oz
   [12.7a]

8. 3 g = _____ kg
   [12.7b]

9. 50 qt = _____ gal
   [12.4b]

10. 28 gal = _____ pt
   [12.4b]

11. 60 mL = _____ L
   [12.4b]

12. 0.4 L = _____ mL
   [12.4b]

13. 0.7 T = _____ lb
   [12.7a]

14. 0.2 g = _____ mg
   [12.7b]

15. 4.7 kg = _____ g
   [12.7b]

16. 4 cg = _____ g
   [12.7b]

17. 4 yd^2 = _____ ft^2
   [12.2a]

18. 0.7 km^2 = _____ m^2
   [12.2b]

19. 1008 in^2 = _____ ft^2
   [12.2a]

20. 570 cm^2 = _____ m^2
   [12.2b]

21. Find the circumference of a circle of radius 5 m.
   Use 3.14 for π.   [12.3b]

22. Find the length of a radius of the circle.   [12.3b]

23. Find the length of a diameter of the circle.   [12.3b]

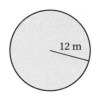

Find the area of each figure in Exercises 24–29.   [12.3a, b]

24.

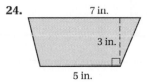

25.

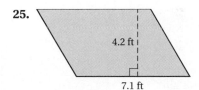

26.

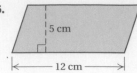

5 cm

|← 12 cm →|

27.

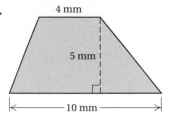

4 mm

5 mm

|← 10 mm →|

28. Use $\frac{22}{7}$ for π.

7 ft

29. Use 3.14 for π.

10 cm

30. A "Norman" window is designed with dimensions as shown. Find its area. Use 3.14 for π. [12.3b]

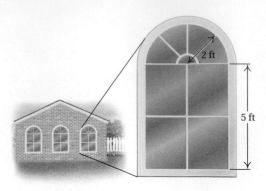

2 ft

5 ft

31. Find the measure of a complement and of a supplement of $\angle BAC$. [12.5c]

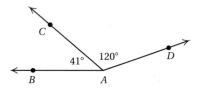

C

41° 120° D

B A

32. List two pairs of vertical angles. [12.5c]

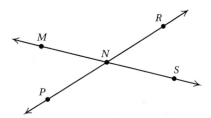

R

M

N

P

S

Find the volume of each figure. Use 3.14 for π. [12.4a]

33.

2.6 m
12 m
3 m

34.

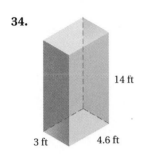

14 ft
3 ft
4.6 ft

35.

90 cm
10 cm

36.

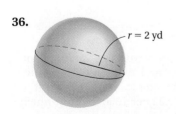

$r = 2$ yd

37.

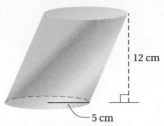

12 cm
5 cm

For each right triangle, find the length of the side not given. Find an exact answer and an approximation to three decimal places. Assume that c represents the length of the hypotenuse. [12.6c]

38. $a = 15$, $b = 25$ **39.** $a = 4$, $c = 10$

40.

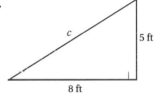

c
5 ft
8 ft

41.

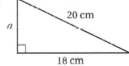

a
20 cm
18 cm

42. Convert 35°C to Fahrenheit. [12.7c]

43. A physician prescribed 650 mL per hour of a saline solution for a patient. How many liters of fluid did this patient receive in one day? [12.4c]

44. Dr. Tanner prescribes 400 mcg of alprazolam. How many milligrams is this dosage? [12.8a]

45. D_W Is a square a special type of parallelogram? Why or why not? [12.3a]

46. D_W Is it possible for a triangle to contain two 90° angles? Why or why not? [12.5e]

47. Find the simple interest on $5000 at 9.5% for 30 days. [8.6a]

48. Convert to percent notation: 0.47 . [8.1b]

49. Convert to decimal notation: 56.7%. [8.1b]

50. Solve: $9x + 4 = 3x - 23$. [5.7b]

51. A hot air balloon travels 5 mi in $2\frac{1}{2}$ hr. At this rate, how far will the balloon travel in 12 hr? [7.4a]

52. Solve: $5(x - 1.5) = x + 2.5$. [5.7b]

53. D_W Which is a larger measure of volume: $1\ m^3$ or $27\ ft^3$? Explain how you can tell without using a calculator. [12.1c], [12.4a]

54. D_W What weighs more: 32 oz or 1 kg? Explain how you can tell without using a calculator? [12.7a, b]

55. ▦ Find the area of the largest round pizza that can be baked in a 35-cm by 50-cm pan. [12.3b]

56. ▦ One lap around a standard running track is 440 yd. A marathon is 26 mi, 385 yd long. How many laps around a track does a marathon require? [12.1a]

57. Lumber that starts out at a certain measure must be trimmed to take out warps and get boards that are straight. Because of trimming, a "two-by-four" is trimmed to an actual size of $1\frac{1}{2}$ in. by $3\frac{1}{2}$ in. What percent of the wood in an untrimmed 10-ft two-by-four is lost by trimming? [12.4c]

58. A community center has a rectangular swimming pool that is 50 ft wide, 100 ft long, and 10 ft deep. The center decides to fill the pool with water to a line that is 1 ft from the top. Water costs $2.25 per 1000 ft^3. How much does it cost to fill the pool? [12.4c]

Complete.

1. 8 ft = _____ in.

2. 280 cm = _____ m

3. 2 yd^2 = _____ ft^2

4. 5 km = _____ m

5. 9.1 mm = _____ cm

6. 4520 m^2 = _____ km^2

7. 2983 mL = _____ L

8. 3.8 kg = _____ g

9. 10 gal = _____ oz

10. 0.69 L = _____ mL

11. 9 lb = _____ oz

12. 4.11 T = _____ lb

13. Find the length of a radius of this circle.

16 cm

14. Find the area of a circle of radius 4 m. Use 3.14 for π.

15. Find the circumference of a circle of radius 14 ft. Use $\frac{22}{7}$ for π.

Find each area. Use 3.14 for π.

16.

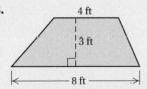
2.5 cm
10 cm

17.

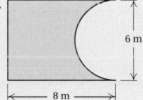
6 m
8 m

18.

4 ft
3 ft
8 ft

19. A 5-in. by 7-in. diploma is mounted on matting board that is 6 in. by 8 in. What is the area of the border?

20. Find the measure of a supplement of $\angle CAD$.

21. Find the measure of $\angle GAF$.

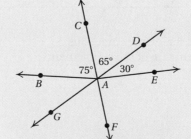
C
D
75° 65° 30°
B   A   E
G
F

22. A gift box for earrings measures 6 cm by 8 cm by 4 cm. What is its volume?

In Exercises 23–25 find the volume in each figure. Use 3.14 for π.

23.

5 ft

8 ft

24.

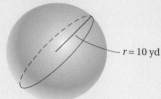

$r = 10$ yd

25.

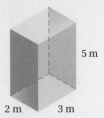

5 m

2 m   3 m

26. Dr. Pietrofiro wants a patient to receive 0.5 L of a dextrose solution every 8 hr. How many milliliters will the patient have received after one 48-hr period?

For each right triangle, find the length of the side not given. Find an exact answer and an approximation to three decimal places.

27.

c

1

1

28.

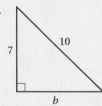

10

7

b

29. Find $\sqrt{121}$.

30. Convert 32°F to Celsius.

31. An antihistamine solution contains 25 mg of medication in 5 mL of liquid. Pat is directed to take a 30-mg dose of the antihistamine. How many mL's of the solution should Pat take?

⎯(**SKILL MAINTENANCE**)⎯⎯⎯⎯⎯⎯⎯⎯⎯⎯⎯⎯⎯⎯⎯⎯⎯⎯⎯⎯⎯⎯⎯⎯⎯⎯

32. Find the simple interest on $5000 at 8.8% for 1 year.

33. Convert to percent notation: 0.93 .

34. Convert to decimal notation: 93.2%.

35. Solve: $5 - 2x = 7(3 - x) + 4$.

36. If 5 gal of gas costs $7.70, how much will 9 gal cost?

37. Solve: $7x - 3.6 = 3x + 6.4$.

⎯(**SYNTHESIS**)⎯⎯⎯⎯⎯⎯⎯⎯⎯⎯⎯⎯⎯⎯⎯⎯⎯⎯⎯⎯⎯⎯⎯⎯⎯⎯⎯⎯⎯⎯⎯⎯

38. The measure of $\angle SMC$ is three times that of its complement. Find the measure of the supplement of $\angle SMC$.

39. ▦ A *board foot* is the amount of wood in a piece 12 in. by 12 in. by 1 in. A carpenter places the following order for a certain kind of lumber:

     25 pieces: 2 in. by 4 in. by 8 ft;
     32 pieces: 2 in. by 6 in. by 10 ft;
     24 pieces: 2 in. by 8 in. by 12 ft.

The price of this type of lumber is $225 per thousand board feet. What is the total cost of the carpenter's order?

Perform the indicated operations and, if possible, simplify.

1. $4\dfrac{2}{3} + 5\dfrac{1}{2}$

2. $\left(\dfrac{1}{4}\right)^2 \div \left(\dfrac{1}{2}\right)^3 \times 2^4 + (10.3)(4)$

3. $120.5 - 32.98$

4. $-27{,}148 \div 22$

5. $14 \div [33 \div 11 + 8 \times 2 - (15 - 3)]$

6. $8^3 + 45 \cdot 24 - 9^2 \div 3$

7. Write 1.2 as an equivalent fraction. Simplify, if possible.

8. Write $\dfrac{9}{20}$ as an equivalent percent.

Use $<$, $>$, or $=$ for $\square$ to write a true sentence.

9. $\dfrac{5}{6} \square \dfrac{7}{8}$

10. $\dfrac{5}{12} \square \dfrac{3}{10}$

Complete.

11. 6 oz = _____ lb

12. 100°C = _____ °F

13. 0.087 L = _____ mL

14. 2.5 yd = _____ in.

15. 3 yd^2 = _____ ft^2

16. 37 cm = _____ m

17. Find the perimeter and the area.

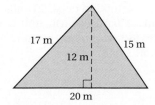

17 m   15 m   12 m   20 m

18. Combine like terms: $12a - 7 - 3a - 9$.

19. Graph: $y = -\dfrac{1}{3}x + 2$.

The following graph records Vermont Medicaid spending on clients of the Department of Prevention, Assistance, Transition and Health Access (PATH).

Source: *Burlington Free Press*, 1/5/03

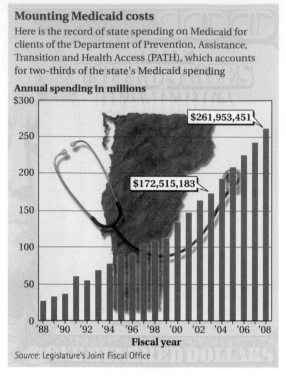

Mounting Medicaid costs

Here is the record of state spending on Medicaid for clients of the Department of Prevention, Assistance, Transition and Health Access (PATH), which accounts for two-thirds of the state's Medicaid spending

Annual spending in millions

$261,953,451

$172,515,183

Fiscal year

Source: Legislature's Joint Fiscal Office

20. Estimate the Medicaid spent on PATH clients in 1998.

21. In what year was Medicaid spending on PATH clients first projected to exceed $200 million?

Solve.

22. $\dfrac{12}{15} = \dfrac{x}{18}$

23. $1 - 7x = 4 - (x + 9)$

24. $-15x = 280$

25. $x + \dfrac{3}{4} = \dfrac{7}{8}$

26. In several states, empty soda and beer bottles can be redeemed for a deposit. A case of returnable bottles contains 24 bottles. Several students find that together they have 168 bottles. How many cases can they fill?

27. Americans own 52 million dogs, 56 million cats, 45 million birds, 250 million fish, and 125 million other creatures as house pets. How many pets do Americans own?

28. Find the mean: 49, 53, 60, 62, 69.

29. What is the simple interest on $800 at 12% for $\frac{1}{4}$ year?

30. How long must a rope be in order to reach from the top of an 8-m tree to a point on the ground 15 m from the bottom of the tree?

31. The sales tax on a purchase of $5.50 is $0.33. What is the sales tax rate?

32. A bolt of fabric in a fabric store has $10\frac{3}{4}$ yd on it. A customer purchases $8\frac{5}{8}$ yd. How many yards remain on the bolt?

33. What is the cost, in dollars, of 15.6 gal of gasoline at 178.9¢ per gallon? Round to the nearest cent.

34. A box of powdered milk that makes 20 qt costs $4.99. A box that makes 8 qt costs $1.99. Which size has the lower unit price?

35. It is $\frac{7}{10}$ km from Ida's dormitory to the library. She starts to walk there, changes her mind after going $\frac{1}{4}$ of the distance, and returns home. How far did Ida walk?

Consider the following figure.

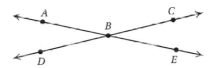

36. If the measure of $\angle ABC$ is 148°, find the measure of $\angle DBE$.

37. If the measure of $\angle ABD$ is 43°, find the measure of $\angle DBE$.

SYNTHESIS

38. A house sits on a lot measuring 75 ft by 200 ft. The lot is a corner lot, and includes sidewalks on two edges of the lot. If the sidewalks are 3 ft wide and 4 in. of snow falls, what volume of snow must be shoveled?

39. The U.S. Postal Service will not ship a box if the sum of the box's lengthwise perimeter and widthwise perimeter exceeds 108 in. Will a 1-ft by 2-ft by 3-ft box be accepted for shipping? Support your answer mathematically.

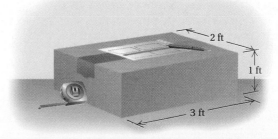

Answers

Chapter R

Margin Exercises, Section R.1, pp. 2–6

1. 9   **2.** 7   **3.** 14   **4.** 16   **5.** 16   **6.** 16   **7.** 8
8. 8   **9.** 7   **10.** 46   **11.** 13   **12.** 58
13.

+	1	2	3	4	5
1	2	3	4	5	6
2	3	4	5	6	7
3	4	5	6	7	8
4	5	6	7	8	9
5	6	7	8	9	10

14.

+	6	5	7	4	9
7	13	12	14	11	16
9	15	14	16	13	18
5	11	10	12	9	14
8	14	13	15	12	17
4	10	9	11	8	13

15. 16   **16.** 9   **17.** 11   **18.** 15   **19.** 59   **20.** 549
21. 9979   **22.** 5496   **23.** 56   **24.** 85   **25.** 829
26. 1026   **27.** 12,698   **28.** 13,661   **29.** 71,328

Exercise Set R.1, p. 7

1. 17   **2.** 15   **3.** 13   **4.** 14   **5.** 12   **6.** 11   **7.** 17
8. 16   **9.** 12   **10.** 10   **11.** 10   **12.** 11   **13.** 7
14. 7   **15.** 11   **16.** 0   **17.** 3   **18.** 18   **19.** 14
20. 10   **21.** 4   **22.** 14   **23.** 11   **24.** 15   **25.** 16
26. 9   **27.** 13   **28.** 14   **29.** 11   **30.** 7   **31.** 13
32. 14   **33.** 12   **34.** 6   **35.** 10   **36.** 12   **37.** 10
38. 8   **39.** 2   **40.** 9   **41.** 13   **42.** 0   **43.** 10   **44.** 0

45. 10   **46.** 6   **47.** 13   **48.** 9   **49.** 8   **50.** 11
51. 12   **52.** 13   **53.** 10   **54.** 12   **55.** 17   **56.** 13
57. 10   **58.** 16   **59.** 16   **60.** 15   **61.** 39   **62.** 89
63. 87   **64.** 999   **65.** 900   **66.** 868   **67.** 999
68. 848   **69.** 877   **70.** 17,680   **71.** 10,873   **72.** 4699
73. 10,867   **74.** 9895   **75.** 3998   **76.** 18,222
77. 16,889   **78.** 64,489   **79.** 99,999   **80.** 77,777
81. 46   **82.** 26   **83.** 55   **84.** 101   **85.** 1643
86. 1412   **87.** 846   **88.** 628   **89.** 1204   **90.** 607
91. 10,000   **92.** 1010   **93.** 1110   **94.** 1227   **95.** 1111
96. 1717   **97.** 10,138   **98.** 6554   **99.** 6111
100. 8427   **101.** 9890   **102.** 11,612   **103.** 11,125
104. 15,543   **105.** 16,774   **106.** 68,675   **107.** 34,437
108. 166,444   **109.** 101,315   **110.** 49,449

Margin Exercises, Section R.2, pp. 9–14

1. 4   **2.** 7   **3.** 8   **4.** 3   **5.** $12 - 8 = 4; 12 - 4 = 8$
6. $13 - 6 = 7; 13 - 7 = 6$ **7.** 8   **8.** 7   **9.** 9   **10.** 4
11. 14   **12.** 20   **13.** 241   **14.** 2025   **15.** 17   **16.** 36
17. 454   **18.** 250   **19.** 376   **20.** 245   **21.** 2557
22. 3674   **23.** 8   **24.** 6   **25.** 30   **26.** 90   **27.** 500
28. 900   **29.** 538   **30.** 677   **31.** 42   **32.** 224   **33.** 138
34. 44   **35.** 2768   **36.** 1197   **37.** 1246   **38.** 4728

Exercise Set R.2, p. 15

1. 7   **2.** 0   **3.** 0   **4.** 5   **5.** 3   **6.** 8   **7.** 8   **8.** 6
9. 7   **10.** 3   **11.** 7   **12.** 9   **13.** 6   **14.** 6   **15.** 2
16. 4   **17.** 3   **18.** 2   **19.** 0   **20.** 3   **21.** 1   **22.** 1
23. 7   **24.** 0   **25.** 4   **26.** 4   **27.** 5   **28.** 4   **29.** 4
30. 5   **31.** 9   **32.** 9   **33.** 7   **34.** 9   **35.** 6   **36.** 6
37. 2   **38.** 6   **39.** 7   **40.** 8   **41.** 33   **42.** 21
43. 247   **44.** 193   **45.** 500   **46.** 654   **47.** 202
48. 617   **49.** 288   **50.** 1220   **51.** 2231   **52.** 4126
53. 3764   **54.** 1691   **55.** 1226   **56.** 99,998   **57.** 10
58. 10,101   **59.** 11,043   **60.** 11,111   **61.** 65   **62.** 29
63. 8   **64.** 9   **65.** 308   **66.** 126   **67.** 617   **68.** 214
69. 89   **70.** 4402   **71.** 3555   **72.** 5889   **73.** 2387
74. 3649   **75.** 3832   **76.** 8144   **77.** 7750   **78.** 10,445
79. 33,793   **80.** 281   **81.** 455   **82.** 571   **83.** 6148

84. 2200 **85.** 2113 **86.** 3748 **87.** 5206 **88.** 1459
89. 305 **90.** 4455

Margin Exercises, Section R.3, pp. 17–22

1. 56 **2.** 36 **3.** 28 **4.** 42 **5.** 0 **6.** 0 **7.** 8
8. 23 **9.**

×	2	3	4	5
2	4	6	8	10
3	6	9	12	15
4	8	12	16	20
5	10	15	20	25
6	12	18	24	30

10.

×	6	7	8	9
5	30	35	40	45
6	36	42	48	54
7	42	49	56	63
8	48	56	64	72
9	54	63	72	81

11. 70 **12.** 450

13. 2730 **14.** 100 **15.** 1000 **16.** 560 **17.** 360
18. 700 **19.** 2300 **20.** 72,300 **21.** 10,000
22. 100,000 **23.** 5600 **24.** 1600 **25.** 9000
26. 852,000 **27.** 10,000 **28.** 12,000 **29.** 72,000
30. 54,000 **31.** 5600 **32.** 56,000 **33.** 18,000
34. 28 **35.** 116 **36.** 148 **37.** 4938 **38.** 6740
39. 116 **40.** 148 **41.** 4938 **42.** 6740 **43.** 5968
44. 59,680 **45.** 596,800

Exercise Set R.3, p. 23

1. 12 **2.** 0 **3.** 7 **4.** 0 **5.** 10 **6.** 30 **7.** 10
8. 63 **9.** 54 **10.** 12 **11.** 0 **12.** 72 **13.** 8 **14.** 0
15. 28 **16.** 24 **17.** 45 **18.** 18 **19.** 0 **20.** 35
21. 45 **22.** 40 **23.** 0 **24.** 16 **25.** 25 **26.** 81
27. 1 **28.** 0 **29.** 4 **30.** 36 **31.** 8 **32.** 0 **33.** 27
34. 18 **35.** 0 **36.** 10 **37.** 48 **38.** 54 **39.** 0
40. 72 **41.** 15 **42.** 8 **43.** 9 **44.** 2 **45.** 32
46. 6 **47.** 15 **48.** 6 **49.** 8 **50.** 20 **51.** 20
52. 16 **53.** 10 **54.** 0 **55.** 80 **56.** 70 **57.** 160
58. 210 **59.** 450 **60.** 780 **61.** 560 **62.** 360
63. 800 **64.** 300 **65.** 900 **66.** 1000 **67.** 345,700
68. 1200 **69.** 4900 **70.** 4000 **71.** 10,000 **72.** 7000
73. 9000 **74.** 2000 **75.** 457,000 **76.** 6,769,000
77. 18,000 **78.** 20,000 **79.** 48,000 **80.** 16,000
81. 6000 **82.** 1,000,000 **83.** 1200 **84.** 200
85. 4000 **86.** 2500 **87.** 12,000 **88.** 6000
89. 63,000 **90.** 120,000 **91.** 800,000 **92.** 120,000
93. 16,000,000 **94.** 80,000 **95.** 147 **96.** 444

97. 2965 **98.** 4872 **99.** 6293 **100.** 3460
101. 16,236 **102.** 13,508 **103.** 87,554 **104.** 195,384
105. 3480 **106.** 2790 **107.** 3360 **108.** 7020
109. 20,760 **110.** 10,680 **111.** 358,800 **112.** 109,800
113. 583,800 **114.** 299,700 **115.** 11,346,000
116. 23,390,000 **117.** 61,092,000 **118.** 73,032,000

Margin Exercises, Section R.4, pp. 25–32

1. 4 **2.** 8 **3.** 9 **4.** 3 **5.** $12 \div 2 = 6$; $12 \div 6 = 2$
6. $42 \div 6 = 7$; $42 \div 7 = 6$ **7.** 7 **8.** 9 **9.** 8 **10.** 9
11. 6 **12.** 13 **13.** 1 **14.** 2 **15.** Undefined **16.** 0
17. Undefined **18.** Undefined **19.** 10
20. Undefined **21.** 0 **22.** 1 **23.** 1 **24.** 1 **25.** 1
26. 17 **27.** 1 **28.** 75 R 4 **29.** 23 R 11 **30.** 969 R 6
31. 47 R 4 **32.** 96 R 1 **33.** 1263 R 5 **34.** 324
35. 417 R 5 **36.** 37 R 8 **37.** 23 R 17

Exercise Set R.4, p. 33

1. 3 **2.** 8 **3.** 4 **4.** 1 **5.** 32 **6.** 9 **7.** 7 **8.** 5
9. 37 **10.** 5 **11.** 9 **12.** 4 **13.** 6 **14.** 9 **15.** 5
16. 8 **17.** 9 **18.** 6 **19.** 3 **20.** 2 **21.** 9 **22.** 2
23. 3 **24.** 7 **25.** 8 **26.** 4 **27.** 7 **28.** 2 **29.** 3
30. 6 **31.** 1 **32.** 4 **33.** 6 **34.** 3 **35.** 7 **36.** 9
37. 0 **38.** Undefined **39.** Undefined **40.** 7 **41.** 8
42. 7 **43.** 1 **44.** 5 **45.** 0 **46.** 0 **47.** 3 **48.** 1
49. 4 **50.** 7 **51.** 1 **52.** 6 **53.** 1 **54.** 5 **55.** 2
56. 8 **57.** 0 **58.** 0 **59.** 8 **60.** 3 **61.** 4
62. Undefined **63.** 4 **64.** 1 **65.** 69 R 1
66. 199 R 1 **67.** 92 R 1 **68.** 138 R 3 **69.** 1723 R 4
70. 2925 **71.** 864 R 1 **72.** 522 R 3 **73.** 527 R 2
74. 2897 **75.** 43 R 15 **76.** 32 R 27 **77.** 47 R 12
78. 42 R 9 **79.** 91 R 22 **80.** 52 R 13 **81.** 29
82. 55 R 2 **83.** 228 R 22 **84.** 20 R 379 **85.** 21
86. 118 **87.** 91 R 1 **88.** 321 R 2 **89.** 964 R 3
90. 679 R 5 **91.** 1328 R 2 **92.** 27 R 8 **93.** 23
94. 321 R 18 **95.** 224 R 10 **96.** 27 R 60 **97.** 22 R 85
98. 49 R 46 **99.** 383 R 91 **100.** 74 R 440

Chapter 1

Pretest: Chapter 1, p. 38

1. Three million, seventy-eight thousand, fifty-nine
2. 6 thousands + 9 hundreds + 8 tens + 7 ones
3. 2,047,398,589 **4.** 6 ten thousands **5.** 956,000
6. $600 \times 100 = 60,000$ **7.** 10,216 **8.** 4,108 **9.** 22,976
10. 503 R 11 **11.** < **12.** > **13.** 5,542 **14.** 22
15. 34 **16.** 25 **17.** 4,500 sheets **18.** $199
19. $369 **20.** $4,862 **21.** 25 **22.** 64 **23.** 0 **24.** 3

Margin Exercises, Section 1.1, pp. 39–42

1. 2 ten thousands **2.** 2 hundred thousands
3. 2 millions **4.** 2 ten millions

5. 4 hundred thousands, 8 ten thousands, 6 thousands, 5 hundreds, 7 tens, 5 ones
6. 1 thousand + 8 hundreds + 9 tens + 5 ones
7. 1 ten thousand + 4 thousands + 2 hundreds + 8 tens + 0 ones, or 1 ten thousand + 4 thousands + 2 hundreds + 8 tens
8. 3 thousands + 0 hundreds + 3 tens + 1 one, or 3 thousands + 3 tens + 1 one
9. 4 thousands + 1 hundred + 0 tens + 0 ones, or 4 thousands + 1 hundred
10. 3 thousands + 8 hundreds + 6 tens + 0 ones, or 3 thousands + 8 hundreds + 6 tens
11. 5689 **12.** 87,128 **13.** 9003 **14.** Eighty-eight
15. Sixteen **16.** Thirty-two **17.** Two hundred four
18. Forty-five thousand, six hundred seventy-eight
19. One million, eight hundred seventy-nine thousand, two hundred four
20. Six billion, two hundred fifty-four million, five hundred forty thousand **21.** 213,105,329

Exercise Set 1.1, p. 44

1. 5 thousands **3.** 5 hundreds **5.** The last 4 **7.** 2
9. 5 thousands + 7 hundreds + 0 tens + 2 ones, or 5 thousands + 7 hundreds + 2 ones
11. 9 ten thousands + 3 thousands + 9 hundreds + 8 tens + 6 ones
13. 2 thousands + 0 hundreds + 5 tens + 8 ones, or 2 thousands + 5 tens + 8 ones
15. 1 thousand + 5 hundreds + 7 tens + 5 ones
17. 2475 **19.** 68,939 **21.** 7304 **23.** 1009
25. Eighty-five **27.** Eighty-eight thousand
29. One hundred twenty-three thousand, seven hundred sixty-five
31. Seven billion, seven hundred fifty-four million, two hundred eleven thousand, five hundred seventy-seven
33. 2,233,812 **35.** 8,000,000,000
37. Five hundred sixty-six thousand, two hundred eighty
39. Four hundred sixty-seven million, three hundred twenty-two thousand, three hundred eighty-eight to one
41. 9,460,000,000,000 **43.** 64,186,000 **45.** D_W
47. 138

Margin Exercises, Section 1.2, pp. 47–52

1. 8 + 2 = 10 **2.** $20 + $13 = $33
3. 100 mi + 93 mi = 193 mi **4.** 5 ft + 7 ft = 12 ft
5. 9745 **6.** 13,465 **7.** 16,182
8. 2 + (6 + 3) = (2 + 6) + 3 **9.** (5 + 1) + 4 = 5 + (1 + 4)
10. 2 + 6 = 6 + 2 **11.** 7 + 1 = 1 + 7 **12.** 27 **13.** 34
14. 27 **15.** 38 **16.** 47 **17.** 61 **18.** 27,474
19. 16 in.; 26 in. **20.** 29 in. **21.** 22 m

Calculator Corner, p. 51

1. 55 **2.** 121 **3.** 1602 **4.** 734 **5.** 1932 **6.** 864

Exercise Set 1.2, p. 53

1. 6 cu yd + 8 cu yd = 14 cu yd
3. 500 acres + 300 acres = 800 acres **5.** 387 **7.** 5198
9. 164 **11.** 100 **13.** 8503 **15.** 5266 **17.** 4466
19. 8310 **21.** 6608 **23.** 16,784 **25.** 34,432
27. 101,310 **29.** 100,111 **31.** (2 + 5) + 4 = 2 + (5 + 4)
33. 6 + (3 + 2) = (6 + 3) + 2
35. (2 + 4) + 6 = 2 + (4 + 6) **37.** 2 + 7 = 7 + 2
39. 6 + 1 = 1 + 6 **41.** 2 + 9 = 9 + 2 **43.** 28 **45.** 26
47. 67 **49.** 230 **51.** 1349 **53.** 18,424 **55.** 2320
57. 31,685 **59.** 114 mi **61.** 20 m **63.** 1086 yd
65. 570 ft **67.** D_W **69.** 7992
70. Nine hundred twenty-four million, six hundred thousand
71. 8 ten thousands **72.** 23,000,000 **73.** D_W
75. 56,055,667
77. 1 + 99 = 100, 2 + 98 = 100, ..., 49 + 51 = 100. Then 49 · 100 = 4900 and 4900 + 50 + 100 = 5050.

Margin Exercises, Section 1.3, pp. 58–61

1. 67 cu yd − 5 cu yd = 62 cu yd
2. 20,000 sq ft − 12,000 sq ft = 8000 sq ft
3. 7 = 2 + 5, or 7 = 5 + 2 **4.** 17 = 9 + 8, or 17 = 8 + 9
5. 5 = 13 − 8; 8 = 13 − 5 **6.** 8 = 12 − 4; 4 = 12 − 8
7. 200 + □ = 348; 348 − 200 = 148
8. 800 + □ = 1200; 1200 − 800 = 400 **9.** 3801
10. 6328 **11.** 4747 **12.** 56 **13.** 205 **14.** 658
15. 2851 **16.** 1546

Calculator Corner, p. 60

1. 28 **2.** 47 **3.** 67 **4.** 119 **5.** 2128 **6.** 2593

Exercise Set 1.3, p. 62

1. 20 − 4 = 16 **3.** 16 oz − 5 oz = 11 oz
5. 7 = 3 + 4, or 7 = 4 + 3 **7.** 13 = 5 + 8, or 13 = 8 + 5
9. 23 = 14 + 9, or 23 = 9 + 14
11. 43 = 27 + 16, or 43 = 16 + 27
13. 6 = 15 − 9; 9 = 15 − 6 **15.** 8 = 15 − 7; 7 = 15 − 8
17. 17 = 23 − 6; 6 = 23 − 17
19. 23 = 32 − 9; 9 = 32 − 23
21. 17 + □ = 32; 32 − 17 = 15
23. 10 + □ = 23; 23 − 10 = 13 **25.** 12 **27.** 44
29. 333 **31.** 1126 **33.** 39 **35.** 298 **37.** 226
39. 234 **41.** 5382 **43.** 1493 **45.** 2187 **47.** 3831
49. 7748 **51.** 33,794 **53.** 2168 **55.** 43,028 **57.** 53
59. 36 **61.** 86 **63.** 454 **65.** 771 **67.** 2191
69. 3749 **71.** 7019 **73.** 5745 **75.** 95,974 **77.** 9975
79. 83,818 **81.** 4206 **83.** 10,305 **85.** D_W **87.** 1024
88. 12,732 **89.** 90,283 **90.** 29,364 **91.** 1345
92. 924 **93.** 22,692 **94.** 10,920
95. Six million, three hundred seventy-five thousand, six hundred two **96.** 7 ten thousands **97.** D_W
99. 2,829,177 **101.** 3; 4

Margin Exercises, Section 1.4, pp. 66–71

1. 40 **2.** 50 **3.** 70 **4.** 100 **5.** 40 **6.** 80 **7.** 90
8. 140 **9.** 470 **10.** 240 **11.** 290 **12.** 600 **13.** 800
14. 800 **15.** 9300 **16.** 8000 **17.** 8000 **18.** 19,000
19. 69,000 **20.** 48,970; 49,000; 49,000
21. 269,580; 269,600; 270,000 **22.** (a) $19,500; (b) Yes
23. Eliminate the driver's seat with 6-way power adjustment,
sunroof, feature package, and sport package. Answers may
vary. **24.** 200 **25.** 1800 **26.** 2600 **27.** 11,000
28. < **29.** > **30.** > **31.** < **32.** < **33.** >

Exercise Set 1.4, p. 72

1. 50 **3.** 470 **5.** 730 **7.** 900 **9.** 100 **11.** 1000
13. 9100 **15.** 32,900 **17.** 6000 **19.** 8000
21. 45,000 **23.** 373,000 **25.** 180 **27.** 5720 **29.** 180
31. 890; incorrect **33.** 16,500 **35.** 5200 **37.** $1500
39. $1300; yes **41.** Answers will vary depending on the
options chosen. **43.** 1600 **45.** 1500 **47.** 31,000
49. 69,000 **51.** < **53.** > **55.** < **57.** > **59.** >
61. > **63.** Thrust SCC; 54 ft > 47 ft
65. 87 yr > 81 yr, or 81 yr < 87 yr **67.** D_W **69.** 7992
70. 23,000,000
71. Two hundred forty-six billion, six hundred five million,
four thousand, thirty-two
72. 8 thousands + 0 hundreds + 1 ten + 7 ones, or
8 thousands + 1 ten + 7 ones
73. 86,754 **74.** 13,589 **75.** 48,824 **76.** 4415
77. D_W **79.** 30,411 **81.** 69,594

Margin Exercises, Section 1.5, pp. 77–82

1. $8 \cdot 7 = 56$ **2.** $10 \cdot 75$ mL $= 750$ mL **3.** $8 \cdot 8 = 64$
4. 116 **5.** 148 **6.** 4938 **7.** 6740 **8.** 1035 **9.** 3024
10. 46,252 **11.** 205,065 **12.** 144,432 **13.** 287,232
14. 14,075,720 **15.** 391,760 **16.** 17,345,600
17. 56,200 **18.** 562,000 **19.** $8 \cdot 7 = 7 \cdot 8$
20. $2 \cdot 6 = 6 \cdot 2$ **21.** $3 \cdot (7 \cdot 9) = (3 \cdot 7) \cdot 9$
22. $(5 \cdot 4) \cdot 8 = 5 \cdot (4 \cdot 8)$ **23.** 40 **24.** 15 **25.** $1600
26. 210,000; 160,000 **27.** 45 sq ft

Calculator Corner, p. 81

1. 448 **2.** 21,970 **3.** 6380 **4.** 39,564 **5.** 180,480
6. 2,363,754

Exercise Set 1.5, p. 83

1. $21 \cdot 21 = 441$ **3.** $8 \cdot 12$ oz $= 96$ oz
5. $1200 \times 600 = 720,000$ **7.** 46 **9.** 138 **11.** 348
13. 684 **15.** 9600 **17.** 56,000 **19.** 65,200
21. 4,371,000 **23.** 1527 **25.** 64,603 **27.** 4770
29. 3995 **31.** 46,080 **33.** 14,652 **35.** 207,672
37. 798,408 **39.** 166,260 **41.** 11,794,332
43. 20,723,872 **45.** 362,128 **47.** 20,064,048
49. 25,236,000 **51.** 302,220 **53.** 49,101,136
55. 30,525 **57.** 298,738 **59.** $50 \cdot 70 = 3500$

61. $30 \cdot 30 = 900$ **63.** $900 \cdot 300 = 270,000$
65. $400 \cdot 200 = 80,000$ **67.** $6000 \cdot 5000 = 30,000,000$
69. $8000 \cdot 6000 = 48,000,000$ **71.** (a) $5,260,000;
(b) $5,400,000 **73.** 529,984 sq mi **75.** 18 sq ft
77. 121 sq yd **79.** 144 sq mm **81.** 8100 sq ft **83.** D_W
85. 12,685 **86.** 10,834 **87.** 427,477 **88.** 111,110
89. 1241 **90.** 8889 **91.** 254,119 **92.** 66,444
93. 6,376,000 **94.** 6,375,600 **95.** D_W
97. 247,464 sq ft **99.** 57,600,000

Margin Exercises, Section 1.6, pp. 90–96

1. $112 \div 14 = \square$ **2.** $112 \div 8 = \square$ **3.** $15 = 5 \cdot 3$, or
$15 = 3 \cdot 5$ **4.** $72 = 9 \cdot 8$, or $72 = 8 \cdot 9$
5. $6 = 12 \div 2; 2 = 12 \div 6$ **6.** $6 = 42 \div 7; 7 = 42 \div 6$
7. 6; $6 \cdot 9 = 54$ **8.** 6 R 7; $6 \cdot 9 = 54, 54 + 7 = 61$
9. 4 R 5; $4 \cdot 12 = 48, 48 + 5 = 53$
10. 6 R 13; $6 \cdot 24 = 144, 144 + 13 = 157$ **11.** 59 R 3
12. 1475 R 5 **13.** 1015 **14.** 134 **15.** 63 R 12
16. 807 R 4 **17.** 1088 **18.** 360 R 4 **19.** 800 R 47

Calculator Corner, p. 95

1. 3 R 11 **2.** 28 **3.** 124 R 2 **4.** 131 R 18 **5.** 283 R 57
6. 843 R 187

Exercise Set 1.6, p. 97

1. $760 \div 4 = 190$ **3.** $455 \div 5 = 91$ **5.** $18 = 3 \cdot 6$, or
$18 = 6 \cdot 3$ **7.** $22 = 22 \cdot 1$, or $22 = 1 \cdot 22$
9. $54 = 6 \cdot 9$, or $54 = 9 \cdot 6$ **11.** $37 = 1 \cdot 37$, or $37 = 37 \cdot 1$
13. $9 = 45 \div 5; 5 = 45 \div 9$ **15.** $37 = 37 \div 1; 1 = 37 \div 37$
17. $8 = 64 \div 8$ **19.** $11 = 66 \div 6; 6 = 66 \div 11$ **21.** 12
23. 1 **25.** 22 **27.** Undefined **29.** 55 R 2 **31.** 108
33. 307 **35.** 753 R 3 **37.** 74 R 1 **39.** 92 R 2
41. 1703 **43.** 987 R 5 **45.** 12,700 **47.** 127
49. 52 R 52 **51.** 29 R 5 **53.** 40 R 12 **55.** 90 R 22
57. 29 **59.** 105 R 3 **61.** 1609 R 2 **63.** 1007 R 1
65. 23 **67.** 107 R 1 **69.** 370 **71.** 609 R 15 **73.** 304
75. 3508 R 219 **77.** 8070 **79.** D_W
81. 7 thousands + 8 hundreds + 8 tens + 2 ones **82.** >
83. $21 = 16 + 5$, or $21 = 5 + 16$ **84.** $56 = 14 + 42$, or
$56 = 42 + 14$ **85.** $47 = 56 - 9; 9 = 56 - 47$
86. $350 = 414 - 64; 64 = 414 - 350$ **87.** 359
88. 21,300 **89.** D_W
91. **93.** 30

a	b	$a \cdot b$	$a + b$
54	68	3672	122
84	33	2772	117
4	8	32	12
16	19	304	35

Margin Exercises, Section 1.7, pp. 102–105

1. No **2.** Yes **3.** 6 **4.** 5 **5.** 5 **6.** 10 **7.** 5
8. 22 **9.** 22,490 **10.** 9022 **11.** 570 **12.** 3661

13. 8 **14.** 45 **15.** 77 **16.** 3311 **17.** 6114 **18.** 8
19. 16 **20.** 644 **21.** 96 **22.** 94

Exercise Set 1.7, p. 106

1. 14 **3.** 0 **5.** 29 **7.** 0 **9.** 8 **11.** 14 **13.** 1035
15. 25 **17.** 450 **19.** 90,900 **21.** 32 **23.** 143
25. 79 **27.** 45 **29.** 324 **31.** 743 **33.** 37 **35.** 66
37. 15 **39.** 48 **41.** 175 **43.** 335 **45.** 104 **47.** 45
49. 4056 **51.** 16,681 **53.** 18,252 **55.** 205 **57.** D_W
59. $7 = 16 - 9; 9 = 16 - 7$ **60.** $6 = 48 \div 8; 8 = 48 \div 6$
61. < **62.** > **63.** > **64.** < **65.** 142 R 5 **66.** 142
67. 334 **68.** 334 R 11 **69.** D_W **71.** 347

Margin Exercises, Section 1.8, pp. 109–116

1. 1,424,000 **2.** 234 home runs **3.** 239 home runs
4. $1874 **5.** $223 **6.** $15,576 **7.** 9180 sq in.
8. 378 cartons with 1 can left over **9.** 34 gal **10.** 181 seats

Exercise Set 1.8, p. 117

1. 178,668 million, or 178,668,000,000
3. 12,113 million, or 12,113,000,000 **5.** 2000
7. 66,672 sq mi **9.** $459,860 **11.** 199,500 people
13. 240 mi **15.** 256 gal **17.** 480,000 pixels
19. $11,976 **21.** 129,000,000 CDs
23. 2,539,000,000 CDs **25.** 35 weeks; 2 episodes left over
27. 168 hr **29.** $247 **31.** 2,959,500 **33.** 21 columns
35. 563 packages; 7 bars left over **37. (a)** 4200 sq ft;
(b) 268 ft **39.** 35 cartons **41.** 56 full cartons; 11 books
left over. If 1355 books are shipped, it will take 57 cartons.
43. 384 mi; 27 in. **45.** 18 rows **47.** 32 $10 bills
49. $400 **51.** 280 min, or 4 hr 40 min
53. 525 min, or 8 hr 45 min **55.** 106 bones **57.** $704
59. D_W **61.** 234,600 **62.** 234,560 **63.** 235,000
64. 22,000 **65.** 16,000 **66.** 8,000 **67.** 4000
68. 320,000 **69.** 720,000 **70.** 46,800,000 **71.** D_W
73. 792,000 mi; 1,386,000 mi

Margin Exercises, Section 1.9, pp. 124–129

1. 5^4 **2.** 5^5 **3.** 13^2 **4.** 10^4 **5.** 100,000 **6.** 225
7. 512 **8.** 32 **9.** 51 **10.** 30 **11.** 584 **12.** 84
13. 4; 1 **14.** 52; 52 **15.** 29 **16.** 1880 **17.** 253
18. 93 **19.** 117 **20.** 305 **21.** 75 **22.** 4
23. 86 in. **24.** 46 **25.** 4

Calculator Corner, p. 125

1. 243 **2.** 15,625 **3.** 20,736 **4.** 2048

Calculator Corner, p. 127

1. 49 **2.** 85 **3.** 36 **4.** 0 **5.** 73 **6.** 49

Exercise Set 1.9, p. 130

1. 3^5 **3.** 5^2 **5.** 7^5 **7.** 10^3 **9.** 49 **11.** 729
13. 20,736 **15.** 121 **17.** 22 **19.** 20 **21.** 100

23. 1 **25.** 49 **27.** 5 **29.** 434 **31.** 41 **33.** 88
35. 4 **37.** 303 **39.** 20 **41.** 70 **43.** 295 **45.** 32
47. 906 **49.** 62 **51.** 102 **53.** 10 sec **55.** $94
57. 110 **59.** 7 **61.** 544 **63.** 708 **65.** 27 **67.** D_W
69. 452 **70.** 835 **71.** 13 **72.** 37 **73.** 2342
74. 4898 **75.** 25 **76.** 100 **77.** 102,600 mi^2
78. 98 gal **79.** D_W **81.** 24; $1 + 5 \cdot (4 + 3) = 36$
83. 7; $12 \div (4 + 2) \cdot 3 - 2 = 4$

Summary and Review: Chapter 1, p. 133

1. 2 thousands + 7 hundreds + 9 tens + 3 ones
2. 5 ten thousands + 6 thousands + 0 hundreds + 7 tens +
8 ones, or 5 ten thousands + 6 thousands + 7 tens + 8 ones
3. 8669 **4.** 90,844 **5.** Sixty-seven thousand,
eight hundred nineteen **6.** Two million, seven hundred
eighty-one thousand, four hundred twenty-seven
7. 476,588 **8.** 2,000,400,000 **9.** 8 thousands **10.** 3
11. 14,272 **12.** 66,024 **13.** 22,098 **14.** 98,921
15. $6 + 4 = 10$, or $4 + 6 = 10$ **16.** $11 - 8 = 3; 11 - 3 = 8$
17. 5148 **18.** 1153 **19.** 2274 **20.** 17,757
21. 345,800 **22.** 345,760 **23.** 346,000
24. $41,300 + 19,700 = 61,000$
25. $38,700 - 24,500 = 14,200$ **26.** $400 \cdot 700 = 280,000$
27. > **28.** < **29.** 420,000 **30.** 6,276,800
31. 506,740 **32.** 27,589 **33.** 5,331,810
34. $8 \times 7 = 56$, or $7 \times 8 = 56$ **35.** $52 \div 13 = 4$ and
$52 \div 4 = 13$ **36.** 12 R 3 **37.** 5 **38.** 913 R 3
39. 384 R 1 **40.** 4 R 46 **41.** 54 **42.** 452 **43.** 5008
44. 4389 **45.** 8 **46.** 45 **47.** 546 **48.** 4^3
49. 10,000 **50.** 36 **51.** 65 **52.** 233 **53.** 56
54. 32 **55.** 260 **56.** 165 **57.** $502 **58.** $484
59. 1982 **60.** 37 cartons **61.** 14 beehives
62. $2,413 **63.** $19,748 **64.** 137 beakers filled, 13 mL
of alcohol left over **65.** $A = 98 \text{ ft}^2; P = 42$ ft
66. D_W A vat contains 1152 oz of hot sauce. If 144 bottles
are to be filled equally, how much will each bottle contain?
Answers may vary. **67.** D_W No; if subtraction were
associative, then $a - (b - c) = (a - b) - c$ for any a, b,
and c. But, for example $12 - (8 - 4) = 12 - 4 = 8$, whereas
$(12 - 8) - 4 = 4 - 4 = 0$. Since $8 \neq 0$, this example shows
that subtraction is not associative. **68.** $d = 8$
69. $a = 8; b = 4$ **70.** 6 days

Test: Chapter 1, p. 136

1. [1.1b] 8 thousands + 8 hundreds + 4 tens + 3 ones
2. [1.1c] Thirty-eight million, four hundred three thousand,
two hundred seventy-seven **3.** [1.1a] 5 **4.** [1.2b] 9,989
5. [1.2b] 63,791 **6.** [1.2b] 34 **7.** [1.2b] 10,515
8. [1.3d] 3,630 **9.** [1.3d] 1,039 **10.** [1.3d] 6,848
11. [1.3d] 5,175 **12.** [1.5a] 41,112 **13.** [1.5a] 5,325,600
14. [1.5a] 2405 **15.** [1.5a] 534,264 **16.** [1.6c] 3 R 3
17. [1.6c] 70 **18.** [1.6c] 97 **19.** [1.6c] 805 R 8
20. [1.8a] 1852 12-packs; 7 cakes left over
21. [1.8a] 1,285,156 sq mi **22.** [1.2c], [1.5c] **(a)** $P = 300$ in.,
264 in.; 220 in.; $A = 5000$ in^2, 3872 in^2, 2888 in^2 **(h)** 2112 in^2

23. [1.8a] 99,076 patents in 1990   **24.** [1.8a] 1808 lb
25. [1.8a] 20 staplers can be filled   **26.** [1.7b] 46
27. [1.7b] 13   **28.** [1.7b] 14   **29.** [1.4a] 35,000
30. [1.4a] 34,580   **31.** [1.4a] 34,600
32. [1.4b] $23{,}600 + 54{,}700 = 78{,}300$
33. [1.4b] $54{,}800 - 23{,}600 = 31{,}200$
34. [1.5b] $800 \times 500 = 400{,}000$ **35.** [1.4c] >
36. [1.4c] <   **37.** [1.9a] 12^4 **38.** [1.9b] 343
39. [1.9b] 8   **40.** [1.9c] 64   **41.** [1.9c] 96   **42.** [1.9c] 2
43. [1.9d] 216   **44.** [1.9c] 18   **45.** [1.9c] 92
46. [1.8a] 336 in^2 **47.** [1.8a] 80 more payments
48. [1.9c] 83   **49.** [1.9c] $a = 9$

Chapter 2

Pretest: Chapter 2, p. 140

1. $-75, +67$ **2.** <   **3.** >   **4.** <   **5.** 73   **6.** 57
7. 32   **8.** 17   **9.** -18 **10.** 6   **11.** -9 **12.** 0
13. -16 **14.** 2   **15.** 18   **16.** -6 **17.** 0   **18.** 48
19. -81 **20.** -5 **21.** 11   **22.** -80 **23.** 0   **24.** 9
25. -13 **26.** $4x + 36$ **27.** $14x - 21y - 7$ **28.** $15a$
29. $-10x + 15$ **30.** 64 ft   **31.** -18 **32.** 22   **33.** 9
34. $12x^2 - 2x - 10$ **35.** $-(6a^3b^2 - 7a^2b - 5)$;
$-6a^3b^2 + 7a^2b + 5$ **36.** $-4x^2 - 17x + 21$ **37.** 57
38. 1   **39.** 48

Margin Exercises, Section 2.1, pp. 142–145

1. -18 **2.** $134; -80$ **3.** $-10; 148$ **4.** $-137; 289$
5. >   **6.** >   **7.** <   **8.** >   **9.** 18   **10.** 9   **11.** 29
12. 52   **13.** -1 **14.** 2   **15.** 0   **16.** 4   **17.** 13
18. -39 **19.** 0   **20.** 7   **21.** 1   **22.** -6 **23.** -2
24. -7 **25.** -39

Calculator Corner, p. 143

Keystrokes will vary by calculator.

Exercise Set 2.1, p. 146

1. -2 **3.** $40; -15$ **5.** $820; -541$ **7.** $-280; 14{,}491$
9. <   **11.** >   **13.** >   **15.** <   **17.** <   **19.** <
21. >   **23.** 57   **25.** 0   **27.** 24   **29.** 53   **31.** 8
33. 7   **35.** -7 **37.** 0   **39.** 19   **41.** -42 **43.** 8
45. -7 **47.** 29   **49.** 22   **51.** -1 **53.** 7   **55.** -9
57. -17 **59.** 23   **61.** -49 **63.** 85   **65.** -47
67. -345 **69.** 0   **71.** -8 **73.** $\mathbf{D_W}$ **75.** 825
76. 125   **77.** 7106   **78.** 4   **79.** 81   **80.** 1550
81. 10   **82.** 42   **83.** $\mathbf{D_W}$
85. $\boxed{5}\,\boxed{4}\,\boxed{9}\,\boxed{+}\,\boxed{3}\,\boxed{8}\,\boxed{7}\,\boxed{=}\,\boxed{+/-}$. Answers may vary.
87. $\boxed{3}\,\boxed{7}\,\boxed{-}\,\boxed{2}\,\boxed{9}\,\boxed{=}\,\boxed{+/-}$ **89.** -8 **91.** -7
93. $-1, 0, 1$ **95.** $-100, -5, 0, |3|, 4, |-6|, 7^2, 10^2, 2^7, 2^{10}$

Margin Exercises, Section 2.2, pp. 149–151

1. -1 **2.** -8 **3.** 4   **4.** 0   **5.** $4 + (-5) = -1$
6. $-2 + (-4) = -6$ **7.** $-3 + 8 = 5$ **8.** -11 **9.** -12

10. -34 **11.** -22 **12.** -17 **13.** 49   **14.** -56
15. 2   **16.** -4 **17.** -2 **18.** 3   **19.** 0   **20.** 0
21. 0   **22.** 0   **23.** -58 **24.** -56 **25.** -12

Exercise Set 2.2, p. 152

1. -5 **3.** -4 **5.** 6   **7.** 0   **9.** -4 **11.** -5
13. 5   **15.** -12 **17.** -11 **19.** 0   **21.** 0   **23.** 6
25. -8 **27.** -25 **29.** -27 **31.** 0   **33.** 0   **35.** 5
37. -9 **39.** -5 **41.** 9   **43.** -3 **45.** 0   **47.** -10
49. -24 **51.** -5 **53.** -21 **55.** 2   **57.** -26
59. -21 **61.** 25   **63.** -17 **65.** 6   **67.** -65
69. -160 **71.** -62 **73.** -23 **75.** $\mathbf{D_W}$
77. 324   **78.** 3625   **79.** 1484   **80.** 23,337
81. 3 ten thousands + 9 thousands + 4 hundreds +
1 ten + 7 ones   **82.** 700   **83.** 33,000   **84.** 2352
85. 32   **86.** 3500   **87.** $\mathbf{D_W}$ **89.** -40 **91.** -6483
93. -1868 **95.** All numbers greater than 7
97. Negative   **99.** Negative

Margin Exercises, Section 2.3, pp. 155–157

1. -10 **2.** 3   **3.** -5 **4.** -2 **5.** -11 **6.** 4   **7.** -2
8. $3 - 10 = 3 + (-10)$; three minus ten is three plus
negative ten.   **9.** $13 - 5 = 13 + (-5)$; thirteen minus five
is thirteen plus negative five.   **10.** $-12 - (-9) = -12 + 9$;
negative twelve minus negative nine is negative twelve plus
nine.   **11.** $-12 - 10 = -12 + (-10)$; negative twelve
minus ten is negative twelve plus negative ten.
12. $-14 - (-14) = -14 + 14$; negative fourteen minus
negative fourteen is negative fourteen plus fourteen.
13. -4 **14.** -16 **15.** 5   **16.** 2   **17.** -6
18. 13   **19.** -9 **20.** 25   **21.** -99, or $99 in debt
22. $19°C$

Exercise Set 2.3, p. 158

1. -5 **3.** -8 **5.** -3 **7.** 0   **9.** -4 **11.** -7
13. -5 **15.** 0   **17.** 0   **19.** 14   **21.** 11   **23.** -14
25. 6   **27.** -8 **29.** -1 **31.** 18   **33.** -10 **35.** -3
37. -21 **39.** 5   **41.** -8 **43.** 12   **45.** -19
47. -68 **49.** -81 **51.** 116   **53.** 0   **55.** 55
57. 19   **59.** -62 **61.** -139 **63.** 6   **65.** 107
67. 219   **69.** 25   **71.** 973 mi   **73.** 17 lb   **75.** 50; no
77. -9 **79.** -9687 ft   **81.** -87, or $87 in debt
83. $\mathbf{D_W}$ **85.** 64   **86.** 4896   **87.** 1   **88.** 4147
89. 8   **90.** 288 oz   **91.** 35   **92.** 3   **93.** 32
94. 165   **95.** $\mathbf{D_W}$ **97.** $-309{,}882$ **99.** False;
$3 - 0 \neq 0 - 3$ **101.** True   **103.** True   **105.** 17
107. Up 15 points

Margin Exercises, Section 2.4, pp. 163–166

1. $20; 10; 0; -10; -20; -30$ **2.** -18 **3.** -100 **4.** -9
5. $-10; 0; 10; 20; 30$ **6.** 12   **7.** 45   **8.** 6   **9.** 0
10. 0   **11.** 120   **12.** -120 **13.** 6   **14.** -8 **15.** 81
16. -1 **17.** 32   **18.** -25 **19.** 25   **20.** Negative
eight squared; the opposite of eight squared

Calculator Corner, p. 166

1. 148,035,889 **2.** −1,419,857 **3.** −1,124,864
4. 1,048,576 **5.** −531,441 **6.** −117,649 **7.** −7776
8. −19,683

Exercise Set 2.4, p. 167

1. −16 **3.** −18 **5.** −48 **7.** −30 **9.** 15 **11.** 18
13. 42 **15.** 20 **17.** −120 **19.** 300 **21.** 72
23. −340 **25.** 0 **27.** 0 **29.** 24 **31.** 420 **33.** −70
35. 30 **37.** 0 **39.** −294 **41.** 36 **43.** −125
45. 10,000 **47.** −16 **49.** −243 **51.** 1 **53.** −729
55. −64 **57.** The opposite of eight to the fourth power.
59. Negative nine to the tenth power. **61.** D_W
63. 532,500 **64.** 60,000,000 **65.** 80 **66.** 2550
67. 5 **68.** 48 **69.** 40 sq ft **70.** 240 **71.** 5 **72.** 4
73. D_W **75.** 243 **77.** 0 **79.** 7 **81.** −2209
83. 130,321 **85.** −2197 **87.** 116,875 **89.** −$23
91. (a) Both m and n must be odd. (b) At least one of m and n must be even.

Margin Exercises, Section 2.5, pp. 169–171

1. −3 **2.** 5 **3.** −3 **4.** 0 **5.** −6 **6.** −5
7. Undefined **8.** 0 **9.** Undefined **10.** 60 **11.** 3
12. −15

Calculator Corner, p. 171

1. −4 **2.** −2 **3.** 787

Exercise Set 2.5, p. 172

1. −7 **3.** −14 **5.** −9 **7.** 4 **9.** −9 **11.** 2
13. −43 **15.** −8 **17.** Undefined **19.** −8 **21.** −23
23. 0 **25.** −19 **27.** −41 **29.** −7 **31.** 19
33. −334 **35.** 23 **37.** 8 **39.** 12 **41.** −10
43. −86 **45.** −9 **47.** 18 **49.** 10 **51.** −25
53. −983 **55.** 82 **57.** −7988 **59.** −3000
61. 60 **63.** 1 **65.** 2 **67.** 7 **69.** Undefined
71. 3 **73.** 2 **75.** 0 **77.** D_W **79.** 28 sq in. **80.** 42
81. 12 gal **82.** 27 gal **83.** 150 calories **84.** 96 g
85. 4; 2 **86.** 4; 4 **87.** D_W **89.** 0 **91.** 0 **93.** −2
95. 992 **97.** $(\boxed{(}\ \boxed{1}\ \boxed{5}\ \boxed{x^2}\ \boxed{-}\ \boxed{5}\ \boxed{y^x}\ \boxed{3}\ \boxed{)}\ )\ \boxed{\div}$
$(\boxed{(}\ \boxed{3}\ \boxed{x^2}\ \boxed{+}\ \boxed{4}\ \boxed{x^2}\ \boxed{)}\ )\ \boxed{=}$ **99.** 5 **101.** Positive
103. Negative **105.** Positive

Margin Exercises, Section 2.6, pp. 175–178

1. 64 **2.** 28 **3.** −70 **4.** $-\dfrac{6}{x}; \dfrac{6}{-x}$ **5.** $\dfrac{-m}{n}; \dfrac{m}{-n}$

6. $\dfrac{-r}{4}; -\dfrac{r}{4}$ **7.** −7; −7; −7 **8.** 50 **9.** 48; 48
10. 81; 81 **11.** 9; −9 **12.** 4; −4 **13.** 32; −32

14.

	$3x + 2x$	$5x$
$x = 4$	20	20
$x = -2$	−10	−10
$x = 0$	0	0

15.

	$4x - x$	$3x$
$x = 2$	6	6
$x = -2$	−6	−6
$x = 0$	0	0

16. $5a + 5b$ **17.** $6x + 6y + 6z$ **18.** $4x - 4y$
19. $3a - 3b + 3c$ **20.** $6m - 24$ **21.** $-16a + 8b - 24c$

Calculator Corner, p. 177

1. 243 **2.** 1024 **3.** −32 **4.** −3125

Exercise Set 2.6, p. 179

1. 14¢ **3.** −2 **5.** 1 **7.** 12 **9.** 13 **11.** 14 ft
13. 14 ft **15.** 21 **17.** 21 **19.** 400 ft **21.** 10 **23.** 0
25. 36 **27.** 100 **29.** $\dfrac{-5}{t}; \dfrac{5}{-t}$ **31.** $\dfrac{n}{-b}; -\dfrac{n}{b}$

33. $\dfrac{-9}{p}; -\dfrac{9}{p}$ **35.** $\dfrac{14}{-w}; -\dfrac{14}{w}$ **37.** −5; −5; −5
39. −27; −27; −27 **41.** 36; −12 **43.** 45; 45
45. 216; −216 **47.** 1; 1 **49.** 128; −128 **51.** $5a + 5b$
53. $4x + 4$ **55.** $2b + 10$ **57.** $7 - 7t$ **59.** $30x + 12$
61. $8x + 56 + 48y$ **63.** $-7y + 14$ **65.** $3x + 6$
67. $-4x + 12y + 8z$ **69.** $8a - 24b + 8c$
71. $4x$ $12y - 28z$ **73.** $20a - 25b + 5c - 10d$
75. D_W **77.** Twenty-three million, forty-three thousand, nine hundred twenty-one **78.** 901
79. $5280 - 2480 = 2800$ **80.** 994 **81.** 17 in.
82. 5 in. **83.** $48 **84.** $63 **85.** D_W **87.** 698
89. 4438 **91.** 279 **93.** 2 **95.** 2,560,000
97. $-32\ \boxed{\times}\ (88\ \boxed{-}\ 29) = -1888$ **99.** True **101.** True
103. D_W

Margin Exercises, Section 2.7, pp. 183–186

1. $5x; -4y; 3$ **2.** $-4y; -2x; \dfrac{x}{y}$ **3.** $9a^3$ and a^3;
$4ab$ and $3ab$ **4.** $3xy$ and $-4xy$ **5.** $9a$ **6.** $7x^2 - 6$
7. $5m - n^2 - 4$ **8.** 26 cm **9.** 35 mm **10.** 12 cm
11. 24 ft **12.** 40 km **13.** 24 ft

Exercise Set 2.7, p. 187

1. $2a, 5b, -7c$ **3.** $9mn, -6n, 8$ **5.** $3x^2y, -4y^2, -2z^3$
7. $14x$ **9.** $-3a$ **11.** $11x + 6z$ **13.** $-13a + 62$

15. $-4 + 4t + 6y$ **17.** $6a + 4b - 2$
19. $-1 + 17a - 12b$ **21.** $6x^2 + 3y$ **23.** $7x^4 + y^3$
25. $6a^2 - 3a$ **27.** $3x^3 - 8x^2 + 4$ **29.** $7a^3 - 3ab + 3$
31. $9x^3y - 2xy^3 + 3xy$ **33.** $-4a^6 - 11b^4 + 2a^6b^4$
35. 10 ft **37.** 42 km **39.** 8 m **41.** 460 yd **43.** 52 yd
45. 36 ft **47.** 56 in. **49.** 260 cm **51.** 64 ft **53.** $\mathbf{D_W}$
55. 17 **56.** 210 **57.** 29 **58.** 7 **59.** 8 **60.** 27
61. 16 **62.** 26 **63.** 16 **64.** 13 **65.** 15 **66.** 25
67. $\mathbf{D_W}$ **69.** $7x + 1$ **71.** $-29 - 3a$
73. $-10 - x - 27y$ **75.** \$29.75 **77.** 912 mm

Margin Exercises, Section 2.8, pp. 191–196

1. Equivalent equations **2.** Equivalent expressions
3. 24 **4.** -3 **5.** 25 **6.** -14 **7.** 6 **8.** -8 **9.** -9
10. -12 **11.** -23 **12.** 3 **13.** 26 **14.** -50
15. -4 **16.** Yes **17.** No **18.** 26 **19.** -15

Exercise Set 2.8, p. 197

1. Equivalent equations **3.** Equivalent expressions
5. Equivalent expressions **7.** Equivalent equations
9. Equivalent expressions **11.** Equivalent equations
13. -3 **15.** -8 **17.** 18 **19.** -14 **21.** 32
23. -17 **25.** 17 **27.** 0 **29.** -4 **31.** -14 **33.** 5
35. 0 **37.** -11 **39.** -56 **41.** 12 **43.** 390 **45.** 4
47. -9 **49.** 35 **51.** 45 **53.** -5 **55.** -4
57. -178 **59.** -50 **61.** 7 **63.** 3 **65.** -3 **67.** -7
69. -8 **71.** 8 **73.** 24 **75.** 6 **77.** 5 **79.** -8
81. $\mathbf{D_W}$ **83.** 177 **84.** 215 **85.** 83 **86.** 154
87. 455 **88.** 249 **89.** 609 **90.** 817 **91.** 3933
92. 6516 **93.** 1220 **94.** 1149 **95.** $\mathbf{D_W}$ **97.** 8
99. 29 **101.** -20 **103.** 1027 **105.** -343 **107.** 17

Margin Exercises, Section 2.9, pp. 200–202

1. $9a^2 + 3a - 1$ **2.** $7x^2y + 3x^2 + 4x + 4$
3. $2a^3 + 2a^2 - 9a + 17$
4. $-(12x^4 - 3x^2 + 4x)$; $-12x^4 + 3x^2 - 4x$
5. $-(-4x^4 + 3x^2 - 4x)$; $4x^4 - 3x^2 + 4x$
6. $-\left(-13x^6 + 2x^4 - 3x^2 + x - \frac{5}{13}\right)$;
$13x^6 - 2x^4 + 3x^2 - x + \frac{5}{13}$
7. $-(-8a^3b + 5ab^2 - 2ab)$; $8a^3b - 5ab^2 + 2ab$
8. $-4x^3 + 6x - 3$ **9.** $-5x^3y - 3x^2y^2 + 7xy^3$
10. $-14x^{10} + \frac{1}{2}x^5 - 5x^3 + x^2 - 3x$ **11.** $2x^3 + 2x + 8$
12. $x^2 - 6x - 2$ **13.** $2x^3 + 3x^2 - 4xy - 2$ **14.** (a) 41
(b) 41 **15.** 132 **16.** 20 m **17.** 80 m

Exercise Set 2.9, p. 204

1. $-4x + 10$ **3.** $x^2 - 8x + 5$ **5.** $2x^2$
7. $6t^4 + 4t^3 + 5t^2 - t$ **9.** $7 + 12x^2$
11. $9x^8 + 8x^7 - 3x^4 + 2x^2 - 2x + 5$
13. $13t^4 + 4t^3 - t^2 + 4t - 3$
15. $-5x^4y^3 + 2x^3y^3 + 4x^3y^2 - 4xy^2 - 5xy$
17. $13a^3b^2 + 4a^2b^2 - 4a^2b + 6ab^2$

19. $-0.6a^2bc + 17.5abc^3 - 5.2abc$ **21.** $-(-5x)$; $5x$
23. $-(-x^2 + 13x - 7)$; $x^2 - 13x + 7$
25. $-(12x^4 - 3x^3 + 3)$; $-12x^4 + 3x^3 - 3$ **27.** $-3x + 5$
29. $-4x^2 + 3x - 2$ **31.** $4x^4 - 6x^2 - \frac{3}{4}x + 8$
33. $7x - 1$ **35.** $4t^2 + 6t + 6$ **37.** $-x^2 - 9x + 5$
39. $5a^2 + 5a - 16$ **41.** $8x^4 + 3x^3 - 4x^2 + 3x - 6$
43. $4.6x^3 + 9.2x^2 - 3.8x - 23$ **45.** $\frac{3}{4}x^3 - \frac{1}{2}x$
47. $6x^3y^3 + 8x^2y^2 + 2x^2y + 4xy$ **49.** -23 **51.** 19
53. -12 **55.** 7 **57.** 4 **59.** 11 **61.** 1024 ft
63. 823 min **65.** About 449 **67.** \$18,750
69. \$155,000 **71.** $\mathbf{D_W}$ **73.** $\mathbf{D_W}$ **75.** 711 min
77. $\mathbf{D_W}$ **79.** (a) 255 mg; (b) 344.4 mg; (c) 0 mg
81. $12y^2 - 23y + 21$ **83.** $-3y^4 - y^3 + 5y - 2$
85. $3x^4, 2x^3, (-7)$, order of answers may vary.

Summary and Review: Chapter 2, p. 209

1. 527; -53 **2.** $>$ **3.** $<$ **4.** $>$ **5.** 39 **6.** 23
7. 0 **8.** 72 **9.** 59 **10.** -9 **11.** -11 **12.** 6
13. -24 **14.** -12 **15.** 23 **16.** -1 **17.** 7 **18.** -4
19. 12 **20.** 92 **21.** -84 **22.** -40 **23.** -3
24. -5 **25.** 0 **26.** -25 **27.** -20 **28.** 7
29. $-6, -6, -6$ **30.** $20x + 36$ **31.** $6a - 12b + 15$
32. $17a$ **33.** $6x$ **34.** $-3m + 6$ **35.** 36 in.
36. 100 cm **37.** -8 **38.** -9 **39.** 11
40. $\mathbf{D_W}$ Equivalent expressions are expressions that have
the same value when evaluated for various replacements of
the variable(s). Equivalent equations are equations that
have the same solution(s). **41.** $\mathbf{D_W}$ A number's absolute
value is the number itself if the number is nonnegative, and
the opposite of the number if the number is negative. In
neither case is the result less than the number itself, so "no,"
a number's absolute value is never less than the number
itself. **42.** $3x - 6$ **43.** $7x^4 - 4x^3 - x - 3$
44. $8a^5 + 12a^3 - a^2 + 4a + 9$ **45.** $5a^3b^3 + 11a^2b^3 - 7$
46. $-(12x^3 - 4x^2 + 9x - 3)$; $-12x^3 + 4x^2 - 9x + 3$
47. -42 **48.** 56 ft **49.** Three hundred eighty-six
thousand, four hundred fifty-one
50. $7300 - 2740 = 4560$ **51.** $2500 - 1700 = 800$
52. 137 **53.** 25,485 **54.** 21,286
55. $\mathbf{D_W}$ The notation "$-x$" means "the opposite of x." If x is
a negative number, then $-x$ is a positive number. For
example, if $x = -2$, then $-x = 2$. **56.** $\mathbf{D_W}$ The
expressions $(a - b)^2$ and $(b - a)^2$ are equivalent for all
choices of a and b because $a - b$ and $b - a$ are opposites.
When opposites are raised to an even power, the results are
the same. **57.** 662,582 **58.** $-88,174$ **59.** -240
60. $x < -2$ **61.** $x < 0$

Test: Chapter 2, p. 212

1. [2.1a] -542; 307 **2.** [2.1b] $>$ **3.** [2.1c] 739
4. [2.1d] -19 **5.** [2.2a] -11 **6.** [2.2a] -21
7. [2.2a] 9 **8.** [2.3a] -12 **9.** [2.3a] -15
10. [2.3a] -24 **11.** [2.3a] 19 **12.** [2.3a] 38

13. [2.4b] -64 **14.** [2.4a] -270 **15.** [2.4a] 0   **16.** [2.5a] 8

17. [2.5a] -8 **18.** [2.5b] -1 **19.** [2.5b] 25

20. [2.3b] 23 min   **21.** [2.6a] -3 **22.** [2.6b] $14x + 21y - 7$

23. [2.7a] $4x - 17$ **24.** [2.8b] 5   **25.** [2.8a] -12

26. [2.9a] $18a^3 - 5a^2 - a + 8$

27. [2.9b] $-(-9a^4 + 7b^2 - ab + 3); 9a^4 - 7b^2 + ab - 3$

28. [2.9c] $3x^4 - x^2 - 11$ **29.** [2.9d] 12.4 m

30. [1.1c] Two million, three hundred eight thousand, four hundred fifty-one

31. [1.4b] $3200 - 1920 = 1280$

32. [1.4b] $9200 - 2900 = 6300$ **33.** [1.8a] 21

34. [1.5a] 5648   **35.** [1.5a] 20,536   **36.** [2.7b] 66 ft

37. [2.5b] $35x - 7$ **38.** [2.5b] $-24x - 57$

39. [2.5b] 103,097   **40.** [2.5b] 1086

Cumulative Review: Chapters 1–2, p. 214

1. [1.1c] 131,451,000   **2.** [1.1c] Five billion, three hundred eighty million, one thousand, four hundred thirty-seven

3. [1.2a] 18,827   **4.** [1.2a] 8857   **5.** [1.3d] 7846

6. [1.3d] 2428   **7.** [1.5a] 16,767   **8.** [1.5a] 8,266,500

9. [2.4a] -344 **10.** [2.4a] 72   **11.** [1.6c] 104

12. [1.6c] 62   **13.** [2.5a] 0   **14.** [2.5a] -5

15. [1.4a] 428,000   **16.** [1.4a] 5300

17. [1.4b] $749,600 + 301,400 = 1,051,000$

18. [1.5b] $700 \times 500 = 350,000$ **19.** [2.1b] $<$

20. [2.1c] 279   **21.** [1.9c], [2.5b] 36   **22.** [1.9d], [2.5b] 2

23. [1.9c], [2.5b] -86 **24.** [1.9b] 125   **25.** [2.6a] 3

26. [2.6a] 28   **27.** [2.6b] $-2x - 10$

28. [2.6b] $18x - 12y + 24$ **29.** [2.2a] -26

30. [2.3a] -31 **31.** [2.3a] -15 **32.** [2.3a] 13

33. [1.7b], [2.8a] 27   **34.** [2.8b] -3 **35.** [2.8a] -3

36. [2.8d] -8 **37.** [1.8a] 104 years   **38.** [1.8a] 13,931

39. [1.8a] $95   **40.** [1.8a] Westside Appliance

41. [2.7a] $10x - 14$ **42.** [2.9a] $10x^5 - x^4 + 2x^3 - 3x^2 + 2$

43. [1.8a] cases: 6; six-packs: 3; loose cans: 4

44. [2.5b] $4a$ **45.** [2.5b] -1071 **46.** [2.8d] ± 3

Chapter 3

Pretest: Chapter 3, p. 218

1. Yes   **2.** Yes   **3.** Prime   **4.** $2 \cdot 2 \cdot 2 \cdot 5 \cdot 7$ **5.** 1

6. $9t$ **7.** 0   **8.** $\frac{-1}{4}$ **9.** $\frac{2}{7}$ **10.** $\frac{12}{28}$ **11.** $\frac{5}{14}$ **12.** -20

13. $\frac{5a}{4}$ **14.** $\frac{13}{9}$ **15.** $\frac{1}{11}$ **16.** 36   **17.** $\frac{-3}{4}$ **18.** $\frac{2}{9x}$

19. $-\frac{2}{7}$ **20.** 30   **21.** $\frac{5}{8}$ **22.** $54   **23.** $\frac{1}{24}$ m

24. 26 ft^2

Margin Exercises, Section 3.1, pp. 219–222

1. $5 = 1 \cdot 5; 45 = 9 \cdot 5; 100 = 20 \cdot 5$

2. $10 = 1 \cdot 10; 60 = 6 \cdot 10; 110 = 11 \cdot 10$

3. 5, 10, 15, 20, 25, 30, 35, 40, 45, 50   **4.** Yes   **5.** Yes

6. No   **7.** Yes   **8.** No   **9.** Yes   **10.** No   **11.** Yes

12. No   **13.** Yes   **14.** Yes   **15.** No   **16.** No   **17.** Yes

18. Yes   **19.** No   **20.** No   **21.** Yes   **22.** No   **23.** Yes

24. No   **25.** Yes   **26.** No   **27.** Yes   **28.** No   **29.** Yes

Calculator Corner, p. 220

1. Yes   **2.** No   **3.** No   **4.** Yes   **5.** No   **6.** Yes

Exercise Set 3.1, p. 223

1. 7, 14, 21, 28, 35, 42, 49, 56, 63, 70

3. 20, 40, 60, 80, 100, 120, 140, 160, 180, 200

5. 3, 6, 9, 12, 15, 18, 21, 24, 27, 30

7. 13, 26, 39, 52, 65, 78, 91, 104, 117, 130

9. 10, 20, 30, 40, 50, 60, 70, 80, 90, 100

11. 9, 18, 27, 36, 45, 54, 63, 72, 81, 90   **13.** No   **15.** Yes

17. Yes   **19.** No   **21.** No

23. 84; 150; 567; 4740; 3609; 6390; 19,458; 2004; 492

25. 84; 150; 4740; 6390; 19,458; 2004; 492; 671,500

27. 150; 235; 4740; 6390; 1775; 671,500

29. 555; 300; 36; 45,270; 711; 13,251; 8064   **31.** 300; 45,270

33. 300; 36; 45,270; 8064

35. 56; 324; 784; 200; 42; 812; 402

37. 55,555; 200; 75; 2345; 35; 1005   **39.** 324   **41.** ^{D}W

43. 53   **44.** 5   **45.** -8 **46.** -24 **47.** $680   **48.** 42

49. 125   **50.** 343   **51.** 1024   **52.** 729   **53.** 9^5

54. 7^6 **55.** ^{D}W **57.** 99,969   **59.** 30   **61.** 60

63. 3655   **65.** 840   **67.** ^{D}W

Margin Exercises, Section 3.2, pp. 226–229

1. 1, 2, 7, 14   **2.** 1, 2, 5, 10   **3.** 1, 2, 4, 8

4. 1, 2, 4, 8, 16, 32   **5.** 2, 13, 19, 41, 73 are prime; 6, 12, 65, 99 are composite; 1 is neither.   **6.** $2 \cdot 3$

7. $2 \cdot 2 \cdot 3$ **8.** $3 \cdot 3 \cdot 5$ **9.** $2 \cdot 7 \cdot 7$ **10.** $2 \cdot 3 \cdot 3 \cdot 7$

11. $2 \cdot 2 \cdot 2 \cdot 2 \cdot 3 \cdot 3$

Exercise Set 3.2, p. 230

1. 1, 2, 3, 6, 9, 18   **3.** 1, 2, 3, 6, 9, 18, 27, 54   **5.** 1, 3, 9

7. 1, 13   **9.** Prime   **11.** Composite   **13.** Composite

15. Prime   **17.** Neither   **19.** Composite   **21.** Prime

23. Prime   **25.** $3 \cdot 3 \cdot 3$ **27.** $2 \cdot 7$ **29.** $2 \cdot 2 \cdot 2 \cdot 2 \cdot 5$

31. $5 \cdot 5$ **33.** $2 \cdot 31$ **35.** $2 \cdot 2 \cdot 5 \cdot 7$ **37.** $11 \cdot 11$

39. $5 \cdot 5 \cdot 7$ **41.** $3 \cdot 3 \cdot 11$ **43.** $2 \cdot 43$ **45.** $7 \cdot 31$

47. $2 \cdot 2 \cdot 2 \cdot 5 \cdot 5 \cdot 5 \cdot 7$ **49.** 1, 2, 4, 5, 10, 20, 25, 50, 100

51. 1, 5, 7, 11, 35, 55, 77, 385   **53.** 1, 3, 9, 27, 81

55. 1, 3, 5, 9, 15, 25, 45, 75, 225   **57.** ^{D}W **59.** -26

60. 256   **61.** 8   **62.** -23 **63.** 1   **64.** 73   **65.** 0

66. 1   **67.** -42 **68.** 0   **69.** ^{D}W **71.** ^{D}W

73. $5 \cdot 11 \cdot 37$ **75.** $11 \cdot 11 \cdot 23 \cdot 37$

77. $2 \cdot 2 \cdot 2 \cdot 3 \cdot 3 \cdot 5 \cdot 7 \cdot 67$ **79.** Answers may vary. One arrangement is a three-dimensional rectangular array consisting of 2 tiers of 12 objects each, where each tier consists of a rectangular array of 4 rows with 3 objects each.

81.

Product	56	63	36	72	140	96	48	168	110	90	432	63
Factor	7	7	2	2	10	8	6	21	10	9	24	3
Factor	8	9	18	36	14	12	8	8	11	10	18	21
Sum	15	16	20	38	24	20	14	29	21	19	42	24

Margin Exercises, Section 3.3, pp. 232–237

1. 5, numerator; 7, denominator
2. $5a$, numerator; $7b$, denominator
3. -22, numerator; 3, denominator **4.** $\frac{1}{2}$ **5.** $\frac{1}{3}$ **6.** $\frac{4}{6}$
7. $\frac{2}{3}$ **8.** $\frac{3}{4}$ **9.** $\frac{15}{16}$ **10.** $\frac{1}{3}$ **11.** $\frac{3}{5}$; $\frac{2}{5}$ **12.** $\frac{5}{4}$ **13.** $\frac{7}{4}$
14. $\frac{95}{66}$; $\frac{95}{161}$; $\frac{66}{161}$ **15.** 1 **16.** 1 **17.** 1 **18.** 1 **19.** 1
20. 1 **21.** 0 **22.** 0 **23.** 0 **24.** 0 **25.** Undefined
26. Undefined **27.** 8 **28.** -10 **29.** -346 **30.** 15

Exercise Set 3.3, p. 238

1. 3, numerator; 4, denominator
3. 7, numerator; -9, denominator
5. $2x$, numerator; $3z$, denominator **7.** $\frac{2}{4}$ **9.** $\frac{1}{8}$ **11.** $\frac{4}{9}$
13. $\frac{3}{4}$ **15.** $\frac{8}{16}$ **17.** $\frac{12}{16}$ **19.** $\frac{7}{16}$ **21.** $\frac{5}{8}$ **23.** $\frac{4}{7}$
25. (a) $\frac{2}{8}$; (b) $\frac{6}{8}$ **27.** (a) $\frac{3}{8}$; (b) $\frac{5}{8}$ **29.** $\frac{9}{8}$ **31.** $\frac{11}{8}$ **33.** $\frac{7}{5}$
35. $\frac{67}{10,000}$ **37.** (a) $\frac{721}{14}$; (b) $\frac{14}{721}$ **39.** (a) $\frac{3}{7}$; (b) $\frac{3}{4}$; (c) $\frac{4}{7}$; (d) $\frac{4}{3}$
41. 0 **43.** 15 **45.** 1 **47.** 1 **49.** 0 **51.** 1 **53.** 1
55. -63 **57.** 0 **59.** Undefined **61.** $7n$
63. Undefined **65.** $\mathbf{D_W}$ **67.** -210 **68.** -322
69. 0 **70.** 0 **71.** \$19,607 **72.** 201 min **73.** $\mathbf{D_W}$
75. $\frac{52}{365}$ **77.** $\frac{1200}{2700}$, $\frac{540}{2700}$, $\frac{360}{2700}$, $\frac{600}{2700}$ **79.** $\frac{6}{33}$
81.

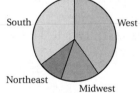

South West Northeast Midwest

83. $\frac{2}{6}$, or $\frac{1}{3}$ **85.** $\frac{6}{16}$, or $\frac{3}{8}$

Margin Exercises, Section 3.4, pp. 243–246

1. $\frac{2}{3}$ **2.** $\frac{5}{8}$ **3.** $\frac{14}{3}$ **4.** $-\frac{33}{10}$ or $\frac{-33}{10}$ **5.** $\frac{68}{5}$ **6.** $\frac{4x}{9}$

7.

$\frac{1}{4}$ $\quad$ $\frac{1}{2} \cdot \frac{1}{4} = \frac{1}{8}$

8.

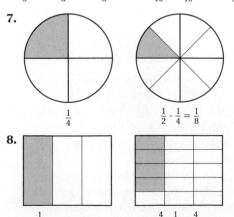

$\frac{1}{3}$ $\quad$ $\frac{4}{5} \cdot \frac{1}{3} = \frac{4}{15}$

9. $\frac{15}{56}$ **10.** $\frac{32}{15}$ **11.** $\frac{3}{100}$ **12.** $-\frac{7a}{b}$ or $\frac{-7a}{b}$ **13.** $\frac{3}{8}$
14. $\frac{63}{100}$ cm^2 **15.** $\frac{3}{40}$

Exercise Set 3.4, p. 247

1. $\frac{3}{8}$ **3.** $\frac{-5}{6}$ or $-\frac{5}{6}$ **5.** $\frac{14}{3}$ **7.** $-\frac{7}{9}$ or $\frac{-7}{9}$ **9.** $\frac{5x}{6}$
11. $\frac{-6}{5}$ or $-\frac{6}{5}$ **13.** $\frac{2a}{7}$ **15.** $\frac{17m}{6}$ **17.** $\frac{6}{5}$ **19.** $\frac{2x}{7}$
21. $\frac{1}{15}$ **23.** $\frac{-1}{40}$ or $-\frac{1}{40}$ **25.** $\frac{2}{15}$ **27.** $\frac{2x}{9y}$ **29.** $\frac{9}{16}$
31. $\frac{14}{39}$ **33.** $\frac{-3}{50}$ or $-\frac{3}{50}$ **35.** $\frac{7a}{64}$ **37.** $\frac{1}{100y}$
39. $\frac{-182}{285}$ or $-\frac{182}{285}$ **41.** $\frac{12}{25}$ m^2 **43.** $\frac{1}{1521}$ **45.** $\frac{10}{3}$ yd **47.** $\frac{9}{20}$
49. $\frac{4}{50}$ **51.** $\mathbf{D_W}$ **53.** 9 **54.** 7 **55.** -50 **56.** -90
57. -7 **58.** -5 **59.** 13 **60.** 6 **61.** 8 thousands
62. 8 millions **63.** 8 ones **64.** 8 hundreds **65.** $\mathbf{D_W}$
67. $\frac{1}{80}$ gal **69.** $-\frac{185,193}{226,981}$ or $\frac{-185,193}{226,981}$ **71.** $-\frac{3}{160}$ or $\frac{-3}{160}$
73. $\frac{4}{105}$ **75.** $-\frac{4836}{30,709}$

Margin Exercises, Section 3.5, pp. 250–255

1. $\frac{8}{16}$ **2.** $\frac{3a}{7a}$ **3.** $\frac{-32}{100}$ **4.** $\frac{-16}{-6}$ **5.** $\frac{12}{9}$ **6.** $\frac{-18}{-24}$ **7.** $\frac{9x}{10x}$
8. $\frac{21}{45}$ **9.** $\frac{-56}{49}$ **10.** $\frac{4}{7}$ **11.** $\frac{-5}{6}$ **12.** 5 **13.** $\frac{4}{3}$ **14.** $\frac{-5}{3}$
15. $\frac{7}{8}$ **16.** $\frac{89}{78}$ **17.** $\frac{-8}{7}$ **18.** $\frac{2}{100} = \frac{1}{50}$; $\frac{4}{100} = \frac{1}{25}$; $\frac{32}{100} = \frac{8}{25}$;
$\frac{44}{100} = \frac{11}{25}$; $\frac{18}{100} = \frac{9}{50}$ **19.** $=$ **20.** $\neq$ **21.** $=$

Calculator Corner, p. 254

1. $\frac{14}{15}$ **2.** $\frac{7}{8}$ **3.** $\frac{138}{167}$ **4.** $\frac{7}{25}$

Exercise Set 3.5, p. 256

1. $\frac{5}{10}$ **3.** $\frac{-36}{-48}$ **5.** $\frac{35}{50}$ **7.** $\frac{11t}{5t}$ **9.** $\frac{20}{48}$ **11.** $\frac{-51}{54}$ **13.** $\frac{15}{-40}$
15. $\frac{-42}{132}$ **17.** $\frac{5x}{8x}$ **19.** $\frac{10a}{7a}$ **21.** $\frac{4ab}{9ab}$ **23.** $\frac{12b}{27b}$ **25.** $\frac{1}{2}$
27. $\frac{-2}{3}$ **29.** $\frac{2}{5}$ **31.** -9 **33.** $\frac{3}{4}$ **35.** $\frac{-12}{7}$ **37.** $\frac{1}{3}$
39. $\frac{-1}{3}$ **41.** $\frac{7}{8}$ **43.** $\frac{9}{8}$ **45.** $\frac{3}{8}$ **47.** $\frac{3y}{2}$ **49.** $\frac{3r}{4}$
51. $\frac{-9}{10b}$ **53.** $=$ **55.** $\neq$ **57.** $=$ **59.** $\neq$ **61.** $\neq$
63. $=$ **65.** $\neq$ **67.** $=$ **69.** $\mathbf{D_W}$ **71.** 3600 yd^2
72. \$928 **73.** 60 **74.** 65 **75.** -63 **76.** -64
77. 5 **78.** 89 **79.** 3520 **80.** 9001 **81.** $\mathbf{D_W}$ **83.** $\frac{17}{19}$
85. $\frac{-23x}{13y}$ **87.** $\frac{137}{149}$ **89.** $\frac{4}{10} = \frac{2}{5}$; $\frac{6}{10} = \frac{3}{5}$
91. No. $\frac{149}{403} \neq \frac{152}{436}$ because $149 \cdot 436 \neq 403 \cdot 152$.

Margin Exercises, Section 3.6, pp. 259–261

1. $\frac{7}{12}$ **2.** $\frac{-1}{3}$ **3.** 6 **4.** $\frac{15}{x}$ **5.** 12 lb **6.** 96 m^2
7. $\frac{66}{5}$ cm^2 **8.** 100 in^2

Exercise Set 3.6, p. 262

1. $\frac{7}{8}$ **3.** $-\frac{1}{8}$ **5.** $\frac{3}{28}$ **7.** $\frac{2}{9}$ **9.** $-\frac{27}{10}$ **11.** $\frac{4x}{9}$ **13.** 3

15. 7 **17.** 12 **19.** $3a$ **21.** 1 **23.** 1 **25.** $\frac{11a}{2}$

27. $\frac{-88}{3}$ **29.** 1 **31.** 3 **33.** $\frac{119}{750}$ **35.** $-\frac{20}{187}$ **37.** $-\frac{42}{275}$

39. $-\frac{16}{5x}$ **41.** $\frac{-11}{40}$ **43.** $\frac{5a}{28b}$ **45.** $\frac{5}{8}$ in.

47. 18 mph **49.** 625 addresses **51.** 30 pounds
53. $\frac{1}{3}$ cup **55.** $115,500 **57.** 90 mi **59.** Food: $9000;
housing: $7200; clothing: $3600; savings: $4000;
taxes: $9000; other expenses: $3200 **61.** 60 in^2
63. $\frac{35}{4}$ mm^2 **65.** $\frac{63}{8}$ m^2 **67.** 92 mi^2 **69.** $\frac{15}{2}$ cm^2
71. D_W **73.** 35 **74.** 85 **75.** 125 **76.** 120
77. 4989 **78.** 8546 **79.** 6498 **80.** 6407 **81.** D_W
83. $\frac{129}{485}$ **85.** $\frac{2}{3}$ **87.** 20 students **89.** 13,380 mm^2
91. 6392 ft^2

Margin Exercises, Section 3.7, pp. 268–270

1. $\frac{8}{7}$ **2.** $\frac{x}{-6}$ **3.** $\frac{1}{2}$ **4.** 5 **5.** $-\frac{10}{3}$ **6.** $\frac{5}{21}$ **7.** $-\frac{8}{3}$
8. $\frac{1}{8}$ **9.** $\frac{100}{a}$ **10.** $\frac{-10}{7}$ or $-\frac{10}{7}$ **11.** $\frac{15}{14}$

Calculator Corner, p. 268

1. $\frac{10}{7}$ **2.** $-\frac{4}{9}$ **3.** $\frac{1}{29}$ **4.** 25

Exercise Set 3.7, p. 271

1. $\frac{3}{7}$ **3.** $\frac{1}{9}$ **5.** 7 **7.** $-\frac{3}{10}$ **9.** $\frac{17}{3}$ **11.** $\frac{m}{-3n}$ **13.** $\frac{-15}{8}$

15. $\frac{1}{7m}$ **17.** $4a$ **19.** $-3z$ **21.** $\frac{4}{7}$ **23.** $-\frac{7}{10}$ **25.** 4

27. -2 **29.** $\frac{25}{7}$ **31.** $\frac{1}{64}$ **33.** $\frac{3}{7x}$ **35.** -8 **37.** $35a$

39. 1 **41.** $-\frac{2}{3}$ **43.** $\frac{99}{224}$ **45.** $\frac{112a}{3}$ **47.** $\frac{14}{15}$ **49.** $\frac{7}{32}$

51. $\frac{-25}{12}$ **53.** $\frac{15}{32}$ **55.** D_W **57.** 67 **58.** 33 R 4
59. 285 R 2 **60.** 103 R 10 **61.** 67 **62.** 264 **63.** 8499
64. 4368 **65.** -9 **66.** 3 **67.** -4 **68.** -4 **69.** D_W
71. $\frac{100}{9}$ **73.** 36 **75.** $\frac{121}{900}$ **77.** $\frac{9}{19}$ **79.** $\frac{220}{51}$

Margin Exercises, Section 3.8, pp. 273–276

1. 12 **2.** -21 **3.** $\frac{-9}{32}$ **4.** $\frac{-3}{4}$ **5.** 320 **6.** 12
7. 200 gal

Exercise Set 3.8, p. 277

1. 15 **3.** 9 **5.** -45 **7.** $\frac{2}{17}$ **9.** $\frac{12}{5}$ **11.** $-\frac{16}{21}$
13. $-\frac{8}{25}$ **15.** $\frac{1}{6}$ **17.** $-\frac{80}{9}$ **19.** $-\frac{1}{6}$ **21.** $-\frac{7}{13}$ **23.** $\frac{27}{31}$

25. $\frac{6}{7}$ **27.** $\frac{12}{5}$ **29.** $\frac{-7}{15}$ **31.** $\frac{9}{5}$ **33.** 6 **35.** $\frac{10}{7}$ **37.** 75
39. 288 km; 108 km **41.** 64 **43.** 20 **45.** $\frac{1}{8}$ T **47.** 8
49. 45 **51.** 32 **53.** $\frac{1}{16}$ in. **55.** D_W **57.** 26
58. -42 **59.** -67 **60.** -65 **61.** 20 **62.** 6
63. $17x$ **64.** $4a$ **65.** $7a + 3$ **66.** $4x - 7$ **67.** D_W
69. $\frac{2}{9}$ **71.** $\frac{7}{8}$ lb **73.** 103 **75.** $510
77. $1608.75, with $\frac{1}{4}$ yd unused

Summary and Review: Chapter 3, p. 281

1. No **2.** No **3.** Yes **4.** $2 \cdot 5 \cdot 7$ **5.** $2 \cdot 2 \cdot 2 \cdot 3 \cdot 3$
6. $2 \cdot 3 \cdot 5 \cdot 5$ **7.** Composite
8. 9, numerator; 7, denominator **9.** $\frac{3}{5}$ **10.** $\frac{3}{8}$ **11.** 0
12. 1 **13.** 48 **14.** 1 **15.** $-\frac{2}{3}$ **16.** $\frac{1}{4}$ **17.** -1
18. $\frac{3}{4}$ **19.** $\frac{2}{5}$ **20.** Undefined **21.** $6x$ **22.** $\frac{1}{3}$ **23.** $\frac{15}{21}$
24. $\frac{-30}{55}$ **25.** $\frac{13}{2}$ **26.** $-\frac{1}{7}$ **27.** 8 **28.** $\frac{5y}{3x}$ **29.** $\frac{14}{45}$
30. $\frac{3y}{7x}$ **31.** $\frac{2}{3}$ **32.** $-\frac{1}{14}$ **33.** $\frac{1}{25}$ **34.** 1 **35.** $\frac{27}{5}$
36. $\frac{1}{4}$ **37.** 200 **38.** $\frac{1}{15}$ **39.** $6a$ **40.** -1 **41.** $\frac{3}{4}$
42. $\frac{7}{144}$ **43.** 42 m^2 **44.** $\frac{35}{2}$ ft^2 **45.** $x = 240$
46. $t = \frac{-3}{10}$ **47.** $n = 28$ **48.** 220 mi **49.** $\frac{3}{8}$ cup
50. $\frac{1}{6}$ mi **51.** 18 bowls **52.** D_W Because $\frac{2}{8}$ simplifies to
$\frac{1}{4}$, it is incorrect to suggest that $\frac{2}{8}$ is simplified form of $\frac{20}{80}$.
53. D_W **1.** Find the largest common factor of the
numerator and denominator. **2.** Use the largest common
factor to express both the numerator and denominator as
a product. **3.** Express the fraction as a product of 1 and
another fraction, using the largest common factor to write
the factor that is equal to 1. **4.** Remove the factor equal to 1.
54. $x = 24$ **55.** 11 **56.** 14 **57.** 27 **58.** $912
59. 559 miles **60.** $7x^3 + 3x^2 + 3x - 6$ **61.** $\frac{17}{6}$
62. 2, 8 **63.** 13, 11, 101, 37 **64.** $a = 11{,}176$; $b = 9{,}887$
65. $\frac{3}{17}$

Test: Chapter 3, p. 284

1. [3.1b] Yes **2.** [3.1b] No **3.** [3.2c] $2 \cdot 2 \cdot 3 \cdot 3$
4. [3.2c] $2 \cdot 2 \cdot 3 \cdot 5$ **5.** [3.2b] Composite
6. [3.3a] 4, numerator; 9, denominator **7.** [3.3a] $\frac{3}{4}$
8. [3.3b] 32 **9.** [3.3b] 1 **10.** [3.3b] 0 **11.** [3.5b] $\frac{-1}{3}$
12. [3.5b] $\frac{1}{5}$ **13.** [3.5b] $\frac{1}{9}$ **14.** [3.5a] $\frac{15}{40}$ **15.** [3.7a] $\frac{42}{a}$
16. [3.7a] $\frac{-1}{9}$ **17.** [3.6a] $\frac{5}{2}$ **18.** [3.7b] $\frac{8}{33}$ **19.** [3.4a] $\frac{3x}{8}$
20. [3.7b] $\frac{-3}{14}$ **21.** [3.6a] $\frac{6}{65}$ **22.** [3.8b] $\frac{3}{20}$ lb
23. [3.6b] 125 lb **24.** [3.8a] 64 **25.** [3.8a] $\frac{-7}{4}$
26. [3.6b] $\frac{91}{2}$ m^2 **27.** [1.9c] 41 **28.** [1.7b], [2.8b] 101
29. [2.2a] -167 **30.** [2.4a] 63 **31.** [3.6b] $\frac{15}{8}$ tsp
32. [3.6b] $\frac{7}{48}$ acre **33.** [3.6a], [3.7b] $\frac{-7}{960}$ **34.** [3.8a] $\frac{7}{5}$

Cumulative Review: Chapters 1–3, p. 286

1. [1.1c] Two million, fifty-six thousand, seven hundred
eighty-three **2.** [1.2b] 10,982 **3.** [2.2a] -43

4. [2.2a] -33 **5.** [1.3d] 2129 **6.** [2.3a] -23
7. [2.3a] -8 **8.** [1.5a] 16,905 **9.** [2.4a] -312
10. [3.6a] $-30x$ **11.** [3.6a] $\frac{7}{15}$ **12.** [1.6c] 235 R 3
13. [2.5a] -17 **14.** [3.7b] -28 **15.** [3.7b] $\frac{2}{3}$
16. [1.4a] 4510 **17.** [1.5b] $900 \times 500 = 450{,}000$
18. [2.1c] 479 **19.** [2.5b] 8 **20.** [3.2b] Composite
21. [2.6a] -21 **22.** [1.7b], [2.8b] 25 **23.** [1.7b], [2.8b] 7
24. [3.8a] -45 **25.** [1.8a] 8 mpg **26.** [1.8a] 8 oz
27. [2.7a] $5x - 5$ **28.** [2.7a] $3x + 7y$ **29.** [3.3b] 1
30. [3.3b] 0 **31.** [3.3b] 63 **32.** [3.5b] $-\frac{5}{27}$ **33.** [3.7a] $\frac{5}{2}$
34. [3.7a] $\frac{1}{57}$ **35.** [3.5a] $\frac{21}{70}$ **36.** [3.6b] $36
37. [3.8b] 12 servings **38.** [3.6b] $\frac{3}{5}$ mile
39. $4x^5 - 4x^3 + 9x^2 - 13$ **40.** 66
41. [2.6a], [3.6a], [3.7b] $\frac{-54}{169}$ **42.** [2.1c], [2.6a], [3.6a] $\frac{-9}{100}$
43. [3.6b] $468

Chapter 4

Pretest: Chapter 4, p. 290

1. 150 **2.** $<$ **3.** $\frac{1}{4}$ **4.** $\frac{11}{90}$ **5.** $-\frac{9}{35}$ **6.** $\frac{43}{8}$ **7.** $3\frac{2}{5}$
8. $397\frac{1}{12}$ **9.** $4\frac{11}{30}$ **10.** $\frac{2}{9}$ **11.** -9 **12.** $18\frac{7}{11}$ **13.** $36\frac{5}{12}$
14. $-7\frac{5}{7}$ **15.** $1\frac{14}{39}$ **16.** $8\frac{26}{35}$ **17.** $87\frac{1}{2}$ lb **18.** $4\frac{1}{4}$ cu ft
19. $1577\frac{1}{2}$ mi **20.** $6\frac{1}{4}$ cups

Margin Exercises, Section 4.1, pp. 291–295

1. 45 **2.** 56 **3.** 18 **4.** 24 **5.** 14 **6.** 200 **7.** 40
8. 360 **9.** 30 **10.** 360 **11.** 100 **12.** xyz **13.** $5a^3b$

Exercise Set 4.1, p. 296

1. 10 **3.** 50 **5.** 40 **7.** 54 **9.** 150 **11.** 120
13. 72 **15.** 420 **17.** 144 **19.** 180 **21.** 42 **23.** 30
25. 72 **27.** 60 **29.** 36 **31.** 900 **33.** 300 **35.** abc
37. $9x^2$ **39.** $4x^3y$ **41.** $8r^3s^2t^4$ **43.** $a^3b^2c^2$
45. Once every 60 yr **47.** $\mathbf{D_W}$ **49.** 14 **50.** -27
51. 7935 **52.** $\frac{2}{3}$ **53.** $-\frac{8}{7}$ **54.** -167 **55.** $\mathbf{D_W}$
57. $\mathbf{D_W}$ **59.** 70,200 **61.** 121,695 **63.** 30
65. 18,900 **67. (a)** Not the LCM because a^2b^5 is not a factor of a^3b^3. **(b)** Not the LCM because a^3b^2 is not a factor of a^2b^5. **(c)** The LCM because both a^3b^2 and a^2b^5 are factors of a^3b^5 and it is the smallest such expression.
69. 27 and 2; 27 and 6; 27 and 18

Margin Exercises, Section 4.2, pp. 299–304

1. $\frac{4}{5}$ **2.** 1 **3.** $\frac{1}{2}$ **4.** $-\frac{3}{8}$ **5.** $-\frac{4}{x}$ **6.** $\frac{2}{5}a$
7. $\frac{7}{19} + \frac{10}{19}x$ **8.** $\frac{5}{6}$ **9.** $\frac{29}{24}$ **10.** $\frac{2}{9}$ **11.** $\frac{38}{5}$ **12.** $\frac{413}{1000}$
13. $\frac{157}{210}$ **14.** $<$ **15.** $>$ **16.** $>$ **17.** $<$ **18.** $<$
19. $<$ **20.** $\frac{9}{10}$ mi

Calculator Corner, p. 304

1. $\frac{5}{8}$ **2.** $\frac{67}{60}$ **3.** $\frac{52}{21}$ **4.** $\frac{201}{140}$ **5.** $\frac{253}{150}$ **6.** $\frac{792}{667}$

Exercise Set 4.2, p. 305

1. $\frac{5}{9}$ **3.** 1 **5.** $\frac{2}{5}$ **7.** $\frac{13}{a}$ **9.** $-\frac{4}{11}$ **11.** $\frac{7}{9}x$ **13.** $\frac{1}{2}t$
15. $-\frac{9}{x}$ **17.** $\frac{7}{24}$ **19.** $-\frac{1}{10}$ **21.** $\frac{23}{24}$ **23.** $\frac{83}{20}$ **25.** $\frac{5}{24}$
27. $\frac{37}{100}x$ **29.** $\frac{19}{20}$ **31.** $-\frac{99}{100}$ **33.** $\frac{29}{12}$ **35.** $-\frac{33}{7}t$
37. $-\frac{17}{24}$ **39.** $\frac{437}{1000}$ **41.** $\frac{5}{4}$ **43.** $\frac{239}{78}$ **45.** $\frac{59}{90}$ **47.** $>$
49. $<$ **51.** $>$ **53.** $<$ **55.** $>$ **57.** $>$ **59.** $\frac{4}{15}, \frac{3}{10}, \frac{5}{12}$
61. $\frac{3}{4}$ lb **63.** $\frac{51}{40}$ mi **65.** $\frac{25}{24}$ cups **67.** $\frac{7}{8}$ in. **69.** $\frac{33}{20}$ mi
71. $\frac{51}{32}$ in. **73.** 690 kg; $\frac{14}{23}, \frac{5}{23}, \frac{4}{23}$; 1 **75.** $\mathbf{D_W}$ **77.** -13
78. 4 **79.** -8 **80.** -31 **81.** $\frac{10}{3}$ **82.** 42; 42
83. $73 **84.** $11 **85.** $3 **86.** $9 **87.** $1558
88. $1684 **89.** $\mathbf{D_W}$ **91.** $\frac{13}{30}t + \frac{31}{35}$ **93.** $7t^2 + \frac{9}{a}t$
95. $>$ **97.** $\frac{4}{15}$; $320 **99.** The largest is $4 + \frac{6}{3} \cdot 5 = 14$, or $4 + \frac{5}{3} \cdot 6 = 14$. **101.** $\frac{3}{4}, \frac{7}{9}, \frac{17}{21}, \frac{19}{22}, \frac{13}{15}, \frac{15}{17}, \frac{13}{12}$

Margin Exercises, Section 4.3, pp. 310–313

1. $\frac{1}{2}$ **2.** $\frac{4}{9a}$ **3.** $-\frac{3}{5}$ **4.** $-\frac{6}{x}$ **5.** $\frac{1}{12}$ **6.** $\frac{1}{6}$ **7.** $-\frac{3}{10}$
8. $-\frac{1}{6}$ **9.** $\frac{9}{112}$ **10.** $\frac{3}{10}x$ **11.** $\frac{3}{5}$ **12.** $\frac{1}{6}$ **13.** $\frac{-59}{40}$
14. $\frac{5}{24}$ mi

Exercise Set 4.3, p. 314

1. $\frac{2}{3}$ **3.** $-\frac{1}{4}$ **5.** $\frac{2}{a}$ **7.** $-\frac{7}{9}$ **9.** $-\frac{1}{2}$ **11.** $\frac{2}{t}$
13. $-\frac{4}{5a}$ **15.** $\frac{13}{16}$ **17.** $-\frac{1}{3}$ **19.** $\frac{7}{10}$ **21.** $-\frac{17}{60}$ **23.** $\frac{47}{100}$
25. $\frac{26}{75}$ **27.** $\frac{-21}{100}$ **29.** $\frac{-13}{24}$ **31.** $\frac{-29}{50}$ **33.** $\frac{-2}{15}$ **35.** $-\frac{41}{72}$
37. $\frac{1}{360}$ **39.** $\frac{2}{9}x$ **41.** $-\frac{7}{20}a$ **43.** $\frac{7}{9}$ **45.** $\frac{4}{11}$ **47.** $\frac{4}{9}$
49. $\frac{9}{8}$ **51.** $\frac{2}{15}$ **53.** $-\frac{7}{24}$ **55.** $\frac{2}{15}$ **57.** $-\frac{5}{4}$ **59.** $\frac{3}{10}$ mi
61. $\frac{1}{32}$ in. **63.** $\frac{3}{16}$ in. **65.** $\frac{2}{3}$ cup **67.** $\frac{5}{12}$ hr **69.** $\frac{5}{12}$ cup
71. $\mathbf{D_W}$ **73.** $\frac{4}{21}$ **74.** $\frac{3}{2}$ **75.** 21 **76.** $\frac{1}{32}$ **77.** 6 lb
78. 9 cups **79.** 11 **80.** 3 **81.** $\mathbf{D_W}$ **83.** $\frac{1}{16}$
85. $-\frac{11}{10}$ **87.** $\frac{-64}{35}$ **89.** $-\frac{37}{1000}$ **91.** $\frac{11}{16}$ **93.** $\frac{43}{50}$
95. 3 hr **97.** $\frac{1}{8}$ **99.** $\frac{14}{3553}$ **101.** 4
103. Day 1: Cut off $\frac{1}{7}$ of bar and pay the contractor.

Day 2: Cut off $\frac{2}{7}$ of the bar's original length and trade it for the $\frac{1}{7}$.

Day 3: Give the $\frac{1}{7}$ back to the contractor.
Day 4: Trade the $\frac{4}{7}$ remaining for the contractor's $\frac{3}{7}$.
Day 5: Give the contractor the $\frac{1}{7}$ again.
Day 6: Trade the $\frac{2}{7}$ for the $\frac{1}{7}$.
Day 7: Give the contractor the $\frac{1}{7}$ again. This assumes that the contractor does not spend parts of the gold bar immediately.

Margin Exercises, Section 4.4, pp. 320–322

1. $\frac{10}{9}$ **2.** $-\frac{18}{7}$ **3.** -16 **4.** -21 **5.** $\frac{10}{9}$

Exercise Set 4.4, p. 323

1. 3 **3.** 5 **5.** 7 **7.** 12 **9.** $\frac{1}{2}$ **11.** $\frac{3}{4}$ **13.** $\frac{8}{3}$
15. $\frac{1}{2}$ **17.** $\frac{8}{7}$ **19.** $\frac{9}{2}$ **21.** $\frac{21}{5}$ **23.** 6 **25.** $\frac{17}{4}$ **27.** $\frac{3}{4}$
29. $\frac{3}{2}$ **31.** $\frac{9}{2}$ **33.** $-\frac{10}{3}$ **35.** $-\frac{1}{5}$ **37.** $-\frac{1}{6}$ **39.** $\frac{35}{12}$
41. $\mathbf{D_W}$ **43.** -13 **44.** -8 **45.** 18 **46.** 27
47. The balance has decreased $150 **48.** $1180 profit
49. $\frac{5}{7m}$ **50.** $20n$ **51.** $\mathbf{D_W}$ **53.** 4 **55.** $-\frac{177,450}{181,843}$
57. $\frac{145}{12}$ **59.** $-\frac{153}{16}$ **61.** $\frac{3}{2}$ cm **63.** $\frac{3}{4}$ cm

Margin Exercises, Section 4.5, pp. 326–328

1. $1\frac{2}{3}$ **2.** $7\frac{1}{4}$ **3.** $15\frac{2}{9}$ **4.** $\frac{22}{5}$ **5.** $\frac{61}{10}$ **6.** $\frac{23}{7}$ **7.** $\frac{73}{8}$
8. $\frac{62}{3}$ **9.** $-\frac{32}{5}$ **10.** $-\frac{65}{9}$ **11.** $2\frac{1}{3}$ **12.** $1\frac{1}{15}$ **13.** $18\frac{1}{3}$
14. $-2\frac{2}{5}$ **15.** $-11\frac{1}{6}$ **16.** $807\frac{2}{3}$ **17.** $55\frac{3}{4}$ qt

Calculator Corner, p. 329

1. $5\frac{4}{7}$ **2.** $8\frac{2}{5}$ **3.** $1476\frac{1}{6}$ **4.** $676\frac{4}{9}$ **5.** $51,626\frac{9}{11}$
6. $7330\frac{7}{32}$ **7.** $134\frac{1}{15}$ **8.** $2666\frac{130}{213}$ **9.** $3571\frac{51}{112}$
10. $12\frac{169}{454}$

Exercise Set 4.5, p. 330

1. $\frac{23}{3}$ **3.** $\frac{25}{4}$ **5.** $-\frac{161}{8}$ **7.** $\frac{51}{10}$ **9.** $\frac{103}{5}$ **11.** $\frac{-58}{7}$
13. $\frac{69}{10}$ **15.** $-\frac{51}{4}$ **17.** $\frac{57}{10}$ **19.** $\frac{-507}{100}$ **21.** $5\frac{1}{3}$ **23.** $7\frac{1}{2}$
25. $5\frac{7}{10}$ **27.** $7\frac{2}{9}$ **29.** $-5\frac{1}{2}$ **31.** $11\frac{1}{2}$ **33.** $-1\frac{1}{2}$
35. $61\frac{2}{5}$ **37.** $8\frac{13}{50}$ **39.** $108\frac{5}{8}$ **41.** $906\frac{3}{7}$ **43.** $40\frac{4}{7}$
45. $-20\frac{2}{15}$ **47.** $-22\frac{3}{7}$ **49.** $2\frac{1}{5}$ g **51.** $2\frac{3}{10}$ g **53.** $\mathbf{D_W}$
55. $\frac{8}{9}$ **56.** $\frac{3}{8}$ **57.** $\frac{1}{4}$ **58.** $\frac{5}{4}$ **59.** $\frac{3}{10}$ **60.** $-\frac{9}{28}$
61. $\mathbf{D_W}$ **63.** $237\frac{19}{541}$ **65.** $8\frac{2}{3}$ **67.** $3\frac{2}{3}$ **69.** $52\frac{1}{7}$

Margin Exercises, Section 4.6, pp. 332–337

1. $9\frac{2}{5}$ **2.** $12\frac{1}{10}$ **3.** $14\frac{7}{12}$ **4.** $1\frac{1}{2}$ **5.** $3\frac{1}{6}$ **6.** $3\frac{2}{3}$
7. $3\frac{5}{18}$ **8.** $12\frac{5}{6}t$ **9.** $2\frac{1}{4}x$ **10.** $14\frac{1}{30}x$ **11.** $17\frac{1}{12}$ yd
12. $23\frac{1}{4}$ gal **13.** $\frac{-3}{4}$ **14.** $-4\frac{1}{4}$ **15.** $-2\frac{1}{2}$ **16.** $-1\frac{5}{6}$
17. $3\frac{3}{10}$ **18.** $-13\frac{7}{30}$

Calculator Corner, p. 338

1. $10\frac{2}{15}$ **2.** $1\frac{1}{28}$ **3.** $2\frac{5}{63}$ **4.** $8\frac{1}{15}$ **5.** $-\frac{60}{209}$ **6.** $-2\frac{64}{255}$

Exercise Set 4.6, p. 339

1. $9\frac{1}{2}$ **3.** $5\frac{11}{12}$ **5.** $13\frac{7}{12}$ **7.** $12\frac{1}{10}$ **9.** $17\frac{5}{24}$ **11.** $21\frac{1}{2}$
13. $27\frac{7}{8}$ **15.** $1\frac{3}{5}$ **17.** $6\frac{1}{10}$ **19.** $21\frac{17}{24}$ **21.** $13\frac{1}{4}$
23. $15\frac{3}{8}$ **25.** $7\frac{5}{12}$ **27.** $11\frac{5}{18}$ **29.** $8\frac{13}{42}t$ **31.** $2\frac{1}{8}x$
33. $8\frac{31}{40}t$ **35.** $11\frac{34}{45}t$ **37.** $6\frac{1}{6}x$ **39.** $9\frac{31}{33}x$ **41.** $5\frac{3}{8}$ yd
43. $7\frac{5}{12}$ lb **45.** $6\frac{7}{20}$ cm **47.** $67\frac{1}{4}$ in. **49.** $19\frac{1}{16}$ in.
51. $20\frac{1}{8}$ in. **53.** $20\frac{3}{160}$ mi **55.** $7\frac{3}{4}$ cups **57.** $3\frac{4}{5}$ hr
59. $51\frac{1}{2}$ in. **61.** $27\frac{3}{4}$ ft **63.** $4\frac{5}{8}$ ft **65.** $7\frac{3}{8}$ ft
67. $1\frac{9}{16}$ in. **69.** $\frac{-4}{5}$ **71.** $-3\frac{1}{4}$ **73.** $-3\frac{13}{15}$ **75.** $-7\frac{3}{5}$
77. $-10\frac{29}{35}$ **79.** $-1\frac{8}{9}$ **81.** $\mathbf{D_W}$ **83.** 16 packages
84. 286 cartons; 2 oz left over **85.** Yes **86.** No **87.** No

88. Yes **89.** No **90.** Yes **91.** Yes **92.** Yes **93.** $\frac{10}{13}$
94. $\frac{1}{10}$ **95.** $\mathbf{D_W}$ **97.** $8568\frac{786}{1189}$ **99.** $-1618\frac{690}{2117}$
101. $10\frac{7}{12}$ **103.** $-28\frac{3}{8}$ **105.** $55\frac{3}{4}$ in.

Margin Exercises, Section 4.7, pp. 345–351

1. 28 **2.** $2\frac{5}{14}$ **3.** $-12\frac{4}{5}$ **4.** $8\frac{1}{3}$ **5.** 12 **6.** $1\frac{7}{8}$
7. $-\frac{7}{10}$ **8.** $175\frac{1}{2}$ **9.** $159\frac{4}{5}$ **10.** $5\frac{3}{4}$ **11.** $227\frac{1}{2}$ mi
12. 20 mpg **13.** $240\frac{3}{4}$ ft^2 **14.** $9\frac{7}{8}$ in.

Calculator Corner, p. 350

1. $10\frac{11}{15}$ **2.** $2\frac{91}{115}$ **3.** $-1\frac{136}{189}$ **4.** $-27\frac{1}{112}$ **5.** $31\frac{47}{143}$
6. $25\frac{107}{221}$

Exercise Set 4.7, p. 352

1. $22\frac{2}{5}$ **3.** $1\frac{2}{3}$ **5.** $-56\frac{2}{3}$ **7.** $16\frac{1}{8}$ **9.** $-10\frac{3}{25}$
11. $35\frac{91}{100}$ **13.** $11\frac{7}{13}$ **15.** $1\frac{1}{5}$ **17.** $2\frac{1}{52}$ **19.** $-2\frac{11}{68}$
21. $1\frac{8}{43}$ **23.** $\frac{-9}{40}$ **25.** $23\frac{2}{5}$ **27.** $15\frac{5}{7}$ **29.** $-28\frac{28}{45}$
31. $-1\frac{1}{3}$ **33.** $12\frac{1}{4}$ **35.** $8\frac{3}{20}$ **37.** 580 **39.** $13\frac{1}{3}$ tsp
41. $\frac{1}{2}$ **recipe:** $1\frac{7}{8}$ cups flour, $\frac{3}{4}$ teaspoon salt, $\frac{3}{8}$ cup shortening, $1\frac{1}{2}$ eggs, $\frac{1}{6}$ cup milk, 4 cups apples, $\frac{3}{4}$ cup sugar, $\frac{1}{2}$ teaspoon cinnamon, $\frac{1}{4}$ teaspoon nutmeg, $\frac{1}{2}$ cup cornflakes, $\frac{1}{2}$ egg white; **5 recipes:** $18\frac{3}{4}$ cups flour, $7\frac{1}{2}$ teaspoons salt, $3\frac{3}{4}$ cups shortening, 15 eggs, $1\frac{2}{3}$ cups milk, 40 cups apples, $7\frac{1}{2}$ cups sugar, 5 teaspoons cinnamon, $2\frac{1}{2}$ teaspoons nutmeg, 5 cups cornflakes, 5 egg whites **43.** 68°F **45.** Yes; $\frac{7}{8}$ in.
47. 25 mpg **49.** $16\frac{1}{2}$ **51.** $343\frac{3}{4}$ lb **53.** $82\frac{1}{2}$ in.
55. 69 kg **57.** $2\frac{41}{128}$ lb **59.** $18\frac{3}{5}$ days **61.** $142\frac{1}{4}$ ft^2
63. $76\frac{1}{4}$ ft^2 **65.** $27\frac{5}{16}$ cm^2 **67.** $\mathbf{D_W}$ **69.** $\frac{21}{100}$ **70.** $\frac{30}{7}$
71. $-\frac{9}{10}$ **72.** 1,429,017 **73.** 4,061,952 **74.** 7,690,718
75. 45,770 **76.** 45,800 **77.** $\mathbf{D_W}$ **79.** $360\frac{60}{473}$
81. $16\frac{25}{64}$ **83.** $\frac{4}{9}$ **85.** $1\frac{4}{5}$ **87.** $r = \frac{240}{13}$, or $18\frac{6}{13}$
89. 104 gallons

Summary and Review: Chapter 4, p. 358

1. 80 **2.** 90 **3.** 30 **4.** $\frac{7}{9}$ **5.** $\frac{9}{x}$ **6.** $\frac{-7}{15}$ **7.** $\frac{7}{16}$
8. $\frac{2}{9}$ **9.** $-\frac{1}{8}$ **10.** $\frac{4}{27}$ **11.** $\frac{11}{18}$ **12.** $>$ **13.** $<$ **14.** $\frac{19}{40}$
15. 4 **16.** $-\frac{5}{6}$ **17.** $\frac{12}{25}$ **18.** $\frac{2}{5}$ **19.** $\frac{15}{2}$ **20.** $\frac{274}{9}$
21. $\frac{-65}{7}$ **22.** $2\frac{3}{5}$ **23.** $-6\frac{3}{4}$ **24.** $7\frac{1}{8}$ **25.** $3\frac{1}{2}$
26. $-877\frac{1}{3}$ **27.** $82\frac{1}{3}$ **28.** $10\frac{2}{5}$ **29.** $11\frac{11}{15}$ **30.** -9
31. $1\frac{3}{4}$ **32.** $7\frac{7}{9}$ **33.** $4\frac{11}{15}$ **34.** $-5\frac{1}{8}$ **35.** $-14\frac{1}{4}$
36. $\frac{7}{9}x$ **37.** $3\frac{7}{40}a$ **38.** 16 **39.** $-3\frac{1}{2}$ **40.** $2\frac{21}{50}$ **41.** 6
42. -24 **43.** $-1\frac{7}{17}$ **44.** $\frac{1}{8}$ **45.** $\frac{9}{10}$ **46.** $13\frac{5}{7}$ **47.** $2\frac{8}{11}$
48. 15 **49.** $3\frac{1}{8}$ pizzas **50.** $\frac{3}{5}$ mi **51.** $8\frac{3}{8}$ cups
52. $177\frac{3}{4}$ in^2 **53.** $50\frac{1}{4}$ in^2 **54.** $\frac{-63}{100}$ **55.** $-1\frac{13}{17}$
56. $30 loss **57.** $7a - 63$ **58.** $\mathbf{D_W}$ The student multiplied the whole numbers and multiplied the fractions. The mixed numerals should be converted to fraction notation before multiplying. **59.** $\mathbf{D_W}$ Yes. We may need to find a common denominator before adding or

subtracting. To find the least common denominator, we use the least common multiple of the denominators.

60. $3 \cdot 23 \cdot 41 \cdot 47 \cdot 59 = 7{,}844{,}817$ **61.** $\frac{600}{13}$

62. **(a)** 6; **(b)** 5; **(c)** 12; **(d)** 18; **(e)** -101; **(f)** -155; **(g)** -3; **(h)** -1 **63.** **(a)** 6; **(b)** 10; **(c)** 46; **(d)** 1; **(e)** -14; **(f)** -28; **(g)** -2; **(h)** -1

Test: Chapter 4, p. 362

1. [4.1a] 48 **2.** [4.2a] 3 **3.** [4.2b] $\frac{-5}{24}$ **4.** [4.3a] $\frac{2}{t}$

5. [4.3a] $\frac{1}{12}$ **6.** [4.3a] $-\frac{1}{12}$ **7.** [4.2c] $>$ **8.** [4.3b] $\frac{1}{4}$

9. [4.4a] $\frac{-12}{5}$ **10.** [4.4a] $\frac{3}{20}$ **11.** [4.5a] $\frac{7}{2}$ **12.** [4.5a] $\frac{-75}{8}$

13. [4.5b] $-8\frac{2}{9}$ **14.** [4.5c] $162\frac{7}{11}$ **15.** [4.6a] $14\frac{1}{5}$

16. [4.6a] $12\frac{5}{12}$ **17.** [4.6b] $4\frac{7}{24}$ **18.** [4.6d] $8\frac{4}{7}$

19. [4.6d] $-5\frac{7}{10}$ **20.** [4.3a] $-\frac{1}{8}x$ **21.** [4.6b] $1\frac{54}{55}a$

22. [4.7a] 39 **23.** [4.7a] -18 **24.** [4.7b] 6 **25.** [4.7b] 2

26. [4.7c] $19\frac{3}{5}$ **27.** [4.7c] $28\frac{1}{20}$ **28.** [4.7d] $7\frac{1}{2}$ lb

29. [4.7d] 80 books **30.** [4.5c] $148\frac{1}{2}$ lb **31.** [4.3c] $\frac{13}{200}$ m

32. [2.6b] $-3x + 12$ **33.** [3.7b] $\frac{-190}{21}$ **34.** [1.4a] 5300

35. [2.3b] 1190 ft **36.** [4.1a] $\frac{24}{25}$ min **37.** [4.3c] Dolores; $\frac{17}{56}$ mi **38.** [4.1a] **(a)** 24, 48, 72; **(b)** 24 **39.** [4.2b] **(a)** $\frac{1}{2}$; **(b)** $\frac{2}{3}$; **(c)** $\frac{3}{4}$; **(d)** $\frac{4}{5}$; **(e)** $\frac{9}{10}$

Cumulative Review: Chapters 1–4, p. 364

1. [1.1a] 5 **2.** [1.1b] 6 thousands + 7 tens + 5 ones **3.** [1.1c] Twenty-nine thousand, five hundred

4. [1.2b] 623 **5.** [2.2a] -8 **6.** [4.2b] $\frac{5}{12}$ **7.** [4.6a] $8\frac{1}{4}$

8. [1.3d] 5124 **9.** [2.3a] 16 **10.** [4.3a] $\frac{-5}{t}$

11. [4.6b] $1\frac{1}{6}$ **12.** [1.5a] 5004 **13.** [2.4a] -145

14. [3.6a] $\frac{3}{2}$ **15.** [3.6a] -15 **16.** [4.7a] $7\frac{1}{3}$

17. [1.6c] 48 R 11 **18.** [1.6c] 56 R 11 **19.** [4.5c] $56\frac{11}{45}$

20. [3.7b] $-\frac{4}{7}$ **21.** [4.7b] $7\frac{1}{3}$ **22.** [1.4a] 38,500

23. [4.1a] 72 **24.** [3.1b] Yes **25.** [3.2a] 1, 2, 4, 8, 16

26. [3.3a] $\frac{1}{6}$ **27.** [4.2c] $>$ **28.** [4.2c] $<$ **29.** [3.5b] $\frac{4}{5}$

30. [3.5b] -14 **31.** [4.5a] $\frac{73}{10}$ **32.** [4.5b] $-5\frac{2}{3}$

33. [1.7b], [2.8a] 55 **34.** [4.3b] $\frac{5}{9}$ **35.** [3.8a] $\frac{-12}{7}$

36. [4.4a] $\frac{2}{21}$ **37.** [2.6a] 4 **38.** [2.6b] $7b - 35$

39. [2.6b] $-3x + 6 - 3z$ **40.** [2.7a] $-6x - 9$

41. [1.8a] \$235 **42.** [1.8a] \$663 **43.** [1.8a] 297 ft^2

44. [1.8a] 31 **45.** [3.6b] $\frac{2}{5}$ tsp **46.** [4.7d] 39 lb

47. [4.7d] 16 **48.** [4.2d] $\frac{19}{16}$ in. **49.** [4.4a], [4.6a] $\frac{3}{7}$

50. [4.6c], [4.7d] 3780 m^2

Chapter 5

Pretest: Chapter 5, p. 368

1. Seventeen and three hundred sixty-nine thousandths
2. Six hundred twenty-five and $\frac{27}{100}$ dollars **3.** $\frac{89}{100}$
4. $5\frac{407}{1000}$ **5.** 2.87 **6.** -0.0079 **7.** 32.0 **8.** 710.318
9. 31.732 **10.** 4.688 **11.** -252.9937 **12.** -30.4

13. $12.9a$ **14.** $-6.9x + 6.8$ **15.** -12.62 **16.** 7.6
17. 1.4 **18.** 4.14 **19.** 1.7835 **20.** 4.34 m^2 **21.** 4.34
22. -84.26 **23.** 5.4 **24.** 6 **25.** 4.55 **26.** \$285.95
27. 1081.6 mi **28.** \$90 **29.** \$3397.71 **30.** 30.8 mi

Margin Exercises, Section 5.1, pp. 370–375

1. Fifteen and three tenths **2.** One hundred sixteen and four hundred sixty-two thousandths **3.** Two hundred forty-five and eighty-nine hundredths **4.** Thirty-four and six hundred forty-seven hundred-thousandths
5. Thirty-one thousand, seventy-nine and seven hundred sixty-four thousandths **6.** Four thousand, two hundred seventeen and $\frac{56}{100}$ dollars **7.** Thirteen and $\frac{98}{100}$ dollars
8. $\frac{549}{1000}$ **9.** $\frac{75{,}069}{1000}$; $75\frac{69}{1000}$ **10.** $-\frac{3129}{10}$; $-312\frac{9}{10}$ **11.** 7.43
12. -0.073 **13.** 6.7089 **14.** -0.9 **15.** -7.03
16. 23.047 **17.** 2.04 **18.** 0.06 **19.** 0.58 **20.** 1
21. 0.8989 **22.** 21.05 **23.** -34.008 **24.** -8.98
25. 2.8 **26.** 13.9 **27.** -234.4 **28.** 7.0 **29.** 0.64
30. -7.83 **31.** 34.70 **32.** -0.03 **33.** 0.943
34. -8.004 **35.** -43.112 **36.** 37.401 **37.** 7459.360
38. 7459.36 **39.** 7459.4 **40.** 7459 **41.** 7460
42. 7500 **43.** 7000

Exercise Set 5.1, p. 376

1. Two hundred forty-nine and ninety-four hundredths
3. Ninety-six and four thousand three hundred seventy-five ten-thousandths **5.** Twenty-eight and thirteen thousand twenty-nine hundred-thousandths **7.** Five and sixty-three hundredths **9.** Five hundred twenty-four and $\frac{95}{100}$ dollars **11.** Thirty-six and $\frac{72}{100}$ dollars **13.** $\frac{73}{10}$; $7\frac{3}{10}$
15. $\frac{2036}{10}$; $203\frac{6}{10}$ **17.** $\frac{-2703}{1000}$; $-2\frac{703}{1000}$ **19.** $\frac{109}{10{,}000}$
21. $\frac{-40{,}003}{10{,}000}$; $-4\frac{3}{10{,}000}$ **23.** $\frac{-207}{10{,}000}$ **25.** $\frac{7{,}000{,}105}{100{,}000}$; $70\frac{105}{100{,}000}$
27. 0.3 **29.** -0.59 **31.** 3.798 **33.** 0.0078
35. -0.00018 **37.** 0.486197 **39.** 7.013 **41.** -8.431
43. 2.1739 **45.** 8.953073 **47.** 0.58 **49.** 0.410
51. -5.043 **53.** 235.07 **55.** $\frac{7}{100}$ **57.** -0.872 **59.** 0.2
61. -0.4 **63.** 3.0 **65.** -327.2 **67.** 0.89 **69.** -0.67
71. 1.00 **73.** -0.03 **75.** 0.572 **77.** 17.002
79. -20.202 **81.** 9.985 **83.** 809.5 **85.** 809.47
87. $\mathbf{D_W}$ **89.** 830 **90.** $\frac{830}{1000}$, or $\frac{83}{100}$ **91.** 182
92. $\frac{182}{100}$, or $\frac{91}{50}$ **93.** $\frac{-12}{55}$ **94.** $\frac{-15}{34}$ **95.** 32,958
96. 10,726 **97.** $\mathbf{D_W}$ **99.** $-1.09, -1.009, -0.989,$ $-0.898, -0.098$ **101.** 6.78346 **103.** 99.99999
105. 1983, 1988, 1990, 1991, 1992, 1995, 1997, 1998, 1999, 2000, 2001, 2002 **107.** 1985

Margin Exercises, Section 5.2, pp. 379–382

1. 10.917 **2.** 34.2079 **3.** 4.969 **4.** 6.7982
5. 10.20434 **6.** 912.67 **7.** 2514.773 **8.** 10.754
9. 0.339 **10.** 2.54 **11.** 0.24238 **12.** 5.26992
13. 1194.22 **14.** 4.9911 **15.** -1.96 **16.** 3.159
17. -13.29 **18.** -4.16 **19.** -9.91 **20.** 12.4
21. -2.7 **22.** $3.7x$ **23.** $1.7a$ **24.** $-2.7y + 5.4$

Exercise Set 5.2, p. 383

1. 464.37 **3.** 1576.215 **5.** 132.56 or 132.560 **7.** 7.823
9. 50.0248 **11.** 0.835 **13.** 771.967 **15.** 20.8649
17. 227.468 or 227.4680 **19.** 41.381 **21.** 49.02
23. 3.564 **25.** 85.921 **27.** 1.6666 **29.** 4.0622
31. 29.999 **33.** 3.37 **35.** 1.045 **37.** 3.703
39. 0.9092 **41.** 605.21 **43.** 53.203 **45.** 161.62
47. 44.001 **49.** -3.29 **51.** -2.5 **53.** -7.2
55. 3.379 **57.** -16.6 **59.** 2.5 **61.** -3.519
63. 9.601 **65.** 75.5 **67.** 3.8 **69.** -10.292 **71.** -8.8
73. $5.7x$ **75.** $4.86a$ **77.** $21.1t + 7.9$ **79.** $-2.917x$
81. $8.106y - 7.1$ **83.** $-0.9x + 3.1y$ **85.** $7.2 - 8.4t$
87. D_W **89.** $\frac{12}{35}$ **90.** $\frac{14}{45}$ **91.** $\frac{63}{1000}$ **92.** -10 **93.** -7
94. 31 **95.** D_W **97.** $-12.001 - 12.2698a + 10.366b$
99. $4.593a - 10.996b - 59.491$ **101.** -138.5 **103.** 2

Margin Exercises, Section 5.3, pp. 388–392

1. 625.66 **2.** 21.4863 **3.** 0.00943 **4.** -12.535374
5. 74.6 **6.** 0.7324 **7.** -0.062 **8.** 0.07236 **9.** 539.17
10. -6241.7 **11.** 83,900 **12.** 570,400 **13.** 24,100,000
14. 1,400,000,000 **15.** 1569¢ **16.** 17¢ **17.** $0.35
18. $5.77 **19.** 6.656 **20.** 8.125 sq cm **21.** 55.107

Calculator Corner, p. 390

1. 48.6 **2.** 6930.5 **3.** 142.803 **4.** 0.5076 **5.** 7916.4
6. 20.4153

Exercise Set 5.3, p. 393

1. 47.6 **3.** 6.72 **5.** 0.252 **7.** 2.574 **9.** 426.3
11. $-783,686.852$ **13.** -780 **15.** 7.918 **17.** 0.09768
19. -0.287 **21.** 43.68 **23.** 3.2472 **25.** 89.76
27. -322.07 **29.** 55.68 **31.** 3487.5 **33.** 0.1155
35. -9420 **37.** 0.00953 **39.** 5706¢ **41.** 95¢ **43.** 1¢
45. $0.72 **47.** $0.02 **49.** $63.99 **51.** 3,156,000,000
53. 63,100,000,000,000 **55.** $13,100,000 **57.** 11,000
59. 26.025 **61.** (a) 44 ft; (b) 118.75 sq ft
63. (a) 37.8 m; (b) 88.2 m² **65.** 60.3 billion **67.** D_W
69. -27 **70.** 36 **71.** 69 **72.** -141 **73.** -21
74. -27 **75.** -141 **76.** -23 **77.** D_W
79. 804,100 billion km **81.** 366.5488175
83. 72.996 cm² **85.** 10^{21} **87.** 6,600,000,000,000
89. $61.45

Margin Exercises, Section 5.4, pp. 396–401

1. 0.6 **2.** 1.7 **3.** 0.47 **4.** 0.32 **5.** -5.75 **6.** 0.25
7. (a) 375 (b) 15 **8.** -4.9 **9.** 12.8 **10.** 15.625
11. -48 **12.** 12.78 **13.** 0.001278 **14.** 0.09847
15. -67.832 **16.** 0.2426 **17.** -7.4 **18.** $2.396 billion

Calculator Corner, p. 398

1. 28 R 2 **2.** 116 R 3 **3.** 74 R 10 **4.** 415 R 3

Exercise Set 5.4, p. 402

1. 12.6 **3.** 23.78 **5.** 7.48 **7.** 7.2 **9.** -0.9
11. -1.143 **13.** 140 **15.** 40 **17.** -0.15 **19.** 48
21. 3.2 **23.** 0.625 **25.** 0.26 **27.** 2.34 **29.** -0.3045
31. -2.134567 **33.** 1023.7 **35.** -9236 **37.** 0.08172
39. 9.7 **41.** -0.0527 **43.** $-75,300$ **45.** -0.0753
47. 2107 **49.** -302.997 **51.** -178.1 **53.** 206.0176
55. -400.0108 **57.** 0.6725 **59.** 5.383 **61.** 10.5
63. 41.04 million **65.** 16.9 miles per gallon **67.** 60.16°
69. D_W **71.** $\frac{3}{4}$ **72.** $\frac{7}{8}$ **73.** $\frac{-3}{2}$ **74.** $\frac{-3}{10}$ **75.** $\frac{a}{3}$
76. $\frac{2x}{5}$ **77.** $\frac{1}{5}$ **78.** $\frac{2}{3}$ **79.** D_W **81.** -56.6916
83. 6.254194585 **85.** 1000 **87.** 100 **89.** 13
91. 450

Margin Exercises, Section 5.5, pp. 406–411

1. 0.4 **2.** -0.625 **3.** $0.1\overline{6}$ **4.** $0.\overline{6}$ **5.** $0.\overline{45}$
6. $-1.\overline{09}$ **7.** $0.\overline{714285}$ **8.** 0.7; 0.67; 0.667
9. 0.6; 0.61; 0.608 **10.** -7.3; -7.35; -7.349
11. 2.7; 2.69; 2.689 **12.** 0.8 **13.** -0.45 **14.** 0.035
15. 1.32 **16.** 0.72 **17.** 0.552 **18.** 4.225 ft²

Calculator Corner, p. 411

1. 123.150432 **2.** 52.59026102

Exercise Set 5.5, p. 412

1. 0.375 **3.** -0.5 **5.** 0.12 **7.** 0.225 **9.** 0.52
11. -0.85 **13.** -0.5625 **15.** 1.4 **17.** 1.12
19. -1.375 **21.** -0.975 **23.** 0.605 **25.** $0.5\overline{3}$
27. $0.\overline{3}$ **29.** $-1.\overline{3}$ **31.** 1.16 **33.** $-1.\overline{27}$ **35.** $-0.41\overline{6}$
37. 0.254 **39.** $0.\overline{12}$ **41.** $-0.2\overline{18}$ **43.** $0.\overline{315}$
45. $0.\overline{571428}$ **47.** -1.48 **49.** 0.4; 0.36; 0.364
51. -1.7; -1.67; -1.667 **53.** -0.5; -0.47; -0.471
55. 0.6; 0.58; 0.583 **57.** -0.2; -0.19; -0.193
59. -0.8; -0.78; -0.778 **61.** 9.485 **63.** $-417.51\overline{6}$
65. 0.09705 **67.** -1.5275 **69.** 24.375 **71.** 1.08 m²
73. 5.78 cm² **75.** 790.92 in² **77.** D_W **79.** 3570
80. 4000 **81.** 79,000 **82.** 19,830,000 **83.** -95
84. -10 **85.** -7 **86.** 1 **87.** D_W **89.** $0.\overline{142857}$
91. $0.\overline{428571}$ **93.** $0.\overline{714285}$ **95.** $0.\overline{1}$ **97.** $0.\overline{001}$
99. 13.86 cm² **101.** 1.76625 ft² or 1.767145868 ft²
103. D_W

Margin Exercises, Section 5.6, pp. 416–418

1. $210 **2.** $260 **3.** $350 **4.** 4 **5.** 16 **6.** 18
7. 470 **8.** 0.07 **9.** 18 **10.** 125 **11.** (c) **12.** (a)
13. (c) **14.** (c)

Exercise Set 5.6, p. 419

1. $200; 170 + 30 **3.** $190; 250 − 60 **5.** $150; 5 · 30
7. 7; 250 · 7 = 1750 **9.** 1.6 **11.** 6 **13.** 60 **15.** 2.3

17. 180 **19.** (a) **21.** (c) **23.** (b) **25.** (b)
27. $1500 \div 0.5 = 3000$; answers will vary **29.** $\mathbf{D_W}$
31. 7 **32.** -2 **33.** -5 **34.** -3 **35.** -6 **36.** 3
37. 16 **38.** 40 **39.** $10x + 16$ **40.** $10t + 9$ **41.** $\mathbf{D_W}$
43. Yes **45.** No **47.** (a) $+, \times$ (b) $+, \times, -$

Margin Exercises, Section 5.7, pp. 422–424

1. 3.6 **2.** -1.9 **3.** 3.5 **4.** 2.2 **5.** -4.5 **6.** 1.25

Exercise Set 5.7, p. 425

1. 5.4 **3.** -12.6 **5.** 6 **7.** 1.8 **9.** -3.7 **11.** -4.7
13. 1.7 **15.** 2.94 **17.** 9 **19.** 3.2 **21.** -1.75
23. 30 **25.** 3.2 **27.** 9 **29.** 2.1 **31.** 4.5 **33.** 5.6
35. -1.9 **37.** 13 **39.** -1.5 **41.** $\mathbf{D_W}$ **43.** 14 m^2
44. 27 cm^2 **45.** $\frac{25}{2} \text{ in}^2$ **46.** 24 ft^2 **47.** 5 ft^2
48. 12 m^2 **49.** $\frac{-29}{50}$ **50.** 0 **51.** -2 **52.** 8 **53.** $\mathbf{D_W}$
55. 3.1 **57.** 36 **59.** 1.1212963

Margin Exercises, Section 5.8, pp. 428–433

1. $8.4°$ **2.** $\$37.28$ **3.** $\$189.50$ **4.** 28.6 mpg
5. 13.76 in^2 **6.** 1.25 hr

Exercise Set 5.8, p. 434

1. $\$230.86$ **3.** $\$35.68$ **5.** $102.8°$ **7.** $\$21,219.17$
9. Area: 8.125 cm^2; Perimeter: 11.5 cm **11.** 22,691.5 mi
13. $\$3.01$ **15.** $3.5°F$ **17.** $\$5.65$ **19.** 148.1 gal
21. 20.2 mpg **23.** 2.66 cc **25.** 233.66 in^2
27. 193.04 cm^2 **29.** $\$10$ **31.** 2.31 cm **33.** 331.74 ft^2
35. 39.585 ft^2 **37.** $\$505.75$ **39.** 3.5 hr **41.** 2.5 hr
43. 2152.56 yd^2 **45.** 17 **47.** $\mathbf{D_W}$ **49.** 0 **50.** $-\frac{1}{10}$
51. $\frac{-20}{33}$ **52.** -4 **53.** $6\frac{5}{6}$ **54.** 1 **55.** $\mathbf{D_W}$
57. 762 **59.** 3 **61.** 25 cm^2. We assume that the figures
are nested squares formed by connecting the midpoints of
consecutive sides of the next larger square. **63.** $\$1.32$

Summary and Review: Chapter 5, p. 440

1. 6,590,000 **2.** 6,900,000
3. Five and two hundred six thousandths
4. Five hundred ninety-seven and $\frac{25}{100}$ dollars **5.** $\frac{9}{100}$
6. $-\frac{30,227}{10,000}$; $-3\frac{227}{10,000}$ **7.** -0.034 **8.** 27.91 **9.** 0.034
10. -0.19 **11.** 39.4 **12.** 39.43 **13.** 499.829
14. 29.148 **15.** 229.1 **16.** 685.0519 **17.** -57.3
18. 2.37 **19.** 12.96 **20.** -1.073 **21.** 24,680 **22.** 3.2
23. -1.6 **24.** 0.2763 **25.** $2.2x - 9.1y$
26. $-2.84a + 12.57$ **27.** 925 **28.** 40.84 **29.** 11.3
30. 20 videotapes **31.** $\$15.49$ **32.** 248.27 **33.** 2.6
34. 1.28 **35.** 3.25 **36.** $-1.1\overline{6}$ **37.** 21.08 **38.** -3.2
39. -3 **40.** -7.5 **41.** 6.5 **42.** 11.16 **43.** $\$15.52$
44. 24.36 cups; 104.4 cups **45.** $\$5788.56$ **46.** $\$224.99$
47. 14.5 mpg **48.** 89.4 sec **49.** 8.4 miles
50. $\mathbf{D_W}$ Since there are 20 nickels to a dollar, $\frac{3}{20}$ corresponds
to 3 nickels, or 15¢, which is 0.15 dollars. **51.** $\mathbf{D_W}$ In
decimal notation, $\frac{1}{3}$ and $\frac{1}{6}$ both must be rounded before they
can be multiplied. The best way to express $\frac{1}{3} \cdot \frac{1}{6}$ as a decimal

is to multiply the fractions and then convert the product $\frac{1}{18}$
to decimal notation. **52.** 1 **53.** $\frac{1}{18}$ **54.** $\frac{3}{10}$
55. $-\frac{1}{4}x - \frac{1}{4}y$ **56.** $-14x^5 + 8x^3 - 5$ **57.** (a) + (b) −
58. $\frac{-13}{15}, \frac{-17}{20}, \frac{-11}{13}, \frac{-15}{19}, \frac{-5}{7}, \frac{-2}{3}$ **59.** $\$35$

60. $\mathbf{D_W}$ The Sicilian pizza, at $\frac{4.4¢}{\text{in}^2}$, is a better buy than the
round pizza which costs $\frac{5.5¢}{\text{in}^2}$.

Test: Chapter 5, p. 443

1. [5.1a] Six and four hundred one ten-thousandths
2. [5.1a] One thousand two hundred thirty-four and
$\frac{78}{100}$ dollars **3.** [5.1b] $\frac{-2}{10}$ **4.** [5.1b] $\frac{7308}{1000}$ **5.** [5.1b] 0.0284
6. [5.1b] -5.28 **7.** [5.1c] 0.162 **8.** [5.1c] -0.173
9. [5.1d] 9.5 **10.** [5.1d] 9.452 **11.** [5.2a] 405.219
12. [5.3a] 0.03 **13.** [5.3a] 0.21345 **14.** [5.2b] 44.746
15. [5.2a] 356.37 **16.** [5.2c] -2.2 **17.** [5.2b] 1.9946
18. [5.4a] 0.44 **19.** [5.4a] 30.4 **20.** [5.4a] -0.34682
21. [5.3b] 17,982¢ **22.** [5.2d] $9.8x - 3.9y - 4.6$
23. [5.3c] 11.6 **24.** [5.4b] 7.6 **25.** [5.6a] 11 gal
26. [5.5b] 48.7 **27.** [5.5c] 1.6 **28.** [5.5c] 5.25
29. [5.5a] -0.4375 **30.** [5.5a] $1.\overline{2}$ **31.** [5.5d] 9.72
32. [5.7a] -3.24 **33.** [5.7b] 10 **34.** [5.7b] 1.4
35. [5.8a] $\$1,199.94$ **36.** [5.8a] 33.46 sec
37. [5.8a] $\$120.49$ **38.** [5.8a] 28.3 mpg
39. [5.8a] 53.9 million passengers **40.** [3.3b] 0
41. [4.2b] $\frac{3}{7}$ **42.** [4.3a] $\frac{-1}{30}$ **43.** [4.3a] $\frac{7}{10}x + \frac{1}{15}y$ **44.** 1
45. [5.3a] (a) Always (b) Never (c) Sometimes
(d) Sometimes **46.** [5.8a] About 0.12 lb per year
47. [5.8a] (a) Fly (b) Drive (c) Drive

Cumulative Review: Chapters 1–5, p. 446

1. [1.1b] Two hundred seven thousand four hundred
ninety-one **2.** [5.1a] Eight hundred two and $\frac{53}{100}$ dollars
3. [5.1b] $\frac{1009}{100}$ **4.** [4.5a] $\frac{35}{8}$ **5.** [5.1b] -0.035
6. [3.2a] 1, 2, 3, 6, 11, 22, 33, 66 **7.** [3.2c] $2 \cdot 7 \cdot 11$
8. [4.1a] 140 **9.** [5.1d] 7000 **10.** [5.1d] 6962.47
11. [4.6a] $6\frac{2}{9}$ **12.** [5.2a] 235.397 **13.** [1.2b] 5495
14. [4.2b] $-\frac{1}{30}$ **15.** [2.3a] -71 **16.** [5.2b] 8446.53
17. [4.3a] $\frac{1}{72}$ **18.** [4.6b] $3\frac{2}{5}$ **19.** [5.3a] 4.78
20. [3.6a] $\frac{-2}{7}$ **21.** [4.7a] $13\frac{7}{11}$ **22.** [3.6a] $\frac{3}{2}$
23. [4.7b] $1\frac{1}{2}$ **24.** [3.7b] $1\frac{13}{35}$ **25.** [5.4a] $-43,795$
26. [5.4a] 20.6 **27.** [4.2c] < **28.** [2.1b] <
29. [2.6a] 12 **30.** [2.6b] $4x - 4y + 12$ **31.** [2.7a] $7p - 8$
32. [2.7a] $14x - 11$ **33.** [5.7a] 0.78 **34.** [2.8b] -28
35. [5.7a] 8.62 **36.** [2.8a] 369,375 **37.** [4.3b] $\frac{1}{18}$
38. [3.8a] $\frac{1}{2}$ **39.** [5.7a] 3.8125 **40.** [4.4a] $\frac{7}{3}$
41. [1.8a] 23,535 transplants **42.** [3.8b] $\$1500$
43. [1.8a] 86,400 **44.** [3.6b] $\$2800$ **45.** [5.8a] $\$258.77$
46. [4.6c] 5 lb **47.** [3.6b] 88 ft^2 **48.** [5.8a] 467.28 ft^2
49. [5.8a] 12 boxes **50.** [5.8a] $\$1.42$

Chapter 6

Pretest: Chapter 6, p. 450

1. (a) $172 **(b)** $134 **2.**

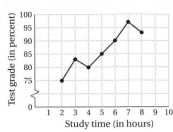

3.

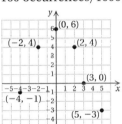

4. 260

5. 160 occurrences/1000 people

6.

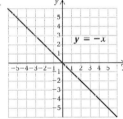

7. II **8.** No

9.

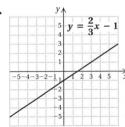

10.

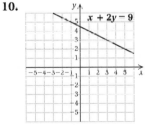

11.

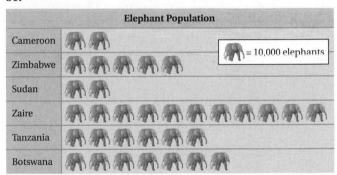

13. (a) 3 **(b)** 3 **(c)** 1, 5   **14. (a)** 12.75 **(b)** 17 **(c)** 4
15. 55 mph   **16.** 86   **17.** 50 occurrences/1000 people
18. $\frac{1}{6}$

Margin Exercises, Section 6.1, pp. 451–454

1. $1192; tuition and required fees at a public 2-yr college
in 1995   **2.** 1998   **3.** $3640   **4.** About 17,400

5. 1992   **6.**

Total Gross Revenue	
Tim McGraw/ Faith Hill	
The Eagles	
Bruce Springsteen	
	= $10,000,000

Exercise Set 6.1, p. 455

1. Cinnamon Life   **3.** Kellogg's Complete   **5.** 1.2 g
7. 483,612,200 mi   **9.** Neptune   **11.** Saturn, Uranus,
Neptune, Pluto   **13.** 92°   **15.** 108°   **17.** 3
19. 90° and higher   **21.** 30% and higher
23. 2000: 59.81°; 2001: 59.69°   **25.** 59.4725°; 59.8925°;
0.42°   **27.** Total Call International   **29.** $7.75 excluding
monthly fee   **31.** Green Saver   **33.** 5.7 cents/min
35. 1.0 billion   **37.** 2070   **39.** 1650 and 1850
41. 3 billion   **43.** About 2.25 births per 100 citizens
45. China   **47.** United States
49.

Coffee Consumption	
Germany	
United States	
Switzerland	
France	
Italy	= 100 cups

51.

Elephant Population	
Cameroon	= 10,000 elephants
Zimbabwe	
Sudan	
Zaire	
Tanzania	
Botswana	

53. ᴰ**w**   **55.** $-\frac{1}{16}$ **56.** $-\frac{31}{35}$ **57.** -2 **58.** -3
59. 1   **60.** 0.375   **61.** 1.16   **62.** $0.8\overline{3}$ **63.** ᴰ**w**
65. 285 min   **67.** ᴰ**w**

Margin Exercises, Section 6.2, pp. 463–468

1. 36 g   **2.** Burger King's Whopper
3. Subway's Meatball Sandwich, KFC's Original Recipe
Chicken Sandwich   **4.** 60   **5.** 85+   **6.** 60–64   **7.** Yes

8.

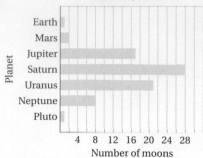

Planetary Moons

9. Graph is not drawn to scale. Bar for Australia should be shorter or U.S. bar should be longer.　**10.** Month 7
11. Months 1 and 2, 4 and 5, 6 and 7, 11 and 12
12. Months 2, 5, 6, 7, 8, 9, 12　**13.** About $900
14. About 40 yr　**15.** About $1300
16.

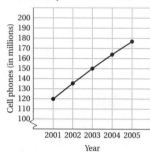

Exercise Set 6.2, p. 469

1. 190 calories　**3.** 1 cup of premium chocolate ice cream
5. About 120 calories　**7.** About 920 calories
9. 1970: $11,000; 2000: $58,000; $47,000
11. 1970: $6000; 2000: $18,000; $12,000　**13.** $4000
15. $14,000　**17.** 920,000 hectares　**19.** Latin America
21. Latin America　**23.** About 854,000 hectares
25.

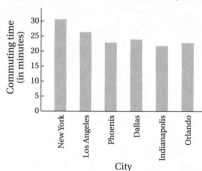

27. Indianapolis　**29.** 24.8 min　**31.** 580 calories
33. 1930 calories　**35.** 2002　**37.** About $1.5 million
39. 1994 and 1995

41.

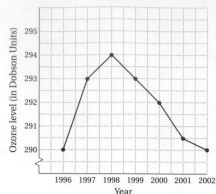

Ozone Layer

43. 1996 and 1997　**45.** About 291.4 Dobson Units
47. 1995 and 1996　**49.** $53.6 million　**51.** D_W
53. 34　**54.** $\frac{9}{50}$　**55.** 72 fl oz　**56.** 32　**57.** 50
58. 18　**59.** 6　**60.** −7　**61.** D_W
63. Lost 657.5 calories　**65.** D_W

Margin Exercises, Section 6.3, pp. 476–479

1 and 2.

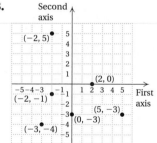

3–8.

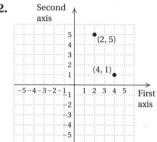

9. A: $(-5, 1)$; B: $(-3, 2)$; C: $(0, 4)$; D: $(3, 3)$; E: $(1, 0)$; F: $(0, -3)$;
G: $(-5, -4)$　**10.** Both are negative numbers.
11. The first, or horizontal, coordinate is positive; the second, or vertical, coordinate is negative.　**12.** I　**13.** III
14. IV　**15.** II　**16.** No　**17.** Yes

Calculator Corner, p. 479

1. Yes　**2.** No　**3.** No　**4.** Yes　**5.** No　**6.** Yes
7. Yes　**8.** No

Exercise Set 6.3, p. 480

1.

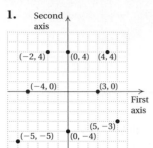

3.

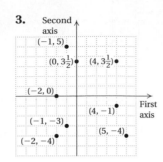

5. A: $(3,3)$; B: $(0,-4)$; C: $(-5,0)$; D: $(-1,-1)$; E: $(2,0)$;
F: $(-3,5)$ **7.** A: $(5,0)$; B: $(0,5)$; C: $(-3,4)$; D: $(2,-4)$;
E: $(2,3)$; F: $(-4,-2)$ **9.** II **11.** IV **13.** III **15.** I
17. Positive; negative **19.** III **21.** IV; positive
23. Yes **25.** No **27.** Yes **29.** No **31.** No
33. Yes **35.** D_W **37.** 7 **38.** 9 **39.** 3 **40.** 14
41. 0 **42.** $\frac{30}{17}$ **43.** $\frac{61}{33}a$ **44.** $7x-24$ **45.** D_W
47. Yes **49.** I, IV **51.** I, III **53.** $(-1,-5)$
55. Answers may vary, but all points should appear on the
following graph. **57.** 26

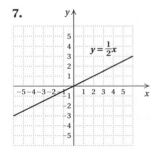

9.

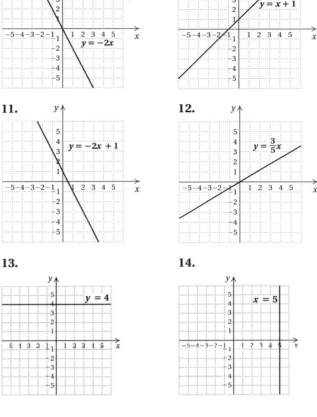

10.

11.

12.

13.

14.

Margin Exercises, Section 6.4, pp. 484–489

1. $(8,5)$ **2.** $(1,5)$; $(3,-5)$ **3.** $(1,3)$, $(7,0)$, $(5,1)$
4. $(0,7)$, $(2,3)$, $(-2,11)$

5.

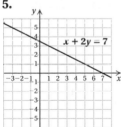

6.

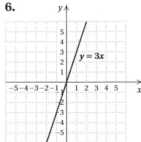

7.

8.

Calculator Corner, p. 490

1. $y = \frac{2}{3}x$

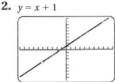

2. $y = x+1$

3. $y = -2x+1$

4. $y = \frac{3}{5}x$

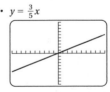

Exercise Set 6.4, p. 491

1. $(5,3)$ **3.** $(3,1)$ **5.** $(5,14)$ **7.** $(10,-3)$ **9.** $(1,3)$
11. $(2,-1)$ **13.** $(1,3)$; $(-1,5)$ **15.** $(7,3)$; $(10,6)$
17. $(3,3)$; $(6,1)$ **19.** $(3,1)$; $(-2,4)$ **21.** $(1,4)$; $(-2,-8)$
23. $\left(0,\frac{3}{5}\right)$; $\left(\frac{3}{2},0\right)$ **25.** $(0,9)$, $(4,5)$, $(10,-1)$
27. $(0,0)$, $(1,4)$, $(2,8)$ **29.** $(0,13)$, $(1,10)$, $(2,7)$
31. $(0,-1)$, $(2,5)$, $(-1,-4)$ **33.** $(0,0)$, $(1,-7)$, $(-2,14)$
35. $(0,-4)$, $(4,0)$, $(1,-3)$ **37.** $(0,6)$, $(4,0)$, $\left(1,\frac{9}{2}\right)$
39. $(0,2)$, $(3,3)$, $(-3,1)$

41.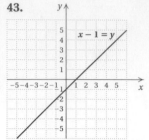

43.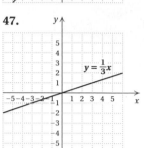

45.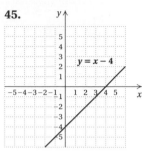

47.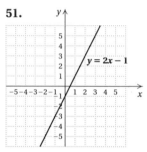

49.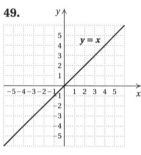

51.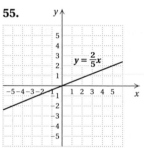

53.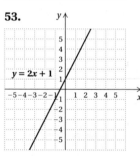

55.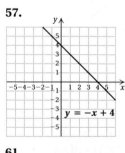

57.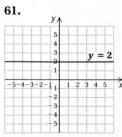

59.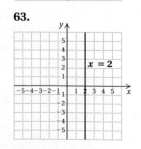

61.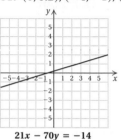

63.

65.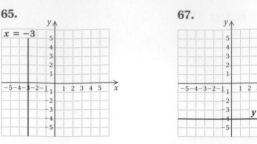

67.

69. D𝗪   **71.** 9 min   **72.** 319.75 pages   **73.** $1\frac{7}{8}$ cups
74. $-\frac{7}{11}$ **75.** 42   **76.** $-\frac{5}{8}$ **77.** 2.6   **78.** 2   **79.** D𝗪
81. $(0, 0.2)$, $(-4, -1)$, $(1, 0.5)$; answers may vary.

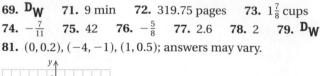

$$21x - 70y = -14$$

83. $(-3, 4.4)$, $(-3.9, 5)$, $(3, 0.4)$; answers may vary.

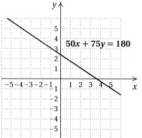

$$50x + 75y = 180$$

85. $(2, 4)$, $(-3, -1)$, $(-5, -3)$; answers may vary.
87. Answers may vary, but all should appear on this graph.

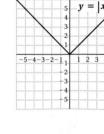   **89.**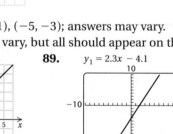
$y_1 = 2.3x - 4.1$

Margin Exercises, Section 6.5, pp. 497–501

1. 75   **2.** 54.9   **3.** 81   **4.** 19.4   **5.** 0.4 lb   **6.** 2.5
7. 94   **8.** 17   **9.** 17   **10.** 91   **11.** $1700   **12.** 67.5
13. 45   **14.** 34, 67   **15.** No mode exists.
16. (a) 17 g **(b)** 18 g **(c)** 19 g   **17.** Wheat A: mean stalk
height ≈ 25.21 in.; wheat B: mean stalk height ≈ 22.54 in.;
wheat B is better.

Calculator Corner, p. 498

1. $203.\overline{3}$ **2.** The answers are the same.

Exercise Set 6.5, p. 502

1. Average: 21; median: 18.5; mode: 29
3. Average: 21; median: 20; modes: 5, 20
5. Average: 5.2; median: 5.7; mode: 7.4
7. Average: 239.5; median: 234; mode: 234
9. Mean: 21.2; median: 21; mode: 23   **11.** 38 mpg
13. 2.7   **15.** Average: $8.19; median: $8.49; mode: $6.99
17. 18,037   **19.** 90   **21.** 263 days   **23.** Bulb A: mean
time ≈ 11171.25 hr; bulb B: mean time ≈ 1251.58 hr; bulb B
is better.   **25.** D_W **27.** 196   **28.** $\frac{4}{9}$ **29.** 1.96
30. 1.999396   **31.** 225.05   **32.** 126.0516   **33.** $\frac{3}{35}$
34. $\frac{14}{15}$ **35.** 2.5 hr   **36.** 6 hr   **37.** D_W **39.** 181
41. 10   **43.** $3475   **45.** 480.375 mi   **47.** D_W

Margin Exercises, Section 6.6, pp. 507–509

1. 88.5 million   **2.** 94%   **3.** (a) $\frac{4}{25}$, or 0.16 (b) $\frac{6}{25}$, or 0.24
(c) $\frac{3}{5}$, or 0.6   **4.** (a) $\frac{1}{4}$, or 0.25 (b) $\frac{2}{13}$

Exercise Set 6.6, p. 510

1. 83   **3.** About $40 million   **5.** About $27 billion
7. About 53.9 thousand tons   **9.** $\frac{1}{6}$, or $0.1\overline{6}$ **11.** $\frac{1}{2}$, or 0.5
13. $\frac{1}{52}$ **15.** $\frac{2}{13}$ **17.** $\frac{3}{26}$ **19.** $\frac{4}{39}$ **21.** $\frac{34}{39}$ **23.** D_W
25. $\frac{11}{14}$ **26.** $\frac{69}{80}$ **27.** $\frac{13}{24t}$ **28.** $\frac{11}{30x}$ **29.** 3   **30.** $-\frac{5}{2}$
31. $-\frac{11}{5}$ **32.** $0.\overline{4}$ **33.** $1.1\overline{3}$ **34.** -0.625 **35.** D_W
37. $\frac{1}{4}$, or 0.25   **39.** $\frac{1}{36}$ **41.** D_W

Summary and Review: Chapter 6, p. 513

1. $29.50   **2.** $41.00   **3.** $17.50   **4.** $16.00
5. No   **6.** 14,000   **7.** Los Angeles   **8.** Houston
9. 12,200   **10.** About 2.5 million   **11.** Birds
12. Reptiles   **13.** 6 million   **14.** True   **15.** False
16. Under 20   **17.** About 12   **18.** About 13   **19.** 45–74
20. About 12   **21.** Under 20
22.

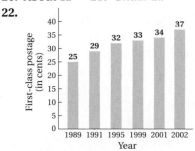

23.

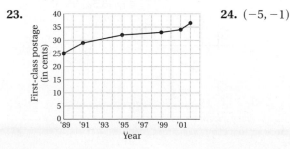

24. $(-5, -1)$

25. $(-2, 5)$ **26.** $(3, 0)$ **27.** $(4, -2)$
28–30.

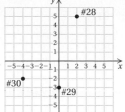

31. IV   **32.** III   **33.** I

34. $(1, 2); (9, -2)$ **35.**

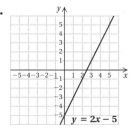

36.

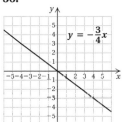

37.

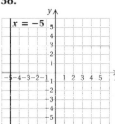

38.

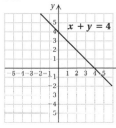

39.

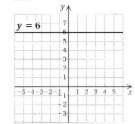

40. (a) 36 (b) 34 (c) 26   **41.** (a) 14 (b) 14 (c) 11, 17
42. (a) 322.5 (b) 375 (c) 470   **43.** (a) 1800 (b) 1900
(c) 700   **44.** (a) $37,500 (b) $27,500 (c) None
45. 96   **46.** 18   **47.** $\frac{1}{52}$ **48.** $\frac{1}{2}$ **49.** D_W It is possible
for the mean of a set of numbers to be larger than all but
one number in the set. To see this, note that the mean of the
set $\{6, 8\}$ is 7, which is larger than all of the numbers in the
set but one.   **50.** D_W The median of a set of four
numbers *can* be in the set. For example, the median of the
set $\{11, 15, 15, 17\}$ is 15, which is in the set.
51. -135 **52.** $\frac{1}{3}$ m^2 **53.** -8 **54.** -1.45
55. $\left(0, \frac{100}{47}\right), \left(\frac{100}{34}, 0\right), \left(2, \frac{32}{47}\right)$ (Ordered pairs may vary.)

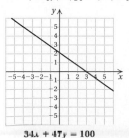

56. $11.52/hr   **57.** 40.8 million   **58.** 35.75 million
59. $18.75
60.   **61.**

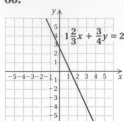   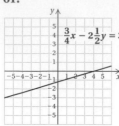

Test: Chapter 6, p. 518

1. [6.1a] Hiking at 3 mph with 20-lb load
2. [6.1a] Hiking at 3 mph with 10-lb load   **3.** [6.1b] Africa
4. [6.1b] North America   **5.** [6.1b] 475,000 gal
6. [6.1b] ≈150,000 gal
7. [6.2b]

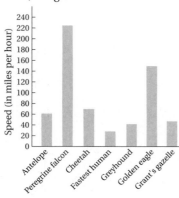

8. [6.2b] 197 mph   **9.** [6.2a, b] **Dw**   **10.** [6.2c] 1992
11. [6.2c] 1994 to 1995   **12.** [6.2c] 1991
13. [6.6a] $33

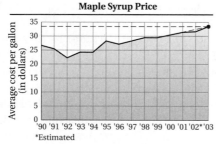

14. [6.3b] II   **15.** [6.3b] III   **16.** [6.3a] (3, 4)
17. [6.3a] (0, −4)   **18.** [6.3a] (−4, 2)   **19.** [6.4a] (4, 2)
20. [6.4b]

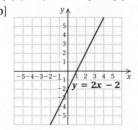

21. [6.4b]   **22.** [6.4b]

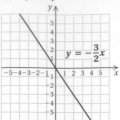   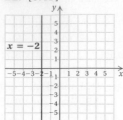

23. [6.5a] 50   **24.** [6.5a] 3   **25.** [6.5a] 15.5
26. [6.5b, c] Median: 50.5; mode: 54
27. [6.5b, c] Median: 3; no mode exists
28. [6.5b, c] Median: 17.5; modes: 17, 18
29. [6.5a] 58 km/hr   **30.** [6.5a] 76   **31.** [6.6b] $\frac{1}{4}$
32. [2.5a] −20   **33.** [3.5b] $\frac{5}{3}$ **34.** [3.4c] $\frac{1}{4}$ lb
35. [5.7a] −1.62
36. [6.4b]   **37.** [6.4b]

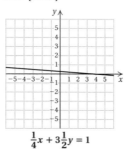   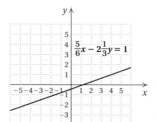

38. [6.3a] 56

Cumulative Review: Chapters 1–6, p. 522

1. [1.1b] 3 thousands + 6 hundreds + 7 tens + 1 one
2. [1.8a] 115 miles   **3.** [1.1c] 8,000,000,000
4. [1.5c], [2.7b] 22 cm; 28 cm^2 **5.** [1.8a] 216 g
6. [1.9a] 7^4 **7.** [2.1a] 8, −7   **8.** [2.1b] >   **9.** [4.2c] >
10. [5.1c] <   **11.** [2.1d] 9   **12.** [2.1d] 17   **13.** [2.6a] −2
14. [2.7a] −2x + y   **15.** [3.2a] 1, 2, 3, 4, 6, 9, 12, 18, 36
16. [3.1b] Yes   **17.** [2.6a] $-\frac{7}{x}$ or $\frac{7}{-x}$
18. [2.6b] 10a − 15b + 5   **19.** [3.3a] $\frac{3}{7}$ **20.** [3.5a] $\frac{10}{35}$
21. [1.3d] 138   **22.** [1.5a] 476   **23.** [2.5a] −9
24. [2.2a] −39   **25.** [4.2a] $\frac{5}{7}$ **26.** [3.7b] $\frac{5}{21}$ **27.** [4.3a] $\frac{13}{18}$
28. [4.2b] $\frac{1}{6}$ **29.** [3.6a] 1   **30.** [4.6a] $\frac{73}{8}$ or $9\frac{1}{8}$
31. [4.6b] $2\frac{5}{12}x$ **32.** [4.7a] $13\frac{1}{5}$ **33.** [5.2a] 83.28
34. [5.4a] 62.345   **35.** [5.3a] −42.282   **36.** [3.3b] 1
37. [3.3b] 4x   **38.** [3.3b] 0   **39.** [4.3b] $-\frac{13}{15}$
40. [4.4a] 24   **41.** [5.7b] $-\frac{17}{4}$ **42.** [6.3b] II
43. [6.4b]   **44.** [6.5a] 36

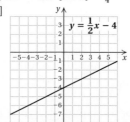

45. [6.5b] 10.5 **46.** [6.5c] 49
47. [6.5a] About 19.7 km/hr
48. [1.9c], [3.6a], [4.6b], [4.7a] $\frac{9}{32}$ **49.** [4.5b], [4.6a] $7\frac{47}{1000}$
50. [6.3a] $(-2, -1), (-2, 7), (6, 7), (6, -1)$

Chapter 7

Pretest: Chapter 7, p. 526

1. $\frac{31}{54}$ **2.** $\frac{3}{7}$ **3.** 41.5 mpg **4.** 20¢ per oz, 16¢ per oz;
34.5 oz package has the lower unit price. **5.** Cleary's
6. Yes **7.** 22.5 **8.** 0.75 **9.** 12 min **10.** 393.75 mi
11. $x = 3.75, y = 2.5, z = 3.75$ **12.** 60 ft

Margin Exercises, Section 7.1, pp. 527–529

1. $\frac{5}{11}$ **2.** $\frac{57.3}{86.1}$ **3.** $\frac{6\frac{3}{4}}{7\frac{2}{5}}$ **4.** $\frac{8620}{34,500}$ **5.** $\frac{739}{12}$ **6.** $\frac{5}{9}$ **7.** $\frac{38.2}{56.1}$
8. $\frac{73}{27}$ **9.** $\frac{3}{4}$ **10.** 18 is to 27 as 2 is to 3. **11.** 3.6 is to 12
as 3 is to 10. **12.** 1.2 is to 1.5 as 4 is to 5. **13.** $\frac{13}{22}$

Calculator Corner, p. 529

1. $\frac{144}{77}$

Exercise Set 7.1, p. 530

1. $\frac{4}{5}$ **3.** $\frac{178}{572}$ **5.** $\frac{0.4}{12}$ **7.** $\frac{3.8}{7.4}$ **9.** $\frac{56.78}{98.35}$ **11.** $\frac{8\frac{3}{4}}{9\frac{5}{6}}$ **13.** $\frac{1}{4}; \frac{3}{1}$
15. (a) $\frac{60}{100}$ **(b)** $\frac{100}{60}$ **17.** $\frac{21.1}{182.5}$ **19.** $\frac{28}{100}; \frac{100}{28}$ **21.** $\frac{93.2}{906.0}$
23. $\frac{478}{213}; \frac{213}{478}$ **25.** $\frac{2}{3}$ **27.** $\frac{3}{4}$ **29.** $\frac{12}{25}$ **31.** $\frac{7}{9}$ **33.** $\frac{2}{3}$
35. $\frac{14}{25}$ **37.** $\frac{1}{2}$ **39.** $\frac{3}{4}$ **41.** $\frac{51}{49}$ **43.** $\frac{32}{101}$ **45.** $\frac{2}{3}$
47. $\frac{32}{41}$ **49.** $\frac{57}{22}$ **51.** $\frac{148}{129}$ **53.** $\mathbf{D_W}$ **55.** < **56.** <
57. > **58.** < **59.** 50 **60.** 9.5 **61.** 14.5
62. 152 **63.** $6\frac{7}{20}$ cm **64.** $17\frac{11}{20}$ cm **65.** $\mathbf{D_W}$
67. 0.0621968593 to 1 **69.** $\frac{7107}{6629}$ **71.** 1 : 2 : 3

Margin Exercises, Section 7.2, pp. 535–537

1. 2 gal/day **2.** 3 cookies/toddler **3.** 5 mi/hr
4. 12 mi/hr **5.** 0.3 mi/hr **6.** 1100 ft/sec
7. 14.5 ft/sec **8.** 250 ft/sec **9.** 20.64 ¢/oz
10. 24.143 ¢/oz; 25.9 ¢/oz; 24.174 ¢/oz; the 7-oz jar has the
lowest unit price.

Calculator Corner, p. 536

1. About 0.12 home runs per at-bat
2. 0.8 pounds per dollar

Exercise Set 7.2, p. 538

1. 70 beats/min **3.** About 4.17 hot dogs/min
5. 3.9 ¢/min **7.** 0.623 gal/ft^2 **9.** 19 mpg
11. About 25.8 points/game **13.** About 0.325 hits/at-bat
15. 40 km/h **17.** 7.48 mi/sec **19.** 124 km/h
21. 1100 ft/sec **23.** 64 mph; 0.015625 hr/mi

25. 12.030 ¢/oz; 11.56 ¢/oz; 50 fl oz **27.** 47.903 ¢/oz;
43.375 ¢/oz; 8.0 oz **29.** 18.174 ¢/oz; 15.275 ¢/oz; 34.5 oz
31. 1.583 ¢/sq ft; 3.311 ¢/sq ft; 1.537 ¢/sq ft; 2.419 ¢/sq ft;
1.544 ¢/sq ft; 1.904 ¢/sq ft; 61.8 sq ft **33.** 7.94 ¢/oz;
4.99 ¢/oz; 6.12 ¢/oz; 5.99 ¢/oz; 100 fl oz **35.** $\mathbf{D_W}$ **37.** <
38. < **39.** > **40.** > **41.** < **42.** >
43. 1.7 million **44.** $25\frac{1}{2}$ **45.** $\mathbf{D_W}$ **47. (a)** 10.83 ¢/oz;
10.91 ¢/oz **(b)** 1.14 ¢/ft^2; 1.22 ¢/ft^2 **49.** The unit price
increases by 0.76 ¢/oz. **51.** 2 min; 0.0000022 min
53. About 26.2 oz/dollar

Margin Exercises, Section 7.3, pp. 543–544

1. Yes **2.** No **3.** No **4.** Yes **5.** No **6.** 14
7. $11\frac{1}{4}$ **8.** 10.5 **9.** 9 **10.** $10\frac{4}{5}$

Calculator Corner, p. 545

3. 27.5625 **4.** 25.6 **5.** 15.140625 **6.** 40.03952941
7. 39.74857143 **8.** 119

Exercise Set 7.3, p. 546

1. No **3.** Yes **5.** Yes **7.** No **9.** 12 **11.** 45
13. 10 **15.** 20 **17.** 7 **19.** 18 **21.** 22 **23.** 21
25. $9\frac{1}{3}$ or $\frac{28}{3}$ **27.** $2\frac{8}{9}$ or $\frac{26}{9}$ **29.** 0.06 **31.** 5 **33.** 1
35. 1 **37.** 0 **39.** $\frac{51}{16}$, or $3\frac{3}{16}$ **41.** 12.5725 **43.** $\frac{1748}{249}$, or
$7\frac{5}{249}$ **45.** $\mathbf{D_W}$ **47.** -52 **48.** -19.75 **49.** 290.5
50. $1523.\overline{1}$ **51.** 109.608 **52.** 67,819 **53.** 15.2475
54. -162.36 **55.** $\mathbf{D_W}$ **57.** Approximately 2731.4
59. -2
61. $\dfrac{a}{b} = \dfrac{c}{d} \Rightarrow \dfrac{dba}{b} = \dfrac{dbc}{d} \Rightarrow da = bc \Rightarrow \dfrac{da}{ba} = \dfrac{bc}{ba} \Rightarrow \dfrac{d}{b} = \dfrac{c}{a}$

Margin Exercises, Section 7.4, pp. 548–550

1. 19,200 mi **2.** 16 gal **3.** 8 **4.** $42\frac{3}{4}$ in. or less
5. 2074 deer

Exercise Set 7.4, p. 551

1. 6 gal **3.** 600 calories **5.** 168.6 million, or 168,600,000
7. 11.04 hr **9.** 12 lb **11.** $7\frac{1}{3}$ in. **13.** 650 mi **15.** 6
17. 309 **19.** 342 gal **21.** 60 **23.** 2 gal **25.** 477 deer
27. 64 bears **29.** $\mathbf{D_W}$ **31.** $2 \cdot 2 \cdot 2 \cdot 101$, or $2^3 \cdot 101$
32. $2 \cdot 2 \cdot 7$, or $2^2 \cdot 7$ **33.** $2 \cdot 433$ **34.** $3 \cdot 31$
35. $2 \cdot 2 \cdot 5 \cdot 101$, or $2^2 \cdot 5 \cdot 101$ **36.** -79.13 **37.** -2.3
38. -7.3 **39.** -7.2 **40.** -1.8 **41.** $\mathbf{D_W}$
43. (a) 422.50 Australian dollars **(b)** $29.59
45. 17 positions **47.** 2150 earned runs
49. CD player: $133.33; receiver: $400; speakers: $266.67

Margin Exercises, Section 7.5, pp. 555–558

1. 15 **2.** 16.9 in. **3.** 34.9 ft **4.** 21 cm **5.** 29 ft

1. 25 **3.** $\frac{4}{3}$, or $1\frac{1}{3}$ **5.** $x = \frac{27}{4}$, or $6\frac{3}{4}$; $y = 9$
7. $x = 7.5$; $y = 7.2$ **9.** 67.2 ft **11.** 33 ft **13.** $28\frac{4}{9}$ ft
15. 2880 yd **17.** 72 ft **19.** 4 cm **21.** $10\frac{1}{2}$
23. $x = 6$; $y = 5.25$; $z = 3$ **25.** $x = 5\frac{1}{3}$, or $5.\overline{3}$; $y = 4\frac{2}{3}$,
or $4.\overline{6}$; $z = 5\frac{1}{3}$, or $5.\overline{3}$ **27.** 20 ft **29.** 152 ft **31.** $^\mathbf{D}\mathbf{w}$
33. $59.81 **34.** 9.63 **35.** −679.4928 **36.** 2.74568
37. 27,456.8 **38.** 0.549136 **39.** 4.59 **40.** 7.23
41. $^\mathbf{D}\mathbf{w}$ **43.** 13.75 ft **45.** $x \approx 4.13$; $y = 466.2$
47. 1.034 cm **49.** $^\mathbf{D}\mathbf{w}$

Summary and Review: Chapter 7, p. 563

1. $\frac{21}{73}$ **2.** $\frac{42}{31}$ **3.** $\frac{48}{5}$ **4.** 6.55 mph; 0.1527 hr/mi
5. 19.2 min per mi **6.** $0.22 per ounce
7. 128-oz plastic container **8.** Yes **9.** 5 **10.** $\frac{16}{3}$, or $5\frac{1}{3}$
11. $\frac{3}{7}$ **12.** 20 **13.** $8.75 **14.** 80 pairs were flawed
15. 15 students **16.** 275 mi; 55 mph **17.** $52.65
18. 161,419 **19.** $x = 8$ **20.** $x = \frac{64}{7}$; $y = \frac{816}{49}$
21. 195.75 cm **22.** $x = \frac{16}{9}$; $y = \frac{20}{9}$; $z = \frac{8}{3}$ **23.** $1,707.87
24. I, III, II, IV **25.** 614.11 **26.** 17.9 **27.** $^\mathbf{D}\mathbf{w}$ It took
Claire 6 gal of gasoline to drive 114 mi. How many gallons
would she need to drive 418 mi? **28.** $^\mathbf{D}\mathbf{w}$ In terms of cost,
a low faculty-to-student ratio is less expensive. In terms of
quality education and student satisfaction, a high faculty-
to-student ratio is better. To ensure a good education, the
student-to-faculty ratio should be low. **29.** $\frac{570,374}{86,051}$, $\frac{86,051}{656,425}$
30. $\frac{570,374}{1045}$; $\frac{86,051}{234}$ **31.** About 217.2 people per sq mi
32. About 65.8 people per sq mi **33.** 4 bracelets,
100 lavender beads **34.** 240 min or 4 hr **35.** 28 gal

Test: Chapter 7, p. 566

1. [7.1a] $\frac{21}{17}$ **2.** [7.1a] $\frac{0.37}{89}$ **3.** [7.1b] $\frac{32}{15}$ **4.** [7.2a] $\frac{5}{8}$ ft/sec
5. [7.2a] $1\frac{2}{3}$ min/km **6.** [7.2b] $0.25/ounce **7.** [7.3a] No
8. [7.3b] 63 **9.** [7.3b] 57.5 **10.** [7.4a] 1512 km
11. [7.4a] 1.44 min **12.** [7.4a] 525 mi **13.** [7.5a] 66 m
14. [7.5a] $x = 8$; $y = 8.8$ **15.** [7.5b] $x = 8$; $y = 8$; $z = 12$
16. [5.8a] $10.1 billion **17.** [6.3b] IV, III, II, I
18. [5.3a] −6923.93 **19.** [5.4a] −14.8 **20.** [7.3b] $\frac{4}{3}$, or
$1.\overline{3}$ **21.** [7.3b] $\frac{-7}{17}$ **22.** [7.4a] 12 balls of burgundy,
4 sweaters **23.** [7.4a] $47.91 **24.** [7.5a] $\frac{875}{13}$ ft, or
67.308 ft **25.** [7.5a] 10.5 ft

Cumulative Review: Chapters 1–7, p. 568

1. [5.2a] 643.502 **2.** [4.6a] $12\frac{1}{2}$ **3.** [4.2b] $\frac{7}{20}$
4. [5.2b] 1868.216 **5.** [2.3a] −17 **6.** [4.3a] $\frac{7}{60}$
7. [5.3a] 222.076 **8.** [2.4a] −645 **9.** [4.7a] $27\frac{3}{10}$
10. [5.4a] 43 **11.** [2.5a] −51 **12.** [3.7b] $\frac{3}{2}$
13. [1.1b] 3 ten thousands + 7 tens + 4 ones
14. [5.1a] One hundred twenty and seven hundredths
15. [5.1c] 0.7 **16.** [5.1c] −0.799
17. [3.2c] $2 \cdot 2 \cdot 2 \cdot 3 \cdot 3$ **18.** [4.1a] 546 **19.** [3.3a] $\frac{5}{8}$
20. [3.5b] $\frac{27}{32}$ **21.** [5.5d] 5.718 **22.** [5.4b] −25.56
23. [6.5a] 48.75 **24.** [7.3a] No

25. [6.4b]
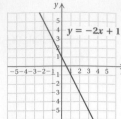
26. [2.6a] 5

27. [7.3b] $30\frac{6}{25}$ **28.** [2.8b], [3.8a] $-\frac{423}{16}$ **29.** [2.8d] −4
30. [5.7b] 3 **31.** [5.7a] 33.34 **32.** [3.8a] $\frac{8}{9}$
33. [7.4a] 209 mi **34.** [7.4a] 26.04 min; 48 wpm
35. [5.8a] 49.8 mi **36.** [7.1a, b] (a) $\frac{900}{600}$, or $\frac{3}{2}$ (b) $\frac{600}{900}$, or $\frac{2}{3}$
37. [3.6b] 12 sq ft **38.** [7.2a], [7.4a] 17.5
39. [4.6c] $2\frac{1}{4}$ cups **40.** [7.2a], [7.4a] 60 mph
41. [7.2b] The 12-oz bag **42.** [7.4a] No; the money will be
gone after 24 weeks. Hans will need $400 more.
43. [7.4a] $750 **44.** [7.4a] Leisure & Incidental Expenses:
$800; Food & Other Necessary Expenses: $2400; Debt
Payments: $1600; Debts: $19,200; Leisure & Incidental
Expenses: $9600

Chapter 8

Pretest: Chapter 8, p. 572

1. 0.133 **2.** 50.4% **3.** 4% **4.** $\frac{19}{100}$ **5.** $0.60 \cdot 75 = a$;
45 **6.** $\frac{N}{100} = \frac{35}{50}$; $N = 70\%$ **7.** 90 lb **8.** 19.2%
9. Tax: $14.30; total price: $300.30 **10.** $5152
11. Discount: $186.25; sale price: $558.75 **12.** $99.60
13. $20 **14.** $7128.60 **15.** $10,079.37
16. Interest: $226.25; amount applied to principal: $115.86

Margin Exercises, Section 8.1, pp. 573–579

1.
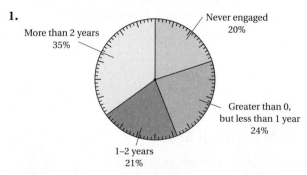

2. $\frac{70}{100}$; $70 \times \frac{1}{100}$; 70×0.01 **3.** $\frac{23.4}{100}$; $23.4 \times \frac{1}{100}$; 23.4×0.01
4. $\frac{100}{100}$; $100 \times \frac{1}{100}$; 100×0.01 **5.** 0.34 **6.** 0.789
7. 0.021 **8.** 0.24 **9.** 0.0008 **10.** 0.29 **11.** 1.43
12. 24% **13.** 347% **14.** 100% **15.** 40% **16.** 25%
17. 62% **18.** 9.4% **19.** 25% **20.** 87.5%
21. $66\frac{2}{3}\%$, or $66.\overline{6}\%$ **22.** 187.5% **23.** 57% **24.** 76%
25. $\frac{9}{5}$ **26.** $\frac{13}{400}$ **27.** $\frac{2}{3}$

28.

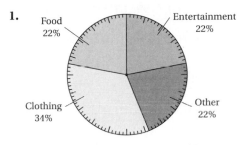

Fraction Notation	$\frac{1}{5}$	$\frac{5}{6}$	$\frac{3}{8}$
Decimal Notation	0.2	$0.83\overline{3}$	0.375
Percent Notation	20%	$83\frac{1}{3}\%$	$37\frac{1}{2}\%$

Calculator Corner, p. 574

1. 0.14 **2.** 0.00069 **3.** 0.438 **4.** 1.25

Calculator Corner, p. 578

1. 52% **2.** 38.46% **3.** 107.69% **4.** 171.43%
5. 59.62% **6.** 28.31%

Exercise Set 8.1, p. 580

1.

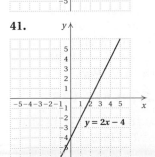

Food 22%
Entertainment 22%
Clothing 34%
Other 22%

3. $\frac{90}{100}$; $90 \times \frac{1}{100}$; 90×0.01 **5.** $\frac{12.5}{100}$; $12.5 \times \frac{1}{100}$; 12.5×0.01
7. 0.67 **9.** 0.456 **11.** 0.5901 **13.** 0.1 **15.** 0.01
17. 2 **19.** 0.001 **21.** 0.0009 **23.** 0.0018 **25.** 0.2319
27. 1.094 **29.** 3.198 **31.** 0.29 **33.** 1.1 **35.** 47%
37. 3% **39.** 870% **41.** 33.4% **43.** 75% **45.** 90%
47. 0.6% **49.** 1.7% **51.** 27.18% **53.** 137.4%
55. 52.6% **57.** 17% **59.** 42.8% **61.** 41% **63.** 5%
65. 20% **67.** 28% **69.** 15% **71.** 62.5%, or $62\frac{1}{2}\%$
73. 80% **75.** $66.\overline{6}\%$, or $66\frac{2}{3}\%$ **77.** 58% **79.** 36%
81. $\frac{17}{20}$ **83.** $\frac{5}{8}$ **85.** $\frac{1}{3}$ **87.** $\frac{1}{6}$ **89.** $\frac{29}{400}$ **91.** $\frac{1}{125}$ **93.** $\frac{11}{20}$
95. $\frac{19}{50}$ **97.** $\frac{11}{100}$ **99.** $\frac{33}{125}$ **101.** $\frac{39}{100}$

103.

FRACTION NOTATION	DECIMAL NOTATION	PERCENT NOTATION
$\frac{1}{8}$	0.125	$12\frac{1}{2}\%$, or 12.5%
$\frac{1}{6}$	$0.1\overline{6}$	$16\frac{2}{3}\%$, or $16.\overline{6}\%$
$\frac{1}{5}$	0.2	20%
$\frac{1}{4}$	0.25	25%
$\frac{1}{3}$	$0.\overline{3}$	$33\frac{1}{3}\%$, or $33.\overline{3}\%$
$\frac{3}{8}$	0.375	$37\frac{1}{2}\%$, or 37.5%
$\frac{2}{5}$	0.4	40%
$\frac{1}{2}$	0.5	50%

105.

FRACTION NOTATION	DECIMAL NOTATION	PERCENT NOTATION
$\frac{1}{2}$	0.5	50%
$\frac{1}{3}$	$0.\overline{3}$	$33\frac{1}{3}\%$, or $33.\overline{3}\%$
$\frac{1}{4}$	0.25	25%
$\frac{1}{6}$	$0.1\overline{6}$	$16\frac{2}{3}\%$, or $16.\overline{6}\%$
$\frac{1}{8}$	0.125	$12\frac{1}{2}\%$, or 12.5%
$\frac{3}{4}$	0.75	75%
$\frac{5}{6}$	$0.8\overline{3}$	$83\frac{1}{3}\%$, or $83.\overline{3}\%$
$\frac{3}{8}$	0.375	$37\frac{1}{2}\%$, or 37.5%

107. D_W **109.** $33\frac{1}{3}$ **110.** $-37\frac{1}{2}$ **111.** 6 **112.** 75
113. 23.125 **114.** 25.5 **115.** D_W **117.** $11.\overline{1}\%$
119. $257.\overline{46317}\%$ **121.** $0.01\overline{5}$ **123.** $1.04\overline{142857}$

Margin Exercises, Section 8.2, pp. 587–589

1. $\frac{12}{100} = \frac{a}{50}$ **2.** $\frac{40}{100} = \frac{a}{60}$ **3.** $\frac{130}{100} = \frac{a}{72}$ **4.** $\frac{20}{100} = \frac{45}{b}$
5. $\frac{120}{100} = \frac{60}{b}$ **6.** $\frac{N}{100} = \frac{16}{40}$ **7.** $\frac{N}{100} = \frac{10.5}{84}$ **8.** $225
9. 35.2 **10.** 6 **11.** 50 **12.** 30% **13.** 12.5%

Exercise Set 8.2, p. 590

1. $\frac{29}{100} = \frac{a}{84}$ **3.** $\frac{N}{100} = \frac{4.3}{5.9}$ **5.** $\frac{25}{100} = \frac{8}{b}$ **7.** $\frac{9}{100} = \frac{37}{b}$
9. $\frac{80}{100} = \frac{a}{730}$ **11.** 140 **13.** 2.88 **15.** 25% **17.** 102%
19. 25% **21.** 93.75% **23.** $72 **25.** 180 **27.** 88
29. 20 **31.** 25 **33.** $780.20 **35.** 7.9 **37.** D_W

39.

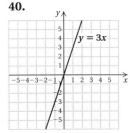

$y = -\frac{1}{2}x$

40.

$y = 3x$

41.

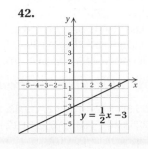

$y = 2x - 4$

42.

$y = \frac{1}{2}x - 3$

43. $\frac{43}{48}$ qt   **44.** $\frac{1}{8}$ T   **45.** 800   **46.** 18.75   **47.** 8
48. 7   **49.** ^{D}W   **51.** $1200; can vary. $1118.64
53. 20%   **55.** 39%

Margin Exercises, Section 8.3, pp. 592–594

1. $0.12 \cdot 73 = a$ **2.** $a = 0.40 \cdot 60$ **3.** $45 = 0.20 \cdot t$
4. $1.20 \cdot y = 79$ **5.** $16 = p \cdot 40$ **6.** $p \cdot 84 = 10.5$
7. 8.4   **8.** $35.20   **9.** 225   **10.** $50   **11.** 40%
12. 12.5%

Calculator Corner, p. 595

1. 1.2   **2.** $5.04   **3.** 48.64   **4.** $22.40   **5.** 0.0112
6. $29.70

Exercise Set 8.3, p. 596

1. $a = 0.32 \cdot 78$ **3.** $89 = p \cdot 99$ **5.** $13 = 0.25 \cdot b$
7. 234.6   **9.** 60   **11.** $18   **13.** 1.9   **15.** 78%
17. 200%   **19.** 50%   **21.** 125%   **23.** 40   **25.** $80
27. 88   **29.** 20   **31.** 6.25   **33.** $846.60   **35.** 41.1
37. ^{D}W   **39.** $\frac{623}{1000}$ **40.** $\frac{19}{10}$ **41.** $\frac{237}{100}$ **42.** 0.009
43. 0.39   **44.** 5.7   **45.** 18   **46.** 20   **47.** ^{D}W
49. $880, answers may vary; $843.20   **51.** 108 to 135 tons

Margin Exercises, Section 8.4, pp. 599–602

1. About 9.5%   **2.** 750 mL   **3.** 4%   **4.** $21,730
5. About 16.2%

Calculator Corner, p. 600

2. $80,040

Calculator Corner, p. 603

1. 30.54; 1.31%   **2.** 32.05; 1.20%   **3.** 34.47; 1.19%
4. 26.47; 1.00%   **5.** 11.98; 4.32%   **6.** 17.52; 0.89%

Exercise Set 8.4, p. 604

1. (a) About 67.7% (b) 90%   **3.** 1634
5. Overweight: 168.6 million; obese: 70.25 million
7. 20.4 mL; 659.6 mL   **9.** 638 field goals   **11.** 95%; 5%
13. 3.6 incorrect   **15.** 95 items   **17.** 25%
19. 166; 156; 146; 140; 122   **21.** 8%   **23.** 20%
25. About 0.1%   **27.** $30,030   **29.** $53.00
31. 34.375%, or $34\frac{3}{8}$%   **33.** About 25%
35. (a) 5.7% (b) 539,452   **37.** 71%   **39.** $1560
41. 80%   **43.** 46,069; 8.2%   **45.** 1,027,429; 21.1%
47. 4,891,769; 9.6%   **49.** $36,400   **51.** 40%
53. (a) 3% (b) 89.5% (c) 107,400 (d) 2235   **55.** ^{D}W
57. $2.\overline{27}$ **58.** 0.44   **59.** 3.375   **60.** $4.\overline{7}$ **61.** 0.92
62. $0.8\overline{3}$ **63.** 0.4375   **64.** 2.317   **65.** 3.4809
66. 0.675   **67.** ^{D}W   **69.** About 5 ft, 6 in.   **71.** $83\frac{1}{3}$%
73. About $1.365 billion   **75.** 19%   **77.** ^{D}W

Margin Exercises, Section 8.5, pp. 612–616

1. $53.52; $722.47   **2.** $9.43; $144.18   **3.** 6%   **4.** $420
5. $2251.20   **6.** 12.5%, or $12\frac{1}{2}$%   **7.** $1675
8. $56; $294   **9.** 20%

Exercise Set 8.5, p. 617

1. $10.95   **3.** $1.03   **5.** $18.55; $283.55   **7.** 5%
9. 4%   **11.** $3000   **13.** $800   **15.** $719.86   **17.** 6.2%
19. $2700   **21.** 5%   **23.** $980   **25.** $5880   **27.** 12%
29. $420   **31.** $30; $270   **33.** $2.55; $14.45
35. $125; $112.50   **37.** 40%; $360   **39.** $387; 30.4%
41. $460; 18.043%   **43.** ^{D}W   **45.** 18   **46.** $\frac{22}{7}$
47. 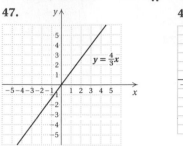   **48.**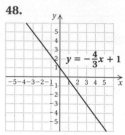

49. $0.\overline{5}$ **50.** $2.\overline{09}$ **51.** 84.872   **52.** 75.712   **53.** ^{D}W
55. 1.1% to 55.6%   **57.** $2.69   **59.** $33\frac{1}{3}$%   **61.** ^{D}W

Margin Exercises, Section 8.6, pp. 622–625

1. $301   **2.** $225.75   **3.** $37.48; $4837.48   **4.** $2464.20
5. $8103.38   **6.** $9064.33

Calculator Corner, p. 625

1. $16,357.18   **2.** $12,764.72

Exercise Set 8.6, p. 626

1. $16   **3.** $84   **5.** $113.52   **7.** $1525   **9.** $671.88
11. (a) $225; (b) $10,225   **13.** (a) $200; (b) $5200
15. (a) $128.22; (b) $6628.22   **17.** (a) $46.03; (b) $5646.03
19. $484   **21.** $2,802.50   **23.** $7,853.38
25. $125,562.26   **27.** $4,284.90   **29.** $28,225.00
31. $9,270.87   **33.** $129,871.09   **35.** $4101.01
37. $1324.58   **39.** $9049.44   **41.** $20,165.05   **43.** ^{D}W
45. 4.5   **46.** 8.75   **47.** 8   **48.** 87.5   **49.** $-3\frac{13}{17}$
50. $3\frac{5}{11}$ **51.** $\frac{18}{17}$ **52.** $\frac{209}{10}$ **53.** 32 cm   **54.** 33 ft
55. 36 in.   **56.** 36 m   **57.** ^{D}W   **59.** $40,524.14
61. 9.38%   **63.** $7883.24

Margin Exercises, Section 8.7, pp. 631–635

1. (a) $97 (b) Interest: $86.40; amount applied to principal:
$10.60 (c) Interest: $55.17; amount applied to principal:
$41.83 (d) The interest at 13.6% is $31.23 less than at 21.3%.
2. (a) Interest: $197.44; amount applied to principal:
$186.56 (b) $34.04 (c) $2520   **3.** Interest: $909.18;
amount applied to principal: $69.46
4. (a) Interest: $909.69; amount applied to principal:
$328.73 (b) $99,915.60 (c) There is $129,394.80 less in
interest with the 15-yr loan than with the 30-yr loan.
5. (a) Interest: $666.25; amount applied to principal:
$405.21 (b) $69,862.80 (c) The Sawyers will pay $30,052.80
less in interest with the 15-yr loan at $6\frac{1}{2}$% than with the
15-yr loan at $8\frac{7}{8}$%.

1. (a) $98; (b) Interest: $86.56; amount applied to principal: $11.44; (c) Interest: $51.20; amount applied to principal: $46.80; (d) The interest at 12.6% is $35.36 less than at 21.3%. **3.** (a) Interest: $241.37; amount applied to principal: $264.60; (b) $74.26; (c) $16,156.40; $21,737.60; $5581.20 **5.** (a) Interest: $872.50; amount applied to principal: $123.44; (b) $208,538.40; (c) New principal: $149,876.56; interest: $871.78; amount applied to principal: $124.16 **7.** (a) Interest: $872.50; amount applied to principal: $474.07; (b) $92,382.60; (c) The Martinez family will pay $116,155.80 less in interest with the 15-yr loan than with the 30-yr loan. **9.** $99,917.71; $99,834.94 **11.** $99,712.04; $99,422.15 **13.** $149,882.75; $149,764.79 **15.** $199,382.07; $198,760.41 **17.** (a) Interest: $112.38; amount applied to principal: $260.82; (b) New principal: $14,739.18; $1.96 less interest in second payment; (c) $2913.60 **19.** (a) $790; $7110; (b) interest: $74; amount applied to principal: $163.82; (c) $1451.52 **21.** D_W **23.** 40 cm^2 **24.** 10 in^2 **25.** 21 m^2 **26.** 84 ft^2 **27.** 36 in^2 **28.** 49 mi^2 **29.** D_W

Summary and Review: Chapter 8, p. 639

1. 87.1% **2.** 60% **3.** 37.5% **4.** $33\frac{1}{3}$% or $33.\overline{3}$%
5. 0.735 **6.** 0.065 **7.** $\frac{6}{25}$ **8.** $\frac{63}{1000}$ **9.** $\frac{28}{100} = \frac{20.72}{b}$;
74 **10.** $\frac{N}{100} = \frac{36}{30}$; 120% **11.** $\frac{10.5}{100} = \frac{a}{84}$; 8.82
12. $30.6 = p \cdot 90$; 34% **13.** $63 = 0.84 \cdot b$; 75
14. $a = 0.385 \cdot 146$; 56.21 **15.** $598 **16.** 15%
17. 82,400 **18.** 44% **19.** 32.58 million **20.** $14.40
21. 5% **22.** 11% **23.** $54; $396 **24.** $52.50; $322.50
25. $1470 **26.** $36 **27.** (a) $394.52; (b) $24,394.52
28. $121 **29.** $7727.26 **30.** Approximately 25%
31. Interest: $301.67; amount applied to principal: $154.48
32. 104 cm^2 **33.** 49 in^2 **34.** 30 m^2 **35.** 20 cm^2
36. 2.4 **37.** 73.29 **38.** $3\frac{2}{3}$ **39.** $5\frac{1}{4}$
40. $-6x^4 - 10x^3 + x^2 - 2$ **41.** D_W No; the 10% discount was based on the original price rather than on the sale price. **42.** D_W A 40% discount is better. When successive discounts are taken, each is based on the previous discounted price, not the original price. A 20% discount followed by a 22% discount is the same as a 37.6% discount off the original price. **43.** About 19.5%
44. $0.27 to $0.64 **45.** $66\frac{2}{3}$% **46.** 7 times

Test: Chapter 8, p. 642

1. [8.1b] 0.26 **2.** [8.1b] 67.4% **3.** [8.1c] 137.5%
4. [8.1c] $\frac{13}{20}$ **5.** [8.3a, b] $a = 0.40 \cdot 55$; 22
6. [8.2a, b] $\frac{N}{100} = \frac{65}{80}$; 81.25% **7.** [8.4a] 2500 mL
8. [8.4b] 8.8% **9.** [8.5a] $16.20; $340.20 **10.** [8.5b] $630
11. [8.5c] Discount: $40; sale price: $160
12. [8.6a] $43.70 **13.** [8.6a] $5356 **14.** [8.6b] $3307.50

15. [8.6b] $10,226.69 **16.** [8.5c] $131.95; 52.8%
17. [8.4b]

Occupation	Number of Jobs in 1998 (in thousands)	Number of Jobs in 2008 (in thousands)	Change	Percent of Increase
Restaurant waitstaff	2019	2322	303	15.0%
Dental assistant	229	326	97	42.4%
Nurse psychiatric aide	1461	1794	333	22.8%
Child-care worker	905	1141	236	26.1%
Hairdresser/ hairstylist/ cosmetologist	608	670	62	10.2%

Source: Handbook of U.S. Labor Statistics

18. [8.7a] Interest: $603.33; amount applied to principal: $308.97 **19.** [3.6b] 54 m^2 **20.** [7.3b] 16
21. [5.5a] $1.41\overline{6}$ **22.** [4.5b] $3\frac{3}{5}$ **23.** [8.5b] $117,800
24. [8.5b], [8.6b] $2546.16 **25.** (a) [3.6a], [4.2d] #1 pays $\frac{1}{25}$, #2 pays $\frac{9}{100}$, #3 pays $\frac{47}{300}$, #4 pays $\frac{77}{300}$, #5 pays $\frac{137}{300}$;
(b) [8.1c], [8.4a] 4%, 9%, $15\frac{2}{3}$%, $25\frac{2}{3}$%, $45\frac{2}{3}$%
(c) [8.1c], [8.4a] 87%

Cumulative Review: Chapters 1–8, p. 644

1. [5.1b] $\frac{91}{1000}$ **2.** [5.5a] $2.1\overline{6}$ **3.** [8.1b] 0.03
4. [8.1c] 112.5% **5.** [7.1a] $\frac{3}{40}$ **6.** [7.2a] $23\frac{1}{3}$ km/hr
7. [4.2c] $<$ **8.** [5.1c] $>$ **9.** [5.6a] 296,200
10. [1.4b] 50,000 **11.** [1.9d] 13 **12.** [2.7a] $-2x - 14$
13. [4.6a] $3\frac{1}{30}$ **14.** [5.2c] -14.2 **15.** [1.2b] 515,150
16. [5.2b] 0.02 **17.** [4.6b] $\frac{2}{3}$ **18.** [4.3a] $-1\frac{47}{63}$
19. [3.6a] $\frac{1}{6}$ **20.** [2.4b] -384 **21.** [5.3a] 1.38036
22. [4.7b] $\frac{3}{2}$ **23.** [5.4a] -12.25 **24.** [1.6c] 123 R 5
25. [2.8b], [3.8a] 95 **26.** [5.7a] 8.13 **27.** [4.4a] 49
28. [4.3b] $\frac{1}{12}$ **29.** [5.7b] $\cdot 1\frac{7}{9}$ **30.** [7.3b] $8\frac{8}{21}$
31. [6.3b] III **32.** [6.4b]

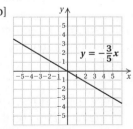

33. [6.5a] 33.2 **34.** [6.5b] 12 **35.** [2.7b] 60 in.
36. [1.5c] 3600 yd^2 **37.** [7.2b] 30 ¢/oz
38. [7.4a] 608 km **39.** [8.4b] 43.2% **40.** [8.4a] 223, 105
41. [4.7d] 5 **42.** [4.2d] $1\frac{1}{2}$ km **43.** [8.4b] 12.5% increase
44. [4.7d], [6.5a] 33.6 mpg **45.** [6.2a] 1906, 1912, 1920, 1924, 1928 **46.** [6.2a] 1977 **47.** [8.5c] $168

Chapter 9

Pretest Answers, Chapter 9, p. 648

1. {January, February, March, April, May, June, July, August, September, October, November, December}
2. 0, {1}, {2}, {1, 2}   **3. a.** {3, 4, 5} **b.** {1, 2, 3, 4, 5, 6, 7}
4. {b, d, f, g, h, j}   **5.** 4
6.

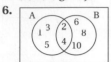

7. yes   **8.** "2 is not less than 6"

Margin Exercises 9.1

1. (a) {John Q. Adams, George W. Bush}
(b) {. . . , −20, −15, −10, −5}   **2. (a)** not a subset
(b) a subset   **(c)** a subset   **3. (a)** $U = \{a, b, c, . . . , z\}$
(the ellipsis indicates all of the letters between c and z).
(b) ∅ **4. (a)** $|A| = 6$ **(b)** $|B| = 4$ (Note that we do not repeat elements in a set, so $B = \{m, i, s, p\}$.) **(c)** $|C| = 42$
(d) $|D| = 0$

Section 9.1 Exercises

1. (a) {Alaska, Arkansas, Alabama, Arizona}   **(b)** {Monday, Tuesday, Wednesday, Thursday, Friday, Saturday, Sunday}
(c) {10, 20, 30, . . .}   **(d)** {2, 3, 5, 7, 11, 13}
2. (a) {January, June, July}   **(b)** {7, 14, 21, . . .}
(c) {1, 3, 4, 5, 9}   **(d)** {−6, −12, −18, . . .}   **3. (a)** {a, e, i, o, u}
(b) ∅   **(c)** {0, 1, 2, 3, 4, 5, 6, 7}   **(d)** ∅
4. (a) {Z, X, C, V, B, N, M}   **(b)** ∅   **(c)** {Hawaii}
(d) {0, 1, 2, . . ., 9, A, B, . . ., E}   **5. (a)** subset
(b) not a subset   **(c)** subset   **(d)** not a subset   **6. (a)** subset
(b) not a subset   **(c)** subset   **(d)** subset   **(e)** not a subset
7. (a) not a subset   **(b)** subset   **(c)** subset   **8. (a)** subset
(b) not a subset   **(c)** subset   **(d)** subset   **(e)** not a subset
9. (a) 4   **(b)** 5   **(c)** 10   **(d)** infinite   **(e)** 1   **(f)** 50   **10. (a)** 10   **(b)** 4   **(c)** 0   **(d)** infinite   **(e)** 1

Margin Exercises 9.2

1. $A \cup B = \{1, 2, 3, 5, 7, 9, 11\}$ **2.** $A \cap B = \{3, 5, 7\}$
3. $A \cap B = \varnothing$ or $A \cap B = \{\}$ **4.** $A' = \{1, 3, 5, 7, 9, B, D, F\}$, which is also the set of odd hexadecimal digits.
5. $|A \cap B| = 27$ **6.** 42   **7. (a)** a CD that costs more than $15, is played on WILD in its entirety, or that contains at least one single from a hit movie **(b)** $|A \cup B \cup C| = 51$

Section 9.2 Exercises

1. (a) {1, 2, 4, 5, 6, 7, 8, 9}   **(b)** {2, 5, 8}   **(c)** {0, 1, 3, 6}
(d) {0, 3, 4, 7, 9}   **(e)** 8   **(f)** 3   **(g)** 6   **(h)** 4   **(i)** 10
2. (a) {1, 3, 5, 6, 7, 9}   **(b)** {3, 9}   **(c)** {0, 1, 2, 3, 4, 5, 6, 7, 8, 9}
(d) ∅   **(e)** 10   **(f)** 0   **(g)** 3   **(h)** 7   **(i)** 0   **3. (a)** {1, 3, 4, 6, 9}
(b) {0, 3, 4, 5, 8, 9}   **(c)** {3, 4, 9}   **(d)** {0, 1, 2, 5, 6, 7, 8}

(e) {3, 4, 9}   **(f)** The answers to parts c and e are equal.
4. (a) {2, 3, 5, 7, 8, 11}   **(b)** {5, 11}   **(c)** {0, 2, 4, 6, 8, 10}
(d) {0, 1, 3, 4, 6, 7, 9, 10}   **(e)** {0, 1, 2, 3, 4, 6, 7, 8, 9, 10}
(f) {0, 1, 2, 3, 4, 6, 7, 8, 9, 10}
(g) The answers to parts e and f are equal.
5. (a) {Raging Bull, Casino, Goodfellas}   **(b)** {Raging Bull, Casino, Goodfellas, Home Alone, Lethal Weapon 2, Braveheart, Road Warrior, Hamlet}   **(c)** ∅
(d) {Home Alone, Lethal Weapon 2, Braveheart, Road Warrior, Hamlet}   **(e)** {Taxi Driver, Cape Fear, Braveheart, Road Warrior, Hamlet}   **(f)** {Lethal Weapon 2}
6. (a) {Aladdin, The Lion King, The Little Mermaid}   **(b)** ∅
(c) ∅   **(d)** {Escape to Witch Mountain, Fantasia, Herbie, Mary Poppins, Snow White}   **(e)** {Aladdin, Escape to Witch Mountain, Fantasia, Flubber, Herbie, Mary Poppins, Snow White, The Lion King, The Little Mermaid, The Parent Trap}
(f) {Aladdin, Fantasia, Snow White, The Lion King, The Little Mermaid}   **7.** 15   **8.** 8   **9.** 14   **10.** 46   **11. (a)** an element of the set $P \cup R \cup D$ is a computer that would have at least ONE of the following: a Pentium IV processor, 256 MB of RAM, or a DVD-ROM drive.   **(b)** 131
12. Two computers have Winamp, Realplayer, and a CD writer.

Margin Exercises 9.3

1.

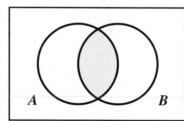

2.

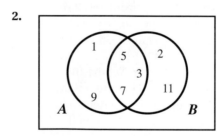

3.

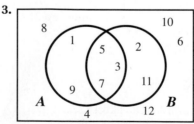

4.

A'

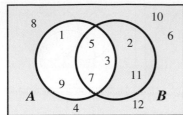

5.

$(A \cap B)' = A' \cup B'$

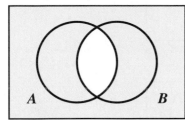

6. Recall that $|A \cup B| = |A| + |B| - |A \cap B|$, $|A \cap B| = 25$.

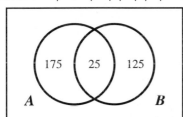

7.

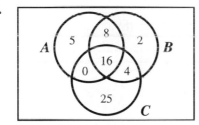

Section 9.3 Exercises

1.

$A \cup B$

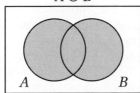

B'

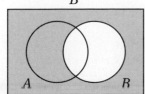

2.

A'

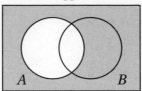

U

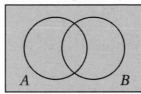

3.

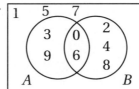

4.

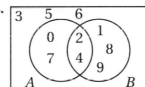

5.

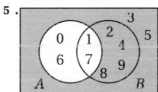

6.

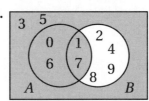

7.

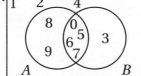

8.

$A \cup B'$

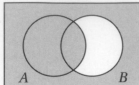

$A \cap B'$

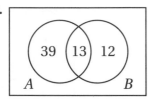

9.

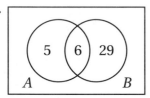

$|A \cup B| = |A| + |B| - |A \cap B| = 52 + 25 - 13 = 64$

10.

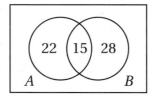

$|A \cap B| = 6$

11.

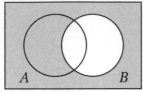

12.

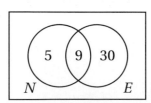

13.

$A \cup C$ ⬛ $(A \cap B)'$

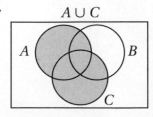

14.

C' ⬛ $A' \cap (B \cup C)$

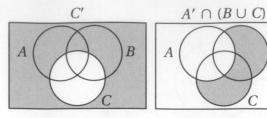

15.

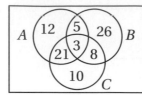

$|A \cap B \cap C| = 3$

16.

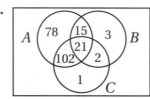

$|A \cup B \cup C| = 222$

17. (a) **(b)** 1 **(c)** 78

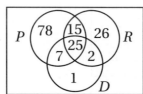

18. (a) **(b)** 97 **(c)** 8 **(d)** 37

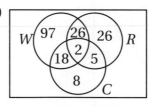

Margin Exercises 9.4

1. (a) "8 − 2 = 5" is a proposition. (It is never true.)
(b) "Is this difficult for you?" is not a proposition.
(c) "The final will be 12 pages long." is a proposition.
(d) "The surface is slippery when wet." is a proposition.
(e) "Turn left at the next light." is not a proposition.
2. *Note*: There may be more than one correct answer to these problems.
(a) Trinh is not going to law school.
(b) Maria did not get an A on her math test.
(c) $12_{16} + 9_{16} \ne 1B_{16}$
(d) $x - 5 > -2$

3.

r	s	$\sim s$	$\sim r$
1	1	0	0
1	0	1	0
0	1	0	1
0	0	1	1

Section 9.4 Exercises

1. (a) No **(b)** Yes **(c)** Yes **(d)** No **(e)** Yes **(f)** No
(g) Yes **(h)** No **2. (a)** The proposition "$x = -10$" is
equivalent to the proposition "$x + 7 = 3$".
(b) The proposition "7 is greater than 4" is equivalent to the
proposition "4 is less than 7". **(c)** The proposition "It is the
third day of the week" is equivalent to the proposition "It is
Tuesday". **(d)** The proposition "$10 > 0$" is equivalent to the
proposition "$4 > -6$". **(e)** The proposition "$51 < 0$" is
equivalent to the proposition "$25 < -26$".
3. (a) $x - 7 \neq 2$ **(b)** 5 is less than or equal to 3
(c) It is not 97° F outside **(d)** $12 \leq -4$ **(e)** Math is not fun
(f) $9 \geq 2$ **4. (a)** $x + 7 = 10$ **(b)** It is raining today
(c) He sometimes takes out the trash **(d)** $12 \leq 13$
(e) $4 > -6$ **(f)** Mark failed the test
5.

p	q	$\sim p$	$\sim q$	$\sim(\sim p)$	$\sim(\sim q)$	$\sim(\sim(\sim p))$	$\sim(\sim(\sim q))$
1	1	0	0	1	1	0	0
1	0	0	1	1	0	0	1
0	1	1	0	0	1	1	0
0	0	1	1	0	0	1	1

6.

p	$\sim q$	$\sim p$	$\sim(\sim q)$	$\sim(\sim p)$	$\sim(\sim(\sim q))$	$\sim(\sim(\sim p))$	$\sim(\sim(\sim(\sim q)))$
1	0	0	1	1	0	0	1
1	1	0	0	1	1	0	0
0	0	1	1	0	0	1	1
0	1	1	0	0	1	1	0

7. (a) Pat sometimes has none of the answers
(b) John has no friends
8. In logic, if two negations occur successively, the result is
the original proposition. In English, this is also the case,
although, colloquially, a double negation often serves to
reinforce a single negation. The property similar in
mathematics is $-(-a) = a$.

Margin Exercises 9.5

1. (a) $1 \wedge 0 = 0$ **(b)** $1 \vee 1 = 1$ **(c)** $0 \wedge 0 = 0$
(d) $\sim 0 = 1$

p	q	$p \vee q$	$\sim(p \vee q)$
1	1	1	0
1	0	1	0
0	1	1	0
0	0	0	1

3. $f(0, 0) = 1$ **4.** We can let $f(p, q) = \sim p \wedge \sim q$ and
$g(p, q) = \sim(p \vee q)$.

p	q	$\sim p$	$\sim q$	$f(p, q)$	$p \vee q$	$g(p, q)$
1	1	0	0	0	1	0
1	0	0	1	0	1	0
0	1	1	0	0	1	0
0	0	1	1	1	0	1

$f(p, q) = g(p, q)$
5. (a) Babe Ruth OR 1927 Yankees
(b) Missouri OR MO (many Web sites will use the postal
abbreviation)
6. (a) mathematics AND Escher
(b) car seat AND child safety
7. (a) Marx Brothers NOT Karl
(b) snake AND python NOT Monty
(c) pollution AND rivers NOT oceans

Section 9.5 Exercises

1. (a) Austin can have coffee with cream and sugar.
(b) Austin can have coffee with cream or sugar.
2. (a) Jane went to the movies and the beach.
(b) Jane went to the movies or the beach.
3. The two propositions are logically equivalent in that they
are true when either or both of the situations occur. The two
propositions are different in that the situations for 1b
(cream and sugar) can happen simultaneously whereas the
situations for 2b (movies and beach) cannot.
4.

p	q	$\sim p$	$q \vee \sim p$
1	1	0	1
1	0	0	0
0	1	1	1
0	0	1	1

5. Austin can have coffee with sugar or without cream.
6. Austin can have coffee without sugar or with cream.

7.

p	q	$\sim q$	$\sim q \lor p$
1	1	0	1
1	0	1	1
0	1	0	0
0	0	1	1

8.

p	q	$\sim p$	$\sim p \lor p$
1	1	0	1
1	0	0	1
0	1	1	1
0	0	1	1

9.

p	q	$\sim q$	$\sim q \land q$
1	1	0	0
1	0	1	0
0	1	0	0
0	0	1	0

10. According to the truth tables in Exercises 8 and 9, the proposition $\sim p \lor p$ is always true and the proposition $\sim q \land q$ is always false.

11.

A	B	$\sim A$	$f(A, B)$
1	1	0	0
1	0	0	0
0	1	1	1
0	0	1	0

12.

A	B	$\sim B$	$g(A, B)$
1	1	0	1
1	0	1	1
0	1	0	0
0	0	1	1

13. (a) 0   **(b)** 0   **(c)** 0

14. (a) 1   **(b)** 1   **(c)** 1

15. The last columns of the truth tables in Exercises 11 and 12 are negations of each other, thus demonstrating De Morgan's law, which in this case takes the form $\sim(\sim A \land B) \Leftrightarrow A \lor \sim B$ [Version 2: $\sim(p \land q) \Leftrightarrow \sim p \lor \sim q$, where $p = \sim A$ and $q = B$].

16. He is not going to both the store and the bank.

17. Abby is playing softball or she is not playing soccer.

18. Answers may vary.   **19.** Answers may vary.

20. Answers may vary.   **21.** Answers may vary.

22. Answers may vary.

Chapter 9   Review Exercises

1. {Canada, USA, Mexico}   **2.** {Greg, Marsha, Jan, Peter, Bobby, Cindy}   **3.** {red, orange, yellow, green, blue, indigo, violet}   **4.** {11, 13}   **5.** {w, i, n, d, o, s}   **6.** {5, 10, 15, ...}
7. (a) Y   **(b)** N   **(c)** N   **(d)** Y   **(e)** Y   **8. (a)** Y
(b) N   **(c)** N   **(d)** Y   **(e)** Y   **9.** {Ore, Nev, Az}
10. {0, 1, 2, ..., 9, A, B, ..., F}   **11.** {Gilligan, Skipper, the Professor, Mr. Howell, Mrs. Howell, Ginger, Mary Ann}
12. {Capricorn, Pisces, ..., Sagitarius}   **13.** {3, 5, 7, ..., 97, 99}
14. 4   **15.** 100   **16.** 9   **17.** infinite   **18.** 6
19. (a) {0 2 3 4 5 6 7 8 A B C D E}   **(b)** {2}   **(c)** {0, 6, C}
(d) {0, 1, 4, 6, 8, 9, A, C, E, F}   **(e)** {1, 5, 7, B, D}   **(f)** 8
(g) 11   **(h)** 16   **20. (a)** {SIL, B}
(b) {E, SIL, B, TTMR, S, P, SD, GWH, D, PH, P, A, CL, CA, BR}
(c) {GWH, D, CA}
(d) {E, TTMR, S, P, SD, BI, ST, ATPH, CUF, MP}   **(e)** ∅
(f) 11   **(g)** 0   **(h)** 20   **(i)** 2   **21.** 43   **22.** 5
23.

24.

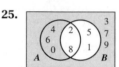

25.

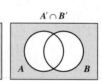

26.

27.

28.

29. 8;

30.

31. 5

32. (a)

(b) computer with Nero, 2 CD-drives, and WinMX **(c)** none **(d)** 8

33. (a) Yes **(b)** No **(c)** Yes **(d)** No **(e)** Yes
(f) Yes **(g)** Yes **(h)** No **34. (a)** $x + 9 \neq 16$
(b) The Bulldogs did NOT win the swim meet.
(c) $6 + 2 \leq 5$ **(d)** Sam did tell the truth. **(e)** $x \neq 1$ and $x \neq 0$ **(f)** The coffee has either cream or sugar.
(g) There is a way out.

35.

p	q	$\sim p$	$\sim(\sim p)$	$\sim(\sim(\sim p))$	$\sim q$
1	1	0	1	0	0
1	0	0	1	0	1
0	1	1	0	1	0
0	0	1	0	1	1

36. (a) Chris can study or watch.

(b) Chris can study and watch. **(c)** Chris can study for his math test. **(d)** Chris can study and Chris can't watch football.

37. (a)

p	q	$\sim p$	$\sim p \vee q$
1	1	0	1
1	0	0	0
0	1	1	1
0	0	1	1

conditional

(b)

p	q	$\sim q$	$\sim q \vee q$
1	1	0	1
1	0	1	1
0	1	0	1
0	0	1	1

tautology

(c)

p	q	$\sim p$	$p \wedge \sim p$
1	1	0	0
1	0	0	0
0	1	1	0
0	0	1	0

fallacy

38.

A	B	$\sim B$	$f(A, B)$
1	1	0	0
1	0	1	1
0	1	0	0
0	0	1	0

39. (a) 0 **(b)** 0 **(c)** 0
40. Allison is working OR not moving. **41.** many answers
42. many answers

Chapter 9 Self-Test

1. (a) {Pacific, Atlantic, Indian, Southern, Arctic}
(b) {23, 29, 31, 37} **(c)** {0, 1, … 7}
(d) {s, p, a, n, k, o, i, t} **(e)** {11, 22, 33, …}
2. (a) Yes **(b)** No **(c)** Yes **(d)** Yes **(e)** No
3. (a) {0, 2, 3, 5, 6, 7, 9, b} **(b)** {3, 5, 7, b}
(c) {0, 2, 4, 6, 8, a} **(d)** {0, 1, 3, 4, 5, 6, 7, 8, 9, a, b}
(e) {0, 6} **(f)** 6 **(g)** 15 **(h)** 12
4.

5. (a) Dolphins
(b) Dolphins, Ravens, Colts, Bengals, Browns, Jags, Broncos, Bills **(c)** Browns, Bills, Broncos, Bengals, Dolphins, Pats, Jets **(d)** Bills, Chargers, Chiefs, Jets, Pats, Raiders, Steelers, Texans, Titans **(e)** 12 **(f)** 1

6. **7.**

8. 98

9. (a) $x + 4 \neq 12$ **(b)** yellow and blue, DO NOT make green **(c)** Stefan was NOT … **(d)** $-3y \not< 15$
10. (a) **(b)** either a flat screen, 100 FB, or DVD and RW drive **(c)** 14

(d) 18 **(e)** 6 **11. (a)** 1 **(b)** 1

(c) 1

A	B	$\sim A$	$f(A, B)$
1	1	0	1
1	0	0	0
0	1	1	1
0	0	1	1

12. many answers, many answers

13. (a) Yes   **(b)** Yes   **(c)** No   **(d)** Yes   **(e)** No

14. (a)

p	q	$\sim p$	$\sim p \wedge p$
1	1	0	0
1	0	0	0
0	1	1	0
0	0	1	0

fallacy

(b)

p	q	$\sim q$	$q \vee \sim q$
1	1	0	1
1	0	1	1
0	1	0	1
0	0	1	1

tautology

(c)

p	q	$\sim p$	$\sim q$	$\sim p \wedge \sim q$
1	1	0	0	0
1	0	0	1	0
0	1	1	0	0
0	0	1	1	1

conditional

Cumulative Review 1–9, p. 693

1. -33 **2.** $\dfrac{14}{27}$ **3.** $10\dfrac{23}{24}$ **4.** 2.6904   **5.** 0.0006

6. $x = 5$ **7.** 23   **8.** 3   **9.** 13   **10. a.** {d, e}

b. {a, b, c, d, e, f, i, h}

Chapter 10

Pretest Answers, Chapter 10, p. 696

1. 100010_2 **2.** 403   **3.** 11000_2 **4.** 1001011_2 **5.** 111_2
6. 11011_2 **7.** 1001_{2*} **8.** -9 **9.** 11100111_{2*} **10.** -79
11. $\dfrac{3}{16}$ **12.** $\dfrac{27}{119}$ **13.** $\dfrac{1111101_2}{1111101000_2}$

14. 2^{21} bytes = 2,097,152 bytes   **15.** 25,769,803,776

Margin Exercises 10.1

1. (a) 2   **(b)** 32   **(c)** 128   **2. (a)** 3   **(b)** 12
(c) 15   **3. (a)** 67   **(b)** 120   **(c)** 255   **4.** 11000111_2

Section 10.1 Exercises

1. 5   **2.** 3   **3.** 13   **4.** 10   **5.** 109   **6.** 198   **7.** 170   **8.** 254
9. 3855   **10.** 3276   **11.** 2049   **12.** 3075   **13.** 0111_2
14. 0010_2 **15.** 1100_2 **16.** 1010_2 **17.** 1111_2 **18.** 110001_2
19. 111001_2 **20.** 1000000_2 **21.** 1101011_2 **22.** 1110000_2
23. 10000000000_2 **24.** 11111010011_2 **25.** 867-5309
26. 555-2743   **27.** 1-800-876-5353   **28.** 1-800-265-5328
29. 9-10-4   **30.** 2468   **31.** $0010_2 = 2$ **32.** $1010_2 = 10$
33. $1011_2 = 11$ **34.** $00110000_2 = 48$ **35.** $10101100_2 = 172$
36. $01111110_2 = 126$

Margin Exercises 10.2

1. 1111_2; $10 + 5 = 15$ **2.** 11011_2; $14 + 13 = 27$
3. 11110110_2; $169 + 77 = 246$ **4.** 1101000_2
5. 1000001_2

Section 10.2 Exercises

1. 0110_2 **2.** 0111_2 **3.** 11_2 **4.** 1101_2 **5.** 10100_2 **6.** 10010_2
7. 100010_2 **8.** 100111_2 **9.** 100111100_2 **10.** 100111000_2
11. 100011011_2 **12.** 11110001_2 **13.** 10110111_2
14. 01010110_2 **15.** 10100000_2 **16.** 1000_2 **17.** 11010_2
18. 11110_2 **19.** 101010_2 **20.** 1011011_2 **21.** 1001101_2
22. No   **23.** Yes

Margin Exercises 10.3

1. 1010_2; $15 - 5 = 10$ **2.** 100_2; $27 - 23 = 4$

3. 1001_2;
$$\begin{array}{r} 1001_2 \\ \times\, 10_2 \\ \hline 0000_2 \\ 10010_2 \\ \hline 10010_2 \end{array}$$

Section 10.3 Exercises

1. 0100_2 **2.** 0101_2 **3.** 1001_2 **4.** 0010_2 **5.** 0011_2 **6.** 0011_2
7. 01111011_2 **8.** 01100110_2 **9.** 5   **10.** 3   **11.** 5   **12.** 3
13. 100001_2 **14.** 10001_2 **15.** 11100_2 R010_2
16. 1111_2 R0010_2

Margin Exercises 10.4

1. $1010_{2*} = -6$ and $1011_{2*} = -5$ **2.** -7 **3.** $1101_{2*} = -3$
4. $(1)0101_{2*} = 5$

Section 10.4 Exercises

1. 0010_{2*} **2.** 0110_{2*} **3.** 1010_{2*} **4.** 1111_{2*} **5.** 5   **6.** -3 **7.** -5
8. 4   **9.** 00000110_{2*} **10.** 11110011_{2*} **11.** 11000010_{2*}
12. 01011111_{2*} **13.** 10010100_{2*} **14.** 10000111_{2*} **15.** 29
16. -5 **17.** -70 **18.** 98   **19.** -1 **20.** -126 **21.** 0111_{2*}
22. $(1)1001_{2*}$ **23.** $(1)0000_{2*}$ **24.** 1010_{2*} **25.** $(1)0100_{2*}$
26. $(1)0010_{2*}$ **27.** $(1)00111000_{2*}$ **28.** $(1)00011011_{2*}$
29. 11110001_{2*}
30. 16 different numbers can be represented in 4-bit, two's complement notation. The minimum value is $1000_{2*} = -8$ and the maximum value is $0111_{2*} = 7$.
31. 256 different numbers can be represented in 8-bit, two's complement notation. The minimum value is $10000000_{2*} = -128$ and the maximum value is $01111111_{2*} = 127$.
32. 4,294,967,296 different numbers can be represented in 32-bit, two's complement notation. The minimum value is 1 followed by 31 zeros, or $-2,147,483,648$, and the maximum value is 0 followed by 31 ones, or 2,147,483,647.

Margin Exercises 10.5

1. 0.0625 or $\dfrac{1}{16}$ **2.** $3.625 = 3\dfrac{5}{8}$ **3.** (a) $\dfrac{101_2}{10000_2}$ (b) $\dfrac{11_2}{100000000_2}$

(c) $\dfrac{11111111_2}{100000000_2}$ **4.** (a) $\dfrac{5}{16}$ (b) $\dfrac{3}{256}$ (c) $\dfrac{255}{256}$

5. (a) $\dfrac{1011101_2}{100000000_2}$ (b) $\dfrac{1011_2}{100000000_2}$

6. (a) $\dfrac{5}{256} = \dfrac{101_2}{100000000_2}$ (b) $\dfrac{80}{256} = \dfrac{1010000_2}{100000000_2}$

7. (a) $0.00110011_2 = \dfrac{51}{256}$ (b) $0.01010101_2 = \dfrac{85}{256}$

8. (a) absolute error $= 0.00078125$, relative error $= 0.39\%$
(b) absolute error $= 0.0013021$, relative error $= 0.39\%$

Section 10.5 Exercises

1. 0.5 **2.** 0.125 **3.** 0.375 **4.** 0.6875 **5.** 0.421875
6. 0.7734375 **7.** 11.625 **8.** 13.875 **9.** 15.390625
10. 0.75 **11.** 0.625 **12.** 0.578125 **13.** 0.9921875
14. 0.453125 **15.** 0.6640625 **16.** 0.01_2 **17.** 0.00001_2
18. 0.1011_2 **19.** 0.1111_2 **20.** 0.0010101_2 **21.** 0.01010101_2
22. 1000.11_2 **23.** 1100.101_2 **24.** 1110.01000001_2
25. 0.001_2 **26.** 0.11_2 **27.** $0.1\overline{0}_2$ **28.** $0.\overline{1001}_2$
29. In base ten, $\dfrac{1}{8}, \dfrac{3}{4}$, and $\dfrac{3}{5}$ terminate.

30. choice (c) is closest to the actual value.
31. choice (b) is the closest to the actual value.

32. The best approximations of the decimal fraction $\dfrac{2}{3}$ using a denominator of 8, of 16, and of 256 are $\dfrac{5}{8}, \dfrac{11}{16}$, and $\dfrac{171}{256}$.

33. The best approximations of the decimal fraction $\dfrac{1}{6}$ using a denominator of 8, of 16, and of 256 are $\dfrac{1}{8}, \dfrac{3}{16}$, and $\dfrac{43}{256}$.

34. 0.125 **35.** 1.375 **36.** 6.375 **37.** 5.25 **38.** 6.30078125

Margin Exercises 10.6

1. $128 \text{ K} = 2^{17}$ bytes $= 2^{20}$ bits
2. $512 \text{ TB} = 2^{49}$ bytes $= 2^{52}$ bits
3. $393,216$ bytes **4.** ≈ 6.1 MB
5. 3×2^{29} bytes 3×2^9 MB
6. (a) 10^1 or 10 (b) 10^{-12}
7. a.e. $= 48,576$ bytes, r.e. $\approx 4.63\%$

Section 10.6 Exercises

1. 1024 **2.** $1,048,576$ **3.** $5,242,880$ **4.** $10,995,116,277,760$
5. $65,536$ **6.** $62,914,560$ **7.** 8192 **8.** $8,589,934,592$
9. $167,772,160$ **10.** $343,597,383,680$ **11.** $5,242,880$
12. $43,980,465,111,040$ **13.** 1000 **14.** 0.1 **15.** 0.01
16. $1,000,000,000$ **17.** 0.000001 **18.** $1,000,000,000,000$
19. 20 **20.** $8.4375 \dfrac{\text{Mb}}{\text{hr}}$ **21.** $2.56 \dfrac{\text{Kb}}{\text{sec}}$ **22.** $38,400$
23. $576,000$ **24.** $921,600$ **25.** $3,145,728$ **26.** 48 MB
27. 144 MB **28.** 191 KB **29.** 703.125 MB

31. the absolute error is given by a.e. $=$
$\left| 1,000,000,000,000 - 1,099,511,627,776 \right| =$
$\left| -99,511,627,776 \right| = 99,511,627,776$ bytes.
The relative error is given by

$$r.e. = \frac{\left| 1,000,000,000,000 - 1,099,511,627,776 \right|}{1,099,511,627,776} =$$

$$\frac{\left| -99,511,627,776 \right|}{1,099,511,627,776} = \frac{99,511,627,776}{1,099,511,627,776} \approx 0.09 = 9\%$$

32. the absolute error is given by a.e.
$= \left| 1,048,576 - 819,200 \right| = \left| 229,376 \right| = 229,376$ bits. The
relative error is given by $r.e. = \dfrac{\left| 1,048,576 - 819,200 \right|}{1,048,576} =$

$\dfrac{\left| 229,376 \right|}{1,048,576} = \dfrac{229,376}{1,048,576} \approx 0.22 = 22\%$

Chapter 10 Review Exercises

1. 4 **2.** 15 **3.** 177 **4.** 228 **5.** 2879 **6.** 1001_2
7. 1110_2 **8.** 11101_2 **9.** 10101100_2 **10.** 111111101_2
11. $503-657-6958$ **12.** $781-944-3700$ **13.** 229
14. 44 **15.** 102 **16.** 111_2 **17.** 10001_2 **18.** 11100_2
19. 11101_2 **20.** 101101000_2 **21.** 1010_2 **22.** 100111_2
23. 110010_2 **24.** 1000_2 **25.** 111_2 **26.** 0010110_2 **27.** 10_2
28. 5 times **29.** 101_2 **30.** 1011_2 **31.** 101_2
32. 101000_2 R 11 **33.** 10010001_2 R 1 **34.** 00000011_2.
35. 11111101_2. **36.** 00011101_2. **37.** 10110101_2.
38. 01100110_2. **39.** 10001101_2. **40.** 2 **41.** -3 **42.** -111
43. 95 **44.** -75 **45.** -35 **46.** (1)1000_2. **47.** (1)0010_2.
48. 1101_2. error **49.** 0.3125 **50.** 0.8125 **51.** 0.8359375
52. 14.6875 **53.** $.875$ **54.** $.28125$ **55.** $.6640625$
56. $.9296875$ **57.** 0.001_2 **58.** $.01011_2$ **59.** 1101.010011_2
60. 1001.0100011_2 **61.** 0.0001_2 **62.** 0.111_2
63. 0.11001101 **64.** $\dfrac{5}{8}, \dfrac{10}{16}, \dfrac{154}{256}$ **65.** 2^{30} **66.** 12×2^{20}
67. 640×2^{10} **68.** 2^{23} **69.** 120×2^{33} **70.** 2^{43}
71. 7.4 or 7 **72.** $2,359,296$

Chapter 10 Self-Test

1. (a) 13 (b) 191 (c) 161 **2.** (a) 10_2 (b) 11011_2
(c) 1110001_2 **3.** (a) 10011_2 (b) 100010011_2
4. (a) 1110_2 (b) 100001_2 (c) 10000010_2
5. (a) 1000_2 (b) 111_2 **6.** (a) 1101_2 (b) 11100 1 R 10
(c) 110110 R 1_2 **7.** (a) 01100010_2. (b) 111100110_2.
(c) 10001100_2. **8.** (a) 14 (b) -3 (c) -111
9. (a) (1)0010_2. (b) 10011_2. error (c) (1)1011_2.
10. (a) $.78125$ (b) 6.5625 (c) $.1328125$ (d) $.8515625$
11. (a) 0.0001_2 (b) 101.01011_2 (c) 1011.010011
12. (a) 0.00001_2 (b) 0.0000110_2 (c) 0.0111001_2
13. (a) 2^{20} (b) 5120 **14.** (a) 40×2^{33} (b) 200×2^{13}
15. 6

Cumulative Review 1–10, p. 745

1. -27 **2.** -2 **3.** $1096 = 2 \cdot 2 \cdot 2 \cdot 137$ **4.** $6\frac{32}{35}$

5. $\frac{2}{3}$ **6.**

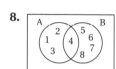

7. 5

8.

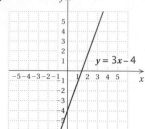

9. 1010011_2 **10.** 110101_2

Chapter 11

Pretest Chapter 11, p. 748

1. 18 **2.** 66_8 **3.** 267_8 **4.** 11011_2 **5.** 1463 **6.** $6E_{16}$
7. $B1_{16}$ **8.** 111000_2 **9.** 14_{16} **10.** $AE1_{16}$ **11.** $172B_{16}$
12. 72 **13.** 106 **14.** 57

Margin Exercises 11.1

1. (a) $6 \times 8^0 = 6$ (b) $7 \times 8^1 = 56$ (c) $2 \times 8^2 = 128$
2. (a) $2 \times 8^2 + 7 \times 8^1 + 6 \times 8^0 = 128 + 56 + 6 = 190$
(b) $2 \times 8^3 + 1 \times 8^2 + 3 \times 8^1 + 3 \times 8^0 =$
$1024 + 46 + 24 + 3 = 1115$

3. $199 = 307_8$

8^3	8^2	8^1	8^0
0	3	0	7

4. $11101101110_2 = 3556_8$

011	101	101	110
3	5	5	6

5. $5624_8 = 101110010100_2$

5	6	2	4
101	110	010	100

6. 8⌊199
8⌊24 R7 Hence, $199 = 307_8$.
3 R0

Section 11.1 Exercises

1. 7 **2.** 2 **3.** 9 **4.** 21 **5.** 32 **6.** 62 **7.** 49 **8.** 84 **9.** 174
10. 275 **11.** 566 **12.** 1022 **13.** 5_8 **14.** 2_8 **15.** 12_8
16. 31_8 **17.** 40_8 **18.** 56_8 **19.** 101_8 **20.** 117_8 **21.** 200_8
22. 765_8 **23.** 3605_8 **24.** 3724_8 **25.** 52_8 **26.** 73_8 **27.** 110_8
28. 357_8 **29.** 252_8 **30.** 376_8 **31.** 7452_8 **32.** 5257_8
33. 7265_8 **34.** 010110_2 **35.** 011001_2 **36.** 111101_2
37. 001010110_2 **38.** 010101101_2 **39.** 011000111_2
40. 110010100_2 **41.** 001000101111_2 **42.** 011001010000_2
43. the octal equivalent of any odd number ends in 1, 3, 5, or 7.

44. the octal equivalent of any even number ends in 0, 2, 4, or 6.
45. 0, 1, 2, 3, 4, 5, 6, 7, and 8.
46. twelve could use 0, 1, 2, 3, 4, 5, 6, 7, 8, 9, A, and B, where A and B are single-character representations of 10 and 11. With this system, the decimal number 11 is written B_{12}.

Margin Exercises 11.2

1. (a) 7_{16} (b) E_{16} (c) $B0_{16}$ (d) $5B_{16}$ (e) $1A0_{16}$
2.

0	C	2	9
0000	1100	0010	1001

$0C29_{16} = 0000110000101001_2$

3. (a) $B21_{16} = 2849$ (b) $9F2C_{16} = 40,748$
4.

16^3	16^2	16^1	16^0
1	7	6	F

$5999 = 176F_{16}$

5. 16⌊2607
16⌊162 R**15**
10 R**2**, hence
$2607 = A2F_{16}$

Section 11.2 Exercises

1. 5 **2.** 14 **3.** 19 **4.** 22 **5.** 161 **6.** 196 **7.** 112 **8.** 2766
9. 3346 **10.** 2776 **11.** 43,962 **12.** 61,776 **13.** 1_{16} **14.** 8_{16}
15. C_{16} **16.** $1F_{16}$ **17.** $2F_{16}$ **18.** 41_{16} **19.** 48_{16} **20.** $6C_{16}$
21. 79_{16} **22.** 154_{16} **23.** $6F7_{16}$ **24.** $14AE_{16}$ **25.** 48_{16}
26. $3B_{16}$ **27.** $2A_{16}$ **28.** AA_{16} **29.** EF_{16} **30.** FE_{16} **31.** $EB5_{16}$
32. AAF_{16} **33.** $F2A_{16}$ **34.** 00100101_2 **35.** 00110111_2
36. 01001010_2 **37.** 11111111_2 **38.** 101100000111_2
39. 110000101001_2 **40.** 111001000001_2
41. 0011011010011100_2 **42.** 1010001011010010_2
43. The octal and hexadecimal equivalents of the binary number 0.1010_2 are 0.5_8 and $0.A_{16}$, respectively.
44. The octal and hexadecimal equivalents of the binary number 0.1110_2 are 0.7_8 and $0.E_{16}$, respectively.
45. The octal and hexadecimal equivalents of the binary number 0.01010100_2 are 0.25_8 and 0.54_{16}, respectively.
46. The octal and hexadecimal equivalents of the binary number 0.01101101_2 are 0.332_8 and $0.6D_{16}$, respectively.
47. The octal and hexadecimal equivalents of the binary number 0.110101101001_2 are 0.6551_8 and $0.D69_{16}$, respectively.
48. The octal and hexadecimal equivalents of the binary number 0.100111101011_2 are 0.4753_8 and $0.9EB_{16}$, respectively.

Margin Exercises 11.3

1. (a) A_{16} (b) E_{16} (c) F_{16} **2.** (a) 12_{16} (b) $1A_{16}$
3. $9FE57_{16}$ **4.** (a) $2F1_{16}$ (b) $1A92_{16}$ **5.** 41_{16}
6. $2AC_{16}$ **7.** (a) $3FF_{16}$ (b) $432DE_{16}$

Section 11.3 Exercises

1. 9_{16} **2.** B_{16} **3.** 11_{16} **4.** $D1_{16}$ **5.** 101_{16} **6.** 168_{16} **7.** $DB2_{16}$
8. $D94_{16}$ **9.** $1A9E_{16}$ **10.** $C2B0_{16}$ **11.** $A780_{16}$ **12.** $B688_{16}$
13. 6_{16} **14.** 1_{16} **15.** B_{16} **16.** $1F_{16}$ **17.** $C3_{16}$ **18.** 45_{16}
19. 542_{16} **20.** $4DC_{16}$ **21.** 450_{16} **22.** $EA1_{16}$ **23.** $2BF_{16}$
24. 2217_{16} **25.** 18_{16} **26.** 28_{16} **27.** BC_{16} **28.** $D6AA_{16}$
29. $6ACD_{16}$ **30.** $3708C_{16}$ **31.** 6_8 **32.** 11_8 **33.** 20_8 **34.** 51_8
35. 117_8 **36.** 112_8 **37.** 5 **38.** 17 **39.** 20 **40.** 40 **41.** 218
42. 6411 **43.** H_{20} **44.** $2A_{20}$ **45.** $9C_{20}$ **46.** $15C_{20}$
47. $28B_{20}$ **48.** 504_{20} **49.** 19_{20} **50.** $2A_{20}$ **51.** HC_{20} **52.** $8E_{20}$
53. $1F4_{20}$ **54.** $1GL_{20}$
55. The number twenty is the sum of the fingers and toes.
56. Bases two, five, and ten make sense. People have two eyes and ears, five fingers per hand and five toes per foot, and ten total fingers and ten total toes.

Margin Exercises 11.4

1. (a) The ASCII for "S" is 01010011_2.
  (b) The ASCII for "G" is 01000111_2.
  (c) The ASCII for "b" is 01100010_2.
  (d) The ASCII for "g" is 01100111_2.
  (c) The ASCII for "5" is 00110101_2.
2. (a) n   (b) 9
3. (a) $1010\ 1001_2$c   does not have odd-parity.
  (b) $1111\ 0100_2$ has odd-parity.
  (c) $0001\ 1010_2$ has odd-parity.
4. (a) $1101\ 1001_2$ represents the character "Y."
  (b) $1011\ 1001_2$ represents the character "9."
  (c) $1011\ 0010_2$ does not have odd-parity.

Section 11.4 Exercises

1. 88 **2.** 70 **3.** 71 **4.** 113 **5.** 57 **6.** 63 **7.** 01011001_2
8. 00110101_2 **9.** 01000010_2 **10.** 01100010_2 **11.** 00110000_2
12. 01111010_2 **13.** $4F_{16}$ **14.** 74_{16} **15.** $4B_{16}$ **16.** 37_{16}
17. 71_{16} **18.** 52_{16} **19.** R2D2 **20.** Seven **21.** Neo
22. Yoda **23.** Spock **24.** Quigon **25.** 4096
26. 16,777,216 **27.** It has an error.
28. It doesn't have an error. **29.** It doesn't have an error.
30. It doesn't have an error. **31.** It doesn't have an error.
32. It has an error. **33.** (a) E (b) q
(c) $0111\ 1010_2$ has an odd number of 1s; it was not correctly transmitted and has an error.
34. No. If an error has been encoded (that is, a bit is on that should be off or a bit is off that should be on), the parity bit will not be correct. But it will not indicate which of the other bits contains the error.
35. The bit that most likely causes the error is the "1" in column B, row 3 because column B and row 3 have odd parity.

36. The message is "U2 ROCKS".
37. To correct an errant message, make all three 3-blocks the same number as the majority in the block; you would be certain as long as each 3-block had at most 1 error.

Chapter 11   Review Exercises

1. 6 **2.** 15 **3.** 53 **4.** 88 **5.** 161 **6.** 835 **7.** 3_8 **8.** 20_8
9. 61_8 **10.** 146_8 **11.** 545_8 **12.** 2724_8 **13.** 16_8 **14.** 75_8
15. 304_8 **16.** 6237_8 **17.** 001101_2 **18.** 111100_2
19. 010011110_2 **20.** 001000100011_2 **21.** 6 **22.** 12
23. 178 **24.** 2781 **25.** 3054 **26.** 61,817 **27.** 3_{16}
28. F_{16} **29.** $2B_{16}$ **30.** 61_{16} **31.** 260_{16} **32.** 714_{16}
33. 9_{16} **34.** 33_{16} **35.** 99_{16} **36.** 81_{16} **37.** $2FB_{16}$
38. $AD7_{16}$ **39.** 01000001_2 **40.** 11111000_2
41. 0010000111110_2 **42.** 110010101011_2
43. 0101001010111001_2 **44.** 1111000001111101_2
45. $0.6_8\ 0.C_{16}$ **46.** $0.3_8\ 0.6_{16}$ **47.** $0.506_8\ 0.A3_{16}$
48. 8_{16} **49.** $1E_{16}$ **50.** 121_{16} **51.** $77F_{16}$ **52.** 19090_{16}
53. $EE6C_{16}$ **54.** 5_{16} **55.** 37_{16} **56.** $EC6_{16}$ **57.** ABE_{16}
58. $C99F_{16}$ **59.** 41_{16} **60.** 1230_{16} **61.** $C27C_{16}$ **62.** 54
63. 105 **64.** 80 **65.** 01100101_2 **66.** 00110111_2
67. 01010001_2 **68.** y **69.** 4 **70.** m **71.** 49_{16} **72.** 39_{16}
73. 72_{16} **74.** S t i n g **75.** B l i n k 1 8 2
76. E n i g m a **77.** P . D i d d y **78.** ERROR
79. OK **80.** ERROR

Chapter 11   Self-Test

1. (a) 11 (b) 38 (c) 175 **2.** (a) 35_8 (b) 116_8 (c) 245_8
3. (a) 13_8 (b) 35_8 (c) 276_8 **4.** (a) 61 (b) 180 (c) 2586
5. (a) ERROR (b) ERROR (c) OK **6.** (a) $3E_{16}$ (b) 69_{16}
(c) ED_{16} **7.** (a) $B3_{16}$ (b) 28_{16} (c) $0.C_{16}$ (d) 83.3_{16}
8. (u) 10100100_2 (b) 101100001110_2 (c) 111111000010_2
9. (a) 84 (b) 52 **10.** (a) 95_{16} (b) $10B_{16}$ (c) 15_{16}
(d) 44_{16} (e) $32A_{16}$ (f) $5FE0_{16}$ **11.** (a) 00111000_2
(b) 01100100_2 **12.** (a) Phoenix (b) Seattle (c) Detroit

Cumulative Reivew 1–11, p. 780

1. 39,362 **2.** $x = 5$ **3.** $7x^3 - 8x^2 + 3x + 12$ **4.** $\dfrac{7}{10}$
5. $9.375 = 9\dfrac{3}{8}$ **6.** 1.98 **7.** 0.00001 **8.** "2 is not less than 9" **9.** 1011011_2 **10.** $2B_{16}$

Chapter 12

Pretest Chapter 12, p. 784

1. 96   **2.** $\frac{3}{4}$ **3.** 7320   **4.** 0.75   **5.** 432   **6.** 12   **7.** 420

8. 896   **9.** 10,000   **10.** 3   **11.** 0.913   **12.** 400,000
13. 130 ft²   **14.** 4 m²   **15.** 235.5 in²   **16.** 18.8 m
17. 220 cm   **18.** 314 cm²   **19.** 0.035 L   **20.** $\angle 1$ and $\angle 3$;
$\angle 2$ and $\angle 4$ **21.** $\angle 1$ and $\angle 2$, $\angle 2$ and $\angle 3$; answers may vary.
22. $m\angle 3$ **23.** 53°   **24.** $c = 20$ **25.** $b = \sqrt{45}$; $b \approx 6.708$
26. 160 cm³   **27.** 1100 ft³   **28.** 38,808 yd³   **29.** 1.8 L

Margin Exercises, Section 12.1, pp. 785–792

1. 2   **2.** 3   **3.** $1\frac{1}{2}$ **4.** $3\frac{1}{4}$ **5.** 288   **6.** 43.5   **7.** 240,768   **8.** 6

9. 8   **10.** 54   **11.** $11\frac{2}{3}$, or $11.\overline{6}$ **12.** 5   **13.** 31,680   **14.** 2 cm,
or 20 mm   **15.** 2.3 cm, or 23 mm   **16.** 3.8 cm, or 38 mm
17. cm; mm   **18.** km   **19.** mm   **20.** m   **21.** cm   **22.** m
23. 37,000   **24.** 500   **25.** 178   **26.** 9040   **27.** 7.814
28. 781.4   **29.** 8.72   **30.** 8,900,000   **31.** 6.78   **32.** 97.4
33. 0.1   **34.** 8.451   **35.** 90.909   **36.** 804.5   **37.** 1479.843

Exercise Set 12.1, p. 793

1. 3.   **3.** $\frac{1}{12}$ **5.** 1760   **7.** 9   **9.** 7   **11.** 16   **13.** 8800   **15.** 4
17. 2.2   **19.** 3   **21.** $2\frac{1}{2}$ **23.** 3   **25.** 1   **27.** 2   **29.** 132,000
31. 126,720   **33.** (a) 1000; (b) 0.001   **35.** (a) 10; (b) 0.1
37. (a) 0.01; (b) 100   **39.** 8300   **41.** 0.98   **43.** 8.921
45. 0.03217   **47.** 28,900   **49.** 4.77   **51.** 688   **53.** 0.1
55. 100,000   **57.** 142   **59.** 0.82   **61.** 450   **63.** 0.000024
65. 0.688   **67.** 230   **69.** 6.21   **71.** 35.56   **73.** 104.585
75. 100   **77.** 70.866   **79.** 32.727   **81.** $\mathbf{D_W}$ **83.** $-\frac{3}{2}$ **84.** –2
85. $101.50   **86.** $44.50   **87.** 47%   **88.** 35%
89. 56 ft; 192 ft²   **90.** 44 ft; 120 ft²   **91.** $\mathbf{D_W}$ **93.** 1.0 m
95. 1.4 cm   **97.** Length: 5400 in., or 450 ft; breadth: 900 in.,
or 75 ft; height: 540 in., or 45 ft   **99.** 321,800   **101.** 85.725 m
103. 0.0041 in.   **105.** <   **107.** <   **109.** <

Margin Exercises, Section 12.2, pp. 797–798

1. 144   **2.** 1440   **3.** 63   **4.** 2.5   **5.** 3200   **6.** 1,000,000
7. 100   **8.** 28,800   **9.** 0.043   **10.** 0.678

Exercise Set 12.2, p. 799

1. 45   **3.** 1008   **5.** 3   **7.** 198   **9.** 2160   **11.** 12,800   **13.** $7\frac{2}{3}$
15. 5   **17.** $\frac{1}{144}$ **19.** $\frac{1}{640}$ **21.** 19,000,000   **23.** 63,100
25. 0.065432   **27.** 0.0349   **29.** 2500   **31.** 0.4728   **33.** 1 ft²
35. $4\frac{1}{3}$ft²   **37.** 84 cm²   **39.** $\mathbf{D_W}$ **41.** $17.50   **42.** $15
43. $6.75   **44.** $8.78   **45.** $35.51   **46.** $86.30   **47.** $\mathbf{D_W}$
49. 1701; 42%   **51.** 6.4516   **53.** 4000   **55.** 5080 cm²
57. 216 cm²

Margin Exercises, Section 12.3, pp. 802–808

1. 43.8 cm²   **2.** 12.375 km²   **3.** 100 m²   **4.** 717.5 cm²   **5.** 9 in.
6. 5 ft   **7.** 62.8 m   **8.** 15.7 m   **9.** 220 cm   **10.** 34.296 yd
11. $78\frac{4}{7}$km²   **12.** 339.6 cm²   **13.** A 12-ft diameter flower bed
is 13.04 ft² larger.

Calculator Corner, p. 807

1. Answers will vary.   **2.** 1417.99 in.; 160,005.91 in²
3. 1729.27 in²   **4.** 125,663.71 ft²

Exercise Set 12.3, p. 809

1. 50 cm²   **3.** 104 ft²   **5.** 64 m²   **7.** 72.45 cm²   **9.** 144 mi²
11. $55\frac{1}{8}$ft²   **13.** 49 m²   **15.** 1.92 cm²   **17.** 68 yd²   **19.** 14 cm
21. $1\frac{3}{4}$in.   **23.** 10 ft   **25.** 0.7 cm   **27.** 44 cm   **29.** $5\frac{1}{2}$in.
31. 62.8 ft   **33.** 4.396 cm   **35.** 154 cm   **37.** $2\frac{13}{32}$in²   **39.** 314 ft²
41. 1.5386 cm²   **43.** The round pie; 6.25 in²
45. The round pie; 9.86 in²   **47.** Two small round pies; 13 in²
49. One extra-large round pizza; 0.96 in²   **51.** 153.86 ft²
53. 153.86 mi²   **55.** 15 in.   **57.** 439.7784 yd   **59.** 45.68 ft
61. 45.7 yd   **63.** 100.48 m²   **65.** 6.9972 cm²   **67.** $\mathbf{D_W}$
69. $\frac{37}{400}$ **70.** $\frac{7}{8}$ **71.** 137.5%   **72.** 66.$\overline{6}$% or $66\frac{2}{3}$%   **73.** 125%
74. 160%   **75.** $\mathbf{D_W}$ **77.** 37.2875 in²   **79.** 3.142   **81.** $\mathbf{D_W}$
83. Circumference   **85.** $\mathbf{D_W}$

Margin Exercises, Section 12.4, pp. 817–823

1. 12 cm³   **2.** 20 ft³   **3.** 128 ft³   **4.** 785 ft³   **5.** 67,914 m³
6. 904.32 cm³   **7.** $\frac{5632}{2625}$in³   **8.** 20   **9.** 32   **10.** mL   **11.** mL
12. L   **13.** L   **14.** 970   **15.** 8.99   **16.** $1.88   **17.** 83.73 mm³

Exercise Set 12.4, p. 825

1. 250 cm³   **3.** 135 in³   **5.** 75 m³   **7.** $357\frac{1}{2}$ yd³   **9.** 4082 ft³
11. 376.8 cm³   **13.** 41,580,000 yd³   **15.** 4,186,666.$\overline{6}$ in³
17. Approximately 124.725 m³   **19.** $1437\frac{1}{3}$km³
21. 1000; 1000   **23.** 59,000   **25.** 0.049   **27.** 27,300   **29.** 40
31. 320   **33.** 3   **35.** 40   **37.** 48   **39.** $1\frac{7}{8}$ **41.** 0.423115 yd³
43. 367.38 m³   **45.** 143.72 cm³   **47.** 263,947,530,000 mi³
49. 4.187 m³   **51.** 646.74 cm³   **53.** $1\frac{3}{4}$ gal; 7.5 gal; $91\frac{1}{4}$ gal;
about 24,000,000,000 gal   **55.** About 346.2 ft³   **57.** $\mathbf{D_W}$
59. $24   **60.** $175   **61.** $10.68   **62.** $\frac{7}{3}$ **63.** –1   **64.** 448 km
65. 59   **66.** 10   **67.** $\mathbf{D_W}$ **69.** About 7546 ft³
71. Audio-cassette cases   **73.** 13,824 cm³   **75.** 57,480 in³

Margin Exercises, Section 12.5, pp. 831–838

1. Angle *DEF*, angle *FED*, angle *E*, $\angle DEF$, $\angle FED$, or $\angle E$
2. Angle *PQR*, angle *RQP*, angle *Q*, $\angle PQR$, $\angle RQP$, or $\angle Q$

3. 127° **4.** 33° **5. Times of Engagement of Married Couples**

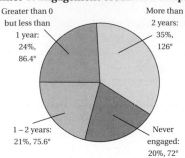

Arrangement of sections may vary.

6. Right **7.** Acute **8.** Obtuse **9.** Straight
10. ∠1 and ∠2; ∠3 and ∠4 **11.** *m*∠*BND* or *m*∠*DNB*;
m∠*CND* or *m*∠*DNC* **12.** ∠1 and ∠2; ∠1 and ∠4;
∠2 and ∠3; ∠3 and ∠4 **13.** 45° **14.** 72° **15.** 5°
16. ∠1 and ∠2; ∠1 and ∠4; ∠2 and ∠3; ∠3 and ∠4
17. 142° **18.** 23° **19.** 90° **20. (a)** △*ABC* **(b)** △*ABC*,
△*MPN* **(c)** △*DEF*, △*GHI*, △*JKL*, △*QRS* **21.** Yes **22.** No
23. (a) △*DEF* **(b)** △*GHI*, △*QRS* **(c)** △*ABC*, △*MPN*, △*JKL*
24. 180° **25.** 64°

Exercise 12.5, p. 839

1. Angle *GHI*, angle *IHG*, angle *H*, ∠ *GHI*, ∠*IHG*, or ∠*H*
3. 10° **5.** 180° **7.** 90°
9.

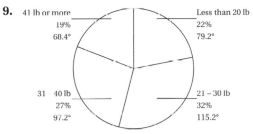

Arrangement of sections may vary.

11.

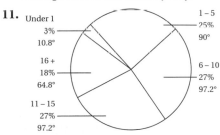

13. Obtuse

Arrangement of sections may vary.

15. Actue **17.** Straight **19.** Right **21.** Acute **23.** Obtuse
25. ∠1 and ∠3; ∠2 and ∠4 **27.** ∠*GME* (or ∠*EMG*) and
∠*AMC* (or ∠*CMA*); ∠*AMG* (or ∠*GMA*) and ∠*EMC* (or ∠*CME*)
29. *m*∠4; *m*∠1 **31.** *m*∠*GME* or *m*∠*EMG*; *m*∠*CME* or
m∠*EMC* **33.** 79° **35.** 23° **37.** 32° **39.** 61° **41.** 177°
43. 41° **45.** 105° **47.** 76° **49.** Scalene; obtuse
51. Scalene; right **53.** Equilateral; acute **55.** Scalene;
obtuse **57.** 46° **59.** 120° **61.** $\mathbf{D_W}$ **63.** $160 **64.** $22.50
65. $148 **66.** $1116. 67 **67.** $33,597.91 **68.** $413,458.31
69. $641,566.26 **70.** $684,337.34 **71.** 29 **72.** 10 **73.** $\mathbf{D_W}$

75. *m*∠2 = 67.13°; *m*∠4 = 79.8°; *m*∠5 = 67.13°;
m∠6 = 33.07° **77.** *m*∠*ACB* = 50°; *m*∠*CAB* = 40°;
m∠*EBC* = 50°; *m*∠*EBA* = 40°; *m*∠*AEB* = 100°;
m∠*ADB* = 50°

Margin Exercises, Section 12.6, pp. 844–848

1. 81 **2.** 100 **3.** 121 **4.** 144 **5.** 169 **6.** 196 **7.** 225
8. 256 **9.** –10, 10 **10.** –9, 9 **11.** –7, 7 **12.** –14, 14 **13.** 7
14. 4 **15.** 11 **16.** 10 **17.** 9 **18.** 8 **19.** 15 **20.** 13 **21.** 1
22. 0 **23.** 2.236 **24.** 8.832 **25.** 12.961 **26.** *c* = 13
27. *a* = $\sqrt{75}$; *a* ≈ 8.660 **28.** *b* = $\sqrt{120}$; *b* ≈ 10.954
29. *a* = $\sqrt{175}$; *a* ≈ 13.229 **30.** $\sqrt{424}$ ft ≈ 20.6 ft

Calculator Corner, p. 845

1. 6.6 **2.** 9.7 **3.** 19.8 **4.** 17.3 **5.** 24.9 **6.** 24.5 **7.** 121.2
8. 115.6 **9.** 16.2 **10.** 85.4

Exercise Set 12.6, p. 849

1. –4, 4 **3.** –11, 11 **5.** –13, 13 **7.** –50, 50 **9.** 8 **11.** 9
13. 15 **15.** 25 **17.** 20 **19.** 100 **21.** 6.928 **23.** 2.828
25. 1.732 **27.** 3.464 **29.** 4.359 **31.** 10.488 **33.** *c* = 15
35. *c* = $\sqrt{98}$; *c* ≈ 9.899 **37.** *a* = 5 **39.** *b* = $\sqrt{45}$; *b* ≈ 6.708
41. *c* = 26 **43.** *b* = 12 **45.** *c* = $\sqrt{41}$; *c* = 6.403
47. *b* = $\sqrt{1023}$; *b* ≈ 31.984 **49.** $\sqrt{208}$ ft ≈ 14.4 ft
51. $\sqrt{8450}$ ft ≈ 91.9 ft **53.** *h* – $\sqrt{500}$ ft ≈ 22.4 ft
55. $\sqrt{211,200,000}$ ft ≈ 14,532.7 ft **57.** $\mathbf{D_W}$ **59.** $468
60. 187,200 **61.** About 324 **62.** 12% **63.** 8 **64.** 125
65. 64 **66.** 27 **67.** $\mathbf{D_W}$ **69.** 47.80 cm² **71.** 64.8 in.
73. Width: 15.2 in.; height: 11.4 in.

Margin Exercises, Section 12.7, pp. 853-857

1. 80 **2.** 4.32 **3.** 32,000 **4.** kg **5.** kg **6.** mg **7.** g **8.** t
9. 6200 **10.** 0.0931 **11.** 77 **12.** 234.4 **13.** –4°C **14.** 85°F
15. –25°C **16.** 50°F **17.** 176°F **18.** 95°F **19.** 35°C
20. 45°C

Exercise Set 12.7, p. 858

1. 16 **3.** 4 **5.** 48 **7.** 9000 **9.** 2.4 **11.** 4.5 **13.** 4000
15. 0.001 **17.** 0.01 **19.** 1000 **21.** 10 **23.** 934,000
25. 6.345 **27.** 0.000897 **29.** 7320 **31.** 9.35 **33.** 6.9
35. 800,000 **37.** 1000 **39.** 0.0034 **41.** 80°C **43.** 60°C
45. 20°C **47.** –10°C **49.** 190°F **51.** 140°F **53.** 10°F
55. 40°F **57.** 86°F **59.** 104°F **61.** 5432°C **63.** 25°C **65.** 55°C
67. 37°C **69.** $\mathbf{D_W}$ **71.** 0.43% **72.** 231% **73.** 10
74.

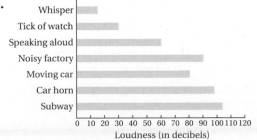

Loudness (in decibels)

75. $\frac{22}{5}$ **76.** 2.5 **77.** $\mathbf{D_W}$ **79.** 0.4536 **81.** –40° **83.** 8.81 oz
85. 60 g **87.** About 5.1 g/cm³ **89.** 144 boxes; 0.1 lb, or 1.6 oz

Margin Exercises, Section 12.8, pp. 863–865

1. 2.4 L **2. (a)** About 59.14 mL; **(b)** About 0.059 L
3. 350 mg; 28 **4.** 3000 **5.** 0.5 mg

Exercise Set 12.8, p. 866

1. 500 mL **3.** 3000 mL **5.** 0.12 g **7.** 4 tables
9. (a) 720 mcg **(b)** About 189 actuations **(c)** 6 inhalers
11. 16 oz **13. (a)** 0.42 g **(b)** 28 **15.** 6 mL **17.** 1000
19. 0.325 **21.** 250 mcg **23.** 125 mcg **25.** 0.875 mg; 875 mcg
27. $\mathbf{D_W}$ **29.** 3358 **30.** 7414 **31.** 854 **32.** 6334
33. $5x + 8$ **34.** $6x + 5$ **35.** $7t - 9$ **36.** $8r - 10$ **37.** $\mathbf{D_W}$
39. (a) 9.1 g **(b)** 162.5 mg **41.** Naproxen. The naproxen
costs 11 cents/day and the ibuprofen costs 25 cents/day.

Summary and Review: Chapter 12, p. 870

1. $3.\overline{3}$ **2.** 30 **3.** 0.17 **4.** 0.006 **5.** 400,000 **6.** $1\frac{1}{6}$ **7.** 80
8. 0.003 **9.** 12.5 **10.** 224 **11.** 0.06 **12.** 400 **13.** 1400
14. 200 **15.** 4700 **16.** 0.04 **17.** 36 **18.** 700,000 **19.** 7
20. 0.057 **21.** 31.4 m **22.** $\frac{14}{11}$in. **23.** 24 m **24.** 18 in²
25. 29.82 ft² **26.** 60 cm² **27.** 35 mm² **28.** 154 ft²
29. 314 cm² **30.** 26.28 ft² **31.** 49°; 139° **32.** $\angle PNM$ and
$\angle SNR$; $\angle MNR$ and $\angle SNP$ **33.** 93.6 m³ **34.** 193.2 ft³
35. 28,260 cm³ **36.** $33\frac{37}{75}$yd³ **37.** 942 cm³ **38.** $c = \sqrt{850}$;
$c \approx 29.155$ **39.** $b = \sqrt{84}$; $b \approx 9.165$ **40.** $c = \sqrt{89}$ ft;
$c \approx 9.434$ ft **41.** $a = \sqrt{76}$ cm; $a \approx 8.718$ cm **42.** 95°F
43. 15.6 L **44.** 0.4 mg
45. $\mathbf{D_W}$ A square is a parallelogram because it is a four-sided figure with two pairs of parallel sides.
46. $\mathbf{D_W}$ No, the sum of the three angles of a triangle is 180°.
If you have two 90° angles, totaling 180°, the third angle
would be 0°. A triangle can't have an angle of 0°.
47. $39.04 **48.** 47% **49.** 0.567 **50.** $-4\frac{1}{2}$ **51.** 24 mi
52. 2.5 **53.** $\mathbf{D_W}$ Since 1 m is slightly more than 1 yd, it
follows that 1 m³ is larger than 1 yd³. Since 1 yd³ = 27 ft³,
we see that 1 m³ is larger than 27 ft³. **54.** $\mathbf{D_W}$ Since 1 kg is
about 2.2 lb and 32 oz is $\frac{32}{16}$, or 2 lb, 1 kg weighs more than
32 oz. **55.** 961.625 cm² **56.** 104.875 laps **57.** 34.375%
58. $101.25

Test: Chapter 12, p. 875

1. [9.1a] 96 **2.** [9.1b] 2.8 **3.** [9.2a] 18 **4.** [9.1b] 5000
5. [9.1b] 0.91 **6.** [9.2b] 0.00452 **7.** [9.4b] 2.983
8. [9.7b] 3800 **9.** [9.4b] 1280 **10.** [9.4b] 690 **11.** [9.7a] 144
12. [9.7a] 8220 **13.** [9.3b] 8 cm **14.** [9.3b] 50.24 m²
15. [9.3b] 88 ft **16.** [9.3a] 25 cm² **17.** [9.3b] 33.87 m²
18. [9.3a] 18 ft² **19.** [9.3a] 13 in² **20.** [9.5c] 115°
21. [9.5c] 65° **22.** [9.4a] 192 cm³ **23.** [9.4a] 628 ft³
24. [9.4a] $4186.\overline{6}$ yd³ **25.** [9.4a] 30 m³ **26.** [9.8a] 3000 mL
27. [9.6c] $c = \sqrt{2}$; $c \approx 1.414$ **28.** [9.6c] $b = \sqrt{51}$; $b \approx 7.141$
29. [9.6a] 11 **30.** [9.7c] 0° **31.** [9.8a] 6 mL **32.** [8.6a] $440
33. [8.1b] 93% **34.** [8.1b] 0.932 **35.** [5.7b] 4
36. [7.4a] $13.86 **37.** [5.7b] 2.5 **38.** [9.6c] 112.5°
39. [9.4c] $188.40

Cumulative Review: Chapters 1-12, p. 877

1. [4.6a] $10\frac{1}{6}$ **2.** [5.5d] 49.2 **3.** [5.2b] 87.52 **4.** [2.5a] –1234
5. [1.9d] 2 **6.** [1.9c] 1565 **7.** [5.1b]$\frac{6}{5}$ **8.** [8.1c] 45%
9. [4.2c] < **10.** [4.2c] > **11.** [9.7a]$\frac{3}{8}$ **12.** [9.7c] 212°
13. [9.4b] 87 **14.** [9.1a] 90 **15.** [9.2a] 27 **16.** [9.1b] 0.37
17. [2.7b], [3.6b] 52 m; 120 m² **18.** [2.7a] $9a-16$
19. [6.4b] **20.** [6.2a] $110 million

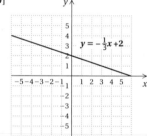

21. [6.2a] 2005 **22.** [7.3b] 14.4 **23.** [5.7b] 1
24. [2.8b], [3.8a] $-18\frac{2}{3}$ **25.** [4.3b]$\frac{1}{8}$ **26.** [1.8a] 7
27. [1.8a] 528 million **28.** [6.5a] 58.6 **29.** [8.6a] $24
30. [9.6d] 17 m **31.** [8.5a] 6% **32.** [4.6c] $2\frac{1}{8}$yd
33. [5.8a] $27.91 **34.** [7.2b] The 8-qt box **35.** [3.6b]$\frac{7}{20}$km
36. [9.5c] 148° **37.** [9.5c] 137° **38.** [9.4c] 272 ft³
39. [2.7b] No; the sum of the perimeters can be measured as
14 ft or 16 ft, both of which exceed 108 in.

Index

Photo Credits

39, Mark Joseph, Digitalvision   44, EyeWire Collection   45, Tony Stone
46, Danny Lehman/Corbis   62, Bohemian Nomad Picturemakers/Corbis
73, Gateway   74, Courtesy of Cytec Fiberite, Inc.   82, Camel   108, UPI
Newspictures   110, Roto Zip Tool Corporation   118, Eyewire   133, Tony Stone
135, Oak Express®   136, Dick Morton   141, Ralph White/Corbis   142,
© AP/Wide World Photos   146, ML Sinibaldi/Corbis   157, Vince Streano/Corbis
160, Erlanson Productions/The Image Bank   162, John Banagan/The Image
Bank   208, Dagmar Ehling/Photo Researchers   232, Corbis   234, all Corbis
except Chung: Pace Gregory/CorbisSygma; Aguilera: Michael Germana, UPI
Photo; Jackson: Mitchell Gerber/Corbis   240, © Ariel Skelly/Corbis Stock Market
278, Greg Probst/Tony Stone Images   298, Lawrence Hughes, Image Bank
308, PhotoDisc   313, Coldwater Creek   316, FoodPix   334, Corbis   340, Tony
Stone   348, Karen Bittinger   351, David Young-Wolff/PhotoEdit   353, Tony
Stone   354, Reprinted with permission from Taste of Home, Greendale, WI
355, PhotoDisc   370, © Reuters NewMedia Inc./Corbis   376, Creative Labs, Inc.
417, Digitalvision   420, © Sohber/Corbis   428, Rebecca Brown   429, Corbis
430, Walter Hodges/Tony Stone Images   441, PhotoDisc   442, Corbis
475 (left), © 1979 Time, Inc. Reprinted by permission.   475 (right), © 1979, Los
Angeles Times. Reprinted with permission.   497, © Duomo/Corbis   498, Penny
Tweedie/Tony Stone Images   502 (left), © Reuters NewMedia Inc./Corbis
502 (right), PBA   503 (left), Karen Bittinger   503 (right), Corbis Images
511, Dots is a registered trademark of Tootsie Roll Industries, Inc. and is used
with permission.   528, David Muench, Corbis   531, Albert J. Copley, PhotoDisc
535, Digitalvision   537, Permission by Heinz North America.   538 (left), Corbis
538 (right), Jeremy Woodhouse, PhotoDisc   539, © AFP Photo, Bruce
Weaver/Corbis   548 (top), Brian Spurlock   548 (bottom), Buccina Studios,
PhotoDisc   550, Nicholas Devore III/Photographers Aspen   551 (left), © 2001
Kellogg Co.   551 (right), Coco Wheats® is a product of Little Crow Foods,
Warsaw, IN.   552 (left), © Kevin Fleming, Corbis   552 (right), Barry Rosenthal,
FPG International   556, Courtesy of Iris and B. Gerald Cantor Foundation;
margin: © Massimo Mastrorillo/Corbis; inset: © Yves Forstier/Corbis   573, FPG
International   574, Kenneth Chen, Envision   581 (top), PhotoDisc
581 (bottom left), David Madison/Stone   581 (bottom right), PhotoDisc
585, Hayden Roger Celestin, UPI Photo Service   601, © AFP/Corbis   602,
Charles Gupton, Stone/Getty Images   604, Jessie Cohen, National Zoo, UPI
PhotoService   605 (left), © AFP/Corbis   605 (right), © Reuters NewMedia
Inc.,/Corbis   607, Photo courtesy of Sharp   617, Mark Peterson/Corbis Saba
618, Christopher Bissell, Stone/Getty Images   620, Photo courtesy Canon
U.S.A., Inc.   630, PhotoLink   632, Eyewire   633, PhotoDisc   640, Chad
Baker/Ryan McVay, PhotoDisc   792, Owen, Franken, Stock Boston
827, © Yogi, Inc./Corbis   829, AP/Wide World Photos   830, © 1988 Al
Satterwhite   861, © Richard T. Nowitz/CORBIS   865, © Tom and Dee Ann
McCarthy/Corbis Stock Market   866, ©Peter Beck/Corbis Stock Market
867, David Young-Wolff/PhotoEdit

Index of Applications

Index of Study Tips

Using a Scientific Calculator

Activates secondary functions printed above certain keys. Also denoted INV or 2nd.

This secondary function takes the square root of number displayed.

Squares number displayed.

Used to raise 10 to any power entered.

Finds reciprocal of number displayed.

Used to raise any base to a power. Also denoted y^x, a^x, or $\wedge$.

Stores number displayed in memory. Also denoted MIN or M.

Recalls number stored in memory. Also denoted MR.

Allows for computation with fraction notation.

Allows for computation with mixed numerals.

Used as an approximation for pi.

Clears all preceding numbers and operations. Also used to turn calculator on.

Used to perform indicated operation.

Used to control order in which certain operations are performed.

Clears last number displayed but not preceding operations.

Used when entering decimal notation.

Used to change sign of number displayed.

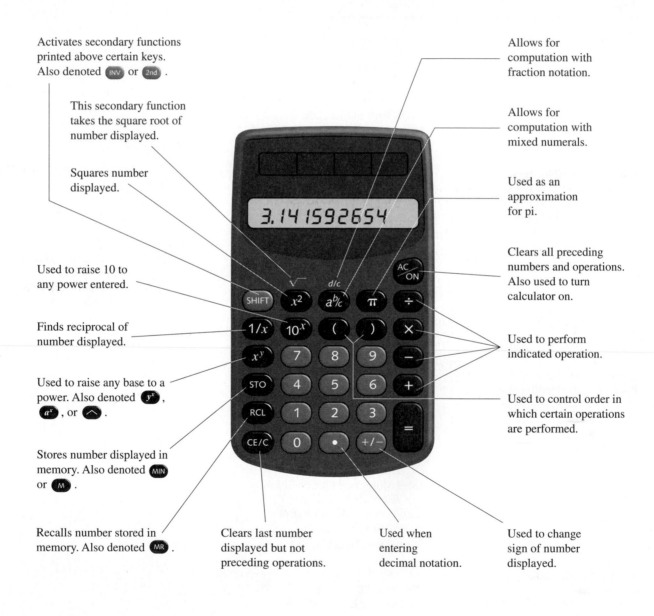